ALLE ZEIT WACH 1842

Finite Elements in WATER RESOURCES

Proceedings of the 6th International Conference,
Lisboa, Portugal, June 1986

Editors:
A. Sá da Costa
A. Melo Baptista
W.G. Gray
C.A. Brebbia
G.F. Pinder

Hosts: Laboratório Nacional de Engenharia Civil
Instituto Superior Técnico – Universidade Técnica de Lisboa

A Computational Mechanics Publication

Springer-Verlag
Berlin Heidelberg New York Tokyo

A. SÁ DA COSTA
Instituto Superior Tecnico
Universidade Tecnica de Lisboa
Av. Rovisco Pais
1096 Lisboa Codex
Portugal

G.F. PINDER
Dept. of Civil Engineering
Princeton University
Princeton
New Jersey 08540
U.S.A.

A. MELO BAPTISTA
Laboratorio Nacional de Engenharia Civil
Av. do Brasil 101
1799 Lisboa Codex
Portugal

W.G. GRAY
Dept. of Civil Engineering
University of Notre Dame
Notre Dame
Indiana 46556
U.S.A.

C.A. BREBBIA
Computational Mechanics Institute
52 Henstead Road
Southampton
SO1 2DD
U.K.

British Library Cataloguing in Publication Data

International Conference on Finite Elements in Water Resources (6th: 1986: Lisbon) Finite elements in water resources: proceedings of the VI International Conference on Finite Elements in Water Resources, Lisboa, Portugal, June 1986.
1. Water resources development – Mathematics
2. Finite element method
I. Title II. Costa, A. Sa da
628.1'61'01515353 TC409
ISBN 0-905451-52-X

ISBN 0-905451-52-X Computational Mechanics Centre, Southampton
ISBN 3-540-16682-3 Springer-Verlag Berlin Heidelberg New York Tokyo
ISBN 0-387-16682-3 Springer-Verlag New York Heidelberg Berlin Tokyo

CONTENTS

SECTION 10 – NUMERICAL TECHNIQUES

PREFACE

This book is the edited proceedings of the Sixth International Conference on Finite Elements in Water Resources, held at the Conference Centre of Laboratório Nacional de Engenharia Civil, Lisboa, Portugal, in June 1986.

This Conference, which is jointly organized by Laboratório Nacional de Engenharia Civil and Instituto Superior Técnico – Universidade Técnica de Lisboa, continues a successful series initiated in 1976. Hosts of previous meetings were the University of Princeton, Princeton, U.S.A. in 1976; the Imperial College, London, U.K. in 1978; the University of Mississippi, Oxford, U.S.A. in 1980; the University of Hannover, Hannover, West Germany in 1982; and the University of Vermont, Burlington, U.S.A. in 1984.

The Conference is intended to provide an exchange of experiences in new developments and in practical applications to Water Resources of Finite Elements and other related methods of discretization. The large number of abstracts submitted for review, and the quality of the selected papers, suggests that this book will become a valuable reference for scientists and engineers, in the area of numerical modelling of groundwater flow and seepage, hydrodynamics, tidal flows and transport phenomena.

Papers have been reproduced directly from the material submitted by the authors, who are totally responsible for them.

The Conference included two parallel activities (the Tidal-Flow Forum and the Convection-Diffusion Forum) which both aim to contribute, through the solution of reference problems, to a systematic comparison of available numerical methods in specific technical areas. Material relative to the forums is not included in this book, due to time constraints, and will be published elsewhere by the working groups that prepared each of them.

We wish to thank the technical contribution to the Conference and to this book of:

* The other members of the Technical Committee (W.G. Gray, C.A. Brebbia and G.F. Pinder).
* The invited lecturers (G.J. Fix, W.G. Gray, S. Neuman, P.M. Gresho) and speakers (J.F. Botha, A. Haugel, P.S. Huyakorn, J.A. Liggett, D.R. Lynch, U. Meissner and G.K. Verboom).
* The authors of the papers.
* The members of the working groups responsible for the Tidal-Flow Forum (G.K. Verboom, W.G. Gray, J.P. Laible, K.P. Holz and D.R. Lynch) and the Convection-Diffusion Forum (A.M. Baptista, P.M. Gresho and W.G. Gray).

We also gratefully acknowledge the sponsorship or endorsement of the following organisations:

Sponsors:
* Laboratório Nacional de Engenharia Civil (LNEC)
* Instituto Superior Técnico – Universidade Técnica de Lisboa (IST-UTL)
* Instituto Nacional de Investigação Científica (INIC)
* U.S. Army Research, Development and Standardization Group, U.K.
* Fundação Calouste Gulbenkian
* Electricidade de Portugal, EP (EDP)
* Câmara Municipal de Lisboa (CML)
* TAP Air Portugal

Endorsers:
* Associação Portuguesa de Recursos Hídricos (APRH)
* Ordem dos Engenheiros
* Society for Computer Simulation (SCS)
* International Society for Computational Methods in Engineering (ISCME)
* American Geophysical Union (AGU)
* International Association of Hydraulics Research (IAHR)
* Wessex Institute of Technology (WIT)

António Sá da Costa
António Melo Baptista
(Local Technical Organizing Committee)
Lisboa, June 1986

SECTION 1 GENERAL LECTURES

VI International Conference on Finite Elements in Water Resources, Lisboa, Portugal, June 1986

Time Integration and Conjugate Gradient Methods for the Incompressible Navier-Stokes Equations

P.M. Gresho
Lawrence Livermore National Laboratory, University of California, Livermore, CA 94550, U.S.A.

I. INTRODUCTION

The rigorous and rather robust Galerkin finite element technique (FEM) for solving the time-dependent, incompressible Navier-Stokes (NS) equations has many advantages, but low cost is not (yet) one of them. This may be due, in part, to its "genealogy", especially when compared to its older relative—the finite difference method (FDM). Whereas the latter was mainly developed during a computer era in which available core storage was ridiculously low and the rate of data transfer to and from peripheral storage devices was ridiculously slow, the FEM is a product of the more modern computer age. It is also largely a product–or at least a spin-off—from the field in which finite elements were born and in which they have had their largest impact—structural mechanics. And there is probably no other field of computation that must regularly address problems of true geometrical complexity in shape—i.e., real world structures. When discretized into finite subdomains—via FEM or FDM—the resulting matrices describing nodal coupling are anything but regular (they are helter skelter). While iterative solution techniques were considered, only the robustness of the expensive but reliable Gaussian elimination method (direct methods) survived in most cases. Hence, direct methods were naturally applied when these same (usually) FEM researchers branched out into CFD (computational fluid dynamics); the "black boxes" were available. On the other hand, FDM CFD began more or less on its own (and much *earlier* than FEM) and took a completely different tack. They focussed on indirect (iterative) methods owing to the primitive computing facilities then available and, probably quite understandably, on *simple* geometries (witness the ubiquitous driven cavity) and uniform meshes. Reasonable and storage-respecting techniques for solving algebraic systems, such as Gauss-Seidel and SOR, were a natural adjunct to these early simulation methods.

But the FEM CFD folk are finding that the brute force direct methods are just too expensive—except for those (special?) cases wherein "cost is no object." The voracious memory demands of these methods, especially when used with fully coupled implicit time integration methods on general meshes, seem destined to cause them to yield to indirect methods because even with the largest supercomputers (e.g., CRAY 2 or equivalent with, say, 256 M-words of fast memory), the memory is too soon filled with "matrix data" from a mesh that is still too coarse and the data transfer rate (of I/O) is still too low—usually. (The CRAY X-MP with SSD is one notable exception.)

In this paper we briefly (and non-expertly) address just one class of iterative methods that are promising for helping to reduce the cost of NS simulations. They all derive from the conjugate gradient (CG) method for solving linear algebraic systems with a symmetric positive-definite (SPD) matrix, which method has a good many theoretically and computationally nice characteristics: monotone convergence (in an appropriate error norm), optimal error minimization, finite termination, the direct exploitation of sparseness in the matrix, and no need to estimate "iteration parameters."

Of course the NS equations also generate unsymmetric indefinite matrices, in which case many of the above features are lost, or nearly lost.

We attempt herein to connect various time integration methods to their respective "best CG-like" solution methods for solving the resulting linear algebraic systems.

II. CONTINUUM EQUATIONS AND SPATIAL DISCRETIZATION

The governing equations of interest here are the conservation equations for momentum, energy, and mass (continuity equation) for a Boussinesq fluid, the "primitive equations," which are (in dimensionless form, for convenience),

$$\frac{\partial \mathbf{u}}{\partial t} + \mathbf{u} \cdot \nabla \mathbf{u} + \nabla P = Re^{-1} \nabla^2 \mathbf{u} + Fr^{-1} \mathbf{k} T, \tag{1a}$$

$$\frac{\partial T}{\partial t} + \mathbf{u} \cdot \nabla T = Pe^{-1} \nabla^2 T, \quad \text{and} \tag{1b}$$

$$\nabla \cdot \mathbf{u} = 0, \tag{1c}$$

where the usual nomenclature applies. (See, e.g., Gresho et al., 1984, for details.) We will also need the pressure Poisson equation, which is easily derived from (1a) and (1c):

$$\nabla^2 P = Fr^{-1} \nabla \cdot (\mathbf{k} T) - \nabla \cdot (\mathbf{u} \cdot \nabla \mathbf{u}), \tag{2}$$

an *elliptic* equation which can be used in lieu of (1c); i.e., just as (1a) and (1c) imply (2), so too do (1a) and (2) imply (1c). (See Gresho and

Sani, 1986, for details.) We remark that if the simpler case of isothermal flow is being considered, we omit (1b) and set $T = 0$ in (1a) and (2).

In the penalty approximation to an incompressible fluid, the mass conservation equation (1b) is replaced by that allowing a very small amount of compressibility, via

$$\nabla \cdot \mathbf{u} = -\epsilon P, \tag{3}$$

where $0 < \epsilon \ll 1$; see, e.g., Reddy (1982) and references therein for further details. The germane point here is that proper implementation of the penalty approximation leads to a system of equations that is generally simpler to solve because the pressure is eliminated a priori and that the resulting solution is acceptably close to that obtained from the true incompressible equations. Thus, inserting (3) into (1a) yields

$$\frac{\partial \mathbf{u}}{\partial t} + \mathbf{u} \cdot \nabla \mathbf{u} = \epsilon^{-1} \nabla (\nabla \cdot \mathbf{u}) + Re^{-1} \nabla^2 \mathbf{u} + Fr^{-1} \mathbf{k} T, \tag{4}$$

in which the pressure no longer appears. The solutions of (4) and (1b) can give results that are close, $O(\epsilon)$, to those of (1); after obtaining $\mathbf{u}$ from (4), the pressure (if needed) can be computed directly from (3).

The spatial discretization of the continuum equations can be performed by the finite difference method or the finite element method. In either case, after augmenting the governing equations with appropriate (see, e.g., Gresho and Sani, 1986) boundary and initial conditions, we can write the semi-discrete equations as

$$M\dot{u} + N(u)u + CP = Ku + f, \quad u(0) = u_0, \tag{5a}$$

$$M_s\dot{T} + N_s(u)T = K_sT + f_s, \quad T(0) = T_0, \tag{5b}$$

and

$$C^T u = g, \quad C^T u_0 = g_0. \tag{5c}$$

The matrix "operators" in (5) are apparent by comparing the various terms with the continuous analogs in (1); the vectors f, f_s, and g reflect the effects of boundary conditions (f also includes the buoyancy force).

Just as (1a) and (1c) were used to derive (2), we now combine (5a) and (5c)—its time-derivative, actually—to obtain the analog of (2) which we call the consistent discretized Poisson equation for the pressure (see, e.g., Gresho et al., 1984):

$$(C^T M^{-1} C)P = C^T M^{-1}[Ku + f - N(u)u] - \dot{g}, \tag{6}$$

a linear algebraic system with a symmetric matrix that is positive semi-definite in general (see Sani et al., 1981a), but frequently positive-definite. Again the reverse implication also generally follows: viz, (5a) and (6) imply (5c); see Gresho and Sani (1986) for further details, including caveats.

<u>Remarks:</u>

(i) If FDM is employed, M is usually just the identity matrix, but the design of schemes in which the "divergence matrix" is the transpose of the "gradient matrix"—regardless of boundary conditions—is a challenge.

(ii) If FEM is employed, M (the consistent mass matrix) is symmetric, positive-definite, banded, and sparse; but its inverse is *dense*. Hence the actual *use* of (6) practically also requires the use of the ad-hoc procedure called mass lumping which "converts" M to a diagonal matrix, thus rendering operations with M^{-1} feasible.

(iii) Equations (5a) and (5c) or (5a) and (6) are examples of systems of differential algebraic equations (DAE's) in contrast to the simpler case of systems of ordinary differential equations (ODE's); see Petzold (1982), Petzold and Lötstedt (1984). The former pair is called an "index 2" DAE system and the latter an index 1 (i.e., "simpler") system. [A conventional (non-singular) ODE system has index 0.]

Finally, the discrete penalty approximation is the discrete approximation to (3) which replaces (5c) by

$$C^T u = g - \epsilon Q P, \tag{7}$$

where Q is the "pressure mass matrix"—see, e.g., Engelman et al. (1982), in which Q is called M, and in which it is stated that replacing Q by I, the identity matrix, appears to be viable. (Indeed, Fortin, 1983, placed that conjecture on solid theoretical ground.) Again, as in the continuum, we can now a priori eliminate the pressure—this time by inserting (7) into (5a) to give, analogous to (4),

$$M\dot{u} + N(u)u = \epsilon^{-1}(CQ^{-1}C^T)u + Ku + f - \epsilon^{-1}CQ^{-1}g, \tag{8}$$

which is a system of ODE's rather than DAE's. After solving (8) for the velocity, the pressure is easily computed (if desired) from (7)—and it is easier yet if Q is diagonal—e.g. via mass lumping or even via $Q = I$.

Remark:

If a certain special-but-useful class of finite element approximations is considered, it is often possible to simplify the "penalty" term in (8); i.e, rather than a product of 2 or 3 matrices (it is a 2 matrix product if Q is replaced by I to give CC^T), it can be equivalently represented by a single matrix [see Malkus and Hughes (1978), Engelman et al. (1982), and Fortin (1983)]; i.e., $CQ^{-1}C^T = B$, where B is generated more easily.

We now turn to the solution; i.e., to the time integration of the various semi-discretized equations.

III. EXPLICIT TIME INTEGRATION

A. Continuity equation approach

The simplest time integration scheme is forward (or explicit) Euler (FE); i.e., to integrate $\dot{y} = f(y)$, use $y_{n+1} = y_n + \Delta t f(y_n)$. But in addition to the usual problems engendered by this method (stability-related, requiring small Δt), the Navier Stokes (NS) equations are *inherently implicit* in the pressure and thus pure and simple time-marching (unless the penalty approximation is employed) is not possible (see, e.g. Gresho et al., 1980a). To help see this, consider first the application of FE to (5a) and (5c): given u_n such that $C^T u_n = g_n$, this yields (using partitioned matrix notation)

$$\begin{pmatrix} \frac{1}{\Delta t}M & C \\ C^T & 0 \end{pmatrix} \begin{pmatrix} u_{n+1} \\ P_n \end{pmatrix} = \begin{pmatrix} \frac{1}{\Delta t}Mu_n + Ku_n + f_n - N(u_n)u_n \\ g_{n+1} \end{pmatrix}, \qquad (9)$$

which, owing to the *intense* (complete) coupling of all velocity components and the pressure, would negate any and all ostensible advantages associated with an explicit method; i.e., (9) requires the solution of the largest possible linear system for the current unknowns, u_{n+1} and P_n.

If, however, the equations are uncoupled, a sequential solution method could be considered; viz combining the second of (9), $C^T u_{n+1} = g_{n+1}$, with the first, gives

$$(C^T M^{-1} C)P_n = C^T M^{-1}[Ku_n + f_n - N(u_n)u_n] - (g_{n+1} - g_n)/\Delta t, \quad (10)$$

which can be solved for P_n. Not surprisingly, however, (10) is simply a discrete time approximation to (6), the consistent discrete Poisson equation; i.e., we *still* do not have a "time-marching" method. Thus we abandon the idea of "simple" marching via an explicit scheme on the primitive form of the incompressible NS equations; the closest we can come is to lump the mass, solve the consistent discrete Poisson equation at each step (but see below), and then "time-march" on the velocity field.

B. Poisson equation approach

Since the previous approach "evolved" to that using the consistent discrete Poisson equation (complete with mass lumping), we can, alternatively and equivalently, *begin* with that approach; viz given u_n satisfying $C^T u_n = g_n$, the 2-step algorithm is:

(i) solve the linear system (10) for P_n;

(ii) apply FE to the momentum eq. (5a) to advance the velocity:

$$u_{n+1} = u_n + \Delta t M^{-1}[Ku_n + f_n - N(u_n)u_n - CP_n]. \qquad (11)$$

The temperature equation, when present, is integrated in time by the simple and obvious analog of (11).

C. Balancing Tensor Diffusivity (BTD) and Subcycling

While the above algorithm is the *simplest* possible for solving the DAE's that approximate the incompressible NS equations, its cost-effectiveness is questionable since stable integration via the FE method requires Δt's that are often (usually) much too small to be reasonable (i.e., considering only the time-accurate integration of the ODE's). This fact, combined with the (time-consuming) requirement of updating the pressure at each time step, lead Gresho et al. (1984) to design and implement two techniques that go far toward increasing the cost-effectiveness of the explicit algorithm.

The first is called BTD and is used to overcome the very stringent time step restriction for FE applied to advection-dominated flows ($Re \gg 1$ and/or $Pe \gg 1$ in (1)); viz (in 1D for simplicity) $c \leq 1/P$ where c is the Courant number and P is the grid Peclet (or Reynolds) number, which is often $\gg 1$. To overcome this stability restriction (and to increase accuracy, believe it or not), the physical diffusion coefficient is augmented by a BTD term as follows (using (1b) as a prototype equation): replace the scalar "diffusivity," Pe^{-1} in $\nabla \cdot (Pe^{-1} \nabla T)$, by the tensor diffusivity, $Pe^{-1} \cdot \delta_{ij} + \frac{1}{2} \Delta t u_i u_j$, where u_i is the i-th component of the (continuum) velocity and δ_{ij} is the Kronecker delta. For this small amount of extra work, the stability of the scheme is improved (for advection-dominated flow) to the "more appropriate" CFL limit, $c \leq 1$. For further details of BTD, including its derivation, see Gresho et al. (1984); for further stability results, see Hindmarsh et al. (1984).

The second technique is called subcycling and is based on the (primary) premise that (even with BTD) the stability-limited Δt associated with FE is often significantly smaller than that required for adequate *accuracy*. Another (secondary) premise is that the continuity equation and associated pressure gradient have little or no effect on the stability of the time integration scheme. The essence of the technique is that the velocity (and temperature) field is integrated via FE (with BTD) at its stability-limited Δt for some pre-determined number of steps (subcycling) during which the pressure gradient is *approximated via extrapolation* (i.e., no discrete Poisson equation need be solved) and the continuity equation is (effectively) ignored. At the conclusion of the subcycling (which can range from ≤ 5 steps during a transient to as many as 50 or 100 steps if a steady state is approached, based on estimates of *accuracy*), the velocity field must be projected back onto the discretely-divergence-free subspace (from which it wandered during subcycling) and the pressure updated. While the details of this procedure are described in Gresho et al. (1984), the two key steps relevant here are those requiring the solution of linear algebraic systems, viz:

(i) Velocity projection: Given an arbitrary velocity vector, $\tilde{u}$, determine its projection onto the discretely-divergence-free subspace. This naturally leads to the 2- step procedure:

(1) solve

$$(C^T M^{-1} C)\lambda = C^T \tilde{u} - g \tag{12}$$

for the associated Lagrange multiplier, λ, and.

(2) compute

$$u = \tilde{u} - M^{-1} C\lambda. \tag{13}$$

Remarks:

(1) u is discretely-divergence-free: $C^T u = g$

(2) u is the "closest possible" divergence-free vector to $\tilde{u}$.

(ii) Given the "solenoidal" velocity field from (13), the concomitant and consistent pressure is obtained from (6); i.e., by solving another algebraic system.

Remarks:

(1) At the conclusion of subcycling, a *sequence* of *two* linear algebraic systems must be solved.

(2) The coefficient matrix, $C^T M^{-1} C$, is the same for each system.

(3) Hence, subcycling can save computer time only if the number of subcycle steps exceeds two—but the savings can be quite large if this number greatly exceeds two.

(4) The solutions obtained *using* subcycling are (as desired/required) usually sufficiently close to those *without* using it to justify the method (a posteriori).

D. Penalty method

While the ODE system [vis-a-vis the DAE's of (5)] given by (8) is *ostensibly* integrable by simple time-marching using an explicit scheme like FE, the "inherent implicitness" of the pressure is still present, albeit in disguised form. If FE were to be applied to (8), presumably (but not necessarily) using lumped mass, it would turn out that the eigenvalues of the "penalty" matrix, $\epsilon^{-1}(CQ^{-1}C^T)$, would set the allowable time step; i.e., one would need $\Delta t < O(\epsilon)$ in order to obtain a stable integration. Since this Δt would (usually) be literally orders of magnitude smaller than that required for accuracy, such a procedure would appear to require too many time steps to be viable, let alone competitive.

IV. SEMI-IMPLICIT TIME INTEGRATION

A. Poisson equation approach

In Gresho and Chan (1985), a cost-effective variation on the scheme using FE (with BTD) was presented, viz. a semi-implicit scheme in which diffusive terms (which includes BTD) were integrated via the trapezoid rule (TR; an implicit, stable, second-order accurate scheme given by, for $\dot{y} = f(y)$, $y_{n+1} = y_n + \Delta t/2[f(y_n) + f(y_{n+1})]$), and the advective terms integrated via FE. The final equations solved are (see Gresho and Chan, 1985, for details):

(i) For AD (temperature), from (5b):

$$\left(M_s - \frac{\Delta t}{2}\widetilde{K}_{n+1}\right) T_{n+1} = \left[M_s + \frac{\Delta t}{2}\widetilde{K}_n - \Delta t N_s(u_n)u_n\right] + \Delta t f_s, \tag{14}$$

where $\widetilde{K}$ is K_s except that the diffusion coefficient is augmented by the BTD correction term. We remark that (i) the coefficient matrix $M_s - \frac{\Delta t}{2}\widetilde{K}_{n+1}$ is symmetric positive-definite, but generally time-dependent (thanks to BTD), (ii) since (14) already requires the solution of a linear algebraic system owing to the use of TR, M needn't be lumped (a great advantage for advection-dominated situations—see e.g., Gresho et al., 1978), and (iii) for (at least) the case of constant velocity on a uniform grid, the scheme is *unconditionally* stable (a somewhat surprising bonus since advection is integrated with an explicit scheme).

(ii) For NS, from (5a) and (6), with some additional approximations ala Gresho and Chan (1985), again a 2-step scheme results:

(1) solve

$$(C^T M^{-1} C)P_n = C^T M^{-1}\left[\widetilde{K}_n u_n + f_n - N(u_n)u_n\right] + (C^T u_n - g_{n+1})/\Delta t \tag{15}$$

for P_n;

(2) solve

$$\left(I - \frac{\Delta t}{2}M^{-1}\widetilde{K}_n\right) u_{n+1} = \left(I + \frac{\Delta t}{2}M^{-1}\widetilde{K}_n\right) u_n + \Delta t M^{-1}\left[f_n - N(u_n)u_n - CP_n\right] \tag{16}$$

for u_{n+1}.

Remarks:

(i) As with the fully explicit scheme, the lumped mass approximation is apparently required in order to make the scheme feasible. The coefficient matrix is still symmetric positive-definite.

(ii) $\widetilde{K}_n = \widetilde{K}(u_n)$ is used rather than $\widetilde{K}_{n+1}$ on the LHS of (16) in order to linearize the equations. This causes:

(iii) $C^T u_{n+1} - g_{n+1} = \delta$ where δ, while $\neq 0$, is "small."

(iv) Stability is not surprisingly not unconditional; stable Courant numbers of only $\sim$ 5–10 have thus far been attained in practice, but there appears to be no diffusive (viscous) stability limit. (The scheme is thus especially useful for diffusion-dominated flows—$Re \ll 1$ and/or $Pe \ll 1$.)

(v) Thus far, we have only implemented this scheme in two dimensions.

B. Continuity equation approach

Using (5a) and (5c), with implicit (TR) treatment of diffusion (including "linearized" BTD) but explicit treatment of all other terms gives

$$\frac{1}{\Delta t} M(u_{n+1} - u_n) + N(u_n)u_n + C\widetilde{P} = \frac{1}{2}\widetilde{K}_n(u_n + u_{n+1}) + f_n$$

and

$$C^T u_{n+1} = g_{n+1},$$

where $C^T u_n = g_n$ is assumed. This can be rewritten as a linear system in u_{n+1} and $\widetilde{P}$:

$$\begin{pmatrix} \frac{1}{\Delta t}M - \frac{1}{2}\widetilde{K}_n & C \\ C^T & 0 \end{pmatrix} \begin{pmatrix} u_{n+1} \\ \widetilde{P} \end{pmatrix} = \begin{pmatrix} f_n + \left[\frac{1}{\Delta t}M + \frac{1}{2}\widetilde{K}_n\right] u_n - N(u_n)u_n \\ g_{n+1} \end{pmatrix}. \tag{17}$$

Remarks:

(1) The coefficient matrix is symmetric, but indefinite.

(2) The consistent mass formulation is available at no extra cost.

(3) The system is *fully* coupled.

(4) The pressure from (17) satisfies

$$(C^T M^{-1} C)\widetilde{P} = C^T M^{-1}\left[f_n + \frac{1}{2}\widetilde{K}_n(u_{n+1} + u_n) - N(u_n)u_n\right] - (g_{n+1} - g_n)/\Delta t \tag{18}$$

wherein, since both u_n and u_{n+1} appear on the RHS, we have avoided the confusion of placing a time index on the pressure—we just call it $\widetilde{P}$ and state that it applies most precisely somewhere *between* t_n and t_{n+1}, the more important point being that it is, for this mixed integration scheme, just *that* pressure that ensures a discretely divergence-free velocity.

C. Penalty method

In this approach, we integrate (8) via TR on both the diffusion term (with BTD; hence, $K \rightarrow \widetilde{K}(u)$, which we linearize, or "drag"—i.e, evaluate, as before, at t_n) *and* the penalty term:

$$= \left[\frac{1}{\Delta t}M - \frac{1}{2}(\widetilde{K}_n + \epsilon^{-1}CQ^{-1}C^T)\right] u_{n+1}$$
$$= \left[\frac{1}{\Delta t}M + \frac{1}{2}(\widetilde{K}_n + \epsilon^{-1}CQ^{-1}C^T) - N(u_n)\right] u_n$$
$$+ f_n - \epsilon^{-1}CQ^{-1}g_n, \tag{19}$$

wherein we note that:

(i) The coefficient matrix is symmetric positive-definite and again the consistent mass matrix is available for no extra cost.

(ii) The solution of (19), and (8) for that matter, will generally suffer a short time penalty transient (à la Sani et al., 1981b), which is nearly innocuous if $C^T u_0 = g_0$, but not if u_0 is "arbitrary." To see this, solve (8) for $\dot{u}$ and apply $C^T \dot{u} = \dot{g} - \epsilon Q \dot{P}$ (the time-differentiated form of (7)) to get

$$\epsilon Q\dot{P} + (C^T M^{-1} C)P = C^T M^{-1}[Ku + f - N(u)u] - \dot{g}, \tag{20}$$

which is "close to" the consistent discretized Poisson equation, (6), and is (implicitly) satisfied by solving (19). Since $\epsilon \ll 1$, the pressure from the penalty method will generally undergo a non-physical short term transient that is completed by $t = O(\epsilon)$, after which it will be in quasi-equilibrium (i.e., it will closely satisfy (6)). Since the velocity field also sees this "startup transient," it is advisable to "avoid" it when solving (19), if possible. To suppress this spurious transient, Sani et al. suggested taking one step at a "reasonable" Δt, Δt_0, [which is usually such that $\Delta t_0 \gg O(\epsilon)$] using the strongly dissipative backward (implicit) Euler method. In the current context, this would mean solving

$$\left[\frac{1}{\Delta t_0}M - (\widetilde{K}_0 + \epsilon^{-1}CQ^{-1}C^T)\right] u_1 = \frac{1}{\Delta t}Mu_0 - N(u_0)u_0$$
$$+ f_0 - \epsilon^{-1}CQ^{-1}g_0$$

for u_1 and then switching to (19) for the rest of the integration.

(iii) Although the pressure is absent (and we truly have a set of ODE's rather than DAE's), the velocities are still fully coupled (an inherent aspect of the penalty method).

V. IMPLICIT TIME INTEGRATION

Thus far, each method considered included the considerable advantage that the coefficient matrices associated with the linear algebraic systems were symmetric. But the price for this advantage (with the exception of certain special cases) was the need to respect a stability limit related to the time integration step size. While certain implicit methods, such as backward Euler or TR, are "unconditionally stable," they are only so for NS if applied "across the board" (to all terms) which, owing to the asymmetry of the advection operator (it is not self-adjoint), leads to unsymmetric matrices in the underlying linear algebra problems. And worse yet, the advection terms are nonlinear, the implicit treatment of which necessarily generates *nonlinear* algebraic equations; these are necessarily solved iteratively, *each* iteration engendering (usually) the requirement of solving an *unsymmetric* linear algebraic system. It is thus already clear that the (alleged) stability advantages of fully implicit methods would need to be quite pronounced to even warrant their *serious* consideration.

Before presenting a viable and proven method, we first state an additional important advantage of such schemes: it is straightforward to generate robust and smart algorithms that vary the time step size so as to control local *accuracy* (since stability is no longer a consideration), thus minimizing the number of steps to achieve a solution of "prescribed" accuracy. In contrast, methods that are stability-limited generally force the analyst (and/or the user) to spend large amounts of time (and many ill-fated computer runs) trying in fact to *estimate* the stability bounds, which are generally rather elusive for the NS equations.

A. Continuity equation approach

In Gresho et al. (1980a, 1980b) we presented a robust but usually expensive scheme based on TR (and Gaussian elimination) which we only summarize here. Application of TR to (5) gives the following nonlinear system, for $(u_{n+1}\ T_{n+1}\ P_{n+1})^T$:

$$
= \begin{bmatrix} \frac{2}{\Delta t}M - K + N(u_{n+1}) & \beta M_s & C \\ 0 & \frac{2}{\Delta t}M_s - K_s + N_s(u_{n+1}) & 0 \\ C^T & 0 & 0 \end{bmatrix} \begin{Bmatrix} u_{n+1} \\ T_{n+1} \\ P_{n+1} \end{Bmatrix}
$$

$$
= \begin{Bmatrix} M\left(\frac{2}{\Delta t}u_n + \dot{u}_n\right) + \overline{f}_{n+1} \\ M_s\left(\frac{2}{\Delta t}T_n + \dot{T}_n\right) + f_{s_{n+1}} \\ g_{n+1} \end{Bmatrix}, \qquad (21)
$$

where, in (5a), $\overline{f} \equiv f + \beta M_s T$ accounts (explicitly) for the buoyancy term. After linearizing the advection matrix, $N(u_{n+1})$ in one way or another (see the above references, and Engelman and Sani, 1983), a matrix similar to the above is generated. (Tho' not containing u_{n+1}, it is still unsymmetric.) Thus we have arrived at the maximum possible coupling of variables.

Remarks:

(i) The coefficient matrix (after linearization) is unsymmetric and indefinite; i.e., it is of the "most difficult" type.

(ii) Consistent mass is again nearly free of cost.

(iii) The analogous "Poisson equation approach" is again possible at the sacrifice of the consistent mass matrix, but not advisable—especially when the next method is considered.

B. Penalty approach

The penalty method is a natural adjunct to an implicit scheme. Thus, TR applied to (5b) and (8) gives

$$\begin{bmatrix} \frac{2}{\Delta t}M - K - \epsilon^{-1}(CQ^{-1}C^T) + N(u_{n+1}) & \beta M_s \\ 0 & \frac{2}{\Delta t}M_s - K_s + N_s(u_{n+1}) \end{bmatrix} \begin{bmatrix} u_{n+1} \\ T_{n+1} \end{bmatrix}$$

$$= \begin{bmatrix} M\left(\frac{2}{\Delta t}u_n + \dot{u}_n\right) + \overline{f}_{n+1} \\ M_s\left(\frac{2}{\Delta t}T_n + \dot{T}_n\right) + f_{s_{n+1}} \end{bmatrix}, \tag{22}$$

with pressure absent. Similar techniques as applied to (21) would also be applicable here (see Engelman and Sani, 1983).

Remarks:

(i) The coefficient matrix, again after linearizing the advection terms, is still unsymmetric and indefinite.

(ii) If the momentum and energy equations were somehow uncoupled, the linearized version of (22) would separate into two smaller linear systems, and a potentially more cost-effective scheme could be devised—see Gresho et al. (1978) for some ideas in this direction.

(iii) Consistent mass is still "free."

VI. BRIEF SURVEY OF CONJUGATE GRADIENT METHODS

The specialized subject of CG-related methods for unsymmetric matrices and "preconditioners" for same may be more of a "moving target" than is the FEM in fluid mechanics; i.e., the literature is already half-vast and growing rapidly so that any scheme that "works OK" today may be made obsolete tomorrow by one that is much better. Even the more established and better understood methods associated with SPD matrices are subject to improvement.

A. Symmetric Matrices

The CG method, first described by Hestenes and Stiefel (1952), is now (thanks in part to the efforts of Reid, 1971, and Concus et al., 1976, to name but two) widely used to solve linear algebraic systems, $Ax = b$, in which the coefficient matrix is sparse, square $(N \times N)$, and SPD [or, if positive-*semi*-definite, the equation set must usually be consistent; see, e.g., Lewis and Rehm (1980), Alexsson (1980)]. CG can be viewed as a direct method that, in the absence of round-off error, gives the exact solution in at most N steps; or as an iterative procedure that gives a good approximation to the solution in far fewer than N steps. It is also referred to as a semi-iterative method; see, e.g., Jackson and Robinson (1985). A feature of the method that makes it particularly suitable for large sparse systems is that all references to A are in the form of a matrix-vector product, say Ax, so that storage requirements can be much lower than for direct methods; i.e., Ax *can* be regarded as rule for generating a vector rather than one for multiplying a vector by a matrix. Such techniques have been called "matrix-free" by some; e.g., Brown and Hindmarsh (1984). Another attractive feature is that, unlike most iterative methods, CG does not require any estimation of parameters—yet it attains the very desirable properties of optimality and monotonicity—which we define momentarily. The CG algorithm in its most efficient form (Elman, 1982) is:

Choose x_0; compute $r_0 = b - Ax_0$ and set $p_0 = r_0$.

For $i = 0,\ 1,\ 2, \ldots,$ until convergence, Do

$$
\begin{aligned}
a_i &= (r_i, r_i)/(p_i, Ap_i), \\
x_{i+1} &= x_i + a_i p_i, \\
r_{i+1} &= r_i - a_i A p_i, \\
b_i &= \| r_{i+1} \|^2 / \| r_i \|^2, \quad \text{and} \\
p_{i+1} &= r_{i+1} + b_i p_i,
\end{aligned}
$$

where $(x, y) \equiv x^T y$ and $\| x \| \equiv \sqrt{(x,x)}$. Another advantage of CG, apparent from the above algorithm, is that it is easy to implement; it also vectorizes quite nicely to provide additional savings (see also Kershaw, 1978).

It can be shown (Hestenes and Stiefel, 1952) that the residuals, $\{r_i\}$, and direction vectors, $\{p_i\}$, satisfy $(r_i, r_j) = 0$ and $(p_i, Ap_j) = 0$ for $i \neq j$ and $(r_i, Ap_j) = 0$ for $i \neq j$ and $i \neq j+1$; i.e., the residual vectors [*gradient* vectors of the quadratic form (Ax, x)] are mutually orthogonal and the direction vectors are mutually A-orthogonal; i.e., *conjugate*. From these properties it also follows that $\| e_{i+1} \| \leq \| e_i \|$ (Hageman and Young, 1981), and that x_i minimizes the error functional over a particular i-dimensional Krylov space given by $E(x_i) \equiv (x - x_i,\ A(x - x_i))$

(Elman, 1982); these are the monotonicity and optimality properties, respectively. Finally, we mention a theoretical upper bound on the number of iterations, I, to make the relative error, $E(x_i)/E(x_0), \leq \epsilon$; viz

$$I \cong \left[\frac{1}{2} \ln \frac{2}{\epsilon}\right] \sqrt{\kappa(A)},$$

where $\kappa(A)$ is the condition number of A (the ratio of the maximum to minimum eigenvalues); see, e.g., Axelsson (1980) or Elman (1982). Note that this estimate is independent of N—*except* insofar as N affects $\kappa(A)$.

To conclude this section, we remark that CG is almost never applied directly to a matrix A that was generated by a discrete approximation to a partial differential equation since $\kappa(A)$ is usually "too large" and convergence correspondingly too slow. We defer the subject of "preconditioning the matrix," however, until a later section.

B. Unsymmetric Matrices with Positive – Definite Symmetric Part

From Mikić and Morse (1985), we quote, "The extension of CG to nonsymmetric, indefinite systems is not trivial. However, there is a need for a method which can be used on such systems *directly*. In the context of conjugate gradients, the search is for a method which improves the solution from the space $\heartsuit_i$ [a Krylov space: $\heartsuit_i \equiv \text{span}\ \{r_o,\ Ar_o,\ A^2r_0,\ \ldots,\ A^ir_0\}$, where r_0 is the initial residual], which has a minimization property in some norm of the error, and which satisfies a simple recursion relation for updating residual and search vectors. A method which possesses all of these properties is not available yet, although partial generalizations have been made."

For reasons that will become clear later, we can improve our lot somewhat by avoiding the worst general case—unsymmetric and indefinite matrices. Recall that any matrix A can be written as the sum of a symmetric part, S, and a skew-symmetric part, U; i.e., $A = S + U$, where $S = \frac{1}{2}(A + A^T)$ and $U = \frac{1}{2}(A - A^T)$. We note that if A is symmetric, $U = 0$ and if A is skew-symmetric, $S = 0$. Herein we restrict attention mainly to those matrices for which $(Sx,\ x) > 0$ which naturally precludes the case where A is skew-symmetric. We further restrict attention (for better or worse) to schemes that are CG-related in that they are variational or descent methods. [We are attracted to decent descent methods since they are related to—or degenerate to, for SPD matrices at least—methods which seek the bottom of a multidimensional "bowl," and these are popular among mathematicians—at least in the U.S.A.—i.e., they generate a multitude of (non-football) "bowl games."]

We next (briefly) present four of the current crop of CG-like algorithms that might work for one or another version of the NS equations:

(1) Generalized conjugate residual method (GCR)

This is a generalization of the conjugate residual method which, for SPD matrices, is closely related to the CG method (Elman, 1982). From Eisenstat et al. (1983), we have:

Choose x_0; compute $r_0 = b - Ax_0$ and set $p_0 = r_0$.

For $i = 0, 1, 2, \ldots,$ until convergence, Do

$$a_i = (r_i, Ap_i) / \| Ap_i \|^2,$$

$$x_{i+1} = x_i + a_i p_i,$$

$$r_{i+1} = r_i - a_i A p_i,$$

$$b_j^{(i)} = -(Ar_{i+1}, Ap_j) / \| Ap_j \|^2,$$

and $p_{i+1} = r_i + \sum_{j=0}^{i} b_j^{(i)} p_j$.

This method is convergent if the symmetric part (S) is positive-definite. The directions $\{p_i\}$ are $A^T A$-orthogonal, $(Ap_i, Ap_j) = 0$ for $i \neq j$ and, as a result, the choice of the step length is such that x_{i+1} is the point in $x_0 + \heartsuit_{i+1}$ with smallest residual norm, $\| r_{i+1} \|$. Thus GCR is optimal with respect to the residual norm. Unlike CG, however, GCR achieves global optimality at a high cost: the recurrence relations for p_{i+1} require $O((i+1)N)$ operations and storage.

A preconditioned form of this algorithm has recently been applied to certain hyperbolic-like problems associated with porous media flow (Obeysekare et al., 1985) and proven more cost-effective than direct sparse matrix solvers.

Two simplifying modifications of this algorithm, described by Eisenstat et al. (1983) are: (i) reduce the number of ($A^T A$-orthogonal) vectors to a predetermined fixed number, k, called Orthomin (k), and (ii) restart the GCR scheme if convergence hasn't been achieved by the k-th iteration, called GCR (k). If $k = 0$ in either Orthomin (0) or GCR (0), the particularly simple scheme called minimum residual results, and this scheme was recommended by Elman (1986) as the one to try first.

(2) Minimum residual (MR)

This simplest of all schemes, which resembles the method of steepest descent for the symmetric system (for which this descent scheme is *not* normally considered to be very decent—e.g., Noble, 1969), is:

Choose x_0; compute $r_0 = b - Ax_0$.

For $i = 0, 1, 2, \ldots,$ until convergence, Do

$$a_i = (r_i, Ar_i) / \| Ar_i \|^2,$$

$$x_{i+1} = x_i + a_i r_i,$$

and $r_{i+1} = r_i - a_i A r_i$.

This scheme, in a preconditioned form (or course), was recently also advocated by Malik et al. (1985), who employed it to solve the NS equations using a semi-implicit time integration scheme.

(3) Biconjugate Gradient (BCG) method

This scheme has the advantage of not being limited to matrices with positive definite symmetric parts, but has some disadvantages, too. It was first described by Fletcher (1976), but our description is from Elman (1983):

$$\text{Choose } x_0, \quad \text{compute } r_0 = b - Ax_0, \quad \text{set } p_0 = r_0 \text{ and } \overline{p}_0 = p_0.$$

$$\begin{aligned} \text{For } i &= 0,\ 1,\ 2,\ \ldots, \text{ until convergence, Do} \\ a_i &= (\overline{r}_i, r_i)/(\overline{p}_i, Ap_i) \\ x_{i+1} &= x_i + a_i p_i, \\ r_{i+1} &= r_i - a_i A p_i \quad \text{and} \quad \overline{r}_{i+1} = \overline{r}_i - a_i A^T \overline{p}_i, \\ b_i &= (\overline{r}_{i+1}, r_{i+1})/(\overline{r}_i, r_i), \\ p_{i+1} &= r_{i+1} + b_i p_i \quad \text{and} \quad \overline{p}_{i+1} = \overline{r}_{i+1} + b_i \overline{p}_i. \end{aligned}$$

Remarks:

(i) This scheme essentially solves two problems at once; one is the desired (physical) problem and the other is its adjoint. It thus has the disadvantage of doing twice as much work as necessary if the problem is symmetric (diffusion-dominated flow, for example).

(ii) There is no minimization property: hence, monotonic error decay is not guaranteed (and often does not occur).

(iii) Although the method will terminate after at most N iterations, it could break down (with $a_i = 0$) before the correct solution is found.

(iv) It has been used with success (and no breakdowns) by Mikić and Morse (1985), in a preconditioned and complex form (to complex equations derived from Fourier-transformed Maxwell equations).

(4) Axelsson's methods

These are too many and too varied to discuss in any detail. Here we summarize one that was presented in Axelsson (1980), applied to the (upwinded) steady convection-diffusion equation in Axelsson and Gustafsson (1979), and compared to GCR by Eisenstat et al. (1983), whose form of the algorithm we present:

$$\text{Choose } x_0; \text{ compute } r_0 = b - Ax_0 \text{ and set } p_0 = r_0.$$

For $i = 0, 1, 2, \ldots,$ until convergence, Do

$$\begin{aligned} x_{i+1} &= x_i + \sum_{j=0}^{i} a_j^{(i)} p_j, \\ r_{i+1} &= b - Ax_{i+1}, \\ b_i &= -(Ar_{i+1}, Ap_i)/ \parallel Ap_i \parallel^2, \\ \text{and } p_{i+1} &= r_{i+1} + b_i p_i, \end{aligned}$$

where the $\{a_j^{(i)}\}$ are computed so that $\parallel r_{i+1} \parallel$ is minimized. This requires the (least-squares) solution of the following symmetric linear system for $a^{(i)}$ of order $i+1$ (hopefully i is small):

$$Ba^{(i)} = g,$$
$$\text{where } B_{kl} = (Ap_k, Ap_l) \text{ and } g_l = (r_i, Ap_l).$$

Eisenstat et al. (1983) show that, while the solution update is more complicated than in GCR, the two methods are mathematically equivalent. This scheme has been called a modified minimum residual conjugate gradient method by Axelsson (1980) and a least squares conjugate gradient residual method by Elman (1982). [What is it, *really*?]

We conclude this section by at least mentioning a few references to related methods that we have not yet considered, but probably should: Saad (1984), Brown and Hindmarsh (1984), Young and Jea (1980), and Manteuffel (1977).

C. Preconditioning Methods

After stating that virtually all CG-like methods utilize some sort of preconditioning in practise, we describe just three; for others, see the references. Recalling that even in the best cases (e.g., CG on SPD matrices), the number of iterations varies as the square root of the condition number, the goal of preconditioning is to convert the original linear system into an equivalent one that has a (much) lower condition number. While this can be done in any of several methods (e.g., left, right, or split preconditioning—see Elman, 1982), we present just one:

$$Ax = b \rightarrow AP^{-1}(Px) \equiv \tilde{A}\tilde{x} = b, \tag{23}$$

where $\tilde{A} \equiv AP^{-1}$ and $\tilde{x} \equiv Px$. P^{-1} is the preconditioning matrix and one goal is to make P "look like" A so that $\tilde{A}$ "looks like" the identity matrix and (most importantly) has a small condition number, $\kappa(\tilde{A}) = 0(1)$. For preconditioning to be effective, the faster convergence must overcome the added costs of *applying* the preconditioning, so that the total cost of solving (23) is lower. Thus, a second goal of "selecting P" is that linear systems with P as the coefficient matrix must be "easy" to solve. Clearly $\tilde{A}$ should remain sparse, although not necessarily as sparse as A. "Thus, preconditioning is a compromise between maintaining sparsity and getting the best approximate inverse of A. When viewed in this framework, the CG method with preconditioning spans the gap between direct and iterative methods."—Mikić and Morse (1985). And the nonsymmetric case is more complicated yet, "The error bounds ... do not suggest a 'best' definition for this concept. Moreover, it is usually difficult to analyze the effect of a particular preconditioning for nonsymmetric matrices. As a result, preconditioning is more of an art than a science, in which approximations P are developed from heuristic notions of closeness to A and from techniques known to be effective for symmetric problems."—Elman (1982).

The preconditioners that we have used or would use for a general finite element mesh, general boundary conditions, etc., are:

(1) Incomplete factorization

"Most preconditionings are based upon the concept of incomplete LU decomposition. The idea behind this is that a sparsity pattern (which may be the same as that of the matrix A) is prescribed, and then a standard LU decomposition is performed, except that where an entry in L or U falls outside the sparsity pattern it is neglected, as are any entries generated by it."—Jackson and Robinson (1985).

This describes the first of the preconditioners that we have used; but only in the symmetric version (where $U \equiv L^T$) described by Kershaw (1978) and implemented by Anderson and Shestakov (1983), called ICCG: Incomplete Cholesky Conjugate Gradient. In these algorithms, the "zero fill-in" strategy is employed; i.e., the sparsity pattern of A is imposed upon P. For the unsymmetric case (which we have not yet tried), the obvious generalization to an incomplete LU decomposition, also described by Kershaw (1978), would be our method of choice.

Perhaps, tho', the ILU technique may be made more robust by a modification that preserves the row sum of A; called $MILU$—Modified Incomplete LU—see Gustafsson (1978) and Elman (1982).

(2) Complete factorization, with a twist

The second technique that we have tested, again for the symmetric case, is one of a family of schemes prescribed by Glowinski et al. (1980), that can be effective if A is a fixed matrix that must be used for many right hand sides (the b vectors). Since this is just the case for the discrete Poisson equation of the NS equations, the algorithm is interesting. The philosophy is that the original cost of preconditioning A is not so important since it will be amortized over many solutions (e.g., one for each time step). Briefly, it begins by performing a full (complete) factorization of A via $A = LL^T$. Then, L is modified (to $\tilde{L}$) by enforcing a specified sparsity pattern on it; i.e., by allowing $\tilde{L}$ to have between 0 and 100% fill-in (relative to A)—the former looking more like ICCG and the latter corresponding to Gaussian elimination (for which $P = A$ so that CG requires but one iteration). It is important to note that while the zero fill-in option gives a preconditioner with the same sparsity pattern as A, the entries are different than those from an *incomplete* factorization.

(3) Diagonal scaling

Diagonal scaling is as simple as it sounds: use a diagonal matrix for P in (23) so that operations with P^{-1} are simple and fast. But what diagonal matrix? It turns out, unusually fortuitously since free lunches are infrequent at best, that the best (or nearly the best) diagonal matrix to use is simply $P = \text{diag}(A)$. That this diagonal matrix is "best" was shown by Bauer (1963) for an SPD matrix and further specialized by Greenbaum (1977) to a Stieltjes matrix, and it applies in the following sense: For A SPD, there is no diagonal preconditioner that will reduce $\kappa(\tilde{A})$ below that using $P = \text{diag}(A)$ except perhaps by a factor of N; and if A is a Stieltjes matrix, this factor is reduced to 2. The low storage and small extra CPU cost (per iteration) of this scheme are its virtues; the larger number of iterations required are its drawbacks.

We end this section on a slightly sour note: Even tho' the symmetric part of A may be positive-definite, the preconditioned version of same may not be (Elman, 1982); and while the effect of this is not known, Murphy's law should tell us in which direction to look.

VII. MATCHING TIME INTEGRATION TO "CG"

Consideration of time integration methods simultaneously with CG-like solution methods narrows the options to some extent. For example, (10) and (11)—with BTD and, usually, subcycling—is a viable option because the coefficient matrix is constant and SPD (or can be made so, by pegging pressures—preferably after verifying that the singular system has a solution). And indeed we have used (and still do use) this scheme. The (additional) advantages are fairly obvious—mainly simplicity—and the main disadvantages are stability and the need to lump the mass (which of course is no problem if FDM is employed). We have tested (mainly) ICCG, but have also limited experience with the Glowinski et al. (1980) method (hereafter referred to as GPP) and with diagonal scaling.

We have also implemented the semi-implicit scheme described by (14)–(16) in the following way: (i) The pressure equation, (15), is solved by ICCG or GPP and (ii) the temperature and velocity, (14) and (16), are solved by diagonally scaled CG which works well since M is rather diagonally dominant and Δt is "small." While consistent mass is precluded in (16), the consistent mass matrix can be used in (14).

The semi-implicit-plus-continuity-equation approach, (17), has little to recommend it, especially when the penalty version, (19), is considered. This looks like a viable scheme and might work well using ICCG or GPP. The eigenvalue spectrum, analyzed by Malkus (1981), appears to be favorable to a (well) pre-conditioned CG method. One potential difficulty might be the design of efficient schemes for the matrix-vector multiplies involving the (consistent—see Engelman et al., 1982) penalty matrix.

Moving finally to implicit time integration, in which an unsymmetric matrix is an inherent part, we remark that, as in the semi-implicit case, the first method of choice would involve the penalty approximation; i.e., we drop (21) and focus on (22). After linearizing the advection matrix (e.g., Newton or quasi-Newton) and even after splitting off the energy equation, we still face an unsymmetric, indefinite matrix problem in the velocities. Also uncertain is whether the symmetric part of the final matrix is positive definite; in general it is probably not, although one's chances are probably better if the advection matrix is designed to be skew-symmetric—see Lee et al. (1982). In any event, after the "best" formulation is available, the selection of a CG-like method is still not easy. The near-concensus of a small group of experts consulted seems to be this: (1) Try the simple MR method, first with no history (search direction) vectors stored, then (2) try a GCR (k) (restart) method or Orthomin (k) with k "small," O (1–10), next (3) try one of the Axelsson schemes, and finally, (4) try BCG. Perhaps items (3) and (4) should be switched in priorities. From this brief and highly speculative look at the unsymmetric NS problem, it is clear that much hard work still lies ahead.

VIII. NUMERICAL RESULTS

Table 1 summarizes most of the results in which one or another CG method was tested. Results are for ICCG unless stated otherwise. The λ/P columns designate the Lagrange multiplier (12) (and sometimes the initial pressure, at $t = 0$) and the pressure (10), respectively, where we note that λ always costs more because our initial guess for P (from the previous time step) is relatively much better. (We briefly tested pressure extrapolation to further improve the initial guess, but were not pleased with the results—which were often not as good as those using P from the old time level.)

Additional observations and comments:

(1) If the matrix is constant *and* can be stored in memory in factored form, a direct method (such as that by Taylor et al., 1981, which we employ) cannot be beat.

TABLE 1: PERFORMANCE SUMMARY OF ICCG (ET ALII)

Run	No.Equations	No.Solutions λ/P	ϵ	No.Iterations λ/P	Comments
		Two-Dimensional Runs			
1	2400	400/1600	10^{-3}	30/7	λ costs more because of less accurate
2	2400	400/1600	10^{-4}	40/15	initial guess.
3	2400	1/25	10^{-3}	54/4	The GPP scheme required $\sim$ 20% fewer
4	2400	1/25	10^{-4}	60/14	iterations for the 3 same runs;
5	2400	1/25	10^{-5}	64/49	averaged over all solutions.
6	3200	1/20	10^{-4}	66/16	Matrix is singular; GPP needs 2× the iterations of ICCG.
7	3200	1/20	10^{-4}	90/20	1 Pressure pegged; GPP needed $\sim$ 1/3 more iterations than ICCG.
8	20,000	–/2400	10^{-4}	–/60	Code + ICCG used 2/3 of the available CRAY 1S memory.
8a	20,000	2/50	10^{-4}	210/56	For $\epsilon = 10^{-3}$, the iterations are 180/8.2.
8b	20,000	2/50	10^{-4}	218/69	GPP method used; like Run 7, hydrostatic mode exists and one pressure is pegged (Ditto for 8a, 8c).
8c	20,000	2/50	10^{-4}	950/240	Diagonal scaling used. Cost per iteration is $\sim$ 1/3 of that for ICCG or GPP.
		Three-Dimensional Runs			
9	3150	1/4	10^{-3}	43/24	GPP scheme required $\sim$ 20% fewer iterations
10	3150	1/4	10^{-4}	49/41	for the same 3 runs.
11	3150	1/4	10^{-5}	55/47	
12	3150	1/4	10^{-8}	72/66	
13	3150	1/1	10^{-8}	897/799	Preconditioned using diag (A) in Run (13); cost per iteration is $\sim$ 1/8 of ICCG.
14	8640	14/50	10^{-3}	80/15	The GPP scheme req'd $\sim$ 25% fewer iterations.
15	9375	135/850	10^{-4}	45/25	
16	16,920	1/1200	10^{-3}	300/1–20	$\sim$ 15 iterations were needed early on—as low as 1 late in the run as flow became $\sim$ steady.

(2) Portions of Run 8 were rerun using the direct solver (and disk, of course) for comparison. The cost (CPU + I/O) was $\sim$ 3 times as much as ICCG and was 88% I/O.

(3) Run 8 was performed with the semi-implicit option, (14)–(16), with diagonal scaling for the velocity and temperature solutions; convergence "rates" were ($\epsilon = 10^{-4}$): 6–10 iterations for u and v, 10–15 for T. We have also tested this option on the "rotating cone"—a pure advection problem—see Gresho and Chan (1985), and the results were quite encouraging: for Courant numbers that yield accurate results (e.g., < 0.2), the consistent mass approach needs only $\sim$ half-a-dozen iterations and the lumped mass approach about half of that.

(4) It is not clear whether ICCG or GPP is "better"; we could "argue" either way, based on our limited experience, but the edge is never more than about 25%. We do note that the ICCG code, á la Kershaw, (1978), does process diagonal entries differently if they would otherwise be ≤ 0. In our version of GPP, no such considerations have yet been addressed.

(5) We stop the iterations when $\| r_{i+1} \| \leq \epsilon \| b \|$ and $\| x_{i+1} - x_i \| \leq \epsilon \| x_{i+1} \|$, criteria installed in the code by Anderson and Shestakov (1980). Comparison of solutions indicated that $\epsilon = 10^{-4} - 10^{-3}$ is a sufficiently small error tolerance for CG.

(6) Run 13 was also performed with 2 other diagonal preconditioners; diag (ICCG) and diag ($\tilde{L}\tilde{L}^T$) of GPP. The costs (iterations, λ/p) were 1046/924 and 1030/915, respectively.

(7) Run 16 required 87% of available memory on a CRAY 1S.

(8) Considering that diagonal scaling uses less storage and vectorizes better, it may be worthy of further exploitation—especially in 3D.

(9) The memory requirements for ICCG in 3D, while much lower than those for direct solvers, are still very "noticeable"; e.g., the largest 3D "cube" ($N \times N \times N$ elements) that we could solve in memory today with ICCG and our explicit code is $N \cong 25 \pm 3$, which would require $\sim 1.3 \pm 0.5$M words of memory and allow 6 dependent variables: u, v, w, P, T, and c (concentration). I.e., $N = 22$ fills a 1M word memory and $N = 28$ fills a 2M word memory. For diagonal scaling, this increases to $N \cong 28 \pm 3$; discouraging, especially when compared to the analogous results for the direct solver: $N =\sim 16 \pm 1$.

IX. SUMMARY AND CONCLUSIONS

Cost effective numerical solutions of the time dependent incompressible Navier-Stokes equations are virtually impossible to obtain without the serious consideration and implementation of efficient methods to solve large sets of linear algebraic equations. While direct methods will probably always have a role to play in solving these systems, iterative techniques have improved rapidly recently and appear to hold out greater hope for further improvement, especially for large—or real world—problems; i.e., three dimensional. Herein we have explored and exploited, briefly, some CG-related methods and found them quite useful. While most of our experience with a symmetric matrix has centered around the incomplete Cholesky technique for preconditioning, we believe that the method of Glowinski et al. (1980) is also worthy of further study and comparative testing. We have also successfully tested the simple technique of diagonal preconditioning for solving the SPD and nearly diagonally dominant matrices associated with the parabolic portion of the problem—i.e., transient diffusion with implicit time integration. Finally we entered the arena of speculation and briefly considered some newer CG-like methods that might be useful in the more general case involving unsymmetric matrices, which, in combination with the associated convective nonlinearity, requires much more careful study of a greater number of options and strategies.

ACKNOWLEDGMENTS

Useful input to this paper was provided by S. T. Chan, J. M. Leone, A. C. Hindmarsh, A. Greenbaum, and G. Rodrique of Lawrence Livermore National Laboratory and by R. L. Sani of the University of Colorado, Z. Mikić of Science Applications, Inc., and H. Elman of the University of Maryland.

This work was performed under the auspices of the U. S. Department of Energy by Lawrence Livermore National Laboratory under Contract W-7405-Eng-48.

REFERENCES

Anderson, D. and A. Shestakov (1983): *Computer Phys. Comm., 30:* 37. Also: *Ibid.*, p. 51.

Axelsson, O. (1980): *Lin. Alg. & Appl., 29:* 1–16.

Axelsson. O. and I. Gustafsson (1979): *J. Inst. Maths. Applics., 23:* 321–337.

Bauer, F. (1963): *Num. Math., 5:* 73–87.

Brown, P. and A. Hindmarsh (1984): LLNL Report UCRL-90770, May 1984.

Concus, P., G. Golub and D. O'Leary (1976): in *Sparse Matrix Computations,* Academic Press, New York NY, PP. 309–332.

Eisenstat, S., H. Elman and M. Schultz (1983): *SIAM J. Num. Anal., 20* (2):345–357.

Elman, H. (1982): Ph.D. Thesis, Yale University, New Haven CT.

Elman, H. (1983): in *Proc. Elliptic Solvers Conference,* Naval Postgraduate School, Monterey CA.

Elman, H. (1986): University of Maryland, personal communication.

Engelman, M. and R. Sani (1983): *Num. Heat Transfer, 6:* 41–54.

Engelman, M., M. Bercovier, P. Gresho and R. Sani (1982): *Int. J. Num. Meth. Fl., 2:* 25–42.

Fletcher, R. (1976): in *Numerical Analysis, Dundee 1975,* Springer-Verlag, New York NY, pp. 73–89.

Fortin, M. (1983): *Int. J. Num. Meth. Fl., 3:* 93–98.

Glowinski, R., J. Periaux and O. Pironneau (1980): *Appl. Math. Mod., 4:* 187.

Greenbaum, A. (1977): LLNL Internal Report, Tech. Memo No. 77-4.

Gresho, P. (1978): in *Recent Advances in Engineering Science,* University of Florida, pp. 549–555.

Gresho, P. and S. Chan (1985): in *Numerical Methods in Laminar and Turbulent Flow,* Pineridge Press, Swansea, UK, pp. 3–21.

Gresho, P. and R. Sani (1986): in preparation.

Gresho, P., R. Lee and R. Sani (1978): in *Finite Elements in Fluids, Vol. 3,* John Wiley & Sons, New York NY, pp. 335–350.

Gresho, P., R. Lee and R. Sani (1980a): in *Recent Advances in Numerical Methods in Fluids, Vol. 1,* Pineridge Press, Swansea, UK, p. 27.

Gresho, P., S. Chan, R. Lee and R. Sani (1980b): in Lecture Notes in Mathematics, No. 771, Springer-Verlag, New York NY.

Gresho, P., S. Chan, R. Lee and C. Upson (1984): *Int. J. Num. Meth. Fl., 4:* 557–598 (Part 1) and 619–640 (Part 2).

Gustafsson, I. (1978): *BIT, 18:* 142–156.

Hageman, L. and D. Young (1981): *Applied Iterative Methods,* Academic Press, New York NY.

Hestenes, M. and E. Stiefel (1952): *J. Res. Nat. Bus. Standards, 49:* 409–436.

Hindmarsh, A., P. Gresho and D. Griffiths (1984): *Int. J. Num. Meth. Fl., 4:* 853–897.

Jackson, C. P. and P. C. Robinson (1985): *Int. J. Num. Meth. Eng., 21* (7):1315.

Kershaw, D. (1978): *J. Comp. Phys., 26* (1):43–65.

Lee, R., S. Chan, M. Cullen, P. Gresho and R. Sani (1982): in *Finite Elements in Fluids, Vol. 4,* Wiley & Sons, New York NY.

Lewis, J. and R. Rehm (1980): *J. Res. Nat. Bus. Stds., 85* (5):367–390.

Malkus, D. (1981): *Int. J. Eng. Sci., 19:* 1299–1310.

Malkus, D. and T. Hughes (1978): *Comp. Meth. Appl. Mech. Eng., 15:* 63.

Manteuffel, T. (1977): *Num. Math., 28:* 307–327.

Mikić, Z. and E. Morse (1985): *J. Comp. Phys., 61:* 154–185.

Noble, B. (1969): *Applied Linear Algebra,* Prentice-Hall, Inc., NJ.

Obeysekare, U., M. Allen, R. Ewing and J. George (1985): submitted to *Int. J. Num. Meth. Fl.*

Petzold, L. (1982): *SIAM J. Sci. Stat. Comp., 3:* 367–384.

Petzold, L. and P. Lötstedt (1984): in Proc. Int. Conf. on *Innovative Methods for Nonlinear Problems,* Pineridge Press, Swansea, UK.

Reddy, J. (1982): AMD-Vol. 51, ASME, New York.

Reid, J. (1971): in *Large Sparse Sets of Linear Equations,* Academic Press, New York NY, pp. 231–254.

Saad, Y. (1984): *SIAM J. Sci. Stat. Comput., 5* (1):203.

Sani, R., P. Gresho, D. Griffiths and R. Lee (1981a): *Int. J. Num. Meth. Fl., 1:* 17–43.

Sani, R., S. Chan, B. Eaton, P. Gresho and R. Lee (1981b): in *Numerical Methods in Laminar and Turbulent Flow,* Pineridge Press, Swansea, UK, pp. 41–51.

Taylor, R., S. Sackett and E. Wilson (1981): in *Nonlinear Finite Element Analysis in Structural Dynamics,* p. 521.

Young, D. and K. Jea (1980): *Linear Alg. Appl., 34:* 159–194.

VI International Conference on Finite Elements in Water Resources, Lisboa, Portugal, June 1986

Evolution of Two-Dimensional FE Wave Equation Models

W.G. Gray, I.P.E. Kinnmark
Department of Civil Engineering, University of Notre Dame, Notre Dame, IN 46556, U.S.A.

BACKGROUND

One of the many interesting water resources problems which has challenged numerical analysts and modelers is the simulation of surface flow in shallow estuaries. The equations which describe this type of flow are obtained by integrating equations for conservation of mass and momentum through the vertical column of fluid under the assumptions that vertical density gradients and fluid accelerations are negligible. Dissipation within the fluid is considered to be much less than bottom friction effects so that the shallow water equations are

Conservation of Mass

$$L(\zeta,\underset{\sim}{v}) \equiv \frac{\partial \zeta}{\partial t} + \underset{\sim}{\nabla} \cdot (H\underset{\sim}{v}) = 0 \tag{1}$$

Conservation of Momentum

$$\underset{\sim}{M}(\zeta,\underset{\sim}{v}) \equiv \frac{\partial(H\underset{\sim}{v})}{\partial t} + \underset{\sim}{\nabla} \cdot (H\underset{\sim}{v}\underset{\sim}{v}) + \tau H\underset{\sim}{v} + f\underset{\sim}{k} \times H\underset{\sim}{v} + gH\underset{\sim}{\nabla}\zeta - \underset{\sim}{A} = \underset{\sim}{0} \tag{2}$$

where ζ is surface elevation above a datum (L),
h is bathymetry (L),
$H = h + \zeta$ is the total depth of flow (L),
$\underset{\sim}{v}$ is the vertically averaged flow velocity (L/T),
τ is the non-linear friction coefficient (1/T),
f is the Coriolis parameter (1/T),
g is the gravitational accerlation (L/T^2),
$\underset{\sim}{A}$ is atmospheric wind forcing (L^2/T^2),
$\underset{\sim}{\nabla}$ is the two-dimensional gradient operator (1/L),
$\underset{\sim}{k}$ is the unit vector in the vertical direction,

t is time (T),
x is positive eastward (L), and
y is positive northward (L).

Although modelers have been simulating flows governed by the shallow water equations for well over a decade using the finite element method, the results of such simulations have been highly varied in quality. This section of the paper is an account of the major problems which have been identified and addressed in the process of evolving simulators with improved representation of physical phenomena and reduced computational cost. The development process is incomplete at present; and, in general, it seems fair to remark that the overall capabilities of finite element surface flow simulators lag behind those of finite difference models. Nevertheless, given the much earlier implementation of finite difference simulators and the more widespread dissemination of that technology, finite element models have progressed to the point where, in some situations (e.g. complex geometry or a fairly limited data base and grid) they are competitive with or superior to the older method. Much effort in finite difference modeling of surface flow today is being devoted to transformation of irregular or odd-shaped regions to simple geometric shapes (e.g. Thompson, 1982). This approach will result in increased sharing of ideas between finite difference and finite element approaches and perhaps will eventually lead to a coalescence of the two methods into one general technique.

The early finite element tidal models were plagued by severe spurious oscillations. In some instances, attempts to control these problems were successful for a limited number of time steps but eventually led to unstable computations. When the non-linear advective terms in the momentum equation are small, the models are sometimes capable of producing stable yet oscillatory simulations superimposed on a reasonable solution. The remedies selected to control this unphysical noise were themselves unphysical: unrealistically large bottom friction coefficients (Brebbia and Partridge, 1976; Niemeyer, 1979); inclusion of an artificial viscosity term in the momentum equation (Adey, 1974; Connor and Wang, 1974); overspecification of boundary conditions (Taylor and Davis, 1975); presentation of numerical solutions averaged over an element such that the solutions appeared smoother (Wang and Connor, 1975); and addition of excessive damping to the model through time-stepping schemes (e.g. Kawahara, et. al. 1978). The use of these techniques, in conjunction with heuristic tuning of the model coefficients and parameters, often led to computed surface elevation and velocity profiles which resembled measured data fields. However, the quality of the finite element method as a tool for investigating the physics of flow in a particular region remained unknown.

Finite difference modelers successfully suppressed spurious oscillations by solving for depth and velocity at different positions in space, the so-called staggered grid approach (Platzman, 1959). A finite element variation on this theme was the choice of different basis functions for surface elevation and velocity. Although this method had the effect of providing solutions for one unknown, typically velocity, at more locations than the other, surface elevation, both variables are computed at the corners of the elements. Recent calculations (Walters, 1983) seem to indicate this procedure is ineffective in removing oscillations from the computed velocity field. Gray (1977) and Gray and Lynch (1979) presented semi-implicit and other numerical solution procedures which reduce, but do not eliminate, spurious modes.

A radically different approach to the elimination of spurious node-to-node oscillations was developed by Lynch and Gray (1979). This method has been called the wave equation approach and is based on a reformulation of continuity equation (1) to a second order in time and space wave propagation form. A generalized presentation of this equation has been introduced by Kinnmark and Gray (1985c) whereby the operators in equation (1) and (2) are combined to form the equation

$$W(\zeta,\underset{\sim}{v};G) \equiv \frac{\partial L}{\partial t} - \underset{\sim}{\nabla} \cdot \underset{\sim}{M} + GL = 0 \qquad (3)$$

where G may be a function of time and space. Equation (3) solved in conjunction with (2) will lead to the same analytic solution as (1) and (2) if the condition that L = 0 at t = 0 is applied. The original formulation of Lynch and Gray (1979) may be obtained as the special case of (3) wherein G is selected as being equal to τ. Substitution for the appropriate operators in (3) yields

$$W(\zeta,\underset{\sim}{v};\tau) \equiv \frac{\partial^2\zeta}{\partial t^2} + \tau\frac{\partial\zeta}{\partial t} - H\underset{\sim}{v} \cdot \underset{\sim}{\nabla}\tau - \underset{\sim}{\nabla} \cdot [\underset{\sim}{\nabla} \cdot (H\underset{\sim}{v}\underset{\sim}{v}) + fH\underset{\sim}{k} \times \underset{\sim}{v}$$

$$+ gH\underset{\sim}{\nabla}\zeta - \underset{\sim}{A}] = 0 \qquad (4)$$

Efficient numerical simulations making use of (4) and (2) have been developed along two lines. Explicit time marching schemes were made highly efficient through the use of integral lumping (Lynch and Gray, 1979) which leads to a diagonal coefficient matrix. Thus the need for matrix solvers is eliminated and the solution for each time step is cheap and involves small core requirements. The main drawback to this scheme is the restriction on the time step size of the explicit scheme. Implicit models were also developed but these require the use of effective matrix solvers to keep costs low. Kinnmark and Gray (1984b) introduced a

Taylor expansion procedure to replace matrix decompositions by back substitutions, thereby decreasing substantially the computational effort for large problems. Alternatively, Kinnmark and Gray (1985c) developed an implicit model based on the generalized wave equation (3) where G is required to be time invariant. By this approach the coefficient matrix, even for an implicit problem, is independent of time. Thus the need to reformulate and decompose the matrix is completely eliminated and the solution procedure is based simply on back substitution at each step.

Current developments involve implementations of a wave type form of momentum equation and application of the existing models to data bases. In the absence of a fully staggered grid, which would be cumbersome for a model making use of general element shapes, the wave equation approach is the only method which has been demonstrated to be capable of noise suppression in finite element models without the need for artificial or physically unrealistic damping.

NUMERICAL ANALYSIS

Numerical analysis of primitive equation formulations has shown that these equations are inherently plagued by spurious spatial oscillations. Field scale simulations based on these equations have invariably required artificial viscosity or implicit numerical damping to achieve stable simulations. The wave equation formulation of the shallow water equations described in the previous section was developed because of its apparent ability to perform without artificial damping and without introducing spurious oscillations. From the earliest consideration of this method (Gray and Lynch, 1977), it was apparent that full scale numerical simulations would be tedious and ineffective in screening alternative equation forms and numerical approximations of these equations. Throughout the years of development of finite element models based on the wave equation formulation, Fourier analysis has played a crucial role in filtering out the optimal formulation. The procedure used makes use of concepts employed by Leendertse (1967) in examining alternative finite difference formulations. The method provides conditions for stability as well as a comparison of numerical wave celerity and damping with the analytical counterparts. The method is applied to linearized versions of the equations and therefore cannot be viewed as a definitive test of fully nonlinear models. However the guidance provided by Fourier analysis has been an invaluable tool leading to successful field simulations.

Figures 1 through 4 from Gray and Lynch (1977) are indicative of the type of results obtained from Fourier analysis and clearly demonstrate the superiority of the explicit wave equation scheme as compared to a leapfrog scheme for the pri-

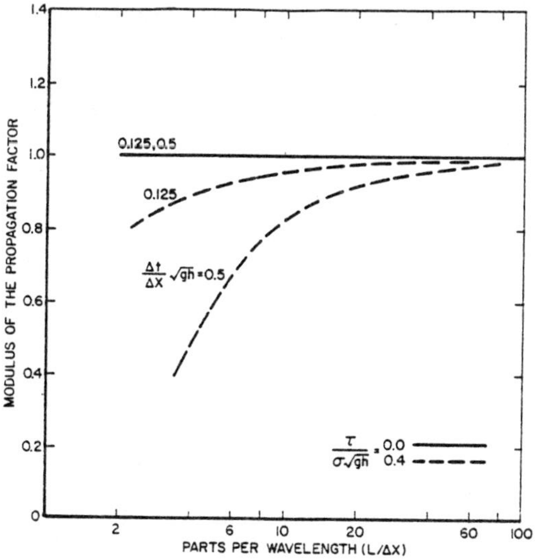

Figure 1. Modulus of the propagation factor for the leapfrog scheme.

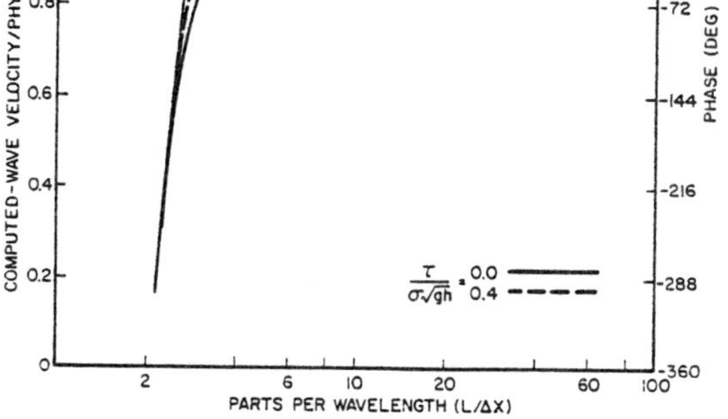

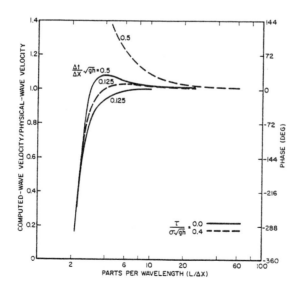

Figure 2. Phase of the propagation factor for the leapfrog scheme.

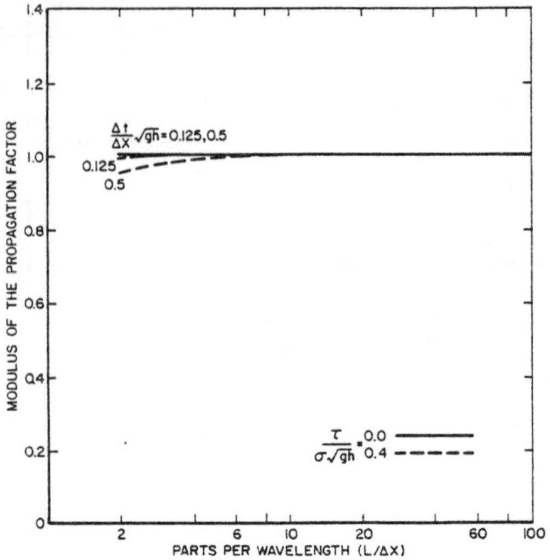

Figure 3. Modulus of the propagation factor for the explicit wave equation scheme.

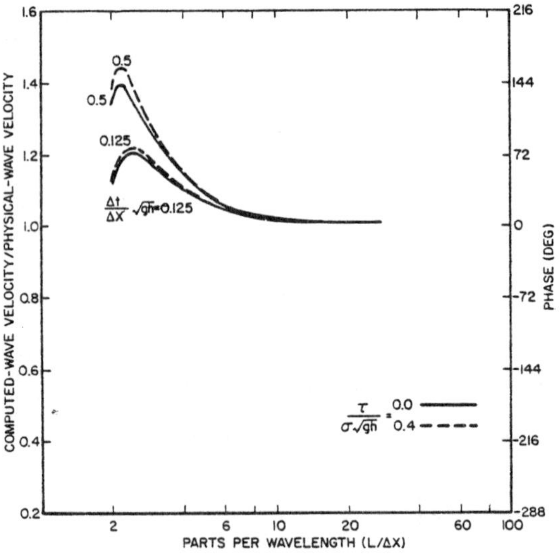

Figure 4. Phase of the propagation factor for the explicit wave equation scheme.

mitive equations. In particular, the wave formulation shows superior simulation of damping due to bottom friction as well as the important property of non-zero phase velocity for the $2\Delta x$ wave. The performance expected based on these figures was later confirmed by full numerical simulations in Lynch and Gray (1979) in which severe node-to-node oscillations of the primitive equation were absent from the wave solutions. These computations clearly show that oscillations in primitive solution schemes arise even for linear problems when the advective terms are neglected. Platzman (1981) analyzed the spatial oscillation problem in terms of numerical resonance frequencies due to forced oscillations. Kinnmark and Gray (1985b) have shown that to correctly explain the ability of numerical schemes to suppress spurious oscillation on higher order elements and/or nonuniform grids, one must perform a direct Fourier analysis on the difference in solution between two neighboring points.

An alternative to the above Fourier analysis which considers discretizations in both time and space is dispersion analysis (see e.g. Platzman, 1978) which discretizes the spatial variables but leaves the time variable continuous. This technique has also been used by Lynch (1978) in analyzing what he refers to as a spectral model. Dispersion analysis is simpler to perform than full analysis and is useful in isolating pathological problems that are entirely attributable to spatial discretization. However, the method does not analyze the effects of different temporal discretizations which are of critical importance in obtaining high quality time evolution of a simulation.

For estuary modeling using the wave equation approach, the most common procedure has been to solve a wave equation formulation of the continuity equation in conjunction with the primitive momentum equations. Kinnmark and Gray (1982,1984a) showed, using Fourier analysis, that the proper time weighting of the momentum equations plays a key role in suppressing spurious temporal oscillations in the velocity solution. This finding was confirmed in their full numerical simulation and is demonstrated in Figure 5 (from Kinnmark and Gray, 1982) and Figure 6 (from Laible, 1984). The chief conclusion from this work is that a two-time-level discretization does not give rise to temporal oscillations while a three level scheme, especially when centered in time, can be a source of serious difficulty. Foreman's (1983) numerical analysis also leads to the conclusion that a three-time-level momentum equation is inappropriate and can result in step-by-step temporal oscillations of velocity, although similar oscillations in surface elevation are eliminated by the wave continuity equation.

Efficiency of the numerical simulation procedure requires that the solution for elevation be uncoupled from the solu-

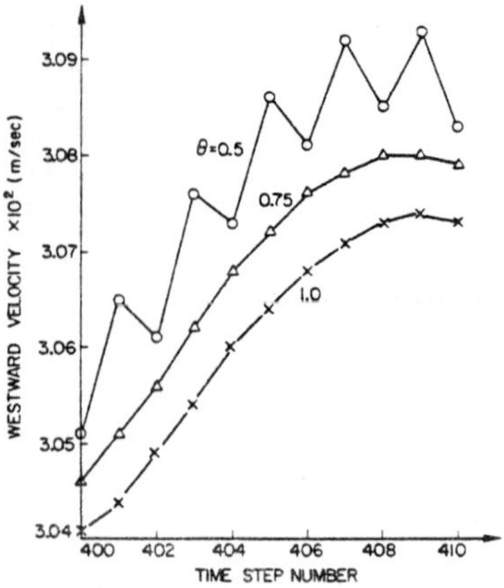

Figure 5. Velocity solutions obtained using various time weightings of the momentum equations. θ = 0.5 is symmetric three time level scheme, θ = 0.75 is an unsymmetric three time level scheme and θ = 1.0 uses a two time level approximation for the time derivative.

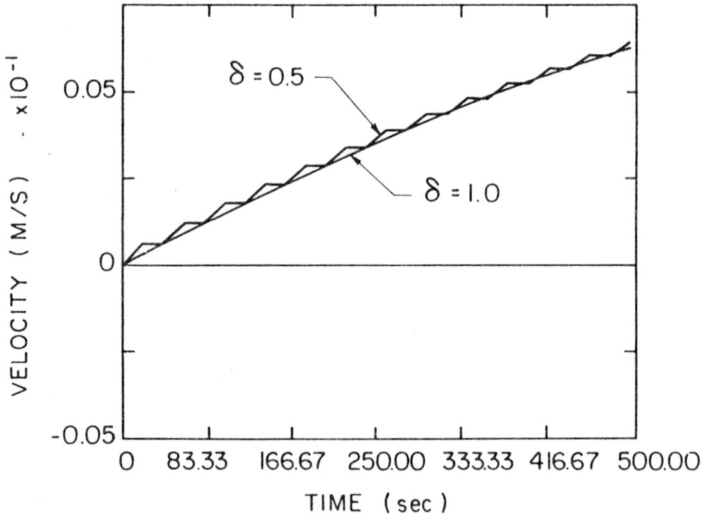

Figure 6. Typical velocity time history response. δ = 1/2 is a symmetric three time level scheme. δ = 1 uses a two time level approximation for the time derivative.

tion for the velocity components. In other words, it is desirable to solve the wave equation for the surface elevation and then to solve the momentum equations for the velocity. Implementation of such a procedure keeps the size of the matrices which must be solved to a minimum. Kinnmark and Gray (1984b) performed a two-dimensional Fourier analysis, amended with the Routh-Hurwitz stability criterion (see e.g. Kinnmark, 1986), which included Coriolis effects and found that the uncoupling of equations can be performed without loss of stability.

Most of the stability analyses performed have considered uniform grids and linear elements in space. These analyses give an indication of expected behavior using more complex formulations. Kinnmark and Gray (1985a) have explicitly developed stability and accuracy constraints for some types of nonuniform grids, variable depths, and higher order elements using Fourier analysis. Quadratic Lagrangian elements were shown to have more restrictive stability conditions than linear elements. The damping of waves is shown to be largely independent of spatial discretization or grid nonuniformity.

Efficient implicit models making use of the wave equation formulation have also been developed with the aid of numerical analysis. For the case where G in equation (3) is held constant such that the coefficient matrix is invariant, Kinnmark and Gray (1985c) have performed a stability analysis which indicates that optimal stability is obtained when G is similar in magnitude to τ. Kinnmark and Gray (1984b) also introduced and numerically analyzed a Taylor expansion for the coefficient matrix which replaces decompositions with back substitutions thereby decreasing the computational effort for large problems.

BOUNDARY CONDITIONS

The appropriate specification of boundary conditions is of critical importance due to the impact these conditions have on the accuracy of a simulation. Among the most important issues are the selection of the correct physical quantities for specification at a boundary, choice of the appropriate equations to be solved in the vicinity of the boundary, and the determination of an appropriate normal direction at a boundary whose slope is discontinuous.

Perhaps the most fundamental question relating to boundary conditions is the identification of the physical quantities which must be specified at the boundary. In tidal problems, the open boundaries transmit the tidal forcing to the interior of the model domain. In a field study, it is generally more convenient to measure the elevation at these boundaries rather than the depth averaged normal velocity or flux. Typically elevation is the only known information at an open boundary and is specified there in a numerical model. However the question of condition specification at an open boundary has not been definitively solved. For example, radiation conditions which allow a wave to pass through a boundary without reflection are sometimes imposed at outflows. Along shorelines or closed boundaries in the absence of flooding, the correct boundary condition is zero flux normal to the boundary. In some simulations, both a zero normal and tangential velocity have been specified. Mathematically, this is correct only at a point where the normal to the boundary is not unique or if a second order artificial damping term is added to the momentum equations. In a discrete numerical model, when a zero tangential velocity is specified at the boundary, a boundary layer of effectively half the width of an element is created. A layer of this size is unrealistically large in field problems and thus routine specification of the tangential velocity should be avoided.

Because of the irregular shape of the shoreline boundary, a typical simulation region will not have a boundary which is collinear with one of the coordinate directions. Therefore the Cartesian components of the velocity or flux vectors must be transformed to tangential-normal coordinates along the boundary. In general, this is accomplished by rotating each component of the momentum equation into local tangential and normal coordinates. This increases the complexity of formulation of the coefficient matrix. An alternative approach is possible when a lumped matrix is used and the solution for surface elevation is decoupled from the solution for the fluxes. For this case, the unrotated momentum equation may be solved for the velocities, and the boundary conditions are applied as a correction to this solution. For example, after solution of the wave equation for the surface elevation, discretization of the momentum equation (2) using a lumped, two-level scheme yields, for node i at time t + Δt

$$(1 + \tau_i \Delta t) H\underset{\sim}{v}_i^{t+\Delta t} + f \Delta t \underset{\sim}{k} \times H\underset{\sim}{v}_i^{t+\Delta t} = \underset{\sim}{r}_i \tag{4}$$

where $\underset{\sim}{r}_i$ are the known quantities in equation (2) and Δt is the time step. Now if the following matrix is defined

$$\underset{\approx}{A}_i = \begin{bmatrix} 1 + \tau_i \Delta t & f\Delta t \\ - f\Delta t & 1 + \tau_i \Delta t \end{bmatrix} \tag{5}$$

then

$$H\underset{\sim}{v}_i^{t+\Delta t} = \underset{\approx}{A}_i \cdot \underset{\sim}{r}_i / |A_i| \tag{6}$$

Equation (6) may be formed at each node i to obtain solutions for $H\underset{\sim}{v}$.

At a boundary where the normal velocity is specified, the solution to (6) may be rotated into normal ($\underset{\sim}{n}$) and tangential ($\underset{\sim}{\lambda}$) coordinates using a rotation matrix $\underset{\approx}{B}_i$ such that

$$H\underset{\sim}{v}^*_i = \underset{\approx}{B}_i \cdot \underset{\approx}{A}_i \cdot \underset{\sim}{r}_i / |A_i| \qquad (7)$$

where the * indicates normal-tangential coordinates. If the normal velocity is then specified to be zero, the tangential velocity is the total velocity and

$$H\underset{\sim}{v}^*_i = \underset{\sim}{\lambda}_i \underset{\sim}{\lambda}_i \cdot \underset{\approx}{B}_i \cdot \underset{\approx}{A}_i \cdot \underset{\sim}{r}_i / |A_i| \qquad (8)$$

Now rotation back to the Cartesian coordinates yields

$$H\underset{\sim}{v}_i^{t+\Delta t} = \underset{\approx}{B}^T \cdot \underset{\sim}{\lambda}_i \underset{\sim}{\lambda}_i \cdot \underset{\approx}{B}_i \cdot \underset{\approx}{A}_i \cdot \underset{\sim}{r}_i / |A_i| \qquad (9)$$

as the velocity vector which incorporates the boundary condition. When the specified normal velocity is non-zero, addition of the normal velocity to the tangential velocity of equation (8) followed by rotation back to Cartesian coordinates is necessary.

Another important issue is the proper selection of the normal direction at a solid boundary where the slope is discontinuous. Consider figure 7 which displays a portion of a grid boundary where the slope at C may be discontinuous. King (1978) has suggested using quadratic elements at such boundaries and locating the midside nodes in adjacent elements such that the normal direction at C is unique. An alternative approach which is successful regardless of element type makes use of an average normal direction such that mass is conserved (Gray, 1977; Engleman, et. al. 1982). One of the interesting aspects of this approach is that the normal direction for a fixed boundary shape and location may vary depending upon the basis functions used to expand H and $\underset{\sim}{v}$ and may even vary with time (Gray, 1984).

Lynch (1985) has proposed a technique which improves the accuracy of the velocity solution at a boundary where the elevation is specified. He noted that the conventional procedure for reducing the number of equations at the boundary when the elevation is specified is to eliminate the wave equation. However by using the wave equation to obtain the normal flux, one obtains better conservation of mass and a higher order approximation for the normal velocity. The normal component of the momentum equation is then neglected at the boundary while the tangential component is solved to complete the velocity solution.

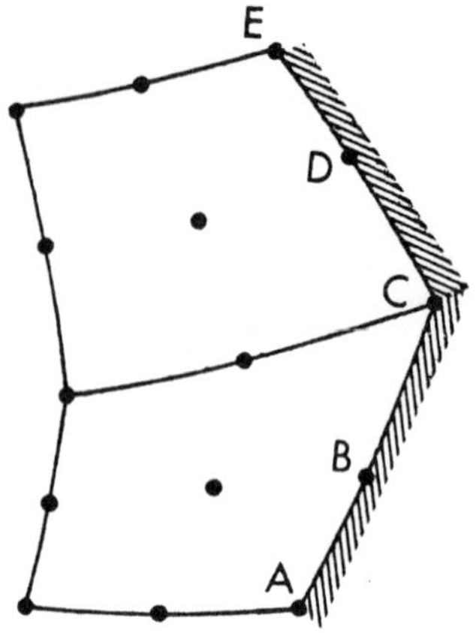

Figure 7. Boundary of finite element grid with nonunique normal direction at nodes.

Although significant advances have been made in properly specifying boundary conditions for two-dimensional shallow water problems, issues relating to the necessary, sufficient, and appropriate boundary conditions on open boundaries remain among the challenges for future research.

IDEALIZED SIMULATIONS

In the previous section, Fourier analysis was presented as the key tool for discriminating among various options for formulation of numerical simulators. Implementation of the selected schemes is best performed by first modeling some standard test case or cases with known analytical solutions. Although such solutions do not exist for complex geometry or in the fully non-linear case, the solutions which do exist are adequate for exercising various terms in the models and assessing various aspects of model behavior. It is important, however, to carefully select analytical test cases which allow for discrimination among alternative simulators. For example, successful simulations of one-dimensional flow in a straight channel with constant bathymetry provide little indication of the ability of a model to simulate two-dimensional flow in an irregular region. In addition to selecting model regions with non-trivial shape and bathymetry, it is of utmost importance to select an appropriate frequency for the tidal forcing. Gray and Lynch (1979) found empirically that the interaction of frequency with the depth and extent of a model region was significant in contributing to the difficulty of a simulation. Platzman (1981) shows that a discretization of the shallow water equations may produce resonance frequencies for the onset of spurious spatial node-to-node oscillations. Thus the forcing frequency for a test case is best chosen close to a resonance frequency such that a simulator will exhibit its tendencies for producing non-physical oscillations.

An analytical test case which has proven very powerful was derived by Lynch and Gray (1978), and the study region is shown in figure 8. The two-dimensional horizontal shallow water equations are solved in the absence of Coriolis force in an annular region. Because the solution depends only on the radial position and time, it is not necessary to consider the entire annulus. Simulations using this analytic solution have typically considered a quarter of the annulus as in figure 8. Boundary conditions include a specified sinusoidally varying elevation along the outer curved edge and zero normal velocity along all other boundaries. A simple discretization using twelve quadratic Lagrangian elements and sixty-three nodes is also shown in figure 8. For the case of a quadratically varying bathymetry, Lynch and Gray (1979) simulated flow in the region using alternative models. Their results for the radial velocity appear in figure 9. The primitive equation leap frog simulation is very poor due to node-to-node oscillations. The semi-implicit scheme provides some improvement but the wave equation method is clearly the best. Although these test simulations do not demonstrate that the wave equation technique will be successful for field simulations, they do indicate that the other methods will be unsatisfactory.

Walters (1983) performed some test calculations for a rectangular region and compared his results to those of another analytical solution in Lynch and Gray (1978). This work demonstrated that different order basis for elevation and velocity (i.e. mixed interpolation) in a primitive equation formulation was incapable of suppressing node-to-node oscillations in the velocity solution. Gray (1982) ran a formulation of the split-step model of Connor and Wang (1974) and Wang and Connor (1975) without using any numerical smoothing to simulate the problem of figure 8. The results are simular to those of the primitive equation model with significant node-to-node oscillations of velocity and surface elevation. These studies all demonstrate the value of simulation on idealized regions as a filter for quality models.

Other analytical solutions which serve as interesting test cases for numerical methods include additional terms. Rahman (1983) extended the work of Lynch and Gray (1978) by

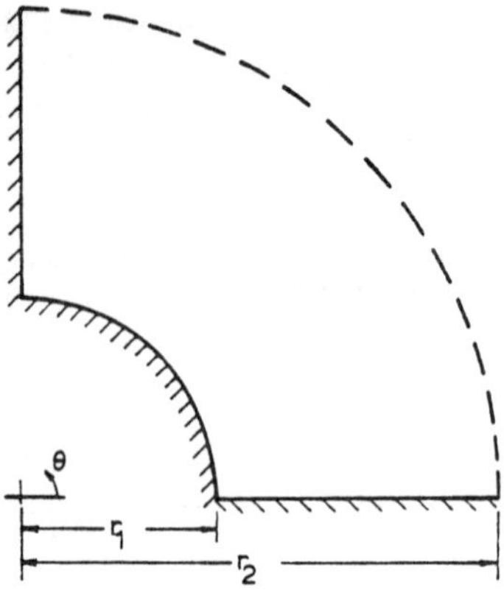

Figure 8.a. Geometry of polar test case. Elevation specified at outer curved edge, zero normal velocity at remaining edges.

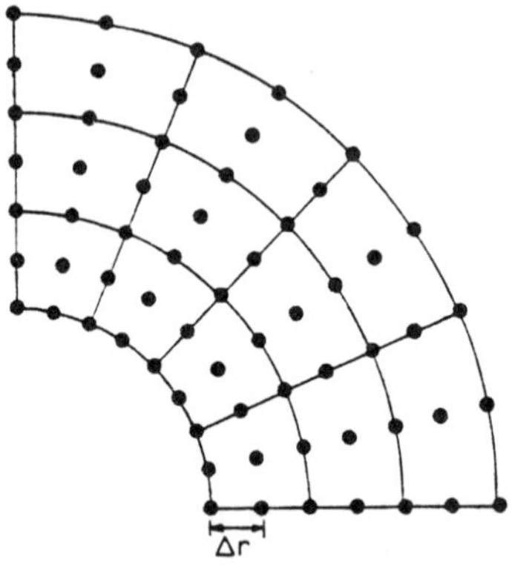

Figure 8.b. Finite element discretization of quarter-annular region employing quadratic Lagrangian elements.

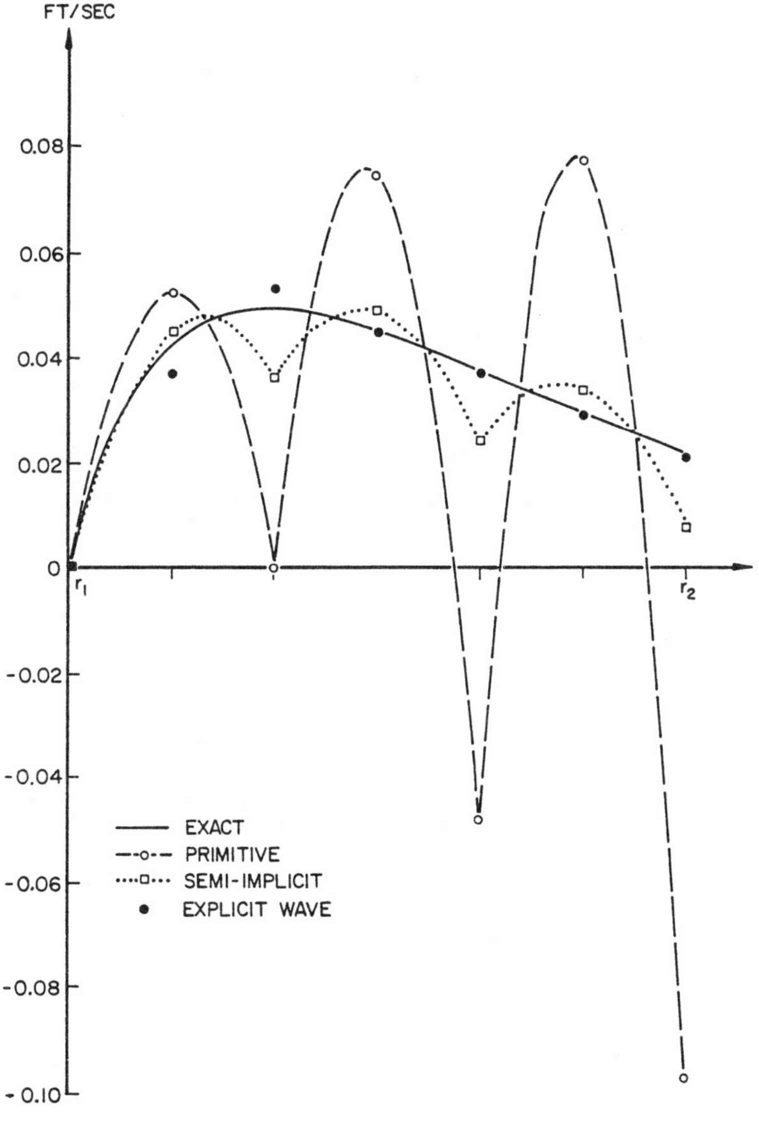

Figure 9. Comparison of lumped results: quadrilateral grid, quadratic bathymetry; Primitive Leapfrog, Semi-Implicit, and Explicit Wave Equation models.

including the Coriolis effect. Askar and Cakmak (1978) used perturbation techniques to solve the shallow water equations including nonlinear convective terms. Lynch and Officer (1985) derive three-dimensional solutions by assembling one-dimensional vertical solutions with two-dimensional lateral solutions.

In summary, idealized simulations have proven to be valuable tools in assessing finite element models when choosen judiciously so as to provide difficult tests of model performance. These tests have verified the conclusion from numerical analysis that the wave equation models are far superior to primitive models in eliminating numerical oscillations without introducing artificial damping.

FIELD APPLICATIONS

The ultimate test of any surface water model is in its application to a wide variety of field data sets. The wave equation approach has now successfully evolved through and been shaped by numerous numerical analyses and analytical test cases. Novel algorithms for increased efficiency and accuracy have also been implemented. More recently wave equation models have been applied to field data: two different data sets in the Southern part of the North Sea (Gray and Kinnmark, 1983; Kinnmark and Gray, 1984b, 1985c); St. Albans Bay on Lake Champlain (Laible, 1984); Lake Maracaibo (Werner and Lynch, 1986). The process of field verification against measured data must continue to be of high priority. The Tidal Flow Forum at this conference should provide a valuable bench mark for the evaluation of surface water models.

ACKNOWLEDGEMENTS

This research has been supported in part through grant number CEE-8419366 from the United States National Science Foundation.

REFERENCES

Adey, R.A. (1974) Numerical Prediction of Transient Water Quality and Tidal Motion in Estuaries and Coastal Waters, Ph.D. Thesis, University of Southampton.

Askar, A. and Cakmak, A.S. (1978) Studies on Finite Amplitude Waves in Bounded Water Bodies, Adv. Water Resources, 1:229-246.

Brebbia, C.A. and Partridge, P.J. (1976) Finite Element Simulation of Water Circulation in the North Sea, Appl. Math. Modelling, 1:101-107.

Connor, J.J. and Wang, J.D. (1974) Finite Element Modelling of Hydrodynamic Circulation, Numerical Methods in Fluid Dynamics, Edited by C.A. Brebbia and J.J. Connor, Pentech Press, London, 355-387.

Engelman, M.S., Sani, R.L. and Gresho, P.M. (1982) The Implementation of Normal and/or Tangential Boundary Conditions in Finite Element Codes for Incompressible Fluid Flow, Intl. J. Num. Meth. Fluids, 2:225-238.

Foreman, M.G.G. (1983) An Analysis of the "Wave Equation" Model for Finite Element Tidal Computations, J. Comput. Phys., 52:290-312.

Gray, W.G. (1977) An Efficient Finite Element Scheme for Two-Dimensional Surface Water Computations, Finite Elements in Water Resources, Edited by W.G. Gray, G.F. Pinder and C.A. Brebbia, Pentech Press, London, 4.33.

Gray, W.G. (1982) Some Inadequacies of Finite Element Models as Simulators of Two-Dimensional Circulation, Adv. Water Resources, 5:171-177.

Gray, W.G. (1984) On Normal Flow Boundary Conditions in Finite Element Codes for Two-Dimensional Shallow Water Flow, Int. J. Numer. Methods Fluids, 4:99-104.

Gray, W.G. and Kinnmark, I. (1983) QUIET: A Reduced Noise Finite Element Model for Tidal Circulation, Adv. Eng. Software, 5:130-136.

Gray, W.G. and Lynch, D.R. (1977) Time-Stepping Schemes for Finite Element Tidal Model Computations, Adv. in Water Resources, 1:83-95.

Gray, W.G. and Lynch, D.R. (1979) On the Control of Noise in Finite Element Tidal Computations: A Semi-Implicit Approach, Computers and Fluids, 7:47-67.

Kawahara, M., Takeuchi, N. and Yoshida, T. (1978) Two Step Explicit Finite Element Method for Tsunami Wave Propagation Analysis, Int. J. Num. Meth. Eng., 12:331.

King, I.P. and Norton, W.R. (1978) Recent Application of RMA's Finite Element Models for Two-Dimensional Hydrodynamics and Water Quality, Proceedings of Second Intl. Conf. on Finite Elements in Water Resources, Pentech Press, 2.81.

Kinnmark, I.P.E. (1986) The Shallow Water Wave Equations Formulation, Analysis and Application, Lecture Notes in Engineering 15, Springer-Verlag, Berlin.

Kinnmark, I.P.E. and Gray, W.G. (1982) Time-Weighting of the Momentum Equation In Explicit Wave Equation Models of Surface Water Flow, Proc. 4th Intl. Conf. on Finite Elements in Water Resources, Edited by K.P. Holz, U. Meissner, W. Zielke, C.A. Brebbia, G. Pinder and W. Gray, Springer-Verlag, Berlin, 5.67-5.77.

Kinnmark, I.P.E. and Gray, W.G. (1984a) A Two-Dimensional Analysis of the Wave Equation Model for Finite Element Tidal Computations, Intl. J. Numer. Methods Eng., 20:369-383.

Kinnmark, I.P.E. and Gray, W.G. (1984b) An Implicit Wave Equation Model for the Shallow Water Equations, Adv. Water Resources, 7:168-171.

Kinnmark, I.P.E. and Gray, W.G. (1985a) Stability and Accuracy of Spatial Approximations for Wave Equation Tidal Models, J. Comput. Phys., 60:447-466.

Kinnmark, I.P.E. and Gray, W.G. (1985b) The 2Δx-Test: A Tool for Analyzing Spurious Oscillations, Adv. Water Resources, 8:129-135.

Kinnmark, I.P.E. and Gray, W.G. (1985c) A Generalized Wave Equation Formulation of Tidal Circulation, Proc. 4th Intl. Conf. on Numerical Methods in Laminar and Turbulent Flow, Pineridge Press, 1312-1324.

Laible, J.P. (1984) A Finite Element/Finite Difference Wave Model for Depth Varying Nearly Horizontal Flow, Adv. Water Resources, 7:2-14.

Laible, J.P. (1984) A Modified Wave Equation Model for 3D Flow in Shallow Bodies of Water, Proceedings of Fourth Intl. Conf. on Finite Elements in Water Resources, Edited by J.P. Laible, C.A. Brebbia, W. Gray and G. Pinder, 609-620.

Leendertse, J.J. (1967) Aspects of a Computational Model for Long Period Water-Wave Propagation, Rand Memorandum RM-5294-PR, Santa Monica, CA.

Lynch, D.R. (1978) Finite Element Solution of the Shallow Water Equations, Ph.D. Thesis, Princeton University.

Lynch, D.R. (1985) Mass Balance in Shallow Water Simulations, Comm. in Applied Num. Methods, (in presss).

Lynch, D.R. and Gray, W.G. (1978) Analytical Solutions for Computer Flow Model Testing, J. of the Hydr. Div., 1409-1428.

Lynch, D.R. and Gray, W.G. (1979) A Wave Equation Model for Finite Element Tidal Computations, Computers and Fluids, 7:207-228.

Lynch, D.R. and Officer, C.B. (1985) Analytic Test Cases for Three-Dimensional Hydrodynamic Models, Intl. J. Num. Meth. Fluids, 5:529-543.

Niemeyer, G. (1979) Long Wave Model Independent of Stability Criteria, ASCE, J. Waterway, Ports, Coastal and Ocean Div., 105:51.

Platzman, G.W. (1959) A Numerical Computation of the Surge of 26 June 1954 on Lake Michigan, Geophysics, 6:407-438.

Platzman, G.W. (1978) Normal Modes of the World Ocean Part I. Design of a Finite-Element Barotropic Model, J. Phys. Oceanogr., 8:323-343.

Platzman, G.W. (1981) Some Response Characteristics of Finite-Element Tidal Models, J. Comput. Phys., 40:36-63.

Rahman, M. (1983) Analytical Solutions for Tidal Propagation in a Rectangular Basin, Adv. Water Resources, 6:44-53.

Taylor, C. and Davis, J.M. (1975) Tidal and Long-Wave Propagation: A Finite Element Approach, Computers and Fluids, 3:125-148.

Thompson, J.F. (1982) Numerical Grid Generation, Proceedings of a Symposium on the Numerical Generation of Curvilinear Coordinate Systems and Their Use in the Numerical Solution of Partial Differential Equations, North-Holland, New York.

Walters, R.A. (1983) Numerically Induced Oscillations in Finite Element Approximations to the Shallow Water Equations, Int. J. Numer. Methods Fluids, 3:591-604.

Wang, J.D. and Connor, J.J. (1975) Mathematical Modelling of Near Coastal Circulation, MIT Parsons Laboratory Report, 200, Cambridge, MA.

Werner, F.E. and Lynch, D.R. *1986) Field Studies with the Wave Equation Formulation, Sixth Intl. Conf. on Finite Elements in Water Resources, (these proceedings).

VI International Conference on Finite Elements in Water Resources, Lisboa, Portugal, June 1986

On Stream Function-Vorticity Formulations

G.J. Fix
Carnegie-Mellon University, Pittsburgh, U.S.A.

Abstract

Stream function vorticity variables have been widely used in computer simulations of incompressible flows. The goal of the paper is to study the accuracy of finite element and finite difference approximations. The analysis reveals that the velocity fields converge at optimal rates but very slow convergence in the vorticity may result. The analysis also reveals when this will occur, and implicates the failure of a vorticity production law as the reason for this phenomena.

§1. Introduction.

The use of stream function-vorticity variables for planar incompressible flows, and vector potentials in three spatial dimensions has been widespread [1], [2]. Their utility stems from the reduced degrees of freedom that are required in comparison with formulations using primitive variables. This presumably means that greater resolution can be achieved for the same amount of computing capability. The major point of this paper is to show that this conclusion, with certain exceptions, is by and large a myth.

The basic issue centers around the accuracy of finite element and finite difference methods based on stream function-vorticity formulations. The term accuracy here refers to actual errors, and not to truncations errors or related quantities. The latter, as will be shown, can be quite deceptive.

(*)This work was supported in part by A.R.O. under contract no. DAAG29-83-K-0084

The major problem with stream function-vorticity formulations is that they are inherently of the mixed type. The same is true of primitive variables, but unlike the latter, the stream function-vorticity are of the weak or nonsmoothing type in a sense that will be defined. This in effect means that truncation errors give no clue to actual errors, and there is generally a serious loss of accuracy in the latter. The one exception to this arises with the use of conforming finite elements, which in this context forces one to use at least C^1 elements or smoother.

Formulations based on finite elements will be used exclusively in this paper. Nevertheless, the analysis and conclusions are also applicable to finite difference formulations as well. The differences between these two approaches in this context is not nearly as great as they may seem. Indeed, the difficulties with what amounts to a finite difference analog of a nonconforming quadratic element has already been pointed out by Roache [1,p.143].

In the second section we review the basic variational principles based on stream function-vorticity formulations. The third section contains a stability analysis, while the final two sections contain an analysis of accuracy for the conforming and nonconforming cases.

§2. Variational Formulations.

We consider the flow region Ω having a boundary Γ and outer normal n. We assume that any inhomogenities in the boundary conditions have been incorporated into a body force f. Thus if u denotes the vorticity and φ the stream function, we have the following:

$$u - \Delta\varphi = 0 \qquad \text{in} \quad \Omega \tag{2.1}$$

$$\nu\Delta u + J(\varphi,u) = f \qquad \text{in} \quad \Omega \tag{2.2}$$

$$\varphi = \frac{\partial\varphi}{\partial n} = 0 \qquad \text{on} \quad \Gamma . \tag{2.3}$$

Here ν denotes the viscosity, and $J(\cdot,\cdot)$ is the bilinear term

$$J(\varphi,u) = \frac{\partial\varphi}{\partial x}\frac{\partial u}{\partial y} - \frac{\partial\varphi}{\partial y}\frac{\partial u}{\partial x} . \tag{2.4}$$

The basic variational principle for this system is in effect a Galerkin formulation where the Laplacians are integrated by parts.

The function spaces associated with this formulation are $H^1(\Omega)$ and $H_0^1(\Omega)$ with

$$u \in H^1(\Omega), \quad \varphi \in H_0^1(\Omega)^{(1)}. \tag{2.5}$$

Thus the second boundary condition in (2.3) is natural. The variational problem consists of finding the pair (2.5) for which

$$\int_\Omega uv + \int \nabla\varphi\nabla v = 0 \quad \text{all} \quad v \in H^1(\Omega) \tag{2.6}$$

$$\nu \int_\Omega \nabla u \nabla \psi + \int_\Omega J(\varphi,u)\psi = \int_\Omega f\psi \quad \text{all} \quad \psi \in H_0^1(\Omega) \tag{2.7}$$

Approximations are obtained by first introducing finite dimensional spaces

$$\mathcal{S}^h \subseteq H^1(\Omega), \ \mathcal{S}_0^h \subseteq H_0^1(\Omega) \ , \tag{2.8}$$

and posing (2.6)-(2.7) on these spaces. That is, we seek

$$u_h \in \mathcal{S}^h, \ \varphi_h \in \mathcal{S}_0^h \tag{2.9}$$

for which

$$\int_\Omega u_h v^h + \int_\Omega \nabla\varphi_h \nabla v^h = 0 \quad \text{all} \quad v^h \in \mathcal{S}^h \tag{2.10}$$

$$\int_\Omega \nabla u_h \nabla \psi^h + \int_\Omega J(\varphi_h, u_h)\psi^h = \int_\Omega f\psi^h \quad \text{all} \quad \psi^h \in \mathcal{S}_0^h \ . \tag{2.11}$$

Once a basis has been chosen for $\mathcal{S}^h$ and $\mathcal{S}_0^h$, (2.10)-(2.11) reduces to a set of nonlinear equations [3].

There are two conservation laws inherent in (2.6)-(2.7) which are physically relevant. First, there is the conservation of vorticity which in this context means

$$\int_\Omega u = 0 \ . \tag{2.12}$$

This follows from (2.6) by putting $v = 1$. Note that this property is also in the approximate scheme (2.10)-(2.11) provided the finite element space $\mathcal{S}^h$ includes the identity function $v^h = 1$ (which will typically be the case since there are no boundary conditions inherent in $\mathcal{S}^h$).

(1) Throughout this paper $H^t(G)$ denotes the t-th order Sobolev space with $H_0^t(G)$ denoting the closure of $C_0^\infty(G)$ in $H^t(G)$. Thus functions in $H_0^1(\Omega)$ have square integrable gradients and vanishes on Γ.

The second conservation law is more subtle, and in many respects more interesting. It is obtained by integrating (2.2) over Ω, and noting

$$\int_{\Omega} J(\varphi,u) = 0 \quad .$$

This gives

$$\nu \int_{\Omega} \Delta u = \int_{\Omega} f \ . \tag{2.13}$$

Integrating the term on the left by parts gives

$$\nu \int_{\Gamma} \frac{\partial u}{\partial n} + \int_{\Omega} f = 0 \quad . \tag{2.14}$$

We recall that vorticity production on boundaries is one of the dominant mechanisms in the flow. The relation (2.14) can thus be interpreted as a constraint on the vorticity flux created on Γ.

Observe that unlike (2.12), the relation (2.14) is not embedded in the approximate scheme (2.10)-(2.11); i.e., it is not derivable from (2.11). This as we shall see is closely related to some of the inaccuracies in the vorticity arising from (2.10)-(2.11).

It should be noted that there are variations of (2.6)-(2.7) which do contain the vorticity production law (2.14). For example, in [4] Lagrange multipliers were used in conjunction in (2.6)-(2.7). This introduces the vorticity flux

$$\lambda = \frac{\partial u}{\partial n} \in H^{-\frac{1}{2}}(\Gamma) \tag{2.15}$$

as a variable, and the scheme consists of finding

$$u \in H^1(\Omega), \ \varphi \in H^1(\Omega), \ \lambda \in H^{-\frac{1}{2}}(\Gamma) \tag{2.16}$$

for which

$$\int_{\Omega} uv + \int_{\Omega} \nabla u \nabla v - \int_{\Gamma} \mu\varphi = 0 \tag{2.17}$$

$$\int_{\Omega} \nabla u \nabla \Psi - \int_{\Gamma} \lambda\varphi = \int_{\Omega} f\psi \tag{2.18}$$

holds for all

$$v \in H^1(\Omega), \ \psi \in H^1(\Omega), \ \mu \in H^{-\frac{1}{2}}(\Gamma) \ . \tag{2.19}$$

Note that all boundary conditions are natural in this setting. Moreover, letting $\psi = 1$ in (2.18) we get the vorticity production law (2.14). Analysis of approximations based on (2.17)-(2.18) will be given in another publication.

To see the difficulties associated with the stream function-vorticity formation consider for the moment the law Reynolds number case where we set $J = 0$. In this setting (2.6)-(2.7) (and (2.10)-(2.11) as well) have the classic structure of a weak (or saddle point) variational principle [5]. In matrix form we can view (2.6)-(2.7) as follows:

$$\begin{bmatrix} I & L \\ L^* & 0 \end{bmatrix} \begin{bmatrix} u \\ \varphi \end{bmatrix} = \begin{bmatrix} 0 \\ f \end{bmatrix} . \tag{2.20}$$

Moreover, this is a weak or nonsmoothing type principle, and in such circumstances the angle conditions of Babuska and Brezzi ([5],[6]) are not valid. This means that the general theory of mixed formulations worked out in [5], [6] is not applicable to (2.10)-(2.11). Moreover, as we shall see, this system can indeed lead to suboptimal approximations.

To verify the above assertion we recall that there are two inequalities required by the Babuska-Brezzi condition. The first requires that there is a number $0 < C < \infty$ for which

$$C \sup \left\{ \frac{\int_\Omega \nabla v \cdot \nabla \psi}{\|v\|_1} \right\} \geq \|\psi\|_1 \tag{2.21}$$

holds for all ψ in $H_0^1(\Omega)$, where the sup is taken over all v in $H^1(\Omega)$. This condition can be verified trivially by putting $v = \psi$.

The second condition uses the null space of L, i.e.,

$$h = \left\{ v \in H^1 : \int_\Omega \nabla v \nabla \psi = 0 \quad \text{all} \quad \psi \in H_0^1(\Omega) \right\} . \tag{2.22}$$

Note that h consists of the (weakly) harmonic functions in Ω. The condition requires that there is a number $0 < C < \infty$ for which

$$C \sup \int_\Omega uv \geq \|u\|_1 \tag{2.23}$$

holds for all u in $\mathcal{h}$, where the sup is taken over all v in $\mathcal{h}$.

Observe that (2.23) amounts to the requirement that the L_2 and H^1 norms be equivalent on the space $\mathcal{h}$ of harmonic functions. That this is false is readily seen by taking Ω to be a circle of unit radius. Using polar coordinates we put

$$u = r^n e^{in\theta} \quad .$$

Then a direct calculation shows that

$$\|u\|_0^2 = \pi/(n + 1)$$

and

$$\|u\|_1^2 = 2\pi n \quad .$$

Our contradiction is obtained by letting $n \to \infty$.

Since the general theory of mixed finite element methods is not applicable to (2.10)-(2.11), a direct analysis is needed. This is done in the three sections. Alternate approaches are given in [7]-[9].

§3. Stability.

Throughout the remainder of this paper we shall consider the low Reynolds number case where $J = 0$. Moreover, we shall assume Ω is polygonal and that

$$\mathcal{S}^h = \mathcal{S}^h(\Omega) \tag{3.1}$$

consists of piecewise polynomials of degree $k - 1$. Further we let

$$\mathcal{S}_0^h = \mathcal{S}^h(\Omega) \cap H_0^1(\Omega), \tag{3.2}$$

and let $\mathcal{S}^h(\Gamma)$ denote the restrictions of functions in $\mathcal{S}^h(\Omega)$ to the boundary Γ. We assume that $\mathcal{S}^h(\Omega)$ has the standard approximation properties in terms of a generic mesh spacing $h > 0$; i.e.,

$$\inf\|u - v_h\|_r \le Ch^{t-r}\|u\|_t^{(2)}, \quad 0 \le r \le 1, \; r < t \le k^{(2)}, \tag{3.3}$$

(2) Throughout this paper $\|\cdot\|_{t,G}$ denotes the norm on $H^t(G)$. The subscript G is omitted if the context is clear. Thus $\|\cdot\|_t = \|\cdot\|_{t,\Omega}$ in (3.3).

where the inf is taken over all $v_h \in \mathcal{S}^h(\Omega)$ if u is in $H^t(\Omega)$, and over all v_h in $\mathcal{S}_0^h(\Omega)$ if u is in $H^t(\Omega) \cap H_0^1(\Omega)$. Finally, since Ω is polygonal we may assume that $\mathcal{S}^h(\Gamma)$ has the same approximation properties; i.e.,

$$\inf \|w - \xi_h\|_{r,\Gamma} \le Ch^{t-r}\|w\|_{t,\Gamma} \qquad 0 \le r \le 1,\ r < t \le k . \tag{3.4}$$

The failure of the Babuska-Brezzi conditions means that the system (2.6)-(2.7) (and (2.10)-(2.11) is not continuous in norms natural to the problem. In this case it is the H^1 norm that is relevant. However, the system is continuous in weaker norms. Indeed, suppose F and G are continuous linear functionals on $H^1(\Omega)$ and $H_0^1(\Omega)$, respectively. Suppose in addition that

$$u_h \in \mathcal{S}^h,\ \varphi_h \in \mathcal{S}_0^h \tag{3.5}$$

satisfies

$$\int_\Omega u_h v^h + \int_\Omega \nabla\varphi_h \nabla v^h = F(v^h) \qquad \text{all } v^h \in \mathcal{S}^h \tag{3.6}$$

$$\int_\Omega \nabla u_h \nabla\psi^h = G(\psi^h) \qquad \text{all } \psi^h \in \mathcal{S}_0^h . \tag{3.7}$$

The weak version of stability is given in the following.

<u>Theorem 3.1</u> In the above context let

$$\mathcal{H}^h = \{v^h \in \mathcal{S}^h : \int \nabla v^h \nabla\psi^h = 0 \quad \text{all } \psi^h \in \mathcal{S}_0^h\} \tag{3.8}$$

denote the space of discrete harmonic functions. Then

$$\|u_h\|_0 \le \sup_{\psi^h \in \mathcal{S}_0^h}\left[\frac{G(\psi^h)}{\|\psi^h\|_1}\right] + \sup_{v^h \in \mathcal{H}^h}\left[\frac{F(v^h)}{\|v^h\|_0}\right] \tag{3.9}$$

$$\|\nabla\varphi_h\|_0 \le \|u_h\|_{-1} + \sup_{v^h \in \mathcal{S}_0^h}\left[\frac{F(v^h)}{\|v^h\|_1}\right] . \tag{3.10}$$

<u>Proof</u>. We start by using the decomposition of u_h into a discrete harmonic part $w_h \in \mathcal{H}^h$ and a part $z_h \in \mathcal{S}_0^h$ which vanishes on Γ; i.e.,

$$u_h = w_h + z_h . \tag{3.11}$$

Note that z_h is determined by

$$\int_\Omega \nabla z_h \nabla \psi^h = \int_\Omega \nabla u_h \nabla \psi^h \qquad \text{all } \psi^h \in \mathcal{S}_0^h . \tag{3.12}$$

Also note that this decomposition is orthogonal in the sense that

$$\int_\Omega \nabla w_h \nabla z_h = 0 . \tag{3.13}$$

Thus,

$$\|\nabla z_h\|_0 \le \sup \frac{G(\psi^h)}{\|\psi^h\|_1} \tag{3.14}$$

is a direct consequence of (3.7). Moreover, from (3.6) we get (letting $v^h = w_h$)

$$\|w_h\|_0 \le \sup_{v^h \in \mathfrak{h}^h} \frac{|F(v^h)|}{\|v^h\|_0} . \tag{3.15}$$

Finally, from (3.6) with v^h restricted to $\mathcal{S}_0^h$ we get

$$\|\nabla \varphi_h\|_0 \le \|u_h\|_{-1} + \sup_{v^h \in \mathcal{S}_0^h} \frac{|F(v^h)|}{\|v^h\|_1} . \tag{3.16}$$

Combining these estimate we get (3.9)-(3.10).

Observe the velocity $\nabla \varphi_h$ is continuous in H^1, however the vorticity is not. It is, in fact, continuous only in the weaker $L^2(\Omega)$ norm. Moreover, this defect is intimately related to the failure of the vorticity production law (2.14).

We can, however, conclude from Theorem 3.1 that the system has a unique solution.

<u>Corollary</u>. Let F be continuous on $H^1(\Omega)$ and G be continuous on $H_0^1(\Omega)$. Then there is exactly one pair

$$(u_h, \varphi_h) \in \mathcal{S}^h \times \mathcal{S}_0^h$$

such that (3.6)-(3.7) holds.

§4. Accuracy. Let $(\tilde{u}_h, \tilde{\varphi}_h)$ be a given pair in $S^h \times S_0^h$. Let

$$e_h = u_h - \tilde{u}_h, \ \varepsilon_h = \varphi_h - \tilde{\varphi}_h \tag{4.1}$$

with

$$e = u - \tilde{u}_h, \ \varepsilon = \varphi - \tilde{\varphi}_h \ . \tag{4.2}$$

Our goal is to bound (4.1) in terms of (4.2), and then appeal to approximation theory (i.e., (3.3)) to estimate the latter.

The first step centers around the stability estimate in the previous section. Indeed, observe that (e_h, ε_h) satisfies (3.6)-(3.7) for appropriate G and F. Indeed, we have

$$\int_\Omega e_h v^h + \int_\Omega \nabla\varepsilon_h v^h = F(v^h) \tag{4.3}$$

$$\int_\Omega \nabla e_h \nabla\psi^h = G(\psi^h) \tag{4.4}$$

where

$$F(v^h) = \int_\Omega e v^h + \int_\Omega \nabla\varepsilon\nabla v^h \tag{4.5}$$

$$G(\psi^h) = \int \nabla e \nabla\psi^h \ . \tag{4.6}$$

The following result has appeared in various papers (see e.g. [10]), however an apparently new proof is included here for completeness.

Lemma 1. The function $\tilde{u}_h \in S^h$ can be chosen such that

$$G(\psi^h) = 0 \quad \text{all} \quad \psi^h \in S_0^h \ . \tag{4.7}$$

Moreover, let g denote the restriction of u to Γ and let g_h denote the orthogonal projection in $L^2(\Gamma)$.
Then

$$\|\nabla(u - \tilde{u}_h)\|_0 = \inf\|\nabla(u - v^h)\|_0 \tag{4.8}$$

$$\|u - \tilde{u}_h\|_0 \le Ch\|u - \tilde{u}_h\|_1 \ . \tag{4.9}$$

The inf in (4.8) is taken over all v^h in S^h for which

$$v^h = g_h \quad \text{on} \quad \Gamma \ . \tag{4.10}$$

The constant $0 < C < \infty$ in (4.9) is independent of u, $\tilde{u}_h$ and h.

<u>Proof</u>. We let $\tilde{u}_h$ be defined by

$$\int \nabla\tilde{u}_h \nabla\psi^h = \int \nabla u \nabla\psi^h \quad \text{all} \quad \psi^h \in S_0^h \tag{4.11}$$

subject to

$$\tilde{u}_h = g_h \quad \text{on} \quad \Gamma . \tag{4.12}$$

The first estimate is immediate from (4.11) once it is noted that $v^h = g_h = \tilde{u}^h$ on Γ and so $v^h - \tilde{u}^h \in S_0^h$.

The second estimate follows a standard duality argument [3], but with a slight twist. Indeed, consider the problem

$$\Delta w = u - \tilde{u}_h \quad \text{in} \quad \Omega \tag{4.13}$$

$$w = 0 \quad \text{on} \quad \Gamma . \tag{4.14}$$

We have

$$\|u - \tilde{u}_h\|_0^2 = \int_\Omega \Delta w(u - \tilde{u}_h) = \int_\Gamma \frac{\partial w}{\partial n}(u - \tilde{u}_h) - \int_\Omega \nabla w \nabla(u - \tilde{u}_h) \tag{4.15}$$

$$= \int_\Gamma \frac{\partial w}{\partial n}(g - g_h) - \int \nabla w \nabla(u - \tilde{u}_h) . \tag{4.16}$$

Since g_h is the $L^2(\Gamma)$ projection of g we have

$$\int_\Gamma (g - g_h)\lambda_h = 0 \quad \text{all} \quad \lambda_h \in S^h(\Gamma) . \tag{4.17}$$

Moreover from (4.11)

$$\int \nabla w_h \nabla(u - \tilde{u}_h) = 0 \quad \text{all} \quad w_h \in S_0^h . \tag{4.18}$$

Thus (4.16) becomes

$$\|u - \tilde{u}_h\|_0^2 = \int_\Gamma \left(\frac{\partial w}{\partial n} - \lambda_h\right)(g - g_h) - \int \nabla(w - w_h)\nabla(u - \tilde{u}_h) \tag{4.19}$$

Using approximation ((3.3)-(3.4)) and regularity of (4.13)-(4.14) (see [11]) we can choose $\lambda_h \in S^h(\Gamma)$, $w_h \in S_0^h(\Omega)$ so that

$$\left\|\frac{\partial w}{\partial n} - \lambda_h\right\|_{-\frac{1}{2},\Gamma} \le Ch\left\|\frac{\partial w}{\partial n}\right\|_{\frac{1}{2},\Gamma} \le Ch\|u - \tilde{u}_h\|_0 \tag{4.20}$$

$$\|\nabla(w - w_h)\|_0 \leq Ch\|w\|_2 \leq Ch\|u - u_h\|_0 \ . \tag{4.21}$$

Also, trace theorems [11] give

$$\|g - g_h\|_{\frac{1}{2},\Gamma} \leq C\|u - \tilde{u}_h\|_1 \ . \tag{4.22}$$

Combining (4.20)-(4.22) with (4.19) gives (4.9).

With the above choice of $\tilde{u}_h$ our system reduces to

$$\int_\Omega e_h v^h + \int_\Omega \nabla\varepsilon_h \nabla v^h = F(v^h) \ \text{all} \ \ v^h \in \mathcal{S}^h \tag{4.23}$$

with e_h being discretely harmonic, i.e., in $\mathcal{H}^h$, and

$$F(v^h) = \int ev^h + \int \nabla\varepsilon\nabla v^h \ . \tag{4.24}$$

Observe that if $\tilde{\varphi}_h \in \mathcal{S}_0^h$ is chosen such that

$$\int \nabla\tilde{\varphi}_h \nabla\psi^h = \int \nabla\varphi\nabla\psi^h \ \ \text{all} \ \ \psi^h \in \mathcal{S}_0^h \ , \tag{4.25}$$

then

$$F(v^h) = \int_\Omega ev^h \ \ \text{all} \ \ v^h \in \mathcal{S}_0^h \subset \mathcal{S}^h \ . \tag{4.26}$$

Moreover $\|\varphi - \tilde{\varphi}_h\|_r$ satisfies the bounds in (3.3). (Both φ and $\tilde{\varphi}_h$ vanish on Γ so Lemma 1 is not needed here.) A direct consequence of these observations is contained in the following:

<u>Corollary 1</u>. Let $\tilde{u}_h$ be given by Lemma 1 and $\tilde{\varphi}_h$ be given by (4.25). Then

$$\|e_h\|_0 \leq \|e\|_0 + \sup_{v^h \in \mathcal{H}^h} \frac{\int_\Omega \nabla\varepsilon\nabla v^h}{\|v^h\|_0} \tag{4.27}$$

$$\|\nabla\varepsilon\|_0 \leq \|e\|_0 + \sup_{v^h \in \mathcal{S}_0^h} \frac{\int_\Omega e_h v^h}{\|v^h\|_1} \ . \tag{4.28}$$

At this point two cases must be considered. The first is the conforming case where

$$\mathcal{H}^h \subset \mathcal{H} ; \tag{4.29}$$

i.e., where discretely harmonic functions are actually harmonic. Since v_h in $\mathcal{H}^h$ means

$$\int_\Omega \nabla v^h \nabla \psi^h = 0 \quad \text{all} \quad \psi^h \in \mathcal{S}_0^h , \tag{4.30}$$

we need for v^h to be in $H^2(\Omega)$ so that (4.30) can be integrated by parts to give

$$\int_\Omega \psi^h \Delta v^h = 0 \quad \text{all} \quad \psi^h \in \mathcal{S}_0^h . \tag{4.31}$$

This in turn will give $\Delta v^h = 0$ (almost everywhere) and hence (4.29). In short, (4.29) requires the use of C^1 elements are better (hence the term conforming). The basic error estimate for this case is given in the following.

<u>Theorem 4.1</u>. Let $\tilde{u}_h$ be chosen by Lemma 1 and $\tilde{\varphi}_h$ by (4.25). Let (4.29) hold. Then

$$\|u - u_h\|_0 \leq 2\|u - \tilde{u}_h\|_0 \tag{4.32}$$

$$\|\nabla(\varphi - \varphi_h)\|_0 \leq \|\nabla(\varphi - \tilde{\varphi}_h)\|_0 + 2\|u - \tilde{u}_h\|_0 . \tag{4.33}$$

<u>Proof</u>. We first note that the sup in (4.27) is zero. Indeed, since v^h is discretely harmonic, it is also harmonic by (4.23). Thus as $\varepsilon = 0$ on Γ

$$\int_\Omega \nabla\varepsilon \nabla v^h = \int_\Gamma \varepsilon \frac{\partial v^h}{\partial n} - \int \varepsilon \Delta v^h = 0 . \tag{4.34}$$

Finally the sup in (4.28) can be bounded above by $\|e_h\|_0$. This (4.28) becomes

$$\|\nabla\varepsilon_h\|_0 \leq \|e\|_0 + \|e_h\|_0 \leq 2\|e\| . \tag{4.35}$$

The final task is to show that the approximation properties (3.3)-(3.4) imply that

$$\|\nabla(\varphi - \tilde{\varphi}_h)\|_0 = O(h^{k-1}), \quad \|u - \tilde{u}_h)\|_0 = O(h^k), \tag{4.36}$$

provided u and φ are sufficiently smooth. This would imply by Theorem 4.1 that the approximate velocity $\nabla\varphi_h$ and vorticity u_h converged at the same optimal rate.

The first of (4.36) is immediate, but the second result suffers from the complication that the inf in (4.8) is taken over v^h in $\mathcal{S}^h$ satisfying (4.10) while $u = g$ on Γ. In [10] the estimate is obtained provided we have extra smoothness in u; i.e.,

$$\|u\|_{k+\frac{1}{2}+2,\Omega} < \infty \tag{4.37}$$

is needed. For a wide class of finite spaces this extra smoothness is not needed. Consider for example, nodal finite element spaces where functions v^h in $\mathcal{S}^h(\Omega)$ are represented

$$v^h = \sum_{z_j \in \Omega} v^h(z_j)\varphi_j + \sum_{z_j \in \Gamma} v^h(z_j)\varphi_j \quad . \tag{4.38}$$

To estimate the inf in (4.8) we let u_h^I denote the interpolant of u:

$$u_h^I = \sum_{z_j \in \Omega} u(z_j)\varphi_j + \sum_{z_j \in \Gamma} g(z_j)\varphi_j \quad . \tag{4.39}$$

Then

$$\|u - u_h^I\|_1 \leq Ch^{k-1}\|u\|_k \tag{4.40}$$

is a standard result. Thus we need to estimate $u_h^I - v^h$ for a suitably chosen v^h. Indeed, let

$$v^h = \sum_{z_j \in \Omega} u(z_j)\varphi_j + \sum_{z_j \in \Gamma} g(z_j)\varphi_j \quad . \tag{4.41}$$

Then

$$u^h = u_h^I - v^h = \sum_{z_j \in \Gamma} [g(z_j) - g_h(z_j)]\varphi_j \tag{4.42}$$

vanishes at all interior nodes $(z_j \in \Omega)$. We assert that for such a function w^h we have

$$\|w^h\|_{1,\Omega} \leq Ch^{-\frac{1}{2}}\|w^h\|_{0,\Gamma} \quad . \tag{4.43}$$

Assuming the validity of (4.43) for the moment, we obtain

$$\|u - v_h\|_{1,\Omega} \leq \|u - u_h^I\|_{1,\Omega} + \|w^h\|_{1,\Omega} . \tag{4.44}$$

Moreover,

$$\|w^h\|_{1,\Omega} \leq Ch^{-\frac{1}{2}}\|w^h\|_{0,\Gamma} = Ch^{-\frac{1}{2}}\|g - g_h\|_{0,\Gamma} . \tag{4.45}$$

By the approximation property, (3.4), we have

$$\|g - g_h\|_{0,\Gamma} \leq Ch^{k-\frac{1}{2}}\|g\|_{k-\frac{1}{2},\Gamma} \leq Ch^{k-\frac{1}{2}}\|u\|_{k,\Omega} . \tag{4.46}$$

Combining these results we obtain

$$\inf \|u - v_n\|_1 \leq Ch^{k-1}\|u\|_k \quad . \tag{4.47}$$

To prove (4.43) we observe that

$$\|w^h\|_{1,\Omega}^2 = \sum_{z_j \in \Gamma} \sum_{z_k \in \Gamma} w^h(z_j)w^h(z_k) \left[\int_\Omega \nabla\varphi_j \nabla\varphi_k + \varphi_j\varphi_k\right] , \tag{4.48}$$

while

$$\|w^h\|_{0,\Gamma}^2 = \sum_{z_j \in \Gamma} \sum_{z_k \in \Gamma} w^h(z_j)w^h(z_k) \left[\int_\Gamma \varphi_j\varphi_k\right] . \tag{4.49}$$

With a quasi-regular grid [3] it can be show that the eigenvalues of the mass matrix

$$\left[\int_\Gamma \varphi_j\varphi_k\right] \qquad z_j, z_k \in \Gamma \tag{4.50}$$

are bounded below by terms of $0(h)$. On the other hand, the eigenvalues of the stiffness matrix

$$\int_\Omega \nabla\varphi_j \nabla\varphi_k + \varphi_j\varphi_k \qquad z_j, z_k \in \Gamma \tag{4.51}$$

(restricted to Γ) are bounded above by terms of $0(1)$ (independent of h). Thus

$$\|w^h\|_{1,\Omega}^2 \leq Ch^{-1}\|w^h\|_{0,\Gamma}^2 \tag{4.52}$$

which is (4.43).

§5. Nonconforming Case. We now consider the nonconforming case where (4.29) does not hold. An important special case occurs when $\mathcal{S}^h(\Omega)$ consists of continuous piecewise linear functions. To treat such cases we must estimate the term

$$\sup_{v^h \in \mathcal{N}^h} \frac{\int_\Omega \nabla \varepsilon \cdot \nabla v^h}{\|v^h\|_0} , \tag{5.1}$$

and

$$\sup_{v^h \in \mathcal{S}_0^h} \frac{\int_\Omega e_h v^h}{\|v^h\|_1} \tag{5.2}$$

appearing in (4.27)-(4.28). The analysis given here is an apparently new and condensed proof of results from [12]. Throughout this section we shall assume that the grid is semiregular so that the inverse inequalities hold; i.e.,

$$\|v^h\|_t \le Ch^{s-t} \|v^h\|_s \quad \text{for} \quad v^h \in \mathcal{S}^h, \ t > s . \tag{5.3}$$

Lemma 1. Let

$$E_j^h = \sup_{v^h \in \mathcal{N}^h} \frac{\int \nabla \varepsilon \nabla v^h}{\|v^h\|_0}$$

for $j = 0,1$. Then for each ε, $0 < \varepsilon < 1$, there is a number $0 < C < \infty$ depending only on ε such that

$$|E_0^h| \le Ch^{k+j-\frac{3}{2}-\varepsilon} \|\varphi\|_{W_\infty^k} . \tag{5.4}$$

For quadratic or higher order elements ($k \ge 3$), C is independent of ε and we may put $\varepsilon = 0$.

Proof. Observe that since

$$\int_\Omega \nabla \varepsilon \nabla \psi^h = 0 \quad \text{all} \quad \psi^h \in \mathcal{S}_0^h \tag{5.5}$$

(see (4.25)), the integral

$$\int_\Omega \nabla \varepsilon \nabla v^h$$

for v^h in $\mathcal{S}^h$ contains contributions only from triangles Δ adjoining the boundary. Thus

$$|\int_\Omega \nabla\varepsilon\nabla v^h| = |\sum_{\Delta\cap\Gamma\neq\emptyset} \int_\Delta \nabla\varepsilon\nabla v^h|$$

$$\leq Ch^2 \sum_{\Delta\cap\Gamma\neq\emptyset} \|\nabla\varepsilon\|_{L^\infty(\Delta)} \|\nabla v^h\|_{L^\infty(\Delta)} \quad . \tag{5.6}$$

We now use the inverse inequality to get

$$\|\nabla v^h\|_{L^\infty(\Delta)} \leq Ch^{-1}\|v^h\|_{L^\infty(\Delta)} \leq Ch^{-2}\|v^h\|_{0,\Delta} \cdot \tag{5.7}$$

Thus

$$|\int_\Omega \nabla\varepsilon\nabla v^h| \leq Ch^{-\frac{1}{2}} \|\nabla\tilde{\varepsilon}\|_{L_\infty} \|v^h\|_{0,\Omega} \quad .$$

We now appeal to sup norm estimates for (4.25) (see [13]) to get

$$\|\nabla\tilde{\varepsilon}\|_{L_\infty} \leq Ch^{k-1-\varepsilon}\|\varphi\|_{W^k_\infty} , \tag{5.8}$$

with $\varepsilon > 0$ required only for linear elements $(k = 2)$. Combining (5.7)-(5.8) and taking sup with $\|v^h\|_0 \leq 1$ gives (5.4) with $j = 0$. The case $j = 1$ is treated in exactly the same manner. The extra power of h arises from the inverse inequality (5.7). Indeed, instead of the latter we can use

$$\|\nabla v^h\|_{L^\infty(\Delta)} \leq Ch^{-1}\|\nabla v^h\|_{0,\Delta} , \tag{5.7'}$$

which gains the desired power of h.

<u>Lemma 2</u>. In the same context as Lemma 1 we have for any $0 < \varepsilon < 1$, a number $0 < C < \infty$, depending only on ε, for which

$$|E_1^h| \leq C\left\{\|e\|_0 + Ch^{\frac{1}{2}-\varepsilon}\|e_h\|_0 + h^{k-\frac{1}{2}-\varepsilon}\|\varphi\|_{W^k_\infty}\right\} . \tag{5.9}$$

Here we can not take $\varepsilon = 0$ for higher order elements.

<u>Proof</u>. We start with the decomposition

$$v_h = y + \Delta z, \tag{5.10}$$

where

$$z \in H^3(\Omega) \cap H_0^2(\Omega) \tag{5.11}$$

and

$$\Delta y = 0 \quad \text{in} \quad \Omega \, . \tag{5.12}$$

Indeed, since $v_h \in \mathcal{S}^h \subset H^1$ we have $\Delta v_h \in H^{-1}$, hence z is determined from

$$\Delta^2 v = \Delta v_h \quad \text{in} \quad \Omega, \; z = \frac{\partial z}{\partial \nu} = 0 \quad \text{on} \quad \Gamma \, . \tag{5.13}$$

Also note that regularity of (5.13) gives

$$\|z\|_3 \le C\|v_h\|_1 \tag{5.14}$$

and hence

$$\|y\|_1 \le C\|v_h\|_1 \quad . \tag{5.15}$$

Observe that with (5.5) we have

$$\int_\Omega e_h v^h = \int_\Omega e_h y + \int_\Omega e_h \Delta z \quad . \tag{5.16}$$

We estimate the two terms on the right hand side of (5.16) separately. First, if $y^h \in h^h$, then using (4.23)-(4.24) (with $v^h = y_h$) we get

$$\int_\Omega e_h y_h = \int_\Omega e_h y_h + \int_\Omega e_h (y - y_h) = \int_\Omega e y_h + \int_\Omega \nabla\varepsilon\nabla y_h + \int_\Omega e_h (y - y_h) \, . \tag{5.17}$$

As a special case of Lemma 1, Section 4 we select $y_h \in h^h$ such that

$$\|y - y_h\|_0 \le Ch\|y\|_1 \le Ch\|v_h\|_1 \tag{5.18}$$

$$\|y_h\|_1 \le C\|y\|_1 \le C\|v_h\|_1 \quad . \tag{5.19}$$

Moreover, Lemma 1 of this section with $j = 1$ gives

$$|\int_\Omega \nabla\varepsilon\nabla y_h| \le Ch^{k-\frac{1}{2}-\varepsilon} \|\varphi\|_{W^k_\infty} \|y_h\|_1 \, . \qquad (\;.20)$$

Thus

$$|\int_\Omega e_h y| \le C(\|e\|_0 + h\|e_h\|_0 + h^{k-\frac{1}{2}-\varepsilon})\|v_h\|_1 \, . \tag{5.21}$$

We now turn to the second term in (5.16). Observe that since $\frac{\partial z}{\partial n} = 0$ on Γ

$$\int e_h \Delta z = -\int \nabla e_h \nabla z = \int_\Omega \nabla e_h \nabla (z_h - z) \tag{5.22}$$

for any $z_h \in \mathcal{S}_0^h$. We choose the latter so that

$$\int \nabla \psi^h \nabla (z_h - z) = 0 \quad \text{all} \quad \psi^h \in \mathcal{S}_0^h . \tag{5.23}$$

This means that the integral on the right hand side of (5.22) has contributions only from triangles Δ adjoining the boundary. Thus as in Lemma 1

$$|\int \nabla e_h \nabla (z_h - z)| = |\sum_{\Delta \cap \Gamma \neq \emptyset} \int_\Omega \nabla e_h \nabla (z_h - z)| \tag{5.24}$$

$$\leq Ch^2 \|\nabla (z_h - z)\|_{L^\infty} \sum_{\Delta \cap \Gamma \neq \emptyset} \|\nabla e_h\|_{L^\infty} . \tag{5.25}$$

The use of inverse inequalities given as in Lemma 1

$$\sum_{\Delta \cap \Gamma \neq \emptyset} \|\nabla e_h\|_{L^\infty} \leq Ch^{-2-\frac{1}{2}} \|e_h\|_{0,\Omega} . \tag{5.26}$$

Thus

$$|\int \nabla e_h \nabla (z_h - z)| \leq Ch^{-\frac{1}{2}} \|\nabla (z_h - z)\|_{L^\infty} \|e_h\|_0 . \tag{5.27}$$

We again use sup norm estimates to get

$$\|\nabla (z_h - z)\|_{L^\infty} \leq Ch^{1-\varepsilon} \|z\|_{W_\infty^{2-\varepsilon}} . \tag{5.28}$$

The Sobolev Embedding Theorem plus regularity gives

$$\|z\|_{W_\infty^{2-\varepsilon}} \leq C\|z\|_3 \leq C\|v_h\|_1 . \tag{5.29}$$

Combining with (5.22) we get

$$|\int_\Omega e_h \Delta z| \leq Ch^{\frac{1}{2}-\varepsilon} \|e_h\|_0 \|v_h\|_1 . \tag{5.30}$$

Combining (5.21), (5.30) with (5.16) we get (5.9)

Remark 1. It follows from (4.27) and Lemma 1 that

$$\|u - u_h\|_0 \leq Ch^{k-\frac{3}{2}-\varepsilon} \|\varphi\|_{W_\infty^k} + \text{higher order terms in } h.$$

In particular, with linear elements $k = 2$, the L^2 error in the vorticity is of order $O(h^{\frac{1}{2}-\varepsilon})$. This extremely slow convergence in vorticity has been seen in numerical simulations [12], and is the major defect of nonconforming finite elements. The culprit of course can be traced back to vorticity production on Γ as noted in Section 1.

Remark 2. Observe that the errors in the velocity $\nabla(\varphi - \varphi_h)$ come out much better. Indeed, it follows from Lemma 2 and the above Remark that

$$\|\nabla(\varphi - \varphi_h)\|_0 = O(h^{k-1-\varepsilon})$$

for any $0 < \varepsilon < 1$. This of course is optimal mod the ε-term. These estimates confirm what has been seen in numerical simulations, namely the velocity fields come out rather accurately, while vorticity errors are usually much larger.

Remark 3. With linear elements we have

$$\|u - u_h\|_0 = O(h^{\frac{1}{2}-\varepsilon}), \quad \|\nabla(\varphi - \varphi_h)\|_0 = O(h).$$

By properly selecting the grid one can show that this finite element formulation is exactly the same as standard finite difference schemes. It is interesting to note in this regard that such schemes have second order truncation errors. This is a useful guide to the velocities since if the stream function is second order accurate, its gradient, i.e., the velocity field should be first order accurate. The truncation error, on the other hand, does not give any clue as to the very slow convergence in the vorticity. It is also interesting to note that most finite difference schemes that have been proposed for the stream function-vorticity equation tend to be equivalent to nonconforming finite elements. This is certainly true of the quadratic scheme considered in [1]. This scheme is derivable from a quadratic finite element, but it is only C^0 and not C^1. Hence it is not conforming.

References

[1] Roache, R. J., Computational Fluid Dynamics, Hermosa Publ., 1972.

[2] Peynet, R., Taylor, T. D. Computational Methods for Fluid Flow, Springer-Verlag, 1983.

[3] G. J. Fix and G. Strang, An Analysis of the Finite Element Method, Prentice-Hall, (1973).

[4] G. J. Fix, "Hybrid finite element methods," SIAM Review, 18, (1976), pp. 460-484.

[5] Brezzi, F., "On the existence, uniqueness and application of saddle point problems arising from Lagrange multipliers," RAIRO, 8, 129-150 (1975).

[6] Babuska, I., Aziz, A. K. Mathematical Foundations of the finite element method, Academic Press, 1972.

[7] Brezzi, F. and Raviart, P. Topics in Numerical Analysis III, Academic Press, 1978.

[8] Falk, Rand Osborn, J., RAIRO, Vol. 14, 249-262, 1980.

[9] Scholz, R., RAIRO, Vol. 12, 85-96, 1978.

[10] G. J. Fix, M. D. Gunzburger, and J. S. Peterson, "On finite element approximations of problems having inhomogeneous essential boundary conditions," Computers and Mathematics with Applications, Vol. 9, No. 5 (1983), pp. 687-700.

[11] Lions, J. L., Magenes Monhomogeneous Boundary Value Problems, Springer, 1973.

[12] G. J. Fix, M. D. Gunzburger, R. A. Nicolaides, and J. S. Peterson, "Mixed finite element approximations for the biharmonic equation," Proceedings of the Fifth International Conference on Finite Elements and Flow Problems, January 23-26, 1984, Austin, Texas, Eds., Graham F. Carey and J. Tinsley Oden, (1984), pp. 281-285.

[13] Scott, R., SIAM J. Numer. Anal., Vol. 12, 404-427, 1975.

SECTION 2 SEEPAGE AND UNSATURATED FLOW

VI International Conference on Finite Elements in Water Resources, Lisboa, Portugal, June 1986

Three-Dimensional Finite Element Techniques for Simulating Unconfined Flow with Seepage Faces

P.S. Huyakorn, V. Guvanasen and T.D. Wadsworth
GeoTrans, Inc., Herndon, Virginia 22070, U.S.A.
E.P. Springer
Los Alamos National Lab., New Mexico 87545, U.S.A.

INTRODUCTION

Problems concerning water flow in variably saturated porous media have been studied intensively for over two decades. These problems are difficult to solve for cases involving highly nonlinear soil moisture characteristics and atmospheric boundary conditions associated with seepage faces, infiltration, and evaporation. Most simulations reported in the literature are limited to one- and two-dimensional flow situations. To date, few three-dimensional numerical models have been developed, and most of these models are subjected to certain constraints that make them difficult to apply to complex field situations. In this paper, an improved three-dimensional finite element model designed to alleviate computational restrictions is presented. The model formulation is general and capable of accommodating complex boundary conditions associated with seepage faces. Included in this formulation is an improved Picard algorithm designed to cope with severely nonlinear soil moisture relations. Spatial discretization is performed using a vertical slicing approach in conjunction with simple rectangular and triangular prism elements. Element matrices are evaluated using influence coefficient formulas that avoid costly numerical integration. Matrix solution is achieved using a slice successive over-relaxation (SSOR) scheme that handles several thousand unknowns efficiently on small minicomputers. Three test problems are presented to verify the model and demonstrate its applications.

GOVERNING EQUATION AND GALERKIN APPROXIMATION

Adopting the assumptions from Huyakorn et al. (1984), the governing equation for three-dimensional flow of water in a variably saturated porous medium can be written in the form

$$\frac{\partial}{\partial x_i}\left[K_{ij}k_{rw}\left(\frac{\partial\psi}{\partial x_j}+e_j\right)\right] = \eta\frac{\partial\psi}{\partial t} - q \tag{1}$$

where ψ is the pressure head, K_{ij} is the saturated hydraulic conductivity tensor, k_{rw} is the relative permeability with respect to the water phase, x_i (i = 1,2,3) are Cartesian coordinates, t is the elapsed time, e_j is the unit gravitational vector in the direction of x_2 (assumed to be vertically upward), q is the volumetric flow rate via sources (or sinks) per unit volume of the medium, and η is an overall storage coefficient defined as

$$\eta = S_w S_s + \phi\frac{dS_w}{d\psi} \tag{2}$$

where S_w is the water saturation, S_s is specific storage, and ϕ is porosity.

Application of the Galerkin finite element approximation to equation (1) leads to the following system of ODE:

$$A_{IJ}\,\psi_J + B_{IJ}\frac{d\psi_J}{dt} - F_I = 0 \quad , \quad I = 1, 2, \ldots, n \tag{3}$$

where I and J are nodal subscripts, n is the number of nodes in the finite element network, and the matrix coefficients are given by

$$A_{IJ} = \sum_e A^e_{IJ} = \sum_e \int_{R^e} K_{ij}k_{rw}\frac{\partial N_I}{\partial x_i}\frac{\partial N_J}{\partial x_j}\,dR \tag{4a}$$

$$B_{IJ} = \sum_e B^e_{IJ} = \sum_e \int_{R^e} \eta\, N_I N_J\, dR \tag{4b}$$

$$F_I = \sum_e F^e_I = \sum_e\left(\int_{R^e} - K_{ij}k_{rw}\frac{\partial N_I}{\partial x_i}e_j\,dR\right) \tag{4c}$$

$$+\sum_e\int_{R^e} N_I q\, dR + \sum_e\left(\int_{B^e} V_n N_I dB\right)$$

where R^e is the element subdomain with boundary B^e, V_n denotes the normal Darcy flux intensity at the boundary, and the summation is performed over the total number of elements.

SPATIAL DISCRETIZATION AND ELEMENT MATRIX COMPUTATION

In performing three-dimensional finite element analysis of flow in a complex subsurface system, it is desirable to develop a discretization approach that is adaptable to systematic mesh generation and efficient matrix handling schemes. To achieve this, we adopt the vertical slicing procedure illustrated in Figure 1. The procedure involves two major steps. First, the given region is partitioned into a number of vertical slices. (Note that in the case depicted, each slice is a vertical plane parallel to the x-y plane of the right-handed Cartesian coordinate system. However, the proposed discretization scheme also allows the vertical slices to be nonplanar vertical surfaces provided these surfaces yield the same projection on the x-y plane.) Second, the vertical-block subregions between pairs of adjacent slices are then divided into simple linear prismatic three-dimensional elements. In this paper, only the rectangular prism and triangular prism elements are considered. For coding convenience, the same discretization pattern and hence the same number of nodes are used for each slice. With rectangular and triangular prism elements, the element matrices can be evaluated simply and efficiently using the influence coefficient formulas given below. These formulas contain various influence matrices and a right-hand vector, which can be found in Huyakorn et al. (1986).

Rectangular Prism Element

Assuming that the coordinate system shown in Figure 1 is oriented parallel to the three principal directions of the hydraulic conductivity tensor, the element seepage matrix, $[A]^e$, can be found using the following influence coefficient formula

$$[A]^e = \langle K_{xx} k_{rw} \rangle \frac{mH}{2\ell} [A^{xx}]^e + \langle K_{yy} k_{rw} \rangle \frac{\ell H}{2m} [A^{yy}]^e + \langle K_{zz} k_{rw} \rangle \frac{\ell m}{2H} [A^{zz}]^e \qquad (5)$$

where the angular brackets are used to denote centroidal values of the enclosed quantities, ℓ, m and H are the length, height, and width of the rectangular prism element, and $[A^{xx}]^e$, $[A^{yy}]^e$, and $[A^{zz}]^e$ are (8x8) influence matrices of the element.

Similarly, the element storage matrix, $[B]^e$, and the element right-hand-side vector, $\{F\}^e$, can be computed from

$$[B]^e = \frac{\ell mH}{8} \langle \eta \rangle [M]^e \qquad (6)$$

$$\{F\}^e = -\frac{\ell H}{2} <K_{yy}k_{rw}> \{F_y\}^e \tag{7}$$

where $[M]^e$ and $\{F_y\}^e$ are the element storage influence matrix, and the element influence vector of the rectangular prism.

Triangular Prism Element

The element seepage matrix of the triangular prism may be expressed as

$$[A]^e = \frac{H\Delta}{2}\left(<K_{xx}k_{rw}> [A^{xx}]^e + <K_{yy}k_{rw}> [A^{yy}]^e\right) + \frac{2\Delta}{3H} <K_{zz}k_{rw}> [A^{zz}]^e \tag{8}$$

where Δ is the area of each triangular face, H is the dimension of the prism parallel to the z-axis, $[A^{xx}]^e$, $[A^{yy}]^e$, and $[A^{zz}]^e$ are (6x6) influence coefficient seepage matrices of the triangular prism.

Similarly, the mass matrix $[B]^e$ and the right-hand-side vector $\{F\}^e$ can be evaluated from

$$[B]^e = \frac{H\Delta}{6} <\eta> [M]^e \tag{9}$$

$$\{F\}^e = -\frac{H\Delta}{2} \{F_y\}^e \tag{10}$$

where $[M]^e$ and $\{F_y\}^e$ are the element storage influence matrix, and the element influence vector of the triangular prism.

SOLUTION PROCEDURE

The solution procedure presented herein for three-dimensional problems is an extension of the work presented in Huyakorn et al. (1984) for 2-D problems. Nonlinearities are treated using an implicit Picard iterative scheme. In each iteration, the linearized global matrix equation is formulated and solved using a slice successive over-relaxation (SSOR) solution technique. At the end of an iteration, updating of pressure head values is performed using an empirical auto-relaxation scheme designed to dampen oscillations of head changes from iteration to iteration. After convergence, element velocities and nodal fluxes are computed using a scheme that requires minimal computational effort.

PICARD SCHEME

The Picard scheme used here is a modification of the version given by Huyakorn et al. (1984). It is based on the following finite difference approximation of equation (3):

$$\left(\omega A_{IJ}^{k+\omega} + \frac{B_{IJ}^{k+\omega}}{\Delta t_k}\right) \psi_J^{k+1} = F^{k+\omega} + (\omega - 1)\, A_{IJ}\, \psi_J^k + \frac{B_{IJ}^{k+\omega}}{\Delta t}\, \psi_J^k \qquad (11)$$

where ω is a time weighting factor, indicies k and k+1 denote the previous and current time levels, respectively, and Δt_k is the kth time step. Modifications have been made to the scheme of Huyakorn et al. (1984) to enhance convergence for cases involving combined saturated-unsaturated flow with atmospheric boundary conditions. These modifications relate to

1. Computation of element storage matrix, $[B]^e$. This is done using equation (11) with lumping of the influence matrix $[M]^e$ and a chord-slope approximation of the $dS_w/d\psi$ term of the coefficient η.
2. Updating of the global matrix equation. In each iteration, the global matrix equation is reassembled. The linearized matrix equation is arranged in a form suitable for treatment by the SSOR matrix solution techniques described in the next section.
3. Updating of nodal pressure head values. This is done by applying an under-relaxation formula of the form

$$\{\psi\}^{r+1} = (1 - \gamma)\ \{\psi\}^r + \gamma\{\psi\}^{r+1} \qquad (12)$$

where r and r+1 denote previous and current iterations of time level k+1, and γ is an iteration-dependent relaxation factor ($0 < \gamma \leq 1$). For each iteration, the value of γ is determined using an adaptation of the empirical scheme developed by Cooley (1983).

4. Adjustments to atmospheric boundary conditions associated with seepage faces (and infiltration or evaporation on the soil surface if these exist). The adjustments are made at the end of each Picard iteration.

SSOR MATRIX ALGORITHM

To avoid the problem of a very large three-dimensional matrix bandwidth (or frontwidth), the slice successive over-relaxation (SSOR) technique is used to solve the linearized system of algebraic equations for each iteration of the

Picard scheme. Within each Picard iteration, SSOR matrix subiterations are performed. The matrix formulation and solution algorithm for SSOR consists of four stages:
1. Partitioning of the element matrix equation. The element matrix equation is written as

$$[G]^e \{\psi\}^e = \{R\}^e \tag{13}$$

where

$$[G]^e = \omega[A]^e + [B]^e/\Delta t_k \;;$$

$$\{R\}^e = \{F\}^e + \left((\omega - 1)\ [A]^e + \frac{[B]^e}{\Delta t_k}\right)\{\psi^k\}^e$$

Equation (13) is partitioned so that the nodal unknowns on the two x-y plane faces of the element are separated. Thus,

$$\left[\begin{array}{c|c} \bar{G}_{11} & \bar{G}_{12} \\ \hline \bar{G}_{21} & \bar{G}_{22} \end{array}\right]^e \left\{\begin{array}{c} \bar{\psi}_1 \\ \hline \bar{\psi}_2 \end{array}\right\} = \left\{\begin{array}{c} \bar{R}_1 \\ \hline \bar{R}_2 \end{array}\right\}^e \tag{14}$$

which becomes

$$\left(\bar{G}_{11}\ \bar{\psi}_1\right)^e = \left(\bar{R}_1 - \bar{G}_{12}\ \bar{\psi}_2\right)^e = \left(\bar{R}_1^*\right)^e \tag{15a}$$

$$\left(\bar{G}_{22}\ \bar{\psi}_2\right)^e = \left(\bar{R}_2 - \bar{G}_{21}\ \bar{\psi}_1\right)^e = \left(\bar{R}_2^*\right)^e \tag{15b}$$

The right-hand-side vectors of (15a) and (15b) are evaluated using the most recent estimate of $\bar{\psi}_1$ and $\bar{\psi}_2$.
2. Matrix assembly for individual slices. For a typical slice s, as shown in Figure 1, the assembled matrix equation is given by

$$[G]_s \{\psi\}_s = \{R^*\}_s \tag{16}$$

where $\{\psi\}_s$ contains the nodal unknowns of the slice,

$$[G]_s = \sum_e (\bar{G}_i)^e \;;\; \{R^*\}_s = \sum_e (\bar{R}_i^*)^e \;, \quad i = 1,\ 2$$

and the summation is taken over the number of elements contributing to slice s.

3. Assembly of the global matrix equation. Stage 2 is performed for all slices in the mesh. The slice submatrix equations are then assembled to yield the global matrix equation:

$$\begin{bmatrix} [G]_1 & & & \\ & [G]_2 & & \\ & & \cdot & \\ & & & [G]_{n_s} \end{bmatrix} \begin{Bmatrix} \{\psi\}_1 \\ \{\psi\}_2 \\ \cdot \\ \{\psi\}_{n_s} \end{Bmatrix} = \begin{Bmatrix} \{R^*\}_1 \\ \{R^*\}_2 \\ \cdot \\ \{R^*\}_{n_s} \end{Bmatrix} \qquad (17)$$

where n_s is the total number of vertical slices in the mesh.

4. Matrix solution by successive over-relaxation. For s = 1 through n_s, the solution algorithm consists of four steps.

<u>Step 1: Decomposition</u>

$$[G]_s = [L]_s \, [U]_s \qquad (18)$$

where $[L]_s$ and $[U]_s$ are lower and upper triangular matrices.

<u>Step 2: Back Substitution</u>

$$[L]_s \, \{\chi\}_s = \{R^*\}_s \qquad (19)$$

$$[U]_s \, \{\psi\}_s = \{\chi\}_s \qquad (20)$$

where $\{\chi\}_s$ and $\{\psi\}_s$ are the intermediate and final solution vectors, respectively.

<u>Step 3: Updating of Nodal Unknown Vector</u>
The new pressure head values to be used in the following iteration are obtained by applying an over-relaxation formula to the old head vector, and the final solution vector determined from Step 2.

$$\{\psi\}_s^{new} = \{\psi\}_s^{old} + \Omega \, (\{\psi\}_s - \{\psi\}_s^{old}) \qquad (21)$$

where Ω is an over-relaxation factor.

<u>Step 4: Updating of the RHS Vector</u>
The value of s is incremented by one. Then the updated pressure head values are used to update the right-hand-side vector, $\{R^*\}_s$. We obtain

$$\{R^*\}_s = \sum_e (\bar{R}^*_i)^e \quad , \ i = 1 \text{ or } 2 \qquad (22)$$

Note that step 1 of the matrix solution is performed only once, and steps 2, 3, and 4 are repeated until $\{\psi\}_s$, s = 1 through n_s, converge to within a prescribed head tolerance.

TREATMENT OF THE SEEPAGE FACES

When seepage faces are present, they are taken into account in the Picard scheme. Each seepage face is represented by a series of vertical or inclined grid lines. The potential seepage face nodes are identified before commencing the nonlinear solution. We adopt the procedure used by Neuman et al. (1974) and Rulon (1984) to locate positions of exit points on the identified grid lines. This procedure starts with an initial exit point of each seepage face and proceeds to predict the position of the exit point at the next time level. Within the time step, Picard iterations are performed and if necessary, the location of the exit point on each of the previously identified grid lines is adjusted at the end of each iteration. The aim is to satisfy the conditions of zero ψ-values on the seepage face portions of the grid lines, negative ψ-values at the nodes above the exit point, and negative flux (outflow) values at the seepage face nodes. All nodes expected to be part of a seepage face during the simulation are considered. Their boundary conditions may be switched from prescribed zero pressure head to prescribed zero flux to meet the necessary constraints. To enhance convergence of the solution, the modification of boundary conditions is performed sequentially from node to node, starting at the saturated end of each seepage face grid line. The iterative process continues until a satisfactory convergence is achieved at all nodes in the finite element network.

ILLUSTRATIVE EXAMPLES

A computer code called "FLAMINCO" has been developed to simulate three-dimensional water flow and contaminant transport in variably saturated porous media. The flow module of this code is based on the Galerkin finite element formulation and solution techniques described earlier. To verify these techniques and demonstrate their capability, three illustrative examples are presented.

Example 1: Transient Drainage from a Square Block

The flow system considered was a 10 m square block assumed to be fully saturated with an initial hydraulic head of 10 m above the base. The water level at the right face of the block was then lowered suddenly, from 10 m to 2 m, and maintained at 2 m thereafter. Values of parameters used in the simulation are as follows: $K_{xx} = K_{yy} = K_{zz} = 0.01$ m/d, $S_s = 10^{-4}\ m^{-1}$, $\phi = 0.25$, and $k_{rw} = S_e$, $S_e = (S_w = 0.2)/0.8$, $S_e = 10/(10 + \psi)$ for $\psi < 0$, and $S_e = 1$ for $\psi \geq 0$.

The flow region was discretized using a two-slice grid consisting of 100 rectangular elements and 242 nodes. The nodal spacings were $\Delta x = \Delta y = 1$ m, and $\Delta z = 10$ m. The simulation was performed for 30 time steps. Time step values were generated using the following algorithm: $\Delta t_1 = 0.1$ days, $\Delta t_k = 1.2 \Delta t_{k-1} \leq 5$ days, for $k = 2, \ldots, 30$. The head tolerances for the Picard and the SSOR schemes were specified as 0.01 and 0.001 m, respectively. For the SSOR scheme, the over-relaxation factor, Ω, was set equal to 1. To enhance convergence of the nonlinear Picard iterations, the storage matrix was diagonalized. Computed profiles of the water table are plotted in Figure 2 for typical time values. The results obtained from the present model are compared with those given by a two-dimensional model, UNSAT2, which was used to solve the same problem. As depicted in Figure 2, there is excellent agreement between the two finite element solutions.

We recorded the number of Picard iterations and the number of SSOR subiterations required by the FLAMINCO code for each time step to meet the specified convergence criterion. This information is presented in Figure 3. Note that both the Picard and the SSOR schemes showed improved performance at later time steps. The number of Picard iterations varies from 2 to 6, and the number of SSOR subiterations varies from 4 to 21 over the 30 time steps of the simulation.

Example 2: Three-Dimensional Flow in a Drained Field

This example was selected to demonstrated an application of the proposed model to a steady three-dimensional flow problem. The problem concerns seepage to a line of drains partially penetrating an anisotropic unconfined aquifer. The drains are placed at regular intervals of 400 m between centers. For convenience, we oriented the z-axis along the line joining the centers of these drains. In Figure 4, a cross section of the aquifer passing through the drain is depicted. Because of symmetry, only one representative portion of the aquifer was considered. This portion was taken to be 200 m wide (along the z-axis) and covered a 50 m half-width of one drain. The water table was assumed to be located initially at 20 m above the aquifer base, and was then lowered suddenly to a height of 12.5 m. This height was maintained thereafter. A prescribed hydraulic head condition

($\psi + y = 20$ m) was assumed on the vertical boundary portion located at $x = 200$ m, and $0 \leq y \leq 20$ m. A no-flow condition was assumed on other boundary portions of the flow region. A steady state analysis of the flow problem was performed. Values of the parameters used in the analysis are as follows:

$K_{xx} = 5$ m/d, $K_{yy} = 2$ m/d, $K_{zz} = 0.5$ m/d, and $k_{rw} = S_e^2$,

$S_e = (S_w = 0.05)/0.95$, and $S_e = 1/(1 + 0.25\psi^2)$ for $\psi < 0$, and

$S_e = 1$ for $\psi \geq 0$.

The region was discretized using a rectangular grid comprising 1200 prism elements and 1584 nodes. The nodal spacings in the x, y, and z directions were set equal to 13.33, 2.5, and 25 m, respectively. The steady flow problem was solved in one step with the tolerance for the Picard algorithm specified as 0.05 m. Seven nonlinear iterations were required to reach convergence. Within each nonlinear iteration, the SSOR matrix subiterations were performed using $\Omega = 1.5$. The total number of matrix subiterations necessary to reach the final solution was 37. A perspective view of computed water table positions is shown in Figure 5. Longitudinal and transverse profiles of the water table elevation are plotted in Figure 6. The difference between these profiles is caused by the combined influence of the anisotropic material properties and the lateral boundary conditions. The total discharge into each drain was computed to be 492.4 m^3/d.

Example 3: Flow in an Unconfined Aquifer Subjected to Pumping

This problem is depicted in Figure 7. Initially, the water table was assumed to be located at 60 m above the base of the aquifer. The water level in the well was then lowered to 30 m. A prescribed hydraulic head condition ($\psi + y = 60$ m) was assumed on two vertical boundaries located at $x = 0$ m, $0 \leq y \leq 60$ m, and at $x = 1000$ m, $0 \leq y \leq 60$ m. A no flow condition was assumed on all other boundaries of the flow region. A steady-state analysis of the stated flow problem was performed. Values of the parameters used in the analysis are the same as those used in Example 2. Because of symmetry, one half of the region above AA' was considered. This portion was then discretized using a nonuniform rectangular grid consisting of 1600 prism elements and 2079 (21x11x9) nodes.

The problem was solved in one step using the Picard iterative method with the head tolerance specified as 0.05 m. It took six Picard iterations to reach convergence. Within each iteration, the SSOR matrix subiterations were performed using $\Omega = 1.5$. The total number of subiterations required to reach the final solution was 80. Computed water table elevation versus distance is plotted in Figures 8a and 8b for longitudinal and transverse sections through the pumping well, respectively. The length of the seepage face and the well discharge were determined to be approximately 4 m and 1838.4 m^3/d, respectively.

DISCUSSION AND CONCLUSIONS

Three examples were provided to verify the finite element model described and to demonstrate its capability for performing three-dimensional analysis of variably saturated flow problems. Improved computational performance is achieved by the use of efficient matrix computation and SSOR solution schemes. These schemes facilitate the analysis of 3-D problems involving seepage faces and a few thousand nodal unknowns, on small minicomputers. For example 2, with 1584 nodes, the CPU times required by the VAX 11/750 and PRIME 550-II were 54 and 33 CPU minutes, respectively. For example 3, with 2079 nodes, the corresponding CPU minutes were 177 and 65, respectively.

The present finite element approach can be applied to a wide range of saturated-unsaturated flow problems. Typical examples are hillslope hydrologic response, agricultural water management, and risk assessment for low level and toxic waste sites. With the present model, these problems can be analyzed in three dimensions, taking into account both the saturated and unsaturated zones if needed. Another valuable use of this model is in conceptual studies of heterogeneous porous media to obtain a better understanding of the response of these systems in three dimensions. Efficient solution techniques enable a large number of nodes to be incorporated into the finite element grid. Thus more realistic field simulations can be achieved if appropriate data are available.

ACKNOWLEDGEMENTS

This work was supported, in part, by research funds provided by GeoTrans, Inc. Additional funding was made by the U.S. Dept. of Agriculture through Contract No. 53-3X06-4-82. Portions of this study were completed by E. Springer while stationed with the USDA-ARS Northwest Watershed Research Center in Boise, Idaho. Thanks are due to V.M. Guvanasen for technical help in manuscript preparation.

REFERENCES

Cooley, R.L. (1982). Some new procedures for numerical solution of variably saturated flow problems, Water Resour. Res. 19(5):1271-1285.

Davis, L.A., and Neuman, S.P. (1983). Documentation and User's Guides UNSAT2 Variably Saturated Flow Model, U.S. Nuclear Regulatory Commission Report, NUREG/CR-3390, Washington, DC.

Huyakorn, P.S., Thomas, S.D., and Thompson, B.M. (1984). Techniques for making finite elements competitive in modeling flow in variably saturated porous media, Water Resour. Res. 20(8):1099-1115.

Huyakorn, P.S., Springer, E.P., and Guvanasen, V. (1986). A three-dimensional finite element model for simulating water flow in variably saturated porous media, submitted to Water Resour. Res.

Neuman, S.P., Feddes, R.A., and Bresler, E. (1974). Finite element simulation of flow in saturated-unsaturated soils considering water uptake by plants, Hydrodynamics and Hydraulic Engineering Laboratory Report for Project No. ALO-5WC-77, Technion, Hafia, Israel.

Rulon, J. (1984). The development of multiple seepage faces along heterogeneous hillslopes, Ph.D. Thesis, University of British Columbia, Vancouver, Canada.

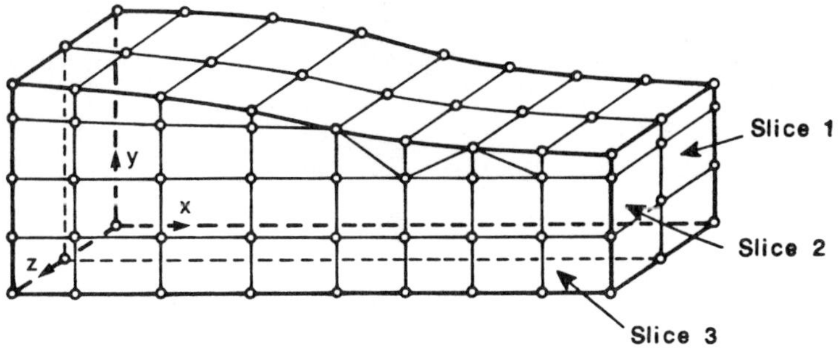

Figure 1. Discretization of a three-dimensional region.

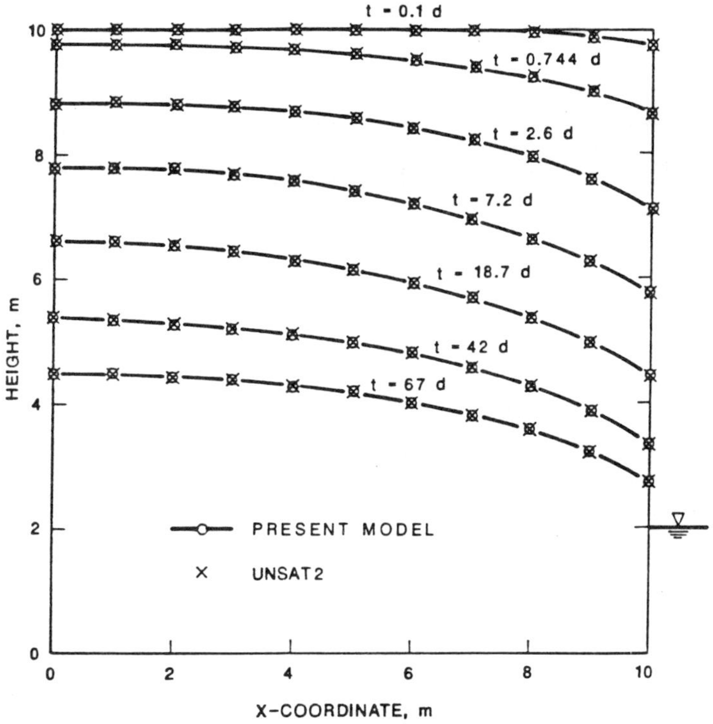

Figure 2. Computer probiles of water table.

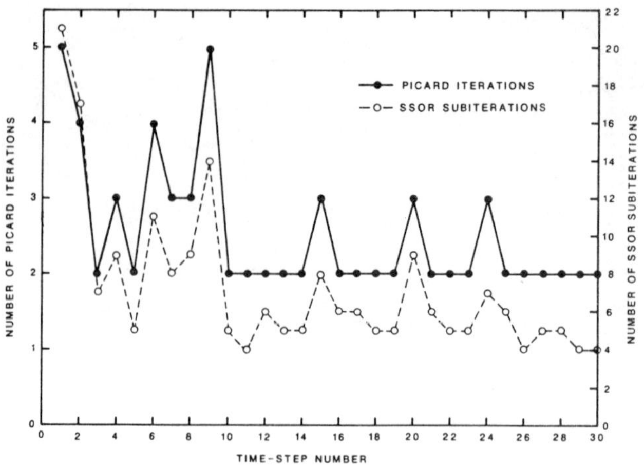

Figure 3. Plot of time step number versus number of Picard iterations and SSOR subiterations.

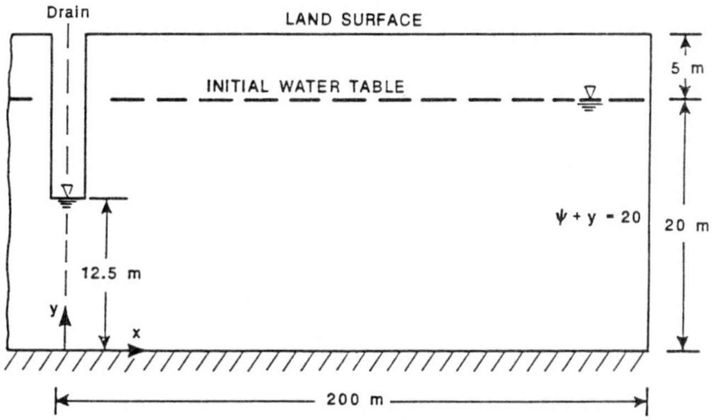

Figure 4. Cross section of the flow region for the drained field problem.

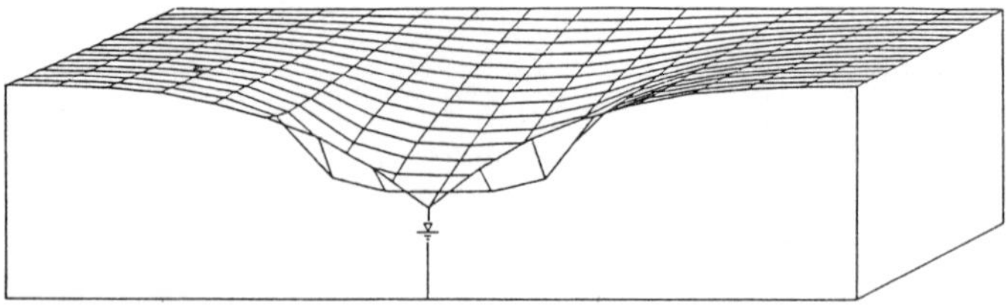

Figure 5. Perspective view of the water table for the drained field problem.

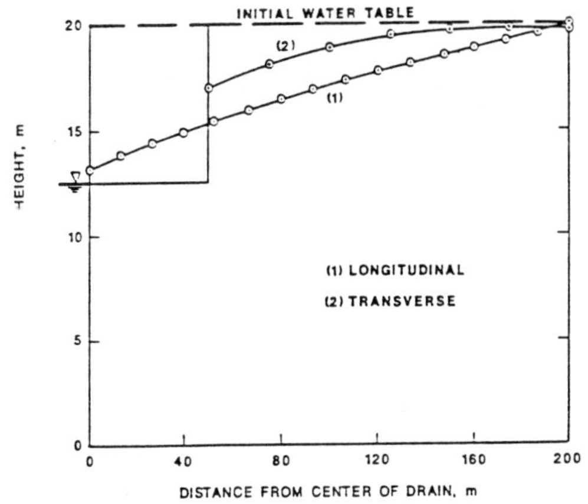

Figure 6. Profiles of the water table for the drained field problem.

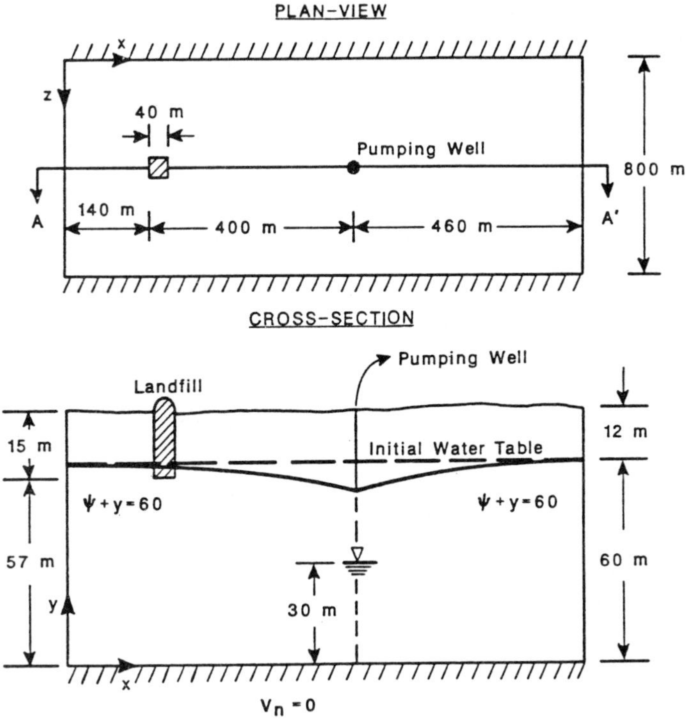

Figure 7. Problem definition for three-dimensional flow in a pumped unconfined aquifer.

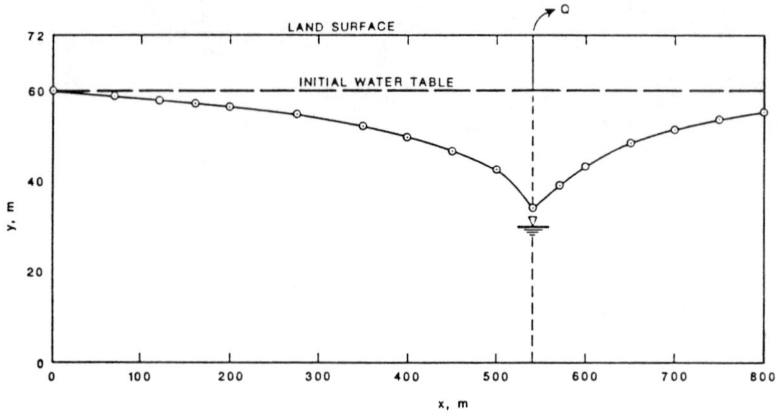

(a) Longitudinal

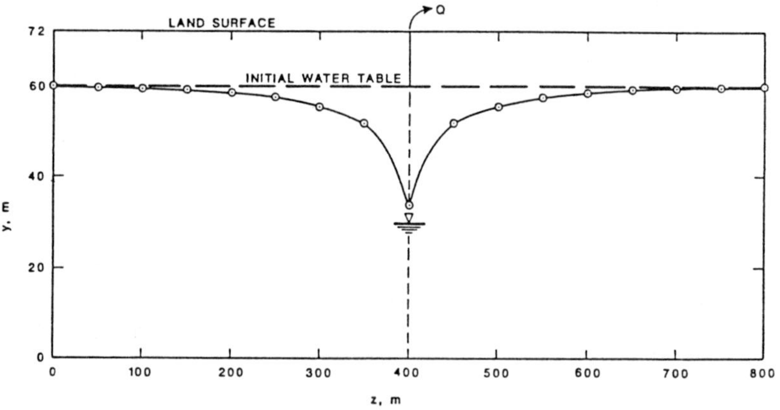

(b) Transverse

Figure 8. Computed profiles of the water table for the pumped aquifer problem.

VI International Conference on Finite Elements in Water Resources, Lisboa, Portugal, June 1986

An Adaptive Eulerian-Lagrangian Approach for the Numerical Simulation of Unsaturated Flow

S. Sorek
Department of Bio-Medical Engineering, Technion – Israel Institute of Technology, Haifa 32000, Israel
C. Braester
Department of Civil Engineering, Technion – Israel Institute of Technology, Haifa 32000, Israel

ABSTRACT

The equation of unsaturated flow with the moisture potential as the state variable is considerable. The classical Eulerian equation is reformulated through an Eulerian-Lagrangian approach, such that the phenomenon is formally decomposed into advection, typical to the Lagrangian concept and propagation of the residual handled by the Eulerian approach.

The moisture potential is decoupled into an advection term and a residual term. Advection is solved by the method of characteristics along pathlines while the residual, discretized within a fixed grid, is solved by a finite element method.

Similar to the dispersion-advection phenomena where the method proved its superiority in the treatment of steep concentration gradients, for the unsaturated flow equation, the method presents advantages in solving flow problems with sharp saturation profiles e.g., as occuring in infiltration into dry soils.

1. INTRODUCTION

Parabolic conduction/flow problems are usually described by an Eulerian representation for the propagation of the state variable in time and space. (Hromadka et al., 1989; Neuman et al., 1982 Tham and Cheung, 1982; Frind, 1982; Kgaran and Sigurdsson, 1981; Van Genuchten, 1983). Let us consider a typical 1-D flow equation of the form

$$\frac{\partial h}{\partial t} = \frac{\partial}{\partial x}\left(G\,\frac{\partial h}{\partial x}\right) \tag{1.1}$$

Eq. 1.1 written in a dimensionless form. (subscript D)

$$\frac{G}{\bar{G}} \frac{\partial h_D}{\partial t_D} = \frac{\partial^2 h_D}{\partial x_D^2} + S_R \frac{\partial h_D}{\partial x_D} \qquad (1.2)$$

where the dimensionless parameters are defined by

$$x_D = x/L \qquad G_D = G/\bar{G}$$

$$h_D = h/\bar{h} \qquad \bar{h} = \frac{1}{\Omega} \int_\Omega h d\Omega \qquad (1.3)$$

$$t_D = t\bar{G}/L^2 \qquad \bar{G} = \frac{1}{\Omega} \int_\Omega G d\Omega$$

here, L is a characteristic length Ω - denotes the solution region and S_R is a dimensionless coefficient defined by

$$S_R = \frac{L|\partial G/\partial x|}{G} = \left(\frac{L}{G} |\partial G/\partial h|\right) \left|\frac{\partial h}{\partial x}\right| \qquad (1.4)$$

The governing equation (1.2) may become hyperbolic or parabolic dominant depending on relative importance of S (see eq. 1.4). This suggests that an Eulerian or a Lagrangian method of solution be considered, depending on the parabolic or the hyperbolic nature of the flow equation.

The proposed method combines the simplicity of a solution within a fixed grid, associated with the Eulerian concept and the computational power of the Lagrangian approach which is especially effective in the regions of high S values, i.e., advection dominated.

Following Neuman and Sorek (Neuman and Sorek, 1982; Neuman, 1984; Sorek, 1984, 1985a,b,c) a technique consisting of follow- ing two steps is used:

(a) a formal decomposition of the potential field into two parts, one controlled by pure Lagrangian advection, and a residual governed by a combination of Euler-Lagrange approaches.

(b) a solution of the resulting advection problem, by the method of characteristics for forward particle tracking. The remainder problem is solved by an implicit finite element scheme on a fixed grid. Both steps are coupled, as will be explained in the following paragraph.

A solution of the advection system requires that particles velocity by continuous no space. Following Yeh (1981) a technique for evaluating a field of continuous spatial particle velocity is described. Thus technique is based on the calculation of the potentials at the element nodes at each time step.

2. The Equation of Flow

The governing equations of flow are the mass conservation equation and the momentum balance expressed by

$$(\phi s\rho)_{,t} + (\rho u_i)_{,i} = 0 \tag{2.1}$$

Where ϕ denotes porosity, S is water saturation, k_r is water density and u_i is Darcy's specific flux, asdescribed by,

$$u_i = \frac{-k_{ij} k_r \rho g}{\mu} (p_{,i}/\rho g + Z_{,i}) \tag{2.2}$$

Where k_{ij} represents the components of the permeability tensor, is relative permeability, g is acceleration of gravity, p is pressure, z is the vertical cartesian coordinate and μ is water viscosity.

We define rock compressibility

$$c_r = \frac{1}{\phi}\frac{d\phi}{dp} \tag{2.3}$$

and fluid compressibility

$$c_f = \frac{1}{\rho}\frac{d\rho}{dp} \tag{2.4}$$

•Assuming that the capillary pressure is the main factor of the moisture potential, and retaining only this term, the pressure in the water phase is equal to

$$p_w = p_a - p_c \tag{2.5}$$

where p_a is the constant atmospheric pressure of stagnant air and p_c is the capillary pressure.

In view of Eqs. (2.3) - (2.5), the first term in eq. (2.1) may be expanded as follows

$$(\phi s\rho)_{,t} = \rho\phi(sc - ds/dp_c)p_{,t} \tag{2.6}$$

where c is the total compresibility of fluid and rock ($c = c_f + c_r$).

Using Hubbert's potential defined as

$$\Phi = \int_{p_a}^{p} \frac{dp}{\rho g} + Z \tag{2.7}$$

where z is the altitude above a reference,

one may express eq. (2.2) as

$$u_i = -\frac{k_{ij}k_r\rho g}{\mu} \Phi_{,i} \tag{2.8}$$

Substitution of eqs. (2.7) and (2.8) into (2.1) yields the flow equation through unsaturated media

$$\rho\phi C\Phi_{,t} - (\rho K_{ij}\Phi_{,i})_{,i} = 0 \tag{2.9}$$

where

$$K_{ij} = \frac{k_{ij}k_r\rho}{\mu} \tag{2.10}$$

$$C = \rho(sc - ds/dp_c) \tag{2.11}$$

Eq. (2.12) must be solved for the unknown Φ , subject to the following initial and boundary conditions, respectively

$$\Phi_{(x_i, o)} = \Phi_{o(x_i)} \tag{2.12}$$

$$(\rho\vec{u})\cdot\vec{n} + \alpha(\Phi - \Phi_\Gamma) = \rho u_\Gamma \tag{2.13}$$

where $\vec{n}$ is the unit normal to the boundary Γ , (positive outwards), Φ_o , Φ_Γ and u_Γ are prescribed functions, and α controls the type of boundary conditions.

For the Dirichlet type of boundary conditions $\alpha \to \infty$ and $\Phi = \Phi_\Gamma$ while for the Neumann type of boundary conditions $\alpha = o$ and $u\ \vec{u} \cdot \vec{n} = u_\Gamma$ For mixed boundary conditions $o < \alpha < \infty$.

The Eulerian Lagrangrian Formulation of the Equation of Flow

Let us define a time derivative operator of the form

$$L/Lt = \partial/\partial t + v_{p_i}\ \partial/\partial x_i \tag{2.14}$$

where v_{p_i} is the velocity vector component of a particle along its path line.

Using this operator we may rewrite the flow equation (Eq. (2.9))

$$\phi C\ L\Phi/Lt = k_{ij}\Phi,_{ii} \tag{2.15}$$

where the particle velocity is defined by a potential function of the form

$$v_{p_i} = - \left(\frac{1}{\rho\phi C}\right) (\rho k_{ij}),_i \tag{2.16}$$

A relationship between particle's velocity $\vec{v}_p$ and Darcy's specific flux $\vec{u}$ may be obtained as follows.

$$u_i = - \left(\frac{k_{ij}\rho k_r}{\mu}\right) \left(\frac{\partial \Phi}{\partial(\rho^2 k_r/\mu)}\right) \left(\frac{k_{ij}k_r\rho^2}{\mu}\right)_{,i} \tag{2.17}$$

Combining eqs. (2.16) and (2.17) we obtain

$$u_i = \left[\Phi C \left(\frac{\rho^2 k_r}{\mu}\right) \left(\frac{\partial \Phi}{\partial(\rho^2 k_r/\mu)}\right)\right] v_{p_i} \tag{2.18}$$

The governing equation, (2.15), is decoupled into two parts, one representing advection along characteristic path lines, and the second describing propagation at a fixed frame of reference. This is obtained by decomposing the variable Φ into an advection potential term $\bar{\Phi}$ solved along path lines described by

$$Lx_i/Lt = v_{p_i} \tag{2.19}$$

and a residual term $\overset{o}{\Phi}$ solved at fixed spatial coordinates. Thus the potential Φ may be written as

$$\Phi = \bar{\Phi} + \overset{o}{\Phi} \tag{2.20}$$

One way to decompose Φ in this form is to let $\bar{\Phi}$ satisfy

$$L\bar{\Phi}/Lt = 0 \tag{2.21}$$

subject to the following initial and boundary conditions

$$\bar{\Phi}_{(x_i,o)} = \Phi_{o(x_i)} \tag{2.22}$$

and

$$\alpha(\bar{\Phi}-\Phi_\Gamma) = \rho u_\Gamma \tag{2.23}$$

The residual $\overset{o}{\Phi}$ is thus solved by

$$\phi C\, L\overset{o}{\Phi}/Lt \;=\; K_{ij}\,\Phi,_{ii} \qquad (2.24)$$

subject to the following initial and boundary conditions

$$\Phi_{(x_i,o)} \;=\; 0 \qquad (2.25)$$

$$\alpha\overset{o}{\Phi} - \rho K_{ij}\,\Phi,_i\, n_i \;=\; 0 \qquad (2.26)$$

Thus the flow equation in the form of eq. (2.15) is rigourously decomposed to a set of two equations, (2.21) and (2.24) that are solved separately.

The method of solution of these equations is as follows: first eq. (2.21) is solved for $\bar{\Phi}$ and then eq. (2.25) with a source term generated by the first solution, is solved for $\overset{o}{\Phi}$.

The complete solution for Φ is obtained by adding at every point the partial solutions for $\overset{o}{\Phi}$ and $\bar{\Phi}$.

Another possibility to solve eq. (2.15) without the need of decomposition of Φ is by using the so-called single-step reverse particle tracking technique. (see numerical implementation).

The proposed numerical method uses both techniques, jointly in an adaptive manner.

3. Numerical Implementation

The numerical calculation scheme starts with the solution of eqs.
(2.21) - (2.23) by continuous forward tracking of particles. The particles are located at selected points, e.g. steep fronts and sources. At the beginning of each time step the field potential is represented by clouds of particles and the residual potential is set to zero.

This is expressed by

$$\bar{\Phi}_{(x_i,t^k)} \;=\; \Phi_{o(x_i,t^k)} \qquad (3.1)$$

$$\Phi_{(x_i,t^k)} \;=\; 0$$

where k indicates the time level.

At the end of the time step, $\bar{\Phi}$ which remains unchanged in time is projected onto the fixed modes of the grid. These values are used for the solution of eqs. (2.24) - (2.26).

Particle Tracking Technique

Let us define a time step Δt as the difference between the time level t^k and the t^{k+1}, i.e.,

$$\Delta t = t^{k+1} - t^k \tag{3.2}$$

Let x_{p_i} be the position vector of the particle p. Denoting the advective potential associated with the particle p at time t^k by $\bar{\Phi}_p^k$ we obtain by virtue of eq. (3.1).

$$\bar{\Phi}_p^k \equiv \bar{\Phi}_{(x_{p_i}, t^k)} = \Phi_{(x_{p_i}, t^k)} \tag{3.3}$$

For a particle along boundary Γ at location x_{Γ_i}, in view of eq. (2.23), we obtain

$$\bar{\Phi}_p^k = \left(\frac{\rho u_\Gamma + \alpha \Phi_\Gamma}{\alpha}\right)_{x_{\Gamma_i}, t^k} \quad ; \quad 0<\alpha<\infty \tag{3.4}$$

In case of an inflow boundary, $\bar{\Phi}_p^k$ may be approximated by

$$\bar{\Phi}_p^k = \left(\frac{\underline{\underline{k}}^{-1} k_r \rho^r}{\mu} u_\Gamma |\underline{x}_\Gamma|\right)_{x_{\Gamma_i}, t^k} \quad \alpha \to 0 \tag{3.5}$$

The potentials defined by eqs. (3.3) and (3.5) remain constant over the elapse of time Δt and are advected forward, along the path to a distance $x_{p_i}^{k+1}$ given by (see eq. 2.22)

$$x_{p_i}^{k+1} = x_{p_i}^k + \int_{t^k}^{t^{k+1}} v_{p_i} \, Lt \tag{3.6}$$

At the end of this period of time $\bar{\Phi}$ values are projected onto fixed nodes covered by the clouds, using a distance weighting

$$w_p = \frac{1/dp}{\sum\limits_{p_t} 1/dp} \tag{3.7}$$

where w_p is a weighting function associated with the particle P , d_p is the distance from a particle P to a fixed node and P_t represents the total number of particles in the clouds covering the latter. The reflected value of $\bar{\Phi}$ upon the node n is denoted by ${}^k\Phi_n$. By virtue of (3.3), we obtain

$${}^k\Phi_n = \bar{\Phi}(x_{n_i}, t^{k+1}) \tag{3.8}$$

We shall now describe the alternative approach called the ''single step reverse particle tracking''.

Let us approximate the potential within an element, using its nodal values Φn and a basis interpolation function ξ_n as follows

$$\Phi(x_i,t) \stackrel{\sim}{=} \hat{\Phi}(x_i,t) = \Phi_n(t)\ \xi_n(x_i) \quad (n=1,2,\ldots,N) \tag{3.9}$$

where, N is the total number of element nodes, and ξ_n are basis functions given by

$$\xi_n(x_m) = \delta_{nm} = \begin{cases} 1 \ ; & n=m \\ 0 \ ; & n \neq m \end{cases} \tag{3.10}$$

where δ_{nm} is the Kronecker delta function.

In the regions where potential fronts are moderate or not covered by clouds, ${}^k\Phi_n$ is evaluated by moving a fictitious point from a backward position so that at the end of the time step it merges with the node. In view of (2.21), we have,

$${}^k x_{n_i} = {}^{k+1}x_{n_i} - \int_{t^k}^{t^{k+1}} v_{p_i}\ Lt \tag{3.11}$$

When $v_{p_i} \neq v_{p_i}(t)$ equation (3.11) yields a constant backward position which means that a single evaluation of ${}^k x_{n_i}$ is sufficient. Thus, by virtue of (3.9) we can write

$$ {}^{k}\overset{\circ}{\hat{\Phi}}_n = \overset{\circ}{\Phi}{}^{k}_n \, \xi_n({}^{k}x_{n_i}) \qquad (n=1,2,\ldots,N) \tag{3.12} $$

This formalism is much more efficient computer-wise compared with forward particle tracking and it is used for the solution of eq. (2.24) after the automatic elimination of the particles.

Fixed Grid Technique

Let A^e, Γ^e denote the element area and its boundary length respectively, Galerkin orthogonalization process, Green's first identity and adopting the lumped-mass finite element approach to eq. 2.24 yields.

$$ \int_{A^e} \left[\Phi C \frac{L\overset{\circ}{\hat{\Phi}}}{Lt} \xi_n + \left(\frac{k_{ij} k_r \rho}{\mu} \xi_n \right)_{,i} \hat{\Phi}_{,i} \right] dA^e - \oint_{\Gamma^e} \frac{k_{ij} k_r \rho}{\mu} \xi_n \hat{\Phi}_{,i} n_i d\Gamma^e = 0 \tag{3.13} $$

Approximating the time derivative by a backwards difference we obtain

$$ \frac{L\overset{\circ}{\Phi}_n}{Lt} = \frac{\overset{\circ}{\Phi}{}^{k+1}_n - {}^{k}\overset{\circ}{\Phi}_n}{\Delta t} = \frac{\Phi^{k+1}_n - (\bar{\Phi}^{k+1}_n + {}^{k}\overset{\circ}{\Phi}_n)}{\Delta t} \tag{3.14} $$

By combining the equations (3.13) and (3.14) we obtain a global matrix in the form

$$ \left(\underline{\underline{A}} + \underline{\underline{B}} + \frac{1}{\Delta t} \underline{\underline{F}} \right) \underline{\Phi}^{k+1} = \frac{1}{\Delta t} \underline{\underline{F}} \, (\underline{\bar{\Phi}}^{k+1} + {}^{k}\underline{\overset{\circ}{\Phi}}) \tag{3.15} $$

where, $\underline{\underline{A}}$ is the ''permeability matrix'', which is symmetric and semi-positive of order M and defined by

$$ A_{mn} = \Lambda_m \int_R \underline{\underline{k}} \, \xi_{m,i} \, \xi_{n,i} \, dR \tag{3.16} $$

where

$$ \Lambda_m = (k_r \rho)_m \tag{3.17} $$

The relative permeability k_r is a function of the wetting saturation S, may be correlated to the capillary pressure p_c through the relative saturation S . The water density ρ is an explicit function of pressure.

$\underline{\underline{B}}$ is the ''boundary matrix'' which is symmetric, of order M and defined by

$$B_{mn} = -\Lambda_m \oint_\Gamma \xi_n \xi_{m,i} n_i d\Gamma \; ; \quad \alpha < \infty \tag{3.18}$$

If m and n are located on an inflow or noflow boundary

$$B_{mn} = 0 \tag{3.19}$$

$\underline{\underline{F}}$ is the ''capacity matrix'' of order M which is diagonal and is defined by

$$F_{mn} = \psi_m \delta_{mn} \int_R \xi_m dR \tag{3.20}$$

where

$$\psi_m = \phi(\mu C)_m \tag{3.21}$$

The viscosity is considered a linear function of pressure, S, ds/dp_c are correlated to the capillary pressure.

Once the nodal potentials are evaluated, the particle potential is modified. In view of equation (3.9) we obtain

$$\Phi_p^{k+1} = \bar{\Phi}_p^k + \Phi_{(x_{p_i}, t^{k+1})} = \bar{\Phi}_p^k + (\Phi_n^{k+1} - {}^k\Phi_n)\, \xi_n(x_{p_i}) \tag{3.22}$$

then $\bar{\Phi}_p^{k+1} = \Phi_p^{k+1}$ is set and the particles are redeployed for the next time step.

It is recommended to cover steep fronts, time dependent sources etc., with clouds of particles, which are eliminated after the fronts have been flattened. The subsequent procedure is based on the fixed grid in con- junction with single-step reverse particle tracking. The criteria for elimination will be described below.

It was found (Neuman and Sorek, 1982) that for a steep gradient of the state variable, application of (3.22) may lead to a situation in which the particle load is lower or higher than the loads at the surrounding element nodes.

$$\Phi_p^{k+1} < \min \Phi_n^{k+1} \tag{3.23}$$

$$\Phi_p^{k+1} > \max \Phi_n^{k+1} \tag{3.24}$$

To overcome this discontinuity, equation (3.22) is replaced by

$$\Phi_p^{k+1} = \Phi_n^{k+1} \xi_n(x_{p_i}) \tag{3.25}$$

which completely eliminates all kinks expressed in (3.23), (3.24). Thus, after a few consecutive time steps when (3.23) and (3.24) are not repeated, ${}^k\underline{\Phi}$ is defined as

$$^{k}\underline{\Phi} = \underline{\bar{\Phi}}^{k+1} + {}^{k}\underline{\Phi} \tag{3.26}$$

Substituting eq. (3.26) into (3.15) we obtain a solution scheme obviating the need for forward particle tracking.

Velocities by Finite Elements

Following is a method for evaluation of nodal velocities with information already determined at elements of the grid. The resulting velocities are spatially continuous to the same degree as the supplied nodal input. Velocities are approximated using the same bases functions as in equations (3.10)

$$v_{p_i} \stackrel{\sim}{=} \hat{v}_{p_i} = v_{p_{i_n}}(t)\ \xi_n(x_i) \qquad (n=1,2,\ldots,N) \tag{3.27}$$

In view of equation (2.16) and by using a finite element Galerkin's method, a global matix form for the solution of particle velocities is yielded.

$$\underline{\underline{H}}\ \underline{v}_{p_i} = \underline{R}_i \tag{3.28}$$

$\underline{H}$ is the ''mass matrix'' symmetric or order M defined as

$$H_{mn} = \int_R \xi_m \xi_n \, dR \tag{3.29}$$

$\underline{R}$ is a ''vector of potential gradients'' of order M, defined as

$$R_{m_i} = -r_m \int_R \xi_m k_{in} \xi_{j,n} (\Phi_j - \lambda_{\ell,i}) dR \tag{3.30}$$

where,

$$r_m = \frac{g}{\phi} \left\{ \frac{\rho^2}{\mu C} \left[k_r (\rho c_f - \eta) - \frac{dk_r}{ds} \frac{ds}{dp_c} \right] \right\}_m \tag{3.31}$$

η is the viscosibility defined as

$$\eta = \frac{1}{\mu} \frac{d\mu}{dp} \tag{3.32}$$

and $\lambda_{e,i}$ is a unit when direction e merges with the i direction, i.e.

$$\lambda_{\ell,i} = \begin{cases} 1 \; ; & \ell = i \\ 0 \; ; & \ell \neq i \end{cases} \tag{3.33}$$

Thus the aforementioned scheme will determine spatially continuous velocities that will yield continuous shifting of particles along these path lines.

CONCLUSION

It was demonstrated that the flow equation may be advection dominated as expressed by hyperbolic terms that are due to steep gradients of permeability factors or steep gradients of the potentials.

The contribution of using an Euler-Lagrange approach, is to handle the propagation of steep gradients, discontinuities and sharp fronts associated with the potential field.

Singularities are imposed on the advection part of the potential and solved explicitly along characteristic lines. Thus no means of numerical smoothing are needed.

The established potential velocity field associated with the particles was proven to be related to Darcy's specific flux.

REFERENCES

Braester, C., et al. (1971). ''A survey of the equations and solutions of ''Saturated flow in porous media'', Research Report p. 176, Technion.

Braester, C. (1973), ''Moisture variation at the soil surface and the advance of the wetting front during infiltration at constant flux''. Water Res. Research Vol. 9, No. 3, 687-694, June.

Frind, E.O., (1982) Simulation of long-term transient density-dependent transport in groundwater. Adv. Wat. Resour. 5, 73-88.

Hromadka, T.V., II & Guyman, G.1. (1980). A note on time integration of unsaturated soil-moisture transport. Adv. Wat. Resour. 3. 181-186.

Kgaran, S.P. & Sigurdsson, S.T. (1981) Treatment of time derivative and calculation of flow when solving groundwater flow problems by Galerki finite element methods. Adv. Wat. Resour. 4, 23-33.

Neuman, S.P. (1984) Adaptive Eulerian-Lagrangian finite element method for advection-dispersion. Int. J. Num. Methods in Engng. 20, 321-337.

Neuman, S.P. & Sorek, S. (1982) Eulerian-Lagrangian methods for advection- dispersion. In: Finite Elements in Water Resources. (Proc. 4th Int. Conf., Hannover, FR Germany), 14, 441-14.68.

Neuman, S.P., Preller, C. & Narasimahan, T.H. (1982) Adaptive explicit-implicit quasi three-dimensional finite element model of flow and subsidence in multiaquifer systems. Wat. Resour. Res. 18 (5), 1551-1561.

Sorek, S. (1984) ADVDSP two-dimensional adaptive Eulerian-Lagrangian method for the solution of mass-transport equations. Computer Documentation.

Sorek, S. (1985a) 2-D adaptive Eulerian-Lagrangian method for mass transport with spatial velocity distribution. (Submitted).

Sorek, S. (1985b) Eulerian-Lagrangian formulation for flow in soils. Adv. Wat. Resour. V.8, 118-120.

Sorek, S. (1985c) Adaptive Eulerian-Lagrangian method for transport problems in soils, scientific basis for water resources management, IAHS Publ. No. 153, 393-403.

Tham, L.G., & Cheung, Y.K. (1982) Numerical solution of heat conduction problems by parabolic time-space element. Int. J. Num. Methods in Engng. 18, 467-474.

Van Genuchten, N. Th. (1983) An Hermitian finite solution of the two-dimensional saturated-unsaturated flow equation. Adv. Wat. Resour. 6, 106-111.

Yeh Gour-Tsyh (1981) On the computation of Darcian velocity and mass balance in the finite element modelling of groundwater flow. Wat. Resour. Res. 17 (5), 1529-1534.

VI International Conference on Finite Elements in Water Resources, Lisboa, Portugal, June 1986

A Finite Element Model for Describing Gas Transport through Unsaturated Soils

D.E. Metcalfe
CANVIRO Consultants Ltd., 178 Louisa Street, Kitchener, Ontario, Canada
G.J. Farquhar
Department of Civil Engineering, University of Waterloo, Waterloo, Ontario, Canada

INTRODUCTION

The movement of gases away from landfill sites and other waste disposal areas continues to be a serious problem in many communities. Methane gas migrating through soils into adjacent structures has produced explosions that have resulted in extensive property damage and, in some cases, loss of life. The transport of harmful vapours from hazardous waste spills or disposal sites through soil into populated areas has also been recognized as a serious environmental health hazard.

In addressing these problems, it is often important to know the extent to which the gas will be transported through soil at some time in the future. It is also of benefit to know how gas transport will be affected by the implementation of control systems such as barriers, passive vents and pumped extraction or injection systems. However, it is not always practical or even feasible to carry out sufficient field experiments to make these judgements. In such cases, the use of mathematical models to simulate gas transport through soil would be of value as they have been in the analogous problem of contaminant transport in groundwater.

More recently, the presence of gaseous volatile organic compounds in the unsaturated zone have been correlated with the detection of these compounds in the groundwater. Lappala and Thompson (1984) have used soil gas samples from depths as shallow as 1 m and 3 m to detect the presence of volatile organic compounds in groundwaters at water table depths of 10 m and 30 m, respectively. Shallow gas samples are considerably more economical to obtain than water samples from below the water table, and Lappala and Thompson (1984) used an on-site gas chromatograph to provide real time assessments of contamination levels. A gas transport model would greatly assist the correlation of gas phase to groundwater aqueous phase volatile contaminant concentrations. It could provide a rapid graphical assessment of the problem with simulations of various situations such as long term hazards or the response to remedial measures.

The physical processes that result in contaminant transport in groundwater are basically the same as those causing gas migration through the unsaturated zone, and there is a wide variety of mathematical models available to simulate contaminant transport in groundwater. The governing equations used to describe the phenomena of contaminant transport in groundwater are (e.g. Bear, 1979), however, usually formulated in terms of mass averaged quantities, which are not as well-suited for describing gas flow as molar averaged quantities. The use of molar quantities permit important simplifications in the equations for gaseous migration through porous media. As such, the mathematical model for gas migration through unsaturated soils that is presented in this paper is developed by first adapting the traditional equations for groundwater flow/contaminant transport to more effectively describe gaseous flow.

Key considerations in the development of mathematical models to describe physical phenomena are the selection of the model dimensionality, configuration and numerical solution scheme. Experience has shown that most of the serious gas migration problems occur at distances on the order of tens of meters from the perimeters of waste disposal sites. When gas excursion distances are small compared to the areal extent of the waste disposal site, the boundary of the waste disposal site can usually be assumed to be a straight line in the area of concern, and perpendicular to the direction of the gas flow. A two-dimensional Cartesian co-ordinate system could therefore be positioned perpendicular to the waste disposal site boundary along the predominant path of outward gaseous migration from the site. A finite element scheme would provide the versatility necessary to accommodate detailed representations of soil profiles and boundary conditions in close proximity to waste disposal sites. In view of the foregoing discussion, the mathematical model for gas migration is developed for a two-dimensional Cartesian co-ordinate configuration and is solved with a finite element scheme.

SYSTEM EQUATIONS

In problems concerning contaminant transport through groundwater, a mass conservation equation is traditionally used to describe the bulk movement of the contaminant/groundwater mixture. Applying the mass conservation approach to gas flow yields:

$$\varepsilon\ \partial\rho/\partial t + \partial(\rho v)/\partial x + \partial(\rho v)/\partial z = 0 \qquad (1)$$

where ε is the gas-occupied porosity, ρ is the mass density of the gas mixture (kg/m^3), v is the Darcy or volume flux of the gas mixture (m/sec), t(sec) is time, and x(m) and z(m) denote the horizontal and vertical axes of the Cartesian co-ordinate system. The mass conservation approach is particularly useful for contaminant transport in groundwater because the fluid density is often essentially constant over the ranges of temperatures, pressures and contaminant concentrations evaluated, and thus the mass conservation equation can be simplified as fluid density does not vary in space or time. The mass density of a gas mixture can, however, be highly dependent on the relative concentrations of its component gases, and the above-mentioned simplification can not be employed. For example, in the field application presented in this paper, the contaminant gas, methane, is approximately half as dense as atmospheric gas (0.69 kg/m^3 as compared with 1.24 kg/m^3) at 10 C and 1 atm.

Rather than use a mass conservation equation to describe gas movement in soils, a conservation equation based on molar quantities is employed:

$$\varepsilon\, \partial C/\partial t + \partial(Cv)/\partial x + \partial(Cv)/\partial z = 0 \qquad (2)$$

where C is the molar density (mol/m^3) of the gas mixture. The molar density for a gas mixture composed of ideal gases is independent of the relative molar concentrations of the component gases. The molar density is a function of temperature and pressure only:

$$C = p_a/RT \qquad (3)$$

where p_a is absolute pressure (Pa), T is absolute temperature (K) and R is the universal gas constant (8.313 $m^3Pa/(molK)$).

Constant temperature and pressure can often be assumed for the unsaturated zone at shallow waste disposal sites. For depths greater than 2 m, Metcalfe (1982) shows that variations in gas molar density due to temperature fluctuations over 2 to 3 month periods are less than 2 percent in Southern Ontario. For the field application presented in this paper, the pressure variation across the area of study due to a gas withdrawal system was approximately 0.5 KPa, which resulted in a variation in molar density of less than 0.5 percent. As such, the molar density of the gas mixture is assumed to be constant in time and space, and Equation (3) is simplified as follows:

$$\partial v/\partial x + \partial v/\partial z = 0 \qquad (4)$$

The x- and z-components of Darcy velocity are expressed as follows:

$$v_x = -k_x/\mu \; (\partial p/\partial x) \qquad (5a)$$

$$v_z = -k_z/\mu \; (\partial p/\partial z + \rho g) \qquad (5b)$$

where k_x (m^2) and k_z (m^2) are intrinsic permeability in the horizontal and vertical directions, μ (Pa.sec) is the absolute viscosity of the gas mixture, p (Pa) is gauge pressure and g (9.81 m/sec^2) is acceleration due to gravity.

The mass density and absolute viscosity of the gas mixture in Equation (5) are dependent on the relative concentrations of the component gases. The mass density of the gas mixture is computed as follows:

$$\rho = \Sigma \, c_i \, M_i/1000 \qquad (6)$$

where c_i (mol/m^3) is the molar concentration of species i, M_i (gm/mol) is the gram molecular mass of species i, and $C = \Sigma c_i$. The absolute viscosity of the gas mixture is computed with the Wilke semi-empirical formula (Bird et al, 1960)

$$\mu = \sum_{i=1}^{n} [X_i \, \mu_i \, / \sum_{j=1}^{n} (X_j \, \Phi_{ij})]$$

$$\Phi_{ij} = 8^{-0.5} \, (1+M_i/M_j)^{-0.5} [1+(\mu_i/\mu_j)^{0.5} + (M_j/M_i)^{0.25}]^2 \qquad (7)$$

where μ_i(Pa.sec) is the absolute viscosity of species i, X_i is the mole fraction (c_i/C) of species i, and n is the number of gas species present.

Hydrodynamic dispersion results in the movement of the contaminant gas relative to the atmospheric gas. This process is superimposed on the contaminant gas flow resulting from the bulk movement of the gas mixture in the continuity equation for the contaminant gas.

$$\varepsilon \frac{\partial c}{\partial t} = -V_x \frac{\partial c}{\partial x} - V_z \frac{\partial c}{\partial z} \qquad (8)$$

$$+ \frac{\partial}{\partial x}(D_{xx} \frac{\partial c}{\partial x} + D_{xz} \frac{\partial c}{\partial z}) + \frac{\partial}{\partial z} (D_{zx} \frac{\partial c}{\partial x} + D_{zz} \frac{\partial c}{\partial z})$$

where D_{xx}, D_{xz}, D_{zx}, and D_{zz} (m^2/sec) are the components of the hydrodynamic dispersion tensor. The contaminant gas molar concentration, c (mol/m^3), is for gas species i=1; however the subscript has been deleted to simplify presentation. Atmospheric gas is assumed to be in sufficient quantity to counterdiffuse and occupy the remaining portion of the available pore space.

Metcalfe (1982) provides additional terms in Equation (8) to account for the dissolution of the contaminant gas in the soil moisture and the movement of the dissolved phase of the gas due to downward-percolating rain water. The mathematical model has, however, only been applied to gases sparingly soluble in water. As such, these additional terms have not been validated with field data.

Bear (1979) provides equations to compute the terms in the hydrodynamic dispersion tensor for hydrodynamic dispersion within the pore spaces of the medium. Expressing Bear's equations in terms of the porous media yields:

$$D_{xx} = \alpha_L v_x^2/v + \alpha_T v_z^2/v + D_e \tag{9a}$$

$$D_{zz} = \alpha_T v_x^2/v + \alpha_L v_z^2/v + D_e \tag{9b}$$

$$D_{xz} = D_{zx} = (\alpha_L - \alpha_T)\, v_x\, v_z/v \tag{9c}$$

where α_L and α_T (m) are the longitudinal and transverse dispersivities, respectively. The parameter D_e (m^2/sec) is the effective diffusion coefficient for porous media for the contaminant gas diffusing into atmospheric gas.

BOUNDARY CONDITIONS

Generally, the solution domain for the evaluation of gas migration scenarios will be quadrangular, with the quadrangle sides contacting the waste-soil interface, the ground surface, the water table or a confining stratum, and a boundary line beyond the zone of influence of the waste disposal site. A gas migration control vent could represent an internal boundary to the flow system. Typical gas pressure and contaminant gas concentration boundary conditions for this boundary configuration are shown in Figure 1 and described below.

Horizontal Limits of the Solution Domain

First or Dirichlet type boundary conditions are imposed for both pressure and concentration at the waste-soil interface,

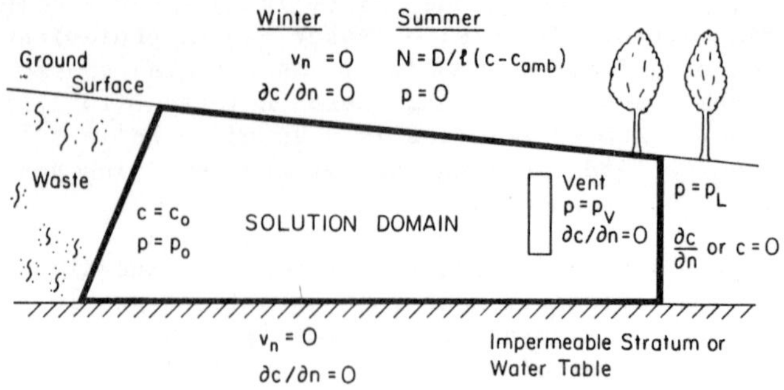

Figure 1. Boundary conditions for gas transport.

based on observed gas production rates for the season under evaluation. At the boundary beyond the zone of influence of the waste disposal site, gas pressures are again prescribed based on observed conditions. Zero gauge pressure is often appropriate at this boundary. The contaminant gas can be assigned zero concentration as the boundary is, by definition, beyond the limit of concern with regard to the contaminant gas. Alternatively, the concentration gradient can be set equal to zero, which is the Neumann or second type boundary condition.

Lower Boundary

The lower boundary is delineated by either a dense, impermeable stratum, or the water table, which can both be assumed to be barriers to gas flow. As such, zero-valued Neumann boundary conditions are used for both gas pressure and contaminant gas concentration at the lower boundary.

Ground Surface

In many areas, snow and ice cover the ground surface and frost penetrates below the ground surface during a significant portion of the year. This can result in an essentially impermeable boundary to gas flow, and the boundary conditions presented for the lower boundary are again appropriate. During the remaining months of the year, the ground surface is open to the atmosphere, providing the potential for mass transfer between the gases in the soil pores and those in the atmosphere. For these times, a gauge pressure of zero is appropriate at ground surface, as the gases at land surface are under atmospheric conditions. A Cauchy or third type boundary condition is used to describe the diffusive transfer of the contaminant gas from the soil pores into the atmosphere across the laminar sublayer immediately adjacent to the earth's surface. The boundary condition is shown in Figure 1, with N equal to the flux of contaminant gas ($mol/m^2/sec$) diffusing into the atmosphere, D(m^2/sec) equal to the free-air or unobstructed diffusion coefficient for the contaminant gas in air, and ℓ(m) equal to the laminar sublayer thickness. Rosenberg (1974) provides a relationship for ℓ as a function of the height of vegative cover.

Vent Boundary

At gas migration control vents, pressures are assigned based on the negative gauge pressure at the vent resulting from the evacuation of gases from the soils by the pumping system. A zero-valued Neumann boundary condition is used for the contaminant gas at vents, implying that gas flow at the vent is due to convective flow only.

SOLUTION PROCEDURE AND CODE VERIFICATION

The finite element formulations developed by Frind (1982) for contaminant transport in variable-density groundwater were adopted for solving the gas transport equations presented in this work. Frind used a classical Galerkin finite element approach with linear elements to eliminate the substantial computational effort associated with numerical integration. The transport equations and boundary conditions used by Frind are similar to those presented for gas transport, and Frind used a two-dimensional Cartesian co-ordinate configuration. Since Frind (1982) presents the finite element formulations for his transport equations in great detail, the finite element formulations for the gas transport equations are not presented here.

In solving the system equations, the gas pressure distribution is computed first through the simultaneous solution of the finite element forms of Equations (4) and (5). The horizontal and vertical components of the Darcy velocities at the centroids of the grid elements are then calculated with the finite element form of Equation (5) from this gas pressure distribution. The elemental Darcy velocities are substituted into the finite element form of Equation (8), and the equation is solved to produce the contaminant gas concentration distribution.

The solution procedure is complicated by the fact that the system equations are nonlinear and, therefore, must be solved iteratively. The nodal gas concentrations, which are calculated in the final step of the solution procedure (Equation (8)), are required to compute the elemental gas mixture mass densities and viscosities for the calculation of the gas pressure distribution and the Darcy velocities (Equations (4) and (5)). The approach used for any intermediate iteration is to compute gas mixture mass densities and viscosities based on the contaminant gas concentrations from the previous iteration. After solving for the gas pressure distribution and then the contaminant gas concentration distribution, the contaminant gas concentrations computed for that iteration are compared with those used to obtain the gas mixture mass densities and viscosities. An absolute error tolerance is used:

$$\left| c^{(m+1)} - c^{(m)} \right| \leq E \quad \text{for all nodes} \qquad (10)$$

where m+1 and m indicate successive iterations and E(mol/m^3) is the absolute error tolerance. If Equation (10) is satisfied for all nodes in the finite element grid, convergence is attained and computations for the next time step commence. The contaminant gas concentrations for the first iteration of the new time step are based on extrapolations of the computed changes in gas concentrations from the previous time step. If Equation (10) is not satisfied, the contaminant gas concentrations computed for the current iteration are used to compute new elemental values for gas mixture mass density and viscosity, and another iteration is performed.

The finite element forms of the system equations, the code listing and the code documentation are presented by Metcalfe (1982). Code verification is also demonstrated through comparison with analytic solutions for one-dimensional flow with one- and two-dimensional dispersion.

FIELD APPLICATION

The mathematical model was applied to two test sites to determine whether or not the mathematical model could be used to represent actual cases of gas transport through heterogenous, naturally occurring geologic deposits. The mathematical model successfully reproduced historical gas pressure and concentration data at both landfill sites. A complete set of model simulations is presented by Metcalfe (1982). The results for the Ottawa Street landfill, Kitchener, Ontario are summarized below.

Site Information

The gas migration study site at the Ottawa Street landfill is shown in Figure 2. Gas monitoring well locations were positioned at eight locations along a line perpendicular to the approximate limit of the refuse. A gas pumping system, which is also shown in Figure 2, was in operation throughout the study period (January 10, 1979 through to December 19, 1979). It imposed a continuous pressure gradient toward the below-ground gas interceptor vents. The gas pumping system proved to be effective in controlling methane gas transport, as evidenced by the fact that methane was not detected at gas monitoring wells G or H, which are located beyond the gas pumping system.

The finite element grid configuration developed for modelling

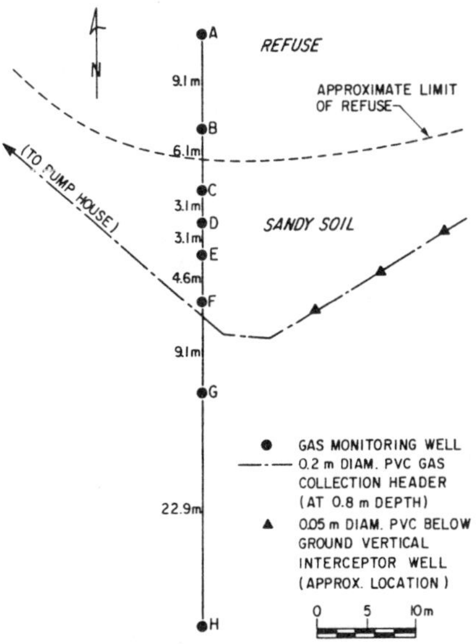

Figure 2. Gas migration study site.

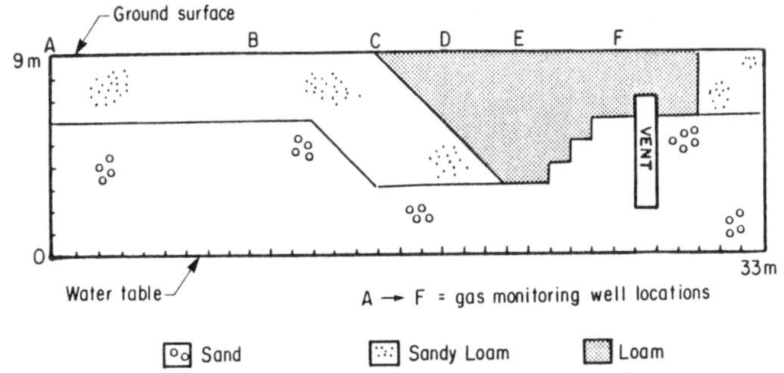

Figure 3. Finite element grid with modelled soil profile.

methane gas transport at the Ottawa Street landfill gas migration study site is presented in Figure 3. The top and bottom of the grid coincide with ground surface and the water table, respectively. Gas monitoring well location A was used as the left grid boundary. A gas interceptor vent was positioned 27 m to the right of this boundary. A gas interceptor vent was not situated directly in line with the gas monitoring wells but one was located nearby (Figure 2). The location of the vent in Figure 3 corresponds with the point where the gas collection header passed through the profile plane. Because methane was not detected beyond the gas pumping system during the year of investigation, the right grid boundary was placed 5 m beyond the gas interceptor vent. Since methane gas flow from the landfill was modelled over a distance of only 27 m, the assumption of two-dimensional flow was deemed to be justified, even though the limit of the refuse as shown in Figure 2 was not a straight line. A complete description of the model parameters and boundary conditions that were used to represent the Ottawa Street Landfill are provided in Metcalfe (1982).

Modelling Methane Transport Under Summer Conditions

Methane gas concentrations and gas pressures were measured on June 26, July 30 and September 5, 1979. The gas concentrations as percent by volume are contoured for the three measurement dates in Figures 4a, 4b and 4c, respectively. Methane migration outward from the landfill is evident between June 26 and July 30, whereas little change occurred between July 30 and September 5. The mathematical model was implemented in an attempt to reproduce the measured methane concentrations for July 30 and September 5, using the June 26 methane gas concentrations as the initial condition.

The modelled methane distributions for July 30, 1979 and September 5, 1979 are superimposed on Figures 4b and 4c, respectively. The comparison between modelled and actual methane concentration distributions is excellent. The mathematical model predicted excursion of the 10 percent contour to the vent for July 30. As well, the modelled methane distribution for September 5 was essentially the same as that predicted for July 30, and thus the modelled system had reached steady state as indicated by the field data. Methane did not accumulate to the right of the vent, which justifies the placement of the right model boundary.

Modelling Methane Transport Under Winter Conditions

During the winter months in Southern Ontario, methane excursion from refuse sites can occur to much greater distances than in the summer months, because the ground surface becomes frozen for extended periods of time. Freezing on the ground surface appeared to occur on November 5, 1979. The greatest methane excursion distances observed during the year of study occurred on December 5, 1979, and the measured data are contoured in Figure 4d. The mathematical model was used in an attempt to reproduce the December 5 measured methane concentrations, with the September 5 methane concentrations used as the initial condition.

Modelled methane concentration contours after one month with winter flow conditions are superimposed on Figure 4d. The modelled methane contours compare well with those measured on December 5. Modelled results for 2 months with winter flow conditions showed the 40 and 50 percent methane contours drawn within 5 m of the vent, confirming the concept that considerable methane migration can occur when the ground surface remains frozen for extended periods of time.

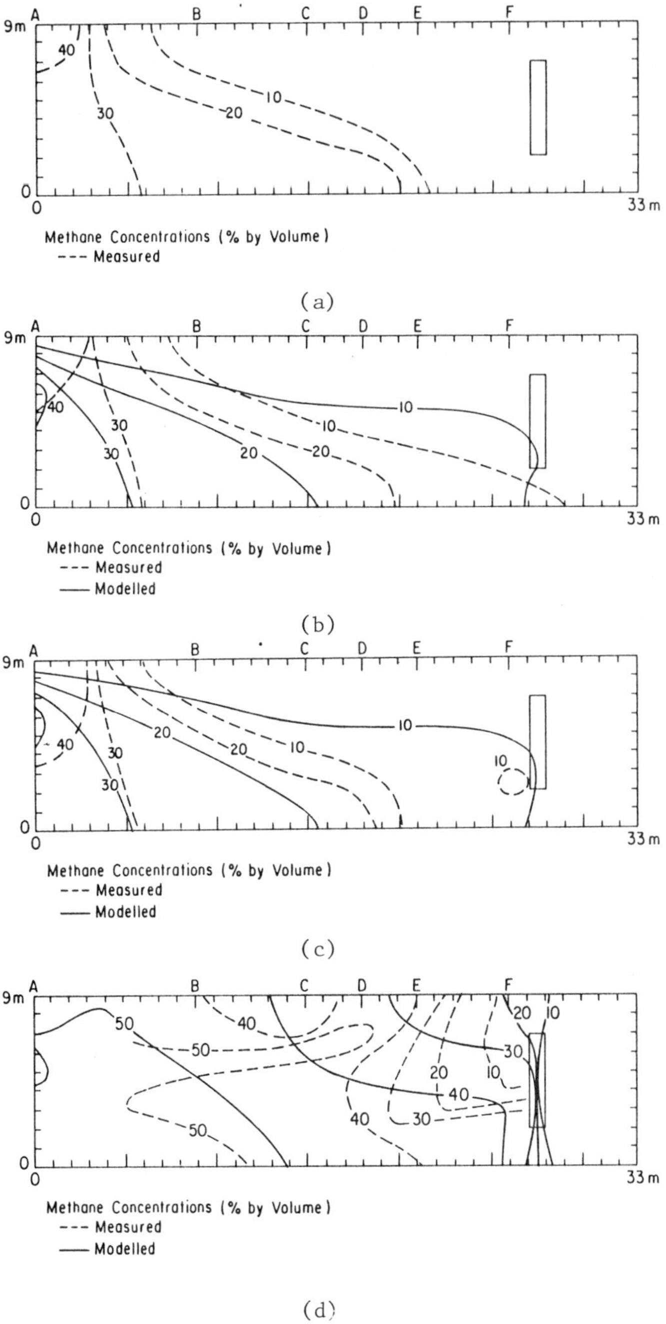

Figure 4. Measured and modelled methane concentrations for: (a) June 26, (b) July 30, (c) September 5, and (d) December 5.

CONCLUSIONS

The mathematical model developed in this work for gas transport through soil was used to simulate methane migration away from an actual landfill site. Comparisons between simulated and actual values were very good. Although not presented in this paper, equally good comparisons were observed at a second field test site.

It is concluded that the mathematical model can be used to provide reasonable gas transport in soil estimates given sufficient input and boundary condition data for the site and provided that the two-dimensional nature of the model is consistent with field conditions. Since the length of the waste disposal site boundary often exceeds gas excursion distances by an order of magnitude, the reduction of the model from three to two dimensions, assuming uniformity along the landfill boundary, is usually justified.

Although originally intended for use in the study of landfill gas problems, it is expected that the model can also provide valuable assistance in assessing the migration of hazardous vapours in soil from spills of volatile chemicals.

ACKNOWLEDGMENTS

This research was funded by the Natural Sciences and Engineering Research Council of Canada (NSERC).

REFERENCES

Bear, J. (1979) Hydraulics of Groundwater, McGraw-Hill, New York.

Bird, R.B., Stewart, W.E. and Lightfoot, E.N. (1960) Transport Phenomena, John Wiley and Sons, Inc., New York.

Frind, E.O. (1982) Simulation of long-term density-dependent transport in groundwater, Adv. Water Resources, 5: 73-88.

Lapalla, E.G. and Thompson, G.M. (1984) Detection of Groundwater Contamination by Shallow Soil Gas Sampling in the Vadose Zone Theory and Applications, Proceedings of the Fifth National Conference on Management of Uncontrolled Hazardous Waste Sites, Hazardous Materials Control Research Institute, Silver Spring, Maryland.

Metcalfe, D.E. (1982) Modelling Gas Transport from Waste Disposal Sites, M.A.Sc. Thesis, Dept. of Civil Engineering, University of Waterloo, Waterloo, Ontario.

Rosenberg, N.J. (1974) Microclimate: The Biological Environment, John Wiley and Sons, Inc., New York.

VI International Conference on Finite Elements in Water Resources, Lisboa, Portugal, June 1986

Heat Transfer Effects on Moisture Movement in Unsaturated Soils – A Numerical Investigation

H.R. Thomas
Department of Civil and Structural Engineering, University College, Cardiff CF2 1TA, Wales, U.K.

INTRODUCTION

Coupled heat and moisture movement in unsaturated soils is a phenomenon of interest in a number of engineering applications. In civil engineering design in general and in water resources studies in particular, the decrease of a soil's moisture content due to surface evaporative moisture losses is a particular problem of interest. Under such circumstances the quantity of water stored in the unsaturated zone decreases and the natural level of the groundwater table is reduced. Obviously a complete understanding of the groundwater regime in a particular region can only be accomplished when this type of behaviour is included in an overall model of groundwater flow.

An understanding of this problem requires an understanding of coupled heat and moisture transfer in unsaturated soil and the inclusion of moisture movement in both liquid and vapour phases. Practical engineering solutions then require a mathematical formulation of the physical problem, followed by a numerical solution of the resulting governing differential equations. Such an approach has been presented in a recent publication (Thomas, 1985) and the method proposed is used as the basis for the work presented in this paper.

The method is derived from Philip and de Vries' (1957) work but an extension of their model is then developed using an approach first proposed by Luikov (1966). The resulting formulation, which is in terms of the two variables temperature and volumetric moisture content, is solved using the finite element method for two dimensional, linear material property, problems.

In this paper the model is used to explore the extent of coupled heat and moisture transfer to be expected in practice. In particular an attempt will be made to identify the range of problems where thermal effects play a significant part in the rate of moisture movement. The results of a series of analyses will be presented, in which various values of both thermal and isothermal moisture diffusivities have been used in the calculations.

THEORY

The governing differential equations of heat and moisture transfer in unsaturated soils are based on the laws of conservation of mass and energy. The phenomenon involved are however complex with moisture transfer taking place in the liquid phase due to capillary potential gradients and in the vapour phase due to a vapour pressure gradient induced by temperature effects. Heat transfer takes place by conduction, by bulk transfer of latent heat effects when vapour transfer occurs and also in some cases by convection.

Limitations of space prevent the presentation here of a full explanation of the derivation of the model used. However full details can be obtained from a recent publication (Thomas, 1985). Philip and de Vries' expressions for moisture content conservation are combined in the model with Luikov's phase conversion factor, to enable a new formulation to be derived. The resulting differential equations describe simultaneous transient heat and moisture transfer and are as follows :

$$C \frac{\partial T}{\partial t} = \underline{\nabla}.(\lambda + L\varepsilon\rho_\ell D_T)\underline{\nabla}T + \underline{\nabla}.(L\varepsilon\rho_\ell D_\Theta)\nabla\Theta_\ell + L\varepsilon\rho_\ell \frac{\partial K}{\partial z} \tag{1}$$

$$\frac{\partial \Theta_\ell}{\partial t} = \underline{\nabla}(D_\Theta \underline{\nabla}\Theta_\ell) + \underline{\nabla}(D_T \underline{\nabla}T) + \frac{\partial K}{\partial z} \tag{2}$$

In these expressions T is the temperature, Θ_ℓ is the volumetric liquid content, t is the time, C is the volumetric heat capacity, λ is the thermal conductivity, L is the latent heat of vaporisation of water, ε is the phase conversion factor, ρ_ℓ is the density of liquid water, D_T is the thermal moisture diffusivity, D_Θ is the isothermal moisture diffusivity, K is the unsaturated hydraulic conductivity and z is the elevation.

A solution to the above equations has been obtained assuming that all the material parameters remain constant and the results presented in this paper are all therefore subject to the validity of this approximation.

APPLICATION

Surface evaporative moisture content losses act in practice over large areas of ground. Their effects can therefore be analysed using a one dimensional approach and to this end a column of soil, 2m high and 0.4m wide is investigated in this work. A depth of 2m is chosen since this is considered to be representative of typically, the depth of soil likely to be affected by both temperature and moisture content gradients. The finite element mesh consists of a column of five square elements of dimension 0.4m.

A number of analyses have been performed using different values of D_Θ and D_T. D_Θ can be expected to vary considerably, depending on the soil type being analysed and in order to represent the range encountered, analyses using the following series of values were performed.

$D_\Theta = 1.0 \times 10^{-5} m^2/s$, $D_\Theta = 1.0 \times 10^{-6} m^2/s$, $D_\Theta = 1.0 \times 10^{7} m^2/s$,
$D_\Theta = 1.0 \times 10^{-8} m^2/s$, $D_\Theta = 1.0 \times 10^{-9} m^2/s$, $D_\Theta = 1.0 \times 10^{-10} m^2/s$

Consideration of the possible variation in values of D_T revealed a more limited range than had been identified for D_Θ. In reflection of this fact, therefore, the following values of D_T were investigated in the analysis :

$D_T = 5.0 \times 10^{-9} m^2/s\,^oC$, $D_T = 1.0 \times 10^{-9} m^2/s\,^oC$,

$D_T = 5.0 \times 10^{-10} m^2/s\,^oC$, $D_T = 1.0 \times 10^{-10} m^2/s\,^oC$

The soil moisture diffusivity and the unsaturated hydraulic conductivity are related by means of the specific moisture capacity of the soil. Assuming that the soil has a constant value of specific moisture capacity of 0.1 m^{-1}, the value of the unsaturated hydraulic conductivity associated with each value of D_Θ can be established for each analysis.

The values of the other material parameters were chosen after a search of the literature and are as follows :

$C = 0.48 \times 10^6$ cal/$m^3\,^oC$, $\lambda = 4 \times 10^{-1}$ cal/m sec ^oC ,

L = 540 cal/g and $\varepsilon = 0.3$. The full range of analyses proposed are given in Table 1.

Initial conditions of a constant temperature of 10^oC throughout the soil has been assumed for all the problems. The initial volumetric moisture content varies linearly with depth from a value of 0.3 at the surface to 0.5 at the base of the column. Boundary conditions of the first kind have been applied at the top surface. Noting Sophocleous (1979) finding that soil temperature and moisture content at depths as little as 50mm varied little during diurnal variation of temperatures in the field of some 16^oC, it was considered appropriate, as a first approximation, to model the boundary temperature and moisture content as constant over the period of time under consideration. Fixed values of a temperature of 25^oC and a volumetric moisture content of 0.2 were in fact applied.

RESULTS

The results presented in this section show temperature and moisture content variation with time at a point near the surface of the column, nodal point 25, a point at mid-height of the column, nodal point 15 and a point at the base of the column, nodal point 3. Therefore considering each analysis in turn, in the order given in table 1, run number 559 was analysed first. The D_Θ value used in this analysis is the highest of all values

RUN NUMBER	D_Θ (m^2/s)	D_T ($m^2/s\ ^oC$)
559	1.0×10^{-5}	5.0×10^{-9}
519	1.0×10^{-5}	1.0×10^{-9}
5510	1.0×10^{-5}	5.0×10^{-10}
5110	1.0×10^{-5}	1.0×10^{-10}
659	1.0×10^{-6}	5.0×10^{-9}
619	1.0×10^{-6}	1.0×10^{-9}
6510	1.0×10^{-6}	5.0×10^{-10}
6110	1.0×10^{-6}	1.0×10^{-10}
759	1.0×10^{-7}	5.0×10^{-9}
719	1.0×10^{-7}	1.0×10^{-9}
7510	1.0×10^{-7}	5.0×10^{-10}
7110	1.0×10^{-7}	1.0×10^{-10}
859	1.0×10^{-8}	5.0×10^{-9}
819	1.0×10^{-8}	1.0×10^{-9}
8510	1.0×10^{-8}	5.0×10^{-10}
8110	1.0×10^{-8}	1.0×10^{-10}
959	1.0×10^{-9}	5.0×10^{-9}
919	1.0×10^{-9}	1.0×10^{-9}
9510	1.0×10^{-9}	5.0×10^{-10}
9110	1.0×10^{-9}	1.0×10^{-10}
1059	1.0×10^{-10}	5.0×10^{-9}
1019	1.0×10^{-10}	1.0×10^{-9}
10510	1.0×10^{-10}	5.0×10^{-10}
10110	1.0×10^{-10}	1.0×10^{-10}

TABLE 1

chosen, signifying relatively rapid movement of moisture through the soil. This is reflected in the results achieved, with moisture content changes effected at the point near the surface in the first day and virtually all changes in moisture content complete within five days. Temperature changes on the other hand have hardly begun to take effect at this time and it can therefore be concluded that the two processes are largely uncoupled in this analysis.

On the basis of results achieved for run 559 it can be concluded that no coupling of heat and mass transfer will be exhibited in runs 519, 5510 and 5110, where lower values of D_T are used.

Results of the next run listed in table 1, run 659, are shown in figure 1. In this case moisture content variations near the surface occur in the first five days while moisture content variations at mid-depth and the base of the column occur more gradually and last over the full time scale presented. Similar rates of variations can be seen to apply to the temperature variations at these points and it can therefore be concluded that, from this point of view, the two processes are definitely coupled in this problem.

To assess the actual influence of temperature gradient on moisture movement, results for run 619, using a lower value of

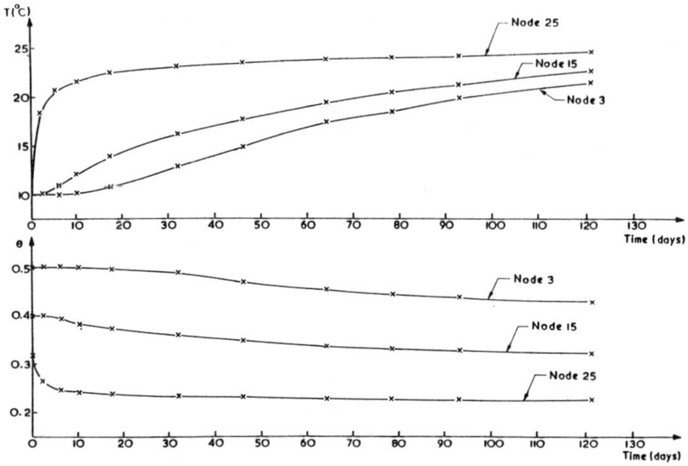

Figure 1. Temperature and moisture content distributions for run 659

D_T, are presented in figure 2. Comparison of the two sets of results give an indication of the actual contribution from temperature induced movement that was contained in run 659. Temperature induced movement occurs due to vapour transfer from hot regions to cold, from the surface down into the soil in this case. The larger this contribution therefore, the slower the outflow of water. This effect is demonstrated clearly in figures 1 and 2, for example, at mid depth where the time taken for the moisture content to reduce to 0.35 is 40 and 14 days respectively. Clearly therefore the two processes are coupled in run 659.

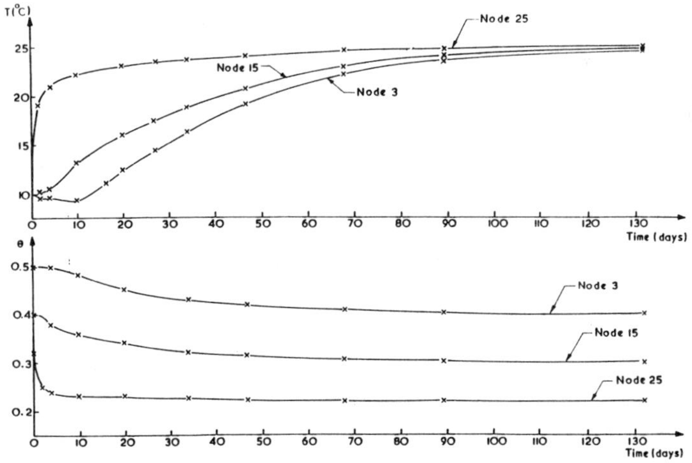

Figure 2. Temperature and moisture content distributions for run 619

On the question of coupling effects in run 619 itself, it can again be seen from figure 2 that the timescale of the two processes are compatible in this run. However to assess the actual importance of temperature effects in this problem comparison must again be made with results of another run using a lower value of D_T. In this case, results for run 6510 were obtained and these showed slight but distinct temperature effects in run 619. Further decreases in D_T as incorporated in run 6110 showed no further changes in moisture content distribution and it was therefore concluded that while the results for run 619 were coupled, this run represented the lower bound of significant temperature effects for this D_Θ value. Realistic temperature distributions for runs 619, 6510 and 6511 were obtained using an ε value of 0.1, this feature being a reflection of the increased rate of moisture movement in these runs.

Results of the series of runs, 759, 719 and 7510 are given in figures 3, 4 and 5. Figure 3 shows temperature effects causing an increase in moisture content at mid-height and the base of the column. This effect occurs in the early stages of the problem when a temperature gradient is operative. Clearly

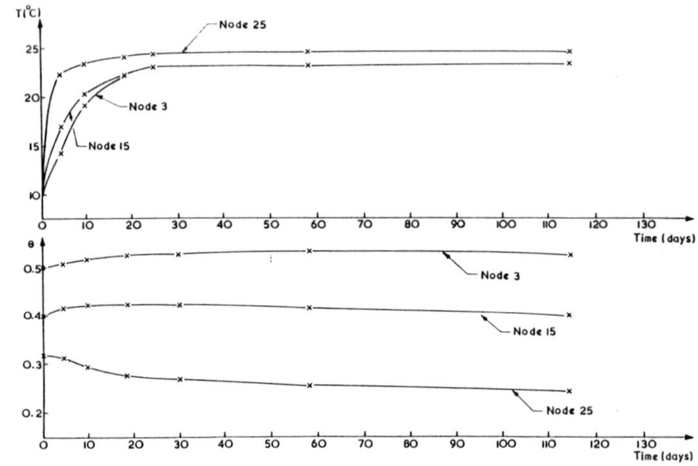

Figure 3. Temperature and moisture content distributions for run 759

therefore the two processes are coupled since moisture outflow is also occurring at these early stages as shown in the results for node 3, near the surface.

The incidence of thermal effects in run 719 can best be seen at the base of the column where again an increase in moisture content can be seen to be taking place. Once again therefore temperature effects are operative while moisture outflow is taking place and the two processes are therefore also coupled in this problem.

Results for run 7510 do not show any increase in moisture content at either the base or the mid-height. Temperature

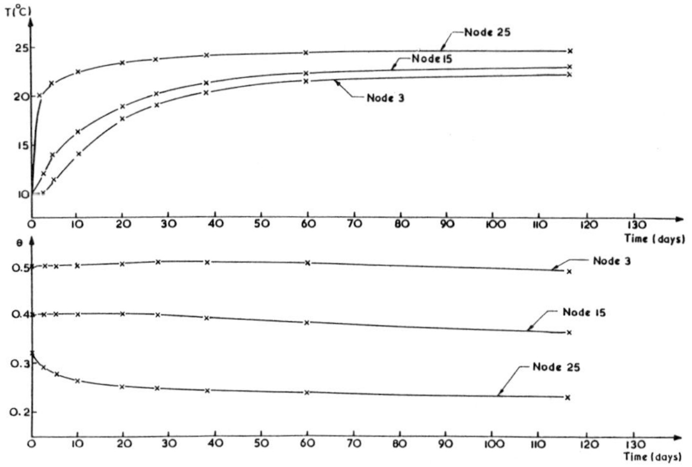

Figure 4. Temperature and moisture content distributions for run 719

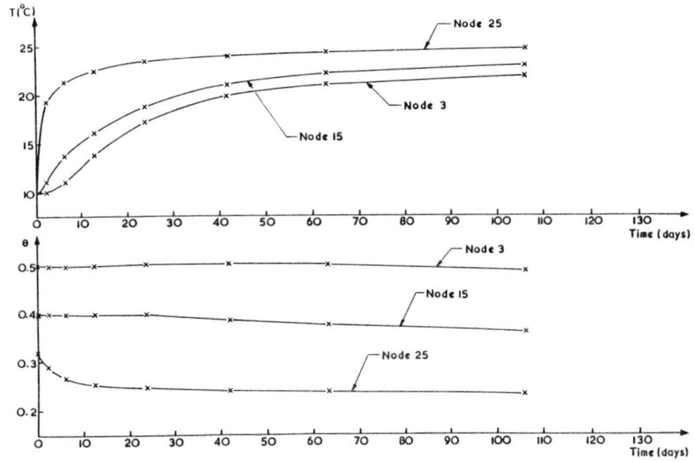

Figure 5 . Temperature and moisture content distributions for run 7510

effects can only therefore be assessed in this case by comparison with another run using a lower value of D_T. Such a comparison was made with results from run 7110 and the conclusion was drawn that while slight differences in results could be observed, the results for run 7510 represent the lower bound of significant temperature effects.

Results of the series of runs, 859, 819 and 8510 are given in figures 6, 7 and 8. Considering first the effect of a decrease in the value of D_Θ, for an isothermal problem, it is clear that for a constant duration of problem, moisture content changes are likely to affect less and less depth of soil as D_Θ decreases. It therefore follows that for a non-isothermal problem the

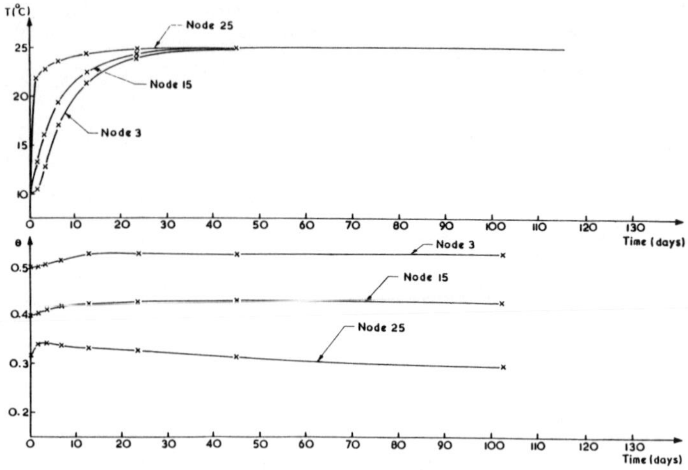

Figure 6 Temperature and moisture content distributions for run 859

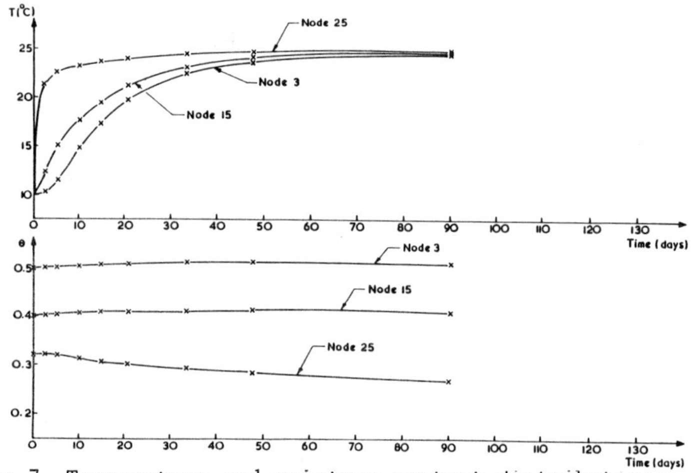

Figure 7 Temperature and moisture content distributions for run 819

domain of interest of possible coupled activity is reduced as the value of D_Θ decreases. This fact can be seen by comparing figures 3, 4 and 5 with 6, 7 and 8.

Considering first the results of run 859 it can be seen that temperature effects, causing an increase in moisture content, dominate flow. At the end of the analysis moisture content at a point near the surface has hardly changed while moisture content at both the mid-height and the base of the column has increased. Temperature effects occur rapidly, compared with the rate of isothermal moisture movement and consequently the two effects are largely uncoupled.

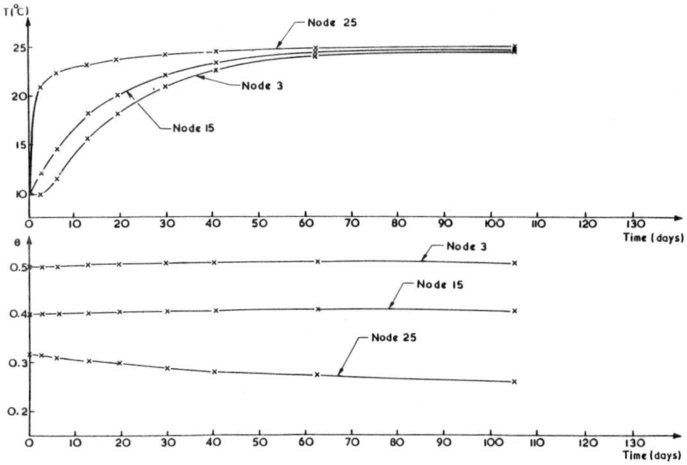

Figure 8 Temperature and moisture content distributions for run 8510

The results for run 819 on the other hand show temperature changes taking place more slowly than in run 859. Furthermore since the D_T value is reduced the effect of temperature induced inflow is more comparable to outflow. Consequently the two effects could be expected to be coupled, particularly at points in the upper half of the column. This fact is confirmed by comparing the results in figure 7 with those in figure 8. Distinct differences in the moisture content variation at a point near the surface can be observed showing that the processes were coupled in run 819.

The influence of coupling effects in run 8510 was examined by comparing the results of run 8110 and 8510. Very slight differences were observed showing that some coupling was operative in run 8510. However run 8510 can be taken as the lower bound of the influence of coupling.

Considering the series of runs carried out with a value of D_Θ equal to $1 \times 10^{-9} m^2/s$, the results obtained showed virtually no changes in moisture content during the specified maximum length of time of analysis. On the other hand the complete change in temperature, from initial to final conditions, occurred entirely during the length of time of the analysis. Therefore the two effects are largely uncoupled for this series of analyses. While it can be argued that theoretically some coupling of the two processes has inevitably occurred in the uppermost layers of the soil, the practical significance of this coupling is small in the overall context of moisture flow throughout the problem.

Similar conclusions can be drawn from the results of the series of runs using $D_\Theta = 1 \times 10^{-10} m^2/s$. Once again the two effects are for all practical purposes uncoupled.

Coupled heat and mass transfer has therefore been identified as taking place during the runs listed in table 2. The influence of temperature effects on moisture movement is obviously related to the relative magnitude of the isothermal and thermal moisture diffusivities. It is therefore instructive to see whether a relationship exists between coupled behaviour in this problem and the ratio of the two diffusivities, D_T/D_Θ, defined by η. The value of η for each analysis which exhibited coupled behaviour is shown in Table 2. The range of values is quite large, spanning two orders of magnitude. However the results do give an indication of the likely range of values of relevance. It can be seen that the values of η which give coupled behaviour are smaller, the greater the value of D_Θ used in the particular series of runs.

Run Number	η ($^oC^{-1}$)
659	5×10^{-3}
619	1×10^{-3}
759	5×10^{-2}
719	1×10^{-2}
7510	5×10^{-3}
819	1×10^{-1}
8510	5×10^{-2}

TABLE 2

In general the ratio η decreases the greater the value of D_Θ or the lower the value of D_T. Under both these conditions moisture movement will take place much more rapidly due to a moisture content gradient than a thermal gradient. On the other hand the ratio η increases the lower the value of D_Θ or the higher the value of D_T. Under such circumstances temperature induced movement is likely to take place before moisture content induced movement can occur. It follows therefore that an upper and lower bound can be expected to exist for η within which coupled heat and moisture transfer occurs. Such bounds have been established for the problem solved.

CONCLUSIONS

Within the overall limitations of the analysis presented and for the problem specified in particular, the range of analyses in which coupled heat and moisture transfer occur have been established. In other analyses either moisture movement took place too quickly for temperature effects to be significant or moisture movement took place too slowly for temperature effects to influence the results. In yet other examples the value of the thermal moisture diffusivity was too small to affect the answers.

The ratio of the thermal to the isothermal moisture diffusivity has been used to characterise those analyses in which coupled behaviour took place. An upper and a lower bound has been established for this parameter, within which coupled behaviour occurs. For the problem analysed these bounds have been found to be 1×10^{-1} and 1×10^{-3} $^{o}C^{-1}$.

REFERENCES

Luikov, A.V., (1966) Heat and Mass Transfer in Capillary Porous Bodies, Pergamon Press, Oxford.

Philip, J.R. and D.A. de Vries, (1957) Moisture movement in porous materials under temperature gradients. Trans. Am. Geophysical Union, 38, 222-232.

Sophocleous, M. (1979) Analysis of water and heat flow in unsaturated-saturated porous media, Water Resources Research, 15, 1195-1206.

Thomas, H.R. (1985) Modelling two-dimensional heat and moisture transfer in unsaturated soils, including gravity effects. Int.J. for Num. and Anal. Meth. in Geomechanics, 9, 573-538.

VI International Conference on Finite Elements in Water Resources, Lisboa, Portugal, June 1986

Finite Element Solution of the Unsaturated Flow Equation Using Hierarchic Basis Functions

L.M. Abriola
Department of Civil Engineering, University of Michigan, Ann Arbor, MI 48109, U.S.A.

INTRODUCTION

A number of problems relating to fluid flow in porous media involve the displacement of a front with time. For the numerical solution of such problems, it is advantageous from the computational standpoint to develop computer models which provide greater resolution at the front, where properties vary most rapidly. Such models are termed "self-adaptive" in the literature. One possible approach to the design of such a model is to generate a mesh in which the spatial discretization at the front is refined. Programming and execution of such mesh generating schemes, however, can be both complex and costly. An alternative approach for the development of a self-adaptive code is to increase the order of the numerical approximation within elements near the front.

A variation of this second approach which utilizes a hierarchic family of basis functions is explored in this paper through its application to the solution of the one dimensional unsaturated flow equation. Hierarchic functions have the property that the shape functions corresponding to an element of lower order are a subset of the functions of all higher order elements. Such functions have previously been used successfully in the Galerkin finite element solution of various problems in linear fracture mechanics and elasticity (Peano, 1976, Pasini, et al, 1977, Szabo, 1978, Peano, et al, 1978). Here the same approach is applied to a non-linear problem.

MODEL FORMULATION

Governing Equation

The equation governing the one dimensional movement of water in an unsaturated vertical soil column is given by:

$$C \frac{\partial \psi}{\partial t} = \frac{\partial}{\partial z} \left(K k_{rw} \left(\frac{\partial \psi}{\partial z} - 1\right)\right) \tag{1}$$

where $C = n\,(ds/d\psi)$ is the soil moisture capacity
n is the matrix porosity
ψ is the suction head
s is the water saturation
z is the vertical coordinate (directed downwards)
t is the time coordinate
K is the saturated hydraulic conductivity
and k_{rw} is the relative permeability of the water phase.

It should be noted that the above equation neglects the effects of matrix and fluid compressibility and assumes a static air phase. Since, in general, both the time derivative coefficient $ds/d\psi$ and the spatial derivative coefficient k_{rw} are functions of ψ, the above equation is a nonlinear partial differential equation in the variable ψ.

<u>Application of the Galerkin Method</u>
For the solution of equation (1), the function ψ is replaced by the trial function:

$$\psi(z,t) \cong \hat{\psi}(z,t) = \sum_j w_j(z)\, \psi_j(t) \tag{2}$$

where $w_j(z)$ are elements of a family of basis functions and $\psi_j(t)$ are undetermined coefficients. Since k_{rw} and $ds/d\psi$ are dependent upon ψ, they will also vary in space and time and may be expanded in terms of the basis functions $w_j(z)$:

$$k_{rw}(z,t) \cong \hat{k}_{rw}(z,t) = \sum_j w_j(z) k_{rwj}(t) \tag{3}$$

$$\frac{ds}{d\psi}(z,t) \cong \frac{d\hat{s}}{d\psi}(z,t) = \sum_j w_j(z) \frac{ds}{d\psi_j}(t) \tag{4}$$

The parameters K and n are assumed piecewise constant over each element.

Substituting expressions (2), (3), and (4) into equation (1) and applying the Galerkin method of weighted residuals yields:

$$\sum_j \sum_k \int_R n \frac{ds}{d\psi_k} w_k w_j \, d\psi_j/dt \; w_i \, dR \tag{5}$$

$$- \sum_j \sum_k \int_R \frac{\partial}{\partial z} \left(Kk_{rw\,k} w_k \left(\psi_j \frac{dw_j}{dz} - 1 \right) \right) w_i \, dR = 0$$

Green's theorem may be applied to the second term to produce the form:

$$\sum_j \sum_k \int_R n \frac{ds}{d\psi_k} w_k w_j \frac{d\psi_j}{dt} w_i \, dR + \sum_j \sum_k \int_R Kk_{rw} w_k \psi_j \frac{dw_j}{dz} \frac{dw_i}{dz} dR$$

$$= \sum_k \int_R Kk_{rw} w_k \frac{dw_i}{dz} dR - \int_\Gamma w_i \, q \, d\Gamma \tag{6}$$

where q is the boundary flux and is positive downwards.

Equations (6) may be written compactly in matrix form as:

$$[A] \{\psi\} + [B] \{d\psi/dt\} = \{f\} \tag{7}$$

where typical matrix and vector elements are given as:

$$A_{ij} = \sum_e \sum_k \int_{R^e} K^e k_{rwk} \; w_k \frac{dw_j}{dz} \frac{dw_i}{dz} dR$$

$$B_{ij} = \sum_e \sum_k \int_{R^e} n^e \frac{ds}{d\psi_k} w_k w_j w_i \, dR$$

and

$$f_i = \sum_e \left\{ \sum_k \int_{R^e} K^e k_{rwk} \; w_k \frac{dw_i}{dz} dR - \int_{\Gamma^e} w_i q d\Gamma \right\}$$

Here the total domain R has been broken up into sub-elements.

If a backward difference approximation is used to approximate the time derivative in equation (7), the resulting matrix equation can be rewritten as:

$$[A]^{n+1}\{\psi\}^{n+1} + [B]^{n+1}(\{\psi\}^{n+1} - \{\psi\}^{n})/\Delta t = \{f\}^{n+1} \quad (8)$$

In equation (8), superscripts indicate the time level of evaluation. Note that the above equation is fully implicit. It may be rearranged to yield:

$$[M]^{n+1}\{\psi\}^{n+1} = \{r\}^{n+1} \quad (9)$$

where

$$[M]^{n+1} = [A]^{n+1} + [B]^{n+1}/\Delta t$$

$$\{r\}^{n+1} = \{f\}^{n+1} + [B]^{n+1}\{\psi\}^{n}/\Delta t$$

<u>Selection of Basis Functions</u>

For this model, basis functions were chosen to be the linear and quadratic members which belong to a family of C^0 hierarchic functions. These functions are shown in Figure 1 for a sample element. The linear functions are the familiar chapeau functions which are represented in local space as:

$$w^1_e = 0.5\,(1 - \xi) \quad (10a)$$

$$-1 \le \xi \le 1$$

$$w^2_e = 0.5\,(1 + \xi) \quad (10b)$$

The quadratic function is a parabola with a zero value at the element nodes and a second derivative of unity at the element midpoint:

$$w^3_e = 0.5\,(\xi^2 - 1\,) \quad (10c)$$

Using basis functions 10 (a-c), the trial function $\hat{\psi}$ can be written over an element as:

$$\hat{\psi}(\xi,t) = \psi_{-1}(t)\, w^1_e + \psi_1(t)\, w^2_e + \psi''_o(t)\, w^3_e \quad (11)$$

where ψ''_o designates the second derivative of ψ with respect to the local spatial coordinate which is evaluated at the element midpoint. Thus, there are three undetermined coefficients in each element. If N elements are present in the domain, the matrix equation (9) will consist of 2N+1 non-linear algebraic equations in 2N+1 unknowns. In this formulation, coefficients $ds/d\psi$ and k_{rw} are expanded across an element only in terms of w^1_e and w^2_e, i.e. they are allowed to vary linearly over an element.

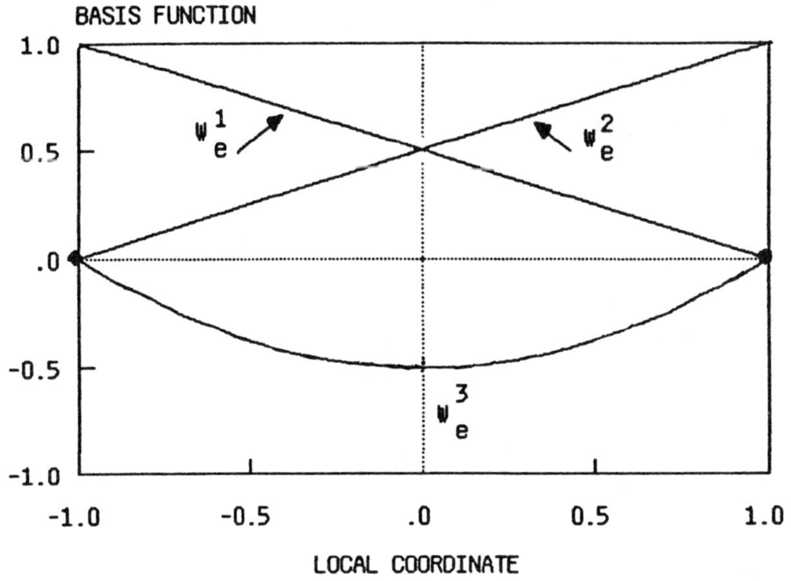

Figure 1: Model basis functions

Iteration Scheme

If the unknowns appearing in equation (9) are ordered so that the element midpoint second derivatives appear following all nodal values of the suction head, the matrix equation (9) may be subdivided as shown below:

$$\left[\begin{array}{c|c} M_{11} & M_{12} \\ \hline M_{21} & M_{22} \end{array}\right] \left\{\begin{array}{c} \psi \\ \hline \psi'' \end{array}\right\} = \left\{\begin{array}{c} r_1 \\ \hline r_2 \end{array}\right\} \tag{12}$$

Here M_{ij} are sub-matrices. The matrix M_{11} is a tridiagonal matrix with the same structure as that of the equivalent Galerkin formulation using linear basis functions only. M_{22} is a diagonal matrix.

Equations (12) are solved at each time step using an iteration scheme based on that employed by Pasini, et al (1977). First the subproblem:

$$[M_{11}]\ \{\psi\} = \{r_1\} \tag{13}$$

is solved using the Thomas algorithm and a Picard iterative scheme. Following convergence, the solution vector is then substituted into the following two step scheme:

$$[M_{22}]\ \{\psi''\}^{k+1} = \{r_2\} - [M_{21}]\ \{\psi\}^{k} \tag{14a}$$

$$[M_{11}]\ \{\psi\}^{k+1} = \{r_1\} - [M_{12}]\ \{\psi''\}^{k+1} \tag{14b}$$

Here superscripts indicate the iteration level. Following each iteration, matrices are updated and steps 14(a) and (b) are repeated until the maximum change in the unknown is less than some specified tolerance. The procedure described above is essentially a block Gauss-Seidel iteration.

EXAMPLE SIMULATION

The model described above was used to solve a problem involving water infiltration into a column of length 50 cm and filled with a homogeneous sand. For this example, saturation and relative permeability have the following functional forms:

$$k_{rw} = A/(A + |\psi|^{B}) \tag{15}$$

$$s = \alpha\,(s_s - s_r)/(\alpha + |\psi|^{\beta}) + s_r \tag{16}$$

where A, B, α, β are empirical constants and s_s and s_r are the saturated and residual levels of water in the medium. Table 1 contains other relevant parameters for this example. Simulation results are plotted in Figure 2. The saturation profile at a time t=0.1 hours after infiltration began is

Table 1 - Parameters for Example Simulation

n	0.30
K	34.0 cm/h
s_s	0.957
s_r	0.250
A	1.175×10^6
B	4.74
α	1.611×10^6
β	3.96

Boundary and Initial Conditions

$s_w = 0.333$	at $t = 0$	$0 \le z \le 50$ cm
$s_w = 0.890$	at $z = 0$	$t \ge 0$
$s_w = 0.333$	at $z = 50$ cm	$t \ge 0$

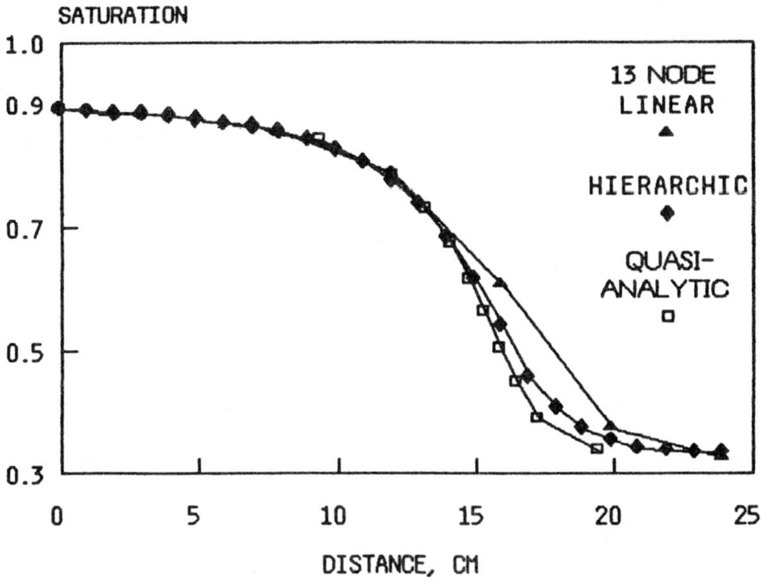

Figure 2: Comparison of Philip's quasi-analytical solution with simulated saturation profiles at t = 0.1 hours

shown in the figure. Philip's quasi-analytical solution for this problem (as computed by Haverkamp, et al, 1977) is plotted against finite element solutions obtained using 13 nodes (Δz = 4 cm). The triangles represent a solution obtained using linear basis functions only. This may be contrasted with the solution (delineated with diamonds) which was derived by employing the hierarchic quadratic basis functions at element midpoints. Note the striking improvement in the solution at the front.

In Figure 3, the 26 (Δz = 2 cm) node linear basis function solution is compared with the 13 node hierarchic solution. Here one sees very close agreement between solutions. The model was made self-adaptive by adding second derivative unknowns only to those elements over which large changes in saturation were occurring ($\Delta s/\Delta z > 0.01$). The self-adaptive solution at this time is also plotted in the figure (triangles). As can be seen, results for both hierarchic methods are essentially indistinguishable in this example. The self-adaptive solution shown here employed on average less than three additional unknowns when compared with the 13 node linear basis function solution. Five to six subiterations of the form 14 (a) and (b) were required to achieve convergence at each time step.

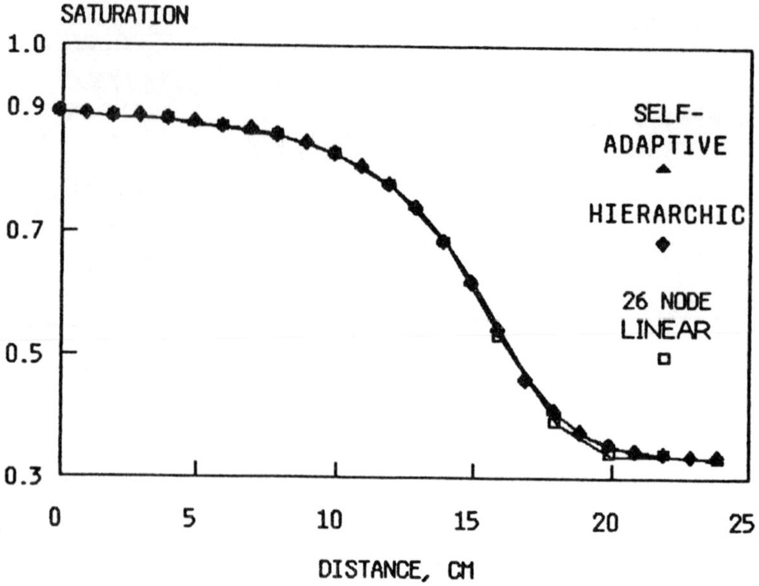

Figure 3: Comparison of 13 node hierachic solutions with a 26 node linear solution at t = 0.1 hours

CONCLUSIONS

A self-adaptive Galerkin finite element model has been developed to solve the non-linear, one dimensional unsaturated flow equation. This model utilizes a family of C^0 hierarchic basis functions along with a block iterative scheme. Simulation results indicate that the method shows promise for the solution of immiscible flow problems. Self-adaptive model solutions were shown to be comparable to solutions obtained using a linear basis function code and twice the number of elements. Extension of the approach to two dimensions appears straightforward. Future work should be directed towards optimization of the iteration scheme.

ACKNOWLEDGMENTS

The author is indebted to William Gray for his helpful suggestions. This work was supported, in part, by the National Science Foundation under grant ECE-8451469.

REFERENCES

Haverkamp, R., M. Vauclin, J. Touma, P.J. Wierenga, and G. Vachaud (1977) A Comparison of Numerical Simulation Models for One-Dimensional Infiltration. Soil Sci. Soc. Am. J., 41, 285-294.

Pasini, A., A. Peano, R. Riccioni, and L. Sbardella (1977) A Self-Adaptive Finite Element Analysis. presented at the IKOSS Congress, Baden Baden, West Germany, November 1977.

Peano, A.G., B.A. Szabo, and A.K. Mehta (1978) Self-Adaptive Finite Elements in Fracture Mechanics. Computer Methods in Appl. Mech. and Eng., 16, 69-80.

Peano, A. (1976) Hierarchies of Conforming Finite Elements for Plane Elasticity and Plate Bending. Comp. and Maths. with Appls., 2, 211-224.

Szabo, B.A. (1979) Some Recent Developments in Finite Element Analysis. Comp. and Maths with Appls., 5, 99-115.

VI International Conference on Finite Elements in Water Resources, Lisboa, Portugal, June 1986

Seepage Analysis in the Foundation of a Dam using a Finite Element Three Dimensional Model

A.T. Mascarenhas, C.S. Martins and L.R. Sousa
Laboratório Nacional de Engenharia Civil (LNEC), Lisbon, Portugal

INTRODUCTION

The creation of a reservoir by means of the construction of a dam, and the consequent marked difference in water levels upstream and downstream, profoundly alters the existing natural flow, which takes place from the slopes towards the valley due to the existence of a natural phreatic level. The resulting flow takes places from upstream to downstream in the direction of the valley downstream, through the rock mass foundation of the dam, including the valley and the slopes.

Seepage in the rock mass foundation of the dam basically produces uplifts in the insertion of the dam in its foundation and body forces in the foundation. Such forces are important in the design of these structures because if not controlled they may endanger stability. The usual means for this control are watertightening and drainage of the rock mass foundation of the dam, Watertightening reduces the permeability of certain zones of the rock mass and drainage usually makes the hydraulic head not exceed a given value in certain surfaces.

Prediction of water actions and the adequate control means (watertightening and drainage) are founded on the study of seepage through the dam's rock mass foundation, with a view to determining the hydraulic head distribution in the domain concerned, as well as the other quantities. The rock mass is assimilated, from the hydraulic point of view, to a fissured medium, through which the seepage equations are solved (Mascarenhas, 1979). For this purpose finite element models weredeveloped by LNEC, in a first phase for plane seepage analysis (Mascarenhas, 1979) and later also for tridimensional flows (Martins, 1984). These models make it possible to simulate confined and unconfined flow by considering a fixed mesh technique that allows to make an overall analysis of the structural and hydraulic behaviour.

This paper presents the study made by means of a finite element tridimensional model to analyse seepage through the foundation of an already constructed multiple arch dam (Mascarenhas et al, 1985), with the characteristics shown in fig. 1.

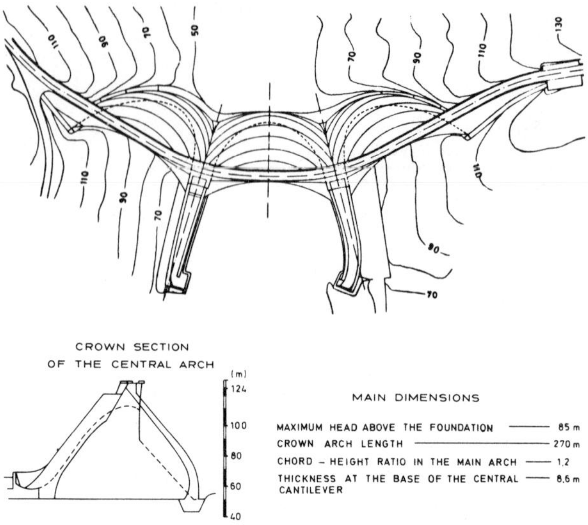

Fig. 1 - Multiple arch dam

THE PROBLEM OF SEEPAGE - ITS RESOLUTION

The rock mass on which the dam is founded consists of phylli - tous, graywackoid and schistous rocks, in successive and altern- ate layers, with some faults and several sets of joints, of which the most frequent are associated with schistosity (Mascarenhas et al., 1985).

The hydraulic characterization of the rock mass was based on Lugeon type tests. Permeability was found to decrease with dep th, values being very low for depths of more than about 30 m.

The watertightening and drainage works for controlling seepa- ge actions are shown in plan in fig. 2. They consist basically of a vertical grout curtain with a depth ranging between 20 and 30 m, drilled from the general drainage gallery, and of an other, also vertical, drilled more downstream (near the power station) down to a depth of 20 m. Drainage works consist essen tially of a general drainage gallery, a foundation gallery run ning about 20 m deep, and a drainage curtain connecting these two galleries. Another drainage curtain, executed from the respective gallery, is located downstream, between the buttres ses.

To solve the problem of seepage, the domain considered presup poses a plane of symmetry passing through the central cantile ver and includes the right bank insertion surface of the dam.

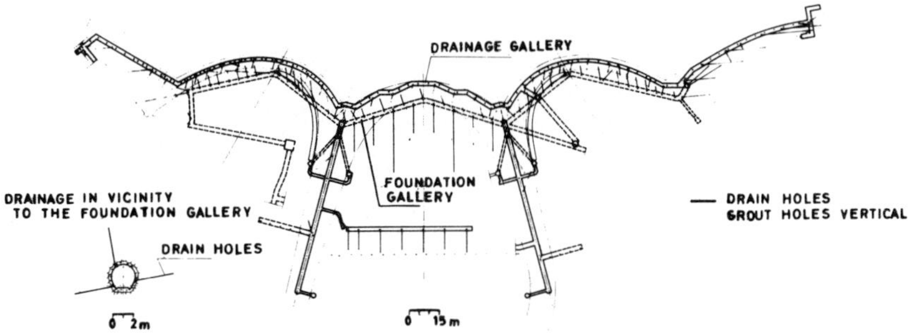

Fig. 2 - Drainage system and watertightening works

From the hydraulic point of view, the rock mass was approximated to a continuous medium, by using a plane fissure conceptual model with low permeability rock matrix (Mascarenhas, 1979). In this media flow follows the generalized Darcy law

$$V_i = - K_{ij} \frac{\partial h}{\partial x_j} \quad (i,\ j = 1,2,3) \qquad (1)$$

V_i being the components of the flow velocity vector, K_{ij} the hydraulic conductivity tensor, and h the hydraulic head; for the adopted hypotheses of flow in permanent laminar conditions the continuity equation is:

$$\frac{\partial}{\partial x_i} (K_{ij} \frac{\partial h}{\partial x_j}) + Q = 0 \qquad (i,\ j = 1,2,3) \qquad (2)$$

Q being the flow per volume unit.

The hypothesis of isotropy of the medium was considered, hydraulic conductivity being as a rule constant in this domain (K_m), and the value of $K_c = 0.1\ K_m$ was adopted for the grout curtains, except for a zone in the upstream curtain, near the insertion surface of the dam, where the value considered was equal to that of the conductivity of the medium (Fig. 3).

The boundary conditions adopted were (Fig.3): i) in the upstream reservoir h = 86.5, (storage level), in the river bed downstream h = 6.5 m, on the slope h = z and q = 0 (free surface condition, being z the hydraulic head that corresponds to the respective elevation and q the flow per surface unit) and, to express natural flow conditions, sufficiently distant from the valley, a phreatic level that is equal to the storage level; ii) in the upstream drainage curtain and foundation gallery, a variable hydraulic head, defined by the expression shown in fig. 3, which gives a decrease of about 70% as regards the upstream hydraulic head; iii) in the downstream drainage curtain, a constant hydrau

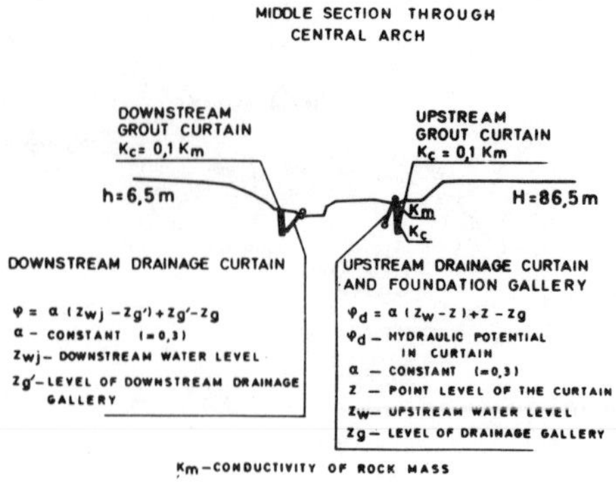

Fig. 3 - Boundary conditions and hydraulic conductivities

lic head equal to 30% of the head that corresponds to the downstream water level; iv) impermeability conditions ($q = 0$) at the lateral transverse surface limits, at the considered symmetry section and at the surfaces of insertion of the dam in the foundation.

FINITE ELEMENT NUMERICAL METHOD

In the formulation of the finite element tridimensional model developed for analysing seepage a variational method was applied which makes possible for each finite element to obtain (Martins, 1984):

$$A^e_{mn} \, h^e_n = F^e_m \tag{3}$$

$$A^e_{mn} = \int_{V_e} K_i \frac{\partial N_m}{\partial x'_i} \frac{\partial N_n}{\partial x'_i} \, dV - \int_{A_e} \alpha \, N_m N_n \, dA \tag{4}$$

$$F^e_{im} = \int_{V_e} Q N_m \, dV + \int_{A_e} q \, N_m \, dA \quad (m,n=1,2,\ldots P) \quad (i = 1,2,3) \tag{5}$$

h^e_m being the hydraulic heads at the nodal points, N_m the interpolating functions ($h = N_m h^e_m$; $m = 1,2,\ldots P$), P the number of nodal points of the element and K_i the main hydraulic conductivities, for a type $q + \alpha h$ surface flow condition.

By ordering the nodal points of the domain we obtain the following system of equations

$$A_{rs} \, h_s = F_r \qquad (r,s = 1,2,\ldots N) \tag{6}$$

A_{rs} being the hydraulic conductivity matrix of the domain, h_s the vector of hydraulic potentials, F_r a vector connected with the flow and N the total number of nodal points.

Regarding seepage through dam foundations, the domain is not well known a priori. It occurs with conditions of free surface boundary and with seepage face type conditions. To determine these surfaces an iterative non-linear calculation sequence is usually adopted, which allows to determine not only the distribution of the hydraulic heads but also the domain of the flow and the consequent boundary surfaces.

A fixed mesh technique was adopted, which permits to consider the same finite element mesh for the analysis of both the hydraulic and the structural behaviour of the foundation and which leads, in the various calculation algorithms used, to equation systems with constant overall conductivity matrices in each iteration, as opposed to the variable finite element mesh technique.

A procedure based on an algorithm proposed by Bathe and Khoshgoftaar (1979) was adopted. It consists in introducing a relation of dependence between the hydraulic conductivity characteristics of the medium and the hydraulic level, which corresponds to considering, for a negative pressure, $K_{ij} = 0$ and, for a nul or positive pressure, a conductivity of the medium equal to the real value. In the iterative process is used a scheme based on the modified Newton-Raphson algorithm and as unknowns, in step i of the iterative process, are considered the variations of the hydraulic head (Δh_s), calculated on the basis of

$$A_{rs}^{(o)} \Delta h_s^{(i)} = F_r^o - (A_{rk}^{(i-1)} h_k^{(i-1)}) \qquad (r,s,k = 1,2,\ldots N) \qquad (7)$$

The initial matrix A_{rs}^{o} is therefore always used to calculate head increases, matrix $A_{rk}^{(i-1)}$ being obtained through a numerical integration scheme.

Convergence accelerators were used in the model and several types of finite elements with 1st degree interpolation functions were formulated for the hydraulic head and transformation of coordinates, which permits the analysis of continuum and discontinuum media (Fig. 4).

The numerical model used (7000 nodal points and 6720 finite elements) is shown in Fig. 5.

OBTAINED RESULTS

Some of the results obtained by the model as regards equipotential lines in several cross-sections are presented in Fig. 6, clearly showing the seepage that takes place through the rock mass foundation of the dam: the equipotential lines in a section passing through the middle section of the central arch, in section B-B', through the right lateral arch, through the surfa-

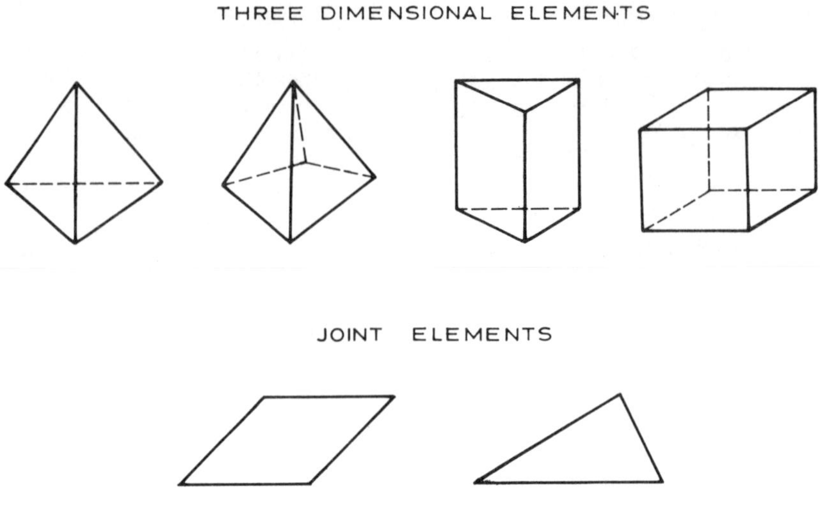

Fig. 4 - Types of finite elements

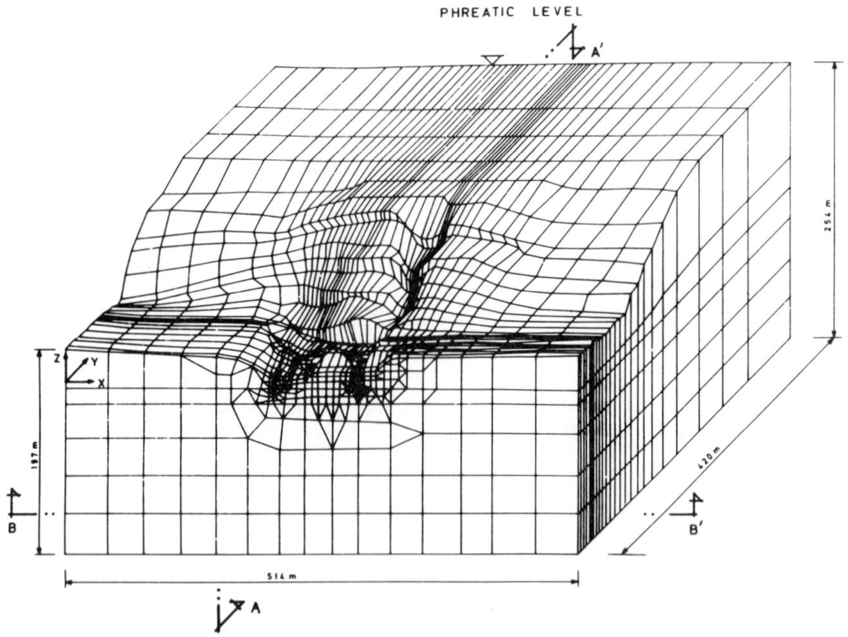

Fig. 5 - Finite element tridimensional model

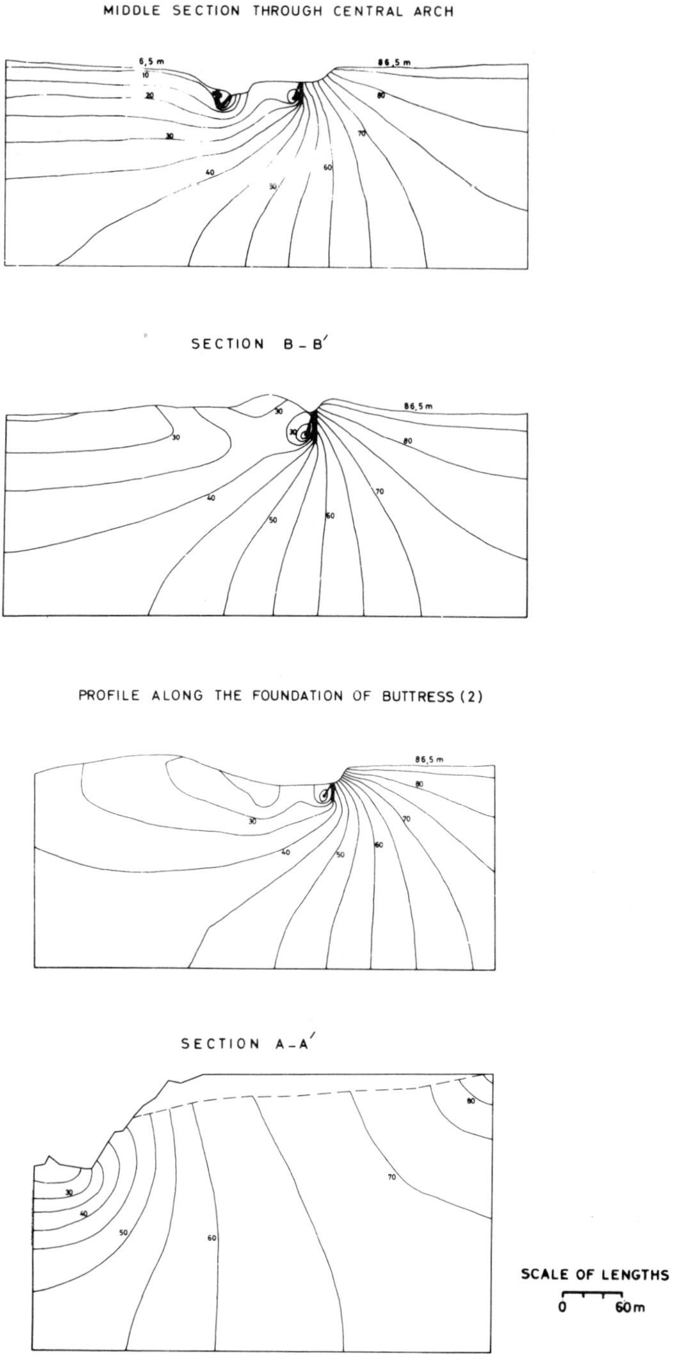

Fig. 6 - Flow analysis by the tridimensional model

ce of insertion of the buttress and also in section A-A' transverse to the river bed downstream, in the neighbourhood of the dam.

It is thus defined the distribution of the hydraulic head, through the foundation of the dam and on the downstream slope, for which it is important to know the actions due to seepage. As can be seen, a free surface occurs on the downstream slope and a considerable decrease in hydraulic heads brought about by the drainage works may be observed.

CONCLUSIONS

The analysis of the results shows the importance of the drainage works to obtain hydraulic heads compatible with those envisaged in the design in a zone of significant influence for the safety of the dam.

It should also be noted that the finite element tridimensional model developed makes it possible to analyse any type of flow as well as the structural effects caused by the mechanical actions of flow and, in the present case, to obtain a reference flow with a view to the interpretation of the future hydraulic behaviour of the dam.

REFERENCES

Bathe, K. and Khoshgoftaar, M. (1979) - Finite element free surface seepage analysis without mesh iteration, J. for Numerical and Analytical Methods in Geomechanics, V3, n 1.

Martins, S. (1984) - Three-dimensional numerical model for seepage analysis in underground openings (in Portuguese), LNEC Internal Report, Lisbon.

Mascarenhas, T. (1979) - Percolation through concrete dams foundations (in Portuguese), LNEC, Research Officer Thesis, Lisbon.

Mascarenhas, T., Sousa, R. and Martins, S (1985) - Uplift, seepage control and observed behaviour of Aguieira dam foundation, ICOLD 15, Lausanne.

VI International Conference on Finite Elements in Water Resources, Lisboa, Portugal, June 1986

Finite Element Assessment of the Method of Fragments for Problems of Confined Seepage

D.V. Griffiths, C.O. Li
Simon Engineering Laboratories, University of Manchester, Oxford Road, Manchester M13 9PL, U.K.

INTRODUCTION

The Methods of Fragments (Pavlovsky 1933) has been around for many years for solving problems of confined seepage, but has not received the attention it deserves. The method claims to give quick and reliable estimates of flow rates, uplift pressures and exit gradients due to seeping water beneath retaining structures. This paper assesses these claims using finite element analysis and finds that for the majority of cases excellent agreement is obtained. The crucial assumption in the method of fragments is that certain equipotentials are vertical. This assumption is found to become less valid as cut-off walls are shortened relative to the depth of the permeable stratum. The assumption that head is lost linearly within fragments is also examined and found to be generally satisfactory. Finally, a novel application of the method of fragments to the problem of non-symmetric double-walled cofferdams is presented. It is found that this can be achieved by the introduction of a vertical impermeable surface between the walls. The 'best' location of this impermeable boundary is presented in chart form as a function of the relative lengths of the cut-off walls.

Many methods are available for tracing the route taken by water as it seeps through a porous soil under steady state conditions. Making the usual assumptions regarding soil/fluid incompressibility and validity of Darcy's law, all the methods must amount to a solution of Laplace's equation

$$k_H \frac{\partial^2 h}{\partial x^2} + k_V \frac{\partial^2 h}{\partial y^2} = 0 \qquad (1)$$

Undoubtedly, the best known and most widely taught method for civil engineers uses 'flow nets', Casagrande (1940). The drawing of flow nets is, however, something of an art, and is rarely straightforward except for the simplest boundary conditions. Small changes in the geometry of a problem, such as the length of a cut off wall or apron, require a completely new flow net and if several different geometries were to be considered for design purposes, much time could be wasted on the trial and error process, only to find that a particular configuration was unsuitable.

The method of fragments can be considered to be a semi-analytical approach which will usually give approximate solutions. The method was first proposed by Pavlovsky (1933) and was 'publicised' by Harr (1962). More recently, Griffiths (1984) has rationalised the method into chart form enabling convenient implementation for engineers. The method, and the inherent assumption contained with it, are summarised in the next section.

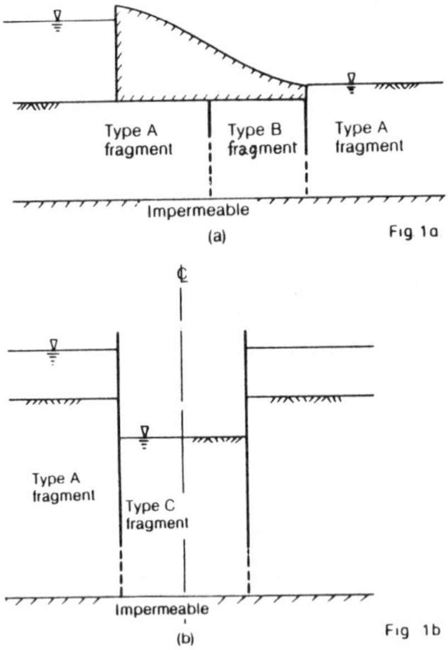

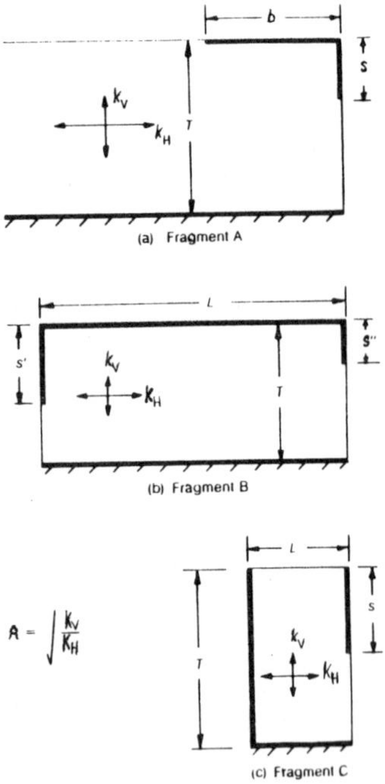

Fig.1 : Subdivision into fragments Fig.2 : Three fragment types

REVIEW OF THE METHOD OF FRAGMENTS

Although the method can also be applied to unconfined flow problems (Harr 1977) the present discussion is concerned with confined flow problems in which all boundary conditions are known.

The crucial assumption in the method is that the equipotential lines at certain locations within the flow regime can be considered vertical. These 'certain locations' are usually chosen to be places where cut-off walls are situated or sharp changes of geometry occur. Figure 1 shows some examples of how confined flow problems could be divided into fragments. The subdivision results in fragments which are rectangular in shape and although this means that the method can only be applied to problems with fairly simple boundaries, the rectangular shapes have the advantage that they can be easily analysed by mapping techniques or finite element approaches.

Three types of fragments have been identified in the present work and are shown in Figure 2. These enable a wide range of problems to be tackled although other fragment types could be developed if required.

THE FINITE ELEMENT MODEL

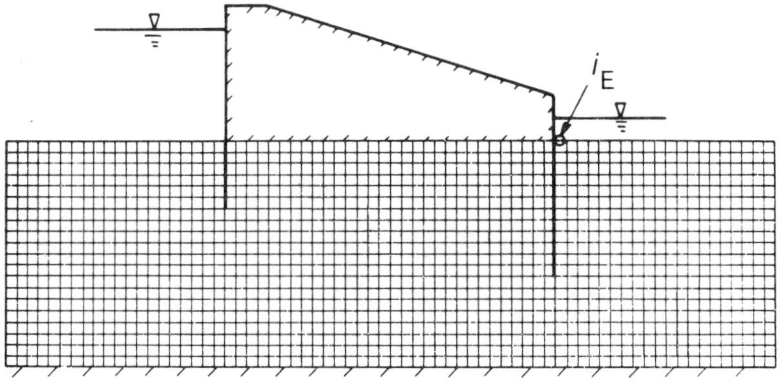

Figure 3 : Typical mesh with two cut-off walls

Four-noded quadrilateral elements were used throughout and a typical mesh is shown in Figure 3 for a dam with two cut off walls. Due to the symmetry of the governing Laplace's equation, and to avoid controversy over aspect ratios, it was decided to use square elements throughout. Boundary conditions involved fixing the potential head at the up- and downstream sides and defining impermeable boundaries ($\partial h/\partial n=0$). The impermeable cut-off walls were assumed to have zero thickness but, in order to model impermeable conditions, each node on the walls had two freedoms, one to the left and one to the right.

For details of the formulation and listings of the programs, the reader is referred to Smith (1982), but in all cases the problem was reduced to the solution of linear simultaneous equations, thus

$$\underline{q} = \underline{k}\,\underline{h} \qquad (2)$$

where $\underline{h}$ is a vector of nodal values of head, $\underline{q}$ is a vector of net nodal inflow/outflow and $\underline{k}$ is the system 'stiffness' matrix.

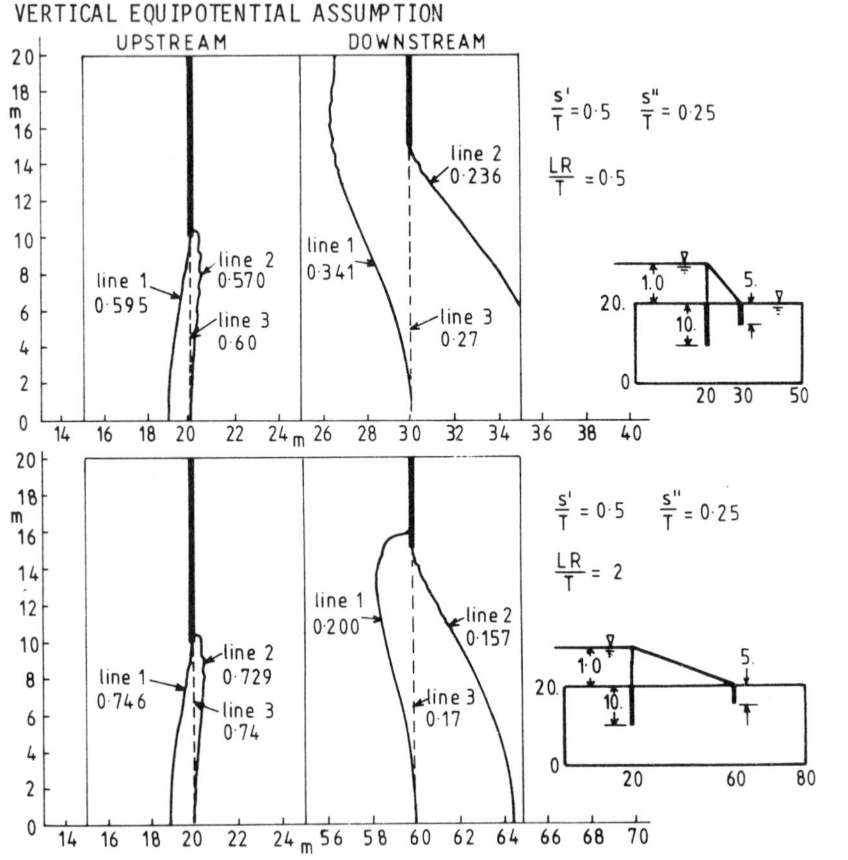

Figure 4 : Assessment of the vertical equipotential assumption

The results of some finite element runs on the mesh of Figure 3 are given in Figure 4. For such a boundary value problem, the method of fragments would place equipotentials directly beneath the cut-off walls, so it is in this vicinity that attention has been focussed. Each of the results in Figure 4 shows a cut-off wall together with three equipotentials - line 1 the upstream equipotential, line 2 the downstream equipotential and line 3 the equipotential by the method of fragments from charts (Griffiths 1984). The two equipotentials from the finite element analysis (line 1 and line 2) were chosen to be those passing through the tip of the wall and through a point on the impermeable surface directly below the wall. Both the up-and downstream walls are considered. The error introduced by assuming a vertical equipotential beneath the walls should be considered relative to the total head loss of 1 unit across the full problem.

Although the equipotentials were not always vertical, the range of values and the error introduced by the fragments assumption was quite small. In the majority of cases the equipotentials drawn through the tip of the wall and the base (lines 1 and 2) lay very close to each other. The downstream wall of the shorter dam (LR/T=0.5) behaved rather differently in that line 1 did not meet the wall itself but intersected the base of the dam. The error was still small, however, as indicated by the head values associated with lines 1 and 2 which had a spread of only 10% of the total head (0.34 - 0.24). This trend would tie in with the results of Figure 5, which shows the fragments assumptions regarding linear loss of head to be less satisfactory for short dams with short cut-off walls.

FLOW RATES, UPLIFT PRESSURES AND EXIT GRADIENTS

The accuracy of the method of fragment for predicting flow rates and exit gradients has been considered in some detail in an earlier publication (Griffiths 1984). Regarding uplift pressures, however, an additional assumption has to be made that head is lost linearly along the uppermost streamline within a Type-B fragment. Figure 5 shows comparisons between the head along line AB beneath a dam by fragments and that computed using a mesh of the type shown in Figure 3. The results indicate that the method of fragments accounts quite well for the uplift pressures, although the assumption of linearity is an approximation. The 'worst' cases are shown in Figures 5(a) and 5(b) where the dam is short relative to the depth of the permeable layer. In these cases, the uplift pressure by the method of fragments was slightly unconservative, but still within 10% of the more rigorously obtained finite element values. In spite of this, all the solutions presented by the method of fragments gave adequate predictions for engineering purposes. It may be noted that when applying the method to obtain uplift pressures due to seepage through anisotropic soils, the 'transformed' width RL, rather than the original width L, should be used.

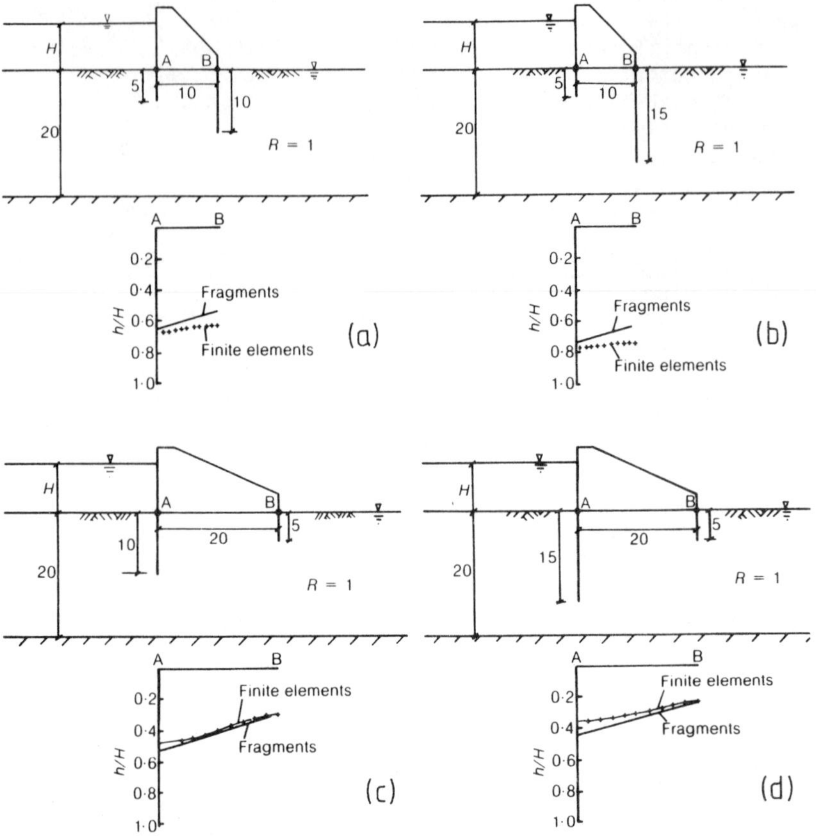

Figure 5 : Uplift pressures by fragments and finite elements

FLOW THROUGH UNSYMMETRICAL COFFERDAMS

An application of the method of fragments to a new problem is now considered. Figure 6 shows an unsymmetrical cofferdam with walls of unequal length. The symmetrical case (Figure 1) is easily dealt with by assuming that an impermeable surface lies at the centreline. This problem is then solved by superposing two identical type -C fragments. It is suggested that a similar approach can be used in the unsymmetrical case by assuming the existence of a vertical impermeable surface. If this assumption is acceptable the problem then amounts to finding the 'best' location of the impermeable surface.

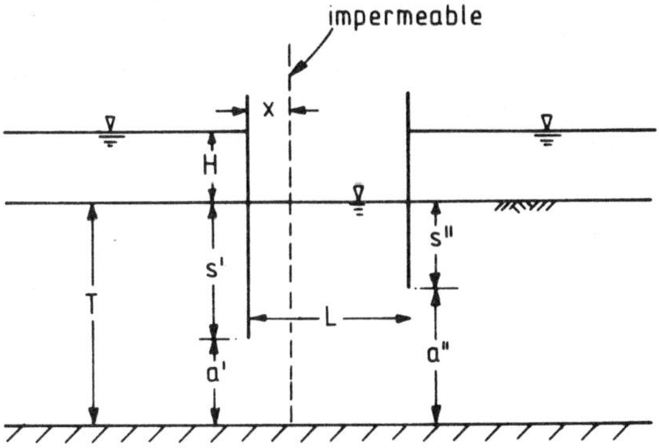

Figure 6 : Unsymmetrical double-wall cofferdam

It seems intuitively likely that the 'best' position depends on the relative size of the gaps beneath the walls thus

$$\frac{x}{L} = f\left(\frac{a'}{a' + a''}\right) \qquad (3)$$

Assuming at all times that $a' \leqslant a''$, finite element runs have been performed on a number of configurations. Boundary conditions of equation (3) that must be satisfied are given by

$$\frac{x}{L} = 0 \text{ when } \frac{a'}{a' + a''} = 0$$

and (4)

$$\frac{x}{L} = 0.5 \text{ when } \frac{a'}{a' + a''} = 0.5$$

The finite element runs involved a full analysis of the unsymmetrical problem which yielded a total flow rate and two exit gradients corresponding to each side. This was followed by a series of runs on the same problem, but with an impermeable wall moved gradually from left (x/L = 0) to right (x/L = 1). By this process the best position of the impermeable wall in order to simulate the full problem was obtained. A series of results for the case LR/T = 0.5 are given in Figure 7. These results emphasised that the solution of a potential problem of this type tends to maximise the kinetic energy of the system. The full solution for the total flow rate in all cases agreed closely with the maximum flow rate achieved by moving the impermeable wall from left to right. This maximum flow rate corresponded to the optimum value of x/L. It was found that this optimum position also gave the best values of the exit gradients on both sides.

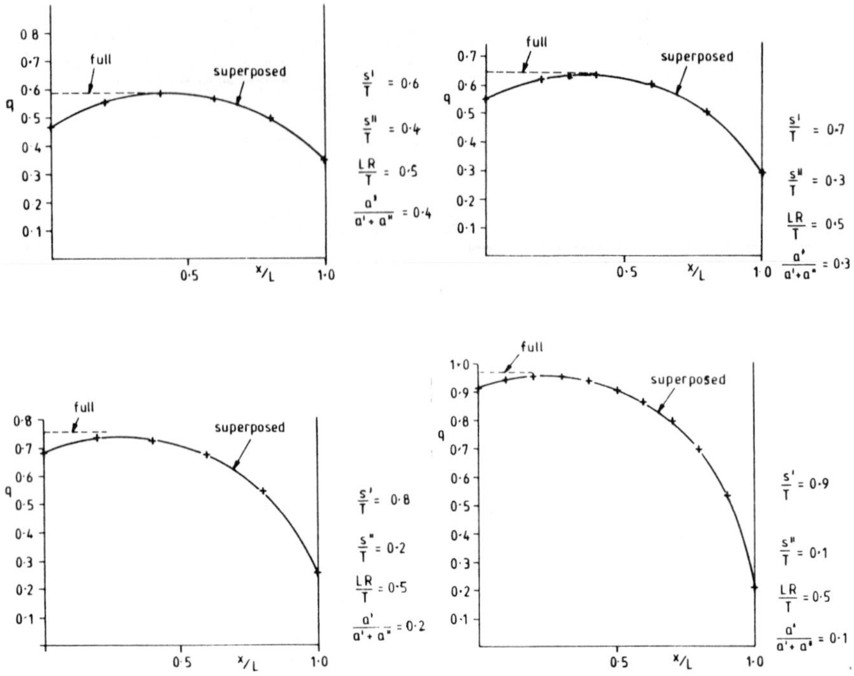

Figure 7 : Effect of impermeable surface on flow rate

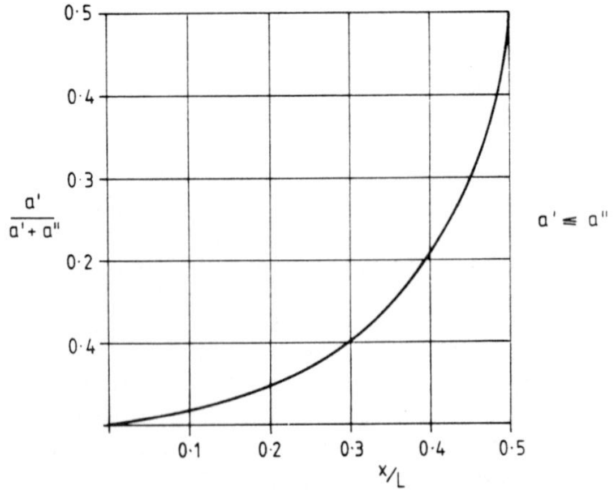

Figure 8 : Suggested location of impermeable surface

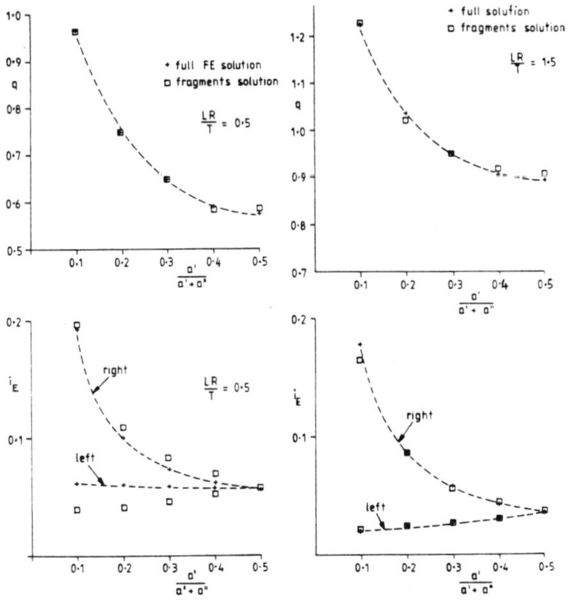

Figure 9 - Comparison of fragments and finite element solution

A series of other configurations involving different values of LR/T have resulted in the empirical curve of Figure 8. This curve estimates the 'best' position of the impermeable surface (x/L) depending on the relative lengths of the cut-off walls (a'/(a' + a")). Figure 9 shows a comparison of flow rates and exit gradients as computed using a full finite element analysis with those that would be obtained using the method of fragments in conjunction with Figure 8. It is seen that quite acceptable agreement is obtained. For the two different LR/T values considered, generally good agreement for both flow rates and exit gradients was observed. For the narrower dam, however, the method of fragments underestimated the exit gradient at the left side, but still gave excellent agreement with the more important and higher gradients to the right.

CONCLUSIONS

The finite element method has been applied to problems of steady state seepage in order to assess the assumptions inherent in the method of fragments. A detailed examination was made of the vertical equipotential assumption beneath cut-off walls. By examining the computed equipotentials in the vicinity of the walls it was found that the assumption was excellent provided the wall was not too short relative to the total depth of the permeable layer. The assumption of linear loss of head within a fragment was also examined with reference to the uplift pressures on water retaining structures. It was found that the assumption was quite acceptable although slightly unconservative for dams that were narrow relative to the depth of the permeable stratum. In all cases, however, the results were certainly of acceptable accuracy for engineering purposes and at least as good as those that could be obtained using a well drawn flow net

Finally, a new approach is suggested for the solution of unsymmetrical double walled cofferdams by the method of fragments. The method involves the assumption of a vertical impermeable surface at some point between the cut-off walls. A chart is presented for finding the 'best' position of the surface, and the accuracy of the ensuing estimates of flow rates and exit gradients is confirmed.

REFERENCES

Casagrande, A. (1940). "Seepage through dams", Boston Soc.Civ.Eng. Contribs. to Soil Mech. 1925-1940.

Griffiths, D.V. (1984). "Rationalised charts for the method of fragments applied to confined seepage", Geotechnique 34, No.2, 229-238.

Harr, M.E. (1962). "Groundwater and seepage", Chaps 3-6, New York, McGraw-Hill.

Harr, M.E. (1977). "Mechanics of particulate media", Chap 5, New York, McGraw-Hill.

Pavlovsky, N.N. (1933). "Motion of water under dams", 1st Congress on large dams, Stockholm, pp 179-192.

Polubarinova-Kochina, P.Ya. (1962).. "Theory of motion of ground water". Chap 3, Princeton Univ.Press.

Smith, I.M. (1982). "Programming the finite element method", Chap.7, Chichester, Wiley.

VI International Conference on Finite Elements in Water Resources, Lisboa, Portugal, June 1986

A Unified Algorithm to Solve Nonlinear Groundwater Flow

F.J. Elorza, L. Ferragut
Departamento de Cálculo Numérico, E.T.S.I. de Minas, Universidad Politécnica de Madrid, Rios Rosas, 21-28003 Madrid, Spain

INTRODUCTION

The problems of flow through porous media occur and play an important role in many disciplines of engineering. The finite element method has been extensively applied to the solution of linear flow through porous media, both in the steady-state case by Zienkiewicz, Mayer and Cheung (1966) or in the nonsteady-state case by Pinder and Frind(1972). The application of the finite element method for the solution of problems that involve nonsteady flow of groundwater with a free surface in the saturated zone has grown very rapidly during the past years. In the early stages the procedures were based on a iterative modification of the finite element mesh as in Neuman and Witherspoon (1972), but they suffer from a number of limitations. In order to avoid this, Desai(1976) proposed a residual flow procedure for the steady-free surface problems in which the mesh remains invariant with iteration and also Bathe and Khoshgoftaar(1979) have proposed another procedure for the some problem. Later, Bathe, Sonnad and Domigan (1982) developed an algorithm for the transient free surface seepage problems and Desai (1984) present a derivation for the residual flow procedure for transient free surface problems.

All the preceding works concern linear flow through porous media. When high velocities take place the Darcy's equation does not describe correctly the relationship between the hydraulic gradient and velocity, thus general expressions have been proposed as:

$i = cv^m$ Missbach equation (1)

$i = av + bv^2$ Forchheimer equation (2)

where i is the hydraulic gradient and v is the velocity of the fluid, a and b are constants of the porous media, however both c and m depend of V, but Pérez Franco (1982) proves that when the hydraulic gradient variations in the flow field are relatively small it is possible to consider c and m as constant --- values. The analysis of this type of problems with the finite element method has been made in the steady-state case by Volker (1969), by McCorquodale (1970), by Elorza and Ferragut (1985), and by Ferragut and Elorza (1985), and in the transient-state case by Rama Rao (1980) but in confined and semi-confined aquifers, and by McCorquodale (1970).

In this work we adopt the Missbach equation (1) to formulate the nonsteady nonlinear flow in porous media with a free surface problem, and we present a derivation of the procedure of -- Desai (1984) for the transient nonlinear free surface problems and present solutions to a number of problems.

NON LINEAR FLOW EQUATIONS IN POROUS MEDIA

Reversing the expression (1) we have, with $i = |\vec{\nabla} u|$, u denoting the isoparametric head:

$$\vec{v} = K_n |\vec{\nabla} u|^{n-1} \, . \, \vec{\nabla} u$$

where $|\cdot|$ denote the vector norm in R^d (d = 1,2 or 3) and K_n and n its dependents on the $|\vec{\nabla} u|$; in the linear case we have n = 1 and in the turbulent case n = 0.5. The governing differential equation of incompressible fluid flow through a porous media of variable permeability will be, Desai (1984)

$$\nabla(k\vec{\nabla} u) + f = S_s \frac{\partial u}{\partial t} \quad \text{in } \Omega_1 \quad \forall \; t \in [0,T] \tag{3}$$

where: u = total fluid potential or head = $p/\gamma + z$, p = pressure head, z = elevation head, γ = density of fluid, k = coefficient of permeability of the medium, f = applied source/sink, Ω_1 = flow domain, and S = specific storage.

In the nonlinear case (3) will be:

$$\nabla(K_n |\vec{\nabla} u|^{n-1} \vec{\nabla} u) + f = S_s \frac{\partial u}{\partial t} \quad \text{in } \Omega_1 \quad \forall \; t \in [0,T] \tag{4}$$

and the boundary conditions associated will be:

$$u = u_1 \quad \text{in } \Gamma_0 \tag{5}$$

$$-K_n |\vec{\nabla} u|^{n-1} \frac{\partial u}{\partial n} = q \quad \text{in } \Gamma_1 \tag{6}$$

where $\Gamma = \Gamma_0 \cup \Gamma_1$ is the boundary of Ω_1, and u_1 and q are known functions which represent the piezometric head on Γ_0 and the flow through Γ_1.

Here, as Desai (1984), the flow domain is extended into the -- whole domain, see Fig. 1, such that

$$\Omega = \Omega_1 \cup \Omega_2$$

and equation (4) is assumed to hold in Ω by introducing a definition of K as follows:

$$K(u,p) = \begin{cases} K_n(u) & \text{on } \Omega_1 \\ K_n(u)-f_1(p) & \text{on } \Omega_2 \end{cases} \qquad (8)$$

where $f_1(p)$ is a smooth continous function of the pressure head, p. Here, a linear permeability-pressure curve is adopted, see Fig. 2. By using the same idea, the specific storage, S_S, is defined in terms of specific storage at saturation, S_S, and a residual function in terms of pressure head, g(p):

$$c(p) = S_S - g(p) \qquad (9)$$

Then the governing equations of the fluid nonlinear flow through the whole domain Ω are:

$$\nabla(K(u,p)|\vec{\nabla}u|^{n-1} \nabla u) + f = c(p)\frac{\partial u}{\partial t} \qquad \text{in } \Omega \quad \forall\, t \in [0,T] \qquad (10)$$

$$u = p/\gamma + z \qquad (11)$$

$$u = u_1 \qquad \text{in } \Gamma_0 \qquad (12)$$

$$-K(u,p)|\vec{\nabla}u|^{n-1}\frac{\partial u}{\partial n} = q \qquad \text{in } \Gamma_1 \qquad (13)$$

$$u(0) = u_0 \qquad \text{in } \Omega \qquad (14)$$

where $\Gamma = \Gamma_0 \cup \Gamma_1$ is the boundary of Ω, and we shall suppose that q=0.

Variational formulation.

The variational formulation associated to the stated problem (10)-(14) is

$$\int_\Omega c(p)\frac{\partial u}{\partial t} v\, dx + \int_\Omega K(u,p)|\vec{\nabla}u|^{n-1} \vec{\nabla}u\, \vec{\nabla}v\, dx =$$

$$= \int_\Omega fv\, dx \qquad (15)$$

$$\forall\, v \in H_0^1(\Omega) \qquad \forall\, t \in [0,T]$$

where $u = p/\gamma + z$, and we seek for a function u(t) that verifies (14) $\forall\, t \in [0,T]$, to simplify the notation, in the following we set:

$$k(u) = k(u,p)|\vec{\nabla}u|^{n-1}$$

and

$$c(u) = c(p)$$

Time discretization.

In this section we consider the time discretization of the problem (15).

A general one step scheme will be:

$$\int_\Omega c(u^{i+\theta})\frac{u^{i+1}-u^i}{\Delta t}\, v\, dx + \int_\Omega k(u^{i+\theta})\, \vec{\nabla} u^{i+\theta}\, \vec{\nabla} v\, dx = \int_\Omega fv\, dx \qquad (16)$$

where u^i is an approximation of the solution at the time t_i, Δt is the time step and θ is a real number in the interval $[0,1]$ $u^{i+\theta}$ is an intermediate value between u^i and u^{i+1}, for example $u^{i+\theta} = (1-\theta)u^i+\theta u^{i+1}$.

In the following we use the notation $c^{i+\theta} = c(u^{i+\theta})$ and $k^{i+\theta} = k(u^{i+\theta})$

The simplest procedure is to take $\theta = 0$ and we obtain the well known Euler explicit scheme:

$$\int_\Omega c^i\, \frac{u^{i+1}-u^i}{\Delta t}\, v\, dx + \int_\Omega k^i \vec{\nabla} u^i \vec{\nabla} v\, dx = \int_\Omega fv\, dx \qquad (17)$$

Taking $\theta = 1$ is the Euler implicit scheme:

$$\int_\Omega c^{i+1}\, \frac{u^{i+1}-u^i}{\Delta t}\, v\, dx + \int_\Omega k^{i+1} \vec{\nabla} u^{i+1} \vec{\nabla} v\, dx = \int_\Omega fv\, dx \qquad (18)$$

For all values of θ the scheme is a first order approximation except for $\theta = 0.5$ that is of order two (Cranc-Nicolson scheme)

Problem (18) is nonlinear and we need an iteration procedure to solve it; if we choose the fixed point method the algorithm should be:

u_n^{i+1}, known we solve

$$\int_\Omega c_n^{i+1}\, \frac{u_{n+1}^{i+1}-u^i}{\Delta c}\, v\, dx + \int_\Omega k_n^{i+1}\, \vec{\nabla} u_{n+1}^{i+1}\, \vec{\nabla} v\, dx = \int_\Omega fv\, dx \qquad (19)$$

where u_n^{i+1} is the approximation of u^{i+1} in the n-th fixed point iteration.

We shall give an incremental formulation of (19) well adapted to the derivation of several algorithms of resolution, from(19) we obtain:

$$\int c_n^{i+1}\, \frac{u_{n+1}^{i+1}-u_n^{i+1}}{\Delta t}\, v\, dx + \int k_n^{i+1}\, \vec{\nabla}(u_{n+1}^{i+1} - u_n^{i+1})\, \vec{\nabla} v\, dx =$$

$$= \int_\Omega fv\,dx + \int_\Omega c_n^{i+1} \frac{u^i}{\Delta t} v\,dx - \int_\Omega c_n^{i+1} \frac{u_n^{i+1}}{\Delta t} v\,dx -$$

$$- \int k_n^{i+1} \vec{\nabla} u_n^{i+1} \vec{\nabla} v\,dx \qquad (20)$$

Setting:

$$\delta = u_{n+1}^{i+1} - u_n^{i+1}$$

$$\Delta u = u^{i+1} - u^i$$

$$(\Delta u)_n = u_n^{i+1} - u^i$$

In each iteration we have to solve the linear problem:

$$\int c_n^{i+1} \frac{\delta}{\Delta t} v\,dx + \int k_n^{i+1} \vec{\nabla}\delta\vec{\nabla} v\,dx = \int_\Omega f^{i+1} v\,dx -$$

$$- \int c_n^{i+1} \frac{(\Delta u)n}{\Delta t} v\,dx - \int_\Omega k_n^{i+1} \vec{\nabla} u_n^{i+1} \vec{\nabla} v\,dx \qquad (21)$$

$$(\Delta u)_{n+1} = (\Delta u)_n + \delta \qquad (22)$$

$$u_{n+1}^{i+1} = u^i + (\Delta u)_{n+1} = u_n^{i+1} + \delta \qquad (23)$$

For a general value of θ we obtain instead of (21) the expression:

$$\int_\Omega c_n^{i+\theta} \frac{\delta}{\Delta t} v\,dx + \theta \int_\Omega k_n^{i+\theta} \nabla\delta\nabla v\,dx = \int_\Omega f^{i+\theta} v\,dx -$$

$$- \int_\Omega c_n^{i+\theta} \frac{(\Delta u)_n}{\Delta t} v\,dx - \theta \int_\Omega k_n^{i+\theta} \vec{\nabla}(\Delta u)_n \vec{\nabla} v\,dx - \qquad (24)$$

$$- \int_\Omega k_n^{i+\theta} \vec{\nabla} u^i \vec{\nabla} v\,dx$$

FINITE ELEMENT APPROXIMATION.

We now consider the finite element approximation of the expression (21). If Z is a partition of the domain Ω into finite elements we search the solution between the functions which are continuous in Ω and polinomials of degree k in each finite element $T \in Z$; Let $\{\psi_i\}_{i=1}^N$ be a base of that finite element space, in each iteration we have to solve the following linear system of equations:

$$\left(\frac{1}{\Delta t}[M] + [K]\right)\{\delta\} = \{f\} - \frac{1}{\Delta t}[M]\{\Delta u\}_n - [K]\{u\}_n^{i+1} \tag{25}$$

where the terms of the matrix [M] and [K] are given by:

$$[M]_{ij} = \int_\Omega c_n^{i+1}\ \psi_i\psi_j\ dx$$
$$[K]_{ij} = \int_\Omega k_n^{i+1}\ \vec{\nabla}\psi_i\vec{\nabla}\psi_j\ dx \tag{26}$$

Different algorithms of resolutions.

The fixed point algorithm in the form of expression (25) is extremely expensive because we need to recalculate the matrix [M] and [K] and to factorize the matrix

$$\frac{1}{\Delta t}[M] + [K]$$

in each iteration, instead we could retain for matrix [M] and [K] the values:

$$[M]_{ij} = \int_\Omega c_0^{i+1}\ \psi_i\psi_j\ dx = \int_\Omega c^i\ \psi_i\psi_j\ dx$$

and

$$[K]_{ij} = \int_\Omega k_0^{i+1}\ \vec{\nabla}\psi_i\vec{\nabla}\psi_j\ dx = \int_\Omega k^i\ \vec{\nabla}\psi_i\vec{\nabla}\psi_j\ dx$$

In fact from expression (25)and choosing different approximations of the matrix

$$[A] = \frac{1}{\Delta t}[M] + [K]$$

we shall obtain a family of algorithms; for example taking

$$[A] \simeq \frac{1}{\Delta t}[M]$$

and limiting the fixed point iterations to one we recover the Euler explicit method; usually we use a numerical integration formula so matrix [M] is diagonal and the solution of the system of equations is an easy task.

Taking

$$[A] \simeq \text{diag}\left(\frac{1}{\Delta t}[M] + [K]\right)$$

we obtain a Jacobi-like algorithm for the resolution of the non linear set of equations; in that case an acceleration parameter should be included in the readaptation formulas (22) and (23). Taking $[A] \simeq \text{diag}([K])$ we obtain, with acceleration parameter, the accelerated viscous relaxation method to solve the steady-state case as proposed by Zienkiewicz and Lohner (1985).

Other techniques are possible, Quasi-Newton techniques instead of the fixed-point ones; Also the diagonal preconditioned conjugate gradient algorithm is a recommended procedure to solve -- the linear system of equations (25); usually a few conjugate gradient iterations should be sufficient for each time step. On the other hand, the iterative methods of resolutions as Jacobi or conjugate gradient do not need to store any matrix as they appear as a matrix-vector product that may be calculated element by element.

Treatment of the boundary condition for seepage surface.

The boundary condition on the seepage surface must be $u = y$ and $\frac{\partial u}{\partial n} = 0$ over the free surface, so we have a nonlinear boundary condition.

We should impose these boundary conditions by using a penalty function in the boundary S with seepage surface we set:

$$-\left.\frac{\partial u}{\partial n}\right|_S = h(u)(u-u_\infty) \tag{27}$$

where $u_\infty = y$ (geometric head) and

$$h(u) = \begin{cases} 0 & \text{if } u < y \\ A & \text{if } u \geqslant y \end{cases}$$

where A is a great constant value which should be adjusted in function of the drawdown.

The problem solved in each iteration of the algorithm for the Euler implicit methods is then:

$$\int_\Omega c_n^{i+1} \frac{\delta}{\Delta t} v\, dx + \int_\Omega k_n^{i+1} \nabla\delta\nabla v\, dx + \int_S h_n^{i+1} \delta\, v\, d\Upsilon =$$

$$= \int_S h_n^{i+1}(y-u_n^{i+1})\, v\, d\Upsilon - \int_\Omega c_n^{i+1} \frac{(\Delta u)_n}{\Delta t} v\, dx - \int_\Omega k_n^{i+1} \nabla u_n^{i+1} \nabla v\, dx$$

$$u_{n+1}^{i+1} = u_n^{i+1} + \delta \tag{28}$$

in this way we have for the nodes on the seepage surface(and under the free surface)

$$\delta \simeq y - u_n^{i+1}$$

$$u_{n+1}^{i+1} = u_n^{i+n} + \delta \simeq y \tag{29}$$

if we use a modified Newton technique setting

$$c_n^{i+1} = c_0^{i+1} = c^i \qquad \text{and} \qquad k_n^{i+1} = k_0^{i+1} = k^i$$

in each time step we may use a partial factorization procedure to handle the terms on S in a similar way of that proposed by Ferragut and Winter (1985).

APPLICATIONS

A number of example problems were solved by using the above procedure. They included both the steady and transient free surface seepage in earth slopes of mines and in a well in an unconfined aquifer.

Open lengthy shape mine (Steady unconfined nonlinear flow)

In this example (Elorza and Ferragut (1985), we present an open lengthy shape mine with a system of wells parallel to the longest axis to avoid the flooding of the mine. Fig. 3 shows a middle section with the hydrological conditions, we have designed with painted-line the future position of the wells. The computations of the nodal reactions in the well should allow us to -- know the necessaryflow to maintain the free surface under the surface of the mine. We have considered K_D=2000m/day and a relation K_n/K_D show by the table 1. We have done two finite element models; the first one with the entire domain and a second model where we have avoided partly the dry zone of the result with the former and a mesh refinement has been considered. In fig. 4 we present the second model as well the position of the free surface obtained. The flow necessary to maintain the free surface in the required position is 2600m^3/d.

The slope mine case (Unsteady unconfined linear flow)

The slope mine shown in Fig.5 is modeled using a finite element mesh consisting of 16x16x2 three-node elements. The domain is initially saturated and a t=0$^+$ the water level on the slope face falls to zero. The coefficient of permeability K_D, is 5m/day and a value of specific storage equal to 0.05m^{-1} is used.

The Fig.6 showsthe results; six time steps are used to reach the steady-state conditions.

Transient axisymmetricnon-linear flow to a well

Fig. 7 shows the two-dimensional axisymmetric well problem analyzed. Tho model consistsof 20x20 four-node bilinear interpolation elements. The initial conditions are fully saturated with zero discharge. The permeability in K_D=40m/day and the specific storage equal to 0'3 m^{-1} is used. The ratio K_n/K_D as well as the exponent n is similar to the former example. At time t=0$^+$ the water level drops fully.

The Fig. 8 shows the results, and the time steps used.

REFERENCES

Bathe, K.J. and Khoshgoftaar, M.R. (1979) Finite element free surface seepage analysis without mesh iteration, Int. J. Num. Anal. Method Geom., 3: 13-22.

Bathe, K.J., Sonnad, V. and Domigan, P. (1982) Some experiences using finite element methods for fluid flow problems. 4° Int. Conference on finite elements in water resources, 9-3 to 9-16.

Desai, C.S. (1976) Finite element residual schemes for unconfined flow. Int. J. Num. Meth. Engng., 10: 1415-1418.

Desai, C.S. (1984) Free surface flow through porous media using a residual procedure, Finite elements in fluids. Ed. Gallagher, R.H., Oden, J.T., Zienkiewicz, O.C., Kawai, T. and Kawahara, M. John Wiley and sons.

Elorza, F.J. and Ferragut, L. (1985) A finite element approximation of nonlinear flow in porous media. 2nd. International Mine Water Congress, 467-477.

Ferragut, L. and Elorza, F.J. (1985) Un método de Lagrangiano aumentado para la resolución de problemas de flujo no lineal en medio poroso. Rev. Int. Metodos Num. Calc. dis. Ing. Vol. 1, n°3: 27-35.

Ferragut, L. and Winter, G. (1985) Efficient implementation of Newton's method. I Simp. Int. Analisis Numérico, Univ. Polit. Madrid.

McCorquodale, J.A. (1970) Variational approach to non-Darcy flow. J. Hydraul. Div. Amer . Soc. Civil. Eng., 99, HY11, 2265-2278.

Neuman, S.P. and Witherspoon, P.A. (1971) Analysis of nonsteady flow with a free surface using the finite element method. Water Resour. Res., 7, n°3, 611-623.

Pérez Franco, D. (1982) Hidráulica subterránea. Ed. Científico Técnica. La Habana.

Pinder, G.F. and Frind, E.O. (1972) Application of Galerkin's procedure to aquifer analysis. Water Resour. Res., 8, n°1, 108-120.

Rama Rao, B.S. (1980) Darcy and Forchheimer flows towards wells with storage in confined and semi-confined aquifers, III Int. Conference on finite elements in Water Resources, 2.111-2.126.

Volker, R.E. (1969) Nonlinear flow in porous media by finite elements. J. Hidraul. Div. Amer. Soc. Civil. Eng. 95, HY6, -- 2093-2114.

Zienkiewicz, O.C. and Lohner, R. (1985) Accelerated "Relaxation" or direct solution? Future prospects for fem., Int. J. Num. Methods Eng., 21: 1-11.

Zienkiewicz, O.C., Mayer, P. and Cheung, Y.K. (1966) Solution of anisotropic seepage problems by finite elements. J. Eng. Mech. Div. Amer. Soc. Civil Eng., 92, EM1, 111-120.

Table 1. n and K_n/K_D values

K_n	K_n/K_D	n	$\lvert\vec{\nabla}u\rvert$
2000.	1.	1-	10^{-4}-10^{-2}
1200.	0.6	0.89	10^{-2}-10^{-1}
580.	0.29	0.69	10^{-1}-10°
520.	0.26	0.56	10°-10^{1}
580.	0.29	0.52	10^{1}-10^{2}

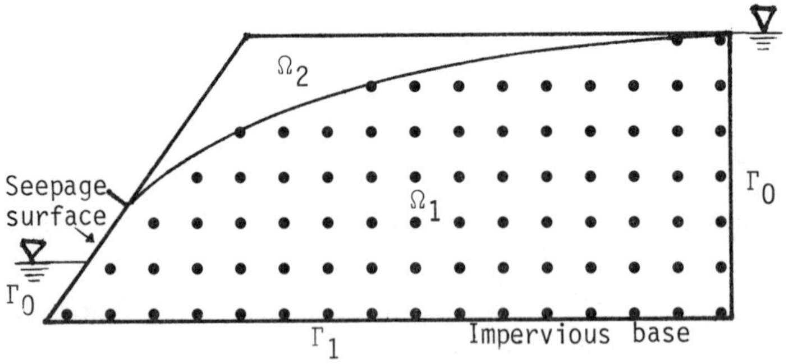

Fig. 1 Schematic of seepage and domain

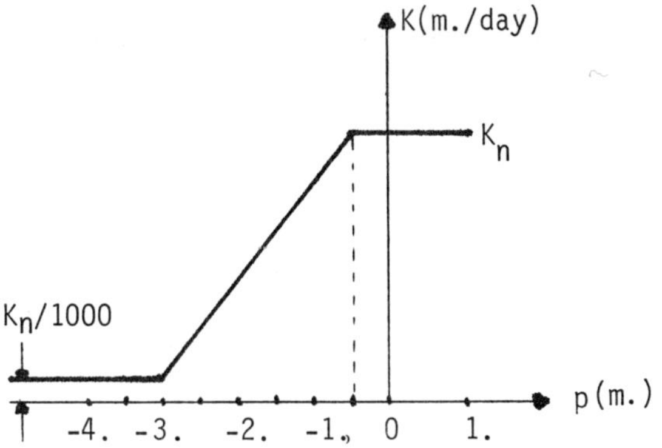

Fig.2 Pressure-permeability curve

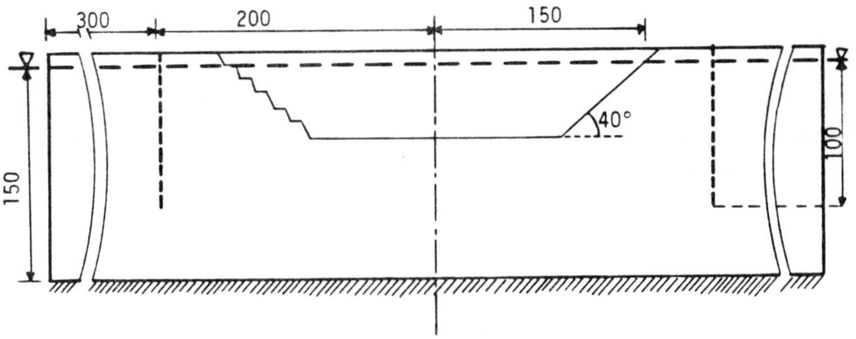

Fig.3 Mine Middle Section

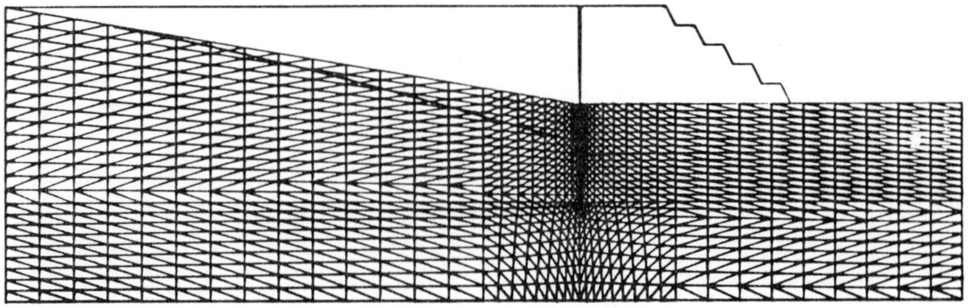

Fig.4 Mesh and free surface solution for the second model.

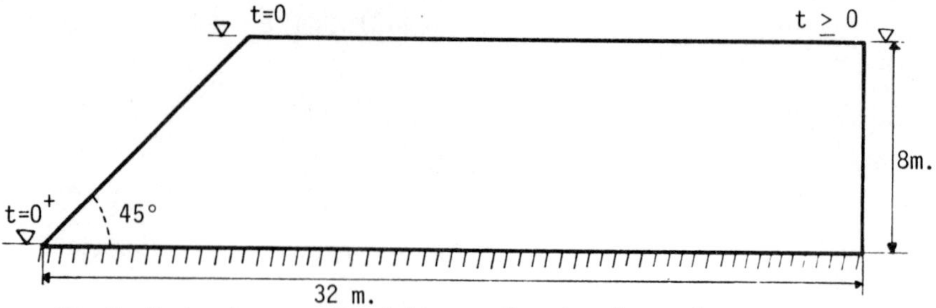

Fig.5 Unsteady unconfined linear flow in slope mine.

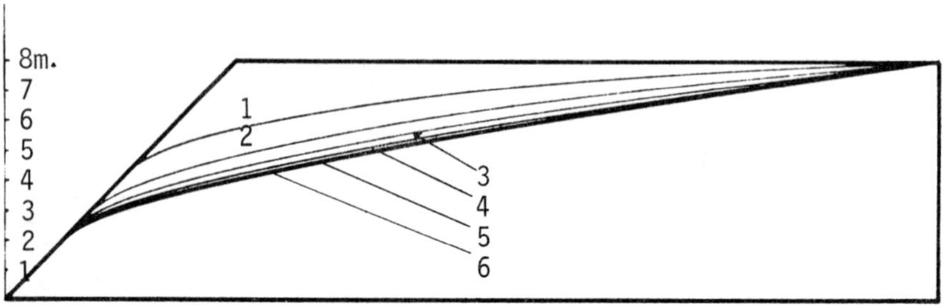

Fig.6 A slope mine solution: drawdown in time

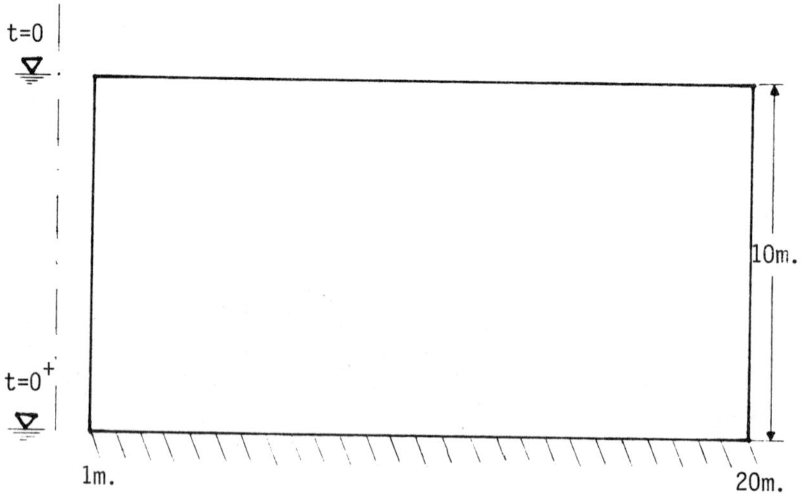

Fig. 7 Axisymmetric nonlinear flow to a well

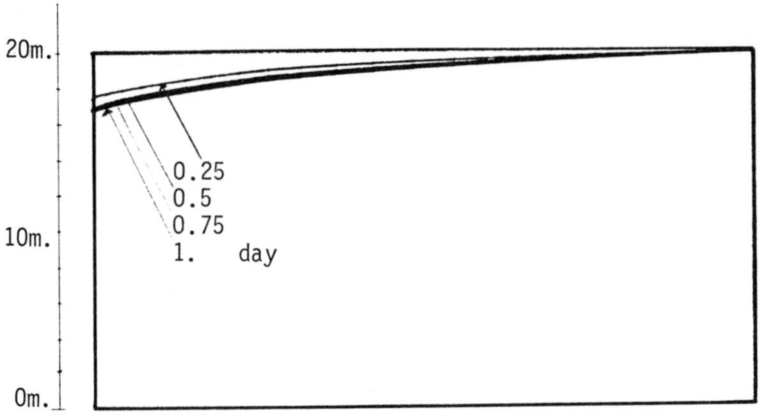

Fig. 8 A well solution: Axisymmetric non linear flow.

VI International Conference on Finite Elements in Water Resources, Lisboa, Portugal, June 1986

Unsteady Flow Between Parallel Drains Solved by Boundary Element Method

R. Cavor, M. Cvjetkovic
Energoprojekt-Energodata, Belgrade, Yugoslavia

INTRODUCTION

Computation of the unsteady flow between parallel drains is a very important part in design and sizing of the drain network. For certain soil conditions it is necessary to find out the proper depth, size and distance between tile drains, in order to drawdown the initial level, to prescribed target level in a given time interval. Fig. 1 shows definition sketch, and illustrates the problem to be solved.

In engineering practice different formulas are used for such a calculation, all of them based on the analytical solution of the Laplace equation usually assuming parallel flow conditions and averaging the soil parameters. Homogeneous permeability condition is the second basic assumption which is in cases of agricultural land drainage far from reality.

This paper presents a solution to the unsteady flow between drains using Boundary Element Method (BEM). BEM offers line discretization, computation procedures and efficiency better than finite differences or finite elements because of their two dimensional discretization and certain numerical difficulties in the free surface computation.

BEM BASIC EQUATION FOR THE UNSTEADY FLOW IN POROUS MEDIA

Free surface, unsteady flow in porous media between parallel drains in two layered region (Fig. 1.) is

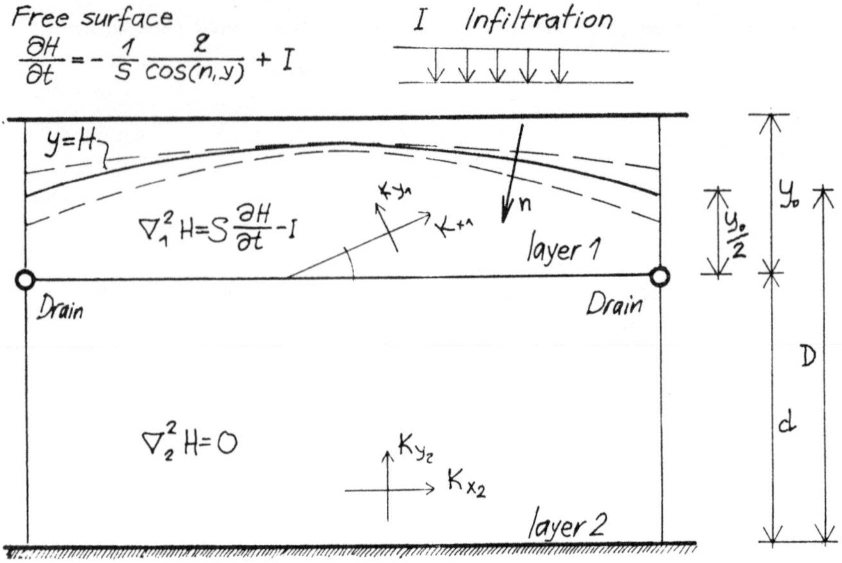

Figure 1. Definition sketch

described by equation:

$$K_x \frac{\partial^2 H}{\partial x^2} + K_y \frac{\partial^2 H}{\partial y^2} = S\left(\frac{\partial H}{\partial t} - I\right) \tag{1}$$

where H is potential and I is infiltration at the free surface. Equation (1) can be divided in two parts which can be solved separately. The linear part:

$$K_x \frac{\partial^2 H}{\partial x^2} + K_y \frac{\partial^2 H}{\partial y^2} = 0 \tag{2}$$

is valid in the whole flow region and will be solved by BEM. Second part:

$$S\left(\frac{\partial H}{\partial t} - I\right) = -\frac{Q_n}{\cos(n,y)} \tag{3}$$

describes additional non-linear, free surface movement condition and should be solved iteratively to be satisfied simultaneously with eq. (2). Qn in eq. (3) represents computed normal flux in the boundary node on the free surface which is treated as prescribed potential node H=y.
By introducing the following substitution in eq. (2):

$$X = \frac{x}{\sqrt{K_x}} \quad ; \quad Y = \frac{y}{\sqrt{K_y}} \tag{4}$$

ordinary Laplace equation is obtained:

$$\frac{\partial^2 H}{\partial X} + \frac{\partial^2 H}{\partial Y} = 0 \tag{5}$$

which can be easily solved by BEM.

Following that manner we can combine different anisotropic, nonhomogeneous subregions (layers) using the same mathematical representation. The basic principles of BEM are shown in [4], [5] and [6], so only the final BEM formulation using linear boundary element discretization will be given here:

$$\sum_{j=1}^{m}\Big[H_j \int_{L_j} W_1 \frac{\partial}{\partial n}(\ln R)\,dl + H_{j+1} \int_{L_j} W_2 \frac{\partial}{\partial n}(\ln R)\,dl -$$

$$- Q_j \int_{L_j} W_1 \ln R\,dl - Q_{j+1} \int_{L_j} W_2 \ln R\,dl \Big] = 0 \tag{6}$$

where W1 and W2 are weight coefficients of function distribution over boundary element;

$$W_1 = \frac{L_2 - l}{L} \quad ; \quad W_2 = \frac{l - L_1}{L} \tag{7}$$

Integrals ie. coefficients of unknowns $h_{i,j}$, $h_{i,j+1}$ $q_{i,j}$, $q_{i,j+1}$ in eq. (6) could be calculated numerically or expressed analytically where the second way gives a more efficient and simpler computer program algorithm.

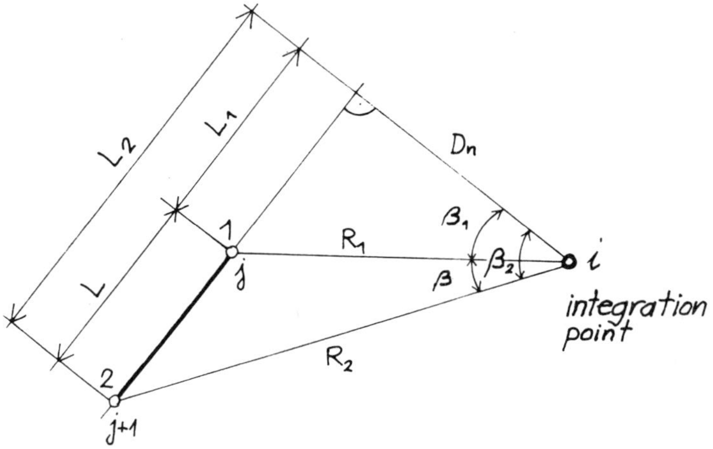

Figure 2. Integration along boundary element

Fig. 2. shows the boundary element and notation of geometrical terms used in the analytical solution for the coefficients from eq. (6) so they have following form:

$$C_h = \frac{D_n}{2}\left(\ln R_2^2 - \ln R_1^2\right) \tag{8}$$

$$C_{q_1} = \frac{1}{4}\left[R_2^2\left(\ln R_2^2 - 1\right) - R_1^2\left(\ln R_1^2 - 1\right)\right] \tag{9}$$

$$C_{q_2} = \frac{1}{2}\left(L_2 \ln R_2^2 - L_1 \ln R_1^2\right) - L + D_n \cdot \beta \tag{10}$$

$$h_{i,j} = \left(C_h - \beta L_2\right)/L \tag{11}$$

$$h_{i,j} = \left(-C_h + \beta L_1\right)/L \tag{12}$$

$$q_{i,j} = \left(C_{q_1} - C_{q_2} \cdot L_2\right)/L \tag{13}$$

$$q_{i,j} = \left(-C_{q_1} + C_{q_2} \cdot L_1\right)/L \tag{14}$$

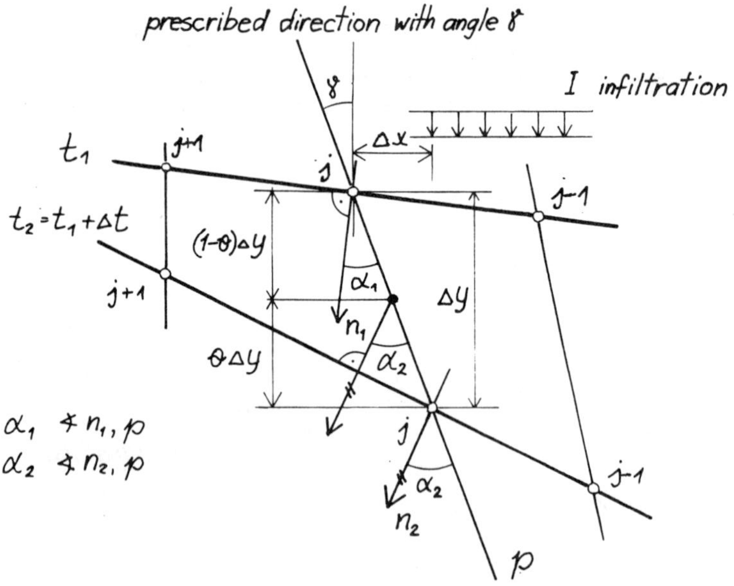

Figure 3. Determination of free surface position

Standard procedure of the system matrix formulation, zoning and system solving, again can be found in [4], [5], [6] and the results are unknown potentials H and potential derivatives (fluxes) in all boundary nodes. The basic components in the solution of the non-linear part of the system, free surface time-dependent position, are shown in Fig. 3. and will be analysed in more details. Generally, the free surface node can be moved not only in a vertical direction, but in some previously defined direction p which forms angle γ with y-direction. In that case α is the angle between direction p and the normal on the free surface, so eq. (3) has the changed shape:

$$\frac{\partial H}{\partial t} = I - \frac{\cos\gamma}{S} \cdot \frac{Q_n}{\cos\alpha} \tag{15}$$

Former equation is solved by means of the weighed, finite differences scheme in which θ is the weight factor, then (15) can be developed in the form suitable for numerical calculation:

$$\Delta H_K = P_I - P^{t_1} - P_K^{t_2} \tag{16}$$

$$P_I = \Delta t\left[(1-\theta)\, I^{t_1} + \theta\, I^{t_2}\right] \tag{17}$$

$$P^{t_1} = \frac{\Delta t \cos\gamma}{S}(1-\theta)\left(\frac{Q_j}{\cos\alpha}\right)^{t_1} \tag{18}$$

$$P_K^{t_2} = \frac{\Delta t \cos\gamma}{S}\,\theta\left(\frac{Q_j}{\cos\alpha}\right)_{K-1}^{t_2} \tag{19}$$

Expressions (16), (17), (18) and (19) are valid for free surface nodes and Qj is the normal flux computed by BEM from the linear part of the eq.(1). Index k denotes the current iteration number, so it should be emphasized that values of (17) and (18) are relative constants for the one time interval, and only third term Pk affects the solution during the iteration process. Condition y=H is valid on the free surface and new positions of the nodes can be evaluated in the following manner:

$$y_K = y_{K-1} + \Psi \Delta H_K \; ; \quad x_K = x_{K-1} + \tan\gamma \cdot \Psi \cdot \Delta H_K \tag{20}$$

To speed up the numerical convergency additional parameter Ψ was introduced with value from 0.55 to 0.70 having in mind the very sensitive behaviour of solution in the vicinity of the drain.

After the correction of all the nodes positions have been done and if the maximal correction at one node is less than the required numerical accuracy then the solution for the next time interval is reached. Otherwise iteration for solving linear part, eq. (6)-(14), and nonlinear part, eq. (15)-(20), should be repeated.

COMPARISON WITH EXPERIMENTS

Maasland and Shery [1], using a Hele-Shaw Model, obtained experimental results for unsteady water-table profiles, produced by parallel drains. Papers [1] and [2] also present comparison of Maasland and Shery experiments with analytical solutions. They found big discrepances between experiments and computational results which lead to significant undersizing of drainage parameters.

For the computation with BEM we chose two experimental cases [1] which show poor agreement with Glower's equation. First case with D/Ld=0.126, and second with D/Ld=0.600 are simulated using BEM. Computational scheme for the BEM given in Fig. 4, consists of 25 external, 8 internal nodes and 2 subregions representing horizontal layers between drains.

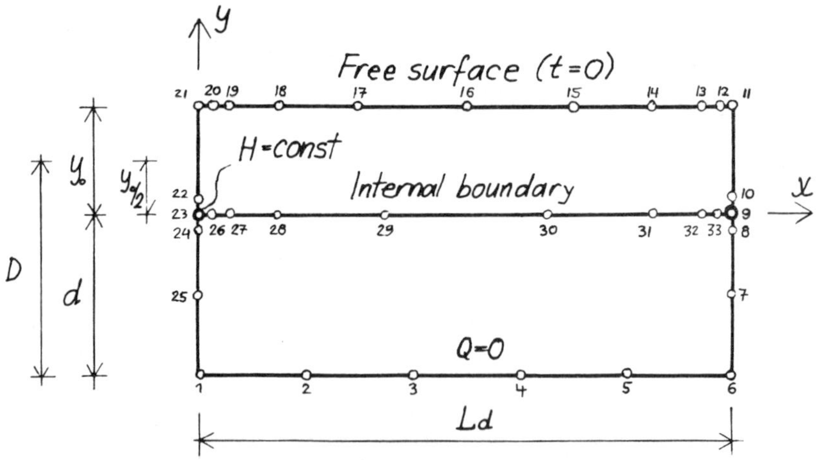

Figure 4. Computational scheme

Experiments deal with homogeneous conditions, where in computation we used two homogeneous layers, because later on nonhomogeneous cases will be investigated with the same computational scheme. Fig. 5 shows computational results with BEM on diagrams of the drawdown at the midpoint, compared with experiments and Glower's solution.

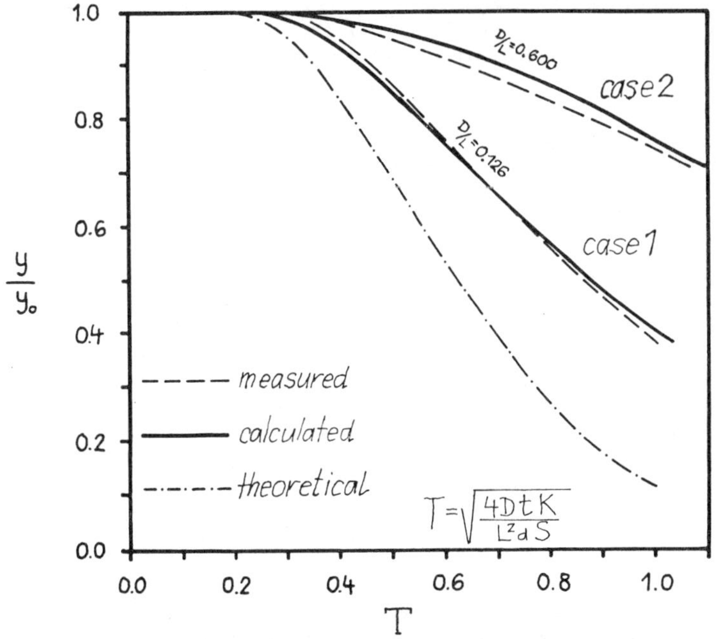

Figure 5. Free surface drawdown at midpoint between drains

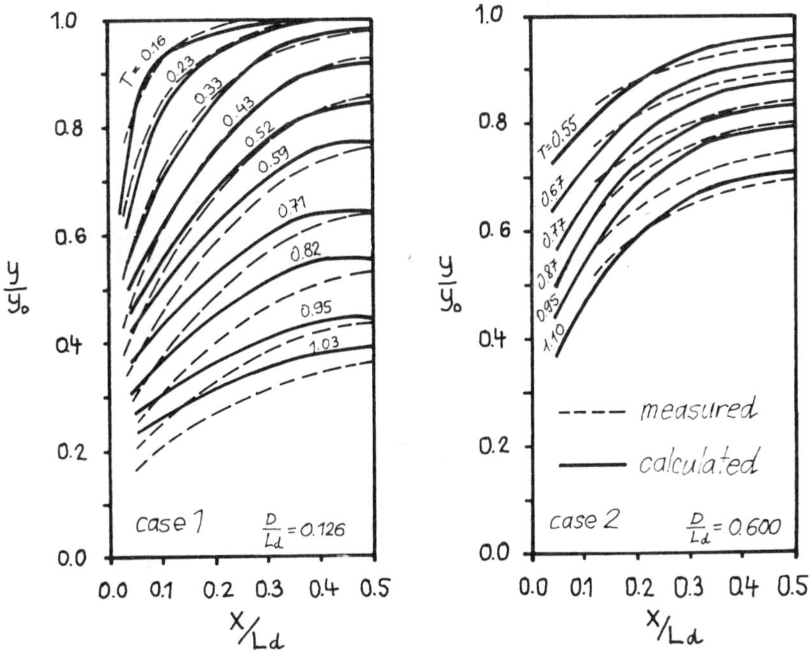

Figure 6. Free surface positions between drains

Free surface time-dependent positions from above computation are given in Fig. 6. Obviously, there is a good agreement between computations and experiments, with few percents maximal difference.

Comparison with experiments from [1] shows the advantage of BEM and full independance from geometrical relations which is of great importance for analytical solutions because of averaging basic flow parameters.

BEM implementation enables simple examination of series of cases, much closer to reality in which drains are embedded in nonhomogeneous layer environment. Results displayed in Fig. 7 show the cases in which the lower layer is the same as the upper one and when the lower layer is 10 and 100 times less permeable than the upper with the ratio D/Ld=0.126 is valid for cases shown. Nonhomogeneity apparently changes the flow field significantly by decreasing drain efficiency, which must not be neglected in drainage sizing.

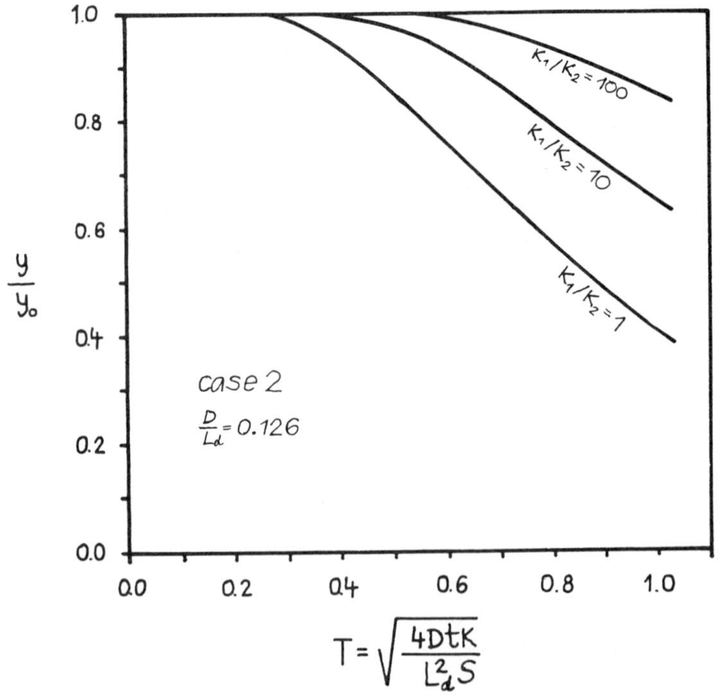

Figure 7. Drawdown at midpoint in nonhomogeneous conditions

CONCLUSION

Efficiency of the BEM for the unsteady flow between parallel drains computation is approved by comparison with experimental results.

Usage of the BEM models is simpler than complicated analytical solutions.

BEM can simulate nonhomogeneous soil conditions, requires simple line discretization end data can be generated automatically for basic geometrical relations

Computer program can be developed and used on the personal computer. For results here presented program is developed on FORTRAN with size of 60 Kb and run on the IBM PC AT.

NOTATION

Kx, Ky - coefficients of permeability,
H - potential - piezometric head,
S - specific yield,
I - infiltration on the free surface,
t - time,
T - dimensionless time
Ld - distance between drains,
d - layer thickness below drains,
yo - initial head above drains at t=0,
Qn, Qj - normal flux on the free surface,
W1, W2 - weight factor of the function distribution over boundary element,
Ch, Cq - arbitrary constants for integral evaluation,
h - unknown potential coefficient,
q - unknown potential derivate coefficient,
Dn - normal distance from integration point to element,
R - distance from integration point to element,
L - oriented element length,
L1 - distance to node 1 (j),
L2 - distance to node 2(j+1),
α - angle between direction p and element normal,
β - central angle from integration point to element,
γ - angle between prescribed direction p and y direction,
θ - weight coefficient in finite difference scheme,
Ψ - convergence coefficient,
k - current iteration number.

REFERENCES

[1] Maasland, D.E.L. and Shery, R.A. (1967) Falling Water Table between Tile Drains, J.Irrigation Drainage Div.,ASCE,93, No.IR2,9-19

[2] Yeh, W.W.G. and Singh, R. (1970) Transient Flow between Parallel Drains, J.Hydrology,11, North-Holland Pub. Co., Amsterdam. ,301-312

[3] Cavor, R., Cvjetkovic, M. and Pavlovic, R. (1984) Development and Application of the Boundary Element Method, Energoprojekt-Energodata Co.,Belgrade

[4] Ligett, J.A. and Liu, P.L-F. (1983) The Boundary Integral Equation Method for Porous Media Flow, George Allen & Unwin, London

[5] Huyakorn, P. and Pinder, G. (1984) Computational Methods in Subsurface Flow, Academic Press, N. Y.

[6] Brebbia, C.A. and Walker, S. (1980) Boundary Element Techniques in Engineering, Newnes-Butterworths, London

SECTION 3 SPECIAL PROBLEMS IN GROUNDWATER

VI International Conference on Finite Elements in Water Resources, Lisboa, Portugal, June 1986

Seawater Intrusion in Coastal Aquifers: Theory, Finite Element Solution, and Verification Tests

P.S. Huyakorn, J.W. Mercer and P.F. Andersen
GeoTrans Inc., Herndon, Virginia, U.S.A.

INTRODUCTION

A Galerkin finite element model for simulating seawater intrusion in single and multiple coastal aquifers is presented. Density-dependent flow and transport are described using two governing equations with hydraulic head and concentration as dependent variables. Flexibility in the numerical approximation allows for either fully three-dimensional simulations or quasi three-dimensional simulations where the aquitards are treated using one-dimensional analytical and/or numerical approximations. Axisymmetric cylindrical coordinates are also allowed in order to examine upconing. Simple rectangular and triangular prism elements are used. The combination of such elements enables flow regions of complex geometry to be modeled accurately. In addition, element matrices can be computed efficiently without numerical integration. Matrix assembly is performed slice by slice, and the matrix solution is achieved using a Slice Successive Relaxation (SSR) scheme. This scheme permits a fairly large number of unknowns to be handled cost effectively. For coupled flow and transport problems, the nonlinearity is handled by Picard iterations. Two test problems are presented to verify the code and check the accuracy of the numerical solution and solution algorithms.

GOVERNING EQUATIONS

The problem of seawater intrusion in coastal aquifers can be formulated in terms of two partial differential equations. The first equation is used to describe flow of variable-density fluid (mixed freshwater and seawater), and the second equation is used to describe the transport of dissolved salt. The three-dimensional flow equation may be written as:

$$\frac{\partial}{\partial x_i}\left[K_{ij}\left(\frac{\partial h}{\partial x_j} + \eta c e_j\right)\right] = S_s \frac{\partial h}{\partial t} + \phi\eta \frac{\partial c}{\partial t} - \frac{\rho}{\rho_0} q \qquad (1)$$

$$i,j = 1,\ 2,\ 3$$

where K_{ij} is the hydraulic conductivity tensor, h is the reference hydraulic head referred to as the freshwater head, x_j (j=1,2,3) are Cartesian coordinates, η is the density coupling coefficient, c is the solute concentration, e_j is the j-th component of the gravitational unit vector, S_s is the specific storage, t is time, ϕ is the porosity, q is the volumetric flow rate of sources (or sinks) per unit volume of the porous medium, and ρ and ρ_0 are the density of the fluid (fresh and seawater), and the reference (freshwater) density, respectively, where density is assumed to be a linear function of concentration.

To describe salt transport, the following form of the convective-dispersion equation is used:

$$\frac{\partial}{\partial x_i}\left(D_{ij}\frac{\partial c}{\partial x_j}\right) - V_i \frac{\partial c}{\partial x_i} = \phi \frac{\partial c}{\partial t} + q\,(c-c^*) \qquad (2)$$

where $D_{ij} = \phi D^*_{ij}$, with D^*_{ij} being the dispersion tensor, V_i is the Darcy velocity vector, and c* is the solute concentration in the injected (or withdrawn) fluid.

To obtain a unique solution to (1) and (2), initial and boundary conditions must be specified. For the flow equation, the initial and boundary conditions may be expressed as

$$h(x_i,0) = h_0(x_i) \qquad (3a)$$

$$h(x_i,t) = \tilde{h} \text{ on } B_1 \qquad (3b)$$

$$V_i n_i = -V_n \text{ on } B_2 \qquad (3c)$$

where h_0 is the initial head, $\tilde{h}$ is the prescribed head on boundary portion B_1, n_i is the outward unit normal vector on the boundary portion B_2, where the fluid flux is prescribed as $-V_n$. The sign convention for V_n is positive for inflow and negative for outflow.

For the transport equation, the initial and boundary conditions take the form

$$c(x_i,0) = c_o \quad (4a)$$

$$c(x_i,t) = \tilde{c} \text{ on } B_1' \quad (4b)$$

$$D_{ij} \frac{\partial c}{\partial x_j} n_i = q_c^D \text{ on } B_2' \quad (4c)$$

$$D_{IJ} \frac{\partial c}{\partial x_j} n_i - V_i n_i c = q_c^T \text{ on } B_3' \quad (4d)$$

where B_1' is the portion of the boundary where concentration is prescribed as $\tilde{c}$, B_2' is the portion of the boundary where dispersive mass flux of solute is prescribed as q_c^D, and B_3' is the portion of the boundary where the total solute mass flux is prescribed as q_c^T. Note that the sign convention for q_c^D and q_c^T are positive for inward mass flux and negative for outward mass flux.

GALERKIN APPROXIMATION

Equations (1) and (2) are approximated using the Galerkin finite element technique. Because the procedure of the Galerkin formulation is now standard and can be found in several references (e.g., Taylor and Huyakorn, 1977), there is no need to include it in this presentation. Thus, only the final systems of differential equations that need to be solved are given. The system of equations for fluid flow takes the form:

$$A_{IJ} h_J + B_{IJ} \frac{dh_J}{dt} = F_I \text{ , } I = 1, 2, \ldots, n \quad (5)$$

where I and J are nodal indices, h_J are nodal head values, n is the number of nodes in the finite element network, and A_{IJ}, B_{IJ}, and F_I are matrices given by

$$A_{ij} = \sum_e A^e_{IJ} = \sum_e \int_{R^e} K_{ij} \frac{\partial N_I}{\partial x_i} \frac{\partial N_J}{\partial x_j} \, dR$$

$$B_{IJ} = \sum_e B^e_{IJ} = \sum_e \int_{R^e} S_s \, N_I N_J \, dR$$

$$F_I = \sum_e F^e_I = \sum_e \left[\int_{B^e} N_I \frac{\rho_o}{\rho} V_n \, dB + \int_{R^e} N_I \frac{\rho}{\rho_o} q \, dR \right.$$

$$\left. - \int_{R^e} (n \, K_{ij} \, N_J c_J \frac{\partial N_I}{\partial x_i} e_j + \phi n N_I N_J \frac{dc_J}{dt}) \, dR \right] \qquad (6)$$

where R^e is the element subdomain with boundary B^e, N_I and c_J are basis functions and nodal values of concentration, respectively, and the summation is performed over the total number of elements.

The system of equations for solute transport may be expressed

$$E_{ij} \, c_J + \tilde{B}_{IJ} \frac{dc_J}{dt} = \tilde{F}_I \quad , \quad I = 1, 2, \ldots, n \qquad (7)$$

where

$$E_{IJ} = \sum_e E^e_{IJ} = \sum_e \int_{R^e} (D_{IJ} \frac{\partial N_I}{\partial x_i} \frac{\partial N_J}{\partial x_j} + V_i \, N_I \frac{\partial N_J}{\partial x_i}) \, dR \qquad (8a)$$

$$\tilde{B}_{IJ} = \sum_e \tilde{B}^e_{IJ} = \sum_e \int_{R^e} \phi N_I N_J \, dR \qquad (8b)$$

$$\tilde{F}_I = \sum_e \tilde{F}_I^e = \sum_e \left[\int_{R^e} N_I \, q \, (c^* - N_J c_J) \, dR + \int_{B^e} N_I \left(D_{ij} \frac{\partial \hat{c}}{\partial x_j} \right) n_i \, dB \right] \qquad (8c)$$

where the dispersive flux on the boundary can be evaluated using equation (4c) or (4d) depending on the type of boundary condition.

SOLUTION STRATEGY

The two matrix systems represented by equations (5) and (7) are linked by the terms containing the density-coupling coefficient η, and by Darcy velocities. The density-coupling terms make the seawater intrusion problem nonlinear. The degree of nonlinearity is dependent on buoyancy effects leading to the upward movement of the mixed seawater and freshwater near the coast. For cases in which the buoyancy effects dominate, convergence difficulties are often encountered in performing steady-state numerical solutions. To develop a three-dimensional finite element model that can handle the problem cost effectively, the following strategy is adopted:

1. Perform spatial discretization using a vertical slicing approach that partitions the matrix system of the three-dimensional network into matrix subsystems of two-dimensional networks interconnected in the third dimension. Such a discretization approach circumvents the computational problems associated with a large matrix bandwidth of the three-dimensional network. In addition, this approach also allows the three-dimensional finite element mesh to be generated automatically using a simple mesh generation scheme.

2. Use simple rectangular and triangular prism elements (or if need be irregular hexahedral elements made up of tetrahedra), and avoid costly numerical integration in computing element matrices and the right-hand-side vector. Numerical integration can be avoided by evaluating the element matrices using an influence coefficient technique.

3. Treat the nonlinearity using an implicit Picard iterative scheme with a sequential solution procedure that incorporates salient features designed to enhance convergence of the nonlinear iterative solution. These features include:

(i) the use of time-extrapolation formulas for obtaining an initial estimate of nodal values of head and concentration at a time step, (ii) the use of an automatic under-relaxation scheme for predicting head and concentration values for the next iteration, and (iii) automatic adjustment of time step values when the prescribed number of nonlinear iterations is exceeded.

4. When dealing with a multi-layer system, provide options to handle flow and transport in aquitards using one-dimensional (vertical leakage) submodels. These submodels are based on analytical and numerical approaches designed to take advantage of the contrasting hydraulic properties of aquifers and aquitards. Note that treating aquitards in the same manner as aquifers is avoided, thus it is not necessary to represent the entire multi-layer system using a fully three-dimensional finite element mesh. Such an approach would be very costly.

5. Perform matrix solution using a Slice Successive Relaxation technique that achieves computational savings by partitioning the overall matrix system into subsystems corresponding to individual slices in the finite element mesh. For each slice, the matrix subsystems for flow and transport are handled using symmetric and nonsymmetric direct solvers, respectively.

VERIFICATION TESTS AND RESULTS

To verify the numerical solution techniques and their coding, and to demonstrate the capabilities of the code to simulate coupled groundwater flow and transport, two typical problems are described. Other problems designed to test additional features of the model are given in Huyakorn et al. (1986).

Transient and Steady Seawater Intrusion in a Confined Aquifer

This problem concerns groundwater flow and salt transport in a coastal confined aquifer. It is known as Henry's seawater intrusion problem (Henry, 1964), and is described schematically in Figure 1. The main objective is to check the density-coupling part of the finite element formulation and to test the reliability of both the nonlinear Picard iteration and the SSR matrix solution schemes.

As depicted in Figure 1, freshwater enters the aquifer on the left face, and the coastal side corresponds to the right face. The z-dimension of the aquifer is assumed to be 100 m wide. Boundary conditions employed in the numerical simulation are also shown. Parameters were chosen so that the case analyzed corresponds to that solved numerically by other researchers (Pinder and Cooper, 1970; Lee and Cheng, 1974; Segol et al., 1975; and Frind, 1982).

A steady-state solution of the density-dependent flow and transport equations was performed in one step using an arbitrary value of time step. The aquifer region was represented by a three-dimensional rectangular grid consisting of 150 elements and 352 nodes. The grid contained two vertical slices each having 176 nodes. To initiate the nonlinear analysis, a zero value of reference hydraulic head and concentration was used as an initial estimate. The maximum allowable iteration errors for head and concentration were prescribed as 0.01 m and 0.01, respectively. The code took 9 Picard iterations to converge. Note that in the SSR matrix solution, the head and concentration tolerances were set to one tenth of the prescribed maximum head and concentration errors to insure reliable accuracy from the SSR subiterations. An over-relaxation factor of 1.8 and an under-relaxation factor of 0.8 were used in performing the SSOR and SSUR solution of the flow and transport matrix equations. On the average, it took 22 SSOR subiterations and 6 SSUR subiterations per Picard iteration. Shown in Figure 2 are the hydraulic head profile along the top of the aquifer and the position of the 0.5 isochlor at steady state. The present finite element result agrees very well with the finite element result of Frind (1982) for the corresponding case. The agreement with the results of Henry (1964) and Lee and Cheng (1974) is also reasonable, although not as good. Possible explanations for the discrepancies between the two finite element solutions and the numerical solutions of Henry, and Lee and Cheng are: (1) different transport boundary conditions that were imposed on the seaward side, and (2) different numerical techniques that are subject to a varying degree of discretization errors. For reference purposes, the sharp interface solution is also depicted in Figure 2.

To test the model further, a transient simulation based on an assumption of zero initial concentration was performed. A detailed description of this simulation is presented in Huyakorn et al. (1986). Shown in Figure 3 is a plot of the position of the 0.5 isochlor at the end of 100 days of simulation. Also shown in Figure 3 are the results for the 0.5 isochlor computed by Frind (1982) and Segol et al. (1975). As may be seen, all three solutions are in excellent agreement. It should be noted that the time scale has been changed from that used by Frind (1982).

Seawater Intrusion in the Biscayne Aquifer, South Florida

This example is based on the Biscayne aquifer in the Cutler area near Miami, Florida. Field data and interpretation have been published Kohout and Klein (1967). This problem has also been simulated by Lee and Cheng (1974) and Segol and Pinder (1976).

The Biscayne aquifer in this area is a water-table aquifer consisting of solution-riddled limestone and calcareous sandstone extending to a depth of 100 ft below mean sea level. Field data indicated that the saltwater front in the Biscayne aquifer is dynamically stable at a position as much as 8 mi seaward of that computed by the Ghyben-Herzberg principle. It is hypothesized that this discrepancy is in part due to a cyclic flow of saltwater induced by the dispersion of salts. In 1958, samples were collected and pressure heads were measured at a test site located in the Cutler area before and after a heavy rainfall which sharply increased the elevation of the water table. Measurements showed that the distribution of chloride before the pulse of recharge could be considered to be indicative of steady-state conditions. This assumption is clearly justified by the fact that the concentration distribution before the rain (Kohout and Klein, 1967, Figure 3) is virtually identical to the distribution observed several months after the end of recharge.

The boundary conditions are shown schematically in Figure 4. As may be seen, the normal velocity and normal concentration gradient are set equal to zero at the bottom and top of the aquifer. The inland boundary is fixed at a relative concentration of 0.0 (freshwater) with a constant hydraulic head of 1.37 ft. This value was used by Segol and Pinder (1976) as the boundary head before the rainfall. The ocean boundary is fixed at a relative concentration of 1.0 (seawater) with a constant reference head that is a function of depth as shown in Figure 4.

The domain of interest to be simulated extends from 600 ft seawater to 1600 ft inland from the shoreline. The finite element grid used for the Biscayne aquifer consists of 666 nodes (2 slices) and 288 elements, which represent a vertical cross-section through the aquifer.

The purpose of this analysis is to reproduce the observed steady-state flow and transport conditions. The aquifer is assumed to be homogeneous. Aquifer properties are similar to those used by Segol and Pinder (1976). Although Kohout and Klein (1967) reported a hydraulic conductivity of about 3800 ft/d, Segol and Pinder (1976) concluded that a value of approximately 1280 ft/d was required to simulate the observed chloride concentration distribution. Note that because the problem is steady-state, the specific storage is zero. The porosity of the Cutler area is approximately 0.25.

To initiate the nonlinear analysis, a zero value of hydraulic head and concentration was used as an initial estimate. The maximum allowable iteration errors for head and concentration were prescribed as 0.01 m and 0.01, respectively. It took 8 Picard iterations to converge. Once again, an over-relaxation factor of 1.8 and an under-relaxation factor of 0.8 were used in performing the SSOR and the SSUR solution of the flow and transport matrix equations. On the average, it took 15 SSOR subiterations and 6 SSUR subiterations per Picard iteration.

The computed steady-state hydraulic head at the top of the aquifer and the computed steady-state position of the 0.5 isochlor are compared to the observed field data in Figure 5. As may be seen, there is satisfactory agreement between observed and computed values. The computed curve is almost identical to that computed by Segol and Pinder (1976).

DISCUSSION AND CONCLUSIONS

Examples presented provide preliminary verifications of the finite element model developed to simulate seawater intrusion in single and multiple aquifers. The model has been designed with special considerations given to alleviating the problems of computational restrictions in performing calculations in three dimensions. Flexibility of the formulation allows for either three-dimensional or quasi three-dimensional simulations in Cartesian or axisymmetric coordinates. The code is currently being applied to several field problems involving multiple aquifers that cover large areal extents. Results from all verification/validation tests and applications indicate that the model is efficient, accurate, and flexible enough to treat lateral intrusion and upconing in layered aquifer systems with the top aquifer being confined or phreatic.

REFERENCES

Frind, E.O., Simulation of long-term transient density-dependent transport in groundwater, Advances in Water Resour., 5, 73-88, 1982.

Henry, H.R., Effects of dispersion on salt encroachment in coastal aquifers, Sea Water in Coastal Aquifers (H.H. Cooper et al.,), U.S. Geological Survey Water Supply Paper 1613-C, 1964.

Huyakorn, P.S., J.W. Mercer, P.F. Andersen, and H.O. White, Jr., Sea water intrusion in coastal aquifers: development and testing of a three-dimensional finite element model, submitted to Water Resour. Res., 1986.

Kohout, F.A., and H. Klein, Effect of pulse recharge on the zone of diffusion in the Biscayne aquifer, Int. Ass. Sci. Hydrol. Publ., 70, 252-270, 1967.

Lee, C.H., and R.T. Cheng, On seawater encroachment in coastal aquifers, Water Resour. Res., 10, 5, 1039-1043, 1974.

Pinder, G.F., and H.H. Cooper, Jr., A numerical technique for calculating the transient position of the salt water front, Water Resour. Res., 6, 3, 875-880, 1970.

Segol, G., and G.F. Pinder, Transient simulation of salt water intrusion in southeastern Florida, Water Resour. Res., 12, 1, 65-70, 1976.

Segol, G., G.F. Pinder, and W.G. Gray, A Galerkin finite element technique for calculating the transient position of the salt water front, Water Resour. Res., 11, 2, 343-347, 1975.

Taylor, C., and P.S. Huyakorn, Finite element analysis of three-dimensional groundwater flow with convective dispersion, Proc. of 2nd Int. Symp. on Finite Element Methods in Flow Problems, Italy, 567-579, June 14-18, 1976.

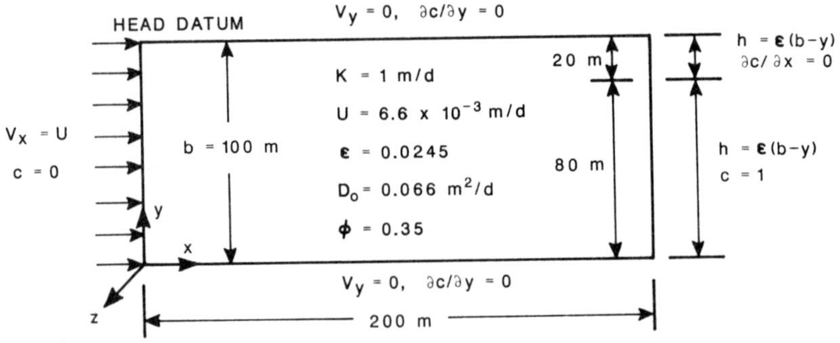

Figure 1. Geometry and boundary conditions of Henry's problem.

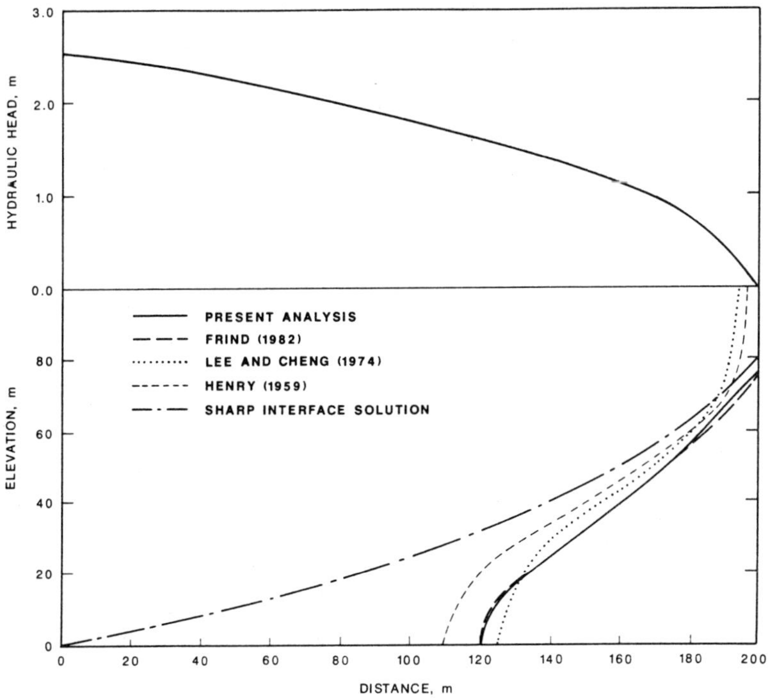

Figure 2. Hydraulic head profile along the top of the aquifer and position of 0.5 isochlor at steady state.

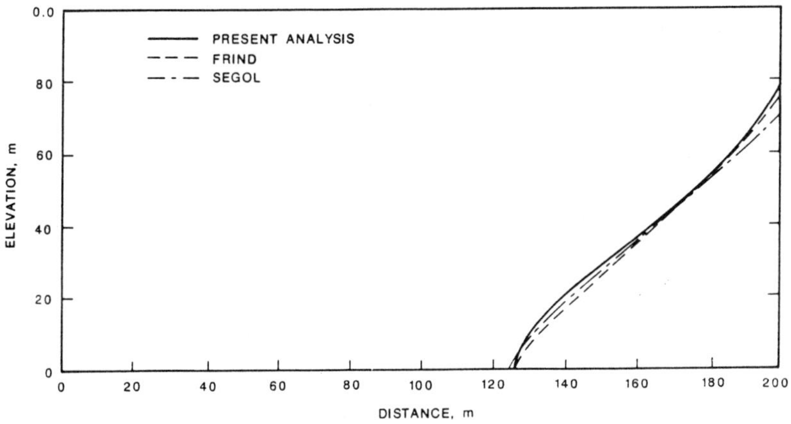

Figure 3. Position of 0.5 isochlor at t = 100 days.

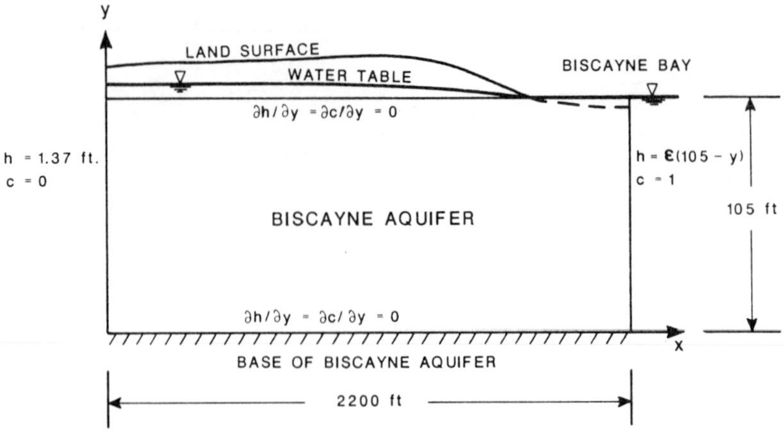

Figure 4. Geometry and boundary conditions for the problem of seawater intrusion in Biscayne aquifer.

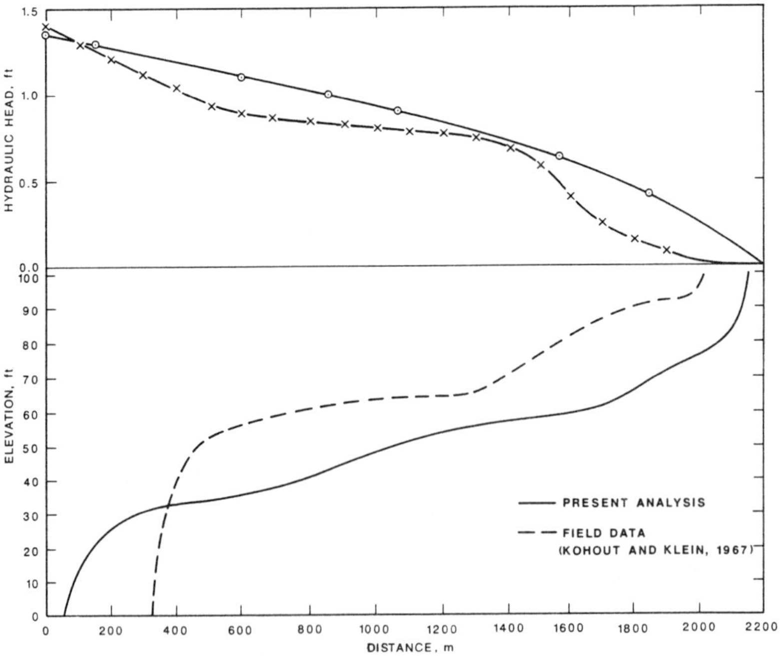

Figure 5. Hydraulic head distribution along the top of the aquifer and position of 0.5 isochlor.

VI International Conference on Finite Elements in Water Resources, Lisboa, Portugal, June 1986

Problems Encountered in Modelling Contaminant Transport using Site Specific Data

J.F. Botha
Institute for Groundwater Studies, University of The Orange Free State, Bloemfontein, 9300, South Africa

1. INTRODUCTION

Contaminant transport in the saturated zone has received considerable attention during the last decade (Princeton, 1984; Frind, 1984; Sudicky, 1983). Most hazardous contaminants are by products of the present technological age and not present in nature. To reach the saturated zone, these contaminants must somehow be transported from the soil surface and deposited in the groundwater. There are a number of mechanisms that can contribute to this process. However, available information indicates that natural and induced infiltration from the soil surface, are probably the most important mechanisms. The prevention of groundwater pollution thus requires that more attention should be directed towards the unsaturated zone.

The development of suitable numerical models have contributed significantly towards the understanding of the flow and transport of contaminants in the saturated zone. It is, therefore, reasonable to expect that the recently published models for contaminant transport (Yeh and Ward,1980, 1981; Voss, 1984) will have the same effect on our understanding of the unsaturated zone. However, there exists a number of significant differences between flow in the saturated and unsaturated zones, which could affect results obtained with these models adversely, if not taken care of consistently. The present paper, is an attempt to draw attention to these differences and the difficulties they cause in modeling the flow of water and contaminant transport in the unsaturated zone. A few precautions that must be taken to ensure a consistent interpretation of the results is also discussed.

The paper starts with a brief summary of the theory underlying flow in the unsaturated zone and a discussion of the major difficulties encountered in

Section 2. The two factors, which in our experience, affect an objective interpretation of the results obtained from a contaminant transport model the most:

(a) the interpretation of the flow parameters,
(b) the existence of an acceptable solution,

and suggestions as how to handle them are discussed in greater detail in Sections 3 and 4 respectively .

2 PROBLEMS ASSOCIATED WITH MODELLING FLOW IN THE UNSATURATED ZONE

Flow in the unsaturated domain is governed by what is known in soil physics literature as the Richards equation (Bear, 1979)

$$C(\psi)D_t\psi(\mathbf{x},t) = \nabla\bullet[K(\psi)\nabla\psi(\mathbf{x},t)] - D_zK(\psi) \qquad (1)$$

where

$\mathbf{x}$ = the usual cartesian coordinates
t = the time
ψ = $-p_c/(\rho_w g)$ is known as the matric head
ρ_w = the density of water
g = the acceleration of gravity
p_c = the capillary pressure
K = the unsaturated hydraulic conductivity
∇ = the gradient operator
C = $-D_\theta\psi$ is known as the moisture capacity
θ = the volumetric moisture content, and
D_u = the partial differential operator with respect to the variable u.

Richards' equation contains two parameters, the moisture capacity C and hydraulic conductivity K, whose dependence on ψ must be known a priori before one can apply it in in modelling unsaturated flow. The determination of C would, at first sight, seem to be trivial. All that need be done, is to determine the dependence of ψ on the moisture content θ - generally referred to as the moisture retention curve. This is a relatively easy experimental exercise that have been conducted for years by soil scientists. However, this is not so simple from the modelling point of view. It turns out that ψ is a non-linear relation (i.e. multi-valued function) of the moisture content, or in physical terms, ψ displays the phenomenon of hysteresis. (See Figure 1). This implies that the modelling of unsaturated flow has to be restricted to either the drying or wetting cycles, unless hysteresis can be accounted for in some way. The latter objective can at present only be achieved empirically or semi-empirically (Scott et al, 1983). Great care should, therefore, be exercised when comparing results of different models to ensure that they use the same water retention curve representation.

The dependence of the unsaturated hydraulic conductivity, $K(\psi)$, on the matric head, suggests that it should also display hysteresis. However, this can be accounted for in a manner similar to that used for the moisture retention curve. A more serious difficulty is the determination of reliable estimates of K. This can be ascribed partly to its extensive variability in the field and partly because it is time-consuming and expensive to measure it accurately in the field. Several investigators have, for these reasons, turned to methods which allow the calculation of K from more easily measured quantities such as the moisture retention curve. This practice is certainly recommendable, until one realize that most methods devised for this purpose have one common denominator - they are based on empirical equations chosen mainly for their ease of evaluation. This implies that one can change the results of a model simply by changing from one representation of K to another. Such a procedure is clearly contrary to the basic philosophy behind any deterministic, and indeed stochastic model, based on Equation (1). The question thus arises whether modellers should not stick to one versatile method for calculating the value of K, at least until such time as better and more objective methods have been developed. The problem is however, which one of the available equations should one use. This will be discussed in more detail in the next section.

Equation (1) is a member of the set of equations generally known as Fokker-Planck equations. These equations are particularly renowned for their non-linear behaviour. The fact that K can, depending on the soil type and moisture content, vary from 10^{-17} - 10^{-4} (m/s), ensures that Equation (1) is probably the most highly non-linear equation encountered in the natural sciences.

A non-linear equation has, as is well known, no unique solution. Small variations in the parameters can cause considerable variation in the solution. As shown by a recent series of numerical experiments, the solution of Equation (1) behaves similarly. The variations in the numerical solution of Equation(1) are, contrary to all expectations, fortunately limited, provided that one use a suitable mesh in the finite element method. The successful application of Equation (1) in modelling unsaturated flow with the finite element method, thus depends on the possibility to devise a suitable mesh. This can be achieved through a knowledge of the convergence properties of the numerical solution. The convergence properties of Fokker-Planck equations have, to the knowledge of the author, not receive any attention in the literature on theoretical numerical analysis. The only useful method for judging the convergence properties of a numerical solution is thus the trial and error adjustment of the mesh used in discretizing Equation (1). This can be a very time consuming exercise, unless one has an automatic mesh generator available. A simple generator developed specifically for the study of mass transport in the unsaturated zone is described in Section 4.

There are other difficulties associated with the use of Equation (1) for the modelling of flow in the unsaturated zone. In arid and semi-arid regions the unsaturated zone may comprise geological formations that do not conform to the usual notions of flow in an unsaturated porous medium. For example (see Figure 2) it is not clear how one can determine a water retention curve for solid, or even highly fractured granite. To incorporate this situation in a model, may require a completely new physical basis for the model and will not be considered here.

3 INTERPRETATION OF THE FLOW PARAMETERS

The moisture retention curve (see Figure 1) is a relation between the water content, θ, and the matric head, ψ, determined experimentally at a small number of points. To use this relation in the calculation of C in Equation (1), requires that it be expressed in some way in terms of an analytical expression. Such an expression should have the following attributes:

(a) represent the experimental results as accurately as possible,
(b) be compatible with the existing theories on groundwater flow, and
(c) not require an exorbitant computational effort to evaluate.

The simplest approximation to use, is certainly some form of polynomial. Such an approximation is easy to evaluate and can match the experimental points exactly in its interpolation form. The only difficulty with this approach is that the number of experimental points are usually very small and not representative of the full relation. Moreover (see Figure 3), the data obtained from in situ or field samples are, due to the inhomogeneity of natural soils, usually scattered considerably. To use a polynomial approximation in such cases for the calculation of C, can only cause unexpected problems when solving Equation (1) numerically. The best that can be done in such cases is to fit a smooth curve by, say the method of least squares, through the data.

Based on the analysis of a large number of experimental data, Brooks and Corey (1964, 1966) concluded that the retention curves for many soils can be fitted reasonably well with the analytical equation

$$\theta = \theta_c(\psi/\psi_c)^{-\lambda} \tag{2}$$

where ψ_c and λ are characteristic constants of the soil that must be determined by the procedure used to fit the data. Let θ_s denote the saturated moisture content, i.e. that value of θ which satisfies

$$\theta \rightarrow \theta_s \text{ as } \psi \rightarrow 0.$$

A moisture capacity calculated from this equation has the property

$$\lim_{\theta \rightarrow \theta_s} C \doteq \lim_{\theta \rightarrow \theta_s} [-\lambda\theta_c(\psi_c/\psi)^{(\lambda+1)}] \rightarrow -\infty.$$

This behaviour implies that there is a discontinuity in flow at the transition from unsaturated to saturated flow. This rather unphysical is avoided by restricting Equation (2) to the range $\psi > \psi_c$ and using the approximation

$$\theta = 1 - \theta_s\psi^{\kappa}$$

when $\psi \leq \psi_c$. Such an approximation has the added disadvantage in that it is only C^0 - continuous.

An equation that is C^{∞} - continuous, behaves in a physical realistic way and is easy to evaluate

$$\Theta = [1 + (\alpha\psi)^n]^{-m}$$

where

Θ = $(\theta - \theta_r)/(\theta_s - \theta_r)$,

θ_r = the residual or irreducible moisture content of the soil (van Genughten, 1980; Bear,1979),

with a and n ($m = 1-1/n$), characteristic constants, has been proposed by van Genughten (1980). There is no doubt that his equation is, at least from the modelling point of view, far superior to any of the other equations used for this purpose. It has only one slight disadvantage in that it is non-linear. However, by using the approximations detailed by van Genughten and an existing non-linear least square subroutine (e.g. E04GBF from the NAG-library) the three unknown parameters, α, n, θ_r and their associated variances, can be determined quite easily. An example of a curve determined in this way, is shown in Figure 3.

The use of an analytic expression for the moisture retention curve, has an added advantage - it allows one to calculate the unsaturated hydraulic conductivity analytically (van Genughten, 1980). The accuracy of such an approach may still be debatable, but all indications are that the differences between the calculated and observed hydraulic conductivities are generally restricted to low moisture values. Since K is small for low values of the moisture content, these differences do not influence the final results seriously.

4 THE EXISTENCE OF AN ACCEPTABLE SOLUTION

As mentioned above an acceptable numerical solution of Equation (1) can only be assured if one uses a suitably refined mesh in the calculations. To generate such a mesh for a real world site can be very time consuming and frustrating. The mesh generators available were all developed for civil engineering applications and not suitable for the present purposes. It was, therefore, decided to develop a simple mesh generator.

A mesh generator for a finite element mesh should, if possible have the following properties.

(a) Number the elements and nodes automatically, the latter optimally in the sense that it will ensure a small bandwidth for the coefficient matrix.

(b) Distinguish between domains with different characteristic properties.

(c) Generate all nodal coordinates required from a limited number of boundary coordinates supplied as input data.

The first two objectives can be easily implemented on a rectangular mesh, or a mesh consisting of a union of rectangular blocks. Such meshes are, unfortunately, very rarely encountered in groundwater problems. The stated objectives for an arbitrary domain can be still obtained by generating a suitable rectangular domain and then map this onto the arbitrary domain.

Let $\mathbf{x}$ represent a set of cartesian coordinates in the arbitrary, henceforth referred to as the global domain, and $\boldsymbol{\xi}$ a similar set in the rectangular, or cardinal domain. The general mapping from $\boldsymbol{\xi}$ to $\mathbf{x}$ is given by the vector-valued function

$$\mathbf{x} = \mathbf{x}(\boldsymbol{\xi}).$$

To be physically acceptable such a mapping must be unique and invertable, i.e. the inverse mapping

$$\boldsymbol{\xi} = \boldsymbol{\xi}(\mathbf{x}).$$

must exists and the Jacobian, $\mathbf{J}$, of the transformation must not change sign over the domain of interest.

Consider the vector valued transformation defined by the Dirichlet problem

$$\nabla^2 \mathbf{x}(\xi) = 0 \qquad (3)$$

$\mathbf{x} = \mathbf{x}_0$ on the boundary $\partial\Gamma$ of the cardinal domain Γ.

Such a transformation has the following properties:

(a) the extreme values of $\mathbf{x}$ occur on the boundary Γ,
(b) since no extrema occur within Γ the first derivatives of $\mathbf{x}$ cannot vanish simultaneously in Γ.

The latter property ensures that **J** will not be zero due to the presence of an extremum in Γ. However, the possibility exists that the first derivatives assume values which can cause **J** to vanish inside Γ. Such a situation can, fortunately, be easily recognized and corrective action taken. The transformation defined by Equation (3) would thus quite suitable for transforming the cardinal to the global domain. This is fortunate as it is extremely simple to solve the Dirichlet problem by the Rayleigh-Ritz finite element method (Botha and Pinder,1983; Schultz, 1973). There are, however a couple of other advantages.

(a) One can use the same basis functions in solving this problem than that for which the global mesh is required.

(b) The boundary points, $\mathbf{x}_0$, can include any points in the interior of the global domain, e.g. borehole positions, which are fixed.

The mesh generator, as implemented at present, requires as input the corner coordinates (in integer format) of a set of rectangular blocks similar to those shown in Figure 4. These coordinates also specifies the number of nodes that must be generated in each direction and should thus be chosen in accordance of the desired discretization of the global domain. These boundary coordinates are then used to generate a cardinal finite element mesh, shown in Figure 5. The cardinal coordinates of the nodes are generated at the same time and the nodes numbered to ensure that the maximum difference between nodes are as small as possible. The cardinal coordinates of the nodes, element numbers and the global coordinates of the boundary points are then used to compute the final discretization of the global domain from Equation (3). A typical example of such a global discretization is shown in Figure 6.

5 SUMMARY

This paper is mainly concerned with difficulties encountered in modelling the transport of contaminants using site specific data. The two major problems encountered are the form in which to supply information on the unsaturated parameters to a suitable computer model and the construction of a sufficiently refined grid in the case where the model is based on the finite element method.

The first difficulty has been solved by using a representation proposed by van Genughten (1980) for the moisture retention curve. This representation has definite advantages, such as C^{∞}- continuity and a better representation of the physical situation, over other representations found in the soil physics literature.

The problem of devising a suitable refined mesh has been solved by developing a versatile mesh generator. Although developed specifically for contaminant transport, the generator can also be applied to other groundwater problems, where a finite element mesh is required.

6 REFERENCES

Bear J. (1979) Hydraulics of Groundwater. McGraw-Hill, New York.

Botha J.F. and Pinder G.F. (1983) Fundamental Concepts in the Numerical Solution of Differential Equations. J. Wiley and Sons, New York.

Brooks R.H. and Corey A.T. (1964) Hydraulic Properties of Porous Media. Hydrology Paper no. 3, Civil Engineering Dept., Colorado State University, Fort Collins, Colorado.

Brooks R.H. and Corey A.T. (1966) Properties of Porous Media affecting Fluid Flow. J. Irrig. Drain.Div., Am. Soc. Civil Eng. 92(IR2): 61 - 88.

Frind E.O. (1984) The Principle Direction Technique for Advective-Dispersive Transport Simulation in Three Dimensions. In Finite Elements in Water Resources, Proc 5th Intl. Conf., Burlington, Vermont.

Princeton University Water Resources Program (1984) Groundwater Contamination from Hazardous Wastes. Prentice-Hall Inc., Englewood Cliffs, New Jersey.

Schultz M.H. (1973) Spline Analysis. Prentice Hall, Inc., Englewood Cliffs, New Jersey.

Scott P.S., Farquhar G.J. and Kouwen N. (1983) Hysteretic Effects on Net Infiltration. In: Advances in Infiltration, Proc Nat. Conf. on Advances in Infiltration, Chicago, Illinois.

Sudicky E.A. (1983) An Advection-Diffusion Theory of Contaminant Transport for Stratified Porous Media. Ph.D.-thesis, Department of Earth Sciences, University of Waterloo, Ontario.

van Genughten M. Th. (1984) A Closed Form Equation for Predicting the Hydraulic Conductivity of Unsaturated Soils. Soil Sci. Soc. Am. J., Vol 44: 892-898.

Voss C.I. (1984) SUTRA Saturated-Unsaturated TRAnsport A Finite Element Simulation Model for Saturated-Unsaturated, Fluid-Density-Dependent Ground-Water Flow with Energy Transport or Chemically reactive Single-Species Solute Transport. U.S. Geological Survey, National Centre, Reston, Virginia.

Yeh G.T. and Ward D.S. (1981) FEMWASTE: A Finite Element Model of Waste Transport through Saturated-Unsaturated Porous Media. ORNL, Environmental Sciences Division, Publication No 1462, Tennessee.

Yeh G.T. and Ward D.S. (1980) FEMWATER: A Finite Element Model of Water Flow through Saturated-Unsaturated Porous Media. ORNL, Environmental Sciences Division, Publication No 1370, Tennessee.

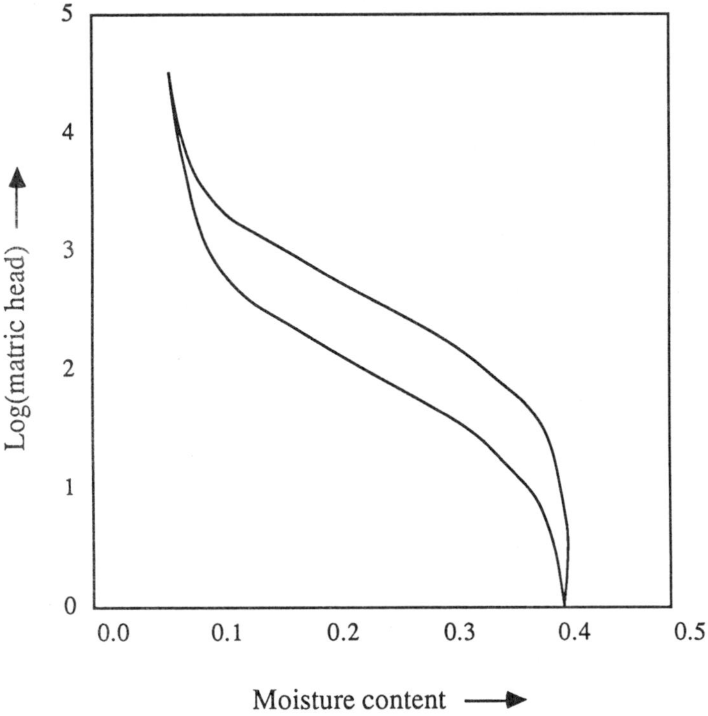

Figure 1 Schematic representation of a typical soil moisture retention curve.

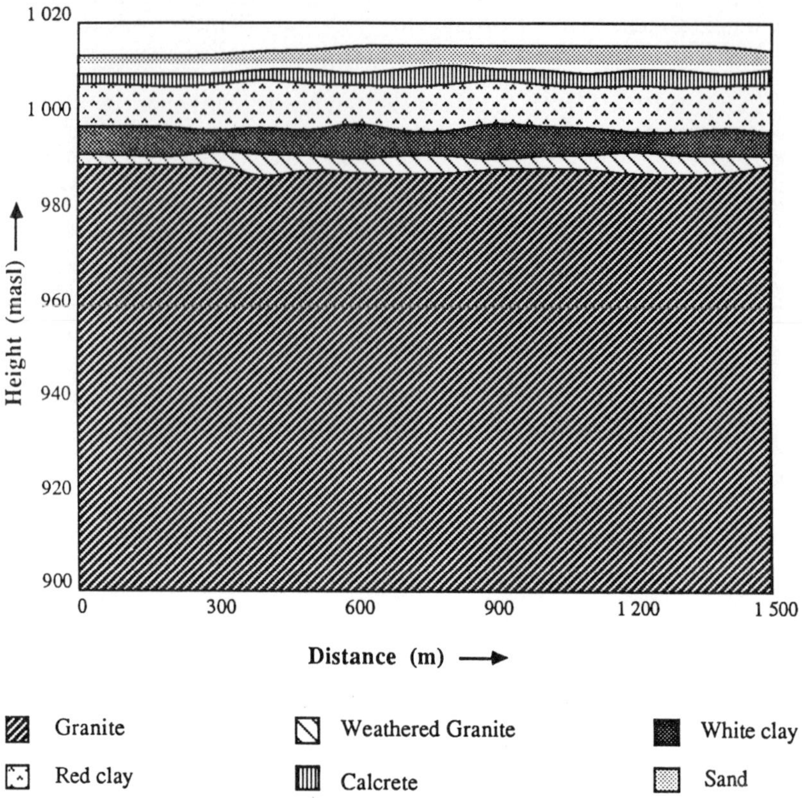

Figure 2 Vertical cross-section showing the various geological layers present in a semi-desert area of South Africa.

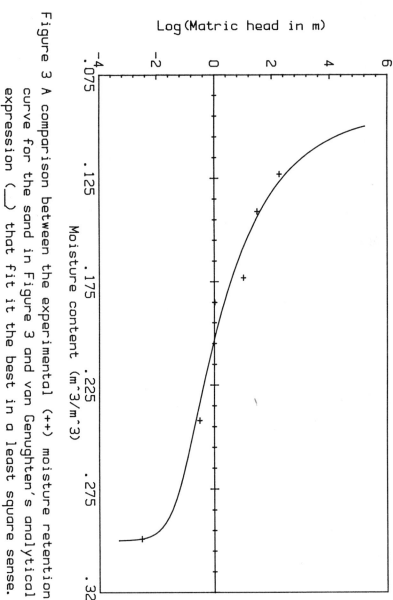

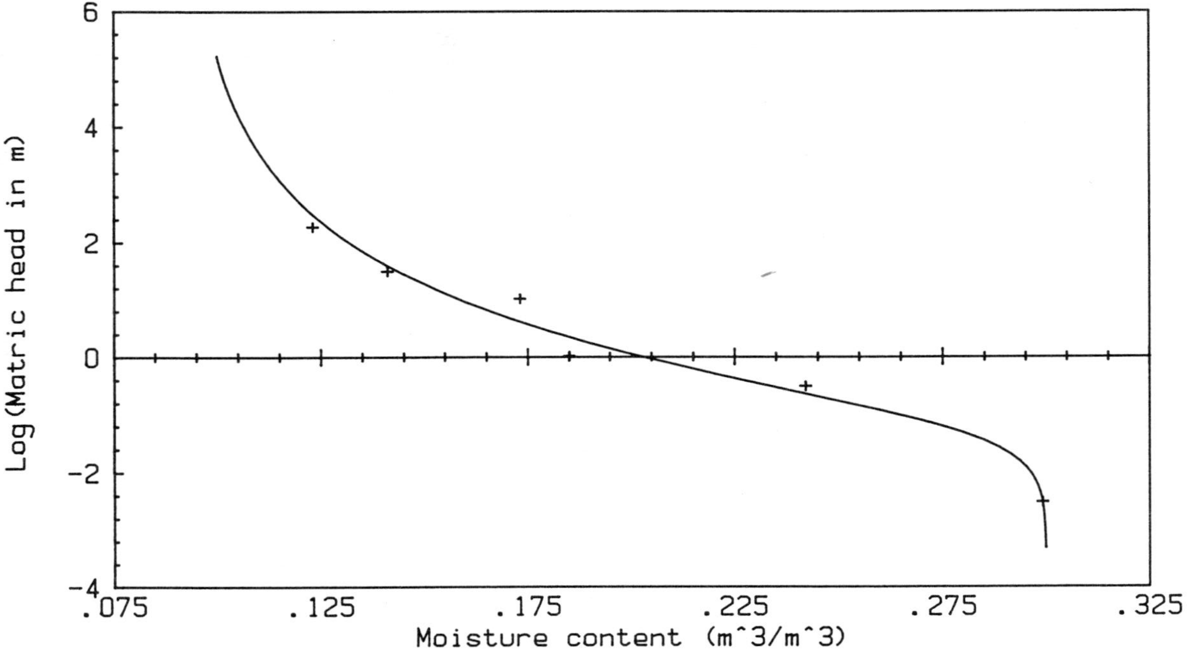

Figure 3 A comparison between the experimental (++) moisture retention curve for the sand in Figure 3 and van Genughten's analytical expression (__) that fit it the best in a least square sense.

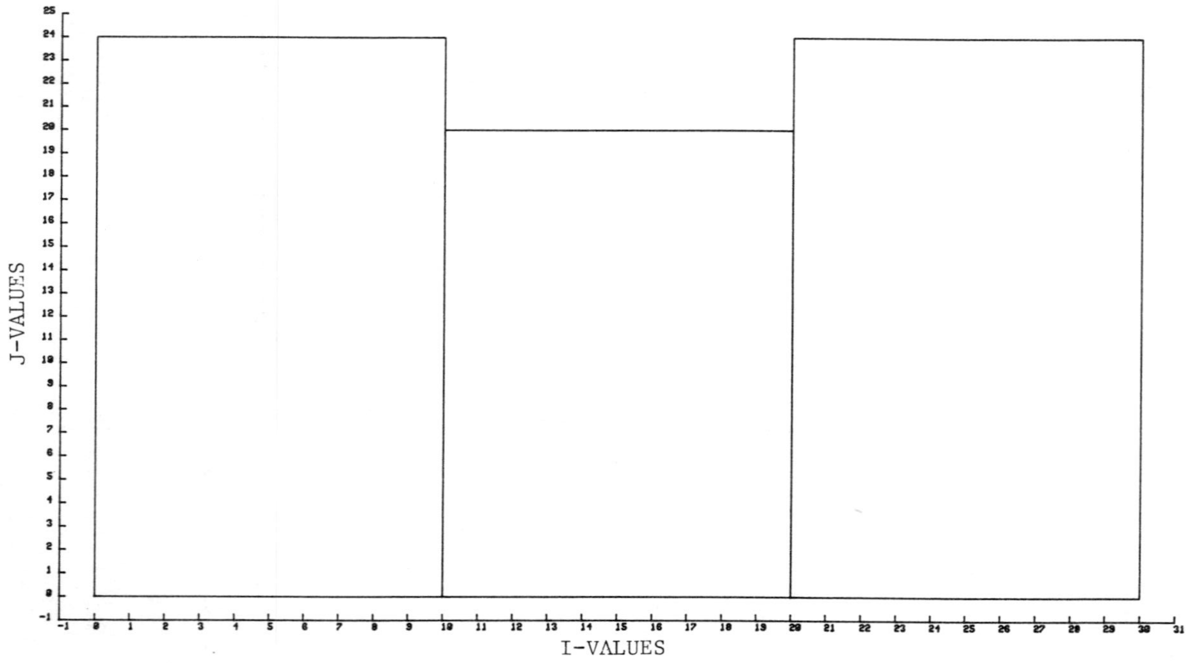

FIGURE 4 BLOCK DIAGRAM USED IN THE CONSTRUCTION OF A TYPICAL CARDINAL FINITE ELEMENT MESH

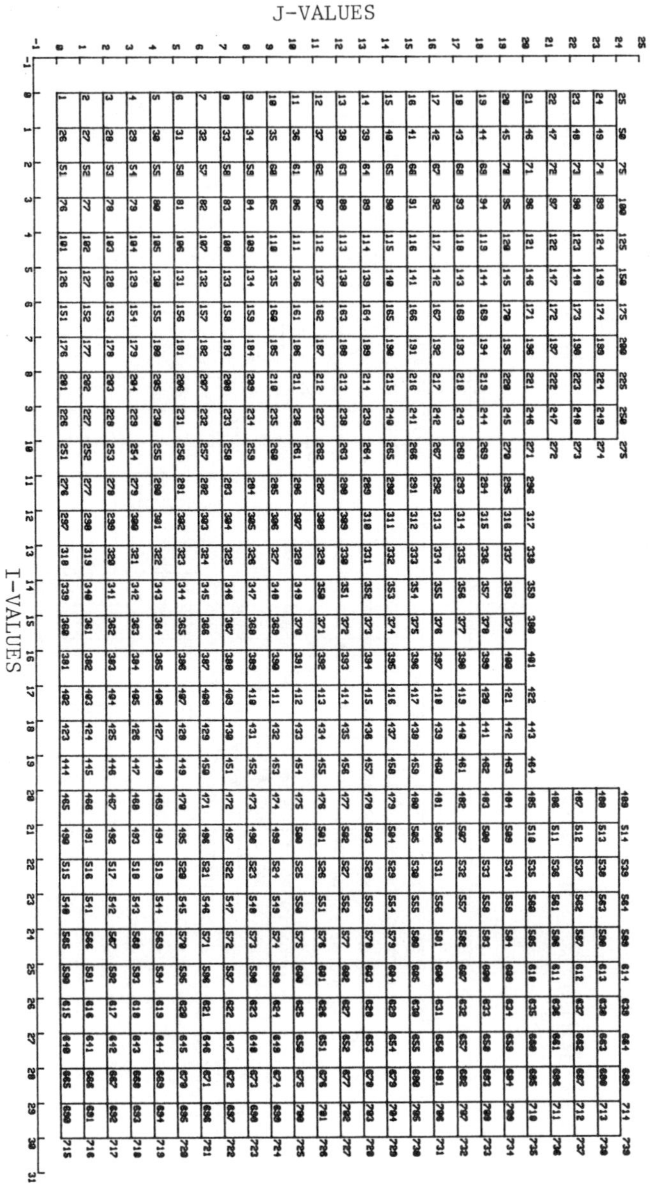

FIGURE 5 CARDINAL FINITE ELEMENT MESH CONSTRUCTED FROM THE BLOCK DIAGRAM IN FIGURE 4.

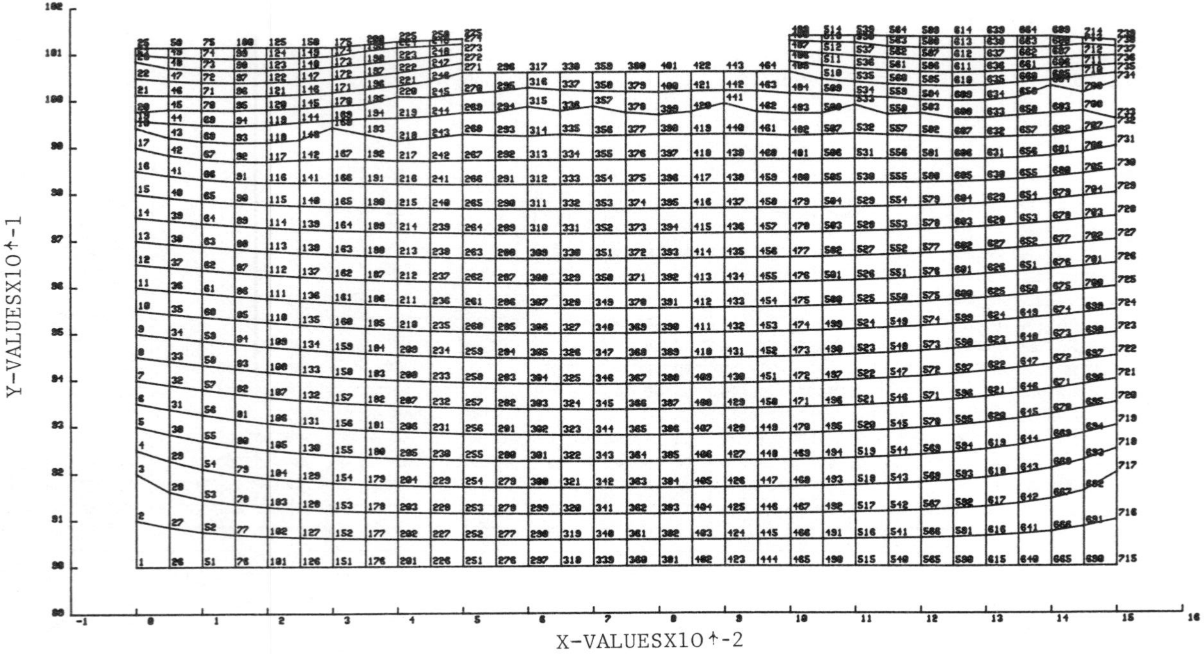

FIGURE 6 GLOBAL FINITE ELEMENT MESH GENERATED FROM THE CARDINAL MESH IN FIGURE 5.

VI International Conference on Finite Elements in Water Resources, Lisboa, Portugal, June 1986

Combining Physical Containment with Optimal Withdrawal for Contaminated Groundwater Remediation

D.P. Ahlfeld, J.M. Mulvey and G.F. Pinder
Department of Civil Engineering, Princeton University, Princeton, NJ 08544, U.S.A.

1. Introduction

Two common techniques for remediation of groundwater plumes of toxic solute are physical containment and groundwater withdrawal. Both methods utilize existing technology and are applicable to aquifers with widely different characteristics. Both methods are also expensive, so that care must be taken in designing systems for their use. This paper considers the use of both methods at a single site and describes an analysis methodology for evaluating the tradeoff between the costs involved in the two methods. The methodology combines contaminant transport simulation modeling with a nonlinear optimization formulation which finds the optimal groundwater withdrawal pumping strategy given a specific physical containment configuration.

Physical containment of contaminated groundwater typically involves the construction of a low permeability barrier (e.g. slurry wall or grout curtain) in the subsurface designed to surround the contaminated groundwater [Glover, 1982]. The ground surface bounded by the barrier is covered with an impermeable cap which prevents further leaching from the contaminated soil and forestalls any increase in water level by precipitation in the contained area. The costs of such a system are related to the length and depth of the barrier structure and the surface area covered by the cap.

Withdrawal methods require the removal of contaminated groundwater from the aquifer by pumping. The design elements in a withdrawal system are the location of the wells and the magnitude of pumping at each well. Careful design of a withdrawal system may include the use of both injection and extraction wells to induce velocity fields which facilitate efficient plume contraction and removal. Because of the ability of a withdrawal system to affect velocity fields over large distances, this method is better suited than containment for large dilute plumes. The costs in a withdrawal system are related to the amount of pumped fluid and to the concentration of the extracted water.

Case histories of groundwater withdrawal and physical containment systems have been reported in the literature, for example, McBride, [1982] and Water Well Journal, [1983]. Methods for determining optimal withdrawal strategies for containment or avoidance of solute plumes which combine flow or solute modeling with optimization techniques have been proposed by Molz and Bell, [1977], Gorelick, et al., [1984], and Colarullo, et al. [1984]. Methods for designing optimal pump strategies for removal of plumes using withdrawal have been suggested by Atwood and Gorelick [1985] and Ahlfeld, et al., [1985].

2. An Analysis Approach

The varying costs and effectiveness of containment and withdrawal suggests that it may be most efficient to combine their use on the same site. Such a scheme might involve the use of containment for the sections of the aquifer with the highest solute concentrations and the use of withdrawal for the remaining sections of the aquifer. To quantify the relative costs of the combined use of containment and withdrawal we propose the following procedure. We begin by assuming that the plume has been well characterized and that a reliable simulation model has been developed which describes groundwater flow in the aquifer and concurrent advective-dispersive solute transport. Given this data base we modify the simulation model so it will represent a containment barrier around a portion of the aquifer which includes the areas of highest concentration. Next we determine the minimum pumping that must be used to remove the contaminant outside of the containment barrier with the approach described by Ahlfeld, et al., [1985] for designing optimal pump strategies. By repeating this process for a number of different containment barrier sizes and configurations the relationship between containment barrier size and the magnitude of pumping in a withdrawal scheme is determined.

2.1. Simulation Model

The physics of the groundwater system are represented using a vertically averaged form of the coupled partial differential equations which describe fluid flow, velocity, and solute transport [Pinder & Bredehoeft, 1973]:

$$\nabla \cdot bK \nabla h - Q\delta(x_k, y_k) = 0 \tag{1.a}$$

$$v = \frac{-K}{\phi}\nabla h \tag{1.b}$$

$$\nabla \cdot D \nabla c - \nabla vc - \frac{Qc_0}{(b\phi)}\delta(x_k, y_k) = \frac{\partial c}{\partial t} \tag{1.c}$$

where

b = saturated thickness (l),
c = solute concentration (m/l^3),

c_0 = solute concentration of source/sink fluids (m/l^3),
D = hydrodynamic dispersion tensor (after Scheidegger [1961]) (l^2/t),
h = hydraulic head (l),
K = hydraulic conductivity tensor (l/t),
Q = source/sink magnitude (l^3/t),
v = average pore velocity (l/t),
$\delta(x_k, y_k)$ = dirac delta function evaluated at nodal point k (x_k, y_k) ($1/l^2$),
ϕ = porosity of medium (*dimensionless*).

These equations are solved using a Galerkin, bi-linear, quadrilateral finite element discretization [Pinder & Gray, 1977].

2.2. Optimization Model

The problem of finding optimal pump strategies for a withdrawal scheme given the presence of a containment barrier is addressed by posing an optimization formulation. The optimization model simultaneously selects pump location and pump rates which cause a reduction in maximum concentration to some specified level at the end of a fixed planning period while minimizing the total required pumping (a surrogate for cost). The pump locations are chosen from a set of potential pump sites at a select number of finite element nodes. The optimization formulation is stated mathematically as :

$$\textit{minimize} \sum_{j \in J} |q_j| \tag{2.a}$$

$$\textit{s.t.} \quad c_{i,T}(\mathbf{q}) \leq c_i^* \quad i \in I \tag{2.b}$$

$$qlow_j \leq q_j \leq qup_j \quad j \in J \tag{2.c}$$

where

J = set of nodes to be considered as potential pump locations,
$\mathbf{q}$ = vector of pump rates located at nodes defined by J with elements q_j,
I = set of nodes at which system concentration behavior will be observed,
$c_{i,T}(\mathbf{q})$ = the concentration at node i at the last time period of the simulation as a function of pump rates. This functional relationship is provided by a solute transport simulation model,
c_i^* = the specified concentration reduction at node i,
$qlow_j$ = lower bound on magnitude of pumping,
qup_j = upper bound on magnitude of pumping.

Equation 2.b describes the design requirement that the concentration at the observation points (contents of set I) must be less than or equal to the specified level (c_i^*). Equation 2.c places bounds on the allowable magnitudes of pumping. Equation 2.a states the design objective of minimizing the total pumping required while satisfying the design requirements.

The optimization constraints (2.b) are nonlinear. The problem is solved using the general purpose nonlinear optimization code MINOS from the Stanford Optimization Laboratory [Murtagh and Saunders,1977,1978].

2.3. Solution Procedure

For each run of the model a containment barrier configuration is selected. The containment barrier is incorporated into the optimization scheme by modifying the simulation model used in (2.b) to include a set of narrow low conductivity elements. Given a fixed barrier configuration the model is allowed to choose from potential pump sites (i.e. the set J) located downgradient of the barrier along the horizontal center line of the mesh. The model is required to select pump rates at the potential pump sites that reduce concentrations at all nodes downgradient of the barrier (or at all nodes in the domain for the case of no barrier) to or below 5% of initial maximum.

3. Test of Methodolgy on a Sample Aquifer

3.1. Sample Aquifer Description

Five sets of optimization runs were made; one with no containment barrier and the other four with barriers of varying size. The mesh and boundary conditions for the 8500 m^2 barrier are shown in Figure 1. The intersecting narrow elements define the boundaries of the containment area. The conductivity in the barrier wall is set to $10^{-7} cm/sec$, a value suggested by the studies of Glover [1982] for slurry walls.

The sample aquifer was constructed with the simulation characteristics shown in Table 1.

Longitudinal Dispersity	2100 cm
Transverse Dispersity	210 cm
Porosity	0.2
Diffusion Coefficient	0.000001 cm^2/sec
Time Step for Mass Transport	2190 hrs (3 months)
Number of Time Steps	12

Table 1: **Hydraulic and Numerical Parameters Used in Sample Aquifer**

The aquifer tested was inhomogenous and of non-uniform thickness. A plan view of the aquifer transmissivity is shown in Figure 2a. The transmissivity values ranged from a minimum of 0.30 cm^2/sec to a maximum of 9.30 cm^2/sec Figure 2b shows the initial concentration conditions used by the optimization model with a maximum normalized to 1.0.

$$\frac{\partial h(x,H)}{\partial y} = 0 \qquad \frac{\partial c(x,H)}{\partial y} = 0$$

$h(0,y) = 19.8m$

$c(0,y) = 0$

$h(L,y) = 12.8m$

$c(L,y) = 0$

$$\frac{\partial h(x,0)}{\partial y} = 0 \qquad \frac{\partial c(x,0)}{\partial y} = 0$$

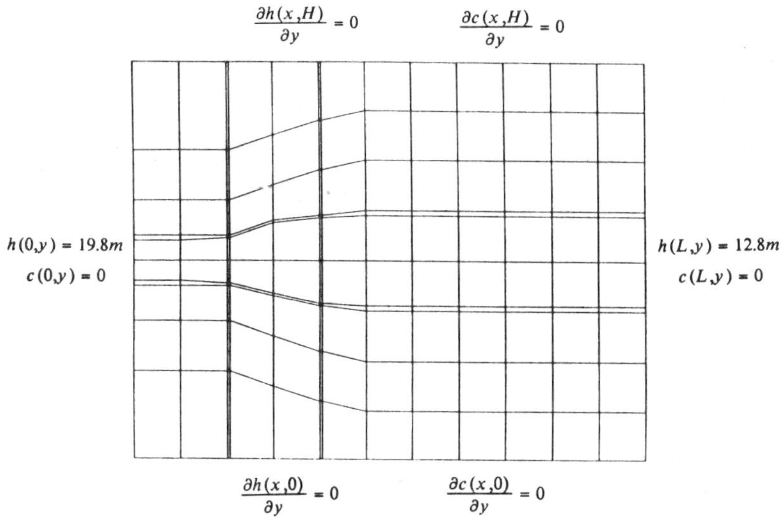

Figure 1 : **Boundary Conditions and Typical Finite Element Mesh for Sample Aquifer**

3.2. Results on Sample Aquifer

Figure 3 depicts the simulated head contours that results from the use of the steady state pump rates selected by the optimization model. The contained area shows a flat head surface in each case. The circles on each figure indicate the location, magnitude, and direction of pumping at each node. The volume of pumping at a point is proportional to the area of the circle. Black circles are for extraction while white circles indicate injection. Although no clear pattern of optimal pumping is present in the various solutions, in general, the optimization model uses extraction wells downgradient of the barrier to create a cone of depression which draws in the contaminant from all sides. Some injection is used to dilute the plume and as a hydraulic tool to increase velocities toward the extraction wells.

Figure 4 shows the relationship between containment barrier size (measured here in area of wall and cap surface) and pumping volume for the sample aquifer. The graph plots the size of containment structure versus the minimum pumping required for the withdrawal scheme as found by the optimization model given the specific containment structure configuration and size. An

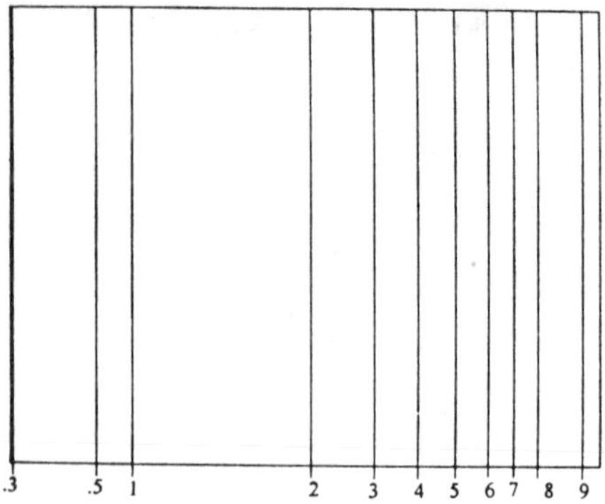

2a)

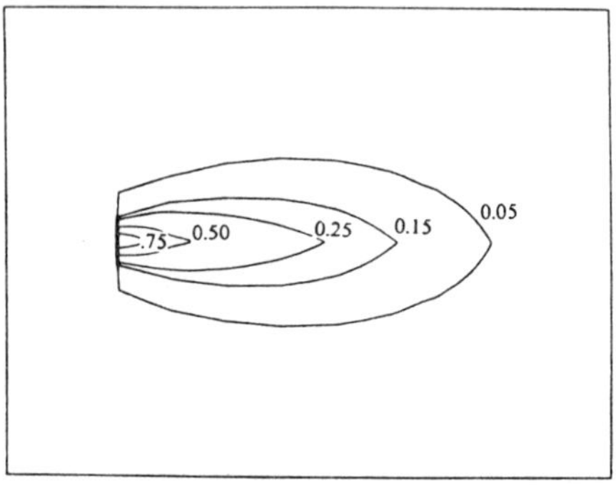

2b)

Figure 2 : **a) Transmissivity** (cm^2/sec) **Used in Sample Aquifer**
b) Initial Concentration Plume

interpolation of the computed points provides a curve from which the least expensive combination of containment and pumping can be estimated. Such a curve for the sample aquifer is shown and indicates that as the barrier size increases the marginal benefit of larger barrier size decreases. When the containment structure is small, an increase in structure size produces a significant decrease in pumping volume. When the containment structure is large, little significant change in pumping volume is realized by an increase in size.

If we assign monetary values to the pumping and containment structure costs the approximate optimal combination of containment structure and withdrawal strategies can be determined. This is done by selecting the point along the curve in Figure 4 that minimizes the combined costs of containment and withdrawal. The middle range of barrier sizes in Figure 4 (i.e. 4500 to 12000) show a nearly constant marginal benefit for barrier size. This suggests that the

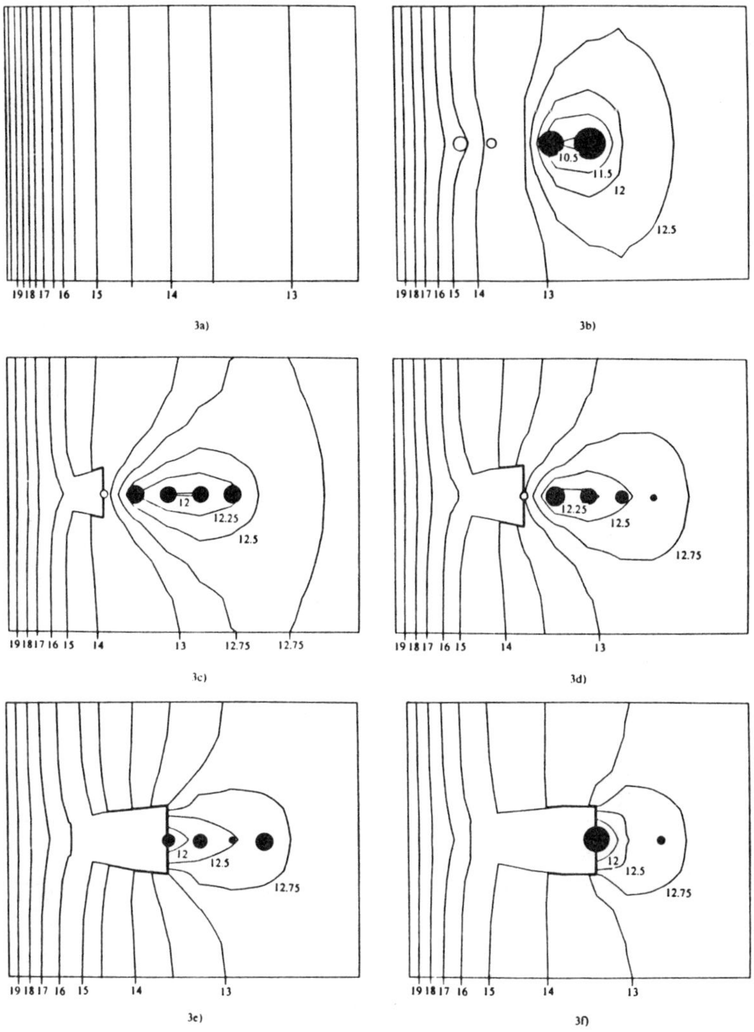

Figure 3 : **Initial and Optimal Head Surfaces for Different Containment Schemes**

a) zero pumping **b) no containment**

c) 4400 m^2 containment **d) 8500 m^2 containment**

e) 12400 m^2 containment **f) 16100 m^2 containment**

best combination of barrier size and withdrawal scheme will be highly dependent on the cost estimates for each remediation technique.

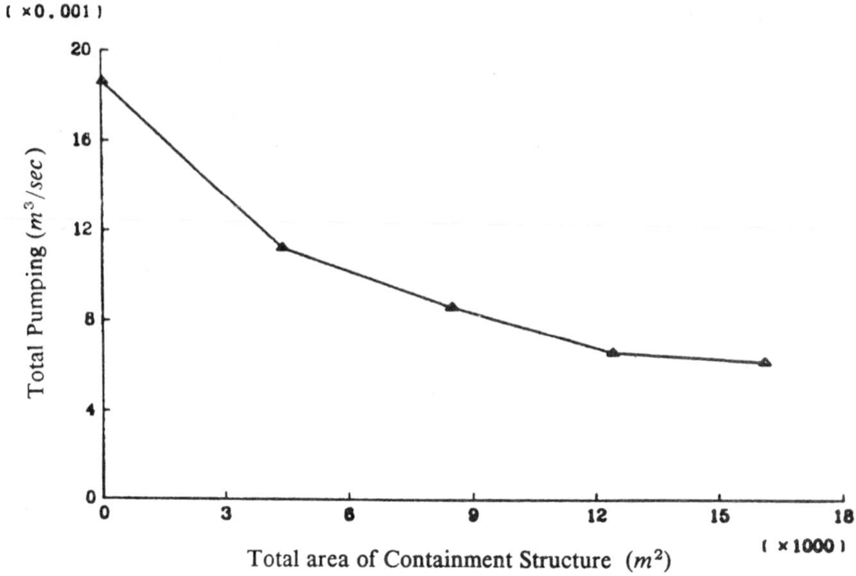

Figure 4 : **Total area of Containment Structure** (m^2) **vs Total Pumping** (m^3/sec)

4. Conclusions

A methodology has been presented for determining the most efficient combination of physical containment and groundwater withdrawal for remediation of a contaminated groundwater aquifer. The method uses solute transport simulation combined with nonlinear optimization to determine the optimal withdrawal strategy while parameterizing on the containment structure size and configuration. The method has been tested on a sample aquifer and has been found to give results useful for an economic interpretation.

5. Acknowledgements

We acknowledge the suggestions of W.G. Gray who prompted our investigation into the use of optimization methods for contaminant clean-up and the generosity of the IBM Corporation which funded this research.

References

1. D. P. Ahlfeld, J. M. Mulvey, and G. F. Pinder, "Designing Optimal Strategies for Contaminated Groundwater Remediation," Report EES-85-12, Civil Engineering Department, Princeton University, 1985. To appear in Advances in Water Resources

2. D. F. Atwood and S. M. Gorelick, "Hydraulic Gradient Control for Groundwater Contaminant Removal," *Journal of Hydrology*, vol. 76, pp. 85-106, 1985.

3. J. D. Bredehoeft and G. F. Pinder, "Mass Transport in Flowing Groundwater," *Water Resources Research*, vol. 9, no. 1, February, 1973.

4. S. J. Colarullo, M. Heidari, and T. Maddock,III, "Identificaton of an Optimal Groundwater Management Strategy in a Contaminated Aquifer," *Water Resources Bulletin*, vol. 20, no. 5, 1984.

5. S. M. Gorelick, C. I. Voss, P. E. Gill, W. Murray, M. A. Saunders, and M. H. Wright, "Aquifer Reclamation Design: The Use of Contaminant Transport SimulationCombined with Nonlinear Programming," *Water Resources Research*, vol. 20, no. 4, 1984.

6. F. J. Molz and L. C. Bell, "Head Gradient Control in Aquifers Used for Fluid Storage," *Water Resources Research*, vol. 13, no. 4, 1977.

7. B. A. Murtagh and M. A. Saunders, "MINOS User's Guide," Report SOL 77-9, Department of Operations Research, Stanford University, California, 1977.

8. B. A. Murtagh and M. A. Saunders, "Large-Scale Linearly Constrained Optimization," *Mathematical Programming*, vol. 14, pp. 41-72, 1978.

9. G. F. Pinder and W. G. Gray, *Finite Element Simulation in Surface and Subsurface Hydrology,* Academic Press, New York, 1977.

10. A. E. Scheidegger, "General Theory of Dispersion in Porous Media," *J. of Geophysical Research*, vol. 66, no. 10, pp. 3273-3278, 1961.

VI International Conference on Finite Elements in Water Resources, Lisboa, Portugal, June 1986

Aquifer Response to Pumping by R-C. Network

S.V.K. Sarma, T.C. da Silva
Department of Civil Engineering; Water Resources Engg. Section, Federal University of Paraiba, C. Grande, Brasil

INTRODUCTION

The design, construction and operation of hydraulic structures demand prior knowledge of the behaviour of the system under varying conditions of operation. As the conventional methods have limited applicability, models based on physical characteristics must be developed so as to easily estimate in advance the input parameters for their calibration and operation, either by physical, analogic or mathematical modelling.

A model should behave as a tool to represent the simplified version of reality, the validity depending on how the model approximates the field condition. Thus, good field data are essential when using the model for predictive purposes. However, an attempt to model a system with inadequate data can also be instructive (Wang and Anderson, 1982) as it might serve to identify those areas, where detailed field data are critical to the success of the model, thus helping guide the data collection activities.

Analogic and Mathematical Models

Of the recent advances for implanting and simulating the conditions in the field are electrical analogy models of the Resistance-Capacity (R-C) type. While these serve to study such conditions as delayed yield in aquifers, sudden drawdown in reservoirs etc, the case discussed here deals with steady state conditions.

A mathematical model consists of a set of differential equations that are known to govern the flow of groundwater. Simplifying assumptions are made to construct a model, as the field conditions are too complex to be exactly simulated and any analytical assumptions are fairly restrictive. To deal with realistic situtations, it is necessary to solve the mathematical model using numerical techniques.

In the case of finite element and finite difference methods, a system of nodal points is superimposed over the problem domain. The concept of elements (the sub-areas delineated by lines connecting model points) is fundamental to the development of equations in finite element methods. While trangular elements are used in some situations, quadrilateral and other elements are also possible. In the finite difference method, the nodes may be located inside the cells or cell intersection of grid lines. The aquifer properties and head are assumed to be constant within each cell and the grid is said to use either block centered or mesh-centered nodes as in figure 1a. Regardless of the representation, an equation is written in terms of each nodal point because the area surrounding the node is not directly involved in the development of finite difference equations.

AQUIFER WITH IMPERVIOUS BARRIER

The grid in figure 1a represents a homogeneous and isotropic confined aquifer with a radius of influence, Ri, pumped at a rate of Qm^3/h, while figures 1b-d show the conditions with impermeable barriers at 1/6 R, 1/2 R and 5/6 R from the center, R/6 wide and 2/3 long and figure 1e is a singular case of a radial barrier of same width and length but extending from the periphery.

Aquifer Simulation on R-C Network

Although the unsteady conditions could be studied with the same network using the capacitors, here the steady state condition is discussed in which the grid consists of 5cm x 5cm units with 51Ω resistors, representing an area of 5m x 5m in the field. Correspondence between yield Q, head H and permeability coefficient K and current I, potential V and inverse of resistance 1/R has been brought out and the following values were adopted. Conversion Factor of Units = 5.71 V/6m
Resistance Used = 51Ω, Grid: 5cm x 5cm on model = 5m x 5m in the field. Peripheral Voltage = 5.7 V = Peripheral Head = 6m. Voltage at the center of well field = 3.43 V = 3.6m (60% of peripheral voltage). Value of Capacitors (used in unsteady case) = 10 μF Number of nodes without barriers = 144
Number of nodes with barriers = 140
Barriers length: 20cm on the model = 20m in the field
Barriers width: 5cm model = 5m in the field
Maximum Current Used in the Homogeneous Aquifer = 82.1 m Amp, corresponding to a yield of $4.4m^3$/day.

ANALYSIS OF THE RESULTS

Results obtained from R-C. network by pumping tests on aquifers, with and without barriers, have been presented in Table 1.

TABLE 1

FLOW AND ELECTRICAL CHARACTERISTICS OF THE MODEL

Characteristic	Homogeneous Aquifer	Barrier at a distance of X from center X=R/6	R/2	5/6R	Radial Barrier
1. Discharge, m^3/h	Q	0.667Q	0.907Q	0.917Q	0.956Q
2. Peripheral Voltage, V	5.71	5.71	5.71	5.71	5.71
3. Voltage of the Center = 60% of Peripheral Voltage, V	0.6 x 5.71	3.43	3.43	3.43	3.43
4. Peripheral Head, m	6	6	6	6	6
5. Head at Center, m	3.6	3.6	3.6	3.6	3.6
6. Current at center m Amp.	82.1	56.2	76.4	77.4	80.5

For the purpose of comparison, the drawdown at the centrally located well is kept constant at (5.71- 3.43) = 2.28 V which is equal to (6-3.6) = 2.4m head and the yield for this drawdown is calculated in each of the cases considered (figs. 1b-e). (Bouwer, 1978).

A glance at table 1 reveals that the maximum yield was obtained in the case of homogeneous aquifer. In all other cases (fig. 1b-e), with the existence of the barrier in the well field, the yield always reduced.

For the case when the barrier was at R/6 from the center, the reduction in yield was a maximum, attaining a value of 33.3% - thus leaving only a discharge of 0.667 Q. However, with distance of the barrier increasing from the center, say from R/6 to R/2 and R/6 to 5/6 R, the yield recuperated to 90.7% and 91.7% of the original yield. Thus, the position of the barrier matters much, while analysing the pumping test results.

In the case of a radial barrier of same length and width, placed from the periphery towards the center, it is observed that this had practically no effect on yield, with only a reduction in yield of 4.4% of discharge. Thus, a barrier across the well - field will have greater effect on yield reduction than a radial barrier of the same dimensions.

The case of oblique barriers, one or more in the well-field is also of interest and although experiments were carried out, using Jacob's theory on this topic, the discussion on this does not form part of this paper.

Computer Simulation of the Model Using Mini-Computers

An attempt is made by the senior author to simulate by way of a finite difference method the problem of heterogeneity in aquifers with impermeable barriers. It is a common experience that in case of alluvial aquifers of shallow nature as in Catole do Rocha near Riacho·Agon, Pb, Brazil, there is possibility of occurrence of rocky barrier within the well field whose effect is to give reduced yields, as compared to those in homogeneous strata. Likewise, an existence of a recharge source increases the yield and as is well known the problem can be solved analytically or graphically by means of images or by use of mini or micro-computers.

The programme originally prepared by Boochs (1985) for a two dimensional well-field problem with rectangular boundaries (as in Dupuits case) was modified suitably by amplifying the grid to accommodate the conditions in the present case where R_i = 6x nodal distance equal to 6 x 5cm of space on R.C Network. Thus the initial and boundary conditions are so manipulated as to simulate a homogeneous well-field and also the barriers of R/6 wide x 2/3 R long. It is interesting to note that the results by numerical analysis with computer simulation coincided within reasonable limits with those obtained by R.C network.

CONCLUSIONS

Aquifer simulation with impermeable barriers on R.C network gave good results, with the capacity to incorporate the conditions in the field, such as impermeable barriers or recharge sources. Computer simulation by simulating the initial and boundary conditions gave results which tally fairly well with those obtained by R.C. network.

ACKNOWLEDGEMENTS

The authors acknowledge the Water Resources Section of UFPb, as also the CNPq for the encouragement and financial help rendered by them. They also thank Dr Peter Boochs for having made available the computer program for use by authors.

REFERENCES

1. ANDERSON, M.P. and WANG, F.W. (1982) "Introduction to Groundwater Modelling", W.H. Freeman, 1-237.

2. BOUWER, H. (1962) "Analysing Groundwater Mounds by Resistance Networks" J. Irr. Drain. Division, Am. Soc. Civil Engg. 88 (IR 3) 15-36.

3. BOUWER, H. (1978) "Groundwater Hydrology" McGraw-Hill 1-488.

4. GroundWater Manual (1981) A Water Resources Technical Publication, U.S.D.A., Denver, Colorado, 1-479.

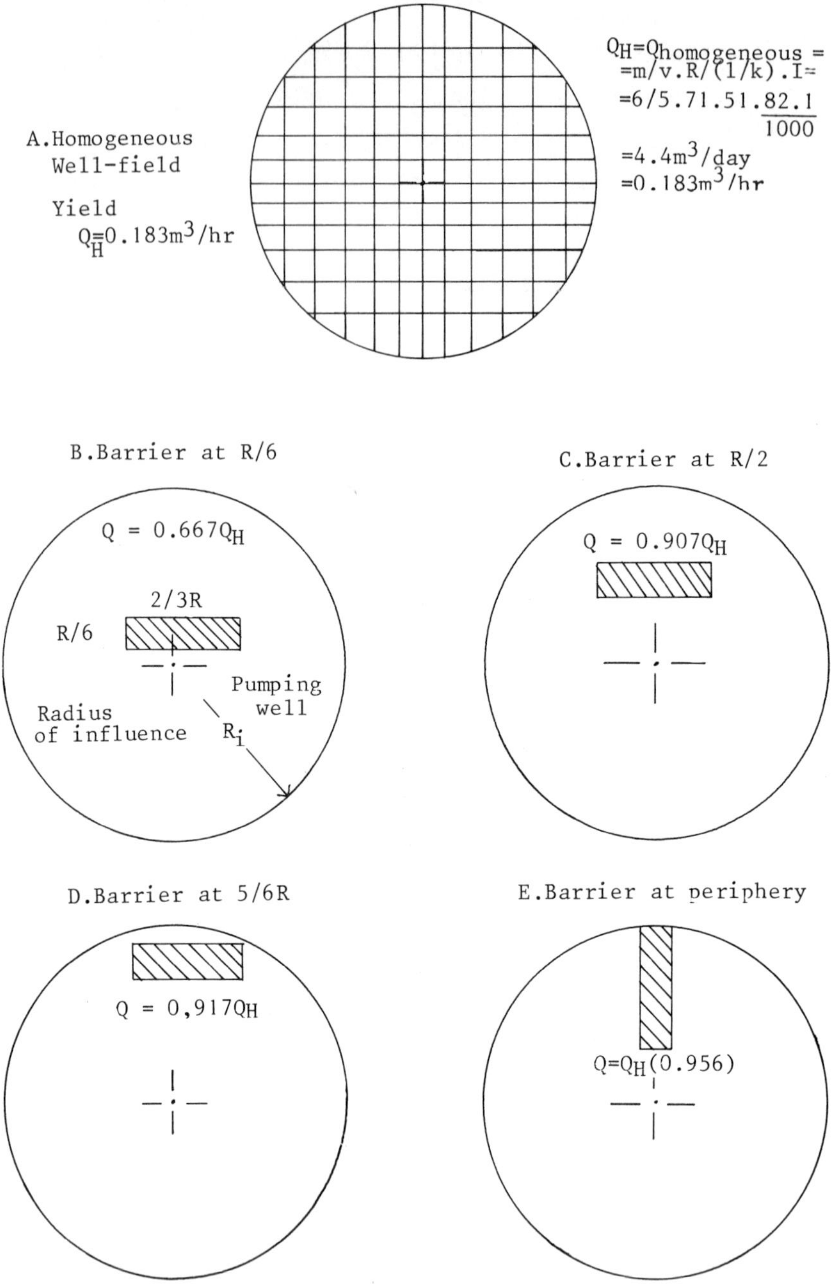

Figure 1 - ARRANGEMENT TO STUDY THE VARIATION IN YIELD WITH CHANGING POSITION OF BARRIERS

VI International Conference on Finite Elements in Water Resources, Lisboa, Portugal, June 1986

Management of Groundwater Systems by Application of Finite Element and Optimization Methods

B. Herrling, A. Heckele
Institute of Hydromechanics, University of Karlsruhe, West Germany

INTRODUCTION

The sufficient supply of groundwater is currently extremely important. However, for ecological reasons, it is often necessary to confine the maximum value of the pumping rate in wells in order to keep the groundwater level above a minimum height. Under these conditions, groundwater extraction can sometimes be enlarged by selecting suitable positions for the wells.

Recently the occurrence of groundwater contamination has been reported with increasing frequency. It is not possible, and in many cases even unnecessary, to investigate the propagation of contaminated groundwater by direct numerical modelling of the transport processes. To restore the aquifer to its original condition, or to confine the contaminant to a limited region, sometimes the only convenient cures are hydraulic. Common hydraulic countermeasures are to pump from a well, or both to induce infiltration (artificial groundwater recharge) and to pump from a well.

Especially when the geometrical situations or the flow conditions are complex, analytical computations for estimating the quantities which have to be pumped or infiltrated, and the place where the inlets and outlets should be located, are extremely complicated. The usual method of solving these problems is to employ numerical models to simulate the groundwater flow, including prescribed sinks and sources; the latter are varied in several computer runs until the admissible groundwater extraction is determined under observation of restricted groundwater levels or until the plotted flow vectors result in flow situations which isolate the contaminated region as demanded.

The present paper describes a method for optimizing the pumping and infiltration rates, and for finding optimal locations for the inlets and outlets. It is based on combining directly the computation of horizontal groundwater flow (finite element method) with a method of linear programming (simplex algorithm) or of quadratic programming for a quadratic objective function. Nonlinearities due to the dependence of the transmissivity on the groundwater level are included in the flow computation.

The objective function of the optimization problem is, for example, to find a maximum pumping rate and the best locations for the wells when the decrease of the groundwater levels is restricted as a consequence of ecological reasons. In connection with hydraulic countermeasures for groundwater contaminations, the objective function is the minimum pumping rate or the minimum in the difference between pumping and infiltration rate. To isolate a prescribed flow region, constraints are formulated such that the gradients of the groundwater surface (and thereby the flow direction) should be less than or equal to zero. The prescribed gradients are directed into the contaminated region.

Another application of the introduced method is to compute unknown influxes into the region of a groundwater model (precipitation, influx from other groundwater stories or from a river, etc) when the groundwater level is known at many measured points. In this case the objective function is the minimum of the difference between measured and computed groundwater levels at prescribed points.

The theory is presented for steady groundwater flow. Moreover, a few remarks will be made about aquifer-management under unsteady conditions being studied by Heckele (1986). Further, an example for steady flow will be demonstrated.

DIRECT COUPLING OF STEADY FLOW COMPUTATION AND OPTIMIZATION ALGORITHMS

Horizonal two-dimensional groundwater flow

In this paper only horizontal two-dimensional groundwater flow will be presented, as these flow computations have the greatest practical importance. The basic equations are the vertically integrated continuity equation

$$q_{i,i} = q^* \qquad (1)$$

and Darcy's flow equation

$$q_i = -T_{ij}\, h_{,j} \qquad (2)$$

with i,j = 1,2. q_i describes the discharge per unit width, $_{,i}$ partial differentiations with respect to the Cartesian coordinates x_i, q^* a sink and source term (precipitation, withdrawal from a well, water exchange with streams etc) and T_{ij} the transmissivity tensor with

$$T_{ij} = k_{ij}\, h^* \quad . \tag{3}$$

In equation (3) k_{ij} denotes the conductivity tensor and h^* the vertical thickness of the saturated aquifer which is dependent on the groundwater level, h, for unconfined flow. Corresponding to Einstein's summation convention, it is summed over the repeated indices in a term.

Substituting equation (2) into equation (1), there results the final equation

$$-(T_{ij}\, h_{,j})_{,i} = q^* \quad . \tag{4}$$

At the boundary of the two-dimensional domain, the groundwater level $\bar{h}$ with

$$h - \bar{h} = 0 \tag{5}$$

or the discharge $\bar{q}$ perpendicular to the boundary with

$$q_i\, n_i + \bar{q} = 0 \tag{6}$$

are prescribed. n_i denotes the direction normal to the boundary.

Definition of the optimization problem

Before defining an optimization problem, an additional variable e is introduced. This decision variable, e, has mostly the same meaning as the prescribed sink and source term q^* in equation (1) or (4); but unlike q^*, e is unknown and has to be computed by the optimization. The decision variable is only defined at specified locations in the computation area and denotes, for example, unknown withdrawal from wells or quantities of artificial recharge.

The objective function, Z, depends on e and h, and can be formulated for the linear problem as

$$Z = c^1 e + c^2 h \rightarrow \text{min/max} \quad . \tag{7}$$

c^1 and c^2 are spatial dependent coefficients of the objective function. Z can be, for example, the sum of withdrawals from all wells in an aquifer. e and h are limited by NR constraints

$$g_T^1\, e + g_T^2\, h \lesseqgtr \bar{R}_T \tag{8}$$

with T = 1,2,...,NR. g^1_T and g^2_T are coefficients of the linear constraints and $\bar{R}_T$ the respectively prescribed values. Examples for these constraints are limitations of upper and lower groundwater levels or a limitation of the pumping rate of a special well for technical reasons. Further, the gradient of groundwater levels between two points can be bounded, which means that the magnitude of the velocity is limited.

A second kind of constraint is the differential equation governing the groundwater flow

$$-e - (T_{ij}\ h,_j),_i = q^* \tag{9}$$

and the boundary conditions belonging to it

$$h - \bar{h} = 0 \tag{10}$$

$$q_i\ n_i + \bar{q} = 0 \quad . \tag{11}$$

Equations (9) to (11) are identical to equations (4) to (6) except for the decision variable e. For transmissivities independent of the groundwater levels the following linear relation between e and h is derived from equations (9) to (11):

$$h = f(x_i,\ T_{ij},\ \bar{h},\ \bar{q},\ q^*) \cdot e \quad . \tag{12}$$

Maddock (1972) was one of the first authors using this relation for optimizing groundwater systems.

Finite element formulation and solution technique

Complex groundwater systems has often been computed using the finite element method. In the present case, triangular elements with linear shape functions and the Galerkin method are applied. Triangular elements are suitable for reproducing any geometrical situation and for local refinements of the discretization which are often necessary in extended models.

Having discretized the model area, there are N nodes. There are fixed NQ (NQ << N) decision variables, e_V (V = 1,2,..,NQ), defining unknown sinks and sources which are located at nodes, element boundaries or spatial distributed over elements. The objective function (equation (7)) can now be rewritten in the form

$$Z = c_V^1\ e_V + c_L^2\ h_L \tag{13}$$

with V = 1,2,...,NQ and L = 1,2,...,N. Depending on the specified objective function, all or most of the N coefficients c_L^2 are zero if equation (13) refers only to the decision variables or if the groundwater levels are extreme only in parts of the model. Respectively, the NQ coefficients, c_V^1, are zero, or generally equal to 1.0.

The constraints of equation (8) are rewritten as

$$g_{TV}^1\ e_V + g_{TL}^2\ h_L \lesseqgtr \bar{R}_T \tag{14}$$

with T = 1,2,...,NR (NR = number of constraints), V = 1,2,..., NQ and L = 1,2,...N. Generally, for a chosen constraint T, either g_{TV}^1 with V = 1,2,...,NQ or g_{TL}^2 with L = 1,2,...,N is zero (constraints either for h_L or for e_V).

Finally, applying the finite element method to equations (9) to (11) results in

$$- D_{LV} \; e_V + K_{LK} \; h_K = R_L \tag{15}$$

with L,K = 1,2,...,N and V = 1,2,...,NQ. Omitting the first term, equation (15) represents the well known algebraic equation set for the numerical approximation of the groundwater flow (equation (4) to (6)). The matrix K_{LK} is symmetrical, banded and positive definite. D_{LV} results from the integration of the unknown decision variables in the element network. Equation (16) demonstrates the special case that e_V represents sinks and sources only defined at nodes, but it is possible to use decision variables characterizing, for example, the unknown ordinate of a spatially distributed infiltration. In the latter case, the coefficients of the matrix D_{LV} result from an integration in space and are dependent on the element sizes.

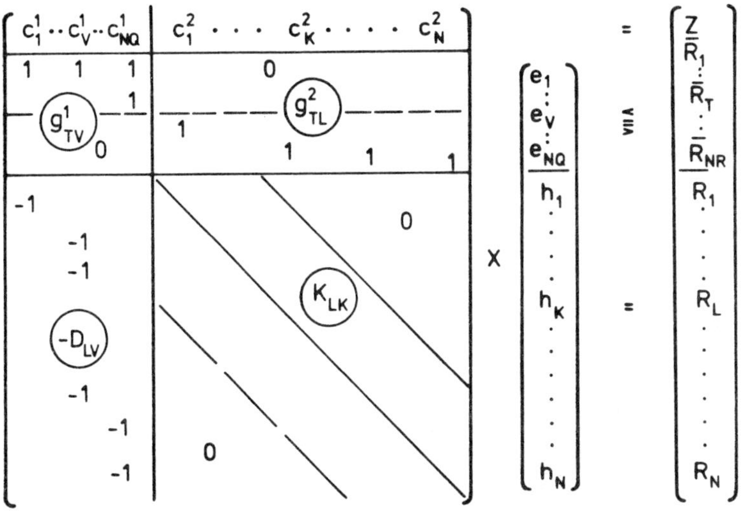

(16)

Equation (13) to (15) or the simplified presentation of equation (16) form a problem well suited to linear programming. The solution of the problem can be obtained by using any linear programming solver f.e. APEX-III from CDC or MPS from IBM. The latter has been done by Elango (1979) using a finite element discretization, and by Aguado and Remson (1974) applying finite differences for the flow constraints.

If a standard optimization method is applied, the economical data storage (see equation (16)) is destroyed and the structure of the matrices can no longer be used. This disadvantage should be explained more clearly: In practical applications, the number of nodes, N, is often considerably greater than 1000. On the other hand the number of decision variables, NQ, and constraints, NR, are both significantly less than one hundred in most practical cases. Further, the matrix K_{LK} is sparse and symmetrical, which means that only half of the banded matrix must be set up and stored. For this reason, attention has been given to the retention of this data structure in the optimization algorithm.

To this purpose, the first step is to multiply equation (15) by the inverse matrix K^{-1}_{HL}, with H,L = 1,2,...,N. In practice, this is realized by applying Cholesky's solution method for (1 + NQ) vectors on the right-hand side consisting of R_L and D_{LV}. This results in

$$h_L = R^*_L + D^*_{LV} \; e_V \quad . \tag{17}$$

Equation (17) corresponds directly to equation (12). In the second step, equation (17) is inserted in the objective function (equation (13)), which yields

$$Z = c_V \; e_V + z^* \tag{18}$$

$$\text{with} \quad c_V = c^1_V + c^2_L \; D^*_{LV} \tag{19}$$

$$\text{and} \quad z^* = c^2_L \; R^*_L \quad . \tag{20}$$

The third step consists of substituting equation (17) into the constraints of equation (14), which gives

$$g_{TV} \; e_V \begin{smallmatrix} \le \\ = \\ \ge \end{smallmatrix} \bar{R}^*_T \tag{21}$$

$$\text{with} \quad g_{TV} = g^1_{TV} + g^2_{TL} \; D^*_{LV} \tag{22}$$

$$\text{and} \quad \bar{R}^*_T = \bar{R}_T - g^2_{TL} \; R^*_L \quad . \tag{23}$$

The matrix operations in equation (19), (20) and (22), (23) are performed only to a limited extent, taking into account the sparse filling of c^2_L and g^2_{TL}.

Now the optimization algorithm can be run only using the objective function of equation (18) and the constraints of equation (21). In addition to the present simplex algorithm, any other optimization method can be applied. When employing a quadratic objective function, as mentioned above, equations (18) to (20) and the optimization algorithm have be to changed, but there is in principle no difficulty.

The result of the optimization yields the decision variables e_V and the value of the objective function, Z. Using equation (17), the groundwater levels can be computed. If the transmissivities are dependent on the groundwater levels (see equation (3)), which is significant in many cases (see below), the computation runs in an iterative circle starting with updated transmissivities in equation (15). As is well known from the conventional flow computation alone (equation (4) to (6)), the iterative process converges in a few steps when solving equation (13) to (15).

MANAGEMENT OF UNSTEADY GROUNDWATER SYSTEMS

Due to lack of space, the computation method can only be presented in detail for steady situations in this paper. But a few remarks should be made for unsteady flow (see Heckele (1986)): Some numerical solution schemes (Futagami (1982), Aguado and Remson (1974) or Shamir and Bear (1984)) combine all the discretized variables of the optimization problem (in space and time) in one equation set. This is extremely voluminous in the application to complex problems. With respect to the linear relation between h and e (see equation (12)) for unsteady situations, the stepping forward in time can be retained as usual for a flow computation alone. It is only necessary to change the conventional method to consider nonlinearities (e.g. transmissivities dependent on the groundwater levels): The iterative procedure has to take place after finishing the calculation of all the decision variables by the optimization algorithm for the total time span of the computation.

APPLICATION TO A STEADY GROUNDWATER FLOW PROBLEM

In the foreland of the Alps in West Germany there are numerous glacial valleys consisting primarily of Quaternary sand and gravel sediments. In these basin and channel systems, the impermeable base often has a slope of more than 1% in the aquifer thalweg. In some regions the distance between the water table and the surface reaches up to 20 m, whereas at other places the streams are recharged by groundwater seepage. In the region near Leutkirch the quantity of groundwater should be enlarged by infiltrating surface water from streams into gravel-pits in regions where the distance is large between the surface and the groundwater table (for more details see Herrling (1982)).

The optimization method is used to find the quantity of recharge that can constantly be infiltrated without detriment to the downstream valley. Due to the increasing groundwater levels agricultural areas and buildings must not be endangered and previous dry gravel-pits, or those filled with refuse, must not be flooded or subjected to throughflow in order to avoid contamination. For the flow computation, the increasing groundwater levels produce an extreme change in the transmissivities in some regions, thus making an iterative solution algorithm necessary.

The model area is discretized into 1041 elements and 592 nodes (figure 1). The artificial recharge is simulated by nodal infiltration at five nodes, each limited to 350 l/s. Areas with

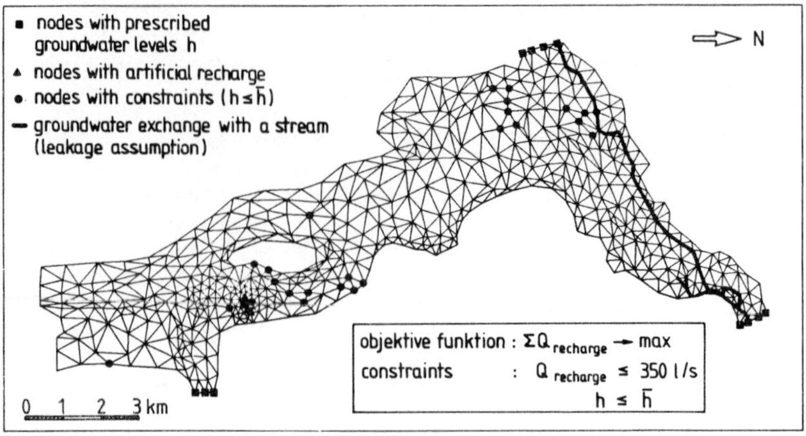

Figure 1. Element network and presentation of the problem.

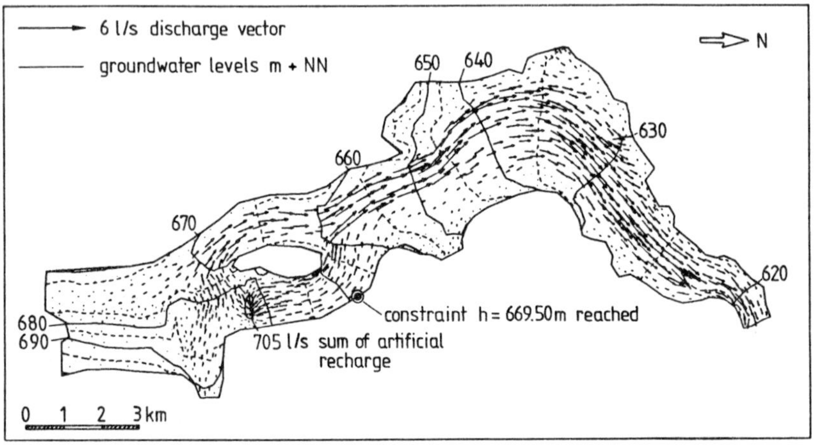

Figure 2. Results of the linear optimization.

constrained groundwater levels as a result of the infiltration are reproduced by 30 nodes, each with a limited groundwater level (see figure 1). The objective function with $c_1 = c_2 = \ldots = c_5 = 1.0$, the constraints of the infiltration, of the groundwater levels and of the flow are defined corresponding to equations (13) to (15) or (16) as follows:

$$Z = c_V \, Q_V \tag{24}$$

$$Q_V \leq 350 \text{ l/s} \tag{25}$$

$$h_I \leq \bar{h}_I \tag{26}$$

$$-D_{LV} \, Q_V + K_{LK} \, h_K = R_L \tag{27}$$

with $V = 1,2,\ldots,5$; $L,K = 1,2,\ldots,592$ and I runs over 30 nodes of the discretization where groundwater levels are limited (see figure 1).

In figure 2, the results of the optimization are shown. Near the gravel pit the transmissivities change extremely as a result of the infiltration; they are iteratively adapted in a few steps. The maximum infiltration rate amounts to $c_V\ Q_V = 705$ l/s. Further, the node in which the constraint of the groundwater level is reached, is shown besides the lines of constant groundwater level and the discharge vectors.

Compared to a flow computation alone, this computation requires double the computer time and the scope for data storage increases only 7.5%.

Instead of using five different decision variables Q_V ($V = 1,2,\ldots,5$) there could be chosen only one,being distributed in equal parts at the five nodes. Further, the artifical recharge could be modelled in another way by using a leakage term. In this case the objective function is the sum of the leakage infiltration, which should be a maximum, and the decision variable is the surface water level in the gravel pit.

CONCLUSION

The paper describes an optimization method for the solution of groundwater management problems. The method consists of a combination of the computation of horizontal plane groundwater flow with a free surface (finite elemente method) and a linear optimization procedure (simplex algorithm). Considering the special structure of data which result from computing the groundwater flow with the finite element method, and modifying the simplex algorithm, the solution of management problems with complex groundwater flow is realized without any difficulties. Compared to a flow computation alone, the additional effort of the optimization (computer time and scope for data storage) is only small. It depends on the number of the decision variables being low in most of the practical cases. The optimization program is designed with the intention that the coupling with an existing flow model (confined or unconfined) can be handled simply.

ACKNOWLEDGEMENT

The investigation was supported by the German Research Community (DFG), grant no. Th 159/13. The authors express their appreciation for their subsidy.

REFERENCES

Aguado, E. and Remson, I. (1974) Ground-Water Hydraulics in Aquifer Management, J. Hydr. Div. ASCE, 100, No. HY1: 103-108.

Elango, K. (1979) Finite Element-Based Optimization and Numerical Simulation Models for Groundwater Systems, Mitteilungen des Instituts für Wasserbau und Wasserwirtschaft, RWTH Aachen, H. 29.

Futagami, T. (1982) The FE (Finite Element) and DP (Dynamic Programming) Method in Optimization of Field Problems, in: Finite Element Flow Analysis, ed. by T. Kawai, North-Holland, Amsterdam: 717-724.

Heckele, A. (1986) Numerische Optimierungsverfahren für den Einsatz in der Grundwasserbewirtschaftung, thesis in preparation.

Herrling, B. (1982) Artifical Groundwater Recharge in Quaternary Gravel Aquifers in the Foreland of the Alps, IAHS Publ. no 136: 33-41.

Maddock, T. (1972) Algebraic Technological Functions from a Simulation Model, Water Res. Research, 8 (1): 129-134.

Shamir, U. and Bear, J. (1984) Optimal Annual Operation of a Coastal Aquifer, Water Res. Res., Vol. 20, No. 4: 435-444.

VI International Conference on Finite Elements in Water Resources, Lisboa, Portugal, June 1986

A Simulation Model for the Transport of Radionuclides by Groundwater in the Vicinity of a Salt-Dome

F. Sauter
R.I.V.M., Postbox 150, 2260 AD Leidschendam, The Netherlands
N. Praagman
Svasek B.V., Coastal Engineering Consultants, Postbox 90, 3000 AB Rotterdam, The Netherlands

INTRODUCTION

The modelling of radionuclide migration in the geosphere outside a salt-dome, where a repository of radionuclides is located, has become an important topic over the last years. The growing amount of radio active waste and the problems to find acceptable storage locations are the main reasons for this increasing importance.
Migration from the salt-dome can only occur after contact of the groundwater with disposed waste. This might happen at short or at long term. Although many precautions during the operational period will be taken to reduce the risk of water intrusion, the possibility of such an intrusion can never completely be excluded. In the following sections the basic steps which led to a numerical model (METROPOL) for the transport of radionuclides by groundwater are treated. Using this model, simulations for different scenarios can be computed.
In section 5 some results of simple applications are given.

THE GEOHYDROLOGY OF A SALT DOME AREA

Before starting with the mathematical model a few remarks concerning the location where the disposal of waste will take place, have to be made. In the present study the location to be investigated is a cross-section, as shown in figure 1, which is representative for several locations in the Netherlands and West-Germany.

Below the first aquitard the transmissivity may be very low

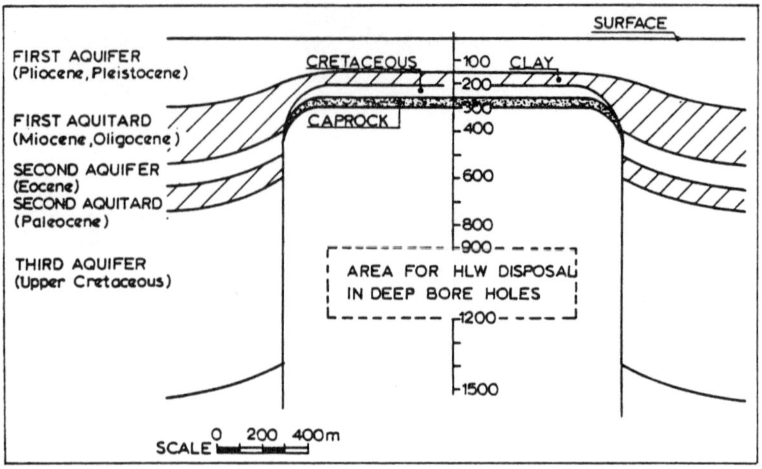

Figure 1

Cross section over reference salt dome.

and the flow rate limited. Another important point is the fact that the salinity of the aquifers below the Oligocene clay is always found to be considerable higher than seawater-salinity. It is therefore that in the simulation model salt cannot be regarded as a species that does not influence the Darcy velocity of the fluid, but has to be treated in a special way. For more geohydrologic information, see [2] .

THE GOVERNING PARTIAL DIFFERENTIAL EQUATIONS

The system of equations describing the transport of pollutants by groundwater is rather complicated. For the derivation of the system used in the following see [4] . It is assumed that the pollutants (radionuclides) do not have, as does the salt, any influences on the Darcy velocity $\underline{q}$. The system consists of the following equations:

- Conservation of mass for the fluid:

$$\frac{\partial}{\partial t}(n\rho) + \nabla \cdot (\rho \underline{q}) = 0 \qquad (1)$$

- Flow equation (modified Darcy-equation):

$$\underline{q} = -\underset{\approx}{K}(\nabla p + \rho \underline{g}) - \underset{\approx}{D}^{f}\nabla C \qquad (2)$$

- Equation for the density ρ:

$$\rho = \rho_{20} \ (1 + \beta(p - p_o)), \qquad (3)$$

with $\rho_{20} = \gamma_1 * C^2 + \gamma_2 * C + \gamma_3$

- Equation for porosity:

$$n = n_o \ (1 + C_r(p-p_o)) \qquad (4)$$

- Conservation of salt:

$$\frac{\partial}{\partial t} (n\rho C) + \nabla \cdot (\rho C \underline{q} + \underline{J}) = 0 \qquad (5)$$

with $\underline{J} = -\underset{\approx}{K}^S \cdot (\nabla p + \rho \underline{g}) - \rho \underset{\approx}{D}^S \cdot \nabla c$

Equations (1),--,(5) form the basis of the mathematical model. For each of the pollutants marked by C^α, a conservation equation has to be added:

$$\frac{\partial}{\partial t} (n\rho C^\alpha) + \nabla \cdot (\rho C^\alpha \underline{q} + \underline{J}^\alpha) = 0 \qquad (6)$$

with $\underline{J}^\alpha = - \rho \underset{\approx}{D}^\alpha . \nabla C^\alpha - \rho \underset{\approx}{D}^{\alpha S} . \nabla C$

$\alpha = 1,2...,n_t$

The unknowns used in these equations are:

- porosity n
- pressure p
- Darcy - velocity $\underline{q}$
- density of fluid $\bar{\rho}$
- mass fraction of salt C
- mass fraction of pollutant C^α

Furthermore the following coefficients, some of which have to be determined empirically, have been used:

$\underset{\approx}{K}$ - permeability coefficient

$\underline{g}$ - acceleration of gravity

$\underset{\approx}{D}^f$ - salt induced flow coefficient

ρ_{20} - reference density

β - compressibility coefficient of the fluid

n_o - reference porosity

C_r - compressibility of rock

p_o - reference pressure

$\underset{\approx}{K}^s$ - coefficient of pressure diffusion for salt
$\underset{\approx}{D}^s$ - dispersion coefficient for salt
$\underset{\approx}{D}^\alpha$ - dispersion coefficient for pollutant α
$\underset{\approx}{D}^{\alpha s}$ - dispersion coefficient for pollutant α due to the gradient in the salt concentration.

In order to have a well-posed problem initial and boundary conditions have to be specified for P, C and C^α on the boundary $\partial\Omega$ of the region of interest Ω.
The following boundary conditions may be specified:

- for the pressure p:

$$(\underline{q} \cdot \underline{n}) \big|_{\partial\Omega_1} = p_n$$

$$p \big|_{\partial\Omega_2} = p_p$$

$$(\underline{q} \cdot \underline{n} + \gamma p) \big|_{\partial\Omega_3} = p_m$$

with p_n, p_p and p_m prescribed functions, $\underline{n}$ the outside pointing normal and

$\partial\Omega_1 \cup \partial\Omega_2 \cup \partial\Omega_3 = \partial\Omega$, the boundary of Ω.

- for the salt C:

$$(p C\underline{q} + \underline{J}) \cdot \underline{n}) \big|_{\partial\Omega_4} = 0$$

and

$$C \big|_{\partial\Omega_5} = C_{s5}$$

with C_{s5} a prescribed function and

$\partial\Omega_4 \cup \partial\Omega_5 = \partial\Omega$.

Finally, for each species C^α : $(\alpha=1,2,\ldots,n_t)$

$$((\rho C^\alpha \underline{q} + \underline{J}^\alpha) \cdot \underline{n}) \big|_{\partial\Omega_6{}^\alpha} = 0$$

and $$C^\alpha \big|_{\partial\Omega_7{}^\alpha} = C_b^\alpha$$

with C_b^α a prescribed function and $\partial\Omega_6{}^\alpha + \partial\Omega_7{}^\alpha = \partial\Omega$

Initial conditions

$$p(x,o) = p_o(x)$$
$$C(x,o) = C_o(x)$$
$$C^{\alpha}(x,o) = C^{\alpha}{}_o(x)$$

have to be given for all $\underline{x} \in \Omega$.

DISCRETIZATION IN SPACE AND TIME

In order to discretize the given system a standard Galerkin finite element method is applied. See for a detailed description of the method [6] , [10] .
In the discretized version two vectors of unknowns

$$\underline{\tilde{p}} = [\tilde{p}_1,\tilde{p}_2,\ldots,\tilde{p}_{np}]^T, \text{ and} \qquad (7)$$
$$\underline{\tilde{C}} = [\tilde{C}_1,\tilde{C}_2,\ldots,\tilde{C}_{np}]^T \qquad (8)$$

have to be solved from the system of ordinary differential equations

$$M \begin{pmatrix} \dot{\underline{\tilde{p}}} \\ \\ \dot{\underline{\tilde{C}}} \end{pmatrix} + S \begin{pmatrix} \underline{\tilde{p}} \\ \\ \underline{\tilde{C}} \end{pmatrix} = \underline{0} \qquad (9)$$

in which both M and S are matrix functions of the unknowns.
System (9) is a strong non-linear system of Ordinary Differential Equations (ODE).
For each of the pollutant vectors $\underline{\tilde{C}}^{\alpha}$ also a system of ODEs is found.
For the discretization in time of these systems a combination of the implicit Euler method and the Trapezoïd rule with stepsize selection is utilized. (See [5]). The system is linearized using the method of successive substitution. The finally resulting system of linear equations is solved using either a preconditioned conjugate gradient method or a successive overrelaxation method. (See [9], [8]).

APPLICATIONS

In order to show the possibilities of the described METROPOL-CODE (See also [7]) some special examples are shortly treated. Examples 1 and 2 have been taken from the HYDROCOIN project.

Steady-state groundwater flow
The stationary flow in a fractured rock has been calculated. In this example the conductivities differ considerably, $K \approx 10^{-8}$ m/s in the rock-matrix and $K \approx 10^{-6}$ m/s in the fracture zones, while constant density and viscosity are assumed.

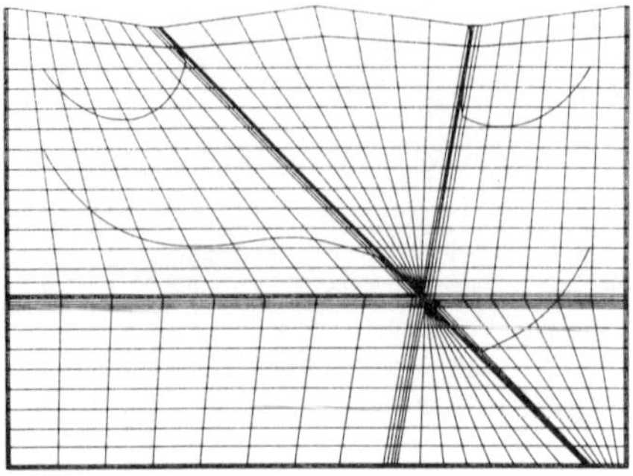

fig. 2 mesh and pathlines for example 1.

The used mesh is given in figure 2, together with path lines for four particles. Results of computations for the hydraulic head are shown in figure 3. In figure 4 the number of iterations required for the different solution techniques are shown. It should be kept in mind that for S.O.R. the relaxation factor has to be estimated, while in the figure $\omega = 1.986$, which did give the best results, has been used.
The results are rather good if compared to the results of other codes (See for instance [3]).

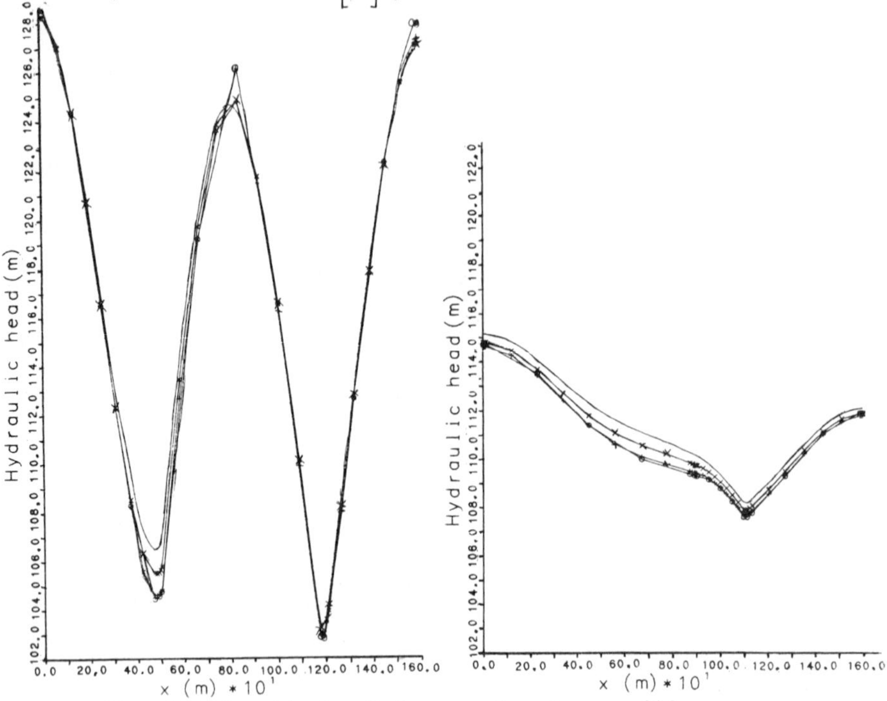

fig. 3 Hydraulic head for z = 0 and z = -400 m.
Different meshes (x is the result of the grid shown in fig. 2).

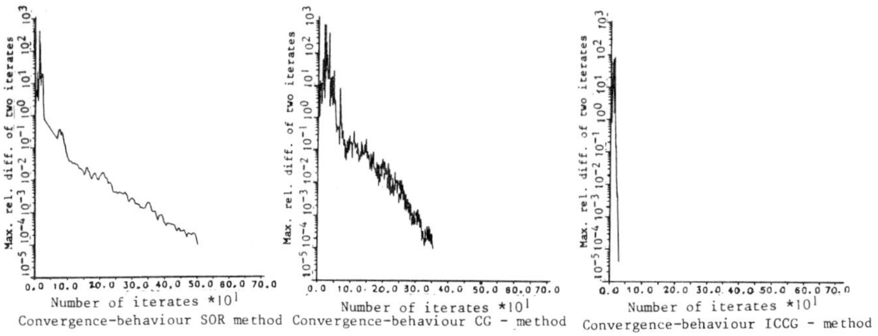

fig. 4 Number of iterations and accuracy for several methods.

Transient groundwaterflow

The transient flow from a borehole in a permeable rock, which is underlain by a fracture has also been simulated.

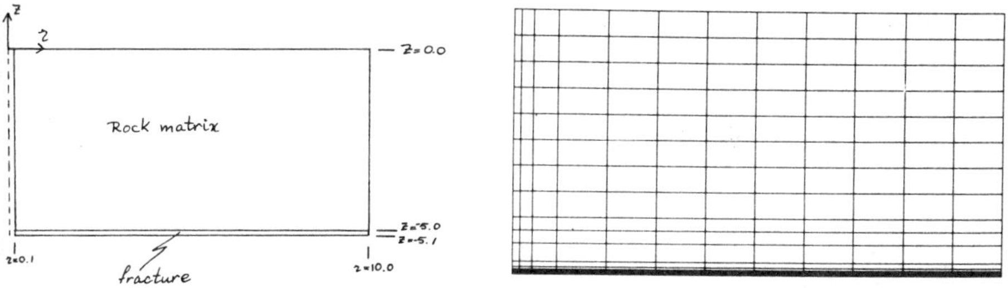

fig. 5: Cross section of cylindrical domain and finite element grid.

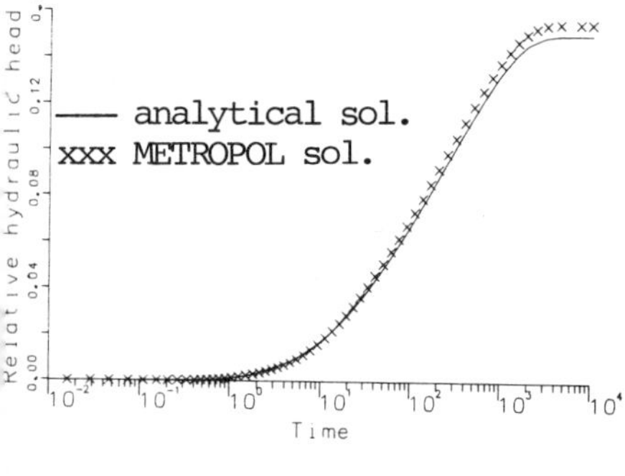

fig. 6 Time-dependent head for $r = 5$, $z = 5$

A plot of domain and grid are given in figure 5. Again the hydraulic conductivity in the fracture (10^{-7} m/s) and in the rockmatrix (10^{-9} m/s) differ considerable. A comparison of the computed and the analytical solution is shown in figure 6. For the time integration the stepsize varied from $\Delta t=.00395$ in the beginning to $\Delta t=2972.23$ at the end of the computation. For the system of linear equations the Incomplete Choleski Conjugate Gradiënt (I.C.C.G.) method has been used.

Break-through curve

A breakthrough-problem (see [1]), has been simulated with METROPOL to show its capability to solve equations like (5) and (6). In figure 7 the concentration at a location at the outflow boundary is plotted, both for the analytical and numerical solution. Results show a good resemblance.

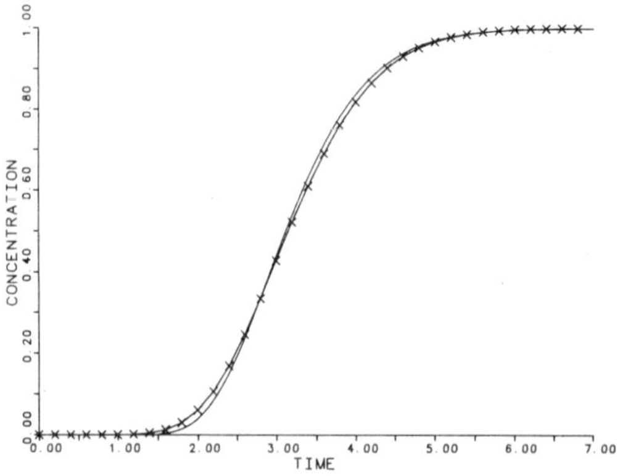

fig. 7: concentration at the outflow boundary

CONCLUSIONS

A simulation model for the transport of pollutants by groundwater has been treated. Results of three simple applications of the model have been given in order to show the different (solving) parts of the model. These results compare satisfactorily in those cases where analytical solutions are available.

REFERENCES

[1] M. Th. van Genuchten, W.J. Alves, Analytical Solutions of the one dimensional convective-dispersive solute transport equation.
U.S. Department of Agriculture, Technical Bulletin, No. 1661 - 1982.

[2] P. Glasbergen, Extreme salt concentrations in deep aquifers in the Netherlands.
The Science of the Total Environment, no. 21, pp 251 - 259

[3] B. Grundfelt, GWHRT - A finite element solution to the coupled groundwater flow and heat transport problem in three dimensions.

[4] M. Hassannisadeh, Derivation of a generalized Darcy's law and Fick's law for the transport of high concentration species in porous media.
R.I.V.M. - report, The Netherlands, 1985.

[5] J.D. Lambert, Computational methods in Ordinary Differential equations.
John Wiley, London, 1973.

[6] A.R. Mitchell, R. Wait, The Finite element method in partial differential equations.
John Wiley, Chicester, 1977.

[7] N. Praagman, F. Sauter, Metropol, a computer package for the simulation of the transport of pollutants by groundwater, R.I.V.M., The Netherlands, 1985.

[8] P. Sonneveld, C.G.S., a fast Lanczos-type solver for large sparse non-symmetric linear systems.
To appear in the SIAM-journal on Scientific and Statistical Computing (1985).

[9] J. Stoer, R. Bulirsch, Einführung in die Numerische Mathematik Springer-Verlag, Berlin, 1978.

[10] G. Strang, G.J. Fix, An analysis of the finite element method.
Prentice Hall, New Jersey, 1973.

VI International Conference on Finite Elements in Water Resources, Lisboa, Portugal, June 1986

A Hybrid Model for the Transient Hydraulic Response of Discretely Fractured Rock Masses

D. Elsworth
Department of Mineral Engineering, The Pennsylvania State University, University Park, PA 16802, U.S.A.

INTRODUCTION

The determination of hydraulic response in sparsely fractured rock masses presents a challenge in present day hydrology with important ramifications to the civil, mining, petroleum and waste engineering industries. The behavior of such rock masses are commonly difficult to quantify using techniques developed for porous and highly fractured aquifers since flow is moderated by the discrete and finite extent of the fissures. Homogenisation concepts used to represent isotropic and anisotropic hydraulic conductivities in aquifers are often invalid where discontinuously fractured masses are encountered. Equivalent anisotropic continuum (Snow, 1965) and dual porosity composite (Barenblatt, 1960) models are applicable only where representative elemental volume (REV) considerations dictate that the discrete behavior of individual fissure conduits may be lumped in an average manner. To define the situations in which a continuum representation may be substituted for a discrete system, effective appraisal of explicitly fractured media must be routinely possible.

Numerical modelling techniques may be used to investigate the phenomenological behavior of discretely fractured masses only if efficient computational procedures are employed. The fundamental requirement, therefore, for such 'numerical testing' is that the number of unknowns representing a realistic system of fractures must be retained within the capacity of currently available computer hardware. For transient analysis, where solution must extend through the time domain, it proves effective to condense system unknowns to a minimum before integrating in time. Although additional effort is expended in reducing the system degrees of freedom prior to execution, it is justified in the light of the large number of operations that must be completed on each of the resulting nodal equations.

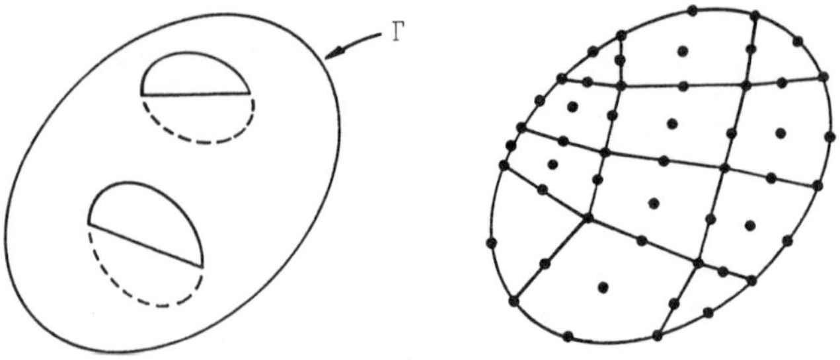

Figure 1. Left; A system of three intersecting fissure discs: Right; Finite element discretisation of central disc. ● Nodal points.

SOLUTION ALTERNATIVES

Existing finite element techniques may be used to evaluate flows in a system of arbitrarily oriented and interconnected fractures in three dimensional space. Plane finite elements may be meshed within the planes of individual fractures, as illustrated in Figure 1, and assembled into global form for the entire fracture network. The matrices formed in this manner are positive definite, symmetric and strongly profiled although a great number of system unknowns will exist. The number of active nodes may be reduced if condensation procedures are invoked to reduce the number of degrees of freedom per fracture disc. This procedure, however, still requires that extensive meshing is completed for each individual fracture disc prior to condensation and represents added computational complexity.

Boundary element procedures are well recognised as exhibiting extremely attractive features with regard to data input requirements. For steady flow within a circular disc, the meshing requirements are illustrated in Figure 2. Nodal and elemental coverage is restricted purely to the fissure edge and internal intersection boundaries. The resulting system of equations required to describe the hydraulic performance of this disc is therefore greatly reduced over the case of finite element representation. Manipulation of the boundary element equations for an individual fissure disc may be completed to describe the performance of the fractures merely in terms of fluid heads at the disc intersections. With this facility, the number of equations required to describe the full system of interconnected fractures may be reduced to a minimum at the elemental disc level to enable efficient transient analysis to be completed.

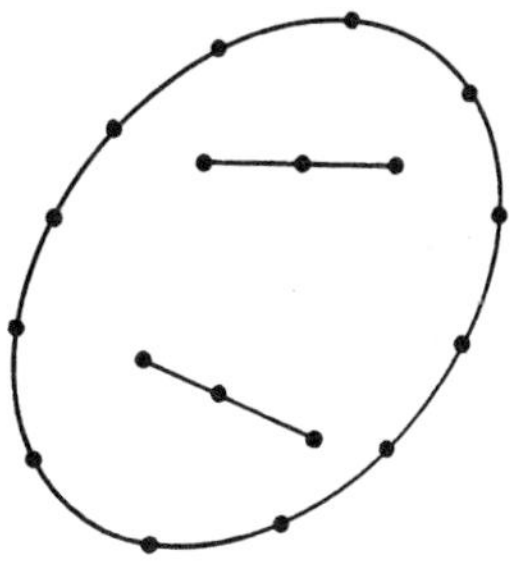

(2)

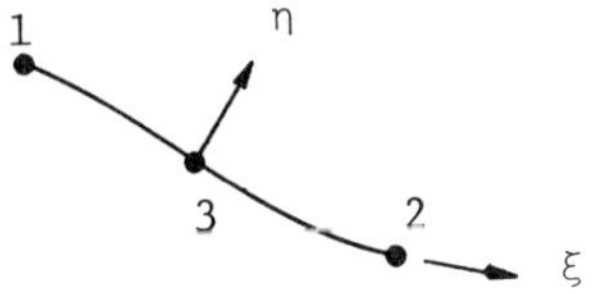

(3)

Figure 2. Boundary element discretisation of a single fissure disc.

Figure 3. Curved isoparametric representation of a boundary element in local coordinates. ● Nodal points.

NUMERICAL FORMULATION

A formulation is presented to evaluate the geometric hydraulic conductivity tensor of a single fissure disc using a direct boundary element procedure. The method may be illustrated to require trivial meshing requirements and result in a reduced degree of freedom system. Once formed, the geometric conductivity tensor, written purely in terms of the nodes present on the interior slit boundaries, may be substituted to yield steady and transient solution by a finite element analogy.

Boundary element analysis

A single fissure disc may be identified as the most basic geometric conduit of a system of interconnected fractures within an impermeable host matrix. For linear flow within a fissure of constant aperture, a single fissure disc may be represented as shown in Figure 2. The boundary constraint equation for this domain within a single plane may be identified in (x, y) space as (Jawson, 1963; Sym, 1963; Kellog, 1953)

$$c(i)\phi(i) + \int_\Gamma V(i,j)\phi(j)d\Gamma = \int_\Gamma \Phi(i,j)v(j)\cdot\bar{n}d\Gamma \qquad (1)$$

$$V(i,j) = -K/2\pi r \qquad (2)$$

$$\Phi(i,j) = \ln(r)/2\pi \qquad (3)$$

$$c(i) = \tfrac{1}{2}\delta_{ij} \text{ when point (i) is on a smooth boundary} \qquad (4)$$

$$= \delta \text{ when point (i) is fully enclosed within the domain}$$

$$r^2 = (x_i-x_j)^2 + (y_i-y_j)^2 \qquad (5)$$

where $\phi(j)$, $v(j)$ are total hydraulic potential and flow velocity at point j on the boundary of the domain due to a unit source at i, K is the hydraulic conductivity of the disc and $\bar{n}$ denotes the domain unit outer normal. All integrations are completed over the boundary of the domain (Γ) which, for the case of a perforated disc, comprises both internal slit and external edge boundaries. For this purpose the boundary of the domain is divided into a number of elements over which both geometry and boundary potential or velocity may be represented parametrically with respect to nodal values (Cruse, 1974; Lachat, 1976). In this particular application, the chosen circular contour of the fissure edge is most effectively represented by curved elements of which a single, three noded example is illustrated in Figure 3.

Shape functions are used to define the magnitude of nodal variables (ϕ, v•n) and geometry (x,y) in terms of the natural coordinate system for each element such that (Zienkiewicz, 1977a)

$$x = \underline{h}^T\underline{x} \; ; \; y = \underline{h}^T\underline{y} \tag{6a}$$

$$\phi = \underline{h}^T\underline{\phi} \; ; \; v \cdot \bar{n} = \underline{h}^T\underline{v \cdot n} \tag{6b}$$

where $\underline{h}^T$ is a vector of Lagrangian shape function terms and $\underline{x}$, $\underline{y}$, $\underline{\phi}$ and $\underline{v \cdot n}$ are vectors of nodal parameters defined over the span of each element.

The Jacobian relating the elemental geometries in mapped and ummapped form is given as

$$\frac{d\Gamma}{d\xi} = \left[\left(\frac{dx}{d\xi}\right)^2 + \left(\frac{dy}{d\xi}\right)^2 \right]^{\frac{1}{2}} \tag{7}$$

where the natural ccordinate system for the bi-unit element is denoted (ξ). Substitution of equations (6b) and (7) into equation (1) allows the boundary constraint identity to be evaluated over the entire boundary (Γ). Gaussian integration (Stroud, 1966) is used to evaluate the integrated velocity kernels (V(i,j)) in all cases where the points i and j are not coincident. Where i and j coincide, the magnitude of the integral and the associated free term $c(i)\phi(i)$ may be evaluated from the sum (Lachat, 1976)

$$c(i) + \int V(i,i)d\Gamma = \sum_{\substack{j=1 \\ i \neq j}} - \int_\Gamma V(i,j)d\Gamma \tag{8}$$

Setting the boundary heads arbitrarily to unity ensures that the right hand side of equation (1) is equal to zero. In all cases, two point quadrature has been found sufficient to evaluate the integrals of velocity kernels.

Integrals containing the potential kernel ($\Phi(i,j)$) are bounded in all cases excepting one where the points i and j coincide. Where unbounded, the integrals are most conveniently evaluated using a logarithmic quadrature formula (Anderson, 1965) with an appropriate change of variable.

$$\int_0^1 f(x)\ln(x) \cong \sum^{k} W_k f(x) \qquad (9)$$

where f(x) in this case contains terms moderated by the shape functions and W_k is an integration weighting applied at k integration points.

With the required integrals of equation (1) evaluated for all source locations (i), the n identities corresponding to the n nodes comprising the solution domain may be arranged in matrix form as

$$\underline{V}\,\underline{\phi} = \underline{\Phi}\,\underline{v} \qquad (10)$$

where the matrices $\underline{V}$, $\underline{\Phi}$ contain the integrated kernel functions and the vectors $\underline{\phi}$, $\underline{v}$ the nodal boundary conditions. Since, in general, only head or boundary flux will be prescribed at each node, appropriate column substitution in equation (8) may be instituted to transfer all known boundary conditions into the vector $\underline{v}$ on the right hand side. For all nodes on the fissure edge, boundary flow velocities are equal to zero. For the nodes present on the internal slit boundaries, neither velocities or heads may be specified since these are unknowns that depend on the global assemblage. A geometric conductivity tensor may, however, be evaluated for the disc if the head at one internal node is set to unity and the heads at all other nodes held at zero. This, if repeated for each of the retained internal nodes will yield a tensor representing the geometric hydraulic conductivity of the disc. This is equivalent to the symbolic rearrangement of equation (10) to yield (Zienkiewicz, 1977b)

$$\underline{v} = [\underline{\Phi}^{-1}\underline{V}]\,\phi \qquad (11)$$

where premultiplication by a matrix of integrated shape functions to convert nodal velocities into discharges may be used such that

$$\underline{q} = \underline{A}\ [\underline{\Phi}^{-1}\underline{V}]\ \underline{\Phi} \tag{12}$$

$$\underline{A} \cong b \int_{\Gamma} \underline{h}^{T}\, d\Gamma \tag{13}$$

where b is the aperture of the fissure aquifer and $\underline{q}$ is the vector of the nodal discharges. Matrix $\underline{A}$ is sparsely populated and will contain only as many entries per column as the number of other nodes connected through direct elemental contacts to a single degree of freedom.

The matrix identity, defined in equation (12), represents the geometric conductivity tensor for a single fissure disc of constant aperture. Formulated in this manner, the conductivity tensor represents that of a 'super element' corresponding to finite element form where interconnection between internal nodes only is retained. This formulation has been illustrated to provide an efficient and attractive method of solving steady potential problems in discretely fractured rock masses (Elsworth, 1986).

Finite element analysis

The geometric conductivity tensor evaluated in equation (12) is directly analogous to a 'super element' of finite element format given by

$$\underline{q} = \underline{K}\ \underline{\phi} \tag{14}$$

where $\underline{K}$ is the geometric conductivity tensor. The system may be solved for both steady and transient states by recourse to the finite element statement for transient flow.

For a system of interconnected discs, the transient response at any time (t) may be represented by the matrix identity

$$\underline{K}\ \underline{\phi}_t + \underline{S}\ \dot{\underline{\phi}}_t = \underline{q}_t \tag{15}$$

where $\underline{\phi}_t$ and $\dot{\underline{\phi}}_t$ are respectively vectors of total head and time derivative of head. Prescribed nodal discharges ($\underline{q}_t$) are known boundary conditions and $\underline{K}$ and $\underline{S}$ are tensors of geometric conductivity and storativity, respectively. If nodal potentials are assumed to vary linearly in a time step Δt, equation (15) may be rewritten for the next time step as

$$\underline{K}^*\ \underline{\phi}_{t+\Delta t} = \underline{q}^*_{t+\Delta t} \tag{16}$$

$$\text{where} \quad \underline{K}^* = (\underline{K} + \underline{S}/\Delta t) \tag{17}$$

$$\underline{q}^*_{t+\Delta t} = \underline{q}_{t+\Delta t} + \underline{\phi}_t\ \underline{S}/\Delta t \tag{18}$$

The modified global conductivity matrix $\underline{K}^*$ may be assembled if it is possible to determine the form of the diagonal storativity matrix $\underline{S}$. This is the final step required to complete the formulation. Since the analysis is required to service large systems of interconnected fissures it has been found appropriate to lump storativity terms at the remaining active nodes. It is known that the sum of storativity terms for a single disc must be equivalent to the total disc storativity thus

$$\text{trace}\,(\underline{S}) = b \int_A S_s \, dA \tag{19}$$

where S_s is the specific storage of the fissure per unit area and the integration is completed over the area of the disc (A). For circular discs, the integral may be calculated in a straightforward manner if it is assumed that the specific storage term (S_s) is constant. The storativity of the disc must then be distributed between nodes in any consistent manner. Since it has already been stated that the objective of the formulation is to represent domains containing many hundreds of fissure discs, this relatively simple mode of distributing storativity terms is entirely adequate for the defined purpose. The storativity terms are distributed proportionally to the diagonal terms of the geometric conductivity matrix ($\underline{K}$) such that

$$\underline{S} = \frac{\text{trace}(S)}{\text{trace}(\underline{K})} \; [\underline{I}\;\underline{K}] \tag{20}$$

where $\underline{I}$ is the identity matrix. Distributing the storativity terms in this manner has proved effective in all validation studies to date.

VALIDATION

The complex geometry of circular fissure discs containing intersection slits necessitates the use of numerical simulation techniques to provide benchmark examples for both steady and transient flow states. Validation studies for the proposed hybrid boundary element-finite element solution procedure have been completed against a finite element representation of a single circular fissure as illustrated in Figure 4. The finite element discretisation contains twin intersection slits symmetrically disposed above and below the horizontal diameter. A total of 28 nine-noded, plane flow elements are used to discretise the domain resulting in a total of 135 nodes. The model is used as a benchmark with which to compare the performance of a disc of identical geometry discretised by 26 boundary nodes as illustrated in Figure 5.

In the validation tests, the fluid head at one slit is raised from zero at time $t=0^-$ to unity at $t=0^+$. To compare performance of the boundary element technique with the

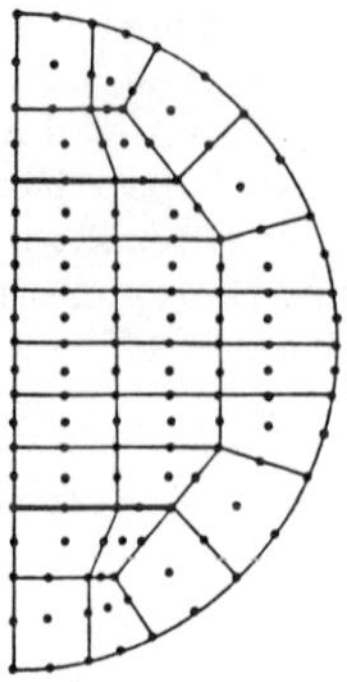

(4)

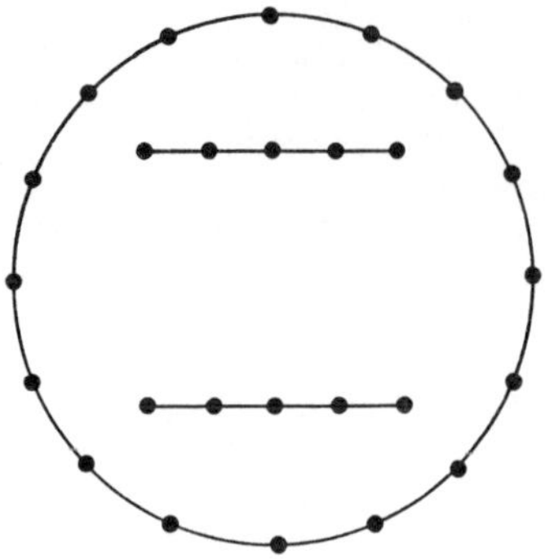

(5)

Figure 4. Finite element mesh for validation studies.
Figure 5. Boundary element discretisation for validation. ● Nodal points.

benchmark finite element solution, the equilibration of fluid pressures at the unconstrained slit is monitored. The performance of the boundary element analyses for the cases where ten and two retained degrees of freedom are used to describe the fissure disc are illustrated in Figure 6. It may be noted that the ten degree of freedom system corresponds directly with the nodal density depicted in Figure 5 while the two degree of freedom system is derived from the former with uniform hydraulic potential assumed for all nodes comprising a single internal slit. The transient performance is not markedly different for these two levels of nodal condensation. The short term hydraulic response of the fissure disc is somewhat lacking in comparison with the finite element solution although the long term agreement between the two solution procedures is favorable.

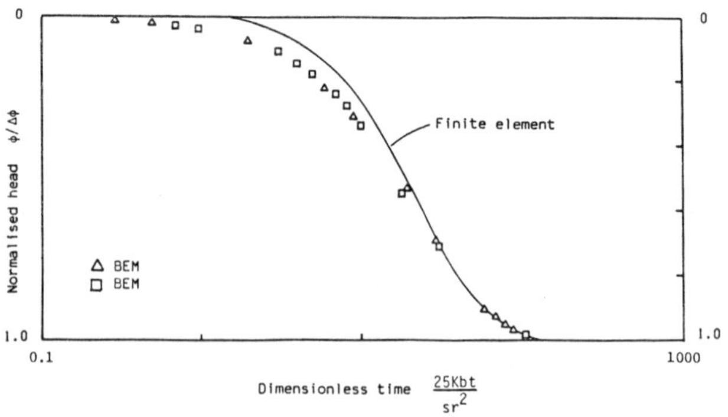

Figure 6. Transient performance of a single, circular fissure disc. - Finite element; △ 10 degrees of freedom; □ 2 degrees of freedom.

The poor agreement in the initial period is attributed to the rather crude manner in which storage is distributed within the fissure disc. As a result, the release of storage from within the disc is governed exclusively by the change in hydraulic potential at the slit elements. Clearly, this does not allow such high fidelity in representing the spatial change in heads over the entire disc as may be afforded in the finite element approximation. For the desired application, however, the results are considered satisfactory. In this light, it would appear that retaining a single degree of freedom per intersection slit would be adequate for most engineering purposes.

CONCLUSIONS

An isoparametric boundary element model is developed for the specific task of efficiently representing the hydraulic performance of three dimensional fracture networks. The boundary element formulation is recast in finite element format and an appropriate procedure applied to distribute the storage of a single fissure disc between the active nodes. The resulting matrices have been observed, in all cases to date, to be positive definite, well conditioned and nominally symmetric.

Benchmark comparisons of the solution procedure with finite element simulations have illustrated that the proposed boundary element method performs favorably. This is especially apparent in considering the drastically reduced numbers of equations (two equations in the ultimate case) utilised in the boundary element procedure compared to the finite element method. It appears, therefore, that the procedure developed in the previous offers considerable promise in ameliorating many of the problems regarding equation size and bandwidth currently inhibiting effective transient solution for large fracture networks.

REFERENCES

Anderson, D. G. (1965) Gaussian quadrature formulae for $\int \ln(x)f(x)dx$. Math. Comp. 19, 447-481.

Barenblatt, G. I., Yu, P. Zheltov and Kochina, I. N. (1960) Basic concepts in the theory of seepage of homogeneous fluids in fissured rocks. J. Appl. Math. Mech., 24, 1286-1303.

Cruse, T. A. (1974) An improved boundary integral equation method for three dimensional elastic stress analysis. Computers and Structures, 4, 741-754.

Elsworth, D. (1986) A hybrid boundary element-finite element procedure for fluid flow in sparsely fractured rock masses. (In press)

Jaswon, M. A. (1963) Integral equation methods in potential theory: I. Proc. Roy. Soc., A, 275, 33-26.

Kellog, O. D. (1953) Foundations of potential theory. Dover.

Lachat, J. C. and Watson, J. O. (1976) Effective numerical treatment of boundary integral equations: a formulation for three-dimensional elastostatics. Int. Journ. for Num. Meth. in Eng., 10, 991-1005.

Snow, D. T. (1965) A parallel plate model of fractured permeable media. Ph.D. Thesis, University of California, Berkeley.

Stroud, A. H. and Secrest, D. (1966). Gaussian quadrature formulas. Prentice-Hall, Englewood Cliffs, NJ.

Symm,G. T. (1963) Integral equation methods in potential theory: II. Proc. Roy. Soc., A, 33-46.

Zienkiewicz, O. C. (1977a) The finite element method. Third edition, McGraw-Hill (UK).

Zienkiewicz, O. C., Kelly, D. W. and Bettes, P. (1977b) The coupling of the finite element method and boundary solution procedures. International Journal for Numerical Methods in Engineering. 11, 355-375.

VI International Conference on Finite Elements in Water Resources, Lisboa, Portugal, June 1986

Numerical Model for the Transport Velocity Representation of Groundwater Flow

M. Nawalany
Warsaw Technical University (Warsaw, Poland) on leave at TNO-DGV Institute of Applied Geoscience (Delft, The Netherlands)

INTRODUCTION

A purpose of the presented model is to discriminate and describe flow subsystems that exist in real groundwater systems under steady state conditions. It is essential for this kind of system analysis to calculate all three components of the flux (or velocity) vector $\underline{q} = (q_x, q_y, q_z)^T$ with sufficient accuracy. The classical approach to the calculations consists of a numerical solution of the flow equation in terms of pressure p followed by the numerical differentiation of $p=p(x,y,z)$ in order to obtain approximate values of $q_x(x,y,z)$, $q_y(x,y,z)$ and $q_z(x,y,z)$. However, in many cases the vertical component q_z (important for discriminating the subsystems) computed this way does not meet the accuracy requirements unless a very dense finite element mesh is applied.
The presented model is based on the so called <u>Transport Velocity Representation</u> (TVR) of groundwater flow. In the representation (W. Zijl, 1984), the components of $\underline{q}$ are considered the primary variables while the pressure is merely a secondary one. The model can be classified as a three-dimensional (3D) and mixed (finite element - finite difference) numerical model of steady state groundwater flow. It solves three coupled partial differential equations for q_x, q_y, q_z using the finite element Galerkin approximation in the horizontal dimensions x,y and the finite difference method for the vertical dimension z. The natural (physical) boundary conditions imposed on the upper, the lower and the side boundaries of a given groundwater system are translated into appropriate boundary conditions for each component of the flux. The system's matrix and right-hand side vector (RHS) for the resultant algebraic equations are assembled with the automatic quad-tree finite element generator, which is capable

of handling the complex geometries of real groundwater systems. Since the matrix obtained is symmetric, positive definite, sparse and usually very large, the Incomplete Cholesky Decomposition Conjugate Gradient method (H.A. van der Vorst, 1982) has been chosen to solve the equations. The ICCG solver is followed by a postprocessor that uses computed values of q_x, q_y, q_z for the pathlines' calculations. The England's method, which is actually applied for these calculations, is used to outline and represent graphically the flow subsystems (M. Nawalany, 1984). After the pathlines' calculations the groundwater system is divided into subsystems which makes it possible to calculate the travel and residence times as well as the recharge/discharge rates related to each subsystem.

TRANSPORT VELOCITY REPRESENTATION OF GROUNDWATER FLOW

The classical approach to the groundwater steady state flow problem consists of the mass balance equation (J. Bear, 1979)

$$\nabla . \underline{q} = 0 \tag{1}$$

where $\underline{q} = (q_x, q_y, q_z)^T$ - mass flux of fluid in some flow domain D, $(kg/m^2/s)$

and the closing formula, which relates the mass flux $\underline{q}$ to the "driving force", that is to the pressure p in the domain D. The closing formula is represented by Darcy's Law (J. Bear, 1979):

$$\underline{q} = - \frac{\rho}{\mu} k \, (\nabla p - \rho g \nabla z) \quad \text{in D} \tag{2}$$

where ρ - fluid density, (kg/m^3)
μ - dynamic viscosity, (Pa.s)
k - intrinsic permeability of the porous medium, (m^2)
p - pressure, (Pa)
g - magnitude of the gravitational acceleration, (m/s^2)
z - z-coordinate oriented in the direction of gravitational acceleration (i.e. downwards), (m)
∇ - gradient operator, (1/m).

Formula (2) can also be written as follows:

$$\beta \underline{q} = - \nabla p + \rho g \nabla z \quad \text{in D} \tag{3}$$

where $\beta = \mu / k\rho$. (4)

Substitution of relationship (3) into equation (1) gives

$$\nabla . (\frac{1}{\beta} (- \nabla p + \rho g \nabla z)) = 0 \quad \text{in D} \tag{5}$$

which, if supplemented with the physical boundary conditions

$$\alpha_1 p + \alpha_2 q_n = 1 \quad \text{on } \partial D, \tag{6}$$

describes the groundwater flow problem completely.
Indeed, after solving equation (5) with boundary conditions (6) one can consequently calculate $\underline{q}$ by substituting the solution obtained (i.e. pressure p in D) into formula (2) or (3). Thus the groundwater flow problem is solved providing the pressure p and/or the normal component of mass flux q_n are prescribed (known or estimated) on the flow domain's boundary ∂D. For a homogeneous fluid having a density equal to ρ=const one can equivalently use the concept of piezometric head ϕ instead of the pressure p and the volumetric flux $\underline{q}_v = \underline{q}/\rho$ instead of the mass flux $\underline{q}$. However, the classical formulation of the groundwater flow problem has one serious disadvantage when approximated numerically. It has been shown by G.F. Pinder and H.G. Gray (G.F. Pinder et al., 1977) that numerical differentiation of p in equation (2) results in a degradation of accuracy of the flux components q_x, q_y and q_z being approximated.
W. Zijl (W. Zijl, 1984) proposed to reverse the procedure of calculating $\underline{q}$ by eliminating the pressure p from equations (1) and (2) and by considering $\underline{q}$ as the primary variable. The resultant Laplacian-like equation for $\underline{q}$ can be solved numerically with the standard finite-element method without any numerical differentiation of and thus without the degradation in accuracy. In this approach the pressure p becomes the secondary variable and can be calculated afterwards.
The Transport Velocity Representation of groundwater flow has the following form:

$$-\nabla^2 \underline{q} = \nabla \times \underline{\Omega} \tag{7}$$

$$\text{where } \underline{\Omega} = \frac{1}{\beta}\left(\nabla(\rho g) \times \nabla z - \nabla\beta \times \underline{q}\right). \tag{8}$$

Equation (8), however, when supplemented only with physical boundary conditions (6) does not represent the well-posed problem. In order to make the new approach, represented by equation (7) and boundary conditions (6), equivalent to the classical approach, represented by equations (1) and (3) and boundary conditions (6), one has to add the following auxiliary boundary conditions, (W. Zijl, 1984):

i) if the pressure p is prescribed on ∂D it is necessary to prescribe in addition

$$\nabla \cdot \underline{q} = 0 \quad \text{on } \partial D, \tag{9}$$

ii) if the normal component of flux $q_n = n.\underline{q}$ is prescribed on ∂D it is necessary to prescribe also

$$\underline{n} \times (\underline{\Omega} - \nabla \times \underline{q}) = \underline{0} \quad \text{on } \partial D. \tag{10}$$

When the auxiliary boundary conditions - i) or ii) - are prescribed on ∂D in addition to the physical boundary conditions (6) every solution of equation (7) satisfies both the mass conservation equation (1) and Darcy's Law in the flow region D. If necessary, the equation for the pressure p

$$\nabla^2 p = -(\nabla\beta)\cdot\underline{q} + \nabla\rho\cdot\underline{g} \tag{11}$$

can also subsequently be solved in D with the physical boundary conditions (6).

NUMERICAL FORMULATION OF THE TVR PROBLEM

When simulating groundwater flow on a regional scale one is usually confronted with a very high aspect ratio between the horizontal and vertical rates of change of the physical and geometrical parameters of the groundwater system. Consequently, the horizontal components of the flux $\underline{q}$ may exhibit discontinuities in the vertical direction z. In order to avoid numerical simulation of the variables which are discontinuous the following transformation of the flux field $\underline{q}$ was proposed (W. Zijl, 1985):

$$\underline{S} = \beta\underline{q}\ . \tag{12}$$

For β having discontinuities in the z-direction the S_x and S_y components of the vector field $\underline{S}$ are continuous. Hence, by combining S_x and S_y with the variable q_z (which is also continuous in z-direction) one obtains the set of p.d.e. that corresponds to flow equation (7):

$$\begin{aligned}
\nabla\cdot(\sigma\nabla S_x) - \sigma S_x \frac{\partial^2\alpha}{\partial x^2} &= \sigma S_y \frac{\partial^2\alpha}{\partial x\partial y} + q_z \frac{\partial^2\alpha}{\partial x\partial z} \\
\nabla\cdot(\sigma\nabla S_y) - \sigma S_y \frac{\partial^2\alpha}{\partial x^2} &= \sigma S_x \frac{\partial^2\alpha}{\partial x\partial y} + q_z \frac{\partial^2\alpha}{\partial y\partial z} \\
\nabla\cdot(\beta\nabla q_z) + \beta q_z\left(\frac{\partial^2\alpha}{\partial x^2} + \frac{\partial^2\alpha}{\partial y^2}\right) &= S_x \frac{\partial^2\alpha}{\partial x\partial z} + S_y \frac{\partial^2\alpha}{\partial y\partial z}
\end{aligned} \tag{13}$$

Since equations (13) are symmetric and positive definite any standard numerical method can be used to obtain approximate solutions for S_x, S_y and $\hat{q}_z$ (so q_x, q_y and q_z) in D. Boundary conditions (6), (9) and (10) are accordingly adapted to the variables S_x, S_y and q_z. Variables S_x, S_y and q_z are approximated with the mixed finite element - finite difference method which was proposed by D.K. Babu and G.F. Pinder (1982).
The discretization nodes are arranged in the series of equally spaced horizontal planes with an identical triangular finite element mesh on each plane - see Figure 1. In the model an automatic quade-tree generator is used to cover all the discontinuities existing in the system with prescribed accu-

racy. For the horizontal plane located at depth z the following approximations are assumed for S_x, S_y and q_z:

$$\hat{S}_x\ (x,y,z) = \sum_{j=1}^{N} a_j(z)\phi_j(x,y)$$
$$\hat{S}_y\ (x,y,z) = \sum_{j=1}^{N} b_j(z)\phi_j(x,y) \qquad (14)$$
$$\hat{q}_z\ (x,y,z) = \sum_{j=1}^{N} c_j(z)\phi_j(x,y)$$

where N - number of nodes in the plane
$\phi_j(j=1,\ldots,N)$ - linear basis functions.

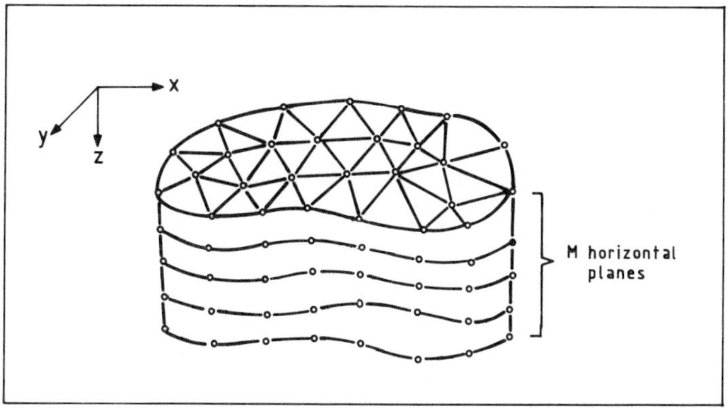

Figure 1. Mixed, finite element - finite difference mesh and the system of coordinates for the model.

By applying the Galerkin approach in the horizontal directions x, y and the finite difference approximation in the z-direction one obtains the set of algebraic equations having both a block and band structure.
Vectors $\underline{a}$, $\underline{b}$ and $\underline{c}$ shown in Figure 2 represent unknown values of the coefficients a_j, b_j and c_j in approximation (14) for NxM nodal points of the mixed mesh, where M is the number of horizontal planes in the model. Consequently, the dimension of the vector $\underline{x} = (\underline{a}^T,\underline{b}^T,\underline{c}^T)^T$ is equal to 3xNxM. Typical values of N and M used in the model were N = 50-200 and M = 5-30; hence the number of unknowns was between 750 and 18000. Sub-matrix $A=A^T(B=B^T,C=C^T)$ of the block matrix $\mathcal{A}$ represents the interactions of the variable $S_x(S_y,q_z)$ with itself. Offdiagonal bands in the matrix A (B,C) correspond to the interactions between the adjacent horizontal planes. Finally,

submatrices D, E and F represent the pairwise interactions between the variables S_x, S_y and q_z. The RHS-vector $\underline{r} = (\underline{r}_x^T, \underline{r}_y^T, \underline{r}_z^T)^T$ is calculated according to the boundary conditions (6) and (9) or (10) prescribed on ∂D.

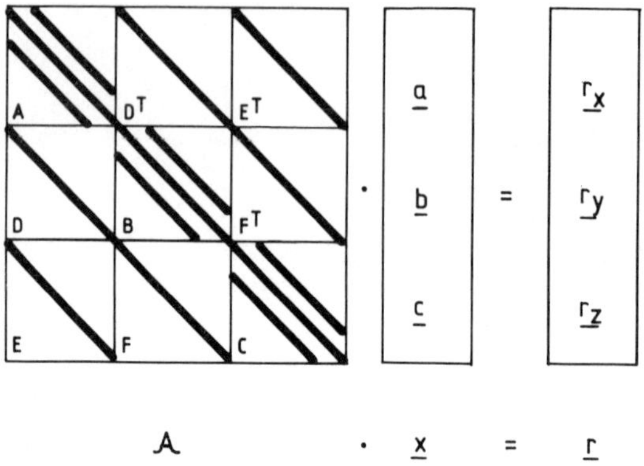

Figure 2. Structure of the algebraic equations.

THE SOLVER

The system of algebraic equations $\mathcal{A}\underline{x} = \underline{r}$ has been decoupled and solved by the outer iterations as shown in Figure 3.

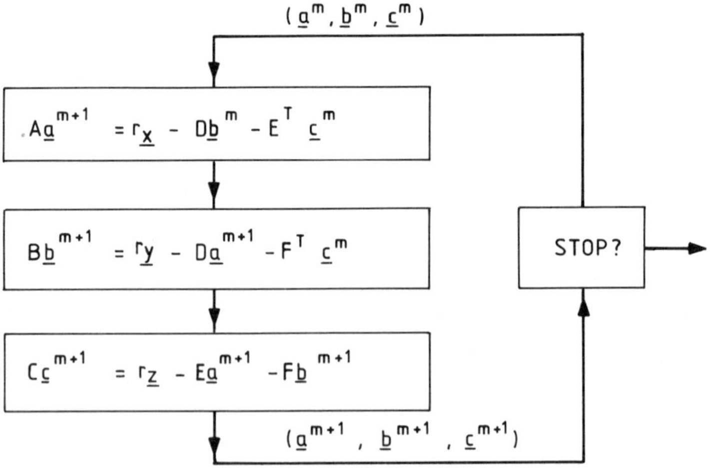

Figure 3. Outer iterations solver.

For each outer iteration three systems of algebraic equations with NxM unknowns are solved by the Preconditioned Incomplete Cholesky Decomposition Conjugate Gradient Method (ICCG). Since the matrices involved are large, sparse and symmetric the compact forms of the matrices, which contain only non-zero entries of the corresponding lower triangular submatrices, are used. The compact matrices are supplemented with the pointer vectors respresenting the structure of the matrices. It was observed that when making an incomplete Cholesky decomposition of matrices A, B and C it was sufficient to store only the corresponding matrices L_A, L_B and L_C because the pointer (structural) vectors were the same as those for the matrices A, B and C by the definition of incomplete decomposition. The ICCG method applied to the problems tested has proven to converge very rapidly to the true solutions. An average as many as three to six outer iterations and two to sixteen inner (Conjugate Gradient) iterations were needed to obtain the desired accuracy of the approximation. Table 1 shows the typical times spent by the VAX 11/780 computer for: assembling of the submatrices of $\mathcal{A}$ creating the pointer vectors for them and generating the RHS-vectors, decomposing the matrices A, B and C with the incomplete Cholesky decomposition method and performing the outer iterations.

Table 1. Computation times for the TVR method

Activity	N=41, M=5	N=41, M=10
Assembling	28.42 CPU	55.37 CPU
Decomposing	02.27 CPU	05.34 CPU
Performing out.iter.	13.05 CPU	27.04 CPU

NUMERICAL VERSUS ANALYTICAL SOLUTIONS

So called Toth's problem (J. Toth, 1963) was chosen as the test example for the numerical model of the TVR equations (13). This problem considers two-dimensional vertical unconfined groundwater flow of a homogeneous fluid ($\rho g=1$) in a homogeneous ($\beta=1$) rectangular domain $D=[0,s]\times[0,z_0]$. The vertical boundaries and the bottom of the system are assumed to be impervious. On the top boundary the pressure is prescribed in the form of a sinusoidal wave superimposed on a linear trend, that is

$$p(x) = cx - \frac{cs}{2\pi}\sin(2\pi x/s) \qquad (15)$$

where c - slope of the trend, (Pa/m).

There exists an analytical solution for this problem in D, namely:

$$q_x(x,z) = \sum_{m=1}^{\infty} B_m C_m \sin(C_m x)\ \cosh(-C_m(z_0-z))/\cosh(-C_m z_o)$$
$$q_z(x,z) = -\sum_{m=1}^{\infty} B_m C_m \cos(C_m x)\ \sinh(-C_m(z_o-z))/\cosh(-C_m z_o) \quad (16)$$

where $C_m = m\pi/s$

$$B_m = \begin{cases} \frac{8cs}{\pi^2} \frac{(1-\cos m\pi)}{m^2(m^2-4)} & \text{- if m is an odd integer} \\ 0 & \text{- otherwise.} \end{cases}$$

The TVR equations (7) were solved for the physical and auxiliary boundary conditions (6), (9) and (10) which, for this case, had the following form:

i) on the side boundaries (x=0 or x=s): $\frac{\partial S_x}{\partial n} = \frac{\partial S_y}{\partial n} = \frac{\partial q_z}{\partial n} = 0$

ii) on the bottom boundary ($z=z_0$): $\frac{\partial S_x}{\partial n} = \frac{\partial S_y}{\partial n} = q_z = 0$

iii) on the top boundary (z=0): $S_x = -c\ (1 - \cos 2\pi x/s)$

$S_y = 0$

$\frac{\partial q_z}{\partial n} = -\frac{2\pi c}{s} .\sin\ (2\pi x/s)$

Table 2 contains a comparison between the analytical (A), the numerical - classical (C) and the TVR (T) - solutions of the Toth problem obtained for c=0.1 Pa/m, s=1.0 m and z_o=1.0 m. The discretization mesh with N=41 and M=5 was used in the numerical models.

Table 2. q_x and q_z values calculated numerically and analytically.

		q_x		q_z	
		x=0.25	x=0.50	x=0.25	x=0.50
z=0.3	C	-0.04360	-0.06320	-0.05050	0.0
	T	-0.04529	-0.06763	-0.04862	0.3x10(-7)
	A	-0.04587	-0.06881	-0.04757	0.0
z=0.5	C	-0.02440	-0.03440	-0.04757	0.0
	T	-0.02539	-0.03646	-0.02447	0.18x10(-7)
	A	-0.02577	-0.03705	-0.02405	0.0
z=0.7	C	-0.01444	-0.02000	-0.01200	0.0
	T	-0.01503	-0.02135	-0.01148	0.9x10(-8)
	A	-0.01527	-0.02169	-0.01130	0.0

The relative error of the TVR numerical solution is in the order of 1%, whereas the classical solution has a relative error of approximately 5%. These quite small errors cause, however, a completely different pattern of pathlines in the system - see Figure 4. Pathlines for the TVR solution almost coincide with those obtained from the analytical solution whereas trajectories based on the classical numerical solution are considerably distorted. It was observed that even for N=41 and M=40 (i.e. for a very dense mesh) the classical trajectories do not match the exact ones. The pathlines for the example have been calculated with the England's method which has proven to be very accurate and efficient.

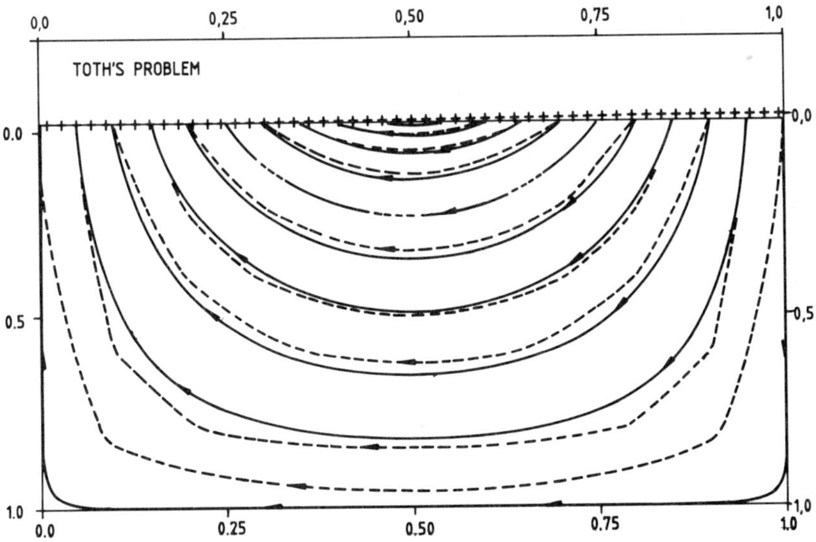

Figure 4. Trajectories of water particles calculated from: (---) classical approach, (——) analytical and TVR approaches. (+) indicates the pressure line on the top boundary of the system.

CONCLUSIONS

The example presented shows that the TVR method can be superior to the classical approach for the type of groundwater flow problems that involve pathlines calculations. The method also allows the application of standard finite element solvers to the symmetric and positive definite set of equations for q_x, q_y and q_z. By considering the flux $\underline{q}$ as the primary variable and using the Zijl flow equations (thus avoiding numerical differentiation), one can calculate the velocity field with an acceptable accuracy even with relatively few discretization nodes.

REFERENCES

Babu, D.K., Pinder, G.F. (1982) A Three Dimensional Hybrid Finite Element - Finite Difference Scheme for Groundwater Simulation in Proc. of 10th IMACS World Congress, Montreal, Canada.

Bear, J. (1979) Hydraulics of Groundwater. McGraw-Hill Int. Publ. Comp. New York.

Nawalany, M. (1984) Pathlines Computations in Groundwater Flow in Proc. of Int.Conf. on Accuracy Estimates and Adaptive Refinements in Finite Element Computations, June 19-22, 1984, Lisbon.

Nawalany, M. (1985) Flow System Analysis (FLOSA-3D), Report no. 9900 DGV-TNO, Delft.

Toth, J. (1963) A theoretical analysis of groundwater flow in small drainage basins. Journal of Geophysical Research, Vol. 68, no. 16.

Van den Vorst, H. (1982) Preconditioning by Incomplete Decompositions, Ph.D. Thesis, Rijksuniversiteit Utrecht, Utrecht.

Zijl, W. (1984) Finite Element Method Based on a Transport Velocity Representation for Groundwater Motion, WRR Vol. 20, No. 1.

Zijl, W. (1985) Subsurface Fluid Dynamics and Transport Phenomena with Vector Computers, 11th IMACS World Congress, August 5-9, 1985, Oslo.

VI International Conference on Finite Elements in Water Resources, Lisboa, Portugal, June 1986

Finite Element Simulation of Fluid and Energy Transport in Deformable Fractured-Porous Media

V. Guvanasen, P.S. Huyakorn
GeoTrans Inc., Herndon, VA 22070, U.S.A.
T. Chan
Atomic Energy of Canada Limited, Pinawa, Manitoba, Canada

INTRODUCTION

The environmental safety of disposal of nuclear fuel waste in geologic formations depends on the degree of isolation afforded by the host rock. Rock masses frequently contain large numbers of discontinuities or fractures which are potential pathways for radionuclides migrating from a repository to the accessible environment. Figure 1 shows some interrelationships between processes affecting the capability of a geologic repository system for isolating radionuclides from the biosphere. As indicated by the arrows, the processes of heat transport, groundwater flow, solute transport, radionuclide transport, and mechanical equilibrium may be coupled in both directions.

The importance of thermohydromechanical coupling to nuclear waste disposal in fractured rock has been recognized by Ayatollahi et al. (1979), who presented a finite-element formulation based on Biot's (1955) consolidation theory and Gurtin's variational principle. Guvanasen and Chan (1980) extended this work to include convective thermal transport and radionuclide transport using a Galerkin finite element formulation. Similar work has also been presented by Witherspoon et al. (1981), whose formulation is based on the isotropic assumption and the combination of the Galerkin formulation and the variational principle.

In the field, effects of fractured rock deformation on the flow of groundwater have been observed. For example, during the excavation of a 250 m shaft in a granitic batholith in Canada in 1984, significant perturbations in water pressure distributions and water flow rates into the excavated shaft were observed (Chan et al., 1985). A preliminary investigation indicated that changes in stress normal to the fracture zones were responsible for these perturbations. The perturbation around a nuclear waste repository is compounded by thermally induced stresses and buoyancy effects. A method for investigating thermohydroelastic effects based on the Galerkin finite element approach is presented in this paper. Two cases of relevance to the investigation of fluid flow around nuclear waste repositories are also discussed.

MATHEMATICAL DEVELOPMENT

Thermohydroelastic equilibrium in a solid matrix Generalized equations describing isothermal hydroelastic equilibrium in poroelastic materials have been given by Biot (1955). Assuming that the thermoelastic dissipation is negligibly small, these equations can be extended to describe thermohydroelastic phenomena. The equations are written in tensorial form as

$$\frac{\partial}{\partial x_j} \tau_{ij} + F_i = 0 \qquad (1)$$

$$\tau_{ij} = C_{ijkl} \varepsilon_{kl} - U_{ij} p - W_{ij} \Delta T \qquad (2)$$

$$\varepsilon_{ij} = \frac{1}{2} \left(\frac{\partial u_i}{\partial x_j} + \frac{\partial u_j}{\partial x_i}\right) \qquad (3)$$

τ_{ij} is the bulk stress tensor, ε_{ij} the strain tensor, C_{ijkl} the elastic constant tensor, U_{ij} the tensor of hydroelastic constants, W_{ij} the tensor of thermoelastic constants, p the fluid pressure, ΔT the increment of temperature, u_i the displacement vector, x_i the Cartesian coordinates, and F_i the body force per unit volume vector.

Flow equation in porous media A modified form of Biot's (1955) equation for flow through deformable porous media is written tensorially as

$$\frac{\partial}{\partial t} (\rho_f \zeta) + \frac{\partial}{\partial x_i} (\rho_f q_i) - \rho_f Q = 0 \qquad (4)$$

where the change of fluid content per unit volume,

$$\zeta = U_{ij} \varepsilon_{ij} + \frac{p}{M} \qquad (5)$$

M is Biot's hydroelastic constant, q_i the Darcy velocity vector, ρ_f the fluid density, Q the rate of fluid volumetric production per unit volume, and t is time.

Heat transport in porous media Assuming that the interconvertibility of mechanical and thermal energy is negligibly small, and that fluid and solid phases are in thermodynamic equilibrium, the equation of heat transport in porous media is written as (Combarnous and Bories, 1971)

$$\frac{\partial}{\partial t}[(\rho c)_e T] + \frac{\partial}{\partial x_i}(\theta\, v_i\, \rho_f\, c_f\, T) - \frac{\partial}{\partial x_i}(E_{ij}\frac{\partial T}{\partial x_j}) - Q_H = 0 \qquad (6)$$

$(\rho c)_e = \theta_f c_f + (1-\theta)\,\rho_s c_s$, c_f is the specific heat capacity of fluid, c_s the specific heat capacity of solid skeleton, θ the porosity, v_i the fluid velocity which equals q_i/θ, T the temperature, E_{ij} the hydrodynamic thermal dispersion tensor which is given by $\rho_f c_f\,(\alpha_T V \delta_{ij} + (\alpha_L - \alpha_T)\, v_i v_j/V) + \lambda_{ij}$, α_L the longitudinal dispersivity, α_T the transversal dispersivity, $V = (v_i v_i)^{\frac{1}{2}}$, λ_{ij} is the thermal conductivity tensor, and Q_H is the specific enthalpy production rate.

Treatment of fractures

Equilibrium analysis The mathematical idealization of fractures has been proposed by several researchers. A fracture is approximated by a pair of surfaces between which normal and shear displacements are permissible, see Figure 2. In this paper the scheme of Goodman and St. John (1976) is adopted. It has the capability for simulating:

(a) normal stress - normal displacement hyperbolic relationship

$$(\sigma_n - \sigma_o)/\sigma_n = -\Delta v/(V_{mc}\frac{\sigma_{st}}{\sigma_o} + \Delta v) \qquad (7)$$

Where σ_n is the normal stress, σ_o the initial stress, σ_{st} the seating stress, V_{mc} the maximum closure of fracture, and Δv is the normal displacement of fracture.

(b) shear displacement

$$\Delta\tau_s = k_s\, \Delta u \qquad (8)$$

Where $\Delta\tau_s$ is the change in shear stress in the fracture plane, Δu the shear displacement along the fracture plane, and k_s is the shear stiffness coefficient (equals 0 when $\tau_s > \tau_{peak}$).

Flow analysis Assuming that hydraulic conductivity of the fracture zone is large compared with the background porous matrix, the flow can be considered dominant along the fracture plane axis. The flow equation for a fracture plane can then be derived by vertically integrating equation (4) along the direction normal to each fracture plane to yield

$$\frac{\partial}{\partial t}[b\,\overline{\rho_f \zeta}] + \frac{\partial}{\partial \xi_i}(b\,\overline{\rho_f q_i}) - \overline{\rho_f Q}\,b + M_L = 0 \qquad (9)$$

where b is the aperture of fracture, ξ_i the coordinates along a fracture plane, M_L the net mass flux from the upper and lower planes bounding the fracture, and the upper bar indicates vertical averaging along the direction normal to the fracture plane.

Thermal transport analysis Based on the assumption of flow dominance along the direction of the fracture plane axis, the transport of thermal energy along a fracture plane is expressed as

$$\frac{\partial}{\partial t}(b[\overline{\rho c}]_e\,\overline{T}) + \frac{\partial}{\partial \xi_i}(b\,\overline{\rho_f \theta c_f\,q_i\,T})$$

$$- \frac{\partial}{\partial \xi_i}(b\,\overline{E_{ij}}\,\frac{\partial \overline{T}}{\partial \xi_j}) - b\overline{Q}_H = 0 \qquad (10)$$

Equations of state
Fluid density (ρ_f) and dynamic viscosity (μ) are expressed as functions of pressure and temperature, thus

$$\rho_f = \rho_f(p,T)\ , \text{ and } \mu = \mu(T) \qquad (11)$$

METHOD OF SOLUTION

The set of nonlinear equations for the solid matrix and fracture planes (equations (1), (4), and (6) to (11)) is solved using equations (2), (3), (5), and Darcy's law

$$q_i = \frac{k_{ij}\,\rho_f^0\,g}{\mu}\frac{\partial}{\partial x_j}(h + e\,x_3) \qquad (12)$$

Where k_{ij} is the permeability tensor, ρ_f^0 the reference fluid density, g the gravitational acceleration, $e = (\rho_f - \rho_f^0)/\rho_f^0$, and the reference hydraulic head, $h = p/\rho_f^0 g + x_3$.

By applying the finite element method in conjunction with the weighted residual technique, the following system equations are obtained:

$$[S^1_{IJ}(u_i)]\{U_J\} = \{F^1_I(u_i, h, T)\} \qquad (13a)$$

$$[M^2_{IJ}(u_i, h, T)]\{\frac{dh_J}{dt}\} + [S^2_{IJ}(u_i, h, T)]\{H_J\} = \{F^2_I\} \qquad (13b)$$

$$[M^3_{IJ}(h, T)]\{\frac{dT_J}{dt}\} + [S^3_{IJ}(h, T)]\{T_J\} = \{F^3_I\} \qquad (13c)$$

Where S^i_{IJ} is the stiffness matrix, M^i_{IJ} the mass matrix, F^i_I the load vector, u_I the displacement vector, H_I the reference hydraulic head vector, and T_I is the temperature vector.

Equations (13a to 13c) are solved iteratively by the Picard method. A finite difference approximation is used for the evaluation of temporal derivatives.

Two two-dimensional finite element representations of fracture planes are illustrated in Figure 2. Four-noded fracture elements for equilibrium analysis, and two-noded fracture elements for flow and thermal transport analysis are shown. Because different numbers of nodes are required to solve equations (13a to 13c) simultaneously, two meshes with identical discretization in the solid matrix zones, but different discretization along the fracture planes, are superimposed.

CASES STUDIED

Two cases have been studied using this finite element scheme. Both involve a fracture traversing a slightly permeable rock block subjected to nonisothermal flow conditions. The elastic properties of the rock block were assumed to be linear, isotropic, and thermally and hydromechanically independent. The fractures were assumed to have uniform apertures and to obey the cubic law (Snow, 1965) (i.e., $k = b^2/12$). The first case involves a horizontal fracture with forced convection, and the second case a vertical fracture with free convection.

Horizontal Fracture

A rock block intersected by a horizontal fracture is shown in Figure 3. The block-fracture configuration was assumed to be under a plain strain condition. Boundary conditions adopted in this analysis are shown in Figure 3. Forced cooling of the rock block along the fracture was effected by maintaining the water reservoir upstream at 20°C.

The system was initially subjected to the following conditions: (i) a uniform compressive initial stress of -1.33 MPa in the vertical direction, (ii) steady flow, and (iii) a uniform temperature of 20°C.

Material properties are given in Table 1. Results from different combinations of phenomenological components, initial aperture (b_o), and maximum closure (V_{mc}), are displayed in Figures 4 through 8. Details are given in Table 2.

Time history curves of dimensionless flow rates along the fracture (flow rate/initial flow rate) are displayed in Figure 4; the temporal variation in flow rate due to aperture size and rock block deformation can be seen. When the block is nondeformable, the flow rate increases with time, due to a rise in temperature which results in a decrease in fluid viscosity and an increase in fracture permeability. The opposite is true when the block is deformable as thermal expansion causes the fracture to close. The above phenomenon is more apparent when the aperture is small.

Time history curves of dimensionless vertical displacements at the outlet of the lower fracture plane are shown in Figure 5. It is evident that heat loss from convection along the fracture tends to dampen the growth of vertical displacements along the joint. With a small aperture (HA-1, HA-2), the difference in displacement diminishes with time as the flow rate along the joint is reduced, causing decreased convective heat flux along the fracture. Contrasting with a large aperture (HB-1, HB-2), the difference tends to increase with time. This is because the reduction in flow rate along the fracture does not significantly reduce the convective heat flux along the fracture (see Figure 4).

Temporal growth of temperatures at the fracture outlet are displayed in Figure 6. The effects of aperture size and deformability of the block can be seen. For small apertures (HA-curves), the deformability of the block causes the temperature growth to depart from that in the rigid block case (HA-3) and approach that of the no-flow case (HA-2) with time. This is not as obvious in larger apertures (HB-curves), because the reduction in convective heat flux along the fracture is small (see Figures 4 and 5).

Table 1. Material Properties.

Property	Rock Matrix	Fracture	Unit
Young's modulus	51.0	--	GPa
Shear stiffness	--	0.1	GPa/m
Poisson's ratio	0.25	--	--
Density	2500	--	kg/m³
Thermal expansion coeff.	$1x10^{-5}$	--	1/°C
Biot's hydroelastic constant	31	--	GPa
Seating stress	--	-1	MPa
Permeability	$1x10^{-16}$	see text	m²
Biot's storativity constant	10	1000	MPa
Porosity	$1x10^{-4}$	1	--
Thermal conductivity	2.5	--	W/(m°C)
Specific heat capacity	4.2	--	kJ/(kg°C)
Longitudinal dispersivity	6	0.6	m
Lateral dispersivity	0.6	--	m

Table 2. Details of Cases Studied.

Case	V_{mc} (m)	b_o (m)	Stress	Flow	Heat	Fracture	Remarks
HORIZONTAL FRACTURE							
HA-1	$.2x10^{-3}$	$.15x10^{-3}$	X	X	X	X	
HA-2	$.2x10^{-3}$	$.15x10^{-3}$	X		X	X	No flow
HA-3	$.2x10^{-3}$	$.15x10^{-3}$		X	X	X	Rigid block
HB-1	$.8x10^{-3}$	$.6x10^{-3}$	X	X	X	X	
HB-2	$.8x10^{-3}$	$.6x10^{-3}$	X		X	X	No flow
HB-3	$.8x10^{-3}$	$.6x10^{-3}$		X	X	X	Rigid block
VERTICAL FRACTURE							
VA-2	--	--		X	X		No fracture
VB-1	$.8x10^{-3}$	$.6x10^{-3}$		X	X	X	Rigid block
VB-2	$.8x10^{-3}$	$.6x10^{-3}$	X	X	X	X	

Figure 7 shows a comparison of isotherms derived from the HA-series cases. The thermal front in the nondeformable block case (HA-3) lags behind those of the other cases. From Figures 4 to 7, the upper and lower bounds of displacement and temperature distribution appear to be without flow and nondeformable, respectively.

The principal stresses calculated in cases HB-2 and HB-1 are displayed in Figures 8(a) and 8(b), respectively. In Figure 8(a), without cooling water in the fracture, compressive stresses are present everywhere in the rock block. With the introduction of cooling water along the fracture plane, the magnitude of the compressive stress, especially in the horizontal direction, is appreciably reduced. The development of thermohydraulically induced tension is shown in Figure 8(b). In all six cases the induced tension is confined to small regions above and below the fracture outlet.

Vertical Fracture

The geometrical configuration and boundary conditions of this problem are shown in Figure 9. Initial conditions are: (i) a uniform horizontal stress of -1.33 MPa, (ii) hydroelastic equilibrium, and (iii) a uniform temperature of 20°C.

Material properties are given in Table 1. Some results from the three cases (Table 2) are given in Figure 10, in which the progress of the 30°C isothermal fronts is displayed. An inspection of Figure 10 indicates that the presence of a fracture enhances the natural convective heat flux along the fracture above the heat source. However, the closure of the fracture caused by thermal expansion of the rock block results in a reduction in heat flux through the fracture. This, in turn, causes the thermal fronts (cases VB-1 and VB-2) to be retarded. A similar trend was also observed with other aperture sizes.

SUMMARY AND DISCUSSION

A finite element solution to the problem of heat and fluid transport in deformable fractured porous media has been presented. Two configurations of a slightly permeable rock block traversed by a fracture have been included to indicate the significance of thermohydroelastic effects. These configurations, involving forced and free convection of fluid and heat flux through a major conduit or fracture, are of fundamental importance to the study of flow and transport of groundwater in fractured rock around nuclear waste repositories. Simulation results indicate that the existence of nonlinear deformable fractures can change the flow and transport behavior drastically. The closure of fractures induced by thermohydrological perturbations may also inhibit the flow of fluid and dissolved contaminants.

In the absence of good field and laboratory data and reliable constitutive relationships, the application of the model presented is restricted to qualitative investigations only. As more laboratory and field data become available, it is hoped that the constitutive relationships will be refined so that this model may be applied quantitatively.

REFERENCES

Biot, M.A., 1955, Theory of elasticity and consolidation for a porous anisotropic solid, J. Appl. Phys., v. 26, pp. 182-5.

Chan, T., Guvanasen, V., and Reid, J.A.K., 1985, Numerical modeling of coupled thermo-hydro-mechanical processes in nuclear fuel waste disposal, Proc. Int. Symposium on Coupled Processes Affecting the Performance of a Nuclear Waste Repository, Lawrence Berkeley Laboratory, University of California, Berkeley, September 18-20, 1985 (in press).

Combarnous, M.A., and Bories, S.A., 1975, Hydrothermal convection in saturated porous media, Advances in Hydroscience, v. 10, pp. 231-307.

Goodman, R.E., and St. John, E.M., 1977, Finite-element analysis for discontinuous rocks, in Numerical Methods in Engineering (Eds. C.S. Desai and J.T. Christian), McGraw-Hill, pp. 148-175.

Guvanasen, V., and Chan, T., 1980, Finite element solution of coupled heat and fluid flow, solute transport, and thermomechanical deformation in fractured porous media, presented at 1980 American Geophysical Union Fall Meeting, Dec. 8-12, San Francisco, Abstract T97, EOS (Trans. AGU) no. 46, 1980 November 11.

Snow, D.T., 1965, A parallel plate model of fractured permeable media, Ph.D. Thesis, University of California, Berkeley.

Witherspoon, P.A., Tsang, Y.W., Long, J.C.S., and Noorishad, J., 1981, New approaches to problems of fluid flow in fracture rock mass, Proc. 22nd U.S. Symposium on Rock Mechanics, pp. 1-20.

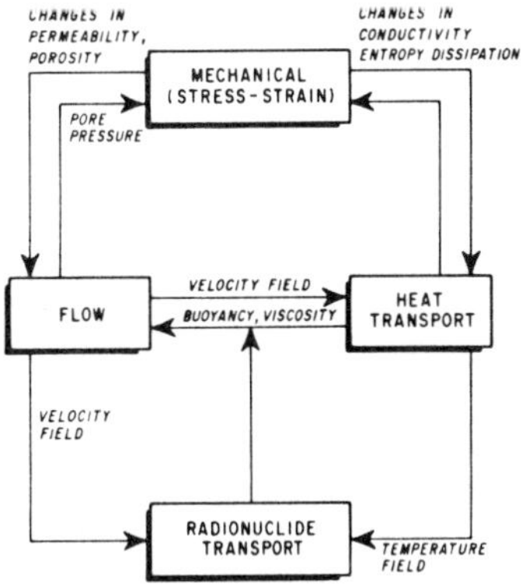

Fig. 1. Interrelationships between thermohydromechanical processes.

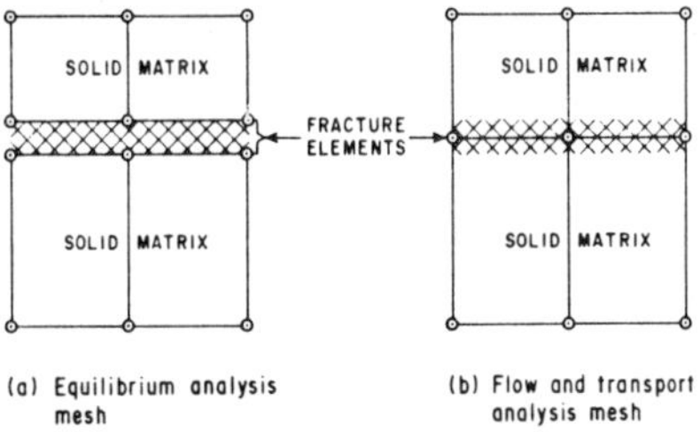

Fig. 2. Typical finite-element discretization.

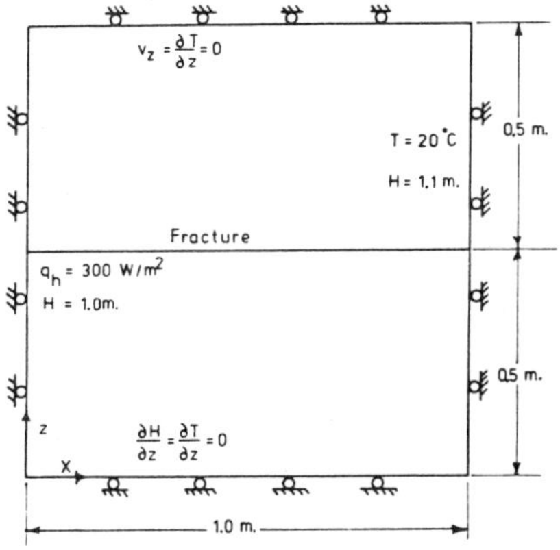

Fig. 3. Definition sketch of horizontal fracture case.

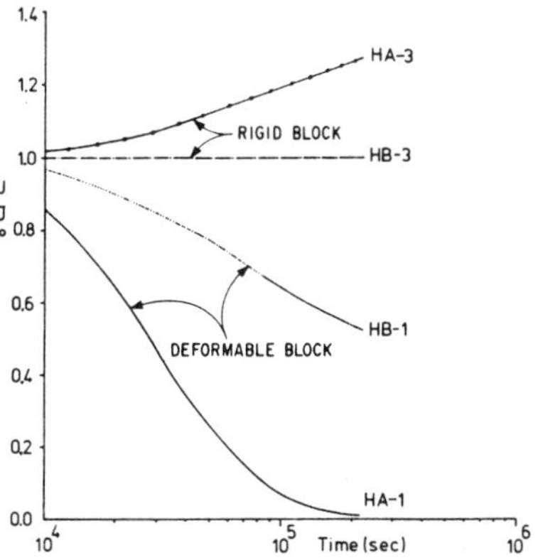

Fig. 4. Time history of flow rates along horizontal fracture (Q^J = volumetric flow rate, Q_o^J = initial volumetric flow rate).

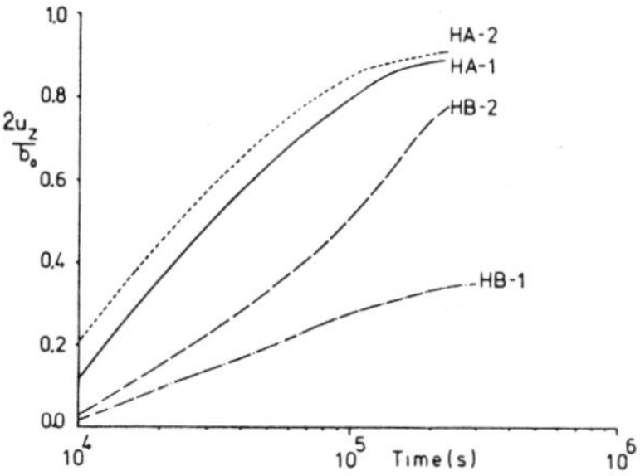

Fig. 5. Time history of vertical displacement at the fracture outlet.

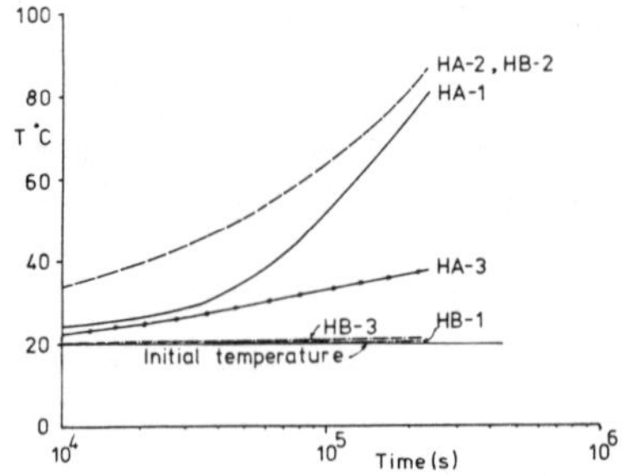

Fig. 6. Time history of temperature at the fracture outlet.

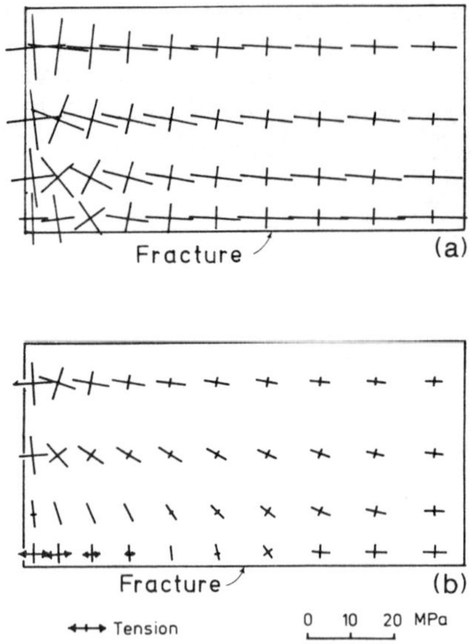

Fig. 8. (a) Stress distribution at 2.3×10^6 s, case HB-2. (b) Stress distribution at 2.3×10^6 s, case HB-1.

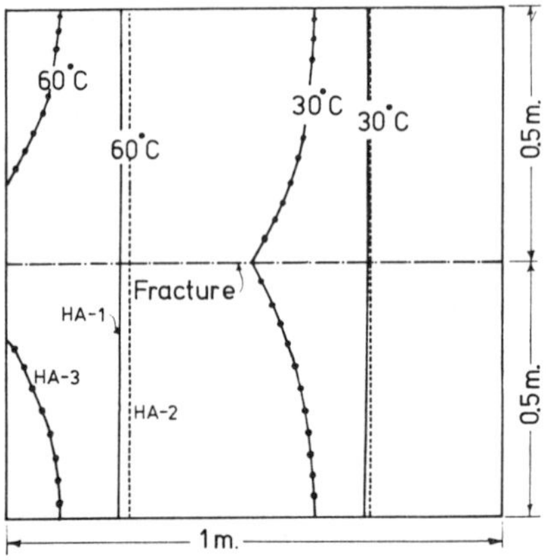

Fig. 7. Temperature contours from cases HA-1, HA-2, and HA-3.

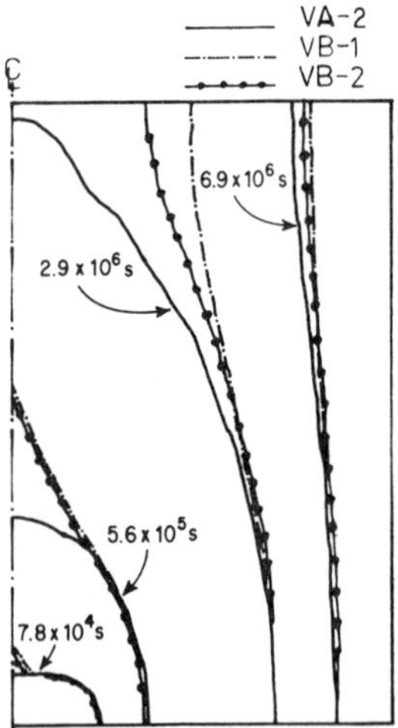

Fig. 10. Temporal movement of 30^oC - isotherms, vertical fracture case.

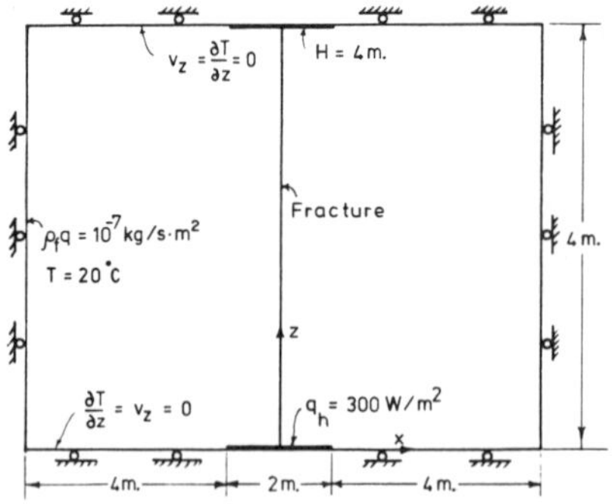

Fig. 9. Definition sketch of vertical fracture case.

VI International Conference on Finite Elements in Water Resources, Lisboa, Portugal, June 1986

Situ-Flow-G – A Computer Program for Groundwater Flow which is Simple to Use

H. Tägnfors, K. Runesson and N.E. Wiberg
Department of Structural Mechanics, Chalmers University of Technology, Sweden

Department of Structural Mechanics, Chalmers University of Technology

INTRODUCTION

A large number of finite element programs for groundwater flow, both in 2D and 3D, are available; see e.g. Pinder et al. (1978), Damrath (1982), Voss (1984). Because of increasing demands from the users much effort should be spent on the development of an effective and versatile software concerning mesh generation of complicated geometries, data management, selected result presentation as well as efficient numerical procedures.

SITU-FLOW-G (Runesson et al. 1986) is a special purpose program within the programming system SITU, which is an abbreviation for the characteristic feature: SImple To Use. (Tägnfors 1984 and Tägnfors et al. 1986). The objectives of this system are to provide the program developer with efficient tools for input and output data handling, for effective data management in both primary and secondary memory, and for the development of new special purpose application programs. SITU is supported by the data base management system PRISEC (Tägnfors et al. 1980), which handles hierarchical data structures with two-dimensional arrays as the operational items.

SITU-FLOW-G can handle confined groundwater flow in aquifers and seepage in 2D. The underlaying theory describing the flow is thus simple and the program may be considered as basic from a physical point of view. Flow in zones of dramatically increased permeability, e.g. cracks or fractured zones, may be modelled by conductors, which are built up by one-dimensional elements. Transient problems are traced by a semi-explicit integration method of Runge-Kutta type, which admits automatic selection of time steps due to the accepted truncation error within each time-step. This minimizes the need for input data and does not require a priori knowledge about the solution from the program user. Sources (prescribed or induced as leakage via change of head) may be prescribed as independent functions of time at each node, element, point, line or area. The same principle applies to prescribed head.

The program can be run in interactive or batch mode, which can be switched at certain stages. The execution is steered by commands which are supplemented by input data. A separate mesh-generator, SITU-MESH, can deal with highly complicated geometries. A separate plotting package, SITU-PLOT, provides plots of isobars for the hydraulic head and vector fields showing the velocity pattern.

SITU - CONCEPTS

Program Design

The code may be subdivided into the parts (in decreasing order of hierarchy):

- Monitor program
- Applications program
- Subprograms
- Modules
- Subroutines

All executions to be performed in an applications program, like SITU-FLOW-G, are described by commands defined in the program specification file, which is read by a monitor program and stored in the data base. When a applications program is run, the monitor program will invoke modules in accordance with the specification in the data base. This program specification written in the specially designed Situ Program Specification Language (SPSL) significantly simplifies the program development and maintenance.

The program specification defines the command tree and executions to be performed for each command; see Figure 1a.

DEFINE	*COMMAND
MESH	POINT
CONDUCTOR	*READ
SOURCE	*FORMAT
INDUCED	1(1R)
POINT	*HELP
LINE	ENTER CONVECTION CONSTANT
AREA	*CALL
SOLVE	PEAC
DISPLAY	

Figure 1a. Command structure   Figure 1b. Specification of command

The order in which the command shall be given depends on the data flow in the program. The user will be guided by help texts, which are defined in the program specification, in order to secure a correct sequence of commands. Detailed information about executions to be performed for a command shall be given in the specification: see Figure 1b. The most important functions are:

- Reading input data
- Invoking modules
- Displaying data

The reading and writing of data are made in the monitor modules in accordance with format specifications. Consequently, a massive amount of FORTRAN-code can be avoided in applications modules. By the database management system the program developer has the opportunity to easily retrieve and inspect given data.

A facility provided in a natural way is the possibility to check the validity of input data against predefined formats or against specified requirements on the value. Consequently, major faults in the computer run can be identified already at the moment when input data are read.

Help texts (keyword HELP) for commands and data may be specified on different levels of sofistication and will be provided upon request. Thus the unexperienced user can virtually reproduce the User's manual on the screen while the experienced user may prepare his input data using simple menus only occasionally.

Arrays which are stored in the data base may be referred either by its full hierarchical name or its reduced (single) name with regard to its residential data node.

THEORETICAL BASIS

Governing equations

A reasonably general class of groundwater seepage problems including aquifer flow can be described by the equation

$$-\underset{\sim}{\nabla} \cdot (\underset{\sim}{K} \cdot \underset{\sim}{\nabla} \theta) + S \frac{\partial \theta}{\partial t} = f(\theta, t) \quad \text{in } V \qquad (1)$$

with the boundary conditions

$$\theta = \bar{\theta}(t) \quad \text{on } S_\theta \qquad (2a)$$

$$q \equiv \underset{\sim}{n} \cdot \underset{\sim}{h} = q(\theta, t) \quad \text{on } S_q \qquad (2b)$$

and the appropriate initial condition on θ for $t = 0$.

The following notation has been used: θ is the hydraulic head, $\underset{\sim}{K}$ is the tensor of hydraulic conductivity (or transmissivity), S is the storage coefficient, $\underset{\sim}{n}$ is the unit outward normal and $\underset{\sim}{h}$ is the velocity vector. The source terms $f(\theta,t)$ and $q(\theta,t)$ may, in the simplest case, account for known percolation and induced infiltration represented by a linear constitutive relation (convective condition)

$$f(\theta,t) = \bar{f}(t) - \gamma_V(\theta - \theta_R(t))$$
$$q(\theta,t) = \bar{q}(t) - \gamma_S(\theta - \theta_R(t)) \qquad (3)$$

where γ_V, γ_S are the convection constants while θ_R is the external (reference) head.

To efficiently model conductors, which are highly conductive flow transmitters with negligable width compared to the characteristic diameter of the region, 1D-theory may be employed. In the computer program the conductors are allowed to occur along the finite element boundaries. In terms of the curvilinear coordinate s along such a conductor, the appropriate differential equation is simply

$$-\frac{\partial}{\partial s}(K_c A_c \frac{\partial \theta}{\partial s}) + S_c A_c \frac{\partial \theta}{\partial t} = 0 \qquad (4)$$

where A_c is the cross-sectional area of the conductor.

Finite element problem

The finite element system of equations corresponding to (1) may be written (on matrix form)

$$[K + G(\gamma_V) + G_S]u + G(S)\frac{\partial u}{\partial t} = f \qquad (5)$$

where

$$K = \int_V B^T \underset{\sim}{K} B dV$$

$$G(\alpha) = \int_V \alpha \Phi^T \Phi dV, \quad \alpha = \alpha(\underset{\sim}{x}) \quad \text{in } V \qquad (6)$$

$$G_S = \int_{S_q} \gamma_S \Phi^T \Phi dS$$

$$f = \int_V \Phi^T \bar{f} dV - \int_{S_q} \Phi^T \bar{q} dS + \int_V \Phi^T \gamma_V \theta_R dV + \int_{S_q} \Phi^T \gamma_S \theta_R dS$$

and u(t) are the nodal values of θ represented via the basis functions Φ as $\theta(\underset{\sim}{x},t) = \Phi u(t)$.

Time integration

Because of the strongly transient character of many groundwater flow problems it is not efficient to keep the time step unchanged in a step-by-step integration algorithm. A procedure is preferable where the next time step is automatically predicted by the program based on a given tolerance for the truncation error. This can be achieved by imbedding technique, which means that the results of two methods of different order are compared in order to obtain the necessary information.

SITU-FLOW-G uses the W(2,4)-method, which is a second order accurate and L-stable two-stage semi-explicit Runge-Kutta method; see Wolfbrandt (1977), Runesson et al. (1979). For the problem

$$Ku + G\dot{u} = f(t)$$

the algorithm becomes:

Given u_n at $t = t_n$ find u_{n+1} at $t = t_{n+1} = t_n + \Delta t$ from

$$u_{n+1} = u_n + \frac{\Delta t}{4}(k_1 + 3k_2) \tag{7a}$$

$$\begin{cases} Wk_1 = -Ku_n + f(t_n) \\ Wk_2 = -K[u_n + (\frac{2}{3} - \frac{4}{3}\alpha)\Delta t k_1] + f(t_n + \frac{2}{3}\Delta t) \end{cases} \tag{7b}$$

where

$$W = G + \alpha \Delta t K, \quad \alpha = 1 - 1/\sqrt{2} \tag{7c}$$

The error estimation necessary for the prediction of next time step is performed by calculating two extra vectors k_3 and k_4 with the same coefficient matrix W in (7c). Thus, a third order estimate of the local truncation error T is given as

$$T = \frac{\Delta t}{8}(k_1 - 5k_2 + 5k_3 - k_4) \tag{8}$$

which may be used to select the next time step; see Runesson et al. (1979).

MESH GENERATOR

The mesh generator program SITU-MESH (Kjellman et al. 1985) supporting all SITU-programs requires the mesh to be composed of an arbitrary number of subregions (areas). Although the geometrical shape is arbitrary, each area is topologically rectangular with respect to the subdivision into finite elements.

The areas may be considered as substructures from input and output points of view. As the mesh is topologically rectangular in each area, output data can be displayed as printed topologically true maps (matrix form) in a clear and instructive way.

A common technique to generate the finite element mesh of a particular area is to map a canonical region onto the true geometry as is done for each individual element at the evaluation of element matrices. The coordinates $\underset{\sim}{x} = (x_1, x_2)$ of each node are then obtained from

$$\underset{\sim}{x} = \Phi(\underset{\sim}{\xi})\tilde{x}^P \tag{9}$$

where $\tilde{x}^P$ is a vector with the coordinates of the points defining the boundaries of the area and $\Phi(\tilde{\xi})$ contains mapping functions.

However, one key problem in practical computation is to ensure that a certain number of (interior) nodes obtain predefined coordinates. This would contradict the requirement of using reasonably low order polynomials. Using Lagrangian elements (bi-polynomial representation in 2D) it is clear that the order of Φ would have to be N-1, where N is the number of nodes with prescribed coordinates.

SITU-MESH employs another method which is more general, but also more expensive, and is therefore optional.

The final geometry is defined as the deformed configuration of an elastic body with simple initial shape. In order to solve a reasonably simple problem small deformation theory is assumed which implies that the distortion of the initial shape must be limited in order that the "deformation" becomes realistic and the final mesh be sufficiently smooth.

The linear finite element problem to be solved may be partitioned as

$$\begin{bmatrix} S & S_P \\ S_P^T & S_{PP} \end{bmatrix} \begin{bmatrix} \tilde{x} \\ \tilde{x}^P \end{bmatrix} = \begin{bmatrix} 0 \\ \tilde{R}^P \end{bmatrix} \tag{10}$$

where $\tilde{x}$ are the nodal coordinates to be calculated while $\tilde{x}^P$ are the predefined nodal coordinates (both on the boundary and in the interior of the region); see Figure 2.

To reduce the computational effort involved (and also the necessary input data) the initial shape may be chosen very simple with "initial elements" of equal size, e.g. squares with unit side as indicated in Figure 2. In order to improve the smoothness of the final mesh, i.e. to reduce the internal distortion, the initial shape may be further adjusted to the final mesh, whereby the initial shape is obtained from conventional polynomial mapping.

The used method is extremely flexible and may be further developed to cope with the various restrictions on the nodal positions that may be set up in practical calculations.

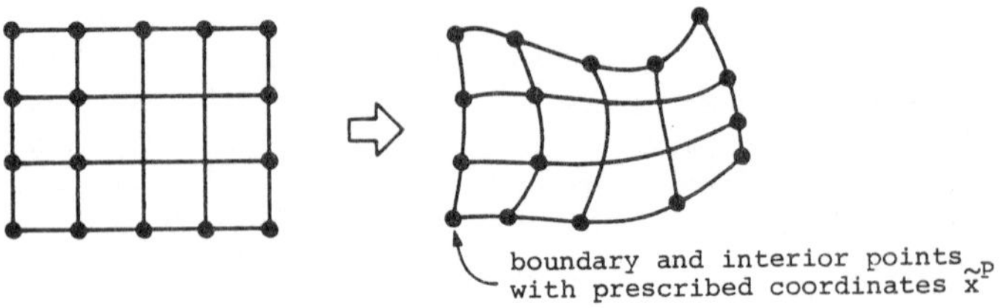

Figure 2. Elastic mapping

EXAMPLE: FLOW IN SUBMERGED ESKER

Problem definition

An aquifer serving as a municipal water supply consists of a submerged esker resting on rock and confined by clay on both sides. Both rock and clay are assumed as impermeable. The esker is at one end in contact with a lake with constant water table At the other end artificial infiltration with the total amount of 0.050 m^3/s starts at the same time as water is discharged from a single well at the rate Q m^3/s; see Figure 3.

The aquifer has an unconfined and a confined part. As very small variation of head is expected, the theory for transient flow in confined aquifers can be adopted. The transmissivity K and the storage coefficient S have been obtained from hydrological investigations.

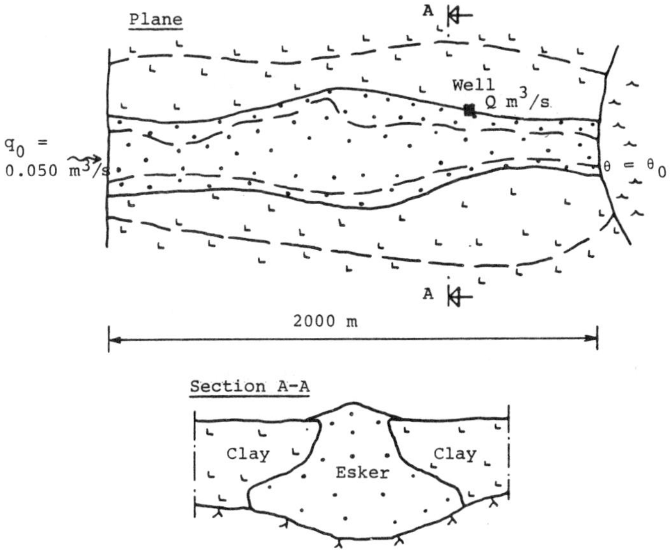

Figure 3. Geology of the aquifer

The finite element model in Figure 4 is used. The given values of K and S shall be considered as mean values for subregions. Isotropic permeability is assumed. The points A and B are observation points for which calculation results are presented below.

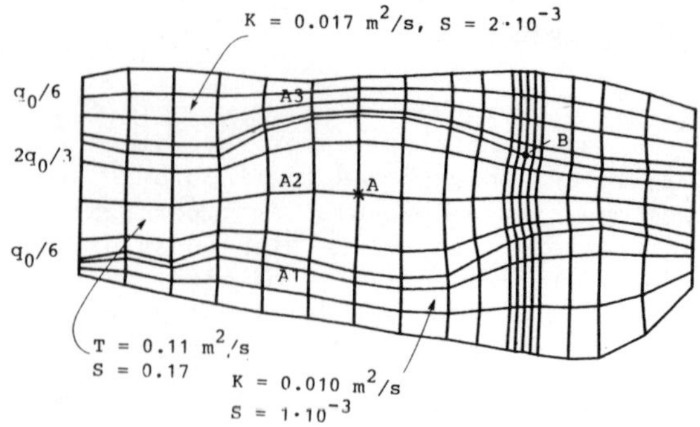

Figure 4. Finite element mesh of aquifer

Calculation result

The change of hydraulic head in points A and B with time is shown in Figure 5 for various well discharge rates: Q = 0.050, 0.075 and 0.100 m^3/s. Stationary conditions are achieved after about 6 months. For Q = 0.100 m^3/s the change of head at stationary conditions is shown in Figure 6. Figure 7 displays, typically, the change of head for area A2 in matrix form. Such matrix displays, which can be obtained for selected objects like areas, lines, points, nodes and/or elements, are most useful.

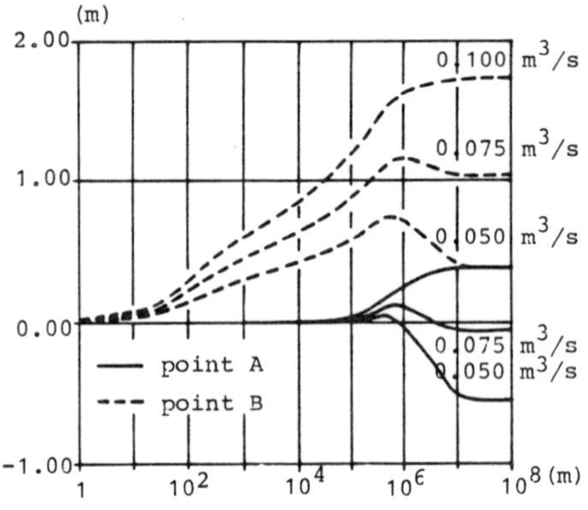

Figure 5. Decrease of hydraulic head for different well discharge rates

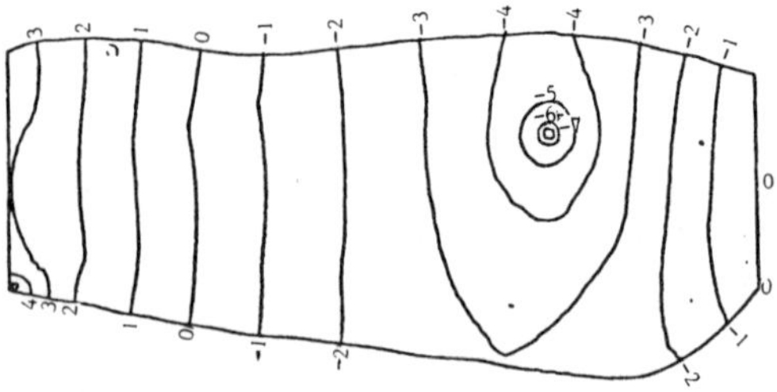

Figure 6. Contour lines for change of hydraulic head at stationary conditions for Q = 0.100 m^3/s

+++ AREA A2 FOR DISPLAY +++
++ MODE NUMBERING ++

ROW/COL	1	2	3	4	5	6	7	8	9	10	11
1	1	4	10	20	34	52	68	86	98	110	122
2	2	3	9	19	33	51	67	85	97	109	121
3	7	8	11	21	35	53	69	87	99	111	123
4	16	17	18	23	37	55	71	89	101	113	125
5	29	30	31	32	39	57	73	91	103	115	127

ROW/COL	12	13	14	15	16	17	18	19
1	134	146	158	170	182	194	206	218
2	133	145	157	169	181	193	205	217
3	135	147	159	171	183	195	207	219
4	137	149	161	173	185	197	209	221
5	139	151	163	175	187	199	211	223

++++++ HYDRAULIC HEAD +

MULTIPLY VALUES BELOW BY 10 RAISED TO -3

ROW/COL	1	2	3	4	5	6	7	8	9	10	11
1	626	451	261	51	-140	-275	-404	-534	-684	-814	-1080
2	597	444	260	65	-112	-263	-400	-537	-688	-819	-1014
3	594	444	263	74	-104	-259	-399	-534	-673	-781	-872
4	615	449	266	81	-101	-259	-400	-529	-653	-737	-798
5	694	446	271	90	-112	-274	-411	-523	-616	-689	-765

MULTIPLY VALUES BELOW BY 10 RAISED TO -3

ROW/COL	12	13	14	15	16	17	18	19
1	-1256	-1647	-1257	-1065	-749	-547	-267	0
2	-1060	-1019	-1054	-997	-743	-544	-264	0
3	-874	-884	-867	-854	-712	-530	-255	0
4	-804	-802	-801	-787	-686	-518	-239	0
5	-777	-783	-784	-776	-684	-516	-228	0

Figure 7. Matrix display of the change of hydraulic head for area A2

CONCLUSION

Flexibility and versatility at the development of new software, the capability of clear and logical input handling and instructive output display are qualities which are emphasized in the SITU-system. The special purpose program SITU-FLOW-G has proved as an efficient tool for, particularly, aquifer analysis and is now used extensively in research as well as in engineering environment. The capability of automatic time step prediction in transient analysis is a considerable advantage of the numerical algorithm.

REFERENCES

Damrath, R. (1982) Software developments for finite element applications. Finite Elements in Water Resources (Hannover 1982), Springer Verlag, Heidelberg.

Kjellman, M., Möller, P., Runesson, K. and Tägnfors, H. (1985) SITU-MESH, A computer program for the two-dimensional mesh generation in finite element analysis, Report 85:19, Dept. of Struct. Mech., Chalmers Univ. of Technology, Göteborg.

Pinder, G.F., Fried, E.O. and Celia, M.A. (1978) Ground water flow circulation using collocation finite elements. Finite Elements in Water Resources (London 1978), Pentech Press, London.

Runesson, K., Wiberg, N-E. and Wolfbrandt, A. (1979) A new Rosenbrock-type method applied to a finite element-discretized nonlinear diffusion-convection equation. The Mathematics of Finite Elements and Applications III, MAFELAP 1978, Academic Press, London.

Runesson, K., Tägnfors, H. and Wiberg, N-E. (1986) SITU-FLOW-G, A computer program for the finite element analysis of two-dimensional groundwater flow, Dept. of Struct. Mech., Chalmers Univ. of Technology, Göteborg. (In preparation).

Tägnfors, H. (1985) Architecture of an adaptive and interactive FEM-program for CAD-purposes, Int. Conf. on Numerical Methods in Engineering, Swansea, U.K., Jan 7th-11th, 1985, 1029-1038.

Tägnfors, H., Runesson, K. and Wiberg, N-E. (1980) PRISEC-VERSION 1, A tool for the data management in FORTRAN-programs, Publ. 80:2, Dept. of Struct. Mech., Chalmers Univ. of Technology, Göteborg.

Tägnfors, H., Runesson, K. and Wiberg, N-E. (1986) SITU, General manual for a programming system which is SImple To Use, Dept. of Struct. Mech., Chalmers Univ. of Technology, Göteborg. (In preparation).

Voss, C. (1984) SUTRA, A finite element simulation model for saturated-unsaturated fluid density dependent ground-water flow with energy transport. U.S. Geological Survey, Water-Resources Investigations Report 84-4369. US Air Force Engineering and Services Centre, Florida.

Wolfbrandt, A. (1977) A study of Rosenbrock Processes with respect to order conditions and stiff stability, Dept. of Comp. Sci., Chalmers Univ. of Technology, Göteborg.

VI International Conference on Finite Elements in Water Resources, Lisboa, Portugal, June 1986

Interactive Modelling for Groundwater Management

D.C. McKinney, D.P. Loucks
School of Civil and Environmental Engineering, Cornell University, Ithaca, New York, 14853, U.S.A.

INTRODUCTION

Contamination of groundwater resources has rapidly become a major problem to be solved by those responsible for environmental and water resources planning. New computer-aided planning tools to aid in understanding the consequences of proposed protection or cleanup strategies may prove helpful to resource managers and engineers. Coupling groundwater flow and transport simulation models with color graphics devices enhances the use of these models in planning and decision making. Through the use of interactive graphic modeling systems, the results of dynamic simulations using varied sets of physical parameters, boundary conditions and design policies can be viewed and evaluated quickly and easily. This capability allows the presentation of modeling results in a manner which is more meaningful to those responsible for planning and policy decisions.

The ease with which models can be used depends on the design of the model input and output characteristics and methods. When simulation models are incorporated into a user-friendly interactive modeling system, the input of data may be accomplished with minimal effort and chance of error. Such an interactive system can provide checks on the completeness and reasonableness of data and transform that data into the format required for a specific simulation model. Using an interactive modeling system the results of simulations may be easily adjusted and displayed to provide the level of detail and organization desired by the user.

The purpose of this paper is to describe an interactive groundwater modeling system design to aid modelers and decision makers in analyzing alternative proposals for the solution of groundwater pollution problems. Color graphics equipment and interactive programming have been used to provide an efficient and user-friendly system for data input and manipulation, model control and execution, and simulation results review and display.

SIMULATION MODEL

The groundwater simulation model incorporated into the interactive modeling system is a subset of the U.S. Geological Survey finite element model SUTRA (Voss, 1984). The subset of SUTRA implemented here allows the simulation of two dimensional (areal) groundwater flow with reactive and sorptive single-species solute transport with constant fluid density. The transient distribution of hydraulic head as a function of the system stresses and boundary conditions is given by the solution of the partial differential equation (Bear, 1979)

$$\nabla \cdot B\underline{K} \cdot \nabla h - \sum_{\omega \in \Omega} Q_{\omega} \delta(x-x_{\omega}) \delta(y-y_{\omega}) = BS_s \frac{\partial h}{\partial t} \qquad (1)$$

where h = hydraulic head [L]
S_s = specific storativity [L^{-1}]
B = aquifer saturated thickness [L]
$\underline{K}$ = hydraulic conductivity tensor [LT^{-1}]
Q_{ω} = volumetric flow rate of the source or sink located at the point (x_{ω}, y_{ω}) [L^3T^{-1}]
$\delta(x-x_{\omega})$ = Dirac delta function
Ω = index set of all sources or sinks in the aquifer
$\vec{q} = -\underline{K} \cdot \nabla h$ = seepage velocity [LT^{-1}]

Initial conditions and general boundary conditions for the hydraulic head are

$$h(x,y,t_0) = h_0(x,y)$$

$$h = f_1(x,y,t) \text{ on } \Gamma_1$$

$$\vec{q} \cdot \vec{\nu} = f_2(x,y,t) \text{ on } \Gamma_2$$

where h_0 are the conditions existing in the aquifer at time t_0, f_1 is a known function, Γ_1 represents all the prescribed hydraulic head boundaries, f_2 is the prescribed flux across the boundary, Γ_2 represents all the prescribed flux boundaries in the system, and $\vec{\nu}$ is the outward pointing normal vector to the boundary.

The transient two dimensional transport of a dilute chemical constituent undergoing linear reactions and sorption in saturated porous media is governed by the equation (Bear, 1979)

$$\nabla\cdot(B\underline{D}\cdot\nabla c)-\nabla\cdot(Bc\vec{q})-nB\gamma c+\sum_{\omega\epsilon\psi} c'_{\omega}Q_{\omega}\delta(x-x_{\omega})\delta(y-y_{\omega}) \qquad (2)$$

$$= \frac{\partial}{\partial t}\{B[n+(1-n)\rho_s k]c\}$$

where c = concentration of the constituent $[ML^{-3}]$
n = aquifer porosity, dimensionless
γ = first-order reaction coefficient for the constituent between the liquid and solid phases $[T^{-1}]$
c'_{ω} = constituent concentration of fluid recharging the aquifer at the point (x_{ω},y_{ω}) through leakage from confining layers, injection wells or other sources $[ML^{-3}]$
ψ = index set of all point sources in the aquifer
$\underline{D}$ = hydrodynamic dispersion tensor $[L^2T^{-1}]$

The boundary conditions which the mass transport equation must satisfy depend on both the type of medium and the fluid present in the region outside the boundaries. Some boundary conditions which are of interest here are:

$$c' = c\ (x,y,t) \text{ on } \Gamma_3$$

$$\nabla c \cdot \vec{\nu} = 0 \text{ on } \Gamma_4$$

where c' is a known function, Γ_3 represents all the prescribed concentration boundaries, and Γ_4 represents all of the boundaries across which no flow of solute takes place. Initial conditions for the aquifer are

$$c(x,y,t_0) = c_0(x,y)$$

where c_0 is the solute concentration condition existing in the aquifer at the time t_0.

The prediction of the concentration of a chemical constituent in an aquifer is obtained by solving the flow and mass transport equations 1 and 2 with an appropriate set of initial and boundary conditions. The state variables of the problem are: mass concentration, c; seepage velocity, $\vec{q}$; and hydraulic head, h. These response equations show the interdependence of the state variables and the possible management decisions, e.g. well locations, pumping and recharge rates, and recharge fluid constituent concentration.

Equations 1 and 2 are solved in the model SUTRA by the Galerkin finite element method, which is a general numerical technique used extensively for the solution of groundwater simulation problems (Huyakorn and Pinder, 1983). For more detailed information on the formulation of the simulation model refer to the model documentation (Voss, 1984).

INTERACTIVE GROUNDWATER MODELING SYSTEM

The interactive modeling system described here is designed to assist model developers and users in simulating the response of groundwater systems to various design and management policies. The modeling system uses a microcomputer coupled with color graphics peripheral devices for ease of problem definition, data input and editing, and display and presentation of results.

Using the interactive groundwater modeling system, the user can simulate the flow and mass transport in groundwater systems as described in the previous section. In particular, the modeling system allows the user to:

1. display videodigitized maps of particular areas of interest in a groundwater modeling study;
2. define, edit and display a finite element modeling mesh for the groundwater problem under consideration;
3. create, edit and display data related to the parameter values required for simulation of the groundwater system;
4. enter, edit and display the data defining the boundary and initial conditions for the groundwater system,
5. specify the values of the parameters which control the execution of the groundwater simulation model (e.g. transient or steady state solution, time steps, etc.); and
6. analyze and display the groundwater system simulation results in various graphic modes.

Description of computer graphics equipment and programs

The computer software was developed for use with an Advanced Electronics Design, Inc. AEDS11 consisting of an LSI 11/23 processor linked to an AED 767 color display monitor. This system is capable of displaying videodigitized images such as maps and pictures on which model results and other data can be overlaid, transparently or opaquely. Data is entered alphanumerically, graphically or pictorially with a keyboard, digitizing pen and tablet, or videodigitizing camera. Model data and simulation results are displayed on the color monitor or computer terminal in the form of tables, graphs or pictures.

The interactive system is menu-driven, which provides a user-friendly environment. The user determines and controls the sequence of modeling operations by selecting desired menu options from a list of possible options displayed on the monitor. The digitizing tablet is used to select menu commands shown on the monitor, draw in geographic data, and enter other data.

General modeling system structure

The interactive groundwater modeling system is broken down into three modules. The overall structure is schematically diagrammed in Figure 1. The three basic modules of the system are (1) a command program, which controls the overall functioning of the system; (2) a geographic data base and manager, which allows the storage of and access to geographic and other information relating to the study area; and (3) a simulation module, which controls the execution of the groundwater simulation model.

The command program module controls the major functions of the modeling system. The command program provides the user with an introduction to the modeling system, calls the system utility routines, accesses the simulation module, and provides for the orderly termination of the modeling session.

The simulation module consists of three major submodules which allow the user to define the input data specific to the simulation model (preprocessor), execute the simulation model using the preprocessed input data, and analyze and display the model results (postprocessor).

The system preprocessor controls the programs and subroutines for (1) defining the finite element mesh geometry used in the simulation model and (2) entering, editing

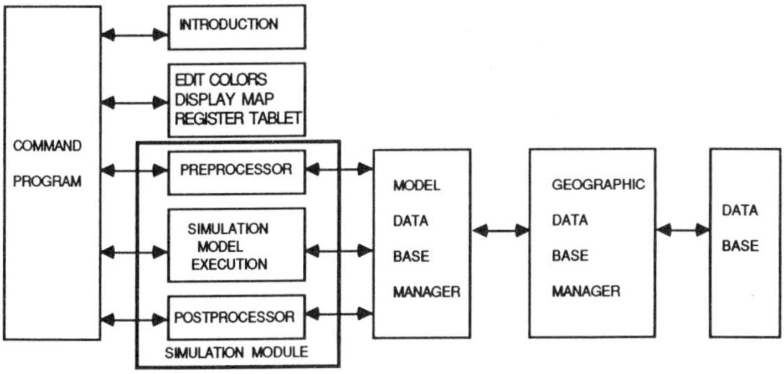

Figure 1. Interactive groundwater modeling system structure.

and displaying the simulation model parameter, boundary condition and initial condition values. The simulation model submodule allows the user to review and modify the parameters governing the control of the simulation execution. The system postprocessor is essentially the same as the preprocessor submodule. This submodule controls the routines for organizing and displaying the simulation results.

SIMULATION EXAMPLE

In this section an application of the interactive groundwater modeling system to a hypothetical aquifer is presented. No attempt has been made to model a real aquifer, but only to illustrate the features and flexibility of the modeling system.

Figure 2 shows a sketch of the hypothetical study area which contains a confined alluvial sand and gravel aquifer. Regional flow exists in the aquifer from the recharge area on the eastern edge to the undisturbed area at the western edge. The study area contains three pumping wells for municipal water supply and one contamination source. The aquifer is recharged by a river on the eastern boundary and also by a recharge area near the eastern edge of the modeled area. An impervious outcrop area exists near the center of the study area. Impervious boundaries exist along the northern and southern limits of the aquifer.

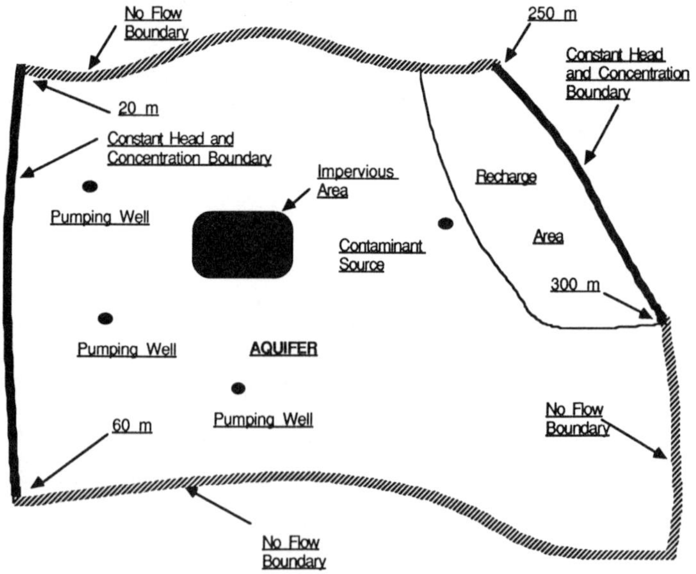

Figure 2. Sketch of example study area and aquifer.

The pumping wells are assumed to have been in operation for a sufficient length of time for steady state head conditions to become established in the area. A contaminant point source of unspecified origin is introduced near the western edge of the recharge area. The goal is to simulate the spreading of the contaminant throughout the aquifer so that any danger to municipal water supplies can be assessed. Table 1 lists all of the data used in this example.

Table 1. Parameter values for simulation example.

Physical Parameters	
Thickness	40-50 m
Porosity	0.30
Storage Coefficient	0.005 m^{-1}
Hydraulic Conductivity	$1x10^{-6}$ - $1x10^{-11}$ m/sec
Long. Dispersivity	200 m
Trans. Dispersivity	100 m
Boundary Conditions	
Point Source Flow	(+ inflow, - outflow)
Recharge Area	$1.9x10^{-3}$ m^3/sec (per node)
Supply Wells	-0.40 m^3/sec (each)
Contaminant Source	.17 m^3/sec
Point Source Concentration	
Recharge Areas	0. mg/ℓ
Contaminant Source	1000. mg/ℓ
Constant Head	
Eastern Edge	250 m to 300 m
Western Edge	20 m to 60 m
Constant Concentration	
Constant Head Nodes	10 mg/ℓ

The software system preprocessor was used to create a finite element mesh and enter the data for this example. The finite element mesh is shown in figure 3. The initial conditions for the example were taken as the steady state hydraulic head and concentration distributions resulting when no contaminant source is present in the system. A transient flow and transport simulation over 30 time steps each of length 182 days was performed. No decay or sorption reactions were modeled in the simulation.

The postprocessor was used to examine the simulation results. With the postprocessor it is possible to examine a time series of interpolated surfaces of contaminant concentration for each time step considered in the simulation model. Interpolated surfaces of concentration results are shown in Figures 4 and 5 for time steps 1 and 30 respectively. Illustrated in these figures is the development of the contamination plume from a small point source at time step 1 (Figure 4) until it has spread throughout a major portion of the aquifer at time step 30 (Figure 5). Figure 5 is typical of all of the interpolated surfaces shown in this example simulation. Shades are used to indicate the range

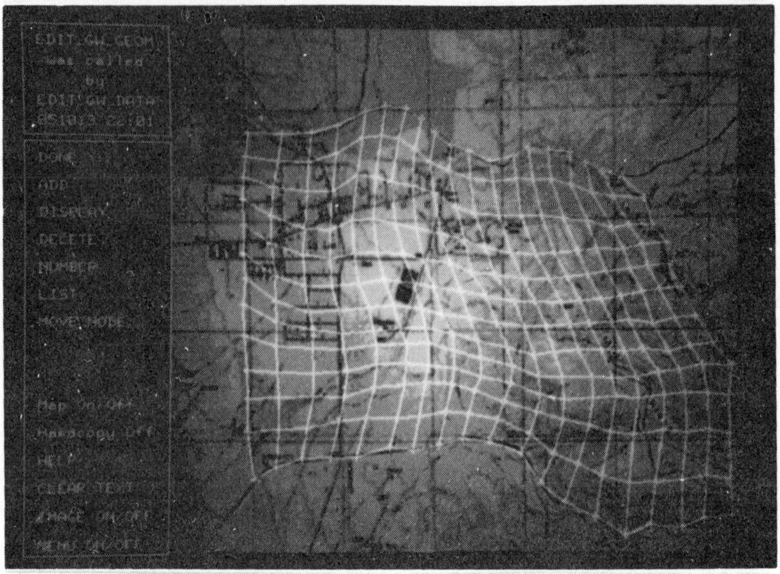

Figure 3. Finite Element Mesh.

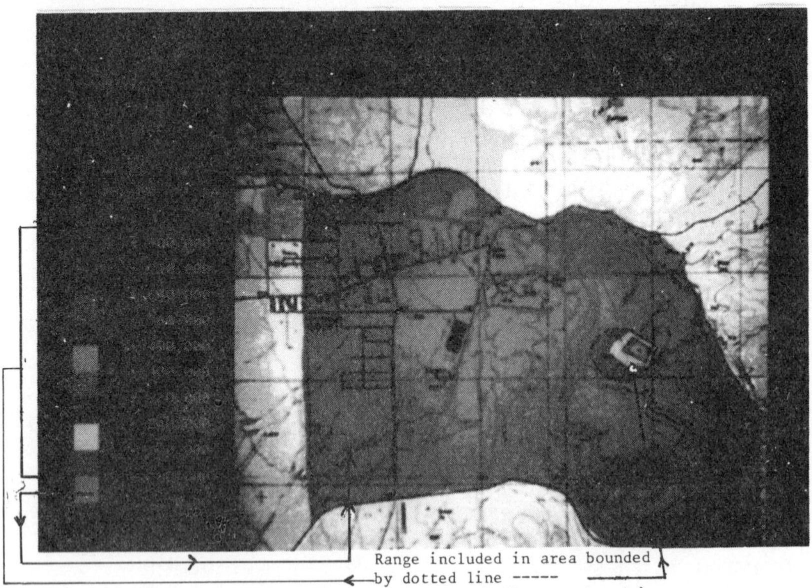

Figure 4. Interpolated Surface of Concentration Values at Time Step 1.

which concentration values fall into at any point on the interpolated surface. For example, points where the interpolated value of concentration falls between 320 and 240 mg/ℓ are colored black, similarly those that fall between 160 and 80 mg/ℓ are hatched.

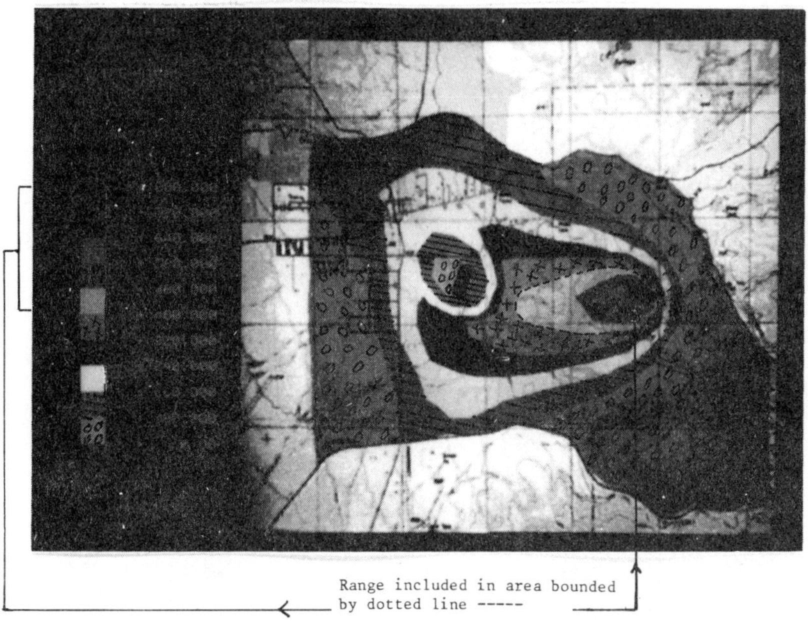

Figure 5. Interpolated Surface of Concentration Values at Time Step 30.

CONCLUSIONS

This work was undertaken with the objective of developing and demonstrating a modeling system which makes the task of simulating complex groundwater systems easier and more understandable. These objectives were met through the use of interactive color computer graphics software and hardware. The microcomputer hardware used has the advantage of being relatively inexpensive and providing high quality color graphics. At the same time, the speed of executing the SUTRA simulation model using the microcomputer (LSI 11/23 processor executing PDP-11 Fortran-77) was extremely slow. This problem, a disadvantage of the type of hardware used, may be alleviated by a microcomputer with a faster computational speed.

The color display capability of the modeling system provides for meaningful display of input data for simulations and makes the display of results convenient and easy to understand. The interactive, menu driven software system provides a user friendly interface so that the user may easily modify the parameters of a simulation and examine the effects of these modifications on the simulation results.

The interactive modeling system is general and not limited to the specific groundwater simulation model incorporated here. The U.S. Geological Survey SUTRA model was used because it represents a general type of model being used by a large number of practicing modelers today. Other groundwater simulation models can be incorporated into the system with only slight modification of the software.

REFERENCES

Bear, J. (1979), Hydraulics of Groundwater, McGraw-Hill, N.Y.

Huyakorn, P.S. and Pinder, G.F. (1983), Computational Methods in Subsurface Flow, Academic Press, N.Y.

Voss, C.I. (1984), SUTRA: a Finite Element Simulation Model for Saturated-Unsaturated, Fluid-Density-Dependent Groundwater Flow with Energy Transport or Chemically-Reactive Single-Species Solute Transport, U.S. Geological Survey, Water Resources Investigation 84-4369.

VI International Conference on Finite Elements in Water Resources, Lisboa, Portugal, June 1986

Transport of Nitrate from a Large Cement Based Waste Form

D.W. Pepper
E.I. de Pont de Nemours and Company, Savannah River Laboratory, Aiken, South Carolina 29808, U.S.A.

ABSTRACT

A finite element model is used to calculate the time-dependent transport of nitrate from a cement-based (saltstone) monolith with and without a clay cap. Model predictions agree well with data from two lysimeter field experiments begun in 1984. The clay cap effectively reduces the flux of nitrate from the monolith. Predictions for a landfill monolith design show a peak concentration occurring within 25 years; however, the drinking water guideline is exceeded for 1200 years. Alternate designs and various restrictive liners are being considered.

INTRODUCTION

A great deal of effort is being spent at the Savannah River site to develop processes to dispose of radioactive waste. A Defense Waste Processing Facility, currently under construction, will process the waste. High-level waste will be converted into glass and stored in a repository. Low-level waste, consisting of approximately 25 million gallons of soluble salts (NaOH, $NaNO_2$, and $NaNO_3$) - about 100 million gallons as salt solution - will be solidified with cement and fly ash to form saltstone. A concerted modeling effort, coupled with experimental tests, is being undertaken to model both processes. In this study, a numerical model is used to calculate the transport of nitrate from a saltstone monolith.

* The information contained in this article was developed during the course of work under Contract No. DE-AC09-76SR00001 with the U.S. Department of Energy.

Preliminary results from laboratory and small-scale field tests[1,2] indicated that simple analytical models underestimated nitrate releases from the saltstone monoliths. A more vigorous model was needed to project long-term impact of the landfill on shallow groundwater and to validate landfill configurations that would meet state and federal regulatory requirements.

A finite element model was developed to solve the time dependent equation for species transport. Steady-state velocities within the soil were solved from Darcy's Law. Time dependent analytical expressions were used to account for the decrease in flux of nitrate from the monolith into the soil.

Three cases are modeled: clay-capped and uncapped field test lysimeters and a reference landfill design. Numerical results from the lysimeter simulations are compared with data obtained from the field tests. Results from the landfill monolith are compared with the drinking water standard for nitrate discharge into the water table.

Lysimeter Field Tests

The saltstone lysimeter tests were begun in January 1984. Approximately 7500 gallons of decontaminated salt solution were mixed with cement (80 wt % ASTM Class C fly ash, 20 wt % API Class H cement) and poured into three monoliths for infield leaching studies. A schematic of the lysimeters is shown in Figure 1. The salt solution consisted of decontaminated radioactive waste.[2]

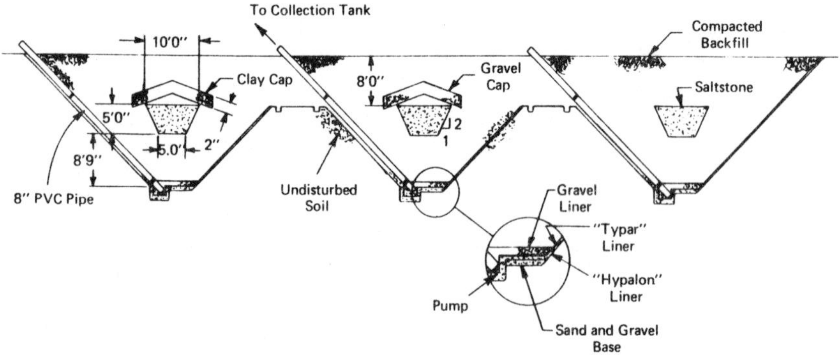

FIGURE 1. Saltstone Lysimeter Tests

The lysimeters were designed to permit monitoring of the leachate. Each monolith had its own pump and leachate collection tank. The trapezoidal shape for the monoliths was based on a preliminary design study conducted by Intera Environmental Consultants, Austin, Texas, to minimize release and migration of contaminants into the groundwater. Both gravel and clay cap tests were designed to evaluate the effects of a barrier in inhibiting ingress of water into the monolith, and groundwater flow around the monolith. Volclay SG-40, a high-swelling Wyoming sodium bentonite with a permeability of 10^{-8} cm^2/sec, was used for the clay cap.

Based on an average rainfall rate of 45 inches/year, (15 inches of infiltration), and a collection area of about 1600 square feet, the average daily water collection from each lysimeter was about 45 gallons. A detailed description of the construction and monitoring setup of the lysimeter tests is discussed by Wolf.[1]

Governing Equations

The transport of a solute in the absence of adsorption is given by the general relation in two-dimensions

$$\phi \frac{\partial c}{\partial t} + \frac{\partial}{\partial x}(\phi cu) + \frac{\partial}{\partial y}(\phi cv) = \frac{\partial}{\partial x}\left(\phi D_L \frac{\partial c}{\partial x}\right) + \frac{\partial}{\partial y}\left(\phi D_T \frac{\partial c}{\partial y}\right) + S \quad (1)$$

where c is concentration, S is source or sink terms, ϕ is porosity, u and v are the horizontal and vertical velocities, D_L = longitudinal diffusivity ($\equiv \alpha_L|v|+K_x$), D_T = transverse diffusivity ($\equiv \alpha_T|v|+K_y$), $\alpha_{L,T}$ the longitudinal and transverse dispersivities, K_x and K_y the hydraulic conductivities, and $|v| = \sqrt{u^2+v^2}$.

The soil at the Savannah River site is relatively sandy, i.e., permeable water-bearing aquifers. From Darcy's law,

$$q_x = -K \frac{\partial \Psi}{\partial y}; \quad q_y = -K \frac{\partial \Psi}{\partial y} \quad (2)$$

where q is the specific discharge (Darcy velocity), K is the hydraulic conductivity and Ψ is the groundwater head. The average linear velocity $\tilde{v}$ is q/ϕ. For a homogeneous soil, K$\equiv$ constant; utilizing the equation for conservation of mass, we can write

$$\frac{\partial^2 \bar{\psi}}{\partial x^2} + \frac{\partial^2 \bar{\psi}}{\partial y^2} = 0; \quad \bar{\Psi} = K\Psi \quad (3)$$

Equation (3) is Laplace's equation for two dimensional steady-state flow in an isotropic, homogeneous aquifer.

For the initial and external boundaries of the problem domain, the following conditions are used (refer to Figure 2).

$$C(S,0) = 0 \text{ (except } S_3); \quad C(S_4,t) = 0$$

$$\frac{\partial C(S_1,t)}{\partial n} = \frac{\partial C(S_2,t)}{\partial n} = 0; \quad -\phi D_T \frac{\partial C(S_1,t)}{\partial y} n + vc(S_5,t)n = q \quad (4)$$

where S denotes surfaces 1 through 5, and n refers to the normal to the surface. The boundary at S_5 is an outflow boundary used to compare with the experimental data from the lysimeters. Zero flux conditions are assumed at the remaining vertical boundaries.

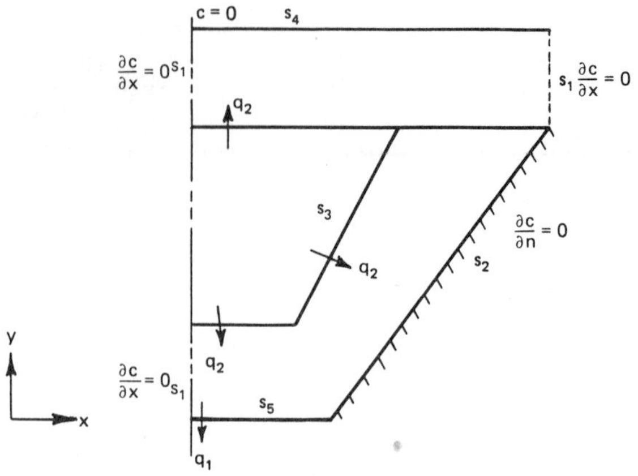

FIGURE 2. Boundary Conditions

An initial insult was used at t=0 on the surface of the saltstone (S_3) to account for the pouring of liquid saltstone into the soil. This insult accounts for the initially high values of the diffusion coefficient (which decreases as the mixture hardens), and suction of the liquid into the soil prior to setting. A factor of 0.02 gm/cm^2 of nitrate was utilized in all the model simulations, based on laboratory experiments of saltstone before setting. After setting, the molecular diffusivity of the saltstone was determined to be ~10^{-9} cm^2/sec. The molecular diffusivity of the soil was ~5×10^{-6} cm^2/sec.

Analytical expressions were used to model the flux of nitrate out the saltstone monolith and clay cap into the soil. Concentration buildup in the soil was not considered -- hence, the flux acts at a maximum rate. The actual release of nitrate from the saltstone is complex; however, laboratory experiments[2,3] indicate that a diffusion model for the flux expression is reasonable. The flux relation used for the uncapped lysimeter simulation was

$$q = C_o \sqrt{\frac{D_s}{\pi t}} \qquad (5)$$

where D_s is the molecular diffusivity of the saltstone, C_o is 6.023, and t is time. The effect of the clay cap is to inhibit the flux of nitrate from the monolith face into the soil, and to inhibit ingress of water. A separate relation was derived for the flux out the clay cap,[4]

$$q = C_o \sqrt{\frac{D_s}{\pi t}} \left[2 \sum_{n=0}^{\infty} (-1)^n e^{-\frac{L^2(1+2n)^2}{4 D_c t}} \right] \tag{6}$$

where L is the thickness of the cap, and D is the molecular diffusivity of the cap (for clay $D_c \simeq 10^{-8}$ cm^2/sec).

Numerical Model

To numerically solve Equations (1) and (3), along with the accompanying boundary conditions and flux relations, the Galerkin finite element method was employed.[5,6] Basis functions based on quadrilateral elements were used to approximate the trial solution,

$$c = N_i(x,y)C_i(t) \quad i = 1,2,\ldots n \tag{7}$$

where $N_i(x,y)$ are the basis functions and $C_i(t)$ are the nodal values of concentration at time t; n is the total number of nodes in the solution domain. Applying the finite element procedure to Equation (1), and employing integration by parts for the second derivative terms, Equation (1) is transformed to

$$\sum_e \int_D \left[D_L \frac{\partial C}{\partial x} \frac{\partial N}{\partial x} + D_T \frac{\partial C}{\partial y} \frac{\partial N}{\partial y} + \left(u \frac{\partial C}{\partial x} + v \frac{\partial C}{\partial y} + \frac{\partial C}{\partial t} \right) N \right] dxdy$$
$$= \int_\Gamma \left(D_L \frac{\partial C}{\partial x} n_x + D_T \frac{\partial C}{\partial y} n_y \right) N ds \tag{8}$$

where $\sum_e$ denotes summation (assembly) over all the elements, and n_x and n_y are unit vectors normal to the surface boundaries. Porosity has been factored into the velocities, and the source/sink term is zero.

Equation (8) can be written in matrix form as

$$[M] \left\{ \frac{dc}{dt} \right\} + ([U] + [K]) \{c\} = \{f\} \tag{9}$$

where the matrices [M], [U], and [K] are defined as

$$[M] = \iint N_i N_j dxdy; \quad [U] = \iint \left(uN_i \frac{\partial N_i}{\partial x} + vN_i \frac{\partial N_i}{\partial y} \right) dxdy$$
$$[K] = \iint \left(D_L \frac{\partial N_i}{\partial x} \frac{\partial N_i}{\partial x} + D_T \frac{\partial N_i}{\partial y} \frac{\partial N_i}{\partial y} \right) dxdy \tag{10}$$

and $\{f\}$ is the column vector consisting of known terms. The time derivative term is approximated using a finite difference expression, allowing implicit, explicit, or Crank-Nicolson averaging. The solution of Equation (9) was obtained using a skyline matrix solver.

Equation (7) was solved analogously like the diffusion terms appearing in Equation (8). The horizontal and vertical velocity components were obtained from the standard relations

$$u = \frac{\partial \Psi}{\partial x} \; ; \; v = \frac{\partial \psi}{\partial y} \tag{11}$$

Time marching of Equation (9) was conducted until the concentration outflow at the sump boundary peaked and began to decrease. In order to keep computational dispersion errors low, the local Peclet numbers ($u\Delta x/D_L$ in the x-direction) were evaluated to ensure a convergent solution ($\leqslant 10$). The Courant number ($U\Delta t/\Delta x$) was kept less than 2.

Since the lysimeters were symmetrical in design, the finite element mesh was created for only half of each domain. The mesh for both the uncapped and capped monoliths are shown in Figure 3(a,b). Figure 4 shows the landfill monolith and two-dimensional mesh of the side view, respectively. Because of the asymmetrical slopes, symmetry could not be assumed. Around 2300 elements were used for this simulation.

To convert the fluxes from the two-dimensional cross-sectional models to three-dimensional values, simple conversion factors were used. The factors were based upon the volumes of the monoliths, surface areas of the outflow boundaries, and volumetric flow rates of the infiltration.

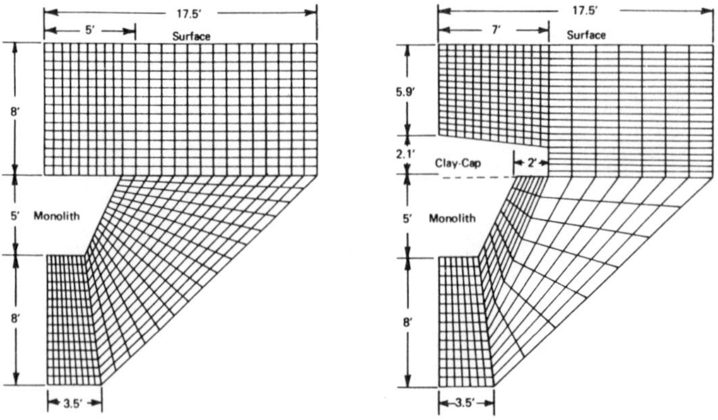

a.) Uncapped Lysimeter

b.) Lysimeter Clay-Capped

FIGURE 3. Mesh for the Uncapped and Clay-Capped Lysimeters

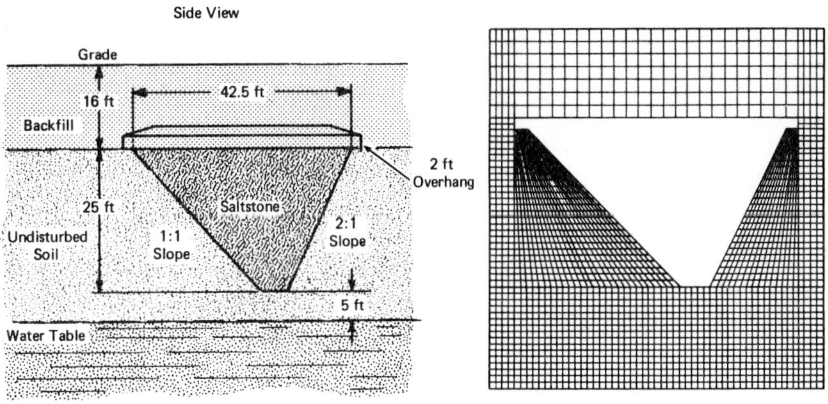

FIGURE 4. Landfill Monolith

Results

The two lysimeter simulations were run on an IBM 3081 computer. A time step of 100 days was used for the test cases. A total time interval of less than 100 years was sufficient for the lysimeter studies. However, in the landfill study, long time periods were required to determine when the nitrate would reach acceptable drinking water standards; this version of the code was run on a Cray X-MP/24 supercomputer.

Model results from the two lysimeter tests agree well with the field data. This is surprising in light of the rather simplistic assumptions made in formulating the model equation set. Figure 5 compares model results at the outflow boundary with field test data from the uncapped lysimeter. The nitrate flux builds up quickly with time, peaking at about 140 ppm in about 4 years, decreasing rather sharply over the next 6-year period, and then declining slowly for many years. Results from the clay-capped lysimeter study are shown in Figure 6. Experimental data shows very little nitrate leaving the monolith over the past two years. The numerical calculations also show very little nitrate initially; a slow buildup of nitrate occurs over a 5-year period. The nitrate at the outflow boundary ultimately peaks to 70 ppm in about 20 years, then slowly starts decreasing over a long period of time.

The difference in results between the two lysimeter studies is better illustrated in Figure 7. The nitrate in the uncapped case diffuses from the top, sides, and bottom of the monolith rapidly. In the capped case, we see some nitrate being emitted through the clay cap. The cap acts like an umbrella, shielding the monolith from the downflow of water.

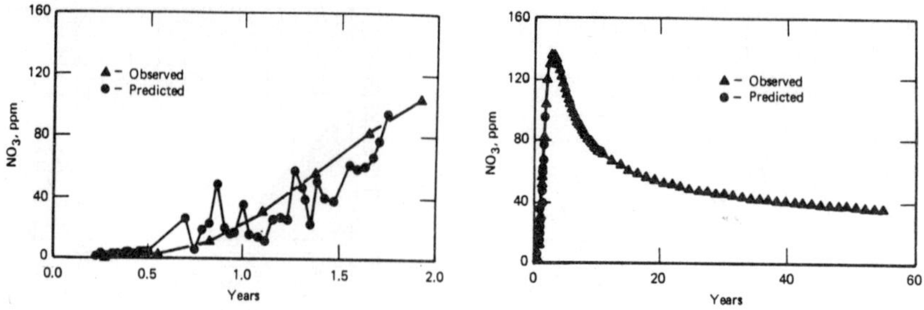

FIGURE 5. Uncapped Lysimeter Results

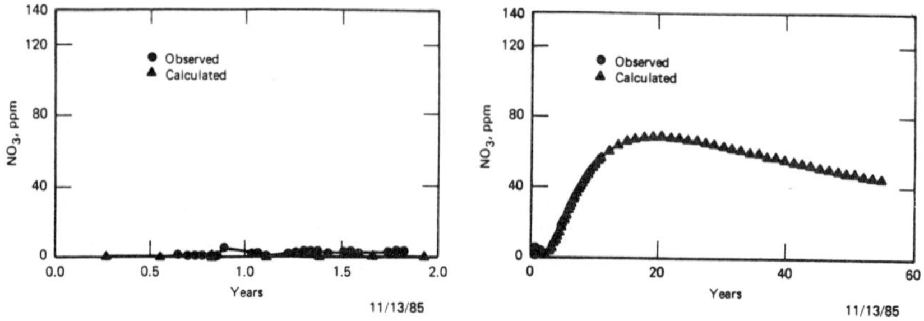

FIGURE 6. Clay-Capped Lysimeter Results

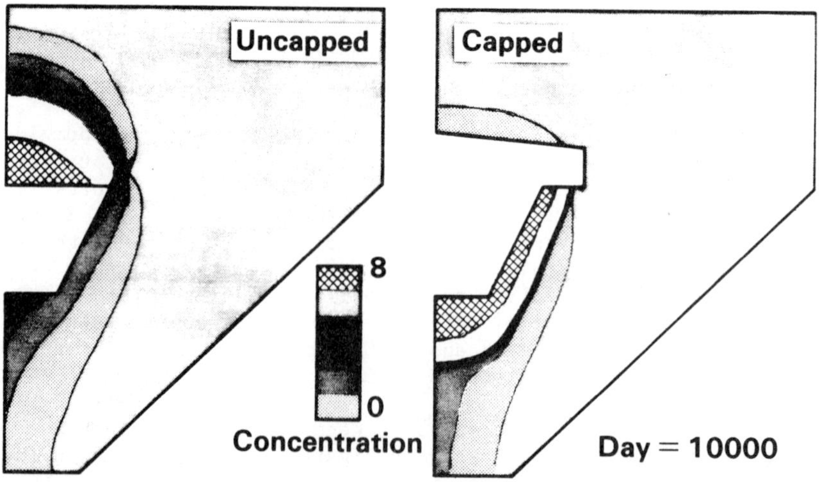

FIGURE 7. Isopleths of Nitrate at Two Time Periods for the Uncapped and Clay-Capped Lysimeter

This results in a low velocity field and higher concentration levels next to the monolith. A color movie of the transport from both lysimeters was made for a simulated time period of 12,000 days.

We assume that the clay cap is saturated, and that groundwater does not flow through the saltstone. While this undoubtedly introduces some error, the results appear quite good. Nevertheless, further work is under way to model transport under saturated conditions with percolation through the saltstone and clay cap.[7]

The landfill simulation was conducted to ascertain the impact of a clay-capped monolith discharging nitrate into the water table over a long period of time. Many of these monoliths are planned for burial at the Savannah River Site. Figure 8 shows the predicted quantity of nitrate discharged into the water table over 150 years. The concentration peaks at 280 ppm within 25 years. The groundwater standard for nitrate (44 ppm) is exceeded for 1200 years.

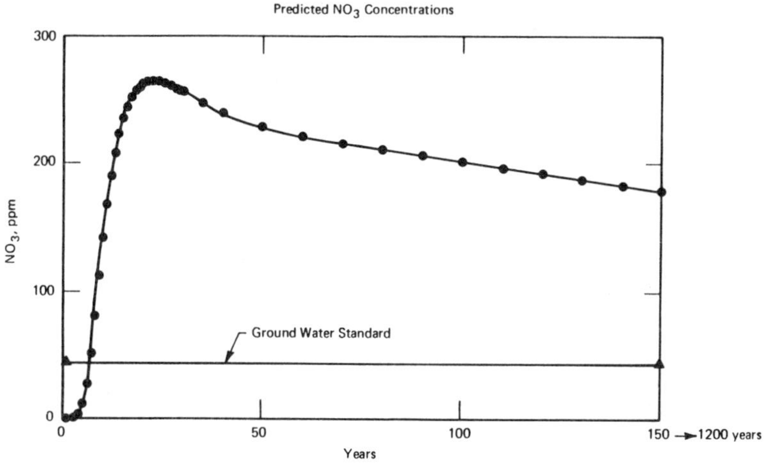

FIGURE 8. Landfill Monolith Results

Exceedance of the drinking water standard is unacceptable; alternate landfill designs are being explored.[8] For example, a two-foot-thick concrete liner placed around the monolith reduces the peak concentration to approximately 23 ppm. However, such an alternative is costly, and time consuming to implement.

Conclusions

Results from a finite element model, using simple assumptions for groundwater flow and transport, agree with field experimental data obtained from uncapped and clay-capped saltstone monoliths (lysimeters). The model predicts a peak concentration of 140 ppm (NO_3) within 4 years for the uncapped lysimeter; a peak concentration of 70 ppm occurrs within 20 years for the clay cap lysimeter. The clay cap acts as a shield over the monolith, reducing advective transport near the monolith surfaces.

The landfill model predicts that nitrate discharge into the water table would exceed drinking water standards for 1200 years. Alternative designs or restrictive liners around the monolith appear necessary.

ACKNOWLEDGEMENT

I wish to acknowledge the support and advice given to me by D. E. Stephenson, B. B. Looney, M. W. Grant, and E. L. Wilhite on development of the model. Special thanks are due to P. A. Watterberg for the color graphics and computer movie of the model results.

REFERENCES

1. H. Charles Wolf. Large-Scale Demonstration of Disposal of Decontaminated Salt as Saltstone. USDOE Report DPST-84-497, E. I. du Pont de Nemours and Company, Savannah River Laboratory, Aiken, SC (1984).

2. S. B. Oblath. Relative Release Rates of Nitrate, Tc, Cs, and Sr from Saltstone, USDOE Report DPST-84-620, E. I. du Pont de Nemours and Company, Savannah River Laboratory, Aiken, SC (1984).

3. B. B. Looney. Assessment of the Simplified Saltstone Release Flux Equations: Estimate of the Magnitude of Possible Error, USDOE Report DPST-85-840, E. I. du Pont de Nemours and Company, Savannah River Laboratory, Aiken, SC (1985).

4. R. M. Wallace, W. W. F. Yau, and M. W. Grant. Sample Approximation of Nitrate Diffusion from Saltstone. USDOE Report DPST-85-939, E. I. du Pont de Nemours and Company, Savannah River Laboratory, Aiken, SC (1985).

5. G. F. Pinder and W. G. Gray (1977). Finite Element Simulation in Surface and Subsurface Hydrology, p. 259 Academic Press, New York.

6. A. Verruijt. Groundwater Flow, p. 144. The Macmillan Press Ltd., London (1982).

7. P. S. Huyakorn, S. D. Thomas, and B. M. Thompson. "Techniques for Making Finite Elements Competitive in Modeling Flow in Variably Saturated Porous Media", Water Resources Research, 20, No. 8, pp. 1099-1115 (1984).

8. E. L. Wilhite. Estimated Release from the Saltstone Landfill Effect of Liners and Monolith Size, USDOE Report DPST-85-764, E. I. du Pont de Nemours and Company, Savannah River Laboratory, Aiken, SC (1985).

VI International Conference on Finite Elements in Water Resources, Lisboa, Portugal, June 1986

Implementation of Finite Element Groundwater Models on Vector and Parallel Computers

W. Pelka, A. Peters
Institute for Hydraulic Engineering and Water Resources Development, Aachen University of Technology, Federal Republic of Germany

ABSTRACT

Finite element models, optimized for running on conventional serial computers, are not suitable to make use of the potentional high performance of today's vector or parallel computers. Also automatic vectorization by the compiler or manual vectorization on local level do by far not lead to the required and expected computational speed.

A new computer-independent programming technique for finite element problems to be implemented on vector computers is proposed and the test results of scalar and vectorized program structures on a conventional serial and on a non-conventional pipeline computer are discussed.

INTRODUCTION

Modern computing, as well as the historical development of computing, has been dominated by sequential monoprocessing based on the von-Neumann-principle of a single instruction stream and a single data stream (SISD). Even when considering future advance in hardware design, computers of this architecture will not be able to supply the performance, necessary to solve future computationally massive numerical problems in engineering science. Super-computers, based on new parallel or pipelined hardware architectures, are the great hope to make use of most advanced numerical models in practice and to give numerical modeling a new impact.

Parallel and pipeline or vector computers realize the principle of a single instruction and multiple data stream (SIMD). The idea behind a pipeline computer is essentially that of an assembly line: if the same arithmetic operation is going to be repeated many times, throughput can be greatly increased by dividing the operation into a sequence of sub-tasks and maintaining flow of operand pairs in various states of completion. In a parallel computer the same entire operation is executed by several processors on various operand pairs simultaneously. Obviously both strategies of processing are especially suited to vector computations, and vectors are taken as fundamental data types on SIMD-computers like e.g. the CDC CYBER 205, the CRAY 1 or the CRAY X-MP.

Applying finite element approaches, large data arrays must be handled in form of vectors and matrices, which are expected to be optimal primary data for processing on a vector-computer. However, conventional finite element programs, implemented and benchmarked on high-speed SIMD-computers showed insignificant speed-up factors of computation (9). Obviously these programs, developed and optimized for running on SISD-computers are not suitable to make use of the potentionally high performance of SIMD-computers.

In the present paper a new computer independent programming technique for finite element problems to be implemented on vector computers is proposed. The test results of vectorized and scalar program structures on a conventional serial (CDC CYBER 175) and a non-conventional pipeline computer (CDC CYBER 205) are discussed.

SOFTWARE PARTICULARITIES OF VECTOR-COMPUTERS

Continuous streams of operands make the pipeline computer very efficient. They are called vectors and a vector is defined to be a contiguous stream of data described by a structural pointer (descriptor) which specifies its beginning address and item count. A vectorizing compiler analyses whether the DO-loops can be executed vectorized and generates vector code with vector instructions. The main difference between a vector and a scalar instruction is that when executing a vector instruction the operations can be performed overlapped. Not all loops of a program can be vectorized. Barriers to vectorization exist in conditional and branch statements, sequential dependencies, nonliniar and indirect indexing, and subroutine calls within the loops. Recursive operations require also special precautions to avoid the data jamming problem (6), (8).

Vectors can be manipulated in vector operations making use of intrinsic vector functions which are not standardized jet, but implemented on any vector-computer with similar names:

Gather - collects into contiguous result vector discontiguous elements from another vector by using an index vector (Fig. 1)

Scatter - stores into discontiguous locations the contiguous elements from another vector by using an index vector (Fig. 2)

Compare - generates a bit vector as a result of comparing two vecto

Mask - put together the elements of two vectors under the control of a bit vector (Fig. 3)

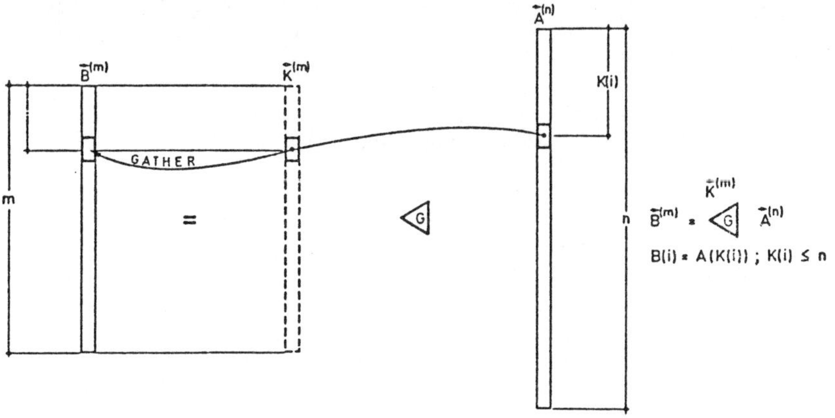

Fig. 1: GATHER-Instruction

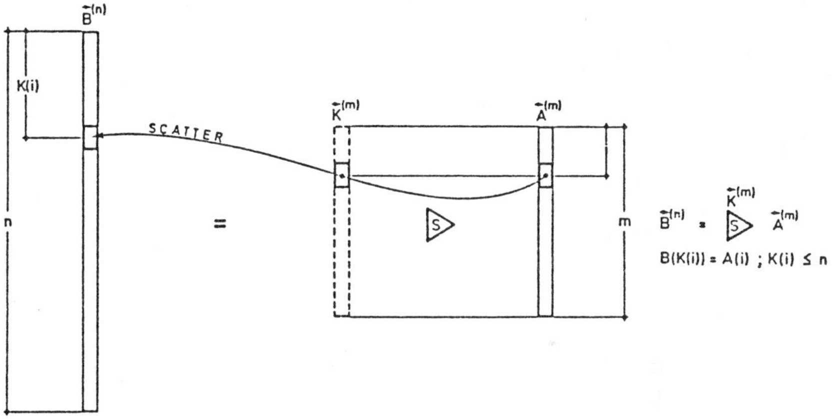

Fig. 2: SCATTER-Instruction

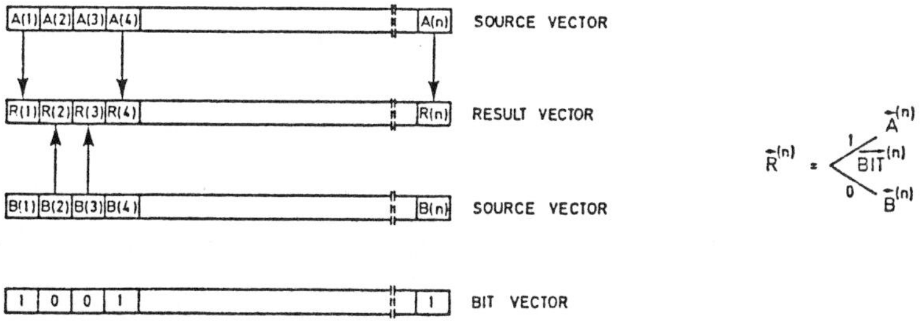

Fig. 3: MASK-Instruction

Strings of binary bits, so called bit-vectors, can carry information about real or integer vectors and can be applied to perform various key functions to these vectors.

A detailed presentation of the vector software features can be found in the specialized manuals (3), (5).

TESTED FINITE ELEMENT MODEL

A finite element model of quasi three-dimensional potentional flow, implemented on the CDC CYBER 175 (which has been for a comparatively long time one of the fastest conventional computers available for numerical computations) was chosen for implementation and testing on the vector computer CDC CYBER 205. For the sake of simplicity triangular elements with linear approximation functions (1), (11) were used in the model solving the equation

$$S \frac{\partial h}{\partial t} + \frac{\partial}{\partial x_j} \left(\underline{T}_{ij}(h) \frac{\partial h}{\partial x_j} \right) + Q(t) = 0 \qquad (1)$$

leading to a linear equation system of the form

$$\underline{D}_{mn} \underline{h}_n + \underline{E}_{mn} \underline{\frac{\partial h_n}{\partial t}} = \underline{F}_m \qquad (2)$$

where

$$\underline{E}_{mn} = \sum_e \int_{A^e} S^e \phi^e_m \phi^e_n \, dA^e$$

$$\underline{D}_{mn} = \sum_e \int_{A^e} \frac{\partial \phi^e_m}{\partial x_i} \underline{T}_{ij} \frac{\partial \phi^e_n}{\partial x_j} \, dA^e$$

h is the unknown piezometric head, S and T represent the specific storativity and the transmissivity of the aquifer, while Q is a time-dependent sink or source term.

CONVENTIONAL PROGRAM STRUCTURE

The results of extensive benchmarks and test-runs showed a minor speed-up on the CDC CYBER 205 in comparison with the CYBER 175, caused by the conventional advance in hardware, e.g. the shorter cyclus-time, and not by taking advantage from the non-conventional, vectorized architecture (9). Relying on the vectorization capability of the compiler, due to various restrictions only a minority of the time-consuming loop constructions could be vectorized automatically. The attempt to transform non-vectorizable loops in vector instructions using intrinsic functions, i.e. a manual vectorization on local level, made the program even slower than not vectorized at all.

A closer look at the internal structure of the three most time consuming phases of the program

- computation of the element matrices and assemblage of the structural matrix
- solving of the equilibrium equations
- computation of the derivatives and balances

makes the reasons for the failure of the automatic compiler vectorization and the manual local vectorization obvious.

The heart of any finite element program is the computation of the element matrices. They are necessary to assemble the general structure matrix and to compute the derivative values, after solving the equilibrium equations. The spatial derivative B-matrices and the element matrices are generated and stored in a peripheral storage device for later use or they are regenerated when required. Common for the both approaches is the sequential process. In a long loop for all elements the B-matrices based on the spatial coordinates are computed and multiplied by the material property tensor of the considered element and integrated over the elements volume. The inner tasks of the loop require many algebraic operations on vectors of short length, preventing the pipeline processor to develop its full potential. Due to the start-up time for short vectors, the vectorized computation may take even longer time than the equivalent row of scalar operations. The start-up time includes the instruction translation time and the delay imposed by fetching and aligning the input streams and by aligning and moving the output streams to memory. To make this initial effort negligible it is essential to operate with long vectors. The same problem occurs, when computing the nodal balances by resubstitution of the solution vector into the equation system and when evaluating the derivatives like velocities and fluxes. Again many operations have to be performed with vectors of very short length, preventing the vectorized hardware to develop its full potential.

Another important part of the finite element program is the solution of the equilibrium equations. Third generation computers are not only characterized by sequential processing but also by a perpetual lack of main storage, only imperfectly patched by virtual memory or background storage. In many program systems direct solvers based on GAUSS-elimination or CHOLESKY-schemes are used quite successfully in connection with skyline-like storage schemes, making use of the global matrix's special properties (2). No coefficients outside of the skyline are stored or processed. This approach requires non-equidistant storage schemes as well as necessary index calculations and logical decisions, which prevent the vectorization.

It can be seen that the finite element programs in the actual form cannot take advantage of the capabilities of the vector computers. A complete redesign becomes necessary.

VECTOR PROGRAM STRUCTURE

The key issue of the vector programming is to structure the computations into vector mode. First of all the user convenient scalar input must be arranged in long vectors in order to feed the execution units with a continuous stream of operands.

Fig. 5 demonstrates the basic procedure. Values like coordinates, evaluated for all nodes of the finite element mesh, are gathered to element node vectors of length m. In this approach system topology vectors, connecting element number and associated node numbers, were used as pointer or filter vectors (Fig. 4). A similar preocedure is used, when converting nodal values to element mean values like shown in Fig. 3 at hand of the bedrock and caprock elevations.

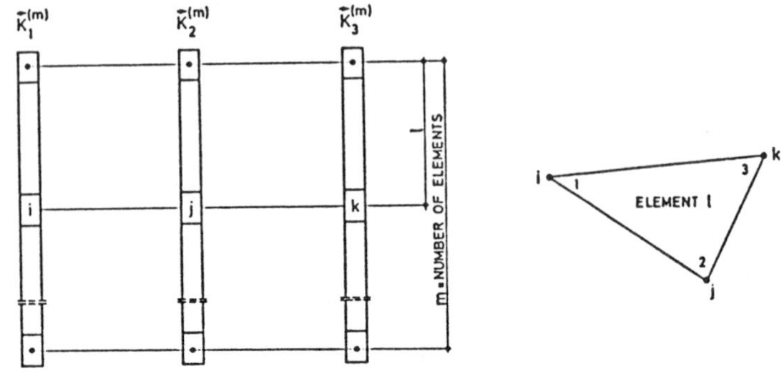

Fig. 4: Generation of the Topology Vectors

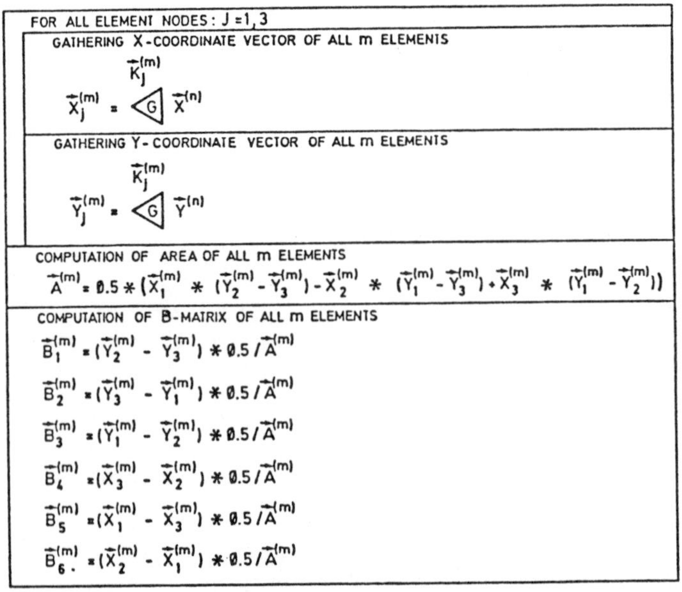

Fig. 5: Vectorized Computation of the B-Matrices

The usual technique of defining certain material types and to use a pointer vector, indicating the material type of each element, is very convenient in the sense of minimizing the manual input and the storage requirements, but will prevent later an effective vectorization, when computing the element matrices. By means of a gather instruction, element vectors of permeability and storativity are built, making use of the material type pointer vector (Fig. 7). A vectorized preparation of the storativity for later use in the storativity matrix may also take place here. The computation of the B- and element matrices and the assembly of the general structure matrix have to be split in operations which are computed vectorized for all elements. The new structure of the geometrical data make the vectorized generation of B-matrices and of element areas easy. Sequences of vectorized operations with vectors of length "m" can be performed now (Fig. 5).

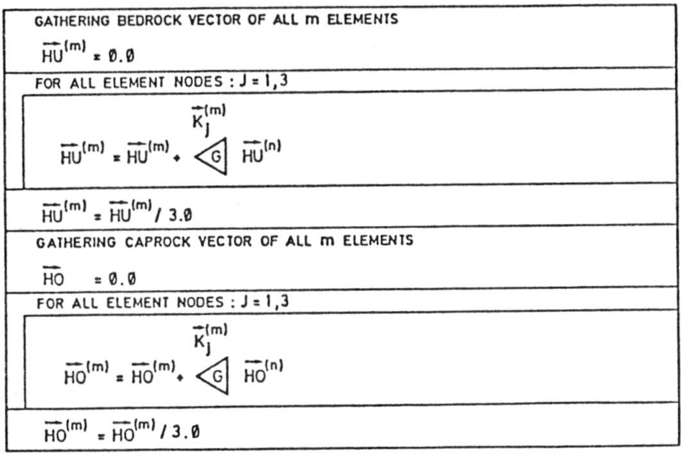

Fig. 6: Rearrangement of Nodal Bedrock and Caprock Elevations

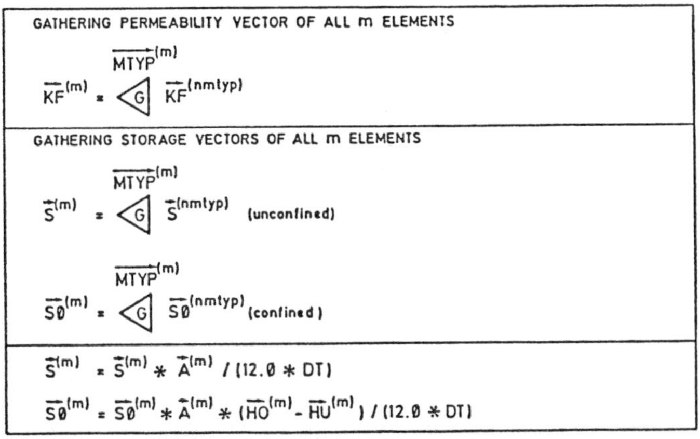

Fig. 7: Vectorized Generation of Material Characteristics

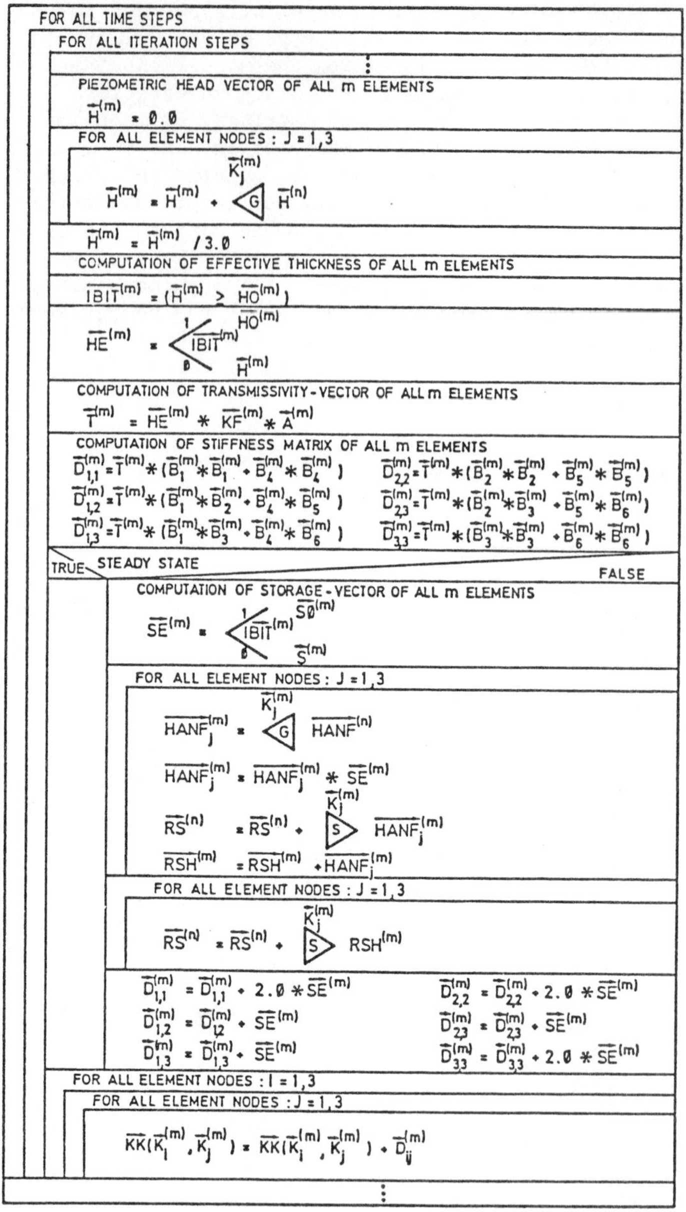

Fig. 8: Vectorized Computation of the Element Matrices and Assemblage of the Global Equation System

Fig. 8 shows the completely vectorized computation of the element matrices, the assembly of the global matrix and of the right side vector. To obtain long vectors, the inner and outer loops were interchanged. By means of this technique the outer non-vectorizable loops are of minor length, while all inner loops, and by this all algebraic computations act on long vectors on length m. Gathering the actual nodal values of piezometric head to element values and applying the bit vector technique in logical decisions, a vectorized computation of all elements' transmissivities takes place. The transmissivity vector and the precalculated derivative matrices were used to compute the element matrices by means of vector instructions. A compare and a mask function are necessary to determine the transmissivities and storativities for the material matrices. The values are different for confined (bit elements "1") and unconfined (bit elements "0") aquifers. The storage matrices were computed in a similar way. Elementary right hand side contributions were scattered to the right hand side vector, again using the mesh topology vectors.

Similar vectorizing techniques as described for the computing of the element matrices are used to calculate the derivative values and balances. The "n" unknowns in the equation system are gathered after solving in vectors of length m using the topology vectors. The computation of derivatives and nodal balances then can be performed completely vectorized.

Already in the past the programmer could choose among various direct and iterative equation solvers with respect to the special structure of the actual problem. There is a lot of literature about vectorization of linear equation solvers available (4), (10), mainly variations of the traditional GAUSS or CHOLESKY and JACOBI or SEIDEL algorithms. As it looks now, some kind of a renaissance of iterative procedures could take place, since they are easy vectorizable to a high degree and especially effective when in the non-linear and time-dependent case the solution of the previous iteration or time step supplies reasonable approximation for the solution of the actual unknown vector. In the present model the GAUSS elimination acting on a skyline matrix was changed against a conjugated-gradient iterative solver, which is very well suited for vectorization in connection with a rectangular storage scheme for the global matrix.

PERFORMANCE OF THE VECTORIZED PROGRAM

Fig. 9 shows the results of the benchmarks in the form of speed-up factors comparing the CPU-time of the global vectorized program running on the CYBER 205 with the sequential program implemented on the CYBER 175 and CYBER 205, respectively. The speed-up of the element matrix computation and the assemblage of the global system (Fig. 9a) increases fast with the number of nodes and reaches maximum values of up to 60. The slow decrease at a further rising numbers of nodes comes from the paging process since the available CYBER 205 was equipped with a comparatively small main memory of only 0,5 MW. Considering the growing share of CPU-time for the solution of the simultaneous equation for larger mesh sizes, the most pleasant property of the vectorized linear equation solver can be seen in Fig. 9b. The speed-up factor continues to increase with the number of unknowns and bandwidth, with values of about 50 to 60 for 3000 to 4000 nodes.

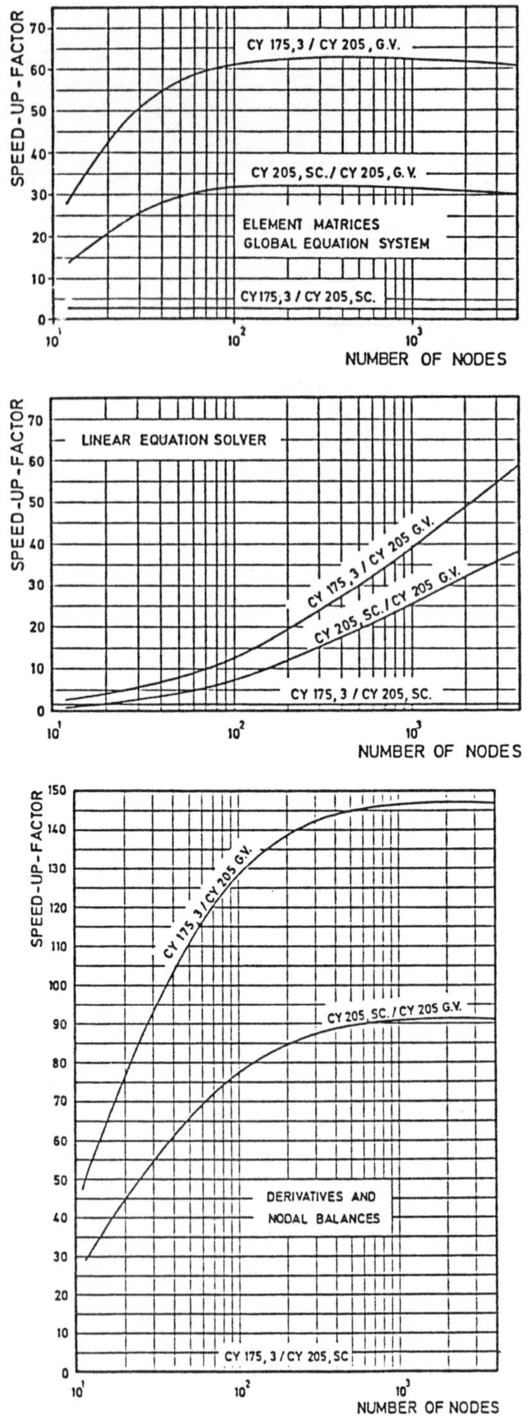

Fig. 9: Speed-Up Factors of Global-Vectorized (G.V.) Compared with Scalar (SC.) Program Version

As it could already be expected, extreme speed-ups can be achieved by the computation of the derivatives and nodal balances, which have been reduced to a few vector operations (Fig. 9c).

CONCLUSION AND OUTLOOK

General theoretical considerations and results of extensive benchmarks show that transporting finite element models, developed and optimized to run on conventional sequential computers, to fourth generation super-computers does by far not lead to the required speed-up to solve future computationally massive problems. The conventional program structures are not suited to make use of the potentionally great performance of today's super-computers, and in extreme, they may run even slower than when not vectorized at all. A global change of the overall program logic, that means more or less a complete redesign, becomes necessary, considering the new hardware characteristics. The global vectorization cannot be achieved by applying the FORTRAN 77 standard only. At least a minimum of additional intrinsic vector functions have to be used. Up to now, every manufacturer supplies his own set of vector instructions, which prevents the portability of programs and the scientific exchange of experience and programs. Since the different vector instruction sets carry out basically the same vector operations, users should insist in establishing a vector language standard as soon as possible. Vectorized programming needs more main memory, since on one hand the definition of additional vectors and storage schemes become necessary and on the other hand slow input/output operations on background storage would not be in coincidence with extremely fast vector operations. With a new generation of programs, developed and optimized to run on fourth generation vector computers, taking maximum advantage from the new advanced hardware architecture of vectorized or parallel processing, considerable speed-ups of more than an order of magnitude can be achieved and the numerical solution of new problem dimensions come into the reach of scientists and engineers.

NOTATION

A	vector of element area
H	vector of piezometric head
HANF	vector of piezometric head of previous timestep
HE	vector of effective aquifer thickness
HO	vector of caprock elevation
HU	vector of bedrock elevation
K	vector of element node number (topology vector)
KF	vector of permeability
MTYP	vector of material type
RSM	vector of element right hand contribution
S	vector of storativity (unconfined)
SE	vector of effective storativity
SO	vector of storativity (confined)
T	vector of transmissivity

REFERENCES

1. A.J. Baker, Finite Element Computational Fluid Mechanics, Mc Graw Hill Book Comp., 1983.

2. K.J. Bathe and E.L. Wilson, Numerical Methods in Finite Element Analysis, Prentice-Hall, Inc., 1976.

3. CDC, Fortran 200 Version 1 Reference Manual 60480200 Rev.C, Rechenzentrum Ruhr-Universitaet Bochum, 1984.

4. P. Concus, G.H. Golub and D.P. O'Leary, A Generalized Conjugate Gradient Method for the Numerical Solution of Elliptical Partial Differential Equations, Sparce Matrix Computations, Academic Press, 1976.

5. CRAY Research, Inc. CRAY X-MP and CRAY-1 Computer Systems, Library Reference Manual SR 0014, 1984.

6. R.W. Hockney and C.R. Jesshope, Parallel Computers, Adam Hilger Ltd., Bristol, 1981.

7. K.H. Huebner, The Finite Element Method for Engineers, John Wiley & Sons, Inc., 1975.

8. R. Mares and R. Wojcieszynski, Vectorisieren in CYBER 200-Fortran, Bochumer Schriften zur Parallelen Datenverarbeitung 3, Rechenzentrum der Ruhr-Universitaet Bochum, 1983.

9. W. Pelka, A. Peters and M. Vogt, Erste Erfahrungen mit dem Einsatz von Groeßtrechnern für mathematisch-numerische Grundwassermodelle, 6. Bochumer Kolloquium über Groeßtrechner und Anwendungen, Bochum, 1984.

10. U. Schendel, Einfuehrung in die parallele Numerik, R. Oldenbourg Verlag, Muenchen Wien, 1981.

11. D. Withum, Elektronische Berechnung ebener und raeumlicher Sicker- und Grundwasserstroemungen durch beliebig berandete inhomogene anisotrope Medien, Mitteilungen des Instituts fuer Wasserwirtschaft und Landwirtschaftlichen Wasserbau der Technische Hochschule Hannover, Heft 10, 1967.

ACKNOWLEDGEMENTS

Funding for this study was provided by the German Research Foundation (DFG) under Ro 365/27. The authors wish to thank the Computer Centers of the University of Technology Aachen and the University Bochum for the continuous co-operation and support.

VI International Conference on Finite Elements in Water Resources, Lisboa, Portugal, June 1986

Finite Element Modelling of Non-Conservative Pollutant Transport in Groundwater Flow

H-W. Dorgarten, W. Pelka
Institute for Hydraulic Engineering and Water Resources Development, Aachen University of Technology, Federal Republic of Germany

INTRODUCTION

A finite element model of non-conservative, temperature dependent pollutant transport in saturated-unsaturated concentration and temperature dependent groundwater flow is presented. To take into account heterogeneous reactions an additional equation describing the relation of fluid and matrix concentration is introduced into the system of coupled differential equations. The solution of the flow field equation, formulated in terms of pressure and mass flow, is generated by a generalized variational approach, while the transport and reaction equations are solved by a weighted residual technique.

CLASSIFICATION OF POLLUTANTS

A general classification of groundwater pollutants is shown by Figure 1 (DORGARTEN, 1984). A solute which, independent from its actual concentration, does not affect the groundwater flow is called a Tracer. Sometimes solutes are called Quasi-Tracer, if the actual concentration is very low and the small changes of density and viscosity don't have any significant effect on the flow field.

If the solute itself is not subject to any reactive changes, the transport is regarded as conservative, otherwise it is non-conservative.

The mathematical description of non-conservative pollutants strongly depends on the relation, or "scale", of transport velocity and reaction rate.

Considering an extremely slow reaction compared with the transport process, the problem may be quasi-conservative. Extremely fast reaction and slow transport lead to a dynamic equilibrium, which can be described by algebraic equations. Everything else between these extreme situations yields time-dependent differential equations governing a kinetic reaction.

If only one phase, for example the fluid phase, takes part in the reaction, the process is called homogeneous. Otherwise, if two or more phases, for example fluid phase and matrix, are involved, the reaction is heterogeneous.

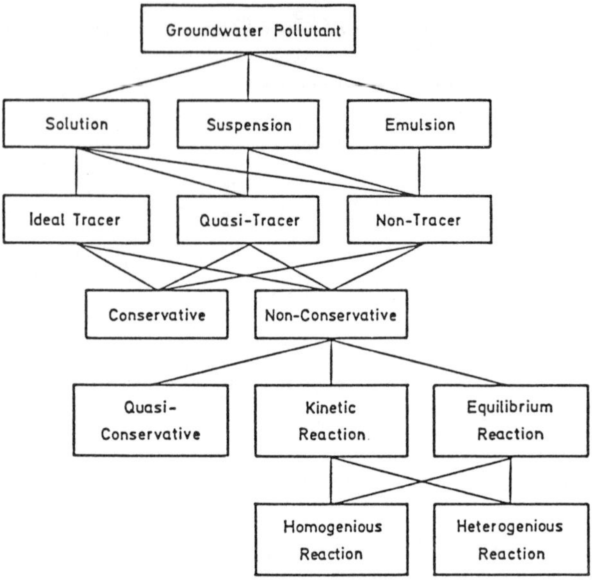

Figure 1 Classification of Groundwater Pollutants

MATHEMATICAL MODEL

Conservative Transport Equation

Considering conservative tracer transport, the three-dimensional, time-dependent concentration field in groundwater flow can be described by the well known tracer equation:

$$\frac{\partial}{\partial t}(nS_r C) + \frac{\partial}{\partial x_i}(\underline{v}_i C) - \frac{\partial}{\partial x_i}\left(\underline{D}_{ij}\frac{\partial C}{\partial x_j}\right) = 0 \quad (1)$$

The first term of this diffusion-convection-equation represents the mass of solute stored in a balance volume due to changes of concentration with time. The second term characterizes the transport by convection and the third term describes the diffusive and dispersive portion of the transport. The tensor of the effective hydrodynamic dispersion combines the velocity dependent tensor of mechanical dispersion and the molecular diffusion tensor. In the saturated-unsaturated case the tensor of hydrodynamic dispersion depends on the actual degree of saturation.

A unique solution of this differential equation requires the definition of boundary conditions on the whole boundary, and, additionally, in the time-dependent case, initial conditions in the whole region under consideration.

Non-Conservative Transport Equation

Experience shows that the most relevant pollutants cannot by far be considered as being conservative, since they are subject to various physical, chemical, or biological reactions.

The partial differential equation governing non-conservative transport, considering kinetic, heterogeneous reactions, is obviously quite different from the conservative transport equation:

$$\frac{\partial}{\partial t}(nS_r C) + \frac{\partial}{\partial t}(\rho_d \bar{C}) + \frac{\partial}{\partial x_i}\cdot(\underline{v}_i C) - \frac{\partial}{\partial x_i}\left(\underline{D}_{ij}\frac{\partial C}{\partial x_j}\right) - f - \bar{f} = 0 \qquad (2)$$

The time-dependent storage term, the convective and diffusive-dispersive transport are still the same, but three new terms have to be introduced into the equation.

The second term comes from the heterogeneous reactions between fluid and matrix, with $\bar{C}$, the matrix concentration. f is a concentration dependent homogeneous reaction in the fluid, while $\bar{f}$ is a concentration dependent reaction in the matrix.

Further it can be seen that the problem is solved at the price of introducing another variable, the concentration of the solid matrix, and two, so far undetermined functions into the equation. A second equation, which is necessary to make a solution of this problem possible, depends on the actual solute and the actual physical, chemical, or biological reactions.

Reaction Equation

Filtration By its porous structure the soil matrix is a filter regarding the pollutants transported with groundwater flow. Assuming the flow field not to be influenced by the filter effect, filtration, a heterogeneous reaction, may be described according to AVOGADRO and DE MARSILY (1983) by

$$\frac{\partial \bar{C}}{\partial t} = \eta v C \qquad (3)$$

i.e. the change of matrix concentration of the pollutant is proportional to the fluid concentration and the flow velocity. The filter coefficient depends on different soil and pollutant parameters.

Exponential decay Homogeneous reactions due to radioactive or various biological processes are governed by the well known exponential decay equation

$$\frac{\partial C}{\partial t} = -\lambda C \qquad (4)$$

Sorption The mostly used mathematical model to describe kinetic adsorption-desorption processes is the differential equation

$$\frac{\partial \bar{C}}{\partial t} = k_1 C - k_2 \bar{C} \tag{5}$$

(LAPIDUS and AMUNDSEN, 1952), which assumes a linear relation between the reaction rate and the concentrations of the solute in fluid and soil matrix. The FREUNDLICH approach

$$\frac{\partial \bar{C}}{\partial t} = k_1 C^n - k_2 \bar{C} \tag{6}$$

and the LANGMUIR approach

$$\frac{\partial \bar{C}}{\partial t} = k_1 (\bar{C}_o - \bar{C}) C - k_2 \bar{C} \tag{7}$$

take into account the non-linearity, which is caused by decreasing reaction rates at high matrix concentrations.

Heterogeneous-homogeneous reaction equation Considering heterogen ous and homogeneous reactions simultaneously and using the linear adsorption equation (5) as well as exponential decay leads to a kinetic equation

$$\frac{\partial \bar{C}}{\partial t} = k_1 C - k_2 \bar{C} - \overline{\lambda C} \tag{8}$$

and an equilibrium equation

$$\bar{C} = kC \qquad \text{with} \qquad k = \frac{k_1}{k_2 + \bar{\lambda}} \tag{9}$$

Heat Transport Equation

Especially when considering chemical and biological reactions, the actual temperature has considerable effects on the non-conservative transport process. The differential equation governing convective-conductive-dispersive heat transport in groundwater flow is analogue to the conservative-transport-equation (1)

$$\frac{\partial}{\partial t}\left(\rho_B c_B T\right) + \frac{\partial}{\partial x_i}\left(\rho c \underline{v}_i T\right) - \frac{\partial}{\partial x_i}\left(\underline{D}_{w,ij} \frac{\partial T}{\partial x_j}\right) = 0 \tag{10}$$

The tensor of effective thermal dispersion combines the velocity and saturation dependent tensor of mechanical dispersion and the effective heat conduction.

Groundwater Flow Equation

Obviously the solution of the transport equations requires the knowledge of the flow field. The convective transport portions strongly depend on the spatial and temporal velocity distribution, and various parameters of the transport equation are functions of the degree of saturation or moisture distribution in the unsaturated or mixed saturated-unsaturated case (PELKA, 1983):

$$\frac{\partial}{\partial t}\left[\left(S_r S + n\rho \frac{\partial S_r}{\partial p}\right) p\right] + \frac{\partial}{\partial x_i}(\rho v_i) = 0 \tag{11}$$

$$v_i = -\frac{1}{\mu} \underline{k}_{ij}\, k_r \left(\frac{\partial p}{\partial x_j} + \rho g \frac{\partial z}{\partial x_j}\right) = 0 \tag{12}$$

Since the fluid density and viscosity are functions of the actual temperature and solute concentration, the flow field depends on the spatial and temporal temperature and concentration field.

NUMERICAL SOLUTION

Decoupling and Linearization

The first steps of solution are decoupling and linearization of the three equation systems (eq. (2) and (8), eq. (10), eq. (11) and (12)) in connection with a stable and fast converging iteration algorithm. In the present model a modified AITKEN-algorithm (PELKA, 1983) is used. Due to the strong non-linearities, especially when considering unsaturated or mixed saturated-unsaturated solution domains, it is necessary to iterate within each timestep instead of using time-coupled iteration schemes (Fig. 2).

Now the decoupled and linearized equations can be solved numerically by application of the finite element method. Since the characters of the flow and transport equations are quite different, appropriate approaches should be used for the formulation of the element equations.

Groundwater Flow

It is important to note that an accurate solution of the transport equations requires a correct representation of velocity, especially a continuous, mass conserving flow field. This can be achieved either by employing a first-order continuous basis function finite element scheme or by solving a multi-equation formulation. The present model is based on a generalized variational approach with independent basic functions defined for pressure and the different velocity components (MEISSNER, 1973), generating the essential continuous flow field.

Heat Transport

Applying the well known classical GALERKIN approach on (10) and integrating by parts the convective and conductive-dispersive transport portions according to the GAUSS integration rules yields element equations, which are summarized to a global equation system of the form

$$\underline{A}_{mn} \frac{\partial \underline{T}_n}{\partial t} + (\underline{B}_{mn} + \underline{D}_{mn})\, \underline{T}_n = \underline{F}_m \tag{13}$$

with

$$\underline{A}_{mn} = \sum_e \int_{V^e} \rho_B^e \, c_B^e \, \phi_m^e \, \phi_n^e \, dV^e$$

$$\underline{B}_{mn} = \sum_e -\int_{V^e} \frac{\partial \phi_m^e}{\partial x_i} \, \rho c \, \phi_l^e \, \underline{v}_{i,l}^e \, \phi_n^e \, dV^e$$

$$\underline{D}_{mn} = \sum_e \int_{V^e} \frac{\partial \phi_m^e}{\partial x_i} \, \phi_l^e \, \underline{D}_{w,ij,l}^e \, \frac{\partial \phi_n^e}{\partial x_j} \, dV^e$$

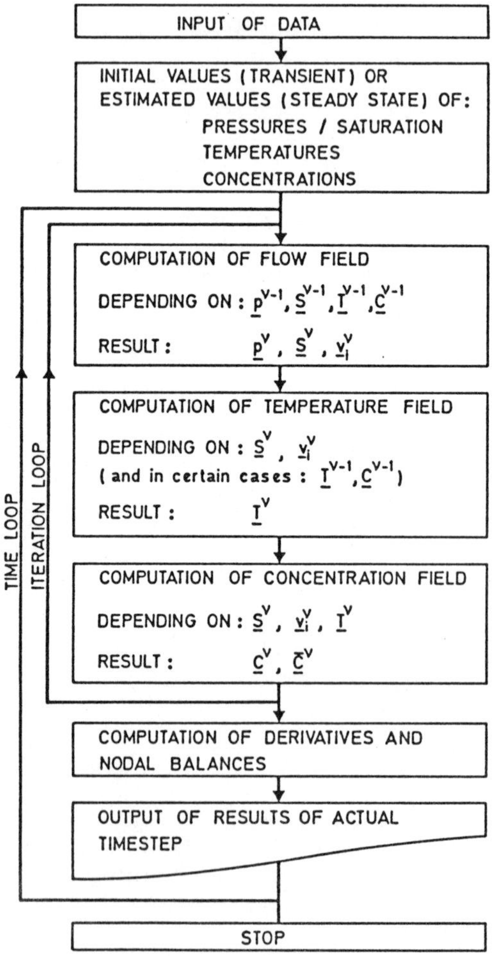

Figure 2 Flow chart of the numerical solution algorithm

Conservative Transport

The solution of the conservative transport equation (1) is analogous to the integration of the heat transport equation yielding the equation system

$$\underline{A}_{l,mn}\,\frac{\partial C_n}{\underline{\partial t}} + (\underline{S}_{l,mn} + \underline{B}_{l,mn} + \underline{D}_{l,mn})\,\underline{C}_n = \underline{F}_{l,m} \tag{14}$$

with

$$\underline{A}_{l,mn} = \sum_e \int_{V^e} n^e\, \phi^e_m\, \phi^e_l\, S^e_{r,l}\, \phi^e_n\, dV^e$$

$$\underline{S}_{l,mn} = \sum_e \int_{V^e} n^e\, \phi^e_m\, \phi^e_l\, \frac{\partial S^e_{r,l}}{\partial t}\, \phi^e_n\, dV^e$$

$$\underline{B}_{l,mn} = \sum_e -\int_{V^e} \frac{\partial \phi^e_m}{\partial x_i}\, \phi^e_l\, \underline{v}^e_{i,l}\, \phi^e_n\, dV^e$$

$$\underline{D}_{l,mn} = \sum_e \int_{V^e} \frac{\partial \phi^e_m}{\partial x_i}\, \phi^e_l\, \underline{D}^e_{ij,l}\, \frac{\partial \phi^e_n}{\partial x_j}\, dV^e$$

Non-Conservative Transport

The numerical solution procedure for non-conservative transport processes is similar to the previous one, since again a GALERKIN weighted residual approach will be applied, but it is reasonably more complicated, since the transport equation (2) and the reaction equation, e.g. (8), have to be solved simultaneously for both unknowns C and $\bar{C}$, the concentration of the fluid phase and the concentration of the soil matrix, respectively. Summarizing the element equations obtained from (2) yields

$$\underline{A}_{l,mn}\,\frac{\partial C_n}{\underline{\partial t}} + (\underline{S}_{l,mn} + \underline{B}_{l,mn} + \underline{D}_{l,mn} + \underline{E}_{l,mn})\,\underline{C}_n$$

$$+ \underline{G}_{l,mn}\,\frac{\partial \bar{C}_n}{\underline{\partial t}} + \underline{H}_{l,mn}\,\underline{\bar{C}}_n = \underline{F}_{l,m} \tag{15}$$

with

$$\underline{E}_{l,mn} = \sum_e \int_{V^e} n^e\, \lambda\, \phi^e_m\, \phi^e_n\, dV^e$$

$$\underline{G}_{l,mn} = \sum_e \int_{V^e} \rho^e_d\, \phi^e_m\, \phi^e_n\, dV^e$$

$$\underline{H}_{l,mn} = \sum_e \int_{V^e} \rho^e_d\, \bar{\lambda}\, \phi^e_m\, \phi^e_n\, dV^e$$

The weighted residual procedure applied to the reaction equation (8) gives another linear equation system

$$\underline{D}_{2,mn}\, \underline{C}_n + \underline{G}_{2,mn} \frac{\partial \overline{C}_n}{\partial t} + \underline{H}_{2,mn}\, \overline{\underline{C}}_n = 0 \tag{16}$$

with

$$\underline{D}_{2,mn} = \sum_e -\int_{V^e} k_1^e\ \phi_m^e\ \phi_n^e\ dV^e$$

$$\underline{G}_{2,mn} = \sum_e \int_{V^e} \phi_m^e\ \phi_n^e\ dV^e$$

$$\underline{H}_{2,mn} = \sum_e \int_{V^e} (k_2^e + \overline{\lambda})\ \phi_m^e\ \phi_n^e\ dV^e$$

Combining the systems (15) and (16) one obtains a system of 2*N linear equations for the solution of 2*N unknown nodal values of fluid and matrix concentration

$$\underline{I}_{mn} \frac{\partial \hat{C}_n}{\partial t} + \underline{J}_{mn}\, \hat{\underline{C}}_n = \underline{R}_m \tag{17}$$

with

$$\underline{J}_{mn} = \begin{bmatrix} \underline{S}_{1,mn} + \underline{B}_{1,mn} + \underline{D}_{1,mn} + \underline{E}_{1,mn} & \underline{H}_{1,mn} \\ \underline{D}_{2,mn} & \underline{H}_{2,mn} \end{bmatrix} \qquad \hat{\underline{C}}_n = \begin{bmatrix} \underline{C}_n \\ \overline{\underline{C}}_n \end{bmatrix}$$

$$\underline{I}_{mn} = \begin{bmatrix} \underline{A}_{1,mn} & \underline{G}_{1,mn} \\ 0 & \underline{G}_{2,mn} \end{bmatrix} \qquad \underline{R}_m = \begin{bmatrix} \underline{F}_{1,m} \\ 0 \end{bmatrix}$$

VERIFICATION

The results of the numerical model were found to be in good agreement with solutions obtained by analytical methods (BEAR, 1979; VAN GENUCHTEN, 1981). But it becomes obvious that an analytical solution covers only a very small sector of the wide range of flow and transport problems, hence numerous analytical solutions must be used to check the numerical model (Fig. 3, Fig. 4).

The numerical model, however, developes its full potential only when used for problems which cannot by far be solved by closed form solutions.

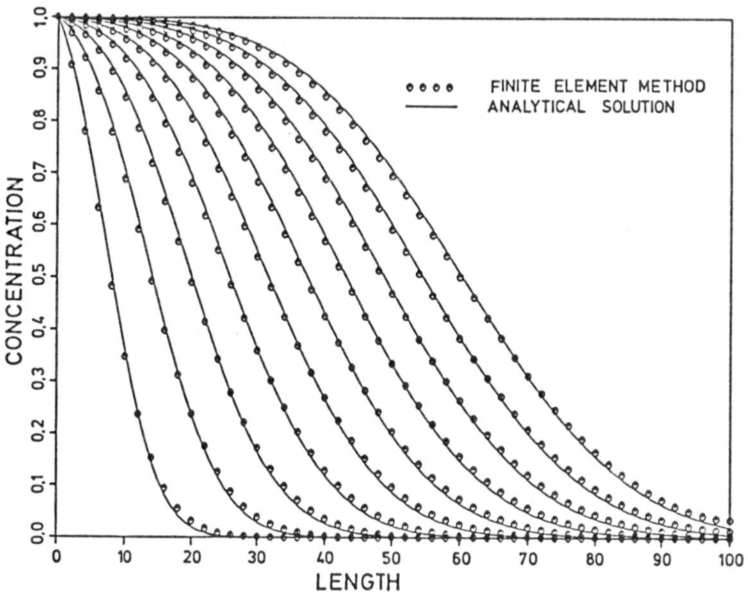

Figure 3 Transport of a conservative pollutant

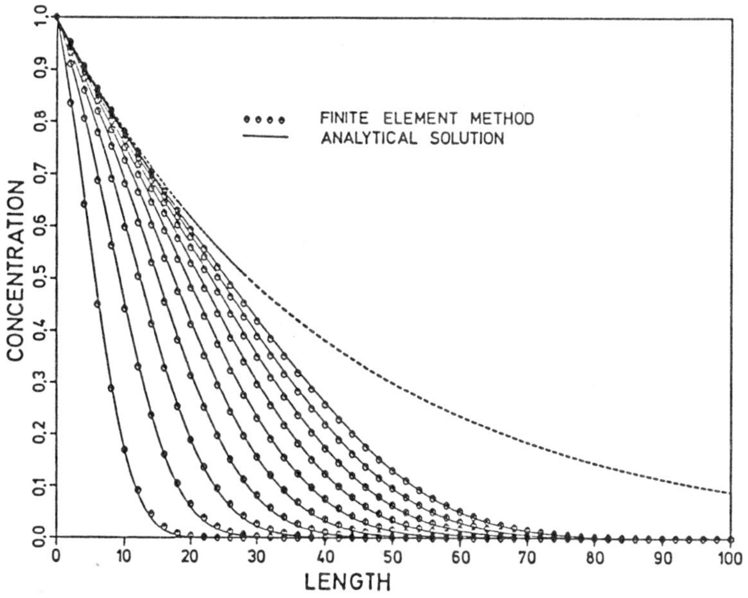

Figure 4 Transport of a non-conservative pollutant

CONCLUSIONS AND OUTLOOK

In consequence of the general formulation of the mathematical model and avoiding the introduction of simplifying and restricting assumptions while obtaining the numerical solution, the present model can be applied to a wide range of flow, mass transport, and heat transport problems:

- salt water intrusion into coastal aquifers,
- invasion of brackish or polluted groundwater from adjacent aquifers,
- infiltration from sanitary landfills or polluted surface waters,
- artificial groundwater recharge,
- groundwater pollution caused by domestic or industrial accidents,
- infiltration of fertilizers or pesticides from agricultural landuse,
- influences of hot or cold water injections from heat pumps, thermal energy storage or air conditioning.

REFERENCES

AVOGADRO, A. and DE MARSILY, G. (1983). The Role of Colloids in Nuclear Waste Disposal. Int. Conf. on Nuclear Waste Management, Boston.

BEAR, J. (1979). Hydraulics of Groundwater. McGraw Hill, New York.

DORGARTEN, H.-W. (1984). Die Berechnung großräumiger nicht-konservativer Stofftransportvorgänge in Grundwasserleitern. Master's Thesis, RWTH Aachen.

LAPIDUS, L. and AMUNDSEN, N.R. (1952). Mathematics of Adsorption in Beds, VI, The Effects of Longitudinal Diffusion in Ion Exchange and Chromatografic Columns. J. Phys. Chem., 6, 984-988.

MEISSNER, U. (1973). A Mixed Finite Element Model for Use in Potential Flow Problems. Int. J. Num. Meth. Eng., 6.

PELKA, W. (1982). Mathematisch-numerische Modelle zur Berechnung von instationären Grundwasserströmungen in großen Einzugsgebieten. Zeitschr. Wasser und Boden, 3.

PELKA, W. (1983). Stoff- und Wärmetransport in gesättigter-ungesättigter Grundwasserströmung. Mitt. Inst. f. Wasserbau und Wasserwirtschaft, RWTH Aachen, 47.

PINDER, G.F. and GRAY, W.G. (1977). Finite Element Simulation in Surface and Subsurface Hydrology. Academic Press, New York.

VAN GENUCHTEN, M.T. (1981). Analytical Solutions for Chemical Transport with Simultaneous Adsorption, Zero-Order Production and First-Order Decay. Journal of Hydrology, 49, 213 - 233.

NOTATION

C	ML^{-3}	Concentration (Fluid)
$\overline{C}$	---	Concentration (Matrix)
c	$L^2T^{-2}K^{-1}$	Specific Heat Capacity (Fluid)
c_B	$L^2T^{-2}K^{-1}$	Specific Heat Capacity (Soil)
$\underline{D}_{ij}$	L^2T^{-1}	Hydrodynamic Dispersion
$\underline{D}_{m,ij}$	L^2T^{-1}	Mechanical Dispersion
$\underline{D}_{d,ij}$	L^2T^{-1}	Molecular Diffusion
$\underline{D}_{w,ij}$	$MLT^{-3}K^{-1}$	Effective Thermal Dispersion
g	LT^{-2}	Gravitation
$\underline{k}_{ij}$	L^2	Permeability
k_r	---	Relative Permeabilty
k	$M^{-1}L^3$	Distribution Coefficient
k_1	$M^{-1}L^3T^{-1}$	Adsorption Rate Coefficient
k_2	T^{-1}	Desorption Rate Coefficient
n	---	Porosity
N	---	Number of Nodes
p	$MT^{-2}L^{-1}$	Pressure
S	T^2L^{-2}	Storage Coefficient
S_r	---	Saturation
t	T	Time
$\underline{v}_i$	LT^{-1}	Darcy-Velocity
x_i	L	Spatial Coordinates
z	L	Vertical Spatial Coordinate
ρ	ML^{-3}	Density (Fluid)
ρ_B	ML^{-3}	Density (Soil)
ρ_d	ML^{-3}	Density (Matrix)
μ	$ML^{-1}T^{1}$	Dynamic Viscosity
$\lambda, \overline{\lambda}$	T^{-1}	Decay Constants
η	$M^{-1}L^2$	Filter Coefficient

VI International Conference on Finite Elements in Water Resources, Lisboa, Portugal, June 1986

Groundwater Model with Consideration of Soil Settlement due to Mining

C. Hoffmann, G. Schmid
Department of Civil Engineering, Ruhr-University Bochum, West Germany

SUMMARY

The impact of mining subsidence on the distance between the ground surface and groundwater table is simulated in a FEM computer model. These settlements may lead to an effluent seepage on the surface if the water table intersects the land surface and will result in swamps. To prevent swamps, the groundwater table has to be lowered by a discharge of the aquifer through wells. In this paper two problems are discussed which had to be solved in a project studied at "Linker Niederrhein" in North-Rhine Westphalia, FRG.

1. The application of the finite element method results in large sets of linear algebraic equations. They require effective equation solvers. Comparative studies of different solvers are performed.
2. In the computer model a large number of rivers and channels has to be simulated by a non-linear leakage function. The implementation of the non-linear leakage function is discussed.

INTRODUCTION

The underground mining of coal and salt causes land subsidence which leads to a reduction of the distance between the ground surface and the water table. If the settlements are large enough the land surface may sink below the water table. This results in swamped zones or in additional springs.

To conserve the original situation - i.e. relative position of the groundwater table to the land surface - wells have to be installed and water has to be discharged from the aquifer. To forecast future groundwater situations the discharge rate of these wells and, in addition the changing base flow in the streams have both to be simulated in the groundwater model. The methods employed as well as the handling of the large data sets is demonstrated in a model of "Linker Niederrhein". Forecasts are given with ground settlements occuring until the year 2005. The situation in "Linker Niederrhein" can be characterized as follows:

1. The land surface investigated covers 475 km^2. To obtain a hydrogeological model a very large number of nodes has to be used in the FEM-discretization.
2. The region considered contains many streams, canals and brooks. Their influence on the groundwater model is simulated by non-linear leakage functions.
3. The discharge of water through wells causes large draw downs of the groundwater table which in a coarse mesh can't be described accurately. Hence, considerable mesh refinements are necessary to obtain a better resolution around the depression cone or in the well screen itself.

In this paper - due to shortage of available space - the discussions are related to the first two topics only: effective equation solvers and iteration procedures of the leakage.

DESCRIPTION OF THE MATHEMATICAL MODEL

The groundwater flow is simulated as a steady state or time dependent two-dimensional FEM-model. It is based on the potential theory and uses the Dupuit assumption. The mesh may consist of arbitrary shaped triangular or four node elements in which the basis functions vary linearly.

STREAM-AQUIFER INTERACTION

Leakage function
The results given by physical or mathematical modelling lead to a qualitative description of the mechanisms involved. In practical applications however, the determination of soil parameters is necessary. This ist especially true in an extended net of surface streams, where a great deal of effort and cost have to be forseen to determine the leakage functions.
In general, the river bed is assumed to be lined by a semipervous blanket of fine material which significantly reduces the exchange of water between the stream and the aquifer. It is common practice in a two-dimensional groundwater model to simulate the stream-aquifer interactions by a "leaky-aquifer principle".
Based on field measurements in the area of "Linker Nierderrhein" the results of discharge measurements in the streams (current meter readings) as well as gauge readings of the groundwater table are evaluated. A schematic description of the procedure involved is depicted in figure 1. In the sections of the rivers with effluent seepage (exfiltration) the hypothesis of a linear leakage function is verified. In the section of the rivers where the stream feds the aquifer (infiltration - the groundwater table is beneath the streambed) a specific rate of infiltration is not exceeded.

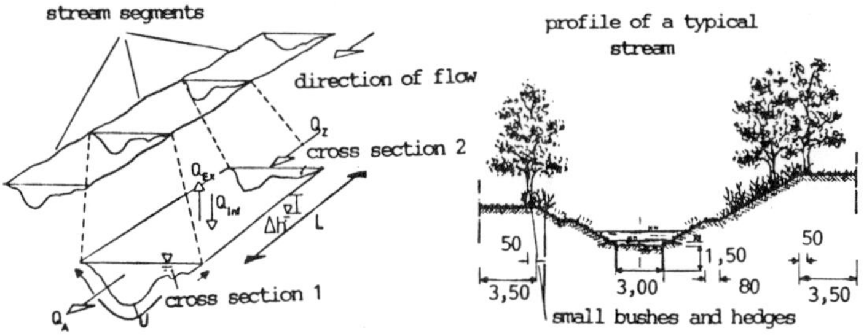

Figure 1: Principle sketch of the field measurements in a cross section of a channel to illustrate the size of the streams investigated

In figure 2 a typical non-linear leakage function is displayed which is quantitatively determined by the field measurements.

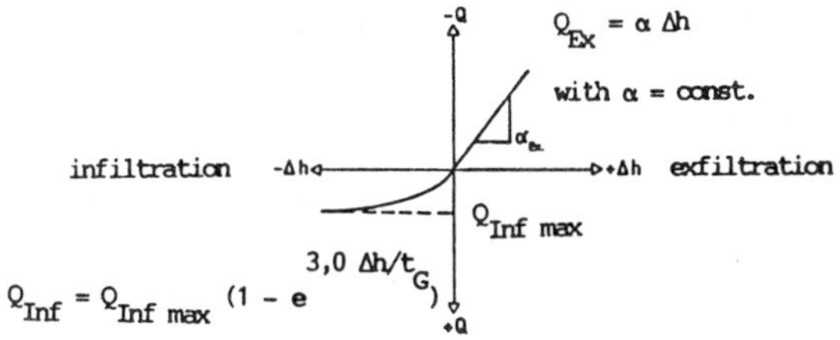

Figure 2: Plot of the leakage function

An analytical formulation of this Q-Δh-relation may be derived heuristically by the equations

$$Q_{Inf} = Q_{Inf\ max} \left(1 - e^{a\ \Delta h/t_G}\right) \tag{1}$$

$$Q_{Ex} = \alpha\ \Delta h \tag{2}$$

where Q_{Inf} is the quantity of water integrated over a specific length of the stream where the aquifer is recharged by the stream, Q_{Ex} the quantity of water which may be interpreted as baseflow, $Q_{Inf\ max}$ the above mentioned seepage rate which is not exceeded in the case of infiltration; t_G is the mean depth in a segment of the stream (a segment is defined as the zone between two vertical crosssections where the discharge is measured), α stands for the leakage function. The slope of this function in the transition from infiltration to exfiltration is mainly described by the coefficient a, which can be derived from a global view of the field observations. From this results a = 3,0.

Non-linear leakage function in a mathematical model

The leakage flow rates are applied to the right-hand side of the equation system which is obtained by the finite element method. The non-linearity is considered in an iterative analysis in which by reasons of stability a damping coefficient D (see Equation (3)) has to be introduced.

The piezometric heads in the aquifer are determined by the FEM-modell. From the difference between the measured streambed- and calculated aquifer-heads with the non-linear leakage function a volume of water for every node $\overline{Q}_{i,n+1}$ is calculated. The quantity which is set up in the next iteration step is defined by:

$$Q_{i,n+1} = Q_{i,n} + D\,(\overline{Q}_{i,n+1} - Q_{i,n}) \tag{3}$$

with $Q_{i,n}$ = volume of last iteration step (n) at node point (i)

$\overline{Q}_{i,n+1}$ = volume defined by the leakage function in step (n+1)

$Q_{i,n+1}$ = volume in step (n+1) using the damping factor

D = damping factor ($0 < D \leq 1$)

The choice of the damping constant depends on different factors:

1. starting point of iteration (Q_o)
2. leakage function in the transition from ex- to infiltration
3. mesh grading around the streams, model parameters - e.g. coefficient a

In particular the postulated continuity of the leakage function in the transition zone between the state where the water table is below and above the streambed respectively leads to difficulties in the convergence of the iteration scheme. The definition of suitable damping factors requires great care; it effects the computing time considerably.

Step size control of the iteration scheme

The idea of the proposed technique is to divide each iteration step of the stream-aquifer interaction in two half steps in which the two vectors (x,y) are defined. The components of these vectors are specified as follows:

$$x_{i,n} = \overline{Q}_{i,n} - Q_{i,n} \tag{4}$$

$$y_{i,n} = \overline{Q}_{i,n+1/2} - Q_{i,n+1/2} \tag{5}$$

with $Q_{i,n+1/2} = Q_{i,n} + D\,(\overline{Q}_{i,n} - Q_{i,n})$ in the second half step

$\overline{Q}_{i,n+1/2}$ = volume defined by the leakage function α and the head difference calculated from the first step

It is the aim of the iteration technique to minimize these deviations in every iteration step. A graphical interpretation of the procedure is given as the shortest distance between a straight line $\bar{g}$ through the endpoints of these vectors and the origin of the coordinate system. $\bar{g}$ is defined in vector-form by

$$\bar{g} = y + t\,(x - y) \tag{6}$$

The scalar coefficient t is specified by the requirement that the distance has to be minimized. In component-form that is:

$$\sum_{i=1}^{k} [t\, x_i + (1-t)\, y_i]^2 = \min ! \qquad (7)$$

k = number of node points located on the stream

By differentiating equation (7) with respect to t and equating to zero one obtains

$$t = \frac{\sum_{i=1}^{k} y_i\,(x_i - y_i)}{\sum_{i=1}^{k} (x_i - y_i)^2} \qquad (8)$$

In the second half step the linear relation given by Darcy's law between the flux and the gradient is used to reduce the computing time used for solving the equations. The procedure is summarized graphically in figure 3:

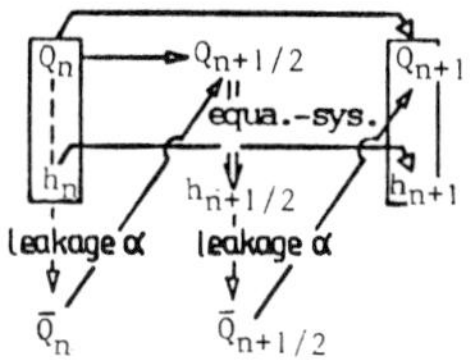

Figure 3: Algorithm to control the step size by a gradient method in the stream-aquifer interaction model

The correlation between field measurements and computed values for the discharge in a river of the project application "Linker Niederrhein" is shown in figure 4.

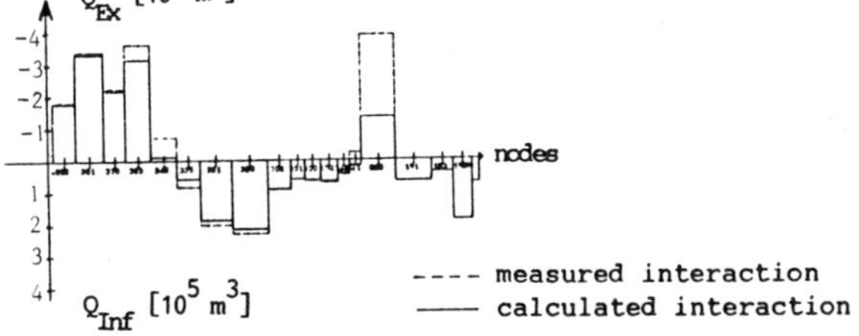

Figure 4: Stream-aquifer interaction in the application "Linker Niederrhein"

COMPARISON OF EQUATION SOLVERS

The efficiency of different equation solvers is judged not only by comparing computer-times but also by their storage capacity.

Prerequisite for the different schemes is a preliminary optimal re-ordering of the unknowns. Two types of meshes are compared in the investigation.
In the last part of this section some properties of the iterative scheme are discussed which are advantegous for use in a repeated solution of the equation system. All computations were performed on a medium size computer, a PRIME 750.

Description of the algorithms

Three equation solvers are discussed:
The Gauss algorithm (GG) with compact column storage and sky-line technique is compared with the direct frontal elimination technique (FG). The immediate advantage of the last named algorithm is a small storage requirement. Only a limited number of equations depending on the bandwidth of the matrix A has to be kept in the central storage of the computer (see Schwarz (1984)).
The third method is the iterative conjugate gradient technique (CG). This algorithm may be accelerated by a preconditioning of the matrix A (PCG - see Axelsson and Barker (1984)):

The matrix $C = H\ H^T$ is a symmetric, positive definite matrix with

$$K\ (C^{-1}\ A) \ll K(A)$$

$$K(.) = \text{condition number of a matrix } (.)$$

and H is obtained by an incomplete Cholesky decomposition in which the "fill-in" for all matrix coefficients H_{ij} is suppressed if A_{ij} equals zero.

Results of the comparison

The comparison is based on two different mesh types:

- regular meshes in a rectangular investigation domain → type R
- meshes which arise from practical applications with an arbitrary shape and a large number of additional constraint equations for constant heads in lakes → type U

Prerequisite for a comparison is an equal number of unknowns which range in the explored problems between 120 and more than 3000 nodes. Some properties of the compared meshes are shown in table 1:

mesh	n_k	n_{el}	m_o	S_s	S_k	mesh	n_k	n_{el}	m_o	S_s	S_k
R1	121	100	13	1442	502	U1	137	140	29	1994	443
R2	529	484	25	12674	2422	U2	512	502	45	12484	1562
R3	1024	961	34	33761	4807	U3	1046	1138	59	41680	3979
R4	1600	1521	42	65561	7607	U4	1569	1739	114	120036	6593
R5	3025	2916	57	169346	14582	U5	3002	3365	105	219822	12159

Table 1: Properties of discretization

In table 1 the following notation is used:

- n_k : number of nodes
- n_{el} : number of elements
- m_o : bandwidth of the matrix A after a bandwidth optimization
- S_s : storage requirements of the A-matrix with skyline technique
- S_k : non-zero elements in the A-matrix

The results of the comparison are summarized in figure 5.

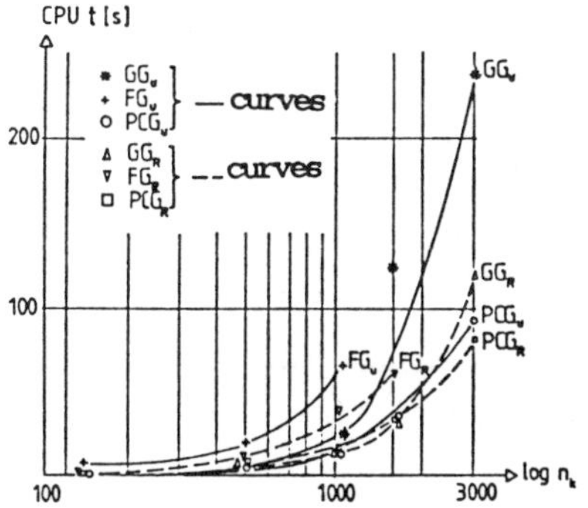

Figure 5: Processing time of the solvers

Obviously the CPU time of the frontal elimination technique is 40 % slower than the time of the Gauss algorithm. The lower storage requirement has to be paid for by an increased processing time not only at the I/O-level.

The PCG technique is more advantageous with the regular shaped meshes if the model has more than 1500 nodes. For meshes of practical applications (type U) the break-even-point is reached already with 500 nodes. The superiority of PCG increases with the problem size: compared with the Gauss algorithm, mesh U4 (for which the elimination schemes are not very suitable) needs 72 % less computer time. A typical gain would be about 60 % in a grid with 3000 unknowns. If the A-matrix is built up in a condensed form which contains only the non-zero elements, then PCG offers a further advantage since it results in a lower storage requirement.

The comparison made so far is based on a single solution of the equation system which is typical for steady state and linear flow problems. If non-linear leakage function or time-dependent problems are solved they demand repeated solutions.

For this kind of problems two properties of PCG are of special value:

- the matrix A is not destroyed in the solution process
- by choosing an appropriate starting vector in each iteration the number of necessary iterations may be reduced.

Table 2 shows the behaviour of the PCG-method in an example (type U) which uses a mesh with 1500 nodes. The stream-aquifer interaction is calculated by the iterative algorithm, discussed above, which required 10 iteration steps.

leakage-iter.	GAUSS GG	PCG1 (x_o^n=0) n_{it}	PCG	PCG2 (x_o^n=x^{n-1}) n_{it}	PCG	PCG3 (x_o^n=x^{n-1} and A=A_o) n_{it}	PCG	
1	66,04	28	22,21	28	21,49	28	21,44	
2	65,80	28	21,67	17	13,65	17	12,82	
3	69,81	28	21,70	18	14,28	17	12,87	
4	65,95	28	21,34	13	10,71	11	8,38	
5	67,65	28	21,33	11	9,20	11	8,37	
6	65,19	28	21,62	12	11,23	10	7,64	
7	65,51	28	21,44	12	9,92	7	5,45	
8	64,21	28	21,59	8	6,97	7	5,47	
9	64,58	28	21,78	6	5,53	7	5,52	
10	65,09	28	21,57	8	7,12	7	5,48	
Σ CPU	884,26		451,55		344,30		177,39	[sec.]
Σ solv.	659,83		216,25		110,10		93,44	

Table 2: Computer time of the PCG-method in an iterativ computation (stream-aquifer interaction) in comparison with a Gauss solver

In table 2 n_{it} is the number of iterations used by the PCG-technique.

The PCG-method is vastly accelerated using the result of the foregoing step as starting vector for the following PCG iteration. Time required is one sixth of that needed for the Gauss algorithm. A further increase of calculation speed is reached if the coefficients of the A-matrix stay constant. In this case (e.g. in a confined aquifer) the sum of the in-core processing time (system assembling, solution of the equations, computation of velocities) may be reduced by one half (Σ CPU).

The presented calculations show that the preconditioned conjugate gradient method is advantegeous above traditional techniques in practical applications if the discretization has more than 500 nodes. For non-linear applications the computing time may again be drastically reduced using the PCG-method.

GROUNDWATER MODEL "LINKER NIEDERRHEIN"

The investigation area of the groundwater model considered here is located between Rhein river and the German boarder to the Netherlands and between the cities Krefeld and Xanten. The large size of the area suggested a splitting in a north- and a south half (see figure 6).

One of the software requirements to handle such a model can be deduced from figure 6. The left half of the "south-model-mesh" shows the fixed points needed for a mesh generation (gauge wells, discharge wells, lakes - the lines stand for the streams which have to be considered in the mesh). From these fixed points a finite element grid is assembled by a mesh generation routine which is based on an algorithm from Nelson (1978).

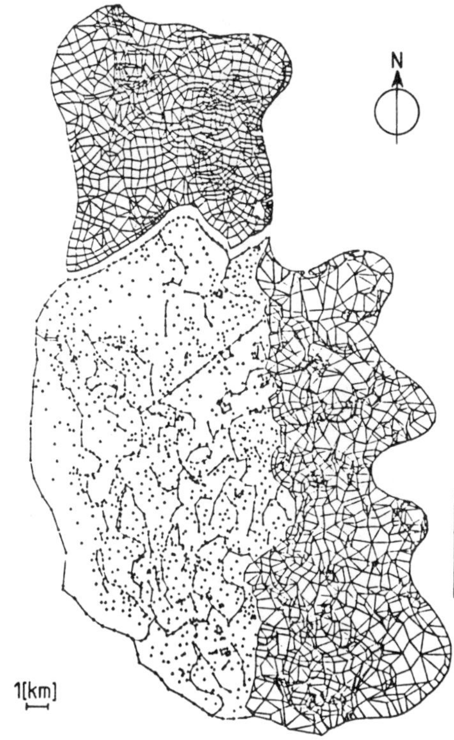

area	[km²]	nodes	elements
"n.-half"	97	1046	1138
"s.-half"	375	3010	3365

Figure 6: Discretization of the groundwater model "Linker Niederrhein"

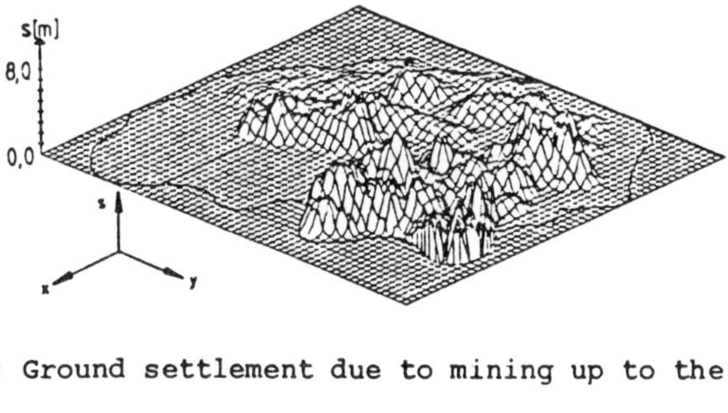

Figure 7: Ground settlement due to mining up to the year 2005

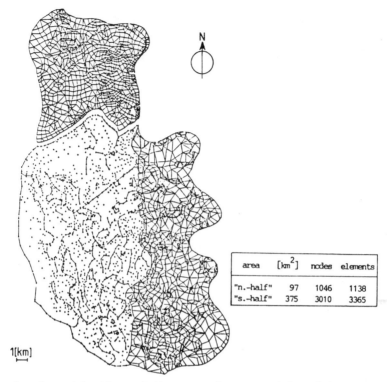

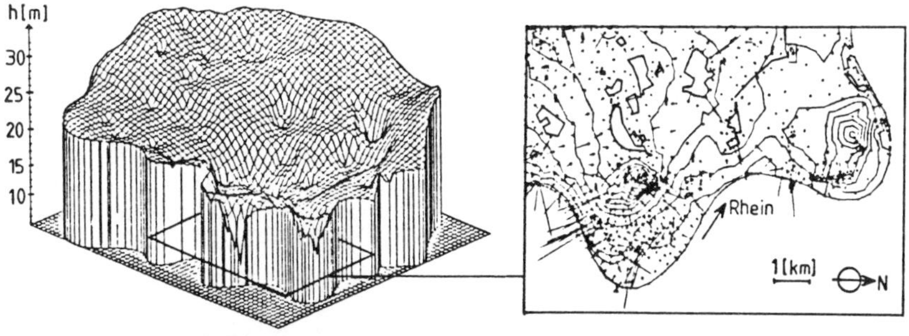

Figure 8: Groundwater contour in a simulation

Figure 7 shows the ground settlement from 1981 up to the year 2005 caused by coal-mining. Figure 8 shows results of a simulation which reveals the interference between pumping wells and drinking water discharge of the aquifer. The model has furnished detailed estimate of future groundwater situations in a rather complex environment.

CONCLUSION

Special attention has to be paid to the non-linear effects in the simulation of a stream-aquifer interaction. An algorithm is presented which ensures convergence of the iterative calculation. The preconditioned conjugate gradient method is an effective tool to solve large size equation systems. The efficiency of the proposed methods is shown in a large practical groundwater model.

ACKNOWLEDGEMENT

Help of Prof. Braess in the mathematical problems in this paper, is gratefully acknowledged. The research has been supported by LINEG, "Linksniederrheinische Entwässerungs-Genossenschaft", Kamp-Lintfort.

REFERENCES

Axelsson, O./ Barker, V.A. (1984) Finite Element Solution of Boundary Value Problems, Academic Press

Bouwer, H. (1969) Theory of Seepage form Open Channels, Advances in Hydroscience, 5

Braess, D. (1985) PRECG, ein Programm zur schnellen Lösung von großen linearen Gleichungssystemen mit positiv definiten, dünn besetzten Matrizen. Kurzfassung einer Programmbeschreibung, Fakultät für Mathematik, RUB

Hoffmann, C. (1986) Einfluß von Bergsenkungen bei der mathematischen Simulation von Grundwasserströmungen, eingereicht als Dissertation in der Fakultät für Bauingenieurwesen der Ruhr-Universität Bochum

Nelson, J.M. (1978) A Trinangulation Algorithm for Arbitrary Planar Domains, Appl. Math. Modelling, Vol. 2, September

Schwarz, H.R. (1984) Methode der Finiten Elemente, Teubner, Studienbücher Mathematik

SICK 100 (1981) Benutzerhandbuch, Programmbeschreibung, Interne Mitteilungen der Arbeitsgruppe IV, Institut für Konstruktiven Ingenieurbau, RUB

SECTION 4 PARAMETER ESTIMATION IN GROUNDWATER

VI International Conference on Finite Elements in Water Resources, Lisboa, Portugal, June 1986

The Inverse Problem for Hysteretic Unsaturated Flow

J.B. Kool, J.C. Parker
Virginia Polytechnic Institute, Blacksburg, VA 24061, U.S.A.
M.Th. van Genuchten
U.S. Salinity Laboratory, Riverside, CA 92501, U.S.A.

ABSTRACT

The application of numerical models to unsaturated flow and transport problems requires detailed knowledge of the soil water retention and unsaturated hydraulic conductivity functions of the medium. A parameter estimation procedure is presented that provides a convenient way for evaluating these functions from transient flow experiments. The hydraulic functions are described with analytical expressions containing five unknown parameters. The inverse problem is solved by combining an efficient linear finite element solution of the unsaturated flow equation with a nonlinear optimization scheme based on Marquardt's method. The procedure was previously applied to transient outflow experiments involving relatively short undisturbed soil cores. Consecutive solution of the inverse problem for outflow (drying) and inflow (wetting) on the same soil core proved to be a practical way for evaluating hysteresis in the hydraulic functions.

INTRODUCTION

Modeling of flow and transport processes in variably saturated porous media requires detailed knowledge of the hydraulic properties of the media. Determination of these properties by traditional methods is generally a time-consuming and tedious task. Moreover, most current methods are based on simplifying assumptions that are known to cause errors. Recently, various researchers have investigated the feasibility of obtaining the hydraulic functions from transient flow measurements by numerical inversion of the governing saturated-unsaturated flow equation (Zachman et al., 1982; Hornung, 1983; Kool et al., 1985a; Parker et al., 1985). These studies were all limited to either monotonic wetting or monotonic drying, thus precluding the determination of hysteresis in the hydraulic functions. Here we present a procedure for determining hysteretic hydraulic properties from transient outflow/inflow experiments on short, undisturbed soil cores. The method is based on the coupling of a finite element solution of the saturated-unsaturated flow equation with a nonlinear least-squares optimization scheme.

THE DIRECT PROBLEM

Consider a flow experiment involving a vertical, homogeneous soil column at some high initial water content that is subjected to a step decrease in pressure head at its lower boundary. Cumulative outflow from the column with time is monitored. After reaching equilibrium, the procedure is reversed by suddenly increasing the pressure head at the lower boundary. Cumulative inflow with time into the column is again measured. The measured outflow and inflow volumes provide the necessary input data for the parameter estimation problem. Thus, the direct problem is given by the one-dimensional unsaturated flow equation,

$$C(h)\,\frac{\partial h}{\partial t} = \frac{\partial}{\partial x}\left[K(h)\left(\frac{\partial h}{\partial x} - 1\right)\right], \qquad (1)$$

subject to the initial and boundary conditions

$$h(x,0) = h_o(x) \qquad 0 \leqslant x \leqslant L \qquad (2a)$$

$$\frac{\partial h}{\partial x}(0,t) = 1 \qquad (2b)$$

$$h(L,t) = \begin{cases} h_{out} & 0 < t \leqslant t_f \\ h_{in} & t > t_f \end{cases} \qquad (2c)$$

where h is the pressure head, $C = d\theta/dh$ is the soil water capacity, θ is the volumetric water content, K is the hydraulic conductivity, t is time, x is distance measured positive down from the soil surface, L is the length of the soil core, h_{out} and h_{in} are the regulated pressure heads at the lower boundary during outflow and inflow, respectively, and t_f is the time at which the flow process is reversed from drying to wetting. Cumulative outflow and inflow volumes, $\tilde{Q}$, are calculated as

$$\tilde{Q}(t \leqslant t_f) = A \int_0^L [\theta(x,0) - \theta(x,t)]\, dx \qquad (3a)$$

and

$$\tilde{Q}(t>t_f) = A \int_0^L [\theta(x,t) - \theta(x,t_f)]\, dx, \tag{3b}$$

respectively, where A is the cross-sectional area of the column normal to the direction of flow.

Equations (1) and (2) were solved numerically by means of a Galerkin-type linear finite element scheme. In previous studies of the inverse problem involving outflow only (Kool et al., 1985b), we used Hermitian cubic basis functions. While the Hermitian scheme proved to be very accurate, its computational efficiency is much less than when lower order basis functions are used (van Genuchten, 1982). Thus, the efficiency of the code was improved by using linear basis functions, by applying mass lumping principles to the time derivative, and also by using a time-implicit scheme. To maintain comparable accuracy, the linear scheme requires a much denser spatial grid system than the Hermitian cubic scheme. Notwithstanding these adjustments in nodal spacing, we were still able to achieve a 50% saving in computer time by reverting back to the lower order basis functions. Since details of the finite element solution (van Genuchten, 1982) and its coupling with a least-squares optimization scheme (Kool et al., 1985b) have been discussed at length previously, we elect to focus here mainly on the hysteretic nature of the outflow/inflow problem.

PARAMETRIC MODEL FOR THE UNSATURATED HYDRAULIC PROPERTIES

We assume that the soil hydraulic properties during monotonic wetting or drying can be described accurately with the equations of van Genuchten (1980):

$$S_e = \frac{\theta - \theta_r}{\theta_s - \theta_r} = \begin{cases} [1 + |\alpha h|^n]^{-m} & h < 0 \\ 1 & h \geq 0 \end{cases} \tag{4}$$

$$C(h) = \alpha(n-1)(\theta_s - \theta_r)\, S_e^{1/m} (1-S_e^{1/m})^m \tag{5}$$

$$K(S_e) = K_s S_e^{1/2} [1 - (1-S_e^{1/m})^m]^2 \tag{6}$$

where $m = 1-1/n$, S_e is effective saturation, $C = d\theta/dh$ is the water capacity, K is hydraulic conductivity, θ is volumetric water content and h is pressure head. The unknown parameters in the above equations are the saturated and residual water contents θ_s and θ_r, respectively, the saturated hydraulic conductivity K_s, and two curve shape parameters α and n.

In this study we consider both wetting and drying, and hence must take into account hysteresis in the soil water retention curve, $\theta(h)$. The outflow phase involves drainage along the boundary drying curve which we describe by the parameter vector $(\theta_s^d, \theta_r^d, \alpha^d, n^d)$. During inflow, the wetting path will generally follow a primary scanning curve rather than the main boundary curve. Scanning curves in this study are described with a modification of the method of Scott et al. (1983): given that the boundary wetting curve is described by $(\theta_s^w, \theta_r^w, \alpha^w, n^w)$, all wetting scanning curves are assumed to have the form $(\theta_s^*, \theta_r^*, \alpha^w, n^w)$. For θ_r^*, the procedure of Scott et al. leads to

$$\theta_r^* = \frac{\theta_1 - \theta_s^* \, S_e^w(h_1)}{1 - S_e^w(h_1)}, \tag{7}$$

where the subscript '1' indicates the point of reversal from drying to wetting, and where $S_e^w(h_1)$ refers to the saturation-pressure head function (Eq. 4) with parameters $(\theta_s^w, \theta_r^w, \alpha^w, n^w)$. The parameter θ_s^* accounts for a non-closed boundary hysteresis loop where $\theta_s^w \leq \theta_s^* \leq \theta_s^d$. If the boundary loop is closed, all values for θ_s are identical, i.e., $\theta_s^* = \theta_s^w = \theta_s^d = \theta_s$. θ_s^* for the non-closed case is evaluated with an expression introduced by Land (1968):

$$\theta_s^* = \theta_s^d - \frac{\theta_s^d - \theta_1}{1 + R(\theta_s^d - \theta_1)} \tag{8a}$$

where

$$R = \frac{1}{\theta_s^d - \theta_s^w} - \frac{1}{\theta_s^d - \theta_r^d} \tag{8b}$$

Equations (7) and (8) lead to a closed-form expression for the hysteretic $C(h)$ when θ_s^* is substituted for θ_s and θ_r^* for θ_r in Equations (4) and (5). Although not needed in this study, the same procedure can also be applied to drying scanning curves.

A more parsimonious parametrization of the hydraulic properties can be obtained by considering their physical characteristics. For example, the $K(\theta)$ relationship is generally observed to exhibit little or no hysteresis. Also, the saturated hydraulic conductivity, K_s, in Equation (6) is taken to correspond to the maximum water content $\theta = \theta_s^d$. To preserve the nonhysteretic nature of $K(\theta)$ in our model, θ_s^d and θ_r^d rather than θ_s^* and θ_r^* are used to calculate the effective saturation, S_e, in (6), i.e., $K(S_e) = K(S_e^d)$. Equation (6) implies then also that for nonhysteretic $K(\theta)$, $n^d \sim n^w = n$. Closure of the hysteresis loop at large negative pressure heads requires furthermore that $\theta_r^w = \theta_r^d = \theta_r$. Thus, the soil hydraulic functions are uniquely defined with seven parameters: K_s, θ_s^w, θ_s^d, α^w, α^d, n and θ_r.

Of these parameters, K_s and θ_s^d are easily obtained by direct measurement. Since θ_s^* and θ_1 are also readily measured for the primary scanning curve during inflow, the value of θ_s^w follows immediately from Equation (8) for given values of θ_r and θ_s^d. Hence, in the two examples to be discussed later we assume that K_s, θ_s^w and θ_s^d are known and restrict ourselves to estimating the four unknown coefficients α^d, α^w, θ_r and n.

PARAMETER ESTIMATION

The determination of the unknown soil hydraulic parameters is posed as a nonlinear least-squares problem, i.e., we seek the parameter vector $b^o = (\alpha^d, \alpha^w, n, \theta_r)$ that minimizes

$$E(b) = \sum_{i=1}^{N} [Q_i - \tilde{Q}_i(b)]^2 \qquad (9)$$

where $Q_i = Q(t_i)$ are the $\underset{\sim}{N}$ measured cumulative inflow/outflow volumes at times t_i, and $\tilde{Q}_i(b)$ are the corresponding volumes obtained by solving Equations (1) - (3) for the current parameter vector b. The Levenberg-Marquardt method (Marquardt, 1963) was used to minimize Equation (9). Further details about the inversion procedure are given by Kool et al. (1985b).

EXAMPLES

The first example is that of a hypothetical soil with known hydraulic properties (Figure 1) and K_s = 75 cm/day (8.7×10^{-6} m/s). Outflow and inflow data were numerically generated for a 4 cm high by 5.4 cm diameter column at initially hydrostatic equilibrium with h=0 at the center of the column. The pressure head at the lower boundary during outflow was taken as h_{out} = -10 m, and during inflow as h_{in} = 0 (saturation). The wetting process thus followed the primary scanning curve as shown in Figure 1. Ten data points each during outflow and inflow (N=20) were selected to represent the 'observed' Q_i in Equation (9). Saturated water contents $\theta_s^w = \theta_s^d = \theta_s$ and hydraulic conductivity K_s were assumed to be measured independently. Our central question thus becomes: are the measured Q_i sufficient to uniquely determine the remaining unknown parameters?

An initial test was carried out with the assumption that θ_r was known, i.e., $b = (\alpha^d, \alpha^w, n)$. Using this assumption, a detailed analysis of the response surface was made involving 630 evaluations of E(b). The range of initial parameter values was 0.002 - 0.025 for α^d, 0.01 - 0.09 for α^w, and 1.40 - 2.50 for n. The analysis indicated the presence of a unique minimum at b^o = (0.01, 0.06, 2.0). In practical situations, the value of θ_r is usually not known beforehand. In that case θ_r becomes an additional unknown and b should remain a 4-dimensional vector: $b = (\alpha^d, \alpha^w, n, \theta_r)$. Considering the escalating expense caused by

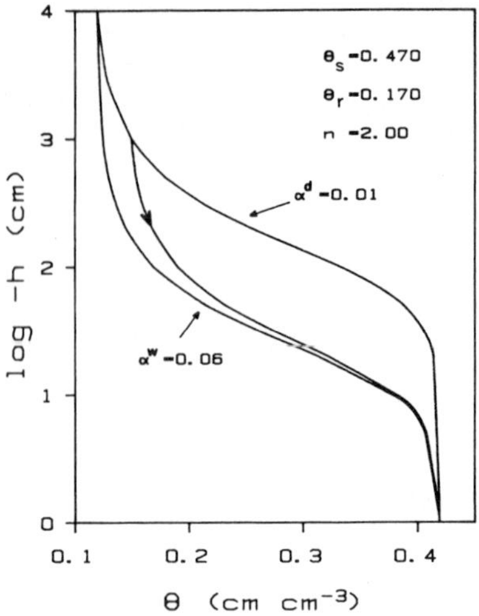

Figure 1. Hysteretic soil water retention curve used for example 1.

including a fourth parameter in the response surface analysis, a less detailed study was carried out for the 4-parameter inversion problem. Since the easiest way to locate minima of E(b) is through the optimization process, we chose to investigate uniqueness by carrying out the minimization starting from different initial points. The assumed initial parameter values were the same as those in our earlier analysis of the outflow problem (Kool et al., 1985b) and represent a range of values that can be expected in practical applications. The inversion process was always carried out with the physical constraint that $\alpha^w \geqslant \alpha^d$.

Results are given in Table 1 as initial and final parameter estimates, residual sum of squares, $E(b^o)$, and number of function evaluations to indicate the relative computational expense of solving each case. For cases 1-5, b^o was found to be quite close to the correct solution (0.01, 0.06, 2.0, 0.170). A relative change in each parameter of less than 1% between iterations was used as the convergence criterion. Higher accuracy could be obtained by setting the convergence criterion to a smaller value, but this would nearly always be at the expense of additional function evaluations (i.e., the number of times the flow problem needs to be solved). The optimization failed to converge to the correct solution for cases 6 and 7. The solution for case 6 is clearly unacceptable. The residual sum of squares $E(b^o)$ for case 7 also remains sufficiently high to use it as a criterion for rejecting the solution. It is of interest to note that by using only outflow

Table 1. Results of 4-parameter optimization for a hypothetical sandy loam soil.

	Parameter Values Initial	Final	Number of Function Evaluations	$E(b^o)$
α^d	0.05	0.010		
α^w	0.05	0.060	19	0.00005
n	1.10	2.001		
θ_r	0.150	0.170		
α^d	0.005	0.0099	151	0.025
α^w	0.005	0.0594		
n	1.10	2.0249		
θ_r	0.225	0.1718		
α^d	0.01	0.0101	50	0.027
α^w	0.01	0.0608		
n	3.0	1.9714		
θ_r	0.075	0.1678		
α^d	0.05	0.0101	42	0.073
α^w	0.05	0.0612		
n	1.50	1.9640		
θ_r	0.150	0.1472		
α^d	0.025	0.0101	37	0.008
α^w	0.025	0.0603		
n	2.50	1.9847		
θ_r	0.150	0.1689		
α^d	0.005	0.007	16	1178.04
α^w	0.005	0.0081		
n	3.00	1.1858		
θ_r	0.005	0.0127		
α^d	0.05	0.0104	26	27.39
α^w	0.05	0.0665		
n	2.75	3.4878		
θ_r	0.225	0.1840		

*Units of α in cm^{-1}, θ in $cm^3\ cm^{-3}$ and n dimensionless.

data for this soil, the starting values α^d=0.05, n=2.75 and θ_r =0.225 also caused the optimization process to converge to a local rather than a global minimum. The residual mean square deviation $E(b^o)/N$=0.095 in this case was small enough to suggest an acceptable solution which, however, corresponded to erroneous $\theta(h)$ and $K(h)$ relationships. From this we concluded that experiments limited to outflow only provide insufficient information to uniquely define the solution of the parameter estimation problem (Hornung, 1983; Kool et al., 1985b). In the study by Kool et al. (1985b) uniqueness was assured by providing additional information about the retention curve. The optimization process here for the combined outflow/inflow case may also fail to converge to the true minimum, but the inclusion of inflow information in the objective function provides a more powerful way to detect erroneous solutions based on the size of the residual $E(b^o)/N = 1.35$. The remedy for this problem is relatively simple: Equation (9) is to be minimized again, starting with different initial parameters, until the fit becomes acceptable.

Although results are quite promising, the practical value of the above example is somewhat limited by the fact that in reality soil hydraulic properties are seldom exactly described with Equations (4) - (8). We therefore consider next the more realistic case of a Guelph loam soil described by Elrick and Bowman (1964). Van Genuchten (1980) showed that the hydraulic functions of this soil can be described well with (4) - (6), provided that different values for α and n are used for both the wetting and drying $\theta(h)$ curves. The following parameters were derived from the measured soil water retention data: θ_s^d= 0.520, θ_s^w=0.434, θ_r^d= θ_r^w=0.218, α^d=0.0115, α^w=0.020, n^d=2.03 and n^w=2.76. In the remainder we assume that these parameters exactly describe the actual soil properties. Main wetting and drying $\theta(h)$ curves are shown in Figure 2a. Notice that for this soil $\theta_s^w \neq \theta_s^d$. For a flow reversal from drying to wetting at h_l = -10 m, we obtain θ_s^* = 0.436 from Equation (7). The re-

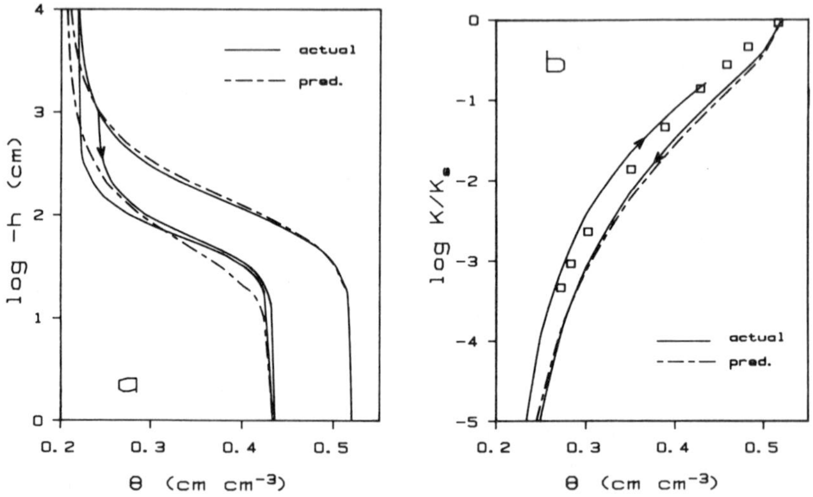

Figure 2. Actual and predicted (a) soil water retention and (b) unsaturated hydraulic conductivity curves. Measured $K(\theta)$ data are shown as open squares.

sulting scanning curve is shown in Figure 2a. This figure also shows the wetting and drying $K(\theta)$ curves predicted with Equation (6) using parameters obtained from the main wetting and drying retention curves. These curves (solid lines in Figure 2b) were assumed to represent the "actual" $K(\theta)$ functions. In reality, the measured $K(\theta)$ for this soil (shown as data points in Figure 2b) exhibited essentially no hysteresis, a feature that is consistent with our assumptions. Outflow and inflow data for this soil were generated by using the $\theta(h)$ and $K(\theta)$ relationships of Figure 2 (solid lines), and assuming the same experimental conditions as in the previous example. Outflow and inflow data for the Guelph loam (N = 20 as before) were fitted with the 4-parameter model $b = (\alpha^d, \alpha^w, n, \theta_r)$. The response surface in this case was much less well-behaved, especially with poor initial guesses, than that of the previous example, with convergence to local minima depending on the assumed intial parameter values. The best-fit solution b^o = (0.011, 0.030, 1.887, 0.206), $E(b^o)$=0.84, resulted from starting values (0.01, 0.03, 1.75, 0.22). Figure 2 shows that the predicted $\theta(h)$ and $K(\theta)$ curves describe the soil hydraulic properties quite well, especially the drying branches.

CONCLUSIONS

Results of the parameter optimization process discussed in this paper indicate a potential for determining hysteretic unsaturated soil hydraulic properties from experimentally simple outflow/inflow experiments. Succes of the inversion depends on the availability of an accurate, yet computationally efficient numerical solution of the unsaturated flow equation. The linear mass-lumped finite element scheme proved to be far more economical than a Hermitian cubic scheme used previously. The two examples discussed above apply to more or less idealized situations. The procedure still must be evaluated with real experimental data that include possible measurement errors in the input data. Results show that a successful performance of the optimization algorithm depends on how close the starting parameter values are to the "true" values. In an earlier paper (Parker et al., 1985) we gave some guidelines for choosing these initial values. The at times slow convergence of the optimization algorithm (case 2, table 1) also suggests room for improvement. For example, determination of the Levenberg-Marquardt parameters by the mode-trust region method as discussed by Moré (1977) could very well improve the overall efficiency of the algorithm.

REFERENCES

Elrick, D.E., and Bowman, D.H. (1964) Note on an improved apparatus for soil moisture flow measurements, Soil Sci. Soc. Am. Proc. 28:450-453.

Hornung, U. (1983) Identification of nonlinear soil physical parameters from an input-output experiment. In P. Deuflhard and E. Hairer (eds.), Workshop on numerical treatment of inverse problems in differential and integral equations, Birkhauser, Boston.

Kool, J.B., Parker, J.C., and van Genuchten, M.Th. (1985a) ONESTEP: A nonlinear parameter estimation program for evaluating soil hydraulic properties from one-step outflow experiments, Virginia Agric. Exp. Sta. Bull. 85-3. 43 p.

Kool, J.B., Parker, J.C., and van Genuchten, M.Th. (1985b) Determining soil hydraulic properties from one-step outflow experiments by parameter estimation, I. Theory and numerical Studies, Soil Sci. Soc. Am. J. 49:1348-1353.

Land, C.S. (1968) The optimum gas saturation for maximum oil recovery from displacement by water. Paper SPE 2216. SPE-AIME, 43rd Annual Fall Meeting, Houston.

Marquardt, D. (1963) An algorithm for least-squares estimation of nonlinear parameters. SIAM J. Appl. Math. 11:431-441.

Moré, J.J. (1977) The Levenberg-Marquardt algorithm: implementation and theory. In G. A. Watson (ed.) Lecture Notes in Mathematics, Springer Verlag, Berlin, pp. 105-116.

Parker, J.C., Kool, J.B., and van Genuchten, M.Th. (1985) Determining soil hydraulic properties from one-step outflow experiments by parameter estimation, II. Experimental studies, Soil Sci. Soc. Am. J. 49:1354-1359.

Scott, P.S., Farquhar, G.J., and Kouwen, N. (1983) Hysteretic effects on net infiltration. In: Advances in Infiltration, ASAE Publ. 11-83, Am. Soc. Agric. Eng., St. Joseph, Michigan, pp. 163-170.

van Genuchten, M.Th. (1980) A closed-form equation for predicting the hydraulic conductivity of unsaturated soils, Soil Sci. Soc. Am. J., 44:892-898.

van Genuchten, M.Th. (1982) A comparison of numerical solutions of the one-dimensional unsaturated-saturated flow and mass transport equations, Adv. Water Resour., 5:47-55.

Zachman, D.W., Duchateau, P.C., and Klute, A. (1982) Simultaneous approximation of water capacity and soil hydraulic conductivity by parameter identification, Soil Sci. 134:157-163.

VI International Conference on Finite Elements in Water Resources, Lisboa, Portugal, June 1986

A Comparative Study of Sensitivity Coefficient Calculation Methods in Groundwater Flow

J. Li
Institute of Geology & Exploration, Shaanxi, People's Republic of China
A. Lu
Rockwell International, Richland, WA 99352, U.S.A.
N.Z. Sun
Dept. of Mathematics, Shandong University, People's Republic of China
W.W-G. Yeh
Civil Engineering Dept., UCLA, Los Angeles, CA 90024, U.S.A.

ABSTRACT

Sensitivity coefficients can be calculated by: (1) the influence coefficient method, (2) the sensitivity equation method, or (3) the variational method. These three methods are summarized for both steady and unsteady state flows in a two-dimensional, inhomogeneous, confined aquifer. All algorithms are based on the finite element method. A comparison of the accuracies of the three calculation methods is made by means of an example for which the sensitivity coefficients can be obtained via analytical solutions. It is shown that the results from the three methods can be close to those of the analytical solutions if the factors that affect the sensitivity coefficient calculation are appropriately treated. It is also shown that the sensitivity equation and the variational methods are superior to the influence coefficient method in many instances because these two methods avoid the difficulty in the selection of the perturbation vector, and that the sensitivity equation and variational methods have the identical accuracies if the same grid size and time step are used.

INTRODUCTION

When the Gauss-Newton or similar methods are used to solve the inverse problem (parameter identification), sensitivity coefficients must be calculated. In groundwater flow, if the storage coefficient is assumed to be known, the parameter to be identified is the transmissivity vector $T = (T_1, T_2, \ldots, T_N)^T$, where superscript T is the transpose. Thus, sensitivity coefficients can be expressed as

$$[J]_{L\times N} = \begin{bmatrix} \frac{\partial h_1}{\partial T_1} & \cdot\ \cdot & \frac{\partial h_1}{\partial T_N} \\ \vdots & & \\ \frac{\partial h_L}{\partial T_1} & \cdot\ \cdot & \frac{\partial h_L}{\partial T_N} \end{bmatrix} \tag{1}$$

where L represents the total number of observations, and N represents the total number of parameters. The sensitivity coefficient matrix can be calculated by : (1) the influence coefficient method, (2) the sensitivity equation method, or (3) the variational method. Several authors have studied these methods. Bard (1974) gave a brief discussion of the influence coefficient method (also referred to as the finite difference method in the literature). Distefano and Rath (1975) used the influence coefficient method for calculating the sensitivity coefficients, and in the same paper they derived the sensitivity equation for unsteady state flow. Yeh and Yoon (1976, 1981) developed the algorithm for the sensitivity equation method based on the Crank-Nicolson scheme. The variational method was used in the problem of parameter identification first by Jacquard (1964) and then by Carter (1974, 1982). Dogru and Seinfeld (1981) compared the computational effort of the sensitivity equation method with that of the variational method. Sun and Yeh (1984) applied the variational method to the finite element scheme.

In this paper, the three methods are summarized for both steady state and unsteady state flows in a two-dimensional inhomogeneous confined aquifer, and the sensitivity equation method is extended to the finite element scheme. A comparison of the accuracies of the three calculation methods is made by means of an example for which the sensitivity coefficients can be obtained via the analytical solutions.

FORMULATION OF THE PROBLEM

Consider both steady and unsteady flows in a two-dimensional, inhomogeneous, isotropic and confined aquifer. The governing equation and boundary conditions for steady flow are

$$\frac{\partial}{\partial x}\left(T\frac{\partial h}{\partial x}\right) + \frac{\partial}{\partial y}\left(T\frac{\partial h}{\partial y}\right) = W$$

$$h(x,y) = g_1(x,y) \qquad (x,y) \in \partial\Omega_1 \tag{2}$$

$$T\frac{\partial h}{\partial n} = g_0(x,y) \qquad (x,y) \in \partial\Omega_2 ,$$

and the governing equation and initial and boundary conditions for unsteady flow are

$$\frac{\partial}{\partial x}(T\frac{\partial h}{\partial x}) + \frac{\partial}{\partial y}(T\frac{\partial h}{\partial y}) = S\frac{\partial h}{\partial t} + W$$

$$h(x,y,0) = g_1(x,y) \qquad (x,y) \in \Omega$$

$$h(x,y,t) = g_2(x,y,t) \qquad (x,y) \in \partial\,\Omega_1 \tag{3}$$

$$T\frac{\partial h}{\partial n} = g_0(x,y,t) \qquad (x,y) \in \partial\,\Omega_2 ,$$

where

h	=	head
T	=	tranmissivity
W	=	source function
S	=	storage coefficient
x,y	=	space variables
t	=	time
Ω	=	flow region
$\partial\Omega$	=	boundary of the aquifer ($\partial\Omega_1 \cup \partial\Omega_2 = \partial\Omega$)
$\partial/\partial n$	=	normal derivative
g_1, g_2, g_0	=	known functions.

Many schemes can be used to solve Equations (2) and (3). The Galerkin finite element scheme is used here. Dividing the flow region into a number of triangular elements, we obtain the following discretization forms of Equations (2) and (3):

$$[B]h + [F] = 0 \tag{4}$$

$$[B]h + [C]\frac{dh}{dt} + [F] = 0 \tag{5}$$

where the elements of the matrices [B], [C] and [F] are

$$B_{p,q} = \iint_{(\Omega)} T\left(\frac{\partial\phi_p}{\partial x}\frac{\partial\phi_q}{\partial x} + \frac{\partial\phi_p}{\partial y}\frac{\partial\phi_q}{\partial y}\right) dxdy; \tag{6}$$

$$C_{p,q} = \iint_{(\Omega)} S\,\phi_p\phi_q\, dxdy; \tag{7}$$

$$F_i = \iint_{(\Omega)} W\phi_i\, dxdy - \int_{(\partial\Omega)} g\phi_i d(\partial\Omega) \tag{8}$$

where ϕ is the basis function. For the triangular element Δijk (Fig. 1), the basis functions ϕ_i, ϕ_j, ϕ_K are defined by

$$\phi_n = \frac{1}{2\Delta}(a_n + b_n x + c_n y) \quad (n = i,j,k) \tag{9}$$

where

$$\begin{aligned}
a_i &= x_j y_k - x_k y_j & b_i &= y_j - y_k & c_i &= x_k - x_j \\
a_j &= x_k y_i - x_i y_k & b_j &= y_k - y_i & c_j &= x_i - x_k \\
a_k &= x_i y_j - x_j y_i & b_k &= y_i - y_j & c_k &= x_j - x_i,
\end{aligned} \tag{10}$$

and Δ is the area of Δijk; (x_i, y_i), (x_j, y_j) and (x_k, y_k) are the coordinates of the nodes i, j, k, respectively.

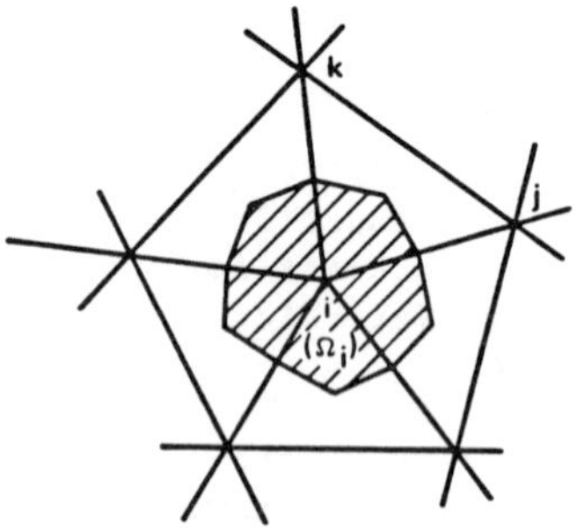

Figure 1: Triangular Element ijk and the Exclusive Subdomain of Node i

SENSITIVITY COEFFICIENT CALCULATION METHODS

Influence Coefficient Method

This is the simplest calculation method and is based on the concept of parameter perturbation (Becker and Yeh, 1972); a finite difference scheme is generally used. Both the forward and the central difference schemes can be employed, but for convenience the forward scheme is used here:

$$\frac{\partial h}{\partial T_i} \simeq [h(x,y,T_1,T_2,\ldots,T_i + \Delta T_i,\ldots,T_N) - h(x,y,T_1,T_2,\ldots,T_i,\ldots,T_N)]/\Delta T_i \tag{11}$$

for steady flow, and

$$\frac{\partial h}{\partial T_i} \simeq [h(x,y,t,T_1,T_2,\ldots,T_i + \Delta T_i,\ldots,T_N)$$

$$- h(x,y,T_1,T_2,\ldots,T_i,\ldots,T_N)]/\Delta T_i \tag{12}$$

for unsteady flow, where $h(x,y,T)$ and $h(x,y,t,T)$ are the solutions of Equations (4) and (5), respectively and ΔT_i is a small increment of T_i. In this method, a key problem is how to choose ΔT_i. From the derivative definition it would seem that the calculated results would be more accurate with smaller ΔT_i. But, this may not be the case, since the piezometric heads obtained with any numerical method are approximate values, and the number of their significant figures is limited. Equations (11) and (12) would have no meaning if ΔT_i were too small to cause any change in the significant figures of h. Hence, the increment ΔT_i should be large enough to cause a change in the significant figures of h, and small enough to reduce the truncation error due to the inexact nature of Equations (11) and (12). In a general case, in order to determine the value of ΔT_i for a practical model, a trial-and-error procedure is required . Bard (1974) suggested

$$\Delta T_i = \alpha T_i \tag{13}$$

where $10^{-5} \leq \alpha \leq 10^{-2}$.

Clearly, N+1 simulation runs are needed in the backward difference approximation.

Sensitivity Equation Method

The sensitivity equations can be derived by taking the partial derivatives with respect to T_i in Equations (2) and (3). For steady flow, we have

$$\frac{\partial}{\partial x}\left(T\frac{\partial h_{T_i}}{\partial x}\right) + \frac{\partial}{\partial y}\left(T\frac{\partial h_{T_i}}{\partial y}\right) = -\left[\frac{\partial}{\partial x}\left(\frac{\partial T}{\partial T_i}\frac{\partial h}{\partial x}\right) + \frac{\partial}{\partial y}\left(\frac{\partial T}{\partial T_i}\frac{\partial h}{\partial y}\right)\right]$$

$$h_{T_i}(x,y) = 0 \qquad (x,y) \in \partial\Omega_1 \tag{14}$$

$$T\frac{\partial h_{T_i}}{\partial n}(x,y) = -\frac{\partial T}{\partial T_i}\frac{\partial h}{\partial n} \qquad (x,y) \in \partial\Omega_2$$

and for unsteady flow,

$$\frac{\partial}{\partial x}\left(T\frac{\partial h_{T_i}}{\partial x}\right) + \frac{\partial}{\partial y}\left(T\frac{\partial h_{T_i}}{\partial y}\right) = S\,\frac{\partial h_{T_i}}{\partial t}$$

$$- [\frac{\partial}{\partial x}(\frac{\partial T}{\partial T_i}\frac{\partial h}{\partial x}) + \frac{\partial}{\partial y}(\frac{\partial T}{\partial T_i}\frac{\partial h}{\partial y})]$$

$$h_{T_i}(x,y,0) = 0 \qquad (x,y)\ \varepsilon\Omega \tag{15}$$

$$h_{T_i}(x,y,t) = 0 \qquad (x,y)\ \varepsilon\partial\Omega_1$$

$$T\frac{\partial h_{T_i}}{\partial n}(x,y,t) = -\frac{\partial T}{\partial T_i}\frac{\partial h}{\partial n} \qquad (x,y)\ \varepsilon\partial\Omega_2$$

where $h_{T_i} = \frac{\partial h}{\partial T_i}$

For practical calculation purposes with the Galerkin finite element scheme, we have to start from the discretized forms, Equations (4) and (5). By taking the partial derivatives of Equations (4) and (5) with respect to T_i, we have (Sun, 1981)

$$[B]h_{T_i} + [B_{T_i}]h = 0 \tag{16}$$

$$[B]h_{T_i} + [C]\frac{dh_{T_i}}{dt} + [B_{T_i}]h = 0 \tag{17}$$

where

$$B_{T_i\,p,q} = \iint_{(\Omega)} \frac{\partial T}{\partial T_i}(\frac{\partial\phi_p}{\partial x}\frac{\partial\phi_q}{\partial x} + \frac{\partial\phi_p}{\partial y}\frac{\partial\phi_q}{\partial y})\,dxdy \tag{18}$$

In Equations (16) and (17), the term $[B_{T_i}]h$ corresponds to [F] in Equations (4) and (5). By solving Equations (4), (5) and (15), the term $[B_{T_i}]h$ can be obtained. Then, h_{T_i} can be obtained by using the same solutions to Equations (16) and (17) as those in Equations (4) and (5).

In this method, N+1 simulation runs are needed.

<u>Variational Method</u>

Following Sun and Yeh (1984), the sensitivity coefficients can be written as

$$\frac{\partial h_1}{\partial T^i} = \frac{1}{12}\sum_{e_i}\frac{1}{\Delta_e}[(b_ih_i + b_jh_j + b_kh_k)(b_iq_i + b_jq_j + b_kq_k)$$

$$+ (c_i h_i + c_j h_j + c_k h_k)(c_i q_i + c_j q_j + c_k q_k)] \quad (19)$$

for steady flow, and

$$\frac{\partial h_1}{\partial T^i} = \frac{1}{12} \sum_{m=1}^{K} \sum_{e_i} \frac{1}{\Delta_e} [(b_i h_i + b_j h_j + b_k h_k)(b_i \bar{q}_j + b_j \bar{q}_j + b_k \bar{q}_k)$$

$$+ (c_i h_i + c_j h_j + c_k h_k)(c_i \bar{q}_i + c_j \bar{q}_j + c_k \bar{q}_k)]|_{m\Delta\tau} \quad (20)$$

with

$$\bar{q}_s|_{m\Delta\tau} = q_s[(K-m+1)\Delta\tau] - q_s[(K-m)\Delta\tau] \quad (s = i,j,k)$$

for unsteady flow. In Equations (19) and (20), h is the solution of Equations (4) and (5). $\sum_{e_i}$ represents the sum of all elements that have a common node i; $\Delta\tau$ is the time step, and K is the number of time steps; q is the solution of the following adjoint problems

$$\frac{\partial}{\partial x}(T\frac{\partial q}{\partial x}) + \frac{\partial}{\partial y}(T\frac{\partial q}{\partial y}) = G_\ell(x,y)$$

$$q(x,y) = 0 \qquad (x,y) \in \partial\Omega_1 \quad (21)$$

$$\frac{\partial q}{\partial n}(x,y) = 0 \qquad (x,y) \in \partial\Omega_2$$

for steady flow, and

$$\frac{\partial}{\partial x}(T\frac{\partial q}{\partial x}) + \frac{\partial}{\partial y}(T\frac{\partial q}{\partial y}) = S\frac{\partial q}{\partial t} + G_\ell(x,y)H(t)$$

$$q(x,y,0) = 0 \qquad (x,y) \in \Omega \quad (22)$$

$$q(x,y,t) = 0 \qquad (x,y) \in \partial\Omega_1$$

$$\frac{\partial q}{\partial n}(x,y,t) = 0 \qquad (x,y) \in \partial\Omega_2$$

for unsteady flow,

where

$$G_\ell(x,y) = \begin{cases} 1/P_\ell, & (x,y) \in (\Omega_\ell) \\ 0, & \text{otherwise} \end{cases} \quad (23)$$

$$H(t) = \begin{cases} 0 , & t \leq 0 \\ 1 , & t > 0 \end{cases} \quad (24)$$

P_ℓ is the area of the subdomain (Ω_ℓ) (Fig.1).

Note that the same time step $\Delta\tau$ should be used, and that L'+1 simulation runs are needed when Equation (20) is used, where L' is the number of observation wells.

EXAMPLES AND ACCURACY COMPARISON

Example 1.

In order to compare the accuracies of the three methods mentioned above, a square, homogeneous, isotropic, and confined aquifer is chosen (Fig. 2). Analytical expressions for the piezometric heads may be derived for this case. The dimension of the aquifer is 1400 m by 1400 m., and it is surrounded by impervious boundaries AB, CD and constant head boundaries BC, DA, where h = 100 m. The transmissivity and storage coefficient of the aquifer are 100 m^2/day and 0.001, respectively. The aquifer is initially at a steady state condition with piezometric head equal to 100 m throughout the aquifer. The flow region is divided into 416 triangular elements, and the total number of the nodes is 237. A pumping well with pumping rate of 10000 m^3/day is located at the center of the square aquifer, node 104. The observation wells are assumed to be located at nodes 14, 28, 42, 56, 70, 84, 93 and 95. For this aquifer, Chan, et al. (1976) have derived an analytical expression for head, h(x,y,t). Note that numerical solutions obtained from Equations (4) and (5) compare favorably with analytical solutions of Chan, et al. using a time step of 0.2 days. For our example, the sensitivity coefficient matrix is reduced to

$$[J] = [\frac{\partial h_1}{\partial T}, \frac{\partial h_2}{\partial T}, \frac{\partial h_3}{\partial T}, \frac{\partial h_4}{\partial T}, \frac{\partial h_5}{\partial T}, \frac{\partial h_6}{\partial T}, \frac{\partial h_7}{\partial T}, \frac{\partial h_8}{\partial T}, \ldots, \frac{\partial h_L}{\partial T}]^T \quad (25)$$

where $\frac{\partial h_1}{\partial T} = \frac{\partial h^{14}}{\partial T}, \frac{\partial h_2}{\partial T} = \frac{\partial h^{28}}{\partial T}, \ldots, \frac{\partial h_8}{\partial T} = \frac{\partial h^{95}}{\partial T}, \ldots$ (Fig. 2);

superscripts are nodal numbers.

By taking the derivatives of h(x,y,t) with respect to T in the analytical expression for h as obtained by Chan, et al. (1976), we obtain the sensitivity coefficients. These values can be considered as the exact solutions and are presented in Table 1.

Table 2 lists the sensitivity coefficients from Equations (11) and (12). An appropriate ΔT_i, obtained experimentally, is 1.0 m^2/day. Table 3 lists the results from Equations (16) and (17). Table 4 lists the sensitivity coefficients calculated by

TABLE 1. Sensitivity Coefficients Calculated by Analytical Solution

Time After Pumping	Nodal Number							
Day	14	28	42	56	70	84	93	95
1	-0.006	-0.010	-0.011	-0.001	0.032	0.121	0.225	0.335
2	-0.002	-0.001	0.008	0.030	0.076	0.174	0.281	0.392
3	0.005	0.014	0.030	0.059	0.110	0.212	0.320	0.431
5	0.017	0.038	0.064	0.102	0.160	0.266	0.375	0.486
10	0.028	0.059	0.094	0.140	0.204	0.314	0.424	0.535
∞	0.030	0.063	0.100	0.147	0.211	0.322	0.432	0.543

TABLE 2. Sensitivity Coefficients Calculated by Influence Coefficient Method (Δt = 0.2 days)

Time After Pumping	Nodal Number							
Day	14	28	42	56	70	84	93	95
1	-0.004	-0.007	-0.007	0.000	0.029	0.115	0.208	0.317
2	-0.001	0.000	0.008	0.029	0.073	0.170	0.267	0.377
3	0.005	0.014	0.029	0.056	0.106	0.208	0.306	0.416
5	0.017	0.036	0.062	0.098	0.154	0.261	0.359	0.469
∞	0.030	0.062	0.099	0.145	0.209	0.320	0.418	0.530

TABLE 3. Sensitivity Coefficients Calculated by Sensitivity Equation Method (Δt = 0.2 days)

Time After Pumping	Nodal Number							
Day	14	28	42	56	70	84	93	95
1	-0.004	-0.007	-0.008	0.000	0.030	0.116	0.210	0.321
2	-0.002	-0.000	0.008	0.029	0.073	0.172	0.270	0.381
3	0.005	0.013	0.029	0.057	0.109	0.211	0.309	0.420
5	0.017	0.036	0.062	0.099	0.156	0.264	0.363	0.475
∞	0.030	0.062	0.100	0.146	0.210	0.322	0.423	0.535

TABLE 4. Sensitivity Coefficients Calculated by Variational Method (Δt = 0.2 days)

Time After Pumping	Nodal Number							
Day	14	28	42	56	70	84	93	95
1	-0.004	-0.007	-0.008	0.000	0.030	0.116	0.210	0.321
2	-0.002	-0.000	0.008	0.029	0.073	0.172	0.256	0.366
3	0.005	0.013	0.029	0.057	0.107	0.211	0.309	0.420
5	0.017	0.036	0.062	0.099	0.156	0.264	0.363	0.475
∞	0.030	0.062	0.100	0.146	0.210	0.322	0.423	0.535

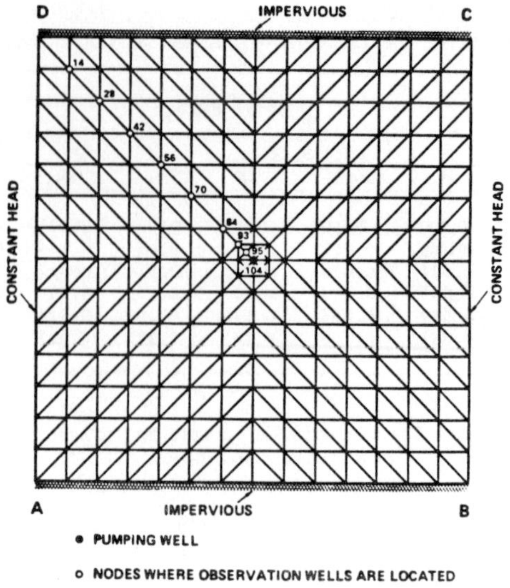

Figure 2: Aquifer Configuration and Discretization

the variational method. Note that due to homogeneity, $\frac{\partial h_1}{\partial T} = \sum_{i=1}^{M} \frac{\partial h_1}{\partial T_i}$, where M is the total number of nodes, and $\frac{\partial h_1}{\partial T_i}$ is calculated by Equation (19) or (20).

Clearly, the results from the sensitivity equation and the variational methods are the same, and very close to those of the analytical solutions. Although the results from the influence coefficient method are not as good as those from the other two methods, the accuracy of the influence coefficient method can be greatly improved if an optimal perturbation value can be chosen. Therefore, in theory, all three methods should produce similar and acceptable results.

CONCLUSIONS

Three methods, the influence coefficient method, the sensitivity equation method and the variational method have been used to calculate the sensitivity coefficients for both steady and unsteady flows in a two-dimensional, inhomogeneous, isotropic, confined aquifer. The results obtained have shown that the sensitivity equation and the variational methods generally have higher accuracies than that of the influence coefficient method. The accuracies of the computed sensitivity coefficients depend on the accuracies of the calculated piezometric heads for any method. The common factors which affect the accuracies of the sensitivity coefficients are the dimension of the elements and the time step sizes.

For a practical groundwater flow model, in order to more accurately calculate the sensitivity coefficients, we suggest:

1. The dimension of the elements, and the time steps should be appropriately selected to produce accurate head calculations.

2. If $N \leq L'$, the sensitivity equation method should be used. If $N > L'$, the variational method is reasonable, especially when parameter dimension corresponds to the number of unknown nodal transmissivity values.

3. The influence coefficient method is easy to implement, but caution must be exercised in choosing an appropriate perturbation vector.

REFERENCES

Bard, Y. (1974), Nonlinear Parameter Estimation, Academic Press, New York, New York.

Becker, L. and Yeh, W.W-G. (1972), Identification of parameters in unsteady open channel flows, Water Resources Research, 8(4): 956-965.

Chan, Y.K., Mullineux, N. and Reed, J.R.(1976), Analytic solutions for drawdowns in rectangular artesian aquifers. J. Hydrol., 31: 151-160.

Carter, R.D., Kemp, L.F., Pierce, A.C. and Williams, D.L. (1974), Performance matching with constraints, Soc. Pet. Engr. J., 14(2): 187-186.

Carter, R.D., Kemp, L.F., and Pierce, A.C. (1974), Discussion of comparison of sensitivity coefficient calculation method in automatic history matching, Soc. Pet. Engr. J., 22(2): 205-208.

Distefano, N., and Rath, A. (1975), An identification approach to Subsurface Hydrological Systems, Water Resources Research, 11(6): 1005-1012.

Dogru, A.H., and Seinfeld, J.H. (1981), Comparison of sensitivity coefficient calculation methods in automatic history matching, Soc. Pet. Engr. J., 21(5): 551-557.

Jacquard, P., and Jain, C. (1965), Permeability distribution from field pressure data, Soc. Petrol. Engr. J., 5(6): 281-294.
Sun, N.Z. (1981), Mathematical Modelings and Numerical Methods in Groundwater Flow (in Chinese), Geological Publishing House, Beijing, China.

Sun, N.Z., and Yeh, W.W-G. (1985), Identification of parameter structure in groundwater inverse problem, Water Resources Research, 21(6): 869-883.

Yeh, W.W-G., and Yoon, Y.S. (1976), A systematic optimization procedure for the identification of inhomogeneous aquifer parameters. In Advances in Groundwater Hydrology, edited by Z.A. Sateem, 72-82, American Water Resources Association, Minneapolis, Minnesota.

Yeh. W.W-G., and Yoon, Y.S. (1981), Parameter identification with optimum dimension in parameterization, Water Resour. Res., 17(3): 664-672.

VI International Conference on Finite Elements in Water Resources, Lisboa, Portugal, June 1986

Optimization Approach to the Identification of Aquifer Parameters in Multilayer Systems

M.M. Aral
School of Civil Engineering, Georgia Institute of Technology, Atlanta, Georgia, U.S.A.

INTRODUCTION

In nature most regional ground water systems consist of several aquifers separated by confining beds that transmit water interconnecting all of the aquifers in the system. Although the bounding formations in such systems usually have relatively high resistance to the flow of water through them, the leakage between semiconfined aquifers cannot be ignored due to large horizontal contact areas involved and also due to large piezometric head differences that might exist between the upper and lower semiconfined layers. Thus, in general the overall flow picture is that of a three-dimensional ground water flow. The description of the physics of flow through porous media for such systems in terms of mathematical expressions leads to the formulation of boundary value problems which, when analyzed through numerical procedures, require a considerable amount of field data. In implementing these models, a problem arises due to the inavailability of the required distributions of such hydrogeologic parameters. Even in cases where hydrogeologic measurements do exist, they reflect conditions at the point of measurement and cannot be considered representative of regional conditions. Thus, numerical models often fail to serve as reliable management tools due to what appears an almost chronic lack of appropriate field data.

To bridge this gap, recently considerable research effort is directed towards determination of such aquifer parameters via numerical methods. Initially, these methods have been widely applied as a manual trial and error procedure, but recently a large number of systematic and computerized methods, based on formal mathematical procedures, have been proposed. In the general terminology of ground water hydraulics, the direct problem formulation implies that the field parameters are treated as known constants. If the input or excitation function and the corresponding response function are considered known, the field parameters can be treated as unknown dependent variables in a new formal boundary value problem. The solution of this boundary value problem is called the inverse problem in ground water modeling, Kitanidis [1976] and Neuman and Yakowitz [1979].

In this study, the finite element least squares optimization algorithm is utilized to identify the hydrogeologic field parameters of a multilayer aquifer system. A typical application is included for demonstration purposes. Field applications of the proposed computation scheme can be seen in Aral [1984].

GOVERNING EQUATIONS

Consider the N-layer aquifer system as shown schematically in Figure 1. Each aquifer and the confining layers may be non-homogeneous. We shall assume that the direction of flow is vertical in the aquitards and horizontal in the main aquifers. The system remains saturated at all times and Darcy's Law applies. Given this configuration, the mathematical model describing the vertically integrated steady state ground water seepage problem for the (i)th layer tapped by several wells can be given as follows, Bear [1979],

$$\frac{\partial}{\partial x}\left(T_i \frac{\partial h_i}{\partial x}\right) + \frac{\partial}{\partial y}\left(T_i \frac{\partial h_i}{\partial y}\right) + \frac{(h_{i+1} - h_i)}{\sigma_{i+1}} + \frac{(h_{i-1} - h_i)}{\sigma_i} + \sum_{k=1}^{w} Q_i(x_k, y_k) = 0 \qquad i = 1,2,3,\ldots,N \qquad (1)$$

where $h_i(x,y)$ denotes the piezometric heads in main aquifers denoted by (i), $\sigma_i = D_i/K_i$ are the resistances of the semipervious layers in which D_i is the thickness of the semiconfining layer and K_i is the permeability of the semi-confining layer in the vertical direction, $T_i(x,y)$ is the transmissivity of the main aquifers, $Q_i(x_k,y_k)$ is the volumetric well discharge from the (i)th aquifer at location (x_k,y_k) and w is the total number of wells in the (i)th aquifer. The formulation assumes that either the confining layers one and (N) are impervious, that is the N-layer system is fully confined or else the piezometric head distributions h_o and h_N are known and do not vary in response to flow situation in the main aquifers. The boundary conditions of the multilayer aquifer system can be given as,

$$h_i(x,y) = f_i(x,y) \qquad \text{for} \quad (x,y) \in B_{i,1} \tag{2}$$

and

$$\vec{n} \cdot (T_i \vec{\nabla} h_i) = g_i(x,y) \qquad \text{for} \quad (x,y) \in B_{i,2} \tag{3}$$

where $f_i(x,y)$ and $g_i(x,y)$ are known functions defined at the boundaries of the regional system, $\vec{\nabla}$ is the vector differential operator and $\vec{n}$ is the outer normal vector at the boundary $B_{i,2}$.

In developing a numerical solution process for the above model a finite element Galerkin process is adopted Zienkiewicz [1971], Aral [1974]. This process can be represented as,

$$\sum_{e=1}^{ne} \iint_{A_i^e} N_j[D_i(h_i)]\, d\, A_i^e = 0 \qquad j = 1,2,3,\ldots,n \quad i=1,2,3,\ldots,N \tag{4}$$

where N_j is the appropriate weighting function, D_i is the differential operator for the (i)th layer, Equation (1), h_i is the piezometric head in the (i)th layer defined for the domain A_i^e, (n) is the number of nodes in each element and (ne) is the total number of elements in A_i. This discretization process eventually leads to a system of matrix equations which can be solved for the unknown piezometric head values in each layer. Details of this formulation and solution process is summarized elsewhere and will not be repeated here, Aral et al. [1984], Aral [1985].

LEAST SQUARES OPTIMIZATION FOR A MULTILAYERED AQUIFER SYSTEM

In this approach the object is the optimal determination of the transmissivity and the resistance coefficients using observations of piezometric head recorded from a number of wells scattered within each aquifer system. The objective function which is to be minimized for each layer can be given as Equation (5),

$$\operatorname*{Min}_{T_{i,1},\ldots,T_{i,L}} F_i(T,\sigma) = \sum_{j=1}^{M} W_j[\bar{h}_i(x_j,y_j) - h_i(x_j,y_j)]^2 \qquad i = 1,2,3,\ldots,N \tag{5}$$

subject to

$$T^{\ell}_{i,k} \leq T_{i,k} \leq T^{u}_{i,k} \quad ; \quad \sigma^{\ell}_{i,k} \leq \sigma_{i,k} \leq \sigma^{u}_{i,k}$$

$$k=1,2,3,\ldots,L \; ; \; i=1,2,3,\ldots,N \qquad (6)$$

in which $\bar{h}_i(x_j,y_j)$ are the observed values of the piezometric head at the location (x_j,y_j) for each layer (i), $h_i(x_j,y_j)$ are the calculated values of the piezometric head at the same locations obtained through a finite element procedure, $T_{i,k}$ are the transmissivity values at a bounded homogeneous region R_e (an element) in each layer, L is the number of bounded homogeneous regions (number of elements) in each layer, M is the number of observation points in each layer which may be larger than the number of elements in a layer, (u.ℓ) denote the upper and lower bounds of transmissivity values in an element for each layer, W_j is the least squares weighting coefficient which is used to scale the data points with respect to their accuracy levels and N is the number of layers in a multilayer system.

The following iterative scheme can now be introduced for the solution of the optimization problem for each layer. Locally, one can state that in a semiconfined layer the piezometric head is a function of the transmissivity of the main aquifer and the resistance parameters of the confining layers above and below the main aquifer.

$$h_{i,j} = f(T_{i,k}, \sigma_{i,k}, \sigma_{i+1,k}) \qquad i = 1,2,3,\ldots,N;$$

$$j=1,2,3,\ldots,M \; ; \; k=1,2,3,\ldots,L \qquad (7)$$

Thus again locally, a change in the piezometric head value can be described in terms of Taylor series expansion of Equation (7),

$$h^{n+1}_{i,j} = h^{n}_{i,j} + (T^{n+1}_{i,k} - T^{n}_{i,k})\left(\frac{\partial h_{i,j}}{\partial T_{i,k}}\right)^{n} + (\sigma^{n+1}_{i,k} - \sigma^{n}_{i,k})\left(\frac{\partial h_{i,j}}{\partial \sigma_{i,k}}\right)^{n}$$

$$+ (\sigma^{n+1}_{i+1,k} - \sigma^{n}_{i+1,k})\left(\frac{\partial h_{i,j}}{\partial \sigma_{i+1,k}}\right)^{n} \qquad (8)$$

$$+ 0\left((T^{n+1}_{i,k} - T^{n}_{i,k})^{2}, (\sigma^{n+1}_{i,k} - \sigma^{n}_{i,k})^{2}, (\sigma^{n+1}_{i+1,k} - \sigma^{n}_{i+1,k})^{2}\right)$$

where $h^{n+1}_{i,j}$ and $h^{n}_{i,j}$ are the computed values of the piezometric head at location (j), layer (i) at iteration sequence (n). Similarly $T^{n+1}_{i,k}$, $T^{n}_{i,k}$, $\sigma^{n+1}_{i,k}$ and $\sigma^{n}_{i,k}$ are the iterated values of the transmissivity and resistance coefficients in each layer (i) for each element (k) and for each iteration sequence (n), that is,

$$T^{n+1}_{i,k} = T^{n}_{i,k} + (\Delta T)^{n}_{i,k} \tag{9}$$

and

$$\sigma^{n+1}_{i,k} = \sigma^{n}_{i,k} + (\Delta\sigma)^{n}_{i,k} \tag{10}$$

Substituting Equation (8) into Equation (5) one may obtain,

$$F_i(T,\sigma) = \sum_{j=1}^{M} W_j[\bar{h}_i(x_j,y_j) - (h^{n}_{i,j} + (\Delta T)^{n}_{i,k}\left(\frac{\partial h_{i,j}}{\partial T_{i,k}}\right)^{n} + (\Delta\sigma)^{n}_{i,k}\left(\frac{\partial h_{i,j}}{\partial \sigma_{i,k}}\right)^{n} + (\Delta\sigma)^{n}_{i+1,k}\left(\frac{\partial h_{i,j}}{\partial \sigma_{i+1,k}}\right)^{n})]^{2}$$

$$i = 1,2,3,\ldots,N \tag{11}$$

which can now be minimized for each layer with respect to the unknown incremental corrections defined as $(\Delta T)^{n}_{i,k}$, $(\Delta\sigma)^{n}_{i,k}$ and $(\Delta\sigma)^{n}_{i+1,k}$.

$$\frac{\partial F(T,\sigma)}{\partial(\Delta T)^{n}_{i,k}} = 0 \quad k = 1,2,3,\ldots,L \; ; \; i = 1,2,3,\ldots,N \tag{12}$$

$$\frac{\partial F(T,\sigma)}{\partial(\Delta\sigma)^{n}_{i,k}} = 0 \quad k = 1,2,3,\ldots,L \; ; \; i = 1,2,3,\ldots,N \tag{13}$$

$$\frac{\partial F(T,\sigma)}{\partial(\Delta\sigma)^n_{i+1,k}} = 0 \quad k = 1,2,3,\ldots,L \quad ; \quad i = 1,2,3,\ldots,N \tag{14}$$

This operation results in standard least squares normal equations given as,

$$[A^n] \ \{\phi^n\} = \{B^n\} \tag{15}$$

where

$$[A^n] = \begin{bmatrix} [J_T]^T [J_T] & [J_T]^T [J_{\sigma_i}] & [J_T]^T [J_{\sigma_{i+1}}] \\ [J_{\sigma_i}]^T [J_T] & [J_{\sigma_i}]^T [J_{\sigma_i}] & [J_{\sigma_i}]^T [J_{\sigma_{i+1}}] \\ [J_{\sigma_{i+1}}]^T [J_T] & [J_{\sigma_{i+1}}]^T [J_{\sigma_i}] & [J_{\sigma_{i+1}}]^T [J_{\sigma_{i+1}}] \end{bmatrix} \tag{16}$$

$$\{\phi^n\} = \begin{Bmatrix} \{\Delta T\}^n \\ \{\Delta\sigma_i\}^n \\ \{\Delta\sigma_{i+1}\}^n \end{Bmatrix} \tag{17}$$

$$\{B^n\} = \begin{Bmatrix} (\bar{h} - h^n) \ [J_T]^T \\ (\bar{h} - h^n) \ [J_{\sigma_i}]^T \\ (\bar{h} - h^n) \ [J_{\sigma_{i+1}}]^T \end{Bmatrix} \tag{18}$$

and $[J_T]$, $[J_{\sigma_i}]$ and $[J_{\sigma_{i+1}}]$ are the Jacobian matrices defined as,

$$[J_T] = \begin{bmatrix} \frac{\partial h^n_{i,1}}{\partial T^n_{i,1}} & \frac{\partial h^n_{i,1}}{\partial T^n_{i,2}} & \cdots & \frac{\partial h^n_{i,1}}{\partial T^n_{i,L}} \\ \frac{\partial h^n_{i,2}}{\partial T^n_{i,1}} & \frac{\partial h^n_{i,2}}{\partial T^n_{i,2}} & \cdots & \frac{\partial h^n_{i,2}}{\partial T_{i,L}} \\ \vdots & \vdots & & \vdots \\ \frac{\partial h^n_{i,M}}{\partial T^n_{i,1}} & \frac{\partial h^n_{i,M}}{\partial T^n_{i,2}} & \cdots & \frac{\partial h^n_{i,M}}{\partial T^n_{i,L}} \end{bmatrix} \tag{19}$$

$$[J_{\sigma_k}] = \begin{bmatrix} \frac{\partial h^n_{i,1}}{\partial \sigma^n_{k,1}} & \frac{\partial h^n_{i,1}}{\partial \sigma^n_{k,2}} & \cdots & \frac{\partial h^n_{i,1}}{\partial \sigma^n_{k,L}} \\ \frac{\partial h^n_{i,2}}{\partial \sigma^n_{k,1}} & \frac{\partial h^n_{i,2}}{\partial \sigma^n_{k,2}} & \cdots & \frac{\partial h^n_{i,2}}{\partial \sigma^n_{k,L}} \\ \vdots & \vdots & & \vdots \\ \frac{\partial h^n_{i,M}}{\partial \sigma^n_{k,1}} & \frac{\partial h^n_{i,M}}{\partial \sigma^n_{k,2}} & \cdots & \frac{\partial h^n_{i,M}}{\partial \sigma^n_{k,L}} \end{bmatrix} \quad k=i,i+1 \qquad (20)$$

The gradient terms in the above equations are further approximated using the difference forms given below,

$$\frac{\partial h^n_{i,j}}{\partial T^n_{i,k}} = \frac{h^n_{i,j} - h^{n-1}_{i,j}}{T^n_{i,k} - T^{n-1}_{i,k}}, \quad \frac{\partial h^n_{i,j}}{\partial \sigma^n_{i,k}} = \frac{h^n_{i,j} - h^{n-1}_{i,j}}{\sigma^n_{i,k} - \sigma^{n-1}_{i,k}},$$

$$\frac{\partial h^n_{i,j}}{\partial \sigma^n_{i+1,k}} = \frac{h^n_{i,j} - h^{n-1}_{i,j}}{\sigma^n_{i+1,k} - \sigma^{n-1}_{i+1,k}} \qquad (21)$$

where the subscripts and the superscripts are as defined earlier .

Solution sequence starts with an initial guess of the transmissivity and resistance values. These values are then used in Equation (1) to obtain computed values of the piezometric head over the aquifer under study. Two consecutive values of the computed piezometric head data are then used to generate least squares equations. Solution of the normal equations of the least squares procedure in turn yields corrections on transmissivity and resistance values for each element. Updated transmissivity and resistance values are again used in solution of equation (1) for piezometric head values in each layer which restarts the solution process.

In this solution sequence two stopping criteria are employed. The first criterion checks the root-mean-square deviations between observed and calculated head values. If this value is small enough, the iterative procedure is stopped and results are printed. The second stopping criterion is the total number of allowable iterations. Because of noise in the observed head data, the root-mean-square deviation should only approach the magnitude of the error in the observed head data.

It is not necessary nor even possible to fit the calculated head values exactly to the observed head data. Since the accuracy of the field data is not usually known a priori a very small RMS value is selected in all computer runs and the second stopping criterion is used to avoid excessive use of computation time.

Similar to the direct solution of the inverse problem, the indirect solution of the inverse problem has its own inherent difficulties. Because the formulation is a nonorthogonal least squares minimization, the matrix [A] will not always be invertible, Levenberg [1944]. Even if the matrix [A] were invertible the procedure may not converge or may converge very slowly, Marquardt [1963]. These are characteristic conditions expected of nonorthogonal least squares formulations. Several techniques are suggested in the literature to overcome these difficulties. Levenbert [1944] suggested the addition of a number to the diagonal of matrix [A] which is in magnitude equal to the 10% of the existing terms of [A]. Similarly multiplication of diagonal terms by a number slightly larger than one is also suggested. This would make the system invertible and behave more as an orthogonal least squares system. The addition of terms to the diagonal is identified as ridge regression by Hoerl and Kennard [1970,a,b], Montgomery and Peck [1982], and Draper and Smith [1966]. Marquardt [1963] suggested that the matrix and vector be scaled such that the diagonal becomes one and that an iterative procedure be used to determine the value of the Levenberg's parameter to be added to the diagonal of the scaled matrix system.

It was found that the least squares normal equations formed in this study were not invertible, thus the three different algorithms mentioned above were tested. It was observed that ridge regression technique was most effective in solving this problem and it was utilized in developing the computer code generated in this study. Marquard's algorithm required longer computation time and was not as effective thus it was abandoned.

NUMERICAL EXAMPLE

Appication of the proposed optimization scheme to a field problem can be found in Aral [1984,1985]. In this paper a two layer confined aquifer problem is studied for demonstration purposes. In this problem it is assumed that the main aquifers are fully confined from above and below and there is leakage between the two. The field parameters and the dimensions of the region are chosen as, Figure (2);

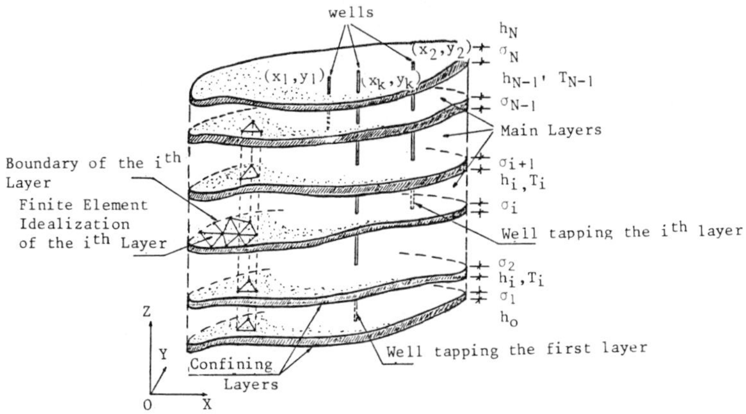

Figure 1. Definition Sketch for a Multiaquifer System

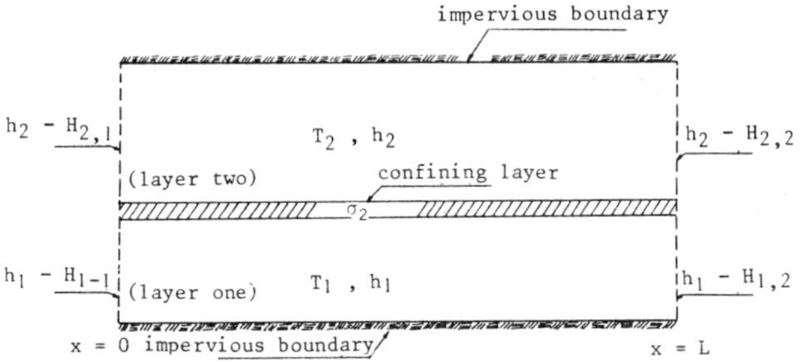

Figure 2. Definition Sketch for a Two Layer System

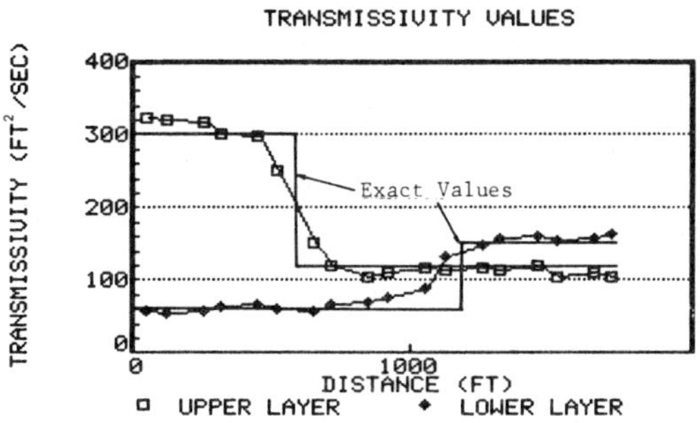

Figure 3. Numerical Results for a Two Layer System

$H_{1,1}$ = 700 ft (213.36 m)

$H_{1,2}$ = 400 ft (121.92 m)

$H_{2,1}$ = 400 ft (121.92 m)

$H_{2,2}$ = 100 ft (30.48 m)

$T_{1,1}$ = 60 ft^2/sec (5.57 m^2/sec) for $0 \leq x \leq 1200$ ft ($0 \leq x \leq 365.76$ m)

$T_{1,2}$ = 150 ft^2/sec (13.94 m^2/sec) for $1200 \leq x \leq 1800$ ft ($365.76 \leq x \leq 548.65$ m)

$T_{2,1}$ = 300 ft^2/sec (27.87 m^2/sec) for $0 \leq x \leq 600$ ft ($0 \leq x \leq 182.88$ m)

$T_{2,2}$ = 120 ft^2/sec (11.15 m^2/sec) for $600 \leq x \leq 1800$ ft ($182.88 \leq x \leq 548.65$ m)

σ_2 = 3000 ft/ft/sec

L = 1800 ft (548.65 m)

Given this data an analytical solution for this unidirectional flow problem in each main aquifer is obtained, Aral [1985]. In this application these analytical results for piezometric heads are used as input data for the optimization algorithm. Comparison of the exact values of the transmissivity with the numerical results obtained are given in Figure 3. The computation of the resistance values yielded the following σ_2 = 3000 $\pm$ 200 ft/ft/sec.

CONCLUSIONS

Aquifer parameter prediction models for multiaquifer systems are indeed rare and the technique proposed here is intended to fill this gap. The proposed algorithm utilizes finite element Galerkin solution technique for the prediction of ground water flow pattern in a multiaquifer system along with a least squares optimization procedure which is used to improve the fit between observed and computed values of piezometric heads at several observation points in the region of study by updating and improving the elemental field parameter values for each layer iteratively. The proposed indirect solution of the inverse problem using the least squares minimization process showed much promise as a method of automating model calibration. The technique is highly dependent on accurate field data on piezometric heads at a number of strategically distributed observation points. The algorithm developed is straightforward and generates a local minimum for the objective function near the initial transmissivity estimates.

ACKNOWLEDGEMENTS

Financial support for this work was partially provided by the United States Department of the Interior, Office of Water Policy, through the Environmental Resources Center of the Georgia Institute of Technology.

REFERENCES

1. Aral, M.M., (1974), "Finite Element Solutions of Selected Partial Differential Equations, FEMAC Computer Program," Middle East Technical University Publication No. 28, Ankara.
2. Aral, M.M. and Zakikhani, M., (1984), "Parameter Identification in Layered Aquifer Systems," Georgia Institute of Technology, Environmental Resources Center, Report No. ERC02-83.
3. Aral, M.M., (1985), "A Simplified Approach to Regional Multilayered Aquifer Analysis," Georgia Institute of Technology, Environmental Resources Center, Report No. ERC02-85.
4. Bear, J., (1979), Hydraulics of Ground Water, McGraw-Hill Book Co., New York, 1979.
5. Draper, N.R. and H. Smith, (1966), Applied Regression Analysis, John Wiley and Sons, New York.
6. Hoerl, Arthur E., and R.W. Kennard, (1970), "Ridge Regression: Biased Estimation for Nonorthogonal Problems," Technometrics, Vol. 12, No. 1, pp. 55-67.
7. Kitanidis, P.K. and E.G. Vomvoris, (1983), "A Geostatistical Approach to the Inverse Problem in Ground Water Modeling and One Dimension Simulations," Water Resources Research, Vol. 19, No. 3, pp. 677-690.
8. Levenberg, K., (1944), "A Method for the Solution of Certain Non-linear Problems in Least Squares," Quarterly Journal of Applied Mathematics, Vol. 2, No. 2, pp. 164-168.
9. Marquardt, D.W., (1963), "An Algorithm for Least-Squares Estimates of Non-Linear Parameters," SIAM J., Vol. 11, No, 2, pp. 431-441.
10. Montgomery, D.C., and E.A. Peck, (1982), Introduction to Linear Regression Analysis, John Wiley and Sons, New York.
11. Neuman, S.P., and S. Yakowitz, (1979), "A Statistical Approach to the Inverse Problem of Aquifer Hydrology," Water Resources Research, Vol. 15, No. 4, pp. 845-860.
12. Zienkiewicz, O.C., (1971), Finite Element Method in Engineering Science, McGraw Hill, New York, N.Y.

SECTION 5 THE COLLOCATION METHOD IN GROUNDWATER

VI International Conference on Finite Elements in Water Resources, Lisboa, Portugal, June 1986

The Boundary Collocation Method

J.F. Botha
Institute for Groundwater Studies, University of The Orange Free State, Bloemfontein, 9300, South Africa

1. INTRODUCTION

The conceptualization of real world phenomena frequently results in a single or a set of partial differential equations. The behaviour of this phenomenon could thus, at least in principle, be studied by solving the associated differential equation(s). In practice this usually implies that the equation(s) has to be solved over a domain with an irregular boundary. Such equations can, of course, be solved accurately by a number of numerical methods, for example the finite element and/or finite difference methods. There exists, however, situations where one would prefer a method that does not require the elaborate mesh generation and data preparation procedures of these methods.

Consider for example the situation of a small town in one of the arid or semi-arid regions of the earth which depends solely on groundwater for its water supply. The town could, with government or institutional help, construct a model that will describe the behaviour of the aquifer quite accurately. However, it is unlikely, that they will have local expertise to supervise and maintain an elaborate finite element or finite difference model. What is really required in such a situation is a model that can predict the behaviour of the aquifer, but with the minimum of supervision and/or maintenance.

Experience gained during the recent drought in Southern Africa, indicates that such a model should be:

(a) able to model the behaviour of the aquifer sufficient accurately for local authorities to take the necessary action before an emergency,

(b) easy to modify in the event that more reliable information requires it,

(c) understandable by any one with a minimum knowledge of groundwater modelling.

Analytical models can be constructed that satisfy the latter two properties. However these models are usually only applicable to one or a couple of boreholes and thus not suitable. The complex nature of groundwater flow necessitates the use of complex modelling techniques.

Discussions held with representatives of various local authorities indicated that a major stumbling block, with either the finite element and finite difference models, is the associated complex mesh. A much more acceptable model would be one based on a square or rectangular mesh which can accommodate any modification of the boundaries without reconstructing the mesh. This implies that one should use a method where the irregular domain of the aquifer is imbedded in the rectangular domain and the boundary conditions applied externally rather than implicitly as is usual in both finite element and difference models.

There are not many numerical methods for the solution of partial differential equations that can be adapted for this purpose. One such a method is the boundary collocation method discussed in Section 3. This method is a modification of the ordinary collocation method which is briefly reviewed in Section 2. Results obtained with this method applied to a simple problem is discussed in Section 4.

2 REVIEW OF THE COLLOCATION METHOD

The collocation method has been applied with excellent results to a number of differential equations ranging from simple ordinary differential equations (Botha, 1977) to complex boundary value problems (Herbst and Botha, 1981) and partial differential equations (Celia, 1982). This discussion will, however, be restricted to the two-dimensional self-adjoint elliptic equation

$$\mathbf{L}u = r, \tag{1}$$

where

$$\mathbf{L} = -\boldsymbol{\nabla}\bullet[p(x,y)\boldsymbol{\nabla}] + q(x,y),$$

defined over the square $\Omega \equiv [0,1] \otimes [0,1]$, and subject to Dirichlet boundary conditions

$$u(x,y) = u_b(x,y) \tag{2}$$

on the boundary $\partial\Omega$ of Ω.

The solution, u(x,y), of Equation (1) can always be approximated on a rectangular domain, Ω, by a tensor product of Hermite interpolation polynomials, $h_i^j(z)$ (Botha and Pinder, 1983) as

$$u(x,y) \approx \hat{u}(x,y) = \sum_{i,j=0}^{n,m} \sum_{k,l=0}^{\nu,\mu} h_i^j(x) h_k^l(y) u_i^j{}_k^l \qquad (3)$$

The symbol, $u_i^j{}_k^l$, is used here, and in what follows, to denote an approximation to the derivative $D_x^j D_y^l(x_i,y_k)$, and z either x or y. Substitution of Equation (3) into Equation (1) yields a set of equations of the form

$$\sum_{i,j,k,l} [q(x,y) a_i^j{}_k^l(x,y) - h_i^j(x) b_k^l(y) - h_k^l b_i^j(x)] u_i^j{}_k^l = r(x,y) \qquad (4)$$

with,

$$a_i^j{}_k^l(x,y) = h_i^j(x) h_k^l(y)$$

$$b_r^s(z) = D_z p(x,y) D h_r^s(z) + p(x,y) D^2 h_s^r(z)$$

When using Hermite polynomials with zero multiplicity of one at the nodes, i.e. $m = \mu = 1$ in Equation (3), Equation (4) contains a set of $4(n+1)(\nu+1)$ unknown parameters $u_i^j{}_k^l$ which have to be determined. This can be easily achieved by choosing a set of $4(n+1)(\nu+1)$ points, $\{\xi_\sigma,\eta_\rho\}$, and substitute these into Equation (4) to obtain a set of linear equations which can be solved for the $u_i^j{}_k^l$, hence the name collocation method.

The collocation points can, in principle, be any set of points, $\{\xi_\sigma,\eta_\rho\} \in \Omega$. However, for a square domain $4n\nu$ of these points are usually chosen to coincide with the $2n \otimes 2\nu$ gaussian points (zeros of the Legendre polynomials $P_{2n}(x)$ and $P_{2\nu}(y)$ suitably scaled). This leaves $4(n+\nu+1)$ points that have to be determined by another method. Such a choice can be avoided by equating $4(n+\nu+1)$ of the parameters $u_i^j{}_k^l$ on the boundary with the prescribed boundary condition $u_b(x,y)$ and its appropriate first derivatives. This method, generally referred to as orthogonal collocation, is super convergent (Percell and Wheeler, 1980).

Equating the $4(n+\nu+1)$ parameters with the boundary conditions, may create the impression of introducing an ad hoc assumption in the derivation of the orthogonal collocation method. However, this choice is actually a very natural one as it corresponds to using the nodal values on the boundary as collocation points for the boundary conditions. To see this consider the approximation of a one-dimensional function by Hermite interpolation polynomials (Botha and Pinder,1983)

$$f(z) = \sum_{r,s=0}^{n,m} h_r^j(z)D^r f(z_s) + E_s^r(z,z_s,\zeta)$$

$$= f^*(z) + E_s^r(z,z_s,\zeta) \qquad (5)$$

where

$$E_s^r(z,z_s,\zeta) = w(z)D^{(r+1)(s+1)}f(\zeta)$$

and

$$w(z) = \prod_s (z - z_s)^r. \qquad (6)$$

The error contained in the approximation defined by Equation (3) can thus be expressed as

$$E_i^j{}_k^l(x,y,\xi,\eta) = W(x,y)D^{(i+1)(j+1)(k+1)(l+1)}u(\xi,\eta)$$

where, using the definition of a tensor product and Equations (5) and (6),

$$W(x,y) = E_i^j(x,x_i,\zeta,y_k)u^*(x,y_k) + E_k^l(y,y_k,\zeta,x_i)u^*(y,x_i) + E_i^j(x,x_i,\zeta,y_k)E_i^j(x,x_i,\zeta,y_k)u^*(x,y)$$

The result now follows from the observation that

$$D^q h_r^s(z_p) = \delta_{rp}\delta_{qs}$$

and

$$E_r^s(z_p,z_r) = 0 \qquad \forall\ p.$$

This also indicates that the interpolation of the boundary conditions does not introduce additional errors into orthogonal collocation.

The accuracy attainable with the orthogonal collocation method depends [see Equation (6)], on

(a) the size of the elements, $(x_{i+1} - x_i)$ and $(y_{k+1} - y_k)$, and
(b) the degree, $[(m+1)(n+1)-1][(\mu+1)(\nu+1)-1]$, used in the calculation.

To investigate the effect of these quantities on the accuracy of the solution, consider the simple elliptic equation

$$\nabla \bullet [(1+x)\nabla u(x,y)] = 0 \qquad (7)$$

defined over the square domain $[0,1]\otimes[0,1]$ and subject to the boundary conditions

$$u(1,y) = 1; \quad u(0,y) = D_n(x,0) = D_n(x,1) = 0.$$

This equation has the analytical solution (Joos,1984)

$$u(x,y) = \ln(1+x)/\ln(2).$$

Figures 1 and 2 display the behaviour of the discrete least square and Chebyshev norms, defined respectively as

$$|u - \hat{u}|_2^0 \equiv \sqrt{[\sum_{q=0}^{N}\{u(x_p,y_q) - \hat{u}(x_p,y_q)\}2/(N+1)]}$$

$$|u - \hat{u}|_\infty^0 \equiv \max_{\forall y_q} |u(x_p,y_q) - \hat{u}(x_p,y_q)|,$$

along the line $x_p = 0.5$ for different numbers of elements and degrees of the basis functions. These results indicate that the global error depends much more on the degree of the basis function used, than the number of intervals.

3 THE BOUNDARY COLLOCATION METHOD

The success of orthogonal collocation, is clearly closely related to the fact that the domain is rectangular. However, this type of domain is not encountered frequently in water resources. The question thus arises how can one adopt the method to problems with curved or irregular boundaries?

Two approaches that immediately spring to mind are :

(a) straightening of the boundaries by mapping the domain on a rectangular one, and

(b) mapping individual elements onto squares.

Both these methods are feasible, but require the construction of rather involved maps, e.g. the use of transfinite interpolation (Gordon and Hall, 1973). There exists, however, other possibilities.

Let Ω_i denote an irregular domain with boundary $\partial\Omega_i$. Such a domain can always be imbedded into a square domain Ω, with boundary $\partial\Omega$. If $u^*(x,y)$ is any solution of Equation (1) on Ω, then $u^*(x,y)$ also satisfies Equation (1) on Ω_i. The problem is of course that $u^*(x,y)$ will not satisfy the boundary conditions associated with $\partial\Omega_i$. One possibility of circumventing this problem is to compute a series of solutions $\{u_q{}^*\}$ and use linear combinations of these to determine a new $u'(x,y)$ that satisfies the boundary conditions on $\partial\Omega_i$. For example one could use the harmonic functions to solve Laplace's equation. Another one is simply to find a general solution of Equation (1) and force this solution to satisfy the prescribed boundary conditions on $\partial\Omega_i$.

The general solution, envisaged above, can be obtained by any available method that allows one to impose boundary conditions externally. The orthogonal collocation method, discussed above, is obviously such a method. The method can also, at least in principle, be easily adapted to irregular boundaries. Instead of taking the boundary conditions explicitly into account one just choose 4(n+n+1) points on $\partial\Omega_i$ as additional collocation points - hence the name boundary collocation method.

As indicated above, the method used to incorporate the boundary values in orthogonal collocation, does not contribute to the global error. This will clearly not be the case when collocation points are chosen so as to coincide with points on curved or irregular boundaries. Since the accuracy attainable with collocation methods depends critically on the position of the collocation points (Botha, 1978), one may expect that the boundary collocation method will be less accurate than orthogonal collocation.

This difficulty is further complicated by the fact that there does not exist a universal theory for Hermite interpolation on curved or irregular domains. Hence it is not possible at present to derive explicit expressions for the position of suitable collocation points. The best that can be done at is to carry out a number of numerical experiments before deciding on the final choice.

4 A NUMERICAL EXAMPLE

To illustrate the boundary collocation method, consider the simple steady state groundwater flow problem defined by Laplace's equation

$$\nabla^2 h(x,y) = 0 \tag{8}$$

over the curvilinear 'rectangle', shown in Figure 3, and subject to the boundary conditions

$$h(1,\theta) = 1$$

$$h(0.5,\theta) = h(r,0) = h(r,\pi/2) = 0.$$

This problem has the analytical solution (Lebedev et al, 1965)

$$h(r,\theta) = (4/\pi)\sum_{q=0}^{\infty} g_q(r)\sin[k(q)\theta]/[(2q+1)c_q]$$

where

$$k(q) = 2(2q + 1)$$

$$c_q = (1/2^{k(q)})(2^{2k(q)} - 1)$$

$$g_q(r) = [(2r)^{k(q)} - (r/2)^{k(q)}]$$

The problem was first solved using the single bicubic Hermite element shown in Figure 3. The collocation points were, using the results of orthogonal collocation, chosen as follows :

(a) interior points - the tensor product of zeros of the Legendre polynomial $P_2(z)$ defined over the domain [0,1], i.e. the same points used in orthogonal collocation,

(b) boundary points - the four corner points and the points where the lines through the interior collocation points, parallel to the x- and y-axes, cut the boundary. (See Figure 4).

Dirichlet boundary conditions where prescribed at all the boundary points. A few trial calculations indicated that these collocation points yield the best results. The discussion that follows, will consequently be restricted to them.

Figures 5 and 6 show the actual errors present in the boundary collocation solution, henceforth abbreviated as BC-solution, of Equation (8). These results seem to indicate that the accuracy of the BC-solution can, similarly to the OC-solution, also be improved by increasing the number of elements. However, as shown by the graphs of the discrete least square and Chebyshev norms in Figure 7, this is only partially true. The accuracy tends to oscillate with a decreasing amplitude as the number of elements is increased, with the best accuracy obtained at odd numbers of elements. The solutions obtained with basis functions of a higher degree, behaved similarly. This result may be problem dependent and should, therefore, not be generalized, unless confirmed by future work.

The way in which the BC-method was introduced, suggests that the extreme errors should occur on the boundaries. This conjecture is supported by the results shown in Figures 5 and 6. To see if this is true in general, the least square and Chebyshev norms were recomputed with the boundary point, $\theta = 0$, excluded. The results are shown in Figure 8. A comparison of Figures 7 and 8 shows that this is indeed the case. The boundary collocation method may thus be applied with confidence to problems, such as groundwater modelling, where there is not much interest in the solution on the boundary.

5 CONCLUSION

The present investigation indicated that the boundary collocation method can be applied to problems with curved or irregular boundaries. The simplicity of the method is particularly attractive. If one is not interested in obtaining an accurate solution on the boundary, then this method has much to offer for problems defined over irregular boundaries.

Judged from the norms used to evaluate the efficiency of the method, the accuracies obtained in the present investigation cannot be considered spectacular. Preliminary calculations indicated that this can be partially explained by the presence of discontinuities in the boundary conditions of the problem. was, however, the choice of suitable collocation points. As shown above, acceptable results can be obtained by using the orthogonal collocation points for the differential equation and 'quasi' gauss points for the boundary. However, more accurate results can only be expected once a suitable method has been devised for determining optimal collocation points. Nevertheless, preliminary calculations indicated that the method may be quite useful for developing a coarse groundwater model. This aspect is at the moment receiving further attention.

6 REFERENCES

Botha J.F. (1977) The Solution of Initial Value Ordinary Differential Equations by Collocation. Symposium on Numerical Mathematics, Department of Computer Science, University of Natal, Durban, South Africa.

Botha J.F. and Pinder G.F. (1983) Fundamental Concepts in the Numerical Solution of Differential Equations. J. Wiley and Sons, New York.

Celia M.A. (1982) Density-dependent transport simulation using alternating direction collocation. Internal Report, Institute for Groundwater Studies, University of the Orange Free State, Bloemfontein, South Africa.

Gordon W.J. and Hall C.A. (1973) Transfinite Element Methods: Interpolation over arbitrary curved Element Domains. Numerische Mathematik, 21 : 109 - 129.

Herbst B.M. and Botha J.F. (1981) Computable Error Estimates for the Collocation Method Applied to Two-point Boundary Value Problems. IMA Journal of Numerical Analysis 1 : 489 - 497.

Joos B. (1984) Private Communication

Lebedev N.N., Skalskaya I.P. and Uflyand Y.S. (1965) Worked Problems in Applied Mathematics. Dover, New York.

Percell, P. and Wheeler, M.F. (1980) A C1-finite Element Collocation Method for Elliptic Equations. SIAM Journal of Numerical Analysis, 17 : 605.

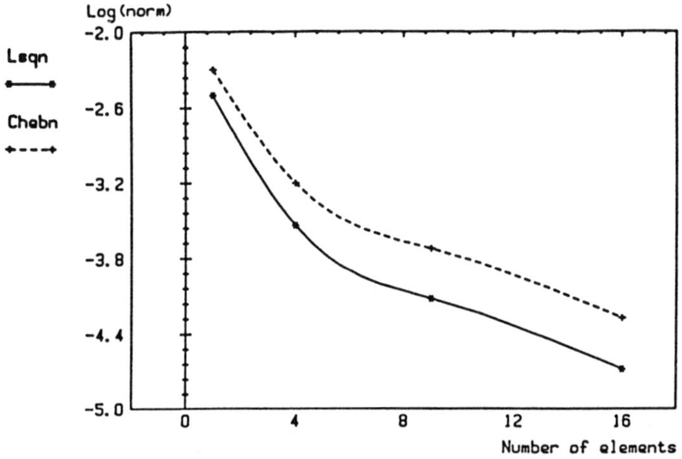

Figure 1 The variation of the least square and Chebyshev norms for the bicubic DC-solution of Equation (7), along the line x = 0.5, as a function of the number of elements.

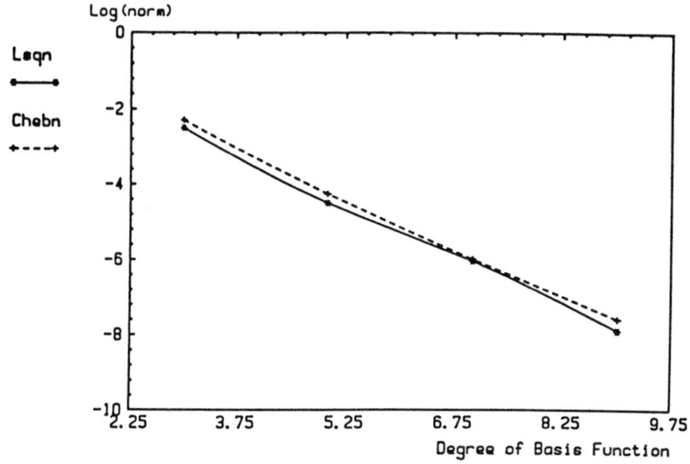

Figure 2 The variation of the least square and Chebyshev norms for the bicubic DC-solution of Equation (7), along the line x = 0.5, as a function of the degree of the basis function used.

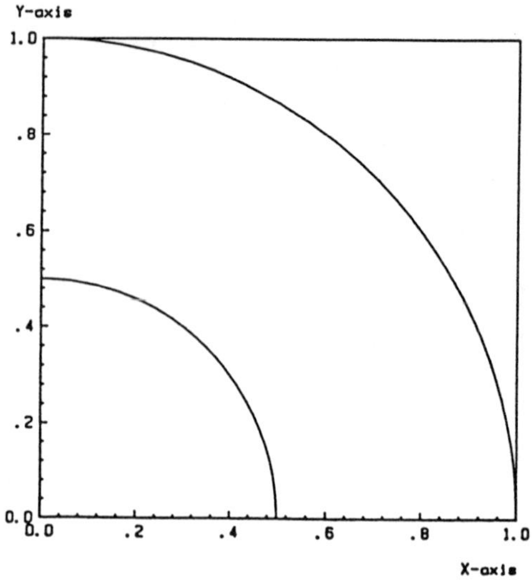

Figure 3 The curvillinear rectangle and associated single element used to solve Equation (8) by the boundary collocation method.

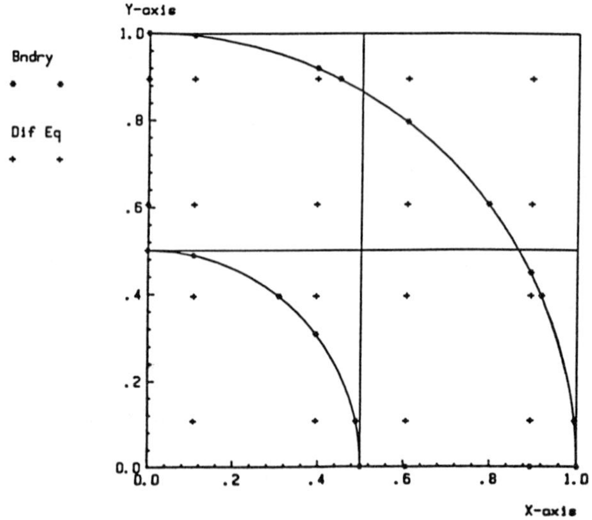

Figure 4 Typical collocation points used to solve Equation (8) with a bicubic Hermite interpolation polynomial. (Number of elements used = 4).

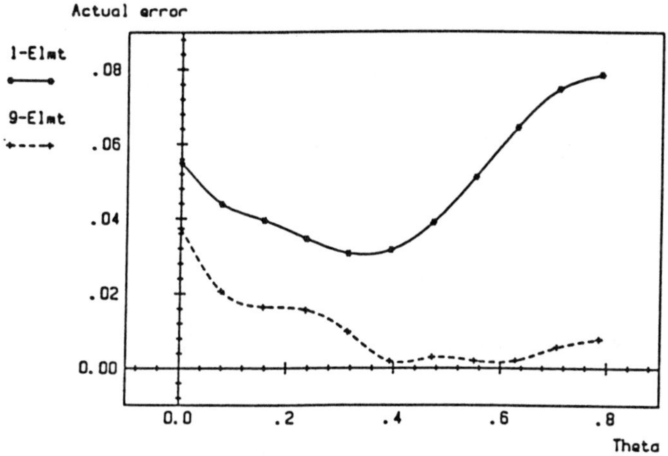

Figure 5 Actual errors present in the BC-solution of Equation (8) as a function of theta for r = 0.75. Bicubic Hermite polynomials, defined over 1 and 9 elements, were used as basis functions.

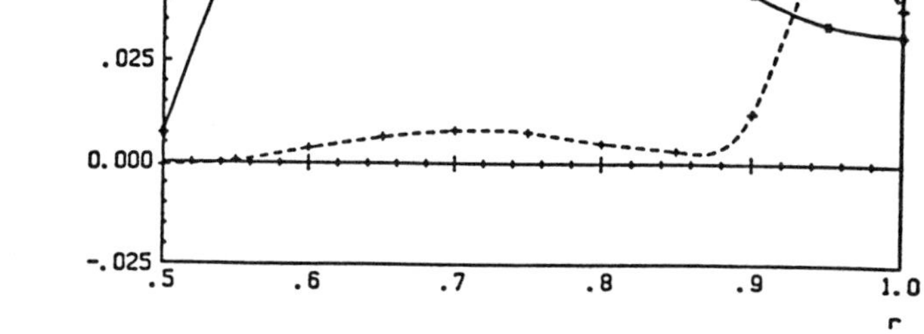

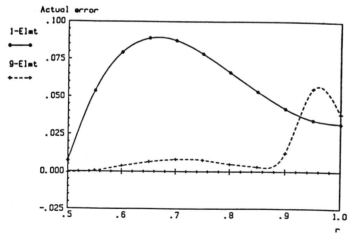

Figure 6 Actual errors present in the BC-solution of Equation (8) as a function of r for theta = pi/4. Bicubic Hermite polynomials, defined over 1 and 9 elements, were used as basis functions.

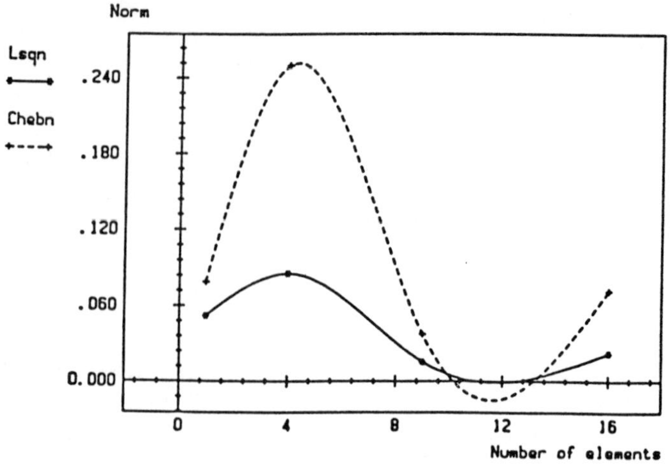

Figure 7 The variation of the least square and Chebyshev norms for the bicubic BC-solution of Equation (8) along the radius r = 0.75 as a function of the number of elements.

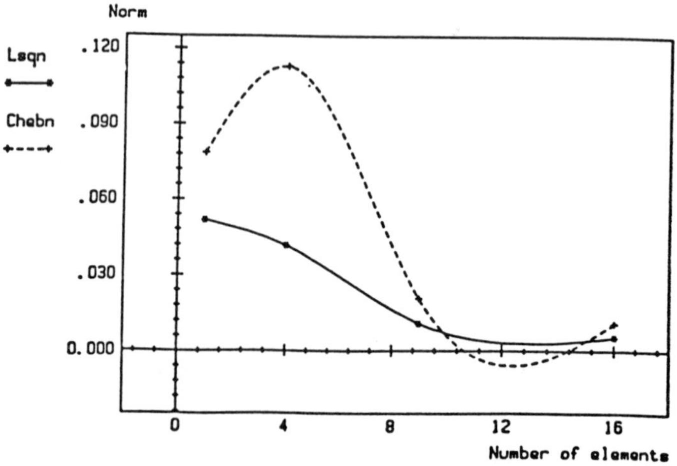

Figure 8 The variation of the least square and Chebyshev norms for the bicubic BC-solution of Equation (8) along the radius r = 0.75 (excluding theta=0) as a function of the number of elements.

VI International Conference on Finite Elements in Water Resources, Lisboa, Portugal, June 1986

Least Squares Collocation Method for Groundwater Flow

B. Joos, G.F. Pinder
Department of Civil Engineering, Princeton University, Princeton, NJ 08544, U.S.A.

ABSTRACT

A new numerical method for solving second order partial differential equations is presented. It combines features of the boundary element method, the finite element collocation method, and the least squares minimization method. After presenting the theoretical underpinnings of this new approach, two potential flow examples in a two-dimensional domain are considered. The results are compared to those of a traditional finite element model.

INTRODUCTION

The method described hereunder has been developed in an attempt to circumvent the problems inherent in the finite element method, while extending the applicability of the boundary element method. The new method proceeds in two steps, as does a traditional analytical approach; firstly, expressions satisfying the operator are found, and then these functions are required to satisfy the boundary conditions. In the first step we construct using a collocation procedure a set of functions satisfying approximately the operator over the domain. The error of approximation is minimized using a least squares technique. This procedure allows us to consider any kind of medium, and to free ourselves from any restriction regarding its heterogeneity. In the second step the set of functions just derived are similarly required to satisfy the boundary conditions using collocation concepts and a least squares approach.

In the first step, the operator and boundary conditions are evaluated at a finite number of points spread over the domain. In the second step the points are aligned along the boundary . We now proceed to detail this procedure.

DEVELOPMENT

Let us consider a set of N linearly independent functions, ϕj, $j=1,\ldots,N$ (e.g. $1,x,y,x^2,xy,y^2,x^2y,\ldots$), and a linear elliptic operator $Lu(x,y) = f(x,y)$.

Firstly we construct a reduced set of n linearly independent functions $u^*_k(x,y)$, $k=1,\ldots,n$. We want these functions to satisfy approximately the homogeneous operator at m collocation points spread over the domain ($m \geq n$).

$$u^*_k(x,y) = \sum_{j=1}^{N} a_{kj}\, \phi_j(x,y) \ , \qquad k = 1,\ldots,n \tag{1}$$

The different u^*_k's are derived independently from one another, and we consider the best approximation in the least squares sense.

$$E_k \equiv \min \sum_{i=1}^{m} A_{k,i}^2 \ , \qquad \text{with } A_{k,i} = L\, u^*_{k,i} \ , \qquad k = 1,\ldots,n$$

where $u^*_{k,i} = u^*_k(xi,yi)$ and $u_i = u(xi,yi)$.

Substituting (1) in the above expression and differentiating with respect to the unknown quantities - i.e. the a_{kj}'s - we get the following system of equations. For an intermediate function k, we have :

$$\frac{\partial E_k}{\partial a_{kl}} = \sum_{i=1}^{m} \frac{\partial E_k}{\partial A_{k,i}} \cdot \frac{\partial A_{k,i}}{\partial a_{kl}} = 0 \ , \qquad l = 1,\ldots,N$$

which, upon expansion of E_k and $A_{k,i}$ yields

$$\sum_{i=1}^{m} \left(\sum_{j=1}^{N} a_{kj}\, L\phi_{j,i}\, L\phi_{l,i} \right) = 0 \ , \qquad l = 1,\ldots,N$$

Reversing the order of summation, we obtain

$$\sum_{j=1}^{N} a_{kj} \sum_{i=1}^{m} L\phi_{j,i}\, L\phi_{l,i} = 0 \ , \qquad l = 1,\ldots,N \tag{2}$$

The procedure for deriving the intermediate functions (IF) is as follows: we arrange the basis functions (BF) in such an order that the same N-n basis functions are always present in every intermediate function (see example to follow). Each of the n IF has in addition one of the n remaining BF's. The coefficients attributed to these linear combinations are defined as :

$$u^{*}_{k} = \sum_{j=1}^{N-n} a_{kj} \phi_{j} + 1.0 \; \phi_{N-n+k} \quad , \quad k = 1,\ldots,n \qquad (3)$$

If the original equation is not homogeneous, a (n+1)th intermediate function is constructed, which satisfies (approximately) $Lu^{*} = f$. This function is made of the N-n first BF's only.

Let us now rewrite (2) as

coefficients of IF's, k=1,...,n

$$\left(b_{1j} = \sum_{i=1}^{m} L\phi_{1,i} \; L\phi_{j,i} \right) \cdot \begin{pmatrix} a_{11} & a_{21} & \cdots & a_{n1} \\ & & & \\ & & & \\ a_{1p} & a_{2p} & \cdots & a_{np} \\ \hline 1 & 0 & \cdots & 0 \\ 0 & 1 & & 0 \\ & & & \\ 0 & 0 & \cdots & 1 \end{pmatrix} = \begin{pmatrix} \\ 0 \\ \\ \end{pmatrix} \qquad (4)$$

(N-n) x N

$l=1,\ldots,N-n$;

$j=1,\ldots,n$

N x n

(N-n) x n

p=N-n

The coefficient 1.0 attributed to the n last BF's enables us to put their contribution to the right hand side of the system. The IF's are thus a linear combination of the BF's; they are themselves linearly independent. In addition, any linear combination of those IF's will satisfy (approximately) the homogeneous operator Lu = 0.

The procedure outlined above enables us to invert only one matrix, and to change only the right hand side of the system as we compute the coefficients of a new intermediate function. This matrix has rank N-n. It must be emphasized that this procedure is valid for all n+1 IF's.

For the boundary conditions, we again use the same procedure, and we express the final approximation u(x,y) to u(x,y) as :

$$\hat{u}(x,y) = \sum_{k=1}^{n} U_k \, u^*_k(x,y) + 1.0 \, u^*_{n+1}(x,y) \tag{5}$$

We seek once again the approximation to the boundary conditions that provides a minimum error in the least squares sense :

$$\min \sum_{i=1}^{M} (B\hat{u}_i - Bu_i)^2$$

where M is the total number of boundary conditions
B is the operator expressing these conditions (Dirichlet or Neumann).

Differentiating with respect to the U_k's, and inverting the summations we obtain a system of n equations and n unknowns :

$$\sum_{k=1}^{n} U_k \sum_{i=1}^{M} Bu^*_{k,i} \, Bu^*_{1,i} = \sum_{i=1}^{M} Bu^*_{1,i} \, (Bu_i - Bu^*_{n+1,i}) \; , \; 1 = 1,\ldots,n \tag{6}$$

Once the U_k's are known, it is quite easy to find the expression relating u directly to the basis functions ϕ_j's. Indeed we have

$$\hat{u}(x,y) = \sum_{j=1}^{N} \alpha_j \, \phi_j(x,y) \; , \quad \text{with } \alpha_j = \alpha_j(a_{kj}, U_j) \; , \quad k=1,\ldots,n+1 \tag{7}$$

Once the basis functions are selected, this set of α_j's bears all the information relative to the solution. This concise form is obviously very convenient computationally.

EXAMPLE 1

We will now illustrate the procedure by a simple two dimensional flow example. The results will be compared to the analytical solution; moreover, and as in the second example, a traditional finite element simulation will also be used as comparison. The domain is homogeneous and circular, centered on (1/2,1/2), with radius r = 1/2, ; the equation is $\nabla^2 u = -10$. The boundary conditions are uniform and equal to zero (see figure 1).

We take as basis functions the power series forming a complete cubic polynomial in x and y, i.e. 1, x, y, x^2, xy, y^2, x^3, x^2y, xy^2, y^3. We therefore have here N=10; we choose n=7 (see "Discussion"). We first rearrange these functions following the rule explained above, and we get the 10 BF's ϕ_1 to ϕ_{10} :

$$x^3,\ x^2y,\ x^2,\quad y^3,\ xy^2,\ y^2,\ xy,\ y,\ x,\ 1.$$

The intermediate functions will therefore be of the form

$$u^*_k = a_{k1}\, x^3 + a_{k2}\, x^2 y + a_{k3}\, x^2 + \phi_{k+3}$$

We will as a demonstration consider the case of u^*_1 .

$$u^*_1 = a_{11}\, x^3 + a_{12}\, x^2 y + a_{13}\, x^2 + y^3.$$

Expressing the value of Lu^*_1 at all interior collocation points, and applying the least squares procedure leads us to the following system of equations :

$$\begin{vmatrix} 409.50 & 111.00 & 222.00 \\ 111.00 & 47.12 & 74.00 \\ 222.00 & 74.00 & 148.00 \end{vmatrix} \begin{vmatrix} a_{11} \\ a_{12} \\ a_{13} \end{vmatrix} = \begin{vmatrix} -333.00 \\ -141.36 \\ -222.00 \end{vmatrix} \qquad (8)$$

The value of the unknowns are thus :

$$a_{11} = 0.000\ ;\quad a_{12} = -3.000\ ;\quad a_{13} = 0.000$$

Similarly for the other six IF's. To take into account the inflow, we construct an eighth IF,

$$u^*_8 = a_{81}\, x^3 + a_{82}\, x^2 y + a_{83}\, x^2.$$

The right hand side of the system (8) is derived accordingly to (2); the values of the coefficients a_{k1} to a_{k3} for all IF's are presented in table I.

BF \ k=	1	2	3	4	5	6	7	8
ϕ_1	0.0	-1/3	0.0	0.0	0.0	0.0	0.0	0.0
ϕ_2	-3.0	0.0	0.0	0.0	0.0	0.0	0.0	0.0
ϕ_3	0.0	0.0	-1.0	0.0	0.0	0.0	0.0	-5.0
ϕ_{k+3}	1.0	1.0	1.0	1.0	1.0	1.0	1.0	---

Table I : coefficients defining the IF's

The final approximation is formed now and is written as

$$\hat{u}(x,y) = \sum_{k=1}^{7} U_k\, u^*_k(x,y) + u^*_8(x,y)$$

We will get a system of 7x7 equations. The contributions of u^*_8 and of the boundary conditions will be put into the right hand side. Table II presents the values of U_k, k=1 to 7.

k	1	2	3	4	5	6	7
U_k	0.0	0.0	-2.50	0.0	2.50	2.50	-.625

Table II : coefficients of $\hat{u}$ as a function of u^*_k's

Finally we can express $\hat{u}$ directly as a combination of the basis functions. The coefficients of this combination are determined simply as follows :

$$\begin{cases} \alpha_j = \sum_{k=1}^{7} a_{kj} U_k + a_{8j}, & j = 1, 2, 3 \\ \alpha_j = U_{j-3}, & j = 4, \ldots, 10 \end{cases}$$

These values are presented in table III.

j	1	2	3	4	5	6	7	8	9	10
α_j	0.0	0.0	-2.50	0.0	0.0	-2.50	0.0	2.50	2.50	-.625

Table III : coefficients of $\hat{u}$ as a function of BF's

The α_j's form the polynomial

$$\hat{u}(x,y) = 2.50\ (x + y - x^2 - y^2) - 0.625$$

As can be easily checked, $L\hat{u} = 2.50\ (-2\ -2) = -10$. Moreover the values of $\hat{u}$ along the circle described by $(x-0.5)^2 + (y-0.5)^2 = 0.25$ are equal to zero.

We have indeed found exactly the analytical solution. And as a final comment, we notice that our set of basis functions was too large; the 6 functions related to a quadratic polynomial in x and y would have been sufficient.

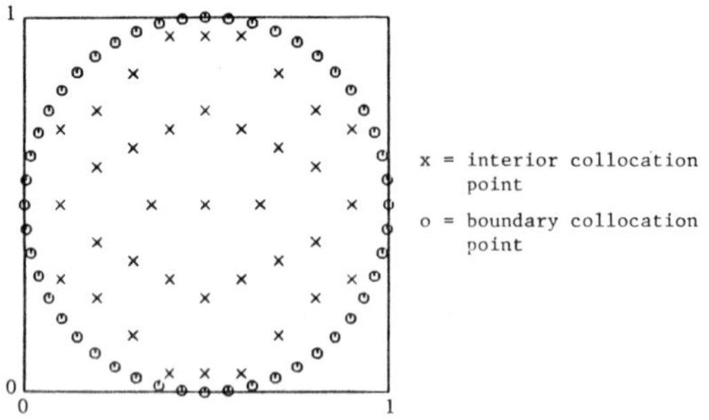

Fig. 1a Least squares collocation (LESCO) domain

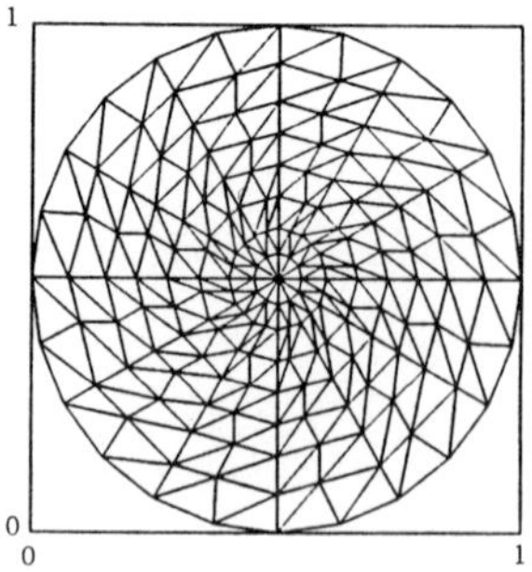

Fig. 1b Finite elements (FE) mesh

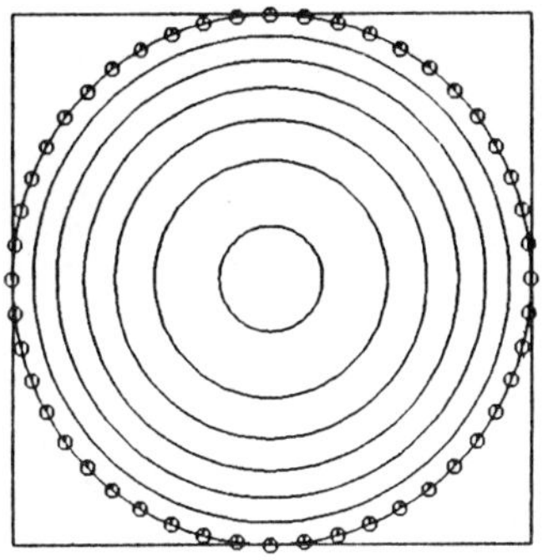

Fig. 2 Solution to problem 1

Table IV and V present all the information pertaining to these simulations.
As can be readily seen, the least squares collocation method is both superior in speed and accuracy to the finite element method.
Moreover its input data file is much more amenable to computational efficiency.

Example	a	b	c	d	e	f	g
1	3	37	48	10	0.0	.006 (1%)	0.37 s
2a	7	130	128	108	-	.56 (6%)	3.08 s
2b	7	130	128	108	-	.06 (3%)	2.82 s

Table IV : LESCO simulations

a - Degree of polynomial
b - No. interior colloc. pts
c - No. boundary + interface pts
d - No. degrees of freedom
e - Max. theoretical error
f - Max. diff. with FE sol.
g - CPU execution time on IBM 3081

Example	a	b	c	d	e	f
1	181	336	157	95	.006 (1%)	0.98 s
2a	279	488	241	40	-	0.84 s
2b	279	488	221	32	-	0.74 s

Table V : FE simulations

a - No. of nodes
b - No. of elements
c - No. degrees of freedom
d - Bandwidth
e - Max. theoretical error
f - CPU execution time

EXAMPLE 2

Example 2a This example is more complicated, in that it addresses a heterogeneous domain of irregular concave geometry. Because of the concavity this particular geometry required division into three subdomains; continuity conditions of the function and of its normal derivative were imposed on the interfaces between elements.

Figure 3 shows the domain as described in term of internal, interface and boundary collocation points. The finite element mesh used for comparison is also shown.

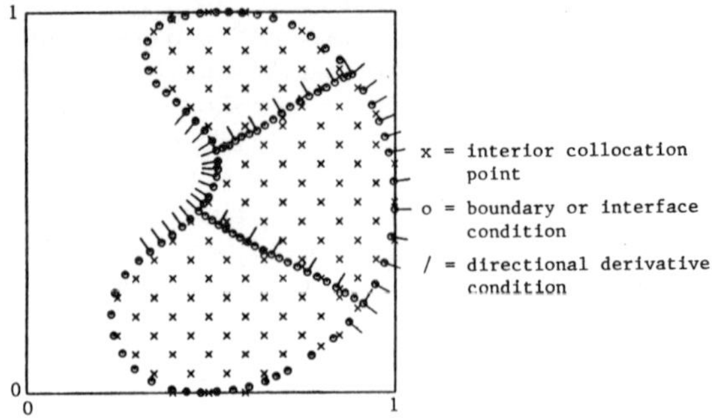

Fig. 3a LESCO domain

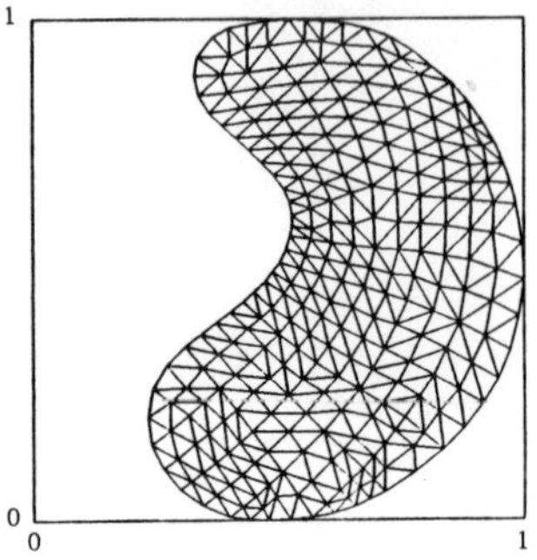

Fig. 3b FE domain

Figure 4 presents the results of the two simulations.

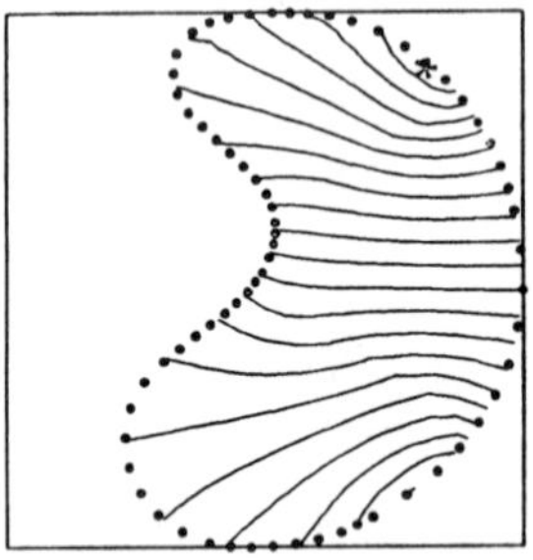

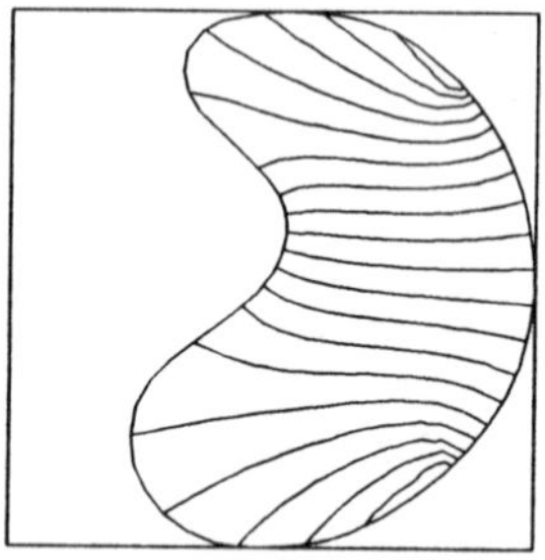

The flow runs from top to bottom in the picture; one should note that the largest difference (*) occurs where the gradient is most pronounced.

Fig. 4a LESCO solution Fig. 4b FE solution

<u>Example 2b</u> Here the boundary conditions are uniform and equal to zero. A uniform inflow f = 100 is imposed over the domain. The same finite element mesh is used; the LESCO data file is the same, too, except for the directional boundary conditions which have been removed, and replaced by Dirichlet conditions.

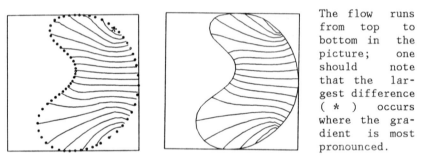

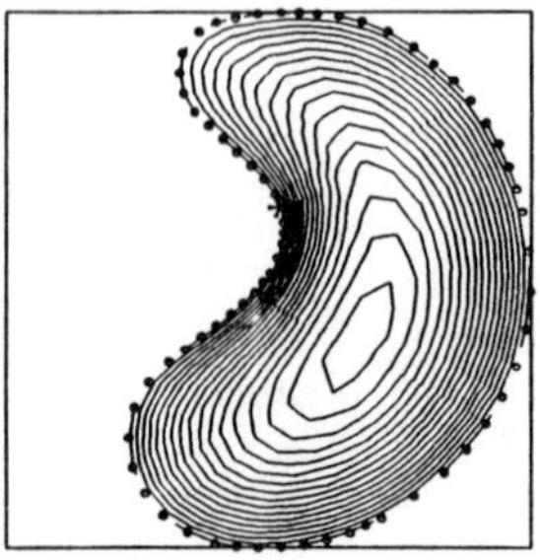

Fig. 5a LESCO solution Fig. 5b FE solution

On figure 5 we see the potential fields obtained with both methods. As can be immediately seen on these pictures, and tabulated on tables IV and V, the difference between both fields is rather small. The computation time however favors the finite elements method.

DISCUSSION

Several features of the new procedure remain to be discussed. First, the number of intermediate functions, n, formally corresponds to the number of independent harmonic polynomials which can be formed in a space of polynomial functions of degree $\leq$ d, d given. Specifically, $n=2 \cdot d + 1$. In our first example, d=3, and n=7. In the second example, there are 15 intermediate functions.

The ratio between the number of interface continuity conditions for the function and for its derivatives, as well as the location of these conditions may vary over a large range without affecting sensibly the final solution. Tests have shown that changing this ratio between 1.0 and 5.0 did not result in significant changes in the potential field.

If directional derivatives of the function are involved in the problem (continuity or boundary conditions), a weighted least squares procedure must be used to accommodate these conditions. We determined experimentally that a weight w1 = 1.0 for the function and w2 = 0.01 for the directional derivatives leads to optimal results. Here too, w2 may vary between 0.001 and 0.1 without noticeable influence on the solution.

Any set of linearly independent functions can be used as basis functions (e.g. Legrendre's polynomials, Chebyshev's polynomials, or others). Power series have been chosen to reduce computation time.

The number and location of the collocation points is of importance, obviously. As long as the number of collocation points over the domain is larger than (N-n) by a few units (see "Development"), the location as well as the number of these points does not dramatically influence the final potential field. The solution is more sensitive to the number and location of the boundary collocation points, though. As a rule of thumb, we discovered that a ratio of 2-3 to 1 between the number of boundary collocation points and the degrees of freedom of the final system leads to the best results.

Finally, checks of the total flux crossing the external boundary revealed that LESCO is very accurate; indeed the error calculated for this flux is smaller than 1%.

CONCLUSION

The method presented here is a valuable alternative to the traditional finite element and boundary element methods. For a comparable computation time, it yields comparable results. Its main advantages are :

1) the simplicity of the data input

2) the condensed form of the results (small number of polynomial coefficients versus large number of mesh node values for the finite elements method)

3) the continuity of the function and of its derivatives over the domain

4) the simplicity of finding the value of the potential at any point (x,y) of the domain by just applying the final polynomial at this point.

ACKNOWLEDGEMENTS

This research was supported in part by the following grants and contracts: NSF - INT - 8305294, NSF - CEE - 8111240, DOE - DE - AC02 - 83ER60170 MODA002 and the Industrial Support Group.

REFERENCES

Brebbia C.A. (1978) - The Boundary Element Method for Engineers. Addison-Wesley, Readings, Mass.

Celia M.A. (1983) - Collocation on Deformed Finite Elements and Alternating Direction Collocation Methods. Ph.D. Thesis, Princeton University.

Cheng A.H.-D. (1984) - Boundary Integral Solution of Darcy's Flow with Variable Permeability. Proceedings of the 5th International Conference in Water Resources, pp. 737-746.

Finlayson B.A. (1972) - The Method of Weighted Residuals and Variational Principles. Academic Press, New York.

Frind O., Pinder G.F. (1979) - A Collocation Finite Element Method for Potential Problems in Irregular Domains. Int. Jour. Num. Meth. in Engrg., 14, pp.681-701.

Pinder G.F., Gray W.G. (1977) - Finite Element Simulation in Surface and Subsurface Hydrology. Academic Press, New York.

VI International Conference on Finite Elements in Water Resources, Lisboa, Portugal, June 1986

An Alternating-Direction Collocation Solution for the Unsaturated Flow Equation

M.A. Celia
Ralph M. Parsons Laboratory, Room 48-207, Department of Civil Engineering, Massachusetts Institute of Technology, Cambridge, MA 02139, U.S.A.
G.F. Pinder
Department of Civil Engineering, Princeton University, Princeton, NJ 08544, U.S.A.

ABSTRACT

The alternating-direction collocation method has recently been developed for general parabolic equations. In order to test the applicability of the procedure to highly nonlinear problems, an alternating-direction collocation algorithm is developed to simulate two-dimensional flow in unsaturated porous media. The algorithm employs a Newton-like iteration within the alternating-direction framework. Results using this new procedure are compared to results from a standard two-dimensional collocation formulation.

INTRODUCTION

Modeling unsaturated flow in porous media is a difficult numerical problem, due to the highly nonlinear nature of the equations. Iteration procedures must be employed to accommodate the nonlinearities. Furthermore, fine grid spacing may be required to effectively propagate sharp moisture fronts. These considerations can preclude economically feasible solutions in more than one space dimension.

An alternating-direction collocation procedure offers the possibility of highly accurate solutions that possess several attractive computational features. The collocation method allows for very efficient formulation of approximating equations, since only point evaluations are involved. This is especially important for nonlinear problems, wherein approximating equations must be formulated a number of times per time step due to the iterative nature of the solution. The efficient equation formulation can be complemented by an efficient equation solver; one such solver is the alternating-direction solution procedure. The coupling of collocation and alternating-direction methods therefore offers the potential for significant computational savings.

The alternating-direction collocation (ADC) method has been developed and applied to several linear (Celia, et al., 1980; Hayes, et al., 1981) and mildly nonlinear (Celia and Pinder, 1986) parabolic partial differential equations. It is the objective of this paper to investigate the applicability of the ADC procedure to the solution of the highly nonlinear parabolic equation that describes unsaturated flow in porous media.

The presentation begins with the formulation of an iterative solution procedure for the two-dimensional unsaturated flow equation. The general, two-dimensional collocation approximation is then defined. Next, the alternating-direction solution procedure is developed, in the framework of the iterative formulation. Finally, an example problem is solved to demonstrate the numerical behavior of the solution procedure.

THE COLLOCATION APPROXIMATION

The general equation that describes two-dimensional fluid flow in an unsaturated porous medium is

$$\frac{\partial \theta(h)}{\partial t} - \frac{\partial}{\partial x}\left[K(h)\frac{\partial h}{\partial x}\right] - \frac{\partial}{\partial y}\left[K(h)\frac{\partial h}{\partial y}\right] - \frac{\partial K}{\partial y} = 0 \qquad (1)$$

where

h = pressure head
θ = moisture content (a function of h)
K = hydraulic conductivity (a function of h)
x = horizontal spatial coordinate
y = vertical spatial coordinate, positive upward
t = time

This equation assumes isotropic hydraulic conductivity, constant porosity, constant water density, and no source or sink terms. It is also assumed that the function dependencies for the nonlinear terms $\theta(h)$ and $K(h)$ are known.

Equation (1) is not amenable to analytic solution and must, in general, be solved numerically. The strongly nonlinear nature of both $\theta(h)$ and $K(h)$ make such a numerical solution inherently difficult. A number of numerical studies have been carried out for the unsaturated flow equation (for example, Neuman, 1973; van Genuchten, 1982; Milly, 1984; Allen and Murphy, 1986). This paper investigates the effectiveness of a special collocation procedure for solving the two-dimensional unsaturated flow equation. This procedure couples the orthogonal collocation approximation in space with a backward Euler approximation in time. Within the iteration cycle for a given time step, an alternating-direction type of solution algorithm is employed.

To develop the numerical procedure, let us first apply a temporal discretization to Equation (1), using a backward Euler method, as

$$\frac{\theta^{n+1} - \theta^{n}}{\Delta t} - \frac{\partial}{\partial x}\left[K^{n+1} \frac{\partial h^{n+1}}{\partial x}\right] - \frac{\partial}{\partial y}\left[K^{n+1} \frac{\partial h^{n+1}}{\partial y}\right] - \frac{\partial K^{n+1}}{\partial y} = 0 \tag{2a}$$

where

$$\theta^{n+1} \equiv \theta(h^{n+1}) \tag{2b}$$

$$K^{n+1} \equiv K(h^{n+1}) \tag{2c}$$

and superscript n denotes time level, with $t^n = n(\Delta t)$. Due to the nonlinear nature of both θ and K, Equation (2) must be solved iteratively for the dependent variable at the new time level, h^{n+1}.

The particular iteration procedure chosen is identical to that used by Allen and Murphy (1986) for the one-dimensional analog of Equation (1). Denoting iteration level by the superscript m, the iteration algorithm is written as

$$\frac{\theta^{n+1,m+1} - \theta^{n}}{\Delta t} - \frac{\partial}{\partial x}\left[K^{n+1,m} \frac{\partial h^{n+1,m+1}}{\partial x}\right]$$

$$- \frac{\partial}{\partial y}\left[K^{n+1,m} \frac{\partial h^{n+1,m+1}}{\partial y}\right] - \frac{\partial K^{n+1,m}}{\partial y} = 0 \tag{3}$$

The following Taylor-like expansion is then written,

$$\theta^{n+1,m+1} = \theta^{n+1,m} + \left(\frac{d\theta}{dh}\right)\Bigg|^{n+1,m} \left(h^{n+1,m+1} - h^{n+1,m}\right) \tag{4}$$

After defining the iteration increment, δh, as

$$\delta h^{m+1} \equiv h^{n+1,m+1} - h^{n+1,m} , \tag{5}$$

Equations (3), (4), and (5) combine to produce the following equation for the dependent variable δh^{m+1},

$$\frac{1}{\Delta t}\left(\frac{d\theta}{dh}\right)\Bigg|^{n+1,m} \delta h^{m+1} - \frac{\partial}{\partial x}\left[K^{n+1,m}\frac{\partial \delta h^{m+1}}{\partial x}\right] - \frac{\partial}{\partial y}\left[K^{n+1,m}\frac{\partial \delta h^{m+1}}{\partial y}\right]$$

$$= \frac{\partial K^{n+1,m}}{\partial y} + \frac{\partial}{\partial x}\left[K^{n+1,m}\frac{\partial h^{n+1,m}}{\partial x}\right] + \frac{\partial}{\partial y}\left[K^{n+1,m}\frac{\partial h^{n+1,m}}{\partial y}\right]$$

$$- \frac{\theta^{n+1,m} - \theta^{n}}{\Delta t} \tag{6}$$

$$\equiv R^{n+1,m}.$$

The right-hand side of Equation (6), defined as $R^{n+1,m}$, is a measure of the amount by which the approximation at the mth iteration fails to satisfy the temporally-discretized Equation (2). It is therefore referred to as the residual. Upon convergence, both $R^{n+1,m}$ and δh^{m+1} should become arbitrarily close to zero.

Equation (6) must now be discretized in space. The orthogonal collocation method is chosen as the spatial approximator. This choice requires that the trial function $\hat{\delta h}$, used to approximate the true solution δh, be at least C^1 continuous, since the governing equation is second order (Prenter, 1975). The natural choice of trial space for second order equations has as a basis the set of C^1 continuous, piecewise cubic Hermite polynomials. Using this basis, the trial function $\hat{\delta h}$ is defined as

$$\delta h \approx \hat{\delta h} = \sum_{j=1}^{N} (\delta h)_j(t)\, \phi_{00j}(x,y) + \frac{\partial(\delta h)_j}{\partial x}(t)\, \phi_{10j}(x,y)$$

$$+ \frac{\partial(\delta h)_j}{\partial y}(t)\, \phi_{01j}(x,y) + \frac{\partial^2(\delta h)_j}{\partial x \partial y}(t)\, \phi_{11j}(x,y) \tag{7}$$

where the $\phi_{k\ell j}$, $k,\ell = 1, 2$, are the Hermite basis functions, N is the total number of nodes, and the four coefficient terms correspond to the function δh and its appropriate derivatives at each node j. These coefficients carry the temporal dependence, while the Hermites carry the spatial dependence. The expansion (7) assumes a rectangular discretization.

The collocation method requires the trial function to exactly satisfy the governing equation at a finite number of discrete points within the domain. These points are referred to as collocation points. For the choice of trial function given by Equation (7), four collocation points are required per element. These points are chosen as the roots of the shifted quadratic Legendre polynomials within each element, in each direction (the Gauss points). A typical rectangular discretization, showing nodes, elements and collocation points, is illustrated in Figure 1.

Implementation of the collocation method is achieved by requiring $\hat{\delta h}$ to exactly satisfy Equation (6) at each collocation point. Since the collocation points are interior to each element, an interpolation procedure must be defined for the coefficients K, θ, and $\frac{d\theta}{dh}$. For the conductivity K(h) and the specific moisture capacity $\frac{d\theta}{dh}$, it is generally held (and relatively easy to demonstrate numerically) that piecewise linear interpolation of nodal values produces significant improvements in solution behavior, as compared to the use of the fully nonlinear expansions for the coefficients. The following expansions are therefore used,

$$K \approx \hat{K} = \sum_{j=1}^{N} K(h_j)\, \Psi\, (x,y) \tag{8a}$$

$$\frac{d\theta}{dh} \approx \widehat{\frac{d\theta}{dh}} = \sum_{j=1}^{N} \frac{d\theta}{dh}\,(h_j)\, \Psi_j(x,y). \tag{8b}$$

In these equations, h_j is the approximate solution for the pressure head at node j, and $\Psi_j(x,y)$ is the piecewise bilinear basis function associated with node j. Allen and Murphy (1986), when solving a one-dimensional unsaturated flow problem with orthogonal collocation, report that numerical experimentation pointed to a cubic Hermite expansion for the moisture content, θ, as the best choice. This result is carried over to the two-dimensional case here, and θ is expanded as

$$\theta \approx \hat{\theta} = \sum_{j=1}^{N} \theta_j \phi_{00j} + \frac{\partial \theta_j}{\partial x} \phi_{10j} + \frac{\partial \theta_j}{\partial y} \phi_{01j} + \frac{\partial^2 \theta_j}{\partial x \partial y} \phi_{11j} \tag{9a}$$

where

$$\frac{\partial \theta_j}{\partial x} = \frac{\partial h_j}{\partial x} \frac{d\theta}{dh} (h_j) \tag{9b}$$

$$\frac{\partial \theta_j}{\partial y} = \frac{\partial h_j}{\partial y} \frac{d\theta}{dh} (h_j) \tag{9c}$$

$$\frac{\partial^2 \theta_j}{\partial x \partial y} = \frac{\partial^2 h_j}{\partial x \partial y} \frac{d\theta}{dh} (h_j) + \frac{\partial h_j}{\partial x} \frac{\partial h_j}{\partial y} \frac{d^2\theta}{dh^2} (h_j) \tag{9d}$$

The standard multi-dimensional collocation solution involves substitution of Equations (7) - (9) into Equation (6), and evaluation of the resulting equation at each of the collocation points. There results a set of linear algebraic equations, with the unknowns being the nodal coefficients of $\delta\hat{h}$, evaluated at the new time (n+1) and iteration (m+1) levels. Implementation of boundary information produces a well-posed system which is solve for the approximation $\delta\hat{h}^{m+1}$. The solution $h^{n+1,m+1}$ is updated, and the procedure is repeated. This iteration leads to a solution for $h^{n+1,m+1}$ such that $||R^{n+1,m+1}||$ is less than a prescribed error tolerance. At this point, the final solution h^{n+1} is defined, and the solution proceeds to the next time step.

ALTERNATING-DIRECTION COLLOCATION

The alternating-direction collocation (ADC) procedure applies a split-step solution algorithm in an attempt to significantly reduce computational effort. As in other alternating-direction methods, the procedure involves two stages, the first corresponding to a series of solutions along one coordinate direction, and the second to solutions along the other coordinate direction. The ADC method has been applied to several parabolic partial differential equations, both linear (Hayes, et al., 1981; Celia, et al., 1980) and nonlinear (Celia and Pinder, 1986). Details of the basic computational procedure can be found in these publications.

In the context of this work, the key is to recognize that Equation (6) is, for any given iteration level, a linear differential equation with variable coefficients. That is, Equation (6) can be written as

$$\delta h^{m+1} - (\Delta t)\, A_x \frac{\partial(\delta h^{m+1})}{\partial x} - (\Delta t)\, A_y \frac{\partial(\delta h^{m+1})}{\partial y} - (\Delta t) B\, \nabla^2(\delta h^{m+1})$$

$$= (\Delta t)\, F^{n+1,m} \tag{10a}$$

where the coefficients A_x, A_y, and B are known functions of the spatial coordinates, defined by

$$A_x = \left(\frac{dh}{d\theta}\right)\Bigg|^{n+1,m} \frac{\partial K^{n+1,m}}{\partial x} \tag{10b}$$

$$A_y = \left(\frac{dh}{d\theta}\right)\Bigg|^{n+1,m} \frac{\partial K^{n+1,m}}{\partial y} \tag{10c}$$

$$B = \left(\frac{dh}{d\theta}\right)\Bigg|^{n+1,m} K^{n+1,m} \tag{10d}$$

$$F = \left(\frac{dh}{d\theta}\right)\Bigg|^{n+1,m} R^{n+1,m}. \tag{10e}$$

Equation (10) can be solved using ADC by a variety of different techniques (see Celia and Pinder, 1985). These include a direct splitting algorithm, a Laplace modification procedure, and related higher-order correction procedures. For the Equation (1), a direct split method appears to give somewhat better results than the other choices, and is therefore applied here. The procedure is briefly described as follows.

The semidiscretized Equation (6) may be written equivalently as

$$[I - (\Delta t)L_x - (\Delta t)L_y]\ \delta h^{m+1} = (\Delta t)F^{n+1,m} \tag{11a}$$

or,

$$[I - (\Delta t)L_x][I - (\Delta t)L_y]\delta h^{m+1} = (\Delta t)F^{n+1,m} + (\Delta t)^2 L_x L_y \delta h^{m+1} \tag{11b}$$

where $L_x \equiv A_x \frac{\partial}{\partial x} + B \frac{\partial^2}{\partial x^2}$, $L_y \equiv A_y \frac{\partial}{\partial y} + B \frac{\partial^2}{\partial y^2}$, I is the identity operator, and the perturbation term P has been added to both sides of Equation (11a) to form (11b). If P is ignored on the right-hand side of Equation (11b), then a two-step solution procedure can be defined as

$$[I - (\Delta t)L_x]\ Z^{m+1} = (\Delta t)F^{n+1,m} \tag{12a}$$

$$[I - (\Delta t)L_y]\ \delta h^{m+1} = Z^{m+1} \tag{12b}$$

In going from Equations (11) to Equations (12), an error corresponding to the neglected perturbation term, P, has been committed.

The ADC procedure can be formulated by developing the numerical analogy of Equations (11) and (12). When the discrete spatial approximation, that is, the trial function of Equation (7), is introduced into the governing Equation (10), the <u>discrete</u> alternating-direction equations, analogous to Equations (12), take the form

$$[\underset{\approx}{M}_x + (\Delta t)\underset{\approx}{S}_x]\ \underset{\sim}{Z}^{m+1} = (\Delta t)\ \underset{\sim}{F}^{n+1,m} \tag{13a}$$

$$[\underset{\approx}{M}_y + (\Delta t)\underset{\approx}{S}_y]\ \delta \underset{\sim}{h}^{m+1} = \underset{\sim}{Z}^{m+1} \tag{13b}$$

In Equations (13), $\underset{\approx}{M}_x$ and $\underset{\approx}{M}_y$ denote mass matrices, while $\underset{\approx}{S}_x$ and $\underset{\approx}{S}_y$ denote stiffness matrices. The detailed form of these matrices can be found in Celia and Pinder (1985). Judicious numbering of both the unknown coefficients and the collocation points produces the desired alternating-direction form. In particular, if the collocation points are numbered consecutively along the x-direction, as indicated in Figure 2a, and if the unknown coefficients are numbered in correspondence to the collocation points, as indicated in Figure 3, then the matrix structure of both $\underset{\approx}{M}_x$ and $\underset{\approx}{S}_x$ is block diagonal. Furthermore, each block along the diagonal corresponds to a one-dimensional collocation matrix, written along each row of collocation points. These blocks can be solved independently, covering all rows of collocation points. Numbering as indicated in Figures 2b and 3 produces a similar block-diagonal structure for the matrices $\underset{\approx}{M}_y$ and $\underset{\approx}{S}_y$. Therefore, the ADC procedure consists of the following two steps,

1) Number the collocation points and unknown coefficients as per Figures 2a and 3, and solve the equation

$$[\underset{\approx}{M}_x + (\Delta t)\underset{\approx}{S}_x]\ \underset{\sim}{Z}^{m+1} = (\Delta t)\underset{\sim}{F}^{n+1,m} \tag{14a}$$

This solution is performed block-by-block and corresponds to a series of one-dimensional solutions.

2) Renumber the collocation points and unknowns as per Figures 2b and 3, and solve

$$[\underset{\approx}{M}_y + (\Delta t)\underset{\approx}{S}_y]\ \delta\underset{\sim}{h}^{m+1} = \underset{\sim}{Z}^{*m+1} \tag{14b}$$

where superscript * implies appropriate renumbering of the elements of the intermediate solution vector $\underset{\sim}{Z}^{m+1}$.

There are several numerical errors in the split Equations (14) that are additional to the usual discretization errors inherent in the standard collocation approximation. These errors are detailed by Celia and Pinder (1985). In the context of the iterative solution given by Equation (6), these errors become arbitrarily small, so long as the iteration converges. This is because these additioinal errors are proportional to δh^{m+1} and its derivatives. Upon convergence, δh^{m+1} approaches zero, and thus the errors must also vanish. Therefore, if the iterative solution procedure converges, the solution h^{n+1} computed from Equations (14) should be arbitrarily close to the solution computed using the standard, two-dimensional collocation procedure.

A NUMERICAL EXAMPLE

An example solution is presented to compare the ADC solution with the standard, two-dimensional collocation (TDC) solution. The example chosen is a hypothetical two-dimensional problem which uses the parametric expressions for K(h) and θ(h) reported by Warrick, et al. (1971). These expressions are based on field measurements, and are given by

$$K(h) = \begin{cases} 1343|h|^{-3.4095}, & h < -29.48 \\ .3589|h|^{.97814}, & h \geq -29.48 \end{cases}$$

$$\theta(h) = \begin{cases} .6829 - .09524 \ln|h|, & h < -29.48 \\ .4531 - .02753 \ln|h|, & h \geq -29.48 \end{cases}$$

The domain, boundary conditions, and numerical discretization are shown in Figure 4. The initial conditions are also taken from the measurements of Warrick, et al., who give an initial moisture distribution of

$$\theta(x,y,0) = \begin{cases} 0.2 - (.05)\left(\frac{y-5}{60}\right), & 5 \leq y \leq 65 \\ 0.2\ , & y \leq 5 \end{cases}$$

Units of length and time are centimeters and minutes, respectively. The patch source of moisture along the top boundary produces a transient infiltration of water.

Both the ADC and TDC procedures were used to compute solutions to the unsaturated flow system of Figure 4. As expected, when both procedures converged, they produced identical results. For example, Figure 5 shows a series of moisture content profiles for times of 30, 60, and 120 minutes. Time steps were taken as $\Delta t = 1$ minute for $0 \leq t < 30$ minutes, $\Delta t = 2$ for $30 \leq t < 60$, and $\Delta t = 4$ for $60 \leq t < 120$.

While the solutions of this example are identical for both ADC and TDC, the numerical behavior of the two methods differs. For example, Figure 6 plots the number of iterations per time step required for convergence of the iteration procedure for the first 30 time steps. The ADC method clearly requires more iterations, especially for the first few time steps. This is a direct result of the additional error terms inherent in the splitting formulation. It was also observed that the TDC method converges for larger initial time steps, whereas the ADC procedure may not. However, the time step size for the ADC method can be increased after the first few time steps to compensate for the small initial step size.

Further insight into the convergence of the methods can be found in Figure 7. Here the maximum residual (the maximum over all collocation points) is plotted as a function of the iteration level for the time step beginning at t = 60 minutes. There is an obvious difference in convergence rates between the ADC and TDC solutions. The slower rate of convergence of ADC dampens the computational advantage of the method, although for these solutions the ADC method is still about five times faster than the corresponding TDC method. The savings in storage requirement remain significant, since the ADC procedure does not store any two-dimensional collocation matrices.

SUMMARY

The alternating-direction collocation solution procedure for the unsaturated flow equation has been developed and applied to an example problem. This solution method can produce significant savings in both execution time and storage requirements, as compared to the standard two-dimensional solution procedure. However, an increased number of iterations required to achieve convergence dampens the computational advantage of the ADC procedure, although it still produces significant savings. For the example problem presented, computation time was reduced by a factor of 5 while storage requirements were also reduced significantly.

ACKNOWLEDGEMENTS

This research was supported in part by the National Science Foundation under Grant CEE-8111240A02, and by the Department of Energy under Grant DE-AC02-83ER60-170 MODA002.

REFERENCES

Allen, M. B. and C. Murphy (1986) "A Finite-element Collocation Method for Variably Saturated Flows in Porous Media," to appear, Numerical Methods for Partial Differential Equations.

Celia, M. A. and G. F. Pinder (1986) "An Alternating-Direction Solution for the Transient Saltwater Intrusion Problem," submitted to Water Resources Research.

Celia, M. A. and G. F. Pinder (1985) "An Analysis of Alternating-Direction Methods for Parabolic Equations," Numerical Methods for Partial Differential Equations, 1:57-70.

Celia, M. A., G. F. Pinder and L.J. Hayes (1980) "Alternating-direction Collocation Simulation of the Transport Equation," Proc. Third Int. Conf. Finite Elements in Water Resources, Wang, et al., eds., University of Mississippi, 3.36-3.48.

Hayes, L. J., G. F. Pinder, and M. A. Celia (1981) "Alternating-direction Collocation for Rectangular Regions," Comp. Meth. Appl. Mech. Engrg., 27:265-277.

Milly, P. C. D. (1984) "A Mass-conservation Procedure for Time-stepping Models of Unsaturated Flow," Proc. Fifth Int. Conf. Finite Elements in Water Resources, Laible, et al., eds., Springer-Verlag, London, 103-112.

Neuman, S. P. (1973) "Saturated-unsaturated Seepage by Finite Elements," ASCE J. Hydr. Div., 99(HY2):2233-2251.

Prenter, P. M. (1975) Splines and Variational Methods, John Wiley, New York.

van Genuchten, M. Th. (1982) "A Comparison of Numerical Solutions of the One-dimensional Unsaturated-saturated Flow and Mass Transport Equations," Adv. Water Resources, 5:47-55.

Warrick, A. W., J. W. Biggar and D. R. Nielsen (1971) "Simultaneous Solute and Water Transfer for Unsaturated Soil," Water Resources Research, 7:1216-1225.

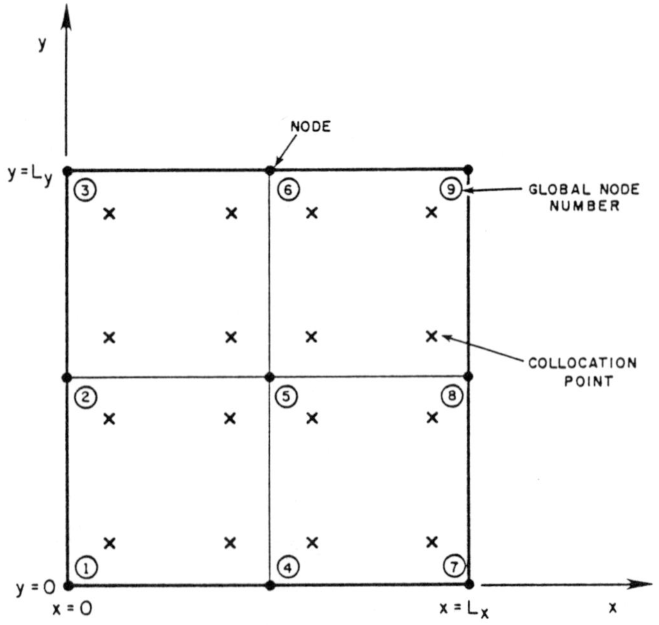

Figure 1 General rectangular domain subdivided into four rectangular elements.

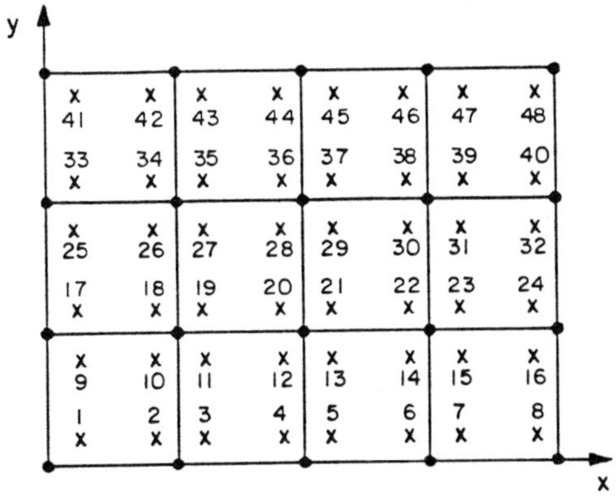

(a)

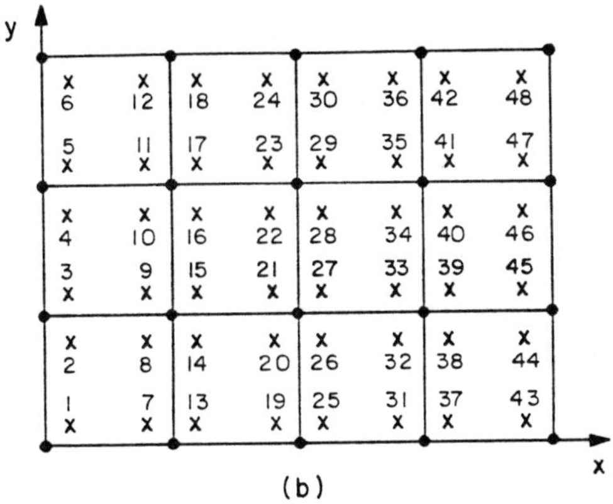

(b)

Figure 2 Numbering of collocation points for the x-direction sweep (a) and y-direction sweep (b) of the ADC procedure. Grid can include any number of elements; this example is 4x3.

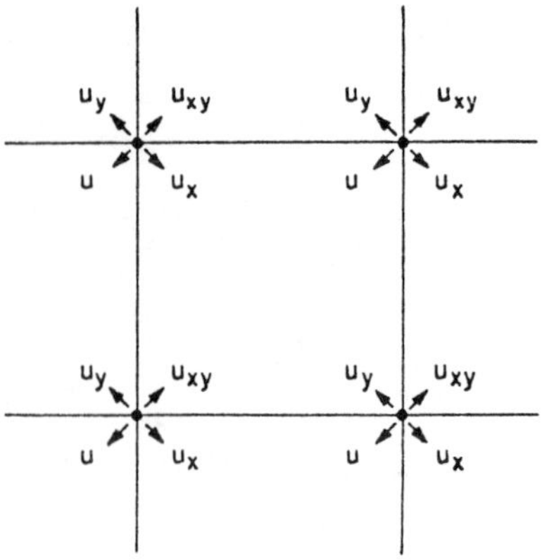

Figure 3 Unknown nodal coefficients (denoted by u, u_x, u_y, u_{xy}) should be numbered to correspond exactly with the numbering of the collocation points with which they are associated in this figure.

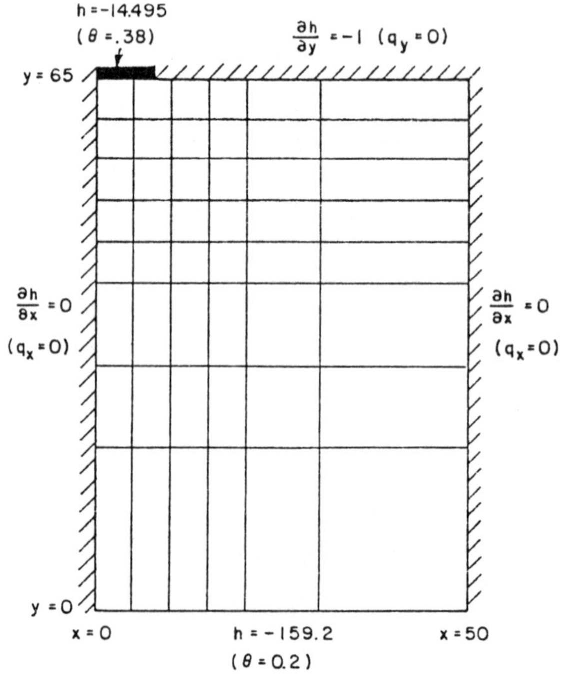

Figure 4 Domain, boundary conditions, and discretization used for the example problem.

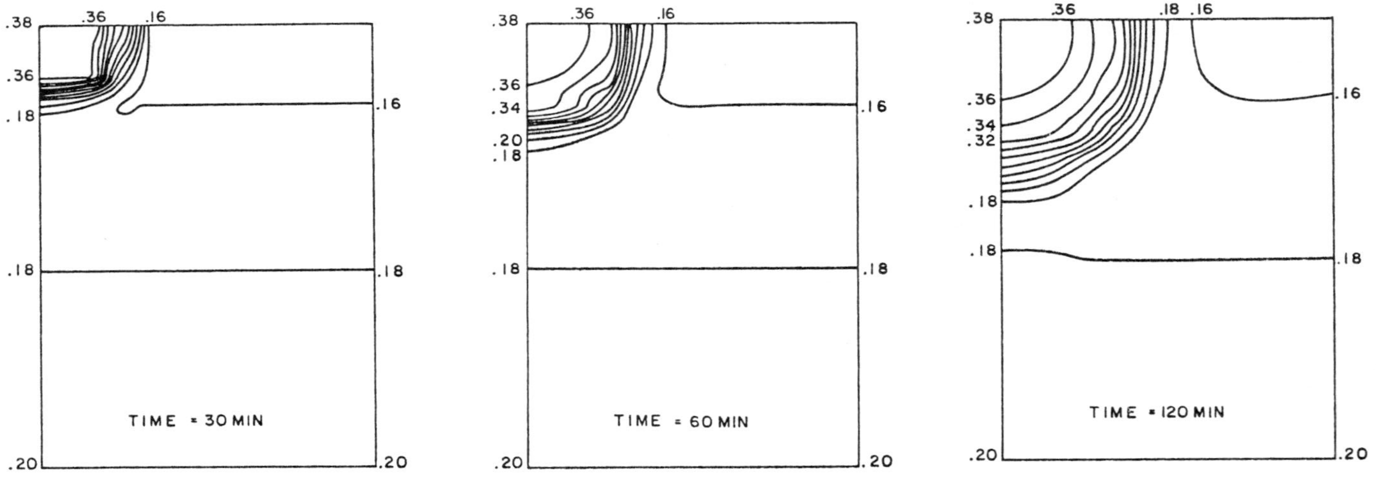

(5a) (5b) (5c)

Figure 5 Contours showing moisture content at several different times for the example problem. Curves are for both ADC and TDC solutions.

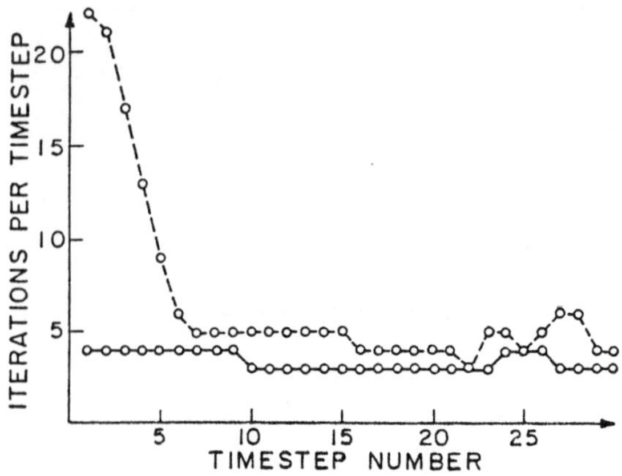

Figure 6 Number of iterations per time step required for the first thirty time steps for ADC (---) and TDC (——).

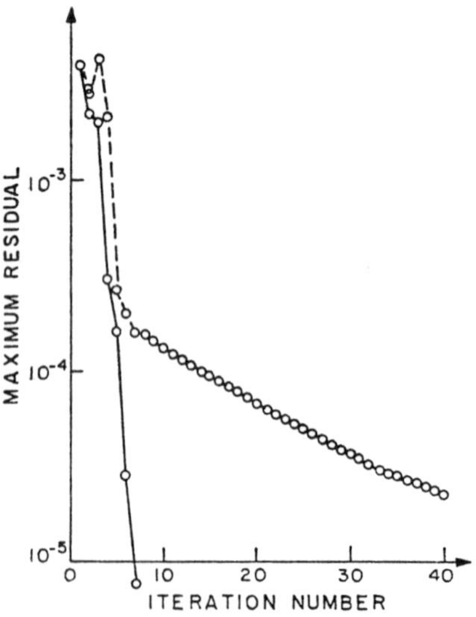

Figure 7 Maximum residual as a function of iteration level for the time step from t = 60 to t = 64. ADC (---) and TDC (——) are plotted.

VI International Conference on Finite Elements in Water Resources, Lisboa, Portugal, June 1986

A Collocation Model of Two-Dimensional Unsaturated Flow

C.L. Murphy
Edwards Air Force Base, California 93532, U.S.A.
M.B. Allen
University of Wyoming, Laramie, Wyoming 82071, U.S.A.

ABSTRACT

This paper introduces a numerical scheme for solving the equation governing two-dimensional flow in a variably saturated porous medium. The scheme uses a mass-conserving time-stepping method together with a computationally efficient collocation formulation of the spatial derivatives. A Newton-like iteration gives a temporally stable implicit scheme. The paper examines a sample problem involving subsurface irrigation in the unsaturated zone.

INTRODUCTION

This paper presents a new numerical scheme for simulating variably saturated flows in two space dimensions. The scheme, based on finite-element collocation, is an extension of a one-dimensional formulation presented earlier (Allen and Murphy, 1985). In that paper we discussed some of the computational advantages of collocation and examined the issue of mass conservation that arises in many numerical approaches to variably saturated flows.

The equation we solve is

$$\nabla \cdot [K(\nabla h - \mathbf{e}_z)] - \frac{\partial \theta}{\partial t} = 0 \qquad (1)$$

where, in two dimensions, $\nabla \equiv (\partial/\partial x, \partial/\partial z)$ with z measuring distance above some datum, and $\mathbf{e}_z$ is the unit vector in the z-direction. In this equation, $h(x, z, t)$ is the pressure head (m), K stands for the soil's hydraulic conductivity (m/s), and θ signifies the moisture content of the soil (dimensionless). Typically, the physics of variably saturated flows dictate that K and θ vary with h, and the relationships $K(h)$ and $\theta(h)$ make Equation (1) nonlinear. Murphy (1985) gives a derivation of this equation.

In the following section we discuss a finite-element formulation of Equation (1) incorporating iterative time-stepping to accommodate the nonlinearity. Then we describe a collocation scheme for obtaining algebraic analogs to the differential equation and review an application to a sample problem.

FINITE-ELEMENT FORMULATION

Our first task in numerically solving two-dimensional unsaturated flows is to discretize the governing equation (1). To do this, we first expand the spatial derivatives using the product rule and use a backward Euler difference scheme to approximate the time derivative on a uniform temporal grid $0 < \Delta t < 2\Delta t < \cdots < n\Delta t < \cdots$:

$$\frac{\partial K^{n+1}}{\partial x}\frac{\partial h^{n+1}}{\partial x} + \frac{\partial K^{n+1}}{\partial z}\frac{\partial h^{n+1}}{\partial z} + K^{n+1}\left(\frac{\partial^2 h^{n+1}}{\partial x^2} + \frac{\partial^2 h^{n+1}}{\partial z^2}\right) - \frac{\partial K^{n+1}}{\partial z} - \frac{\theta^{n+1} - \theta^n}{\Delta t} = 0 \tag{2}$$

This equation furnishes an implicit time-stepping scheme for the approximate pressure head $h^n(x,z) \approx h(x,z,n\Delta t)$, which we regard as the principal unknown.

To solve Equation (2) we must accommodate the dependence of the nonlinear functions $K^{n+1} = K(h^{n+1})$, $\theta^{n+1} = \theta(h^{n+1})$ on unknown values h^{n+1} of the pressure head. To do this, we use an iterative method to advance between time levels, solving for iterative increments $\delta h = h^{n+1,m+1} - h^{n+1,m}$ to progress from the known iteration m to the next unknown iteration $m+1$. This scheme allows us to lag the nonlinear coefficients by an iteration in solving for δh:

$$\left[-\frac{1}{\Delta t}\frac{d\theta^{n+1,m}}{dh} + K^{n+1,m}\left(\frac{\partial^2}{\partial x^2} + \frac{\partial^2}{\partial z^2}\right) + \frac{\partial K^{n+1,m}}{\partial x}\frac{\partial}{\partial x} + \frac{\partial K^{n+1,m}}{\partial z}\frac{\partial}{\partial z}\right]\delta h = -R^{n+1,m} \tag{3}$$

where the expression

$$R^{n+1,m} = -\frac{1}{\Delta t}(\theta^{n+1,m} - \theta^n) + K^{n+1,m}\left(\frac{\partial^2 h^{n+1,m}}{\partial x^2} + \frac{\partial^2 h^{n+1,m}}{\partial z^2}\right) + \frac{\partial K^{n+1,m}}{\partial x}\frac{\partial h^{n+1,m}}{\partial x} + \frac{\partial K^{n+1,m}}{\partial z}\left(\frac{\partial h^{n+1,m}}{\partial z} - 1\right)$$

plays a role analogous to that of the residual in standard Newton-Raphson schemes. In executing the iterative method, we begin each time step by setting $h^{n+1,0} = h^n$ and stop the iteration, setting

$h^{n+1,m+1} = h^{n+1}$, when $\|R^{n+1,m}\|_\infty < \epsilon$ for some prescribed tolerance $\epsilon > 0$.

The formulation leading to Equation (3) differs from standard head-based formulations, which typically use the chain rule to expand the accumulation term as $\partial\theta/\partial t = (d\theta/dh)\partial h/\partial t$. Such an expansion calls for the evaluation of the specific moisture capacity $d\theta/dh$ at some time level in the interval $[n\Delta t, (n+1)\Delta t]$ in the temporally discrete approximation. There seems to be no simple (noniterative) way of choosing this time level to guarantee global mass conservation in the sense

$$\oint_{\partial\Omega} (K^{n+1}\nabla h^{n+1} - K^{n+1}\mathbf{e}_z) \cdot \mathbf{n}\, d\mathbf{x} = \frac{1}{\Delta t}\int_\Omega (\theta^{n+1} - \theta^n)\, d\mathbf{x}$$

where Ω represents the spatial domain of the problem and $\mathbf{n}$ is the unit outward normal vector to the boundary $\partial\Omega$. As discussed in (Allen and Murphy, 1985), discretizing the flow equation as in Equation (3) avoids this difficulty, enforcing global mass conservation to within the iterative convergence criterion at each time step.

To discretize Equation (3) in space, we project the spatially varying quantities $h^{n,m}(x,z)$, $\theta^{n,m}(x,z)$, $K^{n,m}(x,z)$ and $d\theta^{n,m}/dh$ onto finite-element subspaces. In particular, we select for the principal unknown $h^{n,m}(x,z)$ trial spaces spanned by tensor products of piecewise cubic Hermite interpolating functions in the x- and z-directions. Thus, for a rectangular region Ω, we adopt a two-dimensional grid $\{x_0 < x_1 < \cdots < x_M\} \times \{z_0 < z_1 < \cdots < z_N\}$ with nodes (denoted $\mathbf{x}_i$) at the points (x_j, z_k) and, for $\mathbf{x} \in \Omega$, set

$$\delta h(\mathbf{x}) \approx \delta\hat{h}(\mathbf{x}) = \sum_{i=1}^{N}\Big[\delta_i\,\varphi_{00i}(\mathbf{x}) + \delta_i^{(x)}\,\varphi_{10i}(\mathbf{x}) + \delta_i^{(z)}\,\varphi_{01i}(\mathbf{x}) + \delta_i^{(xz)}\,\varphi_{11i}(\mathbf{x})\Big] \qquad (4)$$

Here δ_i, $\delta_i^{(x)}$, $\delta_i^{(z)}$, and $\delta_i^{(xz)}$ represent approximate values of δh, $\partial(\delta h)/\partial x$, $\partial(\delta h)/\partial z$, $\partial^2(\delta h)/\partial x\,\partial z$, respectively, at the node $\mathbf{x}_i$. The basis functions φ_{00i}, φ_{10i}, φ_{01i}, and φ_{11i} are tensor products of the one-dimensional Hermite basis functions (Prenter, 1976, Chapter 3): $\varphi_{pqi}(\mathbf{x}) = H_{pi}(x)\,H_{qi}(z)$, where H_{0i} is the one-dimensional basis function associated with the nodal value of the interpolate, and H_{1i} is associated with its nodal slope.

The projection (4) furnishes a continuously differentiable interpolation scheme for the iterative increment $\delta\hat{h}$ in which the nodal parameters are unknown except where given by boundary data. The head h

inherits this interpolation scheme according to the updating rule

$$h^{n+1,m+1}(\mathbf{x}) \approx \hat{h}^{n+1,m+1}(\mathbf{x})$$
$$= \sum_{i=1}^{N} \Big\{ \left[(h_i)^{n+1,m} + \delta_i\right] \varphi_{00i}(\mathbf{x}) + \left[\left(h_i^{(x)}\right)^{n+1,m} + \delta_i^{(x)}\right] \varphi_{10i}(\mathbf{x})$$
$$+ \left[\left(h_i^{(z)}\right)^{n+1,m} + \delta_i^{(z)}\right] \varphi_{01i}(\mathbf{x}) + \left[\left(h_i^{(xz)}\right)^{n+1,m} + \delta_i^{(xz)}\right] \varphi_{11i}(\mathbf{x}) \Big\}$$

Therefore, given initial and boundary data for $\hat{h}$, one can use Equation (3) to solve for $\delta\hat{h}$ at each iteration, updating $\hat{h}$ to step forward in time.

We also let the moisture content θ have a Hermite cubic expansion, using the chain rule to express spatial derivatives of θ in terms of the nodal unknowns $h_i^{(x)}$, $h_i^{(z)}$, and $h_i^{(xz)}$:

$$\hat{\theta}(\mathbf{x}) = \sum_{i=1}^{N} \Big\{ \theta(h_i)\, \varphi_{00i}(\mathbf{x}) + \frac{d\theta}{dh}(h_i)\, h_i^{(x)}\, \varphi_{10i}(\mathbf{x})$$
$$+ \frac{d\theta}{dh}(h_i)\, h_i^{(z)}\, \varphi_{01i}(\mathbf{x}) + \left[\frac{d^2\theta}{dh^2}(h_i)\, h_i^{(x)}\, h_i^{(z)} + \frac{d\theta}{dh}(h_i)\, h_i^{(xz)}\right] \varphi_{11i}(\mathbf{x}) \Big\}$$

This C^1 projection of θ parallels the successful one-dimensional calculations reported in (Allen and Murphy, 1985).

Finally, for the coefficients K and $d\theta/dh$ in Equation (3) we adopt piecewise bilinear approximations:

$$\hat{K}(\mathbf{x}) = \sum_{i=1}^{N} K(h_i)\, L_i(x)\, L_i(z)$$
$$\widehat{\left(\frac{d\theta}{dh}\right)}(\mathbf{x}) = \sum_{i=1}^{N} \frac{d\theta}{dh}(h_i)\, L_i(x)\, L_i(z)$$

where L_i is just the one-dimensional piecewise linear Lagrange (chapeau) basis function associated with node i.

Substituting all of these finite-element projections into Equation (3) yields a temporally discrete scheme with a finite number of unknown nodal degrees of freedom h_i at each time step.

COLLOCATION SOLUTION SCHEME

To determine the nodal values of $\delta\hat{h}$ and therefore advance the head $\hat{h}$ in time, we need a set of algebraic equations at each iterative step. Some of these equations come from boundary conditions; the rest we will construct using finite-element collocation. Let us begin by reviewing the boundary conditions.

By using the tensor-product basis defined above we have tacitly oriented the computational boundaries parallel to the coordinate axes. For nonrectangular domains, we would isoparametrically transform the (x, y)-plane to a plane endowed with a deformed coordinate system as described in Pinder et al. (1978). In the untransformed system, the unit normal vector $\mathbf{n}$ and unit tangent vector $\boldsymbol{\tau}$ to the boundary will be $\pm\mathbf{e}_x$ or $\pm\mathbf{e}_z$, depending on the position along the boundary. Suppose $\mathbf{x}_i$ is a Dirichlet node. Then $\hat{h}^{n+1}(\mathbf{x}_i) = h_i^{n+1}$ is a fixed, known quantity and therefore $\delta_i = 0$. Moreover, we can differentiate the boundary data tangentially along the Dirichlet boundary $\partial\Omega_D$ to deduce fixed values for $\nabla\hat{h}^{n+1} \cdot \boldsymbol{\tau}$, thus forcing $\delta_i^{(x)} = 0$ if $\boldsymbol{\tau} = \pm\mathbf{e}_x$ and $\delta_i^{(z)} = 0$ if $\boldsymbol{\tau} = \pm\mathbf{e}_z$. Similarly, if $\mathbf{x}_i$ is a Neumann node, then $\nabla\hat{h}^{n+1}(\mathbf{x}_i)$ is a fixed, known quantity, forcing $\delta_i^{(x)} = 0$ if $\mathbf{n} = \pm\mathbf{e}_x$ and $\delta_i^{(z)} = 0$ if $\mathbf{n} = \pm\mathbf{e}_z$. Differentiating the boundary data tangentially in this case will give fixed values for $\nabla(\nabla\hat{h}^{n+1} \cdot \mathbf{n}) \cdot \boldsymbol{\tau}$ along the Neumann boundary $\partial\Omega_N$, forcing $\delta_i^{(xz)} = 0$. Therefore at any boundary node within a boundary line segment the boundary data determine two nodal parameters. At corner nodes the boundary data along the intersecting boundary segments will combine to determine three nodal parameters.

To determine the remaining boundary and interior nodal parameters, we collocate the finite-element approximation to Equation (3) at a set of collocation points $\overline{\mathbf{x}}_k \in \Omega$. This yields a system of linear equations each having the form

$$\left[-\frac{1}{\Delta t}\frac{d\hat{\theta}^{n+1,m}}{dh}(\overline{\mathbf{x}}_k) + \hat{K}^{n+1,m}(\overline{\mathbf{x}}_k)\left(\frac{\partial^2}{\partial x^2} + \frac{\partial^2}{\partial z^2}\right) + \frac{\partial\hat{K}^{n+1,m}}{\partial x}(\overline{\mathbf{x}}_k)\frac{\partial}{\partial x} + \frac{\partial\hat{K}^{n+1,m}}{\partial z}(\overline{\mathbf{x}}_k)\frac{\partial}{\partial z}\right]\delta\hat{h}(\overline{\mathbf{x}}_k) = -\hat{R}^{n+1,m}(\overline{\mathbf{x}}_k)$$

where $\hat{R}$ represents the expression obtained by substituting the appropriate interpolatory projections for the spatially varying quantities in the residual R.

We choose for the collocation points $\overline{\mathbf{x}}_k$ the Gauss points associated with four-point quadrature on each rectangular element $[x_p, x_{p+1}] \times [z_q, z_{q+1}]$ (Pinder et al., 1978). This choice of collocation points furnishes exactly the right number of additional equations for the remaining unknown nodal parameters and gives the best possible accuracy estimates for the linearized problem at each time step (Prenter and Russell, 1976).

SAMPLE PROBLEM

To show the effectiveness of our collocation scheme, we solve a sample problem similar to one solved by van Genuchten (1983) using a Galerkin procedure on Hermite bicubics. This problem describes water infiltrating from a source located 0.15m below the soil surface. The governing differential equation is

$$\nabla \cdot [K(\nabla h - \mathbf{e}_z)] - \frac{\partial \theta}{\partial t} + Q = 0$$

where Q is the water source, measured in s^{-1}. The spatial domain of the problem is $\Omega = (0, 0.61\mathrm{m}) \times (-3.5\mathrm{m}, 0)$. We assume that the left side $\{0\} \times (-3.5\mathrm{m}, 0)$ and right side $\{0.61\mathrm{m}\} \times (-3.5\mathrm{m}, 0)$ are lines of symmetry with no normal flux, that the bottom $(0, 0.61\mathrm{m}) \times \{-3.5\mathrm{m}\}$ is a free-draining boundary, and that the soil surface $(0, 0.61\mathrm{m}) \times \{0\}$ remains at atmospheric pressure. These assumptions lead to the boundary conditions

$$\begin{aligned} \frac{\partial h}{\partial x}(0, z, t) = \frac{\partial h}{\partial x}(0.61\mathrm{m}, z, t) &= 0, \qquad -3.5\mathrm{m} < z < 0,\ t > 0 \\ \frac{\partial h}{\partial z}(x, -3.5\mathrm{m}, t) &= 0, \qquad 0 < x < 0.61\mathrm{m},\ t > 0 \\ h(x, 0, t) &= -0.14495\mathrm{m}, \qquad 0 < x < 0.61\mathrm{m},\ t > 0 \end{aligned}$$

We impose the initial condition $h(\mathbf{x}, 0) = -0.387\mathrm{m}$, $\mathbf{x} \in \Omega$. For the material properties K and θ we assume the same functional forms as van Genuchten, which in SI units are

$$\begin{aligned} K(h) &= (1.157 \times 10^{-7})[96.768 \exp(12.58h)]\mathrm{m/s}, \qquad h \le 0 \\ \theta(h) &= 0.10 + 0.40/[1 + 0.0025(100h)^2]^{1/2}, \qquad h \le 0 \end{aligned}$$

We assume a point source of the form $Q(\mathbf{x}) = Q_0 \delta(x - 0)\delta(z + 0.15\mathrm{m})$ with a source strength $Q_0 = 5 \times 10^{-5}\mathrm{s}^{-1}$. In finite-element collocation we must approximate Q by a square-integrable function. We choose a piecewise bilinear approximation of the form $\hat{Q}(\mathbf{x}) = \sum_{i=1}^{N} Q_i L_i(x) L_i(z)$, where the point $\mathbf{x}_i^{\mathrm{source}} = (0, -0.15\mathrm{m})$ is a node, $Q_i = 0$ if $\mathbf{x}_i \neq \mathbf{x}_i^{\mathrm{source}}$, and $\int_\Omega \hat{Q}\, d\mathbf{x} = \int_\Omega Q\, d\mathbf{x}$.

We solve the resulting collocation equations on the five-element-by-eleven-element grid given in (van Genuchten, 1983) using a time step $\Delta t = 3600\mathrm{s}$ (one hour). Figure 1 shows the structure of the matrix that has to be inverted at each iteration in the nonlinear time-stepping procedure. The bandwidth for this matrix is 31. We use a direct solver executing LU factorization with partial pivoting on banded asymmetric matrices.

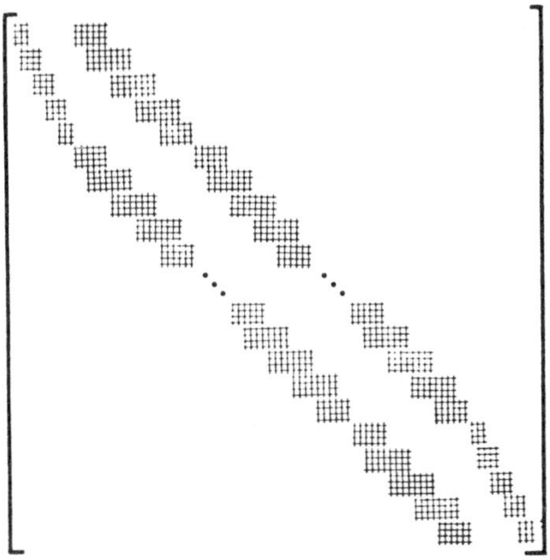

Figure 1. Matrix structure for the sample problem.

Figures 2 through 7 show the spatial variation of $\hat{h}(\mathbf{x}, t)$ at two-hour intervals. At two hours (Figure 2), the source already has a noticeable effect on the pressure head. In the horizontal direction $\hat{h}$ peaks at the source, drops off, and then levels out. In the vertical direction the pressure head gradually increases further down into the column as time progresses. Finally, at $t = 12$ hours (Figure 7) $\hat{h}$ reaches a very close approximation to the steady-state solution in the sense that this solution is virtually identical to solutions at later times.

CONCLUSION

The finite-element collocation method produces good approximations to pressure head distributions in unsaturated flows through porous media. As we have shown, the mass-conserving iterative formulation, demonstrated earlier for one-dimensional flows, extends in a natural way to two space dimensions. One area deserving further investigation is the linear algebra involved at each iterative stage. Since the matrices for the multidimensional problems have an asymmetric block structure without diagonal dominance, better methods for solving the linear iterative systems would be a boon to further applications.

ACKNOWLEDGMENTS

The Wyoming Water Research Center provided partial support for this work. The National Science Foundation also provided support through grants numbered CEE-8404266 and DMS-8504360.

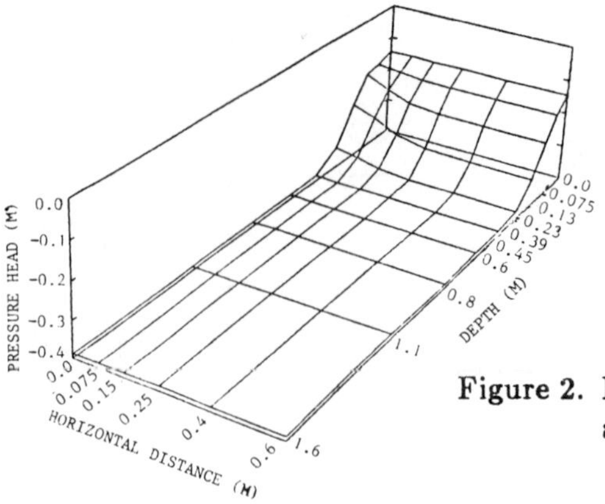

Figure 2. Pressure head solution at 2 hours.

Figure 3. Pressure head solution at 4 hours.

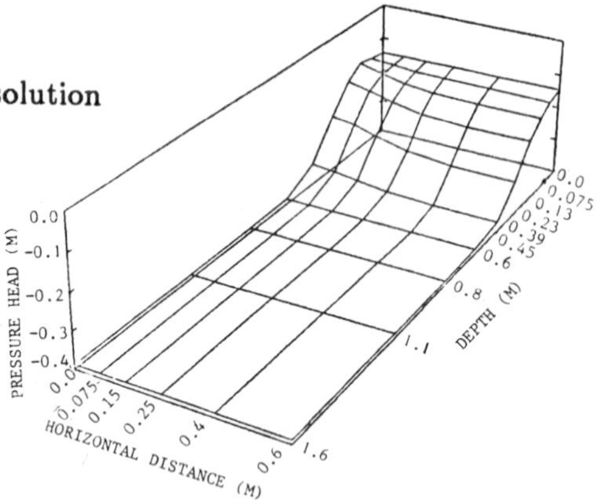

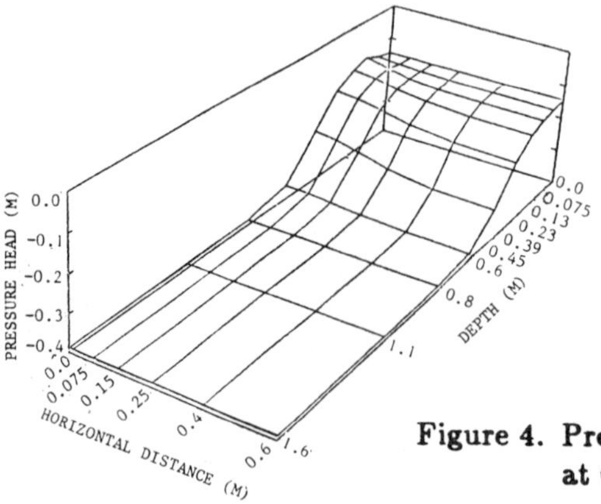

Figure 4. Pressure head solution at 6 hours.

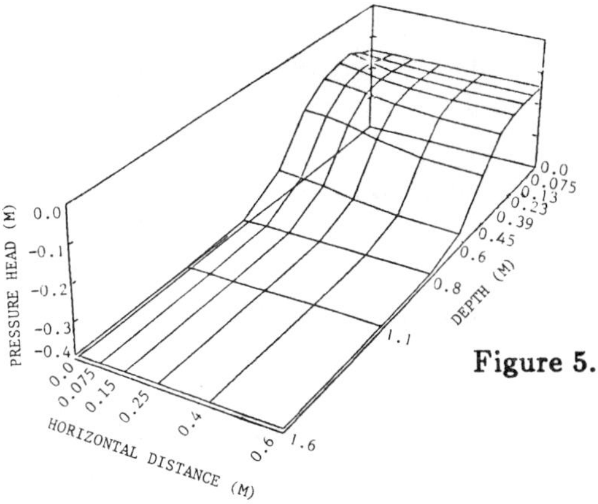

Figure 5. Pressure head solution at 8 hours.

Figure 6. Pressure head solution at 10 hours.

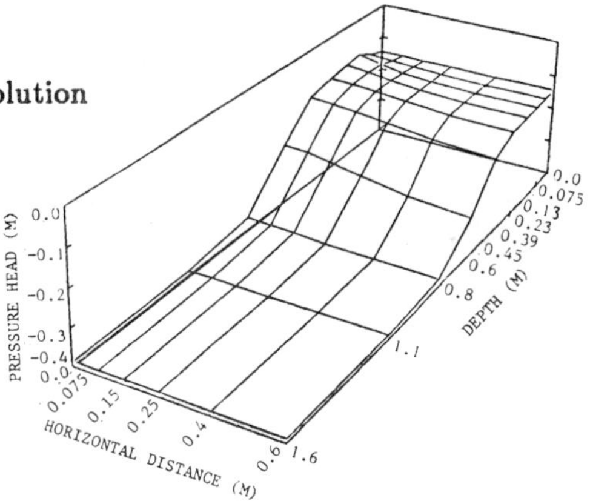

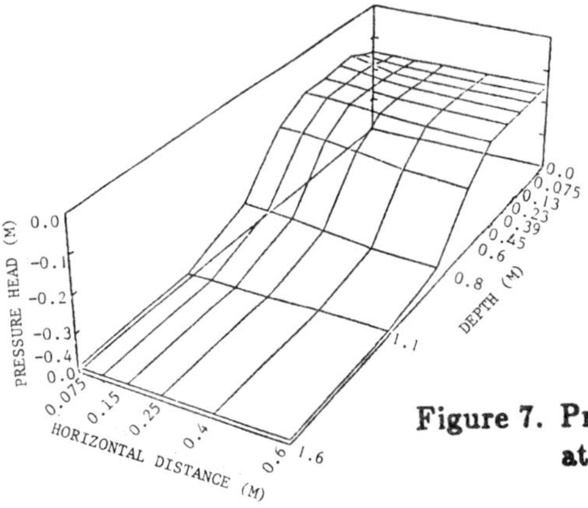

Figure 7. Pressure head solution at 12 hours.

REFERENCES

Allen, M.B. and Murphy, C.L. (1985), A finite-element collocation technique for variably saturated flows in porous media, *Numer. Meth. for PDEs* **3**, 229–239.

Murphy, C.L. (1985), Finite Element Collocation Solution to the Unsaturated Flow Equation, M.S. Thesis, University of Wyoming Department of Mathematics, Laramie, Wyoming, U.S.A.

Pinder, G.F., Frind, E.O. and Celia, M.A. (1978), Groundwater flow simulation using collocation finite elements, in C.A. Brebbia et al., eds., *Proc. Second Intl. Conf. on Finite Elements in Water Resources*, Pentech Press, London, 1.171–1.185.

Prenter, P.M. (1976), *Splines and Variational Methods*, Wiley, New York.

Prenter, P.M. and Russell, R. (1976), Orthogonal collocation for elliptic partial differential equations, *SIAM Jour. Numer. Anal.* **13**, 923–939.

van Genuchten, M.Th. (1983), An Hermitian finite element solution of the two-dimensional saturated-unsaturated flow equation, *Adv. Water Resour.* **6**, 106–111.

SECTION 6 TRANSPORT PHENOMENA

VI International Conference on Finite Elements in Water Resources, Lisboa, Portugal, June 1986

Adjoint State Equations for Advective-Dispersive Transport

F.J. Samper, S.P. Neuman
Department of Hydrology and Water Resources, University of Arizona, Tucson, Arizona 85721, U.S.A.

ABSTRACT

Adjoint state methods have been used extensively to perform sensitivity analysis and to compute the gradient of performance criteria in inverse problems. In this paper we derive adjoint finite element equations for the inverse problem associated with combined steady state and transient subsurface solute transport. Radioactive decay and nonlinear sorption are considered under both steady and transient conditions. Two derivations of the adjoint state finite element equations are given, one involving partial differential equations (continuous approach), the other discrete expressions (discrete approach). The two approaches do not, generally, lead to identical results although, in both cases, the adjoint state equations are linear and similar in character: parabolic for the flow part, and advective-dispersive for the transport part. The adjoint equations for flow and transport are coupled and must be solved in a specific order: (1) the transient adjoint of the concentration followed by the steady state adjoint, and (2) the transient adjoint of the hydraulic head followed by the steady state adjoint. Both transient adjoint equations are solved backward in time. Expressions are also given for the simultaneous transport of several noninteracting species.

STATEMENT OF PROBLEM

We are concerned with subsurface solute transport which, for a radioactive and sorptive dissolved species, obeys the following partial differential equation,

$$\underline{\nabla}\cdot(\phi\underline{\underline{D}}\nabla c-\underline{v}c) - q_d c + q_r c_r - \lambda\phi c - \lambda(1-\phi)\rho s + \phi g = \frac{\partial}{\partial t}\left[\phi c+(1-\phi)\rho s\right] \quad \text{on } D \times T \quad (1)$$

where D is space domain, t is time, T is time interval (t_o, t_f),

ϕ is porosity, $\underline{\underline{D}}$ is dispersion tensor, c is concentration, $\underline{v}$ is specific discharge or Darcy's velocity, q_d and q_r are fluid sink and source terms, respectively, c_r is concentration of the source, q_r, λ is a decay constant, ρ is density of solids, s is adsorbed mass per unit mass of solids, and g is a solute source term. The boundary and initial conditions for (1) are

$$(\phi\underline{\underline{D}}\nabla c-\underline{v}c)\cdot\underline{n} = -\ \beta(c-C) + G - \underline{v}\cdot\underline{n}C \qquad \text{on } \Gamma_1 \times T \quad (2.1)$$

$$(\phi\underline{\underline{D}}\nabla c-\underline{v}c)\cdot\underline{n} = -\ \beta(c-C) + G - \underline{v}\cdot\underline{n}c \qquad \text{on } \Gamma_2 \times T \quad (2.2)$$

$$c = c(0) \quad \text{at} \quad t = t_o \qquad \text{on } D \quad (3)$$

$$s = f(c,\ \kappa_{d1},\ \kappa_{d2}\cdots) \qquad (4)$$

where C is prescribed concentration, G is prescribed solute flux (analogous to g but on the boundary, Γ), β is a parameter controlling the type of boundary condition, $\underline{n}$ is unit vector normal to Γ pointing outward, and f is a linear or nonlinear sorption isotherm. Notice the difference in the last term of the inflow (Γ_1) and outflow (Γ_2) boundary condition.

The function c(0) is either prescribed or represents steady state concentration. In the latter case, it satisfies

$$\underline{\nabla}\cdot\left[\phi\underline{\underline{D}}\nabla c(0)-\underline{v}^0c(0)\right] - q_d^0c(0) + q_r^0c_r^0 - \lambda\phi c(0) -$$

$$-\ \lambda(1-\phi)\rho s(0) = 0 \qquad \text{on } D \quad (5)$$

subject to the boundary conditions

$$\left[\phi\underline{\underline{D}}\nabla c(0)-\underline{v}^0c(0)\right]\cdot\underline{n} = \beta^0\left[c(0)-C^0\right] + G^0 - \underline{v}^0\cdot\underline{n}C^0$$

$$\text{on } \Gamma_1 \qquad (6.1)$$

$$\left[\phi\underline{\underline{D}}\nabla c(0) - \underline{v}^0c(0)\right]\cdot\underline{n} = \beta^0\left[c(0)-C^0\right] + G^0 - \underline{v}^0\cdot\underline{n}c(0)$$

$$\text{on } \Gamma_2 \qquad (6.2)$$

where the null superscript refers to time $t = t_o$. The volumetric fluxes $\underline{v}$ and $\underline{v}^0$ are obtained from Darcy's law as

$$\underline{v} = -\ \underline{\underline{K}}\nabla h \qquad \text{on } D \times T \quad (7)$$

$$\underline{v}^0 = -\ \underline{\underline{K}}\nabla h(0) \qquad \text{on } D \quad (8)$$

where $\underline{\underline{K}}$ is hydraulic conductivity tensor and h and h(0) are transient and steady state hydraulic heads, respectively.

The transient hydraulic head satisfies the flow equation

$$\underline{\nabla}\cdot(\underline{\underline{K}}\nabla h) + q = S_s\frac{\partial h}{\partial t} \qquad \text{on } D \times T \quad (9)$$

where S_s is specific storage and q is net fluid source term, $q = q_r - q_d$. The corresponding boundary and initial conditions are

$$\underline{\underline{K}}\nabla h \cdot \underline{n} = -\alpha(h-H) + Q \qquad \text{on } \Gamma \times T \qquad (10)$$

$$h = h(0) \quad \text{at} \quad t = t_o \qquad \text{on } D \qquad (11)$$

where H is prescribed head, Q is prescribed volumetric flux, and α is a parameter controlling the type of boundary condition. The function h(0) is either prescribed or represents steady state head. In the latter case it satisfies

$$\underline{\nabla} \cdot \left[\underline{\underline{K}}\nabla h(0)\right] + q^0 = 0 \qquad \text{on } D \qquad (12)$$

subject to the boundary condition

$$\underline{\underline{K}}\nabla h(0) \cdot \underline{n} = -\alpha^0\left[h(0)-H^0\right] + Q^0 \qquad \text{on } \Gamma \qquad (13)$$

In solving the inverse problem of subsurface solute transport we wish to minimize an estimation criterion, Ω, having the general form

$$\Omega = \int_D \{J_1[h(0)] + J_2[c(0)]\}d\underline{x}$$
$$+ \int_D \int_T \{J_3[h,h(0)] + J_4[c,c(0)] + J_5(\underline{\gamma})\}d\underline{x}dt \qquad (14)$$

where $\underline{x}$ is vector of spatial coordinates, J_i's are known functions and $\underline{\gamma}$ is a vector of the parameters $\underline{\underline{K}}$, S_s, q, q_d, q_r, α, H, Q, q^0, q_d^0, q_r^0, α^0, H^0, Q^0, ϕ, $\underline{\underline{D}}$, c_r, g, β, C, G, c_r^0, g^0, β^0, C^0, G^0 and κ_{d1}, κ_{d2}, ...

In the process of discretizing (1)-(13) by the finite element method, the dependent variables h, c and the flux $\underline{v}$ are approximated using suitable basis functions, ξ_i. For instance, $h(\underline{x},t)$ is approximated by $h^N(\underline{x},t)$ as

$$h(\underline{x},t) \simeq h^N(x,t) = \sum_{i=1}^{N} h_i(t)\xi_i(\underline{x}) \qquad (15)$$

where N is total number of nodes and h_i is the value of h at node i.

Using the Galerkin finite element method for the spatial discretization on D and Γ, and the finite difference method to discretize the time derivatives, one obtains the matrix equations

$$\underline{\underline{M}}_1\underline{h}^{\ell} - \underline{\underline{M}}_2\underline{h}^{\ell-1} - \underline{b}^{\ell-1} = 0 \qquad \ell = 1,2, \ldots, L \qquad (16)$$

$$\underline{\underline{A}}\underline{h}(0) - \underline{b}^0 = 0 \qquad (17)$$

for hydraulic head, where

$$\underline{\underline{M}}_1 = \underline{\underline{A}}\theta_1 + \underline{\underline{B}}/\Delta t^{\ell} \qquad (18)$$

$$\underline{\underline{M}}_2 = -\underline{\underline{A}}(1-\theta_1) + \underline{\underline{B}}/\Delta t^{\ell} \qquad (19)$$

$$A_{ij} = \int_D \nabla\xi_i \cdot \underline{\underline{K}}\nabla\xi_i d\underline{x} + \int_\Gamma \alpha\xi_i\xi_j d\underline{x} \qquad (20)$$

$$B_{ij} = \int_D S_s \xi_i \xi_j d\underline{x} \qquad (21)$$

$$b_i = \int_D q\xi_i d\underline{x} + \int_\Gamma (\alpha H + Q)\xi_i d\underline{x} \qquad (22)$$

Here $0 \leqslant \theta_1 \leqslant 1$, $\underline{\underline{A}}$ is an N x N conductance matrix, $\underline{\underline{B}}$ is an N x N capacity matrix, $\underline{h}^{\ell}$ is vector of h_i values at time t^{ℓ} where ℓ represents time step number, L is total number of time steps in the interval $[t_o, t_f]$ and $\Delta t^{\ell} = t^{\ell} - t^{\ell-1}$. Similarly, the finite element equations for concentration are

$$\underline{\underline{M}}_3(\underline{v},c)\underline{c}^p - \underline{\underline{M}}_4(\underline{v},c)\underline{c}^{p-1} - \underline{r}^{p-1}(\underline{v}) = 0$$

$$p = 1, 2, \ldots, P \qquad (23)$$

$$\underline{\underline{F}}(\underline{v}^0,c)\underline{c}(0) - \underline{r}^0(\underline{v}^0) = 0 \qquad (24)$$

where

$$\underline{\underline{M}}_3(\underline{v},c) = \underline{\underline{F}}(\underline{v},c)\theta_2 + \underline{\underline{E}}(c)/\Delta t^p \qquad (25)$$

$$\underline{\underline{M}}_4(\underline{v},c) = -\underline{\underline{F}}(\underline{v},c)(1-\theta_2) + \underline{\underline{E}}(c)/\Delta t^p \qquad (26)$$

$$F_{ij}(\underline{v},c) = \int_D [\phi\nabla\xi_j \cdot \underline{\underline{D}}\nabla\xi_i - \underline{v}\cdot\nabla\xi_i\xi_j + (q_d + \lambda\phi)\xi_i\xi_j] d\underline{x}$$
$$+ \int_D \lambda\rho(1-\phi)f^*(c)\xi_i\xi_j d\underline{x} + \int_\Gamma \beta\xi_i\xi_j d\underline{x} +$$
$$+ \int_{\Gamma_2} \underline{v}\cdot\underline{n}\xi_i\xi_j d\underline{x} \qquad (27)$$

$$E_{ij}(c) = \int_D [\phi + \rho(1-\phi)\frac{\partial f}{\partial c}]\xi_i\xi_j d\underline{x} \qquad (28)$$

$$r_i(\underline{v}) = \int_D (q_r c_r + \phi g)\xi_i d\underline{x} + \int_\Gamma (\beta C + G)\xi_i d\underline{x} - \int_{\Gamma_1} \underline{v}\cdot\underline{n} C\xi_i d\underline{x} \qquad (29)$$

Here $0 \leqslant \theta_2 \leqslant 1$, $\underline{\underline{F}}$ is an N x N transport matrix that depends on the Darcy velocity, $\underline{v}$, and concentration, c, $\underline{\underline{E}}$ is an N x N capacity matrix that depends on concentration, $\underline{c}^p$ is vector of nodal concentration values at time t^p, P is total number of time steps at which concentrations are calculated in $[t_o, t_f]$, and $\Delta t^p = t^p - t^{p-1}$. In general, $P \geqslant L$. Although not necessary, we make the time levels t^{ℓ} (at which heads are computed) coincide with time levels t^p in such a way that concentrations are evaluated at $t = t^{\ell-1}$, $t = t^{\ell}$, and possibly at some intermediate times. In order to keep the structure of $\underline{\underline{F}}$ the same for both linear and nonlinear sorption, we have defined $f^*(c)$ such that $s = cf^*(c)$. In this way, if s is linear in c, f^* reduces to a constant (the distribution coefficient); otherwise, f^* is a function of c.

The finite element equations for Darcy velocities are obtained in the manner outlined by Yeh (1981),

$$\underline{v}_m^p = -\underline{\underline{V}}_m \underline{h}^\ell \qquad p = 0,1,2 \ldots P \quad m = 1,2, \ldots \tag{30}$$

where $\underline{v}_m^p$ is a vector containing the m-th component of velocity at each node at time t^p. For a given p, ℓ is such that $t^\ell \leq t^p < t^{\ell+1}$. Matrix $\underline{\underline{V}}_m$ is equal to the product $\underline{\underline{H}}^{-1}\underline{\underline{U}}_m$ where $\underline{\underline{H}}$ and $\underline{\underline{U}}_m$ are N x N matrices defined as

$$H_{ij} = \int_D \xi_i \xi_j d\underline{x} \tag{31}$$

$$U_{ijm} = \int_D \xi_i \sum_{\upsilon} K_{m\upsilon} \frac{\partial \xi_j}{\partial x_\upsilon} d\underline{x} \tag{32}$$

For reasons that will become obvious later, we write

$$\underline{\underline{F}}(\underline{v},c)\ \underline{c}^p = \sum_m \left(\underline{\underline{M}}_{5m}^p\ \underline{v}_m^p + \underline{\underline{M}}_{6m}^p\ \underline{v}_m^{p-1}\right) + \underline{\varepsilon} \tag{33.1}$$

$$\underline{\underline{F}}(\underline{v}^0,c)\ \underline{c}(0) = \sum_m \underline{\underline{M}}_{8m}\ \underline{v}^0 + \underline{\varepsilon}_o \tag{33.2}$$

$$\underline{r}^{p-1}(\underline{v}) = \sum_m \underline{\underline{M}}_{7m}^{p-1}\ \underline{v}_m^{p-1} + \underline{\varepsilon}_r \tag{34.1}$$

$$\underline{r}^0(\underline{v}^0) = \sum_m \underline{\underline{M}}_{9m}\ \underline{v}^0 + \underline{\varepsilon}_{ro} \tag{34.2}$$

where terms not dependent on velocity have been grouped under $\underline{\varepsilon}$, $\underline{\varepsilon}_o$, $\underline{\varepsilon}_r$ and $\underline{\varepsilon}_{ro}$. The superscript of matrices $\underline{\underline{M}}_{5m}$ through $\underline{\underline{M}}_{7m}$ refers to the time level at which they are evaluated. Replacement of h(0), c(0), h and c by their approximate values $h^N(0)$, $c^N(0)$, h^N and c^N in (14) yields a discrete form of Ω.

DERIVATION OF ADJOINT STATE EQUATIONS BY CONTINUOUS METHOD

In the continuous approach, adjoint state equations are derived from the governing partial differential equations (1)-(13). The derivation includes the following steps:

(a) Defining the adjoint state variables Ψ for transient head, $\Psi(0)$ for steady head, τ for transient concentration and $\tau(0)$ for steady concentration;

(b) Taking derivatives of equations (1) through (14) with respect to each parameter, γ

(c) Multiplying each of the resulting expressions for the partial differential equations (1), (5), (9) and (12) by the corresponding adjoint state variable. In particular, the derivative of (1) with respect to γ is multiplied by τ, the derivative of (5) is multiplied by $\tau(0)$, that of (9) by Ψ and the one of (12) by $\Psi(0)$. The resulting expressions are then integrated over D and, if time dependent, also over T;

(d) Applying Green's first identity to replace all divergence terms by terms involving lower order derivatives, and substituting the appropriate boundary conditions into the corresponding boundary integrals. Integrals involving time derivatives are integrated by parts;

(e) Using (7) and (8) to replace all terms that involve $\underline{v}' = \frac{\partial \underline{v}}{\partial \gamma}$ and $\underline{v}'^0 = \frac{\partial \underline{v}^0}{\partial \gamma}$ by terms involving h' and h'(0) respectively;

(f) Subtracting the right-hand side of each expression obtained in this manner from the left-hand side and adding to the derivative, $\Omega' = \frac{d\Omega}{d\gamma}$, of Ω in (14);

(g) Collecting all terms involving the sensitivities h', h'(0), c' and c'(0) into a single term, I, and selecting the adjoint state functions so as to insure that I is identically equal to zero. This yields a system of adjoint state partial differential equations together with associated boundary and terminal conditions.

The partial differential equation for τ, the transient adjoint of c, is

$$\underline{\nabla}\cdot(\phi\underline{\underline{D}}\nabla\tau) + \underline{v}\cdot\nabla\tau - \tau\left[q_d+\lambda\phi+\lambda\rho(1-\phi)\frac{\partial f}{\partial c}\right] + \frac{\partial J_4}{\partial c} = -\frac{\partial\tau}{\partial t}\left[\phi+\rho(1-\phi)\frac{\partial f}{\partial c}\right] \quad \text{on } D \times T \quad (35)$$

subject to the boundary and terminal conditions

$$\phi\underline{\underline{D}}\nabla\tau\cdot\underline{n} = -\tau\beta \quad \text{on } \Gamma_1 \times T \quad (36.1)$$

$$(\phi\underline{\underline{D}}\nabla\tau + \underline{v}\tau)\cdot\underline{n} = -\tau\beta \quad \text{on } \Gamma_2 \times T \quad (36.2)$$

$$\tau = 0 \quad \text{at} \quad t = t_f \quad \text{on } D \quad (37)$$

The steady state adjoint, $\tau(0)$, satisfies

$$\underline{\nabla}\cdot\left[\underline{\underline{D}}\nabla\tau(0)\right] + \underline{v}^0\cdot\nabla\tau(0) - \tau(0)\left[q_d^0+\lambda\phi+\lambda\rho(1-\phi)\frac{\partial f}{\partial c(0)}\right]$$

$$+ \frac{\partial}{\partial c(0)}(J_2+J_4) + \tau(t_o)\left[\phi+\rho(1-\phi)\frac{\partial f}{\partial c(0)}\right] = 0 \quad \text{on } D \quad (38)$$

subject to the boundary conditions

$$\phi \underline{\underline{D}} \nabla \tau(0) \cdot \underline{n} = - \tau(0)\beta^0 \qquad \text{on } \Gamma_1 \qquad (39.1)$$

$$[\phi \underline{\underline{D}} \nabla \tau(0) + \underline{v}^0 \tau(0)] \cdot \underline{n} = - \tau(0)\beta^0 \qquad \text{on } \Gamma_2 \qquad (39.2)$$

From (35) through (39) one can see that the "adjoint solute" having the adjoint "concentration" τ is transported "upstream," its "inflow" boundary being Γ_2 and its "outflow" boundary Γ_1. Moreover, one must solve for τ backward in time and prior to solving for the steady state adjoint, $\tau(0)$. Contrary to the concentrations c and c(0) which are governed by nonlinear equations, the adjoint state equations for τ and $\tau(0)$ are inherently linear.

The transient adjoint, Ψ, of hydraulic head satisfies

$$\underline{\nabla} \cdot (\underline{\underline{K}} \nabla \Psi) + \underline{\nabla} \cdot (c \underline{\underline{K}} \nabla \tau) + \frac{\partial J_3}{\partial h} = -S_s \frac{\partial \Psi}{\partial t} \qquad \text{on } D \times T \qquad (40)$$

subject to the boundary and terminal conditions

$$\underline{\underline{K}} \nabla \Psi \cdot \underline{n} = - c \underline{\underline{K}} \nabla \tau \cdot \underline{n} - \alpha(\Psi + \tau C) \qquad \text{on } \Gamma_1 \times T \qquad (41.1)$$

$$\underline{\underline{K}} \nabla \Psi \cdot \underline{n} = - c \underline{\underline{K}} \nabla \tau \cdot \underline{n} - \alpha(\Psi + \tau c) \qquad \text{on } \Gamma_2 \times T \qquad (41.2)$$

$$\Psi = 0 \quad \text{at} \quad t = t_f \qquad \text{on } D \qquad (42)$$

which, again, must be solved backward in time. The partial differential equation for the steady state adjoint, $\Psi(0)$, of head is

$$\underline{\nabla} \cdot [\underline{\underline{K}} \nabla \Psi(0)] + S_s \Psi(t_0) + \underline{\nabla} \cdot [c(0) \underline{\underline{K}} \nabla \tau(0)] +$$

$$+ \frac{\partial}{\partial h(0)}(J_1 + J_3) = 0 \qquad \text{on } D \qquad (43)$$

subject to the boundary conditions

$$\underline{\underline{K}} \nabla \Psi(0) \cdot \underline{n} = -c(0) \underline{\underline{K}} \nabla \tau(0) \cdot \underline{n} - \alpha^0 [\Psi(0) + \tau(0) C^0] \qquad \text{on } \Gamma_1 \qquad (44.1)$$

$$\underline{\underline{K}} \nabla \Psi(0) \cdot \underline{n} = -c(0) \underline{\underline{K}} \nabla \tau(0) \cdot \underline{n} - \alpha^0 [\Psi(0) + \tau(0) c(0)] \qquad \text{on } \Gamma_2 \qquad (44.2)$$

Expressions for the gradient of Ω with respect to each parameter, in terms of the original and adjoint state functions, are listed in Appendix A.

When the adjoint state equations (35)-(44) are discretized in space by the Galerkin finite element method, and in time by the finite difference method, one obtains the following system of matrix equations:

$$\underline{\tau}^P = 0 \qquad (45)$$

$$(\underline{\underline{F}}_\tau \theta_2 - \underline{\underline{E}}_\tau/\Delta t^p)\,\underline{\tau}^{p-1} + [\underline{\underline{F}}_\tau(1-\theta_2) + \underline{\underline{E}}_\tau/\Delta t^p]\,\underline{\tau}^p = \underline{r}_\tau^p$$

$$p = 1,2\ \ldots\ ,\ P \tag{46}$$

$$\underline{\underline{F}}_{\tau(0)}\ \underline{\tau}(0) = \underline{r}_{\tau(0)} \tag{47}$$

$$\underline{\Psi}^L = 0 \tag{48}$$

$$(\underline{\underline{A}}_\Psi \theta_1 - \underline{\underline{B}}_\Psi/\Delta t^\ell)\,\underline{\Psi}^{\ell-1} + [\underline{\underline{A}}_\Psi(1-\theta_1) + \underline{\underline{B}}_\Psi/\Delta t^\ell]\,\underline{\Psi}^\ell = \underline{b}_\Psi^\ell$$

$$\ell = 1,2,\ \ldots\ L \tag{49}$$

$$\underline{\underline{A}}_{\Psi(0)}\underline{\Psi}(0) = \underline{b}_{\Psi(0)} \tag{50}$$

where

$$F_{\tau ij} = \int_D [\phi \nabla\xi_i \cdot \underline{\underline{D}} \nabla\xi_j - \underline{v}\cdot\nabla\xi_j\,\xi_i + (q_d + \lambda\phi)\,\xi_i\,\xi_j]\,d\underline{x}$$

$$+ \int_D \lambda\rho(1-\phi)\frac{\partial f}{\partial c}\xi_i\,\xi_j d\underline{x} + \int_\Gamma \beta\xi_i\,\xi_j d\underline{x} + \int_{\Gamma_2} \underline{v}\cdot\underline{n}\,\xi_i\,\xi_j d\underline{x} \tag{51}$$

$$E_{\tau ij} = -\int_D [\phi + \rho(1-\phi)\frac{\partial f}{\partial c}]\,\xi_i\,\xi_j d\underline{x} \tag{52}$$

$$r_{\tau i} = \int_D \frac{\partial J_4}{\partial c}\xi_i d\underline{x} \tag{53}$$

$$r_{\tau(o)i} = \int_D \{\frac{\partial}{\partial c(0)}(J_2 + J_4) + \tau(t_0)\,[\phi + \rho(1-\phi)\frac{\partial f}{\partial c(0)}]\}\,\xi_i d\underline{x} \tag{54}$$

$$A_{\Psi ij} = \int_D \nabla\xi_i \cdot \underline{\underline{K}} \nabla\xi_j d\underline{x} + \int_\Gamma \alpha\xi_i\,\xi_j d\underline{x} \tag{55}$$

$$B_{\Psi ij} = -\int_D S_s\,\xi_i\,\xi_j d\underline{x} \tag{56}$$

$$b_{\Psi_i} = \int_D (\frac{\partial J_3}{\partial h}\xi_i - c\,\nabla\xi_i \cdot \underline{\underline{K}} \nabla\tau)\,d\underline{x} - \int_{\Gamma_1} \alpha\tau C\xi_i d\underline{x} - \int_{\Gamma_2} \alpha\tau c\,\xi_i d\underline{x} \tag{57}$$

$$b_{\Psi(0)i} = \int_D [\xi_i \frac{\partial}{\partial h(0)}(J_1 + J_3) - c(0)\,\nabla\xi_i \cdot \underline{\underline{K}} \nabla\tau(0)\,]\,d\underline{x}$$

$$- \int_{\Gamma_1} \alpha^0\,\tau(0)\,C^0\,\xi_i d\underline{x} - \int_{\Gamma_2} \alpha^0\,\tau(0)\,c(0)\,\xi_i d\underline{x}$$

$$+ \int_D S_s\,\Psi(t_0)\,\xi_i d\underline{x} \tag{58}$$

$\underline{\underline{F}}_{\tau(0)}$ and $\underline{\underline{A}}_{\Psi(0)}$ are similar to $\underline{\underline{F}}_\tau$ and A_Ψ, respectively, the only difference being that time dependent terms are evaluated at t_o.

DERIVATION OF ADJOINT STATE EQUATIONS BY DISCRETE METHOD

In the discrete approach, adjoint state equations are derived from the finite element matrix equations (16), (17), (23), (24) and (30) of the original problem. The derivation includes the following steps:

(a) Defining a set of adjoint state vectors $\underline{\Psi}(0)$, Ψ^ℓ, $\ell = 0,1,2\ \ldots\ L$ and $\underline{\tau}(0)$, $\underline{\tau}^p$, $p = 0,1,\ \ldots .\ P$. To facilitate establishing the link between heads and concentrations, it is also convenient to define adjoint state variables $\underline{\sigma}_m^p$, $p = 0,1,2, \ldots, P$, related to the velocity, $\underline{v}_m^p$;

(b) Taking derivatives of the systems of equations (16), (17), (23), (24) and (30) with respect to each parameter, γ;

(c) Premultiplying each of the above expressions by the corresponding adjoint state vector and summing over all time levels. For example, the expression obtained after taking the derivative of (16) with respect to γ is premultiplied by $\underline{\Psi}^{\ell-1}$ and then summed over ℓ from 1 to L. For equation (23), one premultiplies by $\underline{\tau}^{p-1}$ and then sums over p from 1 to P. Equation (30) is premultiplied by $\underline{\sigma}_m^p$ summed over m, and then summed over p from 0 to P. The steady state equations (17) and (24) do not require summation over p;

(d) Subtracting the right-hand side of each expression obtained in this manner from the left-hand side and adding to the derivative, $\Omega' = d\Omega/d\gamma$, of Ω in (14);

(e) Collecting all terms involving sensitivity vectors into a single term, I, and selecting the adjoint state vectors in such a manner that I vanishes.

After performing the previous steps, the gradient of Ω reduces to

$$\frac{d\Omega}{d\gamma} = -\sum_{\ell=1}^{L} \underline{\Psi}^{\ell-1}\cdot\left[\underline{\underline{M}}_1'\underline{h}^{\ell}-\underline{\underline{M}}_2'\underline{h}^{\ell-1}-\underline{b}'^{\,\ell-1}\right] - \underline{\Psi}(0)\cdot\left[\underline{\underline{A}}'\underline{h}(0)-\underline{b}'^{\,0}\right]$$

$$-\sum_{p=1}^{P} \underline{\tau}^{p-1}\cdot\left[\underline{\underline{M}}_3'\underline{c}^{p}-\underline{\underline{M}}_4'\underline{c}^{p-1}-\underline{r}'^{\,p-1}\right] - \underline{\tau}(0)\cdot\left[\underline{\underline{F}}'\underline{c}(0)-\underline{r}'^{\,0}\right]$$

$$-\sum_{p=0}^{P}\sum_{m} \underline{\sigma}_m^{p}\cdot\underline{\underline{V}}_m'\underline{h}^{\ell} + \int_D\int_T \frac{\partial J_5}{\partial\gamma}\,d\underline{x}dt \qquad (59)$$

The transient adjoint, $\underline{\tau}$, of the concentration is solved backward in time starting from the terminal condition

$$\underline{\tau}^P = 0 \qquad (60)$$

and continuing with

$$\underline{\tau}^{p-1}\cdot(\underline{\underline{M}}_3+\underline{\underline{\Phi}}_1) = \underline{\tau}^{p}\cdot\left[\underline{\underline{M}}_4-\underline{\underline{\Phi}}_2\right] + \underline{\zeta}^{p}$$

$$p = 1,2, \ldots, P \qquad (61)$$

where

$$\zeta_i^p = \int_D \int_T \frac{\partial J_4}{\partial c_i{}^p}\, d\underline{x}dt \tag{62}$$

$$\Phi_{1im} = \sum_{j=1}^{N} \left\{\frac{1}{\Delta t^p}(c_j^p - c_j^{p-1})\frac{\partial Eij}{\partial c_m^p} + \frac{\partial Fij}{\partial c_m^p}\left[\theta_2 c_j^p + (1-\theta_2)c_j^{p-1}\right]\right\} \tag{63}$$

$$\Phi_{2im} = \sum_{j=1}^{N} \left\{\frac{1}{\Delta t^{p+1}}(c_j^{p+1} - c_j^{p})\frac{\partial Eij}{\partial c_m^p} + \frac{\partial Fij}{\partial c_m^p}\left[\theta_2 c_j^{p+1} + (1-\theta_2)c_j^{p}\right]\right\} \tag{64}$$

The steady state adjoint, $\underline{\tau}(0)$, satisfies

$$\underline{\tau}(0)\cdot(\underline{\underline{F}} + \underline{\underline{\Phi}}_4) = \underline{\tau}^0\cdot\left[\underline{\underline{M}}_4 - \underline{\underline{\Phi}}_3\right] + \underline{\zeta}(0) \tag{65}$$

where

$$\zeta_i(0) = \int_D \frac{\partial}{\partial c_i(0)}(J_2 + J_4)d\underline{x} \tag{66}$$

$$\Phi_{3im} = \sum_{j=1}^{N} \left\{\frac{1}{\Delta t^1}\left[c_j^1 - c_j(0)\right]\frac{\partial Eij}{\partial c_m(0)} + \frac{\partial Fij}{\partial c_m(0)}\left[\theta_2 c_j^1 + (1-\theta_2)c_j(0)\right]\right\} \tag{67.1}$$

$$\Phi_{4im} = \sum_{j=1}^{N} \frac{\partial Fij}{\partial c_m(0)} c_j(0) \tag{67.2}$$

The adjoint state vectors $\underline{\sigma}_m^p$, which are needed to evaluate $\underline{\psi}^p$, are computed explicitly from

$$\underline{\sigma}_m^p = -\underline{\tau}^{p-1}\cdot\left[\theta_2\underline{\underline{M}}_{5m}^p + (1-\theta_2)\underline{\underline{M}}_{5m}^{p-1}\right] - \underline{\tau}^p\cdot\left[\theta_2\underline{\underline{M}}_{6m}^{p+1} + (1-\theta_2)\underline{\underline{M}}_{6m}^{p} - \underline{\underline{M}}_{7m}^{p}\right]$$

$$p = 1, 2, \ldots P \tag{68}$$

$$\underline{\sigma}_m^o = -\underline{\tau}(0)\cdot\left(\underline{\underline{M}}_{8m} - \underline{\underline{M}}_{9m}\right) - \underline{\tau}^0\cdot\left[\theta_2\underline{\underline{M}}_{6m}^1 + (1-\theta_2)\underline{\underline{M}}_{6m}^0 - \underline{\underline{M}}_{7m}^0\right] \tag{69}$$

The transient adjoint vector, $\underline{\Psi}$, of head is solved backward in time starting from the terminal condition

$$\underline{\Psi}^L = 0 \tag{70}$$

and then continuing with

$$\underline{\Psi}^{\ell-1}\cdot\underline{\underline{M}}_1 = \Psi^{\ell}\cdot\underline{\underline{M}}_2 + \underline{\eta}^{\ell} - \sum_{p=p_1}^{p_2}\sum_m \underline{\sigma}_m^p\cdot\underline{\underline{V}}_m$$

$$\ell = 1, 2, \ldots, L \tag{71}$$

where, for a given ℓ, p_1 and p_2 are such that $t^{p_1} = t^{\ell}$ and $t^{p_2+1} = t^{\ell+1}$ and the vector $\underline{\eta}^{\ell}$ is given by

$$\eta_i^\ell = \int_D \int_T \frac{\partial J_3}{\partial h_i^\ell} \, d\underline{x}dt \tag{72}$$

The steady state adjoint, $\underline{\Psi}(0)$, of head satisfies

$$\underline{\Psi}(0)\cdot\underline{\underline{A}} = \underline{\Psi}^0\cdot\underline{\underline{M}}_2 + \underline{\eta}^0 - \sum_{p=0}^{p^*} \underline{\sigma}_m^p\cdot\underline{\underline{V}}_m \tag{73}$$

where p* is such that t^{p^*} coincides with t^ℓ for ℓ=1 and

$$\eta_i^0 = \int_D \frac{\partial}{\partial hi(0)} (J_1+J_3)d\underline{x} \tag{74}$$

COMPARISON OF RESULTS FROM CONTINUOUS AND DISCRETE DERIVATIONS

Both the continuous and the discrete methods yield linear adjoint state equations that must be solved in a given order, starting from the transient adjoint of concentration, followed by the corresponding steady state adjoint, then the transient adjoint of hydraulic head, and finally the associate steady state adjoint. Both transient adjoint equations are solved backward in time, starting from zero terminal conditions.

A comparison of equations (45)-(58) obtained by the continuous method, with (59)-(74) obtained by the discrete method, shows that:

(a) Both methods yield similar matrices on the left-hand side of the steady state adjoint equations (47) and (65) for $\tau(0)$, and (50) and (73) for $\Psi(0)$. Differences exist between the right-hand side vectors in (47) and (65), and in (50) and (73). However, it can be shown that both methods are consistent in the sense that they lead to two different time discretizations of the same underlying equation. In other words, equations (47) and (65) for $\tau(0)$, and (50) and (73) for $\underline{\Psi}(0)$ can be derived from the same differential adjoint equations using different discretization schemes.

(b) The two methods generally yield different forms for the transient adjoint equations (46) and (61) corresponding to $\underline{\tau}$, and (49) and (71) corresponding to $\underline{\Psi}$. However, one can show that when an appropriate time discretization scheme is used, the left-hand side of (49) and (71) coincide. In addition, one can also show that equations (46) and (61) are consistent as they are two different discretizations of the same differential adjoint equation.

An additional requirement for the two methods to yield similar equations for Ψ and $\underline{\Psi}(0)$ is that both heads and concentrations be solved at the same time levels, P = L and $t^P = t^\ell$.

CASE OF SEVERAL NONINTERACTING SPECIES

The above results are easily extended to the case of N_s noninteracting dissolved species having concentrations $c_i(\underline{x},t), i = 1,2, \ldots N$. For each solute, i, one has a set of partial differential equations similar to (1)-(6), the flow equations being the same for all of them. In deriving the adjoint state equations using (for instance) the continuous approach, one would have to define 2 N_s adjoint state variables for concentration [N_s for τ_i and N_s for $\tau_i(0)$]. Each of these variables will satisfy equations similar to (35)-(39). The adjoint state equations for head, however, would differ from those in (40)-(42) in that they would involve the sum of the τ_i and $\tau_i(0)$. For instance, the steady state adjoint equations would be

$$\underline{\nabla}\cdot\left[\underline{\underline{K}}\nabla\Psi(0)\right] + S_s\Psi(t_o) + \sum_{i=1}^{N_s} c_i(0)\cdot\underline{\underline{K}}\nabla\tau_i(0) + \frac{\partial}{\partial h(0)}(J_1+J_3) = 0 \quad \text{on } D \qquad (75)$$

$$\underline{\underline{K}}\nabla\Psi(0)\cdot\underline{n} = -\sum_{i=1}^{N_s} c_i(0)\cdot\underline{\underline{K}}\nabla\tau_i(0) - \alpha^0\Psi(0) - \alpha^0\sum_{i=1}^{N_s}\tau_i(0)C_i^0 \quad \text{on } \Gamma_1 \qquad (76.1)$$

$$\underline{\underline{K}}\nabla\Psi(0)\cdot\underline{n} = -\sum_{i=1}^{N_s} c_i(0)\cdot\underline{\underline{K}}\nabla\tau_i(0) - \alpha^0\Psi(0) - \alpha^0\sum_{i=1}^{N_s}\tau_i(0)c_i(0) \quad \text{on } \Gamma_2 \qquad (76.2)$$

The expressions for the gradient of Ω would be analogous to those listed in Appendix A with the difference that products of the type τc would have to be replaced by a summation over all solutes. For example $\partial\Omega/\partial\underline{\underline{K}}$ would become

$$\frac{\partial\Omega}{\partial\underline{\underline{K}}} = -\int_D\int_T \nabla\Psi \otimes \nabla h\, d\underline{x}dt - \int_D \nabla\Psi(0)\otimes\nabla h(0)\, d\underline{x}dt$$

$$-\sum_{i=1}^{N_s}\int_D\int_T c_i\nabla\tau_i\otimes\nabla h\, d\underline{x}dt - \sum_{i=1}^{N_s}\int_D c_i(0)\nabla\tau_i(0)\otimes\nabla h(0)\, d\underline{x}$$

$$+\int_D \frac{\partial J_5}{\partial\underline{\underline{K}}}d\underline{x} \qquad (77)$$

CONCLUSIONS

Ajoint state equations for combined transient and steady state advective-dispersive solute transport have been derived by two methods, one involving partial differential equations (continuous approach), the other discrete expressions (discrete approach). We have used the Galerkin finite element method to discretize the space domain and the finite difference method to discretize time derivatives. Although the two methods generally lead to different sets of adjoint state matrix equations, one can show that the two sets of equations are consistent in the sense that they result from two different discretizations of the same governing adjoint partial differential equations. For advection-dominated problems the Galekrin finite element method is not always the best approach. In such cases one may prefer other solution methods such as the adaptive Eulerian-Lagrangian finite element method of Neuman (1984). The associated adjoint state equations will differ from those presented in this paper.

APPENDIX A: GRADIENT OF Ω WITH RESPECT TO EACH PARAMETER (CONTINUOUS APPROACH)

$$\frac{\partial \Omega}{\partial \underline{\underline{K}}} = - \int_D \int_T (\nabla \Psi \otimes \nabla h + c \nabla \tau \otimes \nabla h) d\underline{x} dt$$

$$- \int_D [\nabla \Psi(0) \otimes \nabla h(0) + c(0) \nabla \tau(0) \otimes \nabla h(0)] d\underline{x} + \int_D \frac{\partial J_5}{\partial \underline{\underline{K}}} d\underline{x} \qquad (A.1)$$

where $\otimes$ denotes tensorial product,

$$\frac{\partial \Omega}{\partial \alpha} = - \int_{\Gamma_1} \int_T (\tau C + \Psi)(h-H) d\underline{x} dt - \int_{\Gamma_2} \int_T (\tau c + \Psi)(h-H) d\underline{x} dt$$

$$+ \int_\Gamma \int_T \frac{\partial J_5}{\partial \alpha} d\underline{x} dt \qquad (A.2)$$

$$\frac{\partial \Omega}{\partial \alpha^0} = - \int_{\Gamma_1} [\tau(0) C^0 + \Psi(0)][h(0) - H^0] d\underline{x}$$

$$- \int_\Gamma [\tau(0) c(0) + \Psi(0)][h(0) - H^0] d\underline{x} + \int_\Gamma \frac{\partial J_5}{\partial \alpha^0} d\underline{x} \qquad (A.3)$$

$$\frac{\partial \Omega}{\partial H} = \int_{\Gamma_1} \int_T (\tau C + \Psi) \alpha \, d\underline{x} dt + \int_{\Gamma_2} \int_T (\tau c + \Psi) \alpha \, d\underline{x} dt$$

$$+ \int_\Gamma \int_T \frac{\partial J_5}{\partial H} \, d\underline{x} \qquad (A.4)$$

$$\frac{\partial \Omega}{\partial H^0} = \int_{\Gamma_1} [\tau(0) C^0 + \Psi(0)] \alpha^0 d\underline{x} + \int_{\Gamma_2} [\tau(0) c(0) + \Psi(0)] \alpha^0 d\underline{x}$$

$$+ \int_\Gamma \frac{\partial J_5}{\partial H^0} d\underline{x} \qquad (A.5)$$

$$\frac{\partial \Omega}{\partial Q} = \int_{\Gamma_1} \int_T (\tau C + \Psi) d\underline{x} dt + \int_{\Gamma_2} \int_T (\tau c + \Psi) d\underline{x} dt + \int_\Gamma \int_T \frac{\partial J_5}{\partial Q} d\underline{x} dt \qquad (A.6)$$

$$\frac{\partial\Omega}{\partial Q^0} = \int_{\Gamma_1}[\tau(0)C^0 + \Psi(0)]d\underline{x} + \int_{\Gamma_2}[\tau(0)c(0) + \Psi(0)]d\underline{x}$$

$$+ \int_\Gamma \frac{\partial J_5}{\partial Q^0}d\underline{x} \quad (A.7)$$

$$\frac{\partial\Omega}{\partial Ss} = - \int_D\int_T(\Psi\frac{\partial h}{\partial t} + \frac{\partial J_5}{\partial Ss})d\underline{x}dt \quad (A.8)$$

$$\frac{\partial\Omega}{\partial q} = \int_D\int_T(\Psi + \tau c + \frac{\partial J_5}{\partial q})d\underline{x}dt \quad (A.9)$$

$$\frac{\partial\Omega}{\partial q^0} = \int_\Gamma[\Psi(0) + \tau(0)c(0) + \frac{\partial J_5}{\partial q^0}]d\underline{x} \quad (A.10)$$

$$\frac{\partial\Omega}{\partial\phi} = - \int_D\int_T[\nabla\tau\cdot\underline{\underline{D}}\nabla c + \tau(\lambda c - g - \lambda\rho s + \frac{\partial c}{\partial t})]d\underline{x}dt$$

$$- \int_D\{\nabla\tau(0)\cdot\underline{\underline{D}}\nabla c(0) + \tau(0)[\lambda c(0) - g^0 - \lambda\rho s(0)] + \frac{\partial J_5}{\partial\phi}\}d\underline{x}$$

$$(A.11)$$

$$\frac{\partial\Omega}{\partial\underline{\underline{D}}} = - \int_D\int_T\phi\nabla\tau \otimes \nabla c d\underline{x}dt + \int_D[\frac{\partial J_3}{\partial\underline{\underline{D}}} - \phi\nabla\tau(0) \otimes \nabla c(0)]d\underline{x} \quad (A.12)$$

$$\frac{\partial\Omega}{\partial q_r} = \int_D\int_T[\tau(c_r - c) + \frac{\partial J_5}{\partial q_r}]d\underline{x}dt \quad (A.13)$$

$$\frac{\partial\Omega}{\partial q_r^0} = \int_D\{\tau(0)[c_r^0 - c(0)] + \frac{\partial J_5}{\partial q_r^0}\}d\underline{x} \quad (A.14)$$

$$\frac{\partial\Omega}{\partial c_r} = \int_D\int_T(\tau q_r + \frac{\partial J_5}{\partial c_r})d\underline{x}dt \quad (A.15)$$

$$\frac{\partial\Omega}{\partial c_r^0} = \int_D[\tau(0)q_r^0 + \frac{\partial J_5}{\partial c_r^0}]d\underline{x} \quad (A.16)$$

$$\frac{\partial\Omega}{\partial g} = \int_D\int_T(\tau\phi + \frac{\partial J_5}{\partial g})d\underline{x}dt \quad (A.17)$$

$$\frac{\partial\Omega}{\partial g^0} = \int_D[\tau(0)\phi + \frac{\partial J_5}{\partial g^0}]d\underline{x} \quad (A.18)$$

$$\frac{\partial\Omega}{\partial\beta} = \int_\Gamma\int_T[-\tau(c - C) + \frac{\partial J_5}{\partial\beta}]d\underline{x}dt \quad (A.19)$$

$$\frac{\partial\Omega}{\partial\beta^0} = \int_\Gamma\{-\tau(0)[c(0) - C^0] + \frac{\partial J_5}{\partial\beta^0}\}d\underline{x} \quad (A.20)$$

$$\frac{\partial\Omega}{\partial C} = \int_{\Gamma_1}\int_T\tau(\beta - \underline{v}\cdot\underline{n})d\underline{x}dt + \int_{\Gamma_2}\int_T\tau\beta d\underline{x}dt + \int_\Gamma\int_T\frac{\partial J_5}{\partial C}d\underline{x}dt \quad (A.21)$$

$$\frac{\partial\Omega}{\partial C^0} = \int_{\Gamma_1} \tau(0)\,[\beta^0 - \underline{v}^0\cdot\underline{n}]d\underline{x} + \int_{\Gamma_2} \tau(0)\,\beta^0 d\underline{x} + \int_\Gamma \frac{\partial J_5}{\partial C^0} d\underline{x} \qquad (A.22)$$

$$\frac{\partial\Omega}{\partial G} = \int_\Gamma\int_T (\tau + \frac{\partial J_5}{\partial G}) d\underline{x}dt \qquad (A.23)$$

$$\frac{\partial\Omega}{\partial G^0} = \int_\Gamma [\tau(0) + \frac{\partial J_5}{\partial G^0}] d\underline{x} \qquad (A.24)$$

$$\frac{\partial\Omega}{\partial K_{d_i}} = - \int_D\int_T \tau\rho(1-\phi)\,[\lambda \frac{\partial f}{\partial K_{d_i}} + \frac{\partial}{\partial t}(\frac{\partial f}{\partial K_{d_i}})]d\underline{x}dt$$

$$+ \int_D [-\tau(0)\,\rho(1-\phi)\frac{\partial f}{\partial K_{d_i}} + \frac{\partial J_5}{\partial K_{d_i}}]d\underline{x} \qquad (A.25)$$

For Dirichlet boundary conditions where $\alpha \to \infty$ and $\beta \to \infty$, (A.3)-(A.4) and (A.21)-(A.22) are undetermined. According to (36), (39), (41) and (44) we obtain

$$\frac{\partial\Omega}{\partial H} = \int_\Gamma\int_T [-\underline{\underline{K}}(\nabla\Psi + c\nabla\tau)\cdot\underline{n} + \frac{\partial J_5}{\partial H}] d\underline{x}dt \qquad (A.26)$$

$$\frac{\partial\Omega}{\partial H^0} = \int_\Gamma\int_T [-\underline{\underline{K}}[\nabla\Psi(0) + c(0)\nabla\tau(0)]\cdot\underline{n} + \frac{\partial J_5}{\partial H^0}] d\underline{x} \qquad (A.27)$$

$$\frac{\partial\Omega}{\partial C} = \int_\Gamma\int_T [-(\phi\underline{\underline{D}}\nabla\tau + \underline{v}\tau)\cdot\underline{n} + \frac{\partial J_5}{\partial C}] d\underline{x}dt \qquad (A.28)$$

$$\frac{\partial\Omega}{\partial C^0} = \int_\Gamma \{-[\phi\underline{\underline{D}}\nabla\tau(0) + \underline{v}(0)\,\tau(0)]\cdot\underline{n} + \frac{\partial J_5}{\partial C^0}\} d\underline{x} \qquad (A.29)$$

REFERENCES

Neuman, S. P. (1984) Adaptive Eulerian-Lagrangian finite element method for advection-dispersion, Int. j. numer. methods eng., 20,321-337.

Yeh, G. T. (1981) On the computation of Darcian velocity and mass balance in the finite element modeling of groundwater flow, Water Resour. Res., 17,5:1529-1534.

VI International Conference on Finite Elements in Water Resources, Lisboa, Portugal, June 1986

Unconditionally Stable Explicit Method Applied to Transport Simulations

D.E. Dougherty
Department of Civil Engineering, University of California, Irvine, CA 92717, U.S.A.

INTRODUCTION

Something for nothing -- or at least more for less. These desires are held by computational physicists as well as those in other disciplines. In this regard, I report on an excursion to explore a rational Runge Kutta (RRK) method for use in hydrological calculations.

Physically-based hydrological models lead to transport equations that are generally parabolic and may possess significant first-order (spatial) derivative terms. Common examples in geohydrology include saturated water flow (a diffusion equation) and binary mixture transport (an advection-diffusion equation is generally used). Computer representation of such processes leads to a system of algebraic equations that is frequently quite stiff; this aspect of discrete models for partial differential equations is well known (e.g., Strang, 1986, page 571) and, in addition, practical models are frequently built of computational elements or cells of varying size (characteristic length Δx varies) and material properties. Implicit integration schemes are the most common way to treat stiff systems.

Implicit methods have become the standard time-stepping technique in the analysis of subsurface fluid flow. The main reasons are the stability of implicit methods and the concomitantly large timestep (Δt) that is possible. Groundwater flow problems are frequently only slightly compressible, so the allowable stability limit on Δt for conditionally stable explicit methods (such as the Euler explicit, EE, method) is very small. On the other hand implicit equations require the formation and solution of a matrix equation, which can be a substantial fraction of solution time (except for the case of constant coefficients and fixed Δt). The impact is greatest as the order of the system of equations increases; recall that the effort to compute the direct solution of a banded system is about NB^2, where N is the number of equations and B is the bandwidth (roughly $\sqrt{N}$). Further, in some nonlinear problems the timestep must be quite small in order to track the nonlinear behavior, even for "unconditionally stable" implicit methods such as the Euler implicit (EI) method. Geothermal simulation is one such case.

Hughes and others (Hughes et al., 1979; Park and Fellipa, 1983) have suggested time-partitioning methods as a way to effectively integrate stiff numerical pde's. In this technique one partition of the mesh is integrated differently than other partition(s) of the mesh. Implicit-explicit time partitionings of computational domains have grown common in fluid-structure studies and I have used them in the past as an analysis tool. The basic idea is to write the equations in different parts of a mesh using different time-stepping schemes that are appropriate to the local conditions. Consider the mesh in Figure 1, for a diffusion problem with uniform constant coefficients. Lumping is employed to ensure a diagonal capacitance (mass)

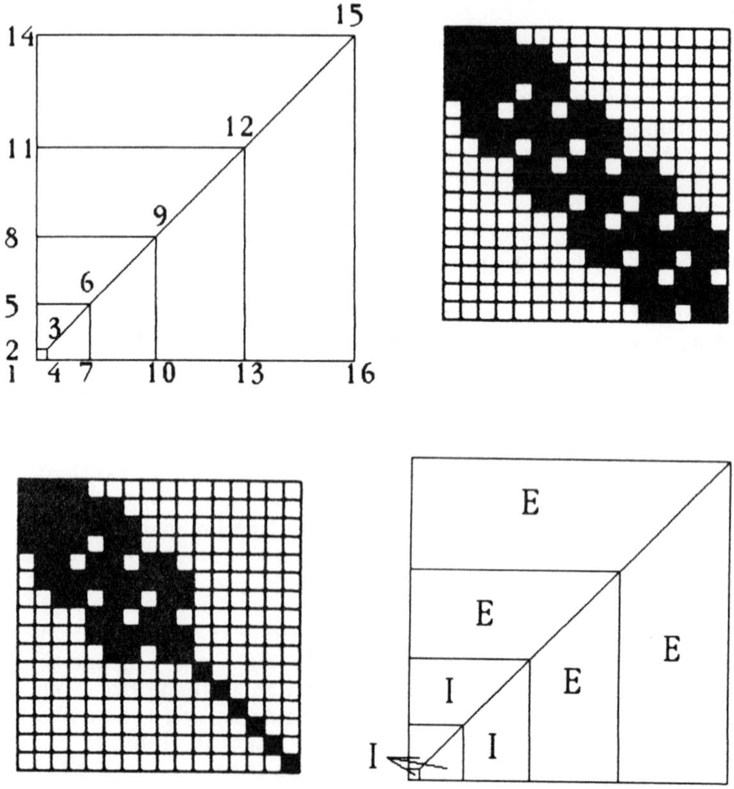

Figure 1. (Clockwise from upper left) A--A graded mesh of bilinear finite elements, B--matrix structure for fully implicit solution, C--an implicit(I)-explicit(E) element partitioning of grid A, and D--matrix structure for the implicit-explicit partitioning. Note the reduced storage and solution effort required.

matrix. The element lengths vary by a factor of 10, and the Euler cricial time step varies by a factor of 100. An implicit method will obviate the problem at the cost of solving simultaneous equations. The matrix structures of $\mathbf{Ax} = \mathbf{b}$ for both the EI and EE cases are given in the figure. If some elements are called explicit and others implicit, then another form of $\mathbf{A}$ arises--the implicit-explicit form, shown in the figure. If an EE method is used with any unconditionally stable implicit integrator (e.g., EI) then (Hughes, 1983) the implicit-explicit algorithm has a stability timestep limit equal to that of the explicit Euler method for the degrees of freedom (dof's) that are incident in explicit elements. The "purely explicit" dof's are solved directly--without any LU factorization or the like--which gives a savings in storage and cpu effort that is attractive. If an unconditionally stable explicit method is coupled with an unconditionally stable implicit integrator then the implicit-explicit method will be unconditionally stable. If in addition both integrators are adequately accurate then implicit-explicit methods may be a very useful tool, especially for nonlinear problems where the stability constraint can vary with the solution.

A RATIONAL RUNGE KUTTA METHOD (SECOND ORDER ACCURATE)

Wambecq (1978) has proposed one-step RRK schemes to solve systems of first-order ordinary differential equations (ode's), $\mathbf{u}' = \mathbf{f}(\mathbf{u})$, where $'$ means d/dt. They are

$$\mathbf{u}^1 = \mathbf{u}^0 + \sum_{i=1}^{s} \sum_{j=1}^{i} w_{ij} \frac{g_i\, g_j}{\sum_{k=1}^{s} b_k\, g_k} \qquad (1)$$

$$g_i = \Delta t\, f\left(u_0 + \sum_{j=1}^{i-1} a_{ij}\, g_j \right), \qquad (2)$$

where a, b, and w are real parameters and s is the number of stages. Hairer (1980) considered the stability properties of the RRK schemes of Wambecq in more detail, with special attention to two-stage, two-parameter RRK method. Hairer's results put constraints on the parameters to ensure A_0- and I-stability, which are defined as follows:

The integrator defined by Equations (1) and (2) is:

A_0-stable: iff $\{x \epsilon R \,|\, x \le 0\}$ is a stability region

I-stable: iff $\{iy \,|\, y \epsilon R\}$ is a stability region

where R indicates the reals and i is $(-1)^{1/2}$.

A_0-stability implies that parabolic equations may be integrated by RRK with unconditional stability. Unconditionally stable explicit time-integrators have been constructed for parabolic numerical pde's (for example see Liu et al, 1984). I-stability suggests that hyperbolic equations may be integrated with unconditional stability by RRK. Peirce and Prevost (1985) and I (Dougherty, 1985) investigated the applicability of RRK to hyperbolic equations at about the same time last year, although my study was more empirical.

Hairer (1980) found that there is an A_0- and I-stable one-step, two-stage explicit RRK method that is second order accurate. The matrix differential equation is integrated by the algorithm (Liu et al., 1984)

$$\mathbf{u}' = \mathbf{A} \cdot \mathbf{u} \tag{3}$$

$$\mathbf{u}^{j+1} = \mathbf{u}^{j} + \Delta t \frac{\mathbf{e}}{\mathbf{b} \cdot \mathbf{b}} \tag{4}$$

where

$$\mathbf{e} = 2(\mathbf{v}_1 \cdot \mathbf{b})\mathbf{v}_1 - (\mathbf{v}_1 \cdot \mathbf{v}_1)\mathbf{b} \tag{5}$$

$$\mathbf{b} = 2\mathbf{v}_1 - \mathbf{v}_2 \tag{6}$$

$$\mathbf{v}_1 = \mathbf{A} \cdot \mathbf{u}^j \tag{7}$$

$$\mathbf{v}_2 = \mathbf{A} \cdot (\mathbf{u}^j + 0.5\Delta t\, \mathbf{v}_1) \tag{8}$$

j is the known time level and j+1 is the unknown time level. Note that all quantities are either at the j level or constructed from it, so the method is truly explicit. Call this method RRK2.

In an earlier paper (Dougherty, 1985) heuristic studies showed that the linear dimensionless advection diffusion equation

$$\frac{\partial u}{\partial t} + \frac{\partial u}{\partial x} - \frac{1}{Pe}\frac{\partial^2 u}{\partial x^2} = 0 \tag{9}$$

could be consistently integrated by RRK2 only if the Courant number were less than or equal to 2,

$$Co = \frac{\Delta t\, v}{\Delta x} \leq 2 \tag{10}$$

where v and Δx are the velocity and spatial mesh increment, respectively.

This limitation was easily explained by a domain of influence argument: if spatial derivatives at node I are computed using information from a compact region that is adjacent to node I, then the two-stage RRK2 method can only propagate information from a limited domain. Consider standard finite differences (or linear Galerkin finite elements) in one dimension; the derivatives at node I include functional information from nodes I−1, I, and I+1. Let us denote by (M,N) the node M and the time level N, and let * and ** represent information at the first and second stage of the RRK2 scheme. The RRK2 method propagates information as indicated in Figure 2; to (I,J+1) from (I,J**) and from (I−1,J*), (I,J*), and (I+1,J*), which in turn propagate from the triads {(I−2,J), (I−1,J), (I,J) }, {(I−1,J), (I,J), (I+1,J) }, and {(I,J), (I+1,J), (I+2,J) }. Thus information can propagate at most 2 elements per time step. Peirce and Prevost (1985) present an almost identical

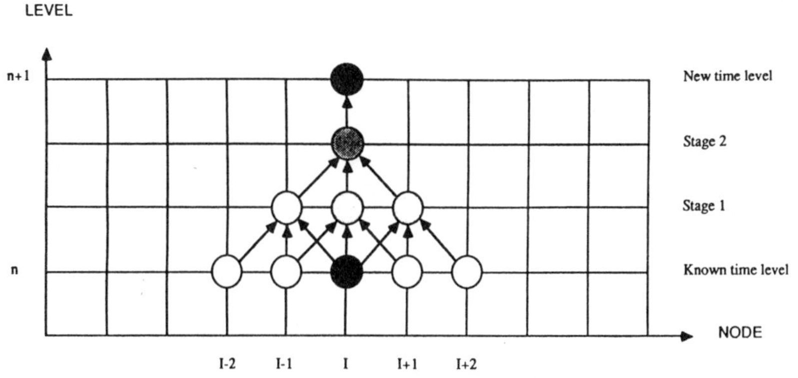

Figure 2. Schematic of the domain of influence argument for the RRK2 stability constraint that Courant number be ≤ 2.

result for the diffusion-free problem. This result says that, for Δt increasing with Δx and v held constant, the RRK2 method for

$$\frac{\partial u}{\partial t} + v\frac{\partial u}{\partial x} = 0 \qquad (11)$$

is actually computed as

$$\frac{\partial u}{\partial t} + 2\frac{\Delta x}{\Delta t}\frac{\partial u}{\partial x} = 0. \qquad (12)$$

Thus the RRK2 method might be called "inconsistent for finite Δt".

When the Courant number is small, RRK2 is consistent (in the usual sense). Peirce and Prevost (1985) show this for the dimensionless form of Equation (11) by substituting Equations (3), (5), (6), (7), and (8) into Equation (4) to obtain

$$\mathbf{u}^{j+1} = \mathbf{u}^{j} + \tau \left\{ 1 + \frac{(0.5\tau)^2 \|\mathbf{u}''^{j}\|^2}{\|\mathbf{u}'^{j} - 0.5\tau\,\mathbf{u}''^{j}\|^2} \right\} \mathbf{u}'^{j} \tag{13}$$

$$+ 0.5\tau^2 \left\{ \frac{\|\mathbf{u}''^{j}\|^2}{\|\mathbf{u}'^{j} - 0.5\tau\,\mathbf{u}''^{j}\|^2} \right\} \mathbf{u}''^{j}$$

where $\|\cdot\|$ is the ℓ_2 or euclidean norm and τ is the dimensionless timestep (Courant number). They next say that Equation (13) becomes

$$\mathbf{u}^{j+1} = \mathbf{u}^{j} + \tau\,\mathbf{u}'^{j} + (0.5\tau)^2\,\mathbf{u}''^{j} + O(\tau^3), \tag{14}$$

and that the truncation error $\mathbf{T}^{j+1}$ obtained by comparing $\mathbf{u}^{j+1}$ with the exact solution at the nodes $\mathbf{U}^{j+1}$ is (using $(1-\beta)\alpha = -0.5$ in their equations)

$$\mathbf{T}^{j+1} = O(\tau^3). \tag{15}$$

Because $\mathbf{T}^{j+1} = O(\tau^3)$ and consistency requires $\mathbf{T} = O(\tau^{k+1})$ with $k \geq 1$, then the RRK2 method is consistent. It is also second-order accurate. Pausing between Equations (13) and (14), we see that this result holds only if

$$\frac{\|0.5\tau\,\mathbf{u}''^{j}\|}{\|\mathbf{u}'^{j}\|} < 1. \tag{16}$$

If this is not satisfied then Equation (14) is not obtained and consistency may be violated.

The notion of "consistency for a finite Δt", advanced earlier, is traditionally identified as a stability constraint (see Roache, 1976, page 47). Therefore, we can say the RRK2 method is conditionally stable when there is a non-zero advection term in the governing equation. Further, the constraint is only half as restrictive as for explicit Euler.

The discovery of stabiility constraints for the RRK2 scheme, while disappointing, does not in and of itself preclude its effective use in transient analysis. If the amount of work required for RRK2 is less than or equal to the work for EE for similar accuracy, etc., then it will be useful. Because each RRK2 step requires two evaluations of the right hand side to EE's one, there must be comparable accuracy for $\Delta t_{RRK2} \geq \Delta t_{EEcr}$, the critical EE timestep.

Liu and Chang (1985) demonstrated the stability of RRK2 for a problem in thermoelasticity with $\Delta t > \Delta t_{EE}$. When one examines their results from the point of view of accuracy, however, the results are disappointing; with $\Delta t_{RRK2} = \Delta t_{EEcr}$ results are similar, but as Δt_{RRK2} goes to $4\Delta t_{EEcr}$ the accuracy wanes considerably, as seen in Figure 3. Thus it appears that RRK2 is marginally useful for transient thermal analysis.

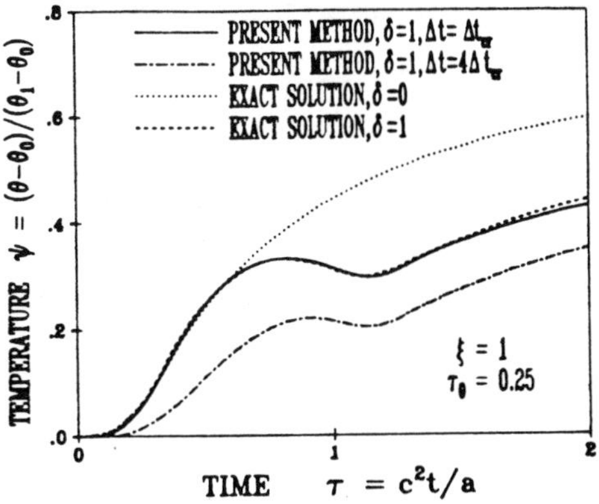

Figure 3. Dimensionless temperature-time plot of results of Sternberg-Chakravorty problem using RRK2 (marked "present method"). Note the relative error of roughly 25% for Δt of 4 times the explicit Euler critical Δt. (From Liu and Chang, 1985.)

I have investigated the use of RRK2 for two transport problems (Dougherty, 1985). The one-dimensional linear advection-diffusion and nonlinear Buckley-Leverett problems were considered, using centered spatial approximations. (It is well known that centered spatial approximations lead to the incorrect admissable solution to the Buckley Leverett but mass is conserved using EE (see Allen and Pinder, 1983).) The results suggested (1) stable solutions are obtained for high Peclet (Reynolds) number if the Courant constraint is satisfied, (2) the speed of the front's advance is slower for RRK2 than expected, and (3) the conventional first-order upwinding scheme for the advection term led to even slower propagation of the front. The Buckley-Leverett solutions also indicated that mass is poorly conserved compared with the EE scheme unless the timestep is a fraction of Δt_{EE}; see Figure 4. RRK2 required 10 times as much work as EE to obtain similar accuracy for this problem.

DISCUSSION

These uninspiring results paint a picture that excludes RRK2 from practical application. The anticipated unconditional stability does not exist for problems with advection terms. Accuracy comparable to the explicit Euler method is obtained by RRK2 with at least as much computational effort as EE. The upwinding tool with which we

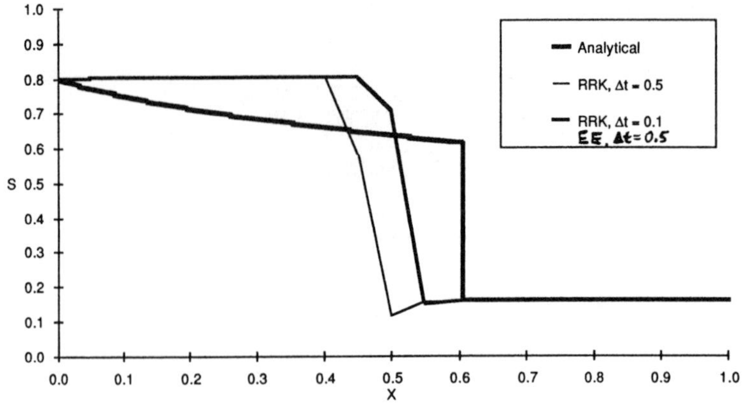

Figure 4. Solutions of Buckley-Leverett problem using orthogonal collocation on Hermite cubics with explicit Euler (EE) and RRK2 time integrators. Note that orthogonal collocation with EE preserves mass although it yields the incorrect solution (Allen and Pinder, 1983). For RRK2 to have same mass balance capability as EE, a time step 1/5 as large can be used, indicating 10 times as much work as EE. (After Dougherty, 1985.)

are familiar does not perform as experience with linear one-step methods have conditioned us.

On the other hand it is true that RRK2 is unconditionally stable for diffusion equations. In addition, these rational Runge Kutta methods are new and relatively undeveloped. Therefore, although the RRK2 scheme presented here may not be useful, future advances may occur to change this conclusion.

REFERENCES

Allen, M.B. and G.F. Pinder (1983) Collocation simulation of multiphase porous-medium flow, Soc. Petrol. Eng. J., 23:135-142.

Dougherty, D.E. (1985) Investigating the use of a rational Runge Kutta method for transport modelling, Adv. Water Resources, 7.

Hairer, E. (1980) Unconditionally stable explicit methods for parabolic equations, Numer. Math., 35:57-68.

Hughes, T.J.R. (1983) Anslysis of transient algorithms with particular reference to stability behavior, Chapter 2, pp. 67-155 in

Computational Methods for Transient Analysis, edited by T. Belytschko and T.J.R. Hughes, Elsevier.

Hughes, T.J.R., K.S. Pister, and R.L. Taylor (1979) Implicit-explicit finite elements in nonlinear transient analysis, Comp. Meth. Appl. Mech. Eng., 17/18:159-182.

Liu, W.K., T. Beytschko, and Y.F. Zhang (1984) Partitioned rational Runge Kutta for parabolic systems, Int. J. Num. Meth. Eng., 20:1581-1597.

Liu, W.K. and H.-G. Chang (1985) A note on numerical analysis of dynamic coupled thermoelasticity, J. Appl. Mech., 52:483-485.

Park, K.C. and C.A. Fellipa (1983) Partitioned analysis of coupled systems, Chapter 3, pp. 157-219 in Computational Methods for Transient Analysis, edited by T. Belytschko and T.J.R. Hughes, Elsevier.

Peirce, A. and J.H. Prevost (1985) On the lack of convergence of unconditionally stable explicit rational Runge-Kutta schemes, to appear, Comp. Meth. Appl. Mech. Engr., 15 pp. manuscript, July.

Roache, P.J. (1976) Computational Fluid Dynamics, Hermosa Press, 446 pp., 2nd edition.

Strang, G. (1986) Introduction to Applied Mathematics, Wellesley-Cambridge Press, 758 pp.

Wambecq, A. (1978) Rational Runge-Kutta methods for solving systems of ordinary differential equations, Computing, 20:333-342.

VI International Conference on Finite Elements in Water Resources, Lisboa, Portugal, June 1986

Mathematical Modelling of Stream Pollution Under Nuclear Accident Conditions

R. Popa
Hydraulics Department, Polytechnical Institute, 77206 Bucharest, Romania

INTRODUCTION

The rapid development of nuclear industries leads to a substantial increase of both theoretical and experimental efforts connected to the study of environmental fate and evolution of radioactive wastes.
A major interest is devoted to the radioactive pollution of water bodies because, directly or indirectly the water represents one of the most usual pathways for radiotoxic contamination of the population. However, relatively few reports deal with the mathematical modelling of radionuclide transport by natural streams. See for example Shih and Gloyna (1967), Armstrong and Gloyna (1968), etc. In all these studies, the attention has been focused on mathematical simulation of radionuclide sorption and release by bottom sediments and aquatic plants, as actual processes coexisting with hydrodynamic transport. A steady state was generally assumed for the flowing water regime.

This paper presents the main features of a mathematical model developed to simulate the radioactive pollution of a large rivers system, under nuclear accident conditions. The hypothesis of a strong, short-time period pollution, but affecting some long river reaches has been accepted. The well-known Saint-Venant equations, governing the unsteady, free surface open channel flows were used in connection with the unsteady, one-dimensional, general equation of mass transfer on rivers. The radionuclide interactions with bottom sediments and plants attached to bed were also included. Some radioactive pollution cases of study, concerning the Danube's river reach belonging to the "Iron Gates" Hydropower Plants (with its major tributaries the Tisa and the Sava rivers) are presented.

MATHEMATICAL MODEL STATEMENT

Because of the assumed hypotheses, a one-dimensional framework in problem statement seems to be the most valuable one.

Governing equations

Unsteady, free-surface flow equations. The model developed by Schaffranek, Baltzer and Goldberg (1981) for simulation of unsteady, free-surface flow in interconnected channels has been adopted. Let be a hypothetical flow network as shown in Figure 1.

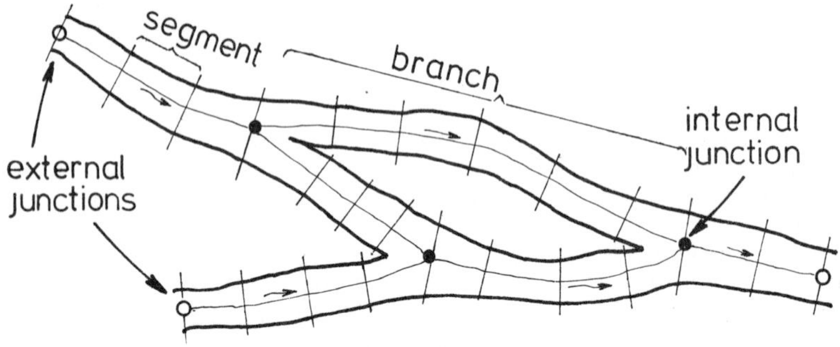

Figure 1. Sketch of hypothetical flow network

The branch is defined as a river reach bounded by two characteristic cross-sections (internal or external junctions). Each branch consists of several segments, bounded by two successive computational cross-sections. It is accepted that the flow along any branch of the network is essentially one-dimensional, obeying the Saint-Venant equations:

$$B\frac{\partial z}{\partial t} + \frac{\partial Q}{\partial x} - q = 0 \tag{1}$$

$$\frac{\partial Q}{\partial t} + \frac{2\beta Q}{A}\frac{\partial Q}{\partial x} - \frac{\beta Q^2}{A^2}\frac{\partial A}{\partial x} + gA\left[\frac{\partial z}{\partial x} + \frac{n^2 Q|Q|}{A^2 R^{4/3}} - D\right] + Vq = 0 \tag{2}$$

where x is the longitudinal distance along stream, t represents the time, z is the water-surface elevation above a horizontal datum, Q is the cross-sectional flow discharge, A represents the cross-sectional area, V denotes the mean velocity in cross section, B is the channel top width, R represents the hydraulic radius, n is the Manning's flow resistance coefficient, β specifies the momentum coeffi-

cient, g is the acceleration of gravity, q denotes the lateral inflow per unit length and D is the lateral inflow contribution to the equation of motion (for lateral inflow normal to the principale flow axis $D = Vq/(gA)$ and the last two terms of Eq. (2) are to be deleted).
The Eqs.(1) and (2) make up a nonlinear, partial-differential, hyperbolic type system of equations which defies an analytical solution. However, these equations can be numerically solved if some adequate initial conditions, boundary conditions (at external junctions) and compatibility conditions (at internal junctions) are provided.

Radionuclide transport and transfer equations. Although the involved processes are much more intricate ones, the general, one-dimensional, unsteady, diffusion-convection equation is accepted as below:

$$\frac{\partial(AC)}{\partial t} - \frac{\partial}{\partial x}\left(AE\frac{\partial C}{\partial x}\right) + \frac{\partial(QC)}{\partial x} = -\lambda CA + \sum_{m=1}^{M} S_m \qquad (3)$$

where C is the radionuclide concentration in river water, expressed as radioactivity (disintegrations per unit time)per unit volume of water; E represents the longitudinal dispersion coefficient; λ is the radioactive decay constant; S_m is the radionuclide exchange rate between the sorbent m and the water, and M is the total number of sorbents interacting with radionuclides.
Following the Shih and Gloyna (1967) approach, the terms S can be detailed for various types of sorbent media. For simplicity, two kind interactions are assumed and some linear reaction functions between radionuclides and sorbents are introduced. The exchange rate of radionuclides between water and bottom sediments is given by

$$S_b = Bk_b(R_b - K_bC) \qquad (4)$$

in which k_b represents a mass-transfer coefficient (having as dimension 1 per unit time); R_b is the number of radionuclides contained by bottom sediment on unit area of bed surface, at a given time-moment, and K_b denotes the equilibrium distribution coefficient of radionuclides in bottom sediments (having as dimension radioactivity per unit area of bed surface/radioactivity per unit volume of water).

The time-variation of radionuclide number from river bed is described by the following partial-differential equation:

$$\frac{\partial R_b}{\partial t} = k_b(K_bC - R_b) - \lambda R_b \qquad (5)$$

The interactions with aquatic plants are simulated by similar relations as:

$$S_p = BM_p k_p (C_p - K_p C) \quad (6) \;; \quad \frac{\partial C_p}{\partial t} = k_p (K_p C - C_p) - \lambda C_p \quad (7)$$

where M_p denotes the weight of plants on unit area of river bed surface; k_p is a radionuclide mass-transfer coefficient between water and plants; C_p represents the radioactive concentration per unit weight of biomass, and K_p is the equilibrium distribution coefficient for radionuclides associated with aquatic plants.
By using the Eqs.(4) and (6), Eq.(3) becomes:

$$\frac{\partial (AC)}{\partial t} - \frac{\partial}{\partial x}\left(AE\frac{\partial C}{\partial x}\right) + \frac{\partial (QC)}{\partial x} = -\lambda CA + Bk_b(R_b - K_b C) +$$

$$+ BM_p k_p (C_p - K_p C) \quad (8)$$

This equation together with Eqs.(5) and (7) describe radionuclides transport by natural streams and their interactions with some parts of environment. A numerical solution can be also derived if the necessary initial, boundary and compatibility at junctions conditions are specified.
Thus, the whole mathematical model will be obtained by coupling the Eqs.(1),(2),(8),(5) and (7).

Finite-difference schemes

Finite-difference scheme for Saint-Venant equations. On a space-time grid as in Figure 2, the computational cross-sections i and i+1 delimit the river segment Δx_i, while j and j+1 represent two computational time-levels.

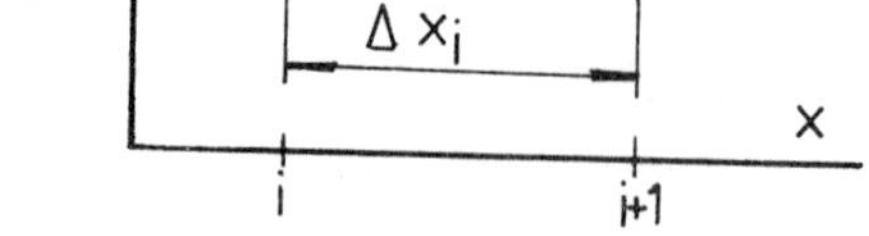

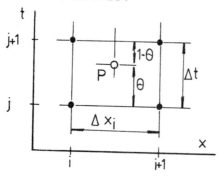

Figure 2. Space-time grid for Saint-Venant equations

The finite-difference forms of Eqs.(1) and (2) are written for the P point, using the values of various quantities from the four neighbouring grid-points. The time derivatives are approximated by centered both in space and time, finite-difference expressions. For the spatial derivatives, some centered in space and weighted in time finite-difference relations are used.

These relations are as follows:

$$\frac{\partial f(P)}{\partial t} = \frac{1}{2\Delta t}(f_{i+1}^{j+1}+f_i^{j+1}-f_{i+1}^{j}-f_i^{j})$$
$$\frac{\partial f(P)}{\partial x} = \frac{1}{\Delta x_i}\left[\theta(f_{i+1}^{j+1}-f_i^{j+1})+(1-\theta)(f_{i+1}^{j}-f_i^{j})\right] ; \quad f \equiv z,Q \tag{9}$$

The nonderivative terms are approximated by:

$$f(P) = \frac{1}{2}\left[\chi(f_{i+1}^{j+1}+f_i^{j+1})+(1-\chi)(f_{i+1}^{j}+f_i^{j})\right] ; \quad f \equiv A,B,\ldots \tag{10}$$

The values of two weighting factors θ and χ decide the type of finite-difference scheme. If $0.5 \leqslant \theta \leqslant 1$, an unconditionally stable, implicit scheme is derived. If $\chi \neq 0$, the functional f(P) is evaluated between the two adjacent time-levels and an iterative procedure must be used. A notation as $\tilde{f}(P)$ denotes the functional value given by Eq.(10), where for f^{j+1} terms, the values from previous iteration on the same time-step Δt were used.
By defining a two-component vector of state at the i-th cross-section as

$$S_i^{j+1} = \begin{bmatrix} z_i^{j+1} \\ Q_i^{j+1} \end{bmatrix} ,$$

using the relations (9) and (10) in Eqs.(1) and (2), and after some computations, the matriceal transformation equation for the i-th segment is obtained as

$$S_{i+1}^{j+1} = U_i S_i^{j+1} + u_i \tag{11}$$

where the transformation matrices and their components are:

$$U_i = \begin{bmatrix} 1 & \zeta_i \\ \gamma_i & 1 \end{bmatrix}^{-1} \begin{bmatrix} 1 & -\omega_i \\ -\gamma_i & 1 \end{bmatrix} ; \quad u_i = \begin{bmatrix} 1 & \zeta_i \\ \gamma_i & 1 \end{bmatrix}^{-1} \begin{bmatrix} \varepsilon_i \\ \delta_i \end{bmatrix}$$

$$\gamma_i = \frac{\Delta x_i}{2\theta\Delta t}\tilde{B} ; \quad \delta_i = \frac{\Delta x_i}{\theta}q_i - \frac{1-\theta}{\theta}(Q_{i+1}^{j}-Q_i^{j})+\gamma_i(z_{i+1}^{j}+z_i^{j}) ;$$

$$\zeta_i = \lambda_i+\sigma_i+\mu_i ; \quad \omega_i = \lambda_i+\sigma_i-\mu_i ; \quad \lambda_i = \frac{\Delta x_i}{2g\theta\Delta t}\frac{1}{\tilde{A}} ; \tag{12}$$

$$\sigma_i = \frac{\chi n_i^2 \Delta x_i}{2\theta}\frac{|\tilde{Q}|}{(\tilde{A}R^{2/3})^2} ; \quad \mu_i = \frac{2\beta}{g}\left(\frac{\tilde{Q}}{A^2}\right) ;$$

$$\varepsilon_i = \left(\lambda_i-\sigma_i\frac{1-\chi}{\chi}\right)(Q_{i+1}^{j}+Q_i^{j})-\mu_i\frac{1-\theta}{\theta}(Q_{i+1}^{j}-Q_i^{j})-\frac{1-\theta}{\theta}(z_{i+1}^{j}-z_i^{j})+\frac{\beta}{g\theta}\left(\frac{\tilde{Q}^2}{A^3}\right)(A_{i+1}^{j+1}-A_i^{j+1})$$

All these expressions contain the values of dependent variables at previous time-level, j, and the values $\tilde{f}(P)$ only.
A branch transformation equation is derived through successive application of Eq.(11) for all segments of the branch. If L segments are involved, one obtains:

$$S_L^{j+1} = U\, S_1^{j+1} + u \qquad (13)$$

and

$$U = U_{L-1}U_{L-2}\ldots U_1 \; ; \quad u = u_{L-1}+U_{L-1}(u_{L-2}+U_{L-2}(u_{L-3}+ \ldots +U_3(u_2+U_2u_1)\ldots)$$

These equations relate the unknown (dependent variables z^{j+1}, Q^{j+1}) at the two boundary cross-sections 1 and L of the branch. For a simple, three-branches flow system as is shown in Figure 3, three matriceal (six algebraic) equations as Eq.(13) and having twelve unknown z, Q values, are derived. Three new equations are provided by the boundary conditions at external junctions 1, M and N, as follows

$$Q_1^{j+1} = Q_1^*(t^{j+1}); \; z_M^{j+1} = z_M^*(t^{j+1}); \; z_N^{j+1} = z_N^*(t^{j+1}) \qquad (14)$$

(for this example). At internal junctions, the compatibility conditions refer to the water-surface elevation equality on all joined branches and to discharge continuity, resulting in three additional equations as:

$$z_J^{j+1} = z_{J+1}^{j+1}; \quad z_J^{j+1} = z_{M+1}^{j+1}; \quad Q_J^{j+1} = Q_{J+1}^{j+1}+Q_{M+1}^{j+1} \qquad (15)$$

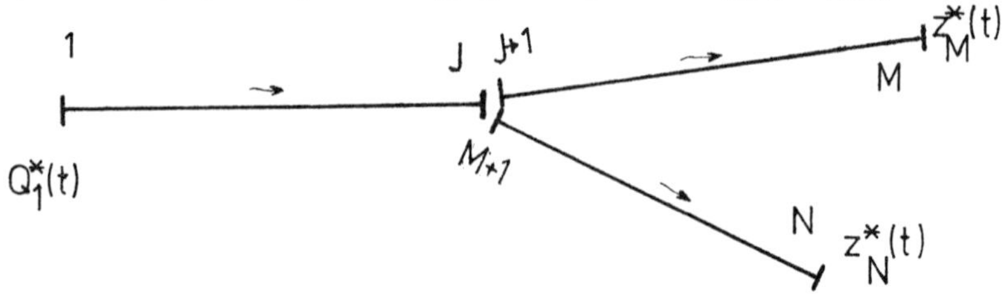

Figure 3. Simple, three-branches network

Finally, the system consisting of the three branch matriceal equations as Eq.(13), and Eqs.(14) and (15) is solved by Gaussian elimination using maximum pivot strategy, to furnish the z^{j+1} and Q^{j+1} values at the six cross-sections bounding the three branches of flow network. For a certain time-step, an iterative computation is to be performed if $\chi \neq o$. At first iteration, the f values are computed with $f^{j+1} = f^j$ (known values) and thereafter, the values derived in last iteration are used. The z, Q values at internal cross-sections for all branches are then obtained by successive application of Eq.(11). The procedure starts with the initial conditions (at time-level t^o), which are to be specified according to the particular nature of each analyzed problem.

Finite-difference scheme for radionuclide transport and transfer equations. These equations are approximated using a computational space-time grid with unequal spatial steps, Δx, and staggered in time by $\Delta t/2$ in respect to the space-time grid for Saint-Venant equations, as in Figure 4.

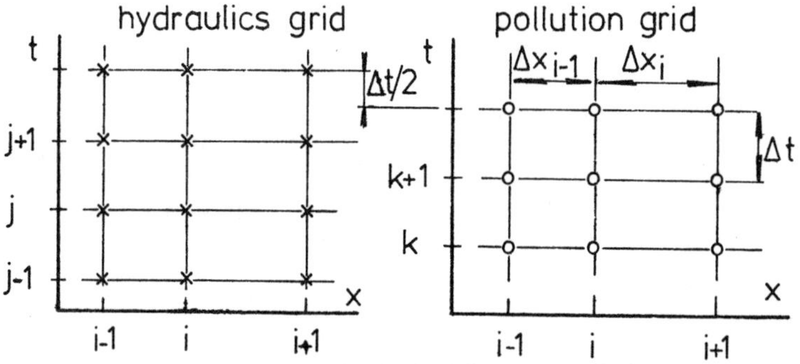

Figure 4. Computational space-time grids for coupled solving procedure

The partial derivatives from Eq.(8) are evaluated for the grid-point x_i, as (see Harleman, Lee and Hall (1968)):

$$\frac{\partial(AC)}{\partial t} = A_i^j(C_i^{k+1}-C_i^k)/\Delta t$$

$$\frac{\partial(QC)}{\partial x} = \frac{1}{2\Delta_{i-1,i}}(Q_{i+1}^j C_{i+1}^{k+1}-Q_{i-1}^j C_{i-1}^{k+1}+Q_{i+1}^j C_{i+1}^k-Q_{i-1}^j C_{i-1}^k)$$

$$(16)$$

$$\frac{\partial}{\partial x}(AE\frac{\partial C}{\partial x}) = \frac{1}{2\Delta_{i-1,i}}\left\{\frac{1}{\Delta x_i}\left[(AE)_{i+1}^j+(AE)_i^j\right](C_{i+1}^{k+1}-C_i^{k+1}+\right.$$

$$\left.+C_{i+1}^k-C_i^k)-\frac{1}{\Delta x_{i-1}}\left[(AE)_i^j+(AE)_{i-1}^j\right](C_i^{k+1}-C_{i-1}^{k+1}+C_i^k-C_{i-1}^k)\right\}$$

where $\Delta_{i-1,i}=\Delta x_{i-1}+\Delta x_i$.

The nonderivative terms in Eqs.(8),(5) and (7) are assumed as

$$f = (f_i^{k+1}+f_i^k)/2; \quad f \equiv C, R_b, C_p \qquad (17)$$

while the time derivatives in Eqs.(5) and (7) are expressed by

$$\frac{\partial f}{\partial t} = (f^{k+1}-f^k)/\Delta t \; ; \quad f \equiv R_b, C_p \qquad (18)$$

Substituting these relations in Eqs.(8),(5) and (7),

an equation as

$$a_i C_{i-1}^{k+1} + b_i C_i^{k+1} + c_i C_{i+1}^{k+1} = d_i \qquad (19)$$

is derived for each grid-point x_i. The coefficients a_i to d_i are given by:

$$a_i = -(\alpha_i^- + Q_{i-1}^j)/\Delta_{i-1,i} \; ; \quad b_i = 2A_i^j/\Delta t\varphi + \eta_i ;$$

$$c_i = -(\alpha_i^+ - Q_{i+1}^j)/\Delta_{i-1,i} \; ; \quad d_i = -a_i C_{i-1}^k + b_i^* C_i^k - c_i C_{i+1}^k + d_i^* ;$$

$$\alpha_i^- = \frac{1}{\Delta x_{i-1}}\left[(AE)_i^j + (AE)_{i-1}^j\right] ; \quad \alpha_i^+ = \frac{1}{\Delta x_i}\left[(AE)_{i+1}^j + (AE)_i^j\right] ; \qquad (2o)$$

$$\varphi = 1 + \Delta t\lambda/2 \; ; \quad \eta_i = B_i^j \varphi(\psi_i K_{b_i} + \varrho_i K_{p_i}) + (\alpha_i^- + \alpha_i^+)/\Delta_{i-1,i}$$

$$\psi_i = k_{b_i}/(\varphi + \Delta t k_{b_i}/2) \; ; \quad \varrho_i = M_{p_i} k_{p_i}/(\varphi + \Delta t k_{p_i}/2) \; ;$$

$$b_i^* = 2A_i^j(\varphi + \lambda\Delta t)/\Delta t - \eta_i ; \quad d_i^* = B_i^j(\psi_i R_{b_i}^k + \varrho_i C_{p_i}^k)$$

The remainder unknowns of the problem can be expressed as:

$$R_{b_i}^{k+1} = \frac{\frac{\Delta t}{2}\left[k_{b_i} K_{b_i}(C_i^{k+1} + C_i^k) - R_{b_i}^k(k_{b_i} + \lambda)\right]}{1 + \Delta t(k_{b_i} + \lambda)/2}$$

$$C_{p_i}^{k+1} = \frac{\frac{\Delta t}{2}\left[k_{p_i} K_{p_i}(C_i^{k+1} + C_i^k) - C_{p_i}^k(k_{p_i} + \lambda)\right]}{1 + \Delta t(k_{p_i} + \lambda)/2} \qquad (21)$$

The boundary conditions to be imposed depend on the place of each branch into the flow network. A very simple, but physically acceptable downstream boundary condition is provided by neglecting the dispersion term and using a backward approximation of spatial derivative $\partial(QC)/\partial x$ in Eq.(8). The upstream boundary condition takes into account the dilution effect at junctions of polluted and unpolluted branches by a mass concentration balance equation, while for all branches issuing from a junction, the same radioactive concentration is to be applied. Some other particular situations lead to different ending conditions. A tridiagonal system of equations as Eq. (19) is derived for each branch, and solved by Thomas algorithm. The hydraulic and pollution computations are alternatively performed, on all time-steps of the analyzed period.

NUMERICAL SIMULATIONS

A Danube sector extended between km.1299 (at upstream end) and km.845 (at downstream end) was modelled as shown in Figure 5.

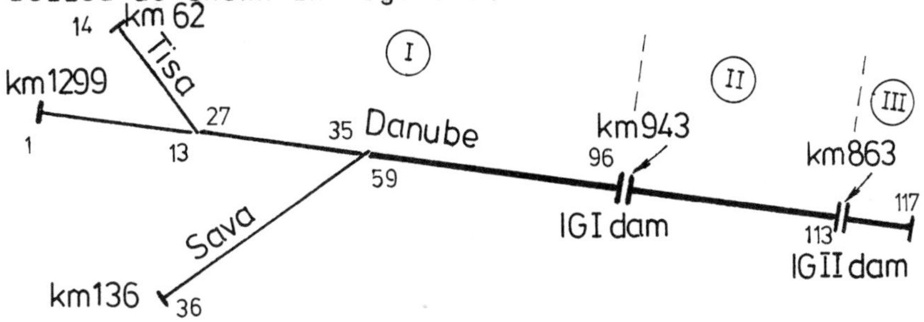

Figure 5. Sketch of modelled Danube sector

The three characteristic river reaches are defined by the two dams placed at km.943 ("Iron Gates I" dam) and km.863 ("Iron Gates II" dam). The upstream reach includes two major tributaries, the Tisa and the Sava rivers. Because of on-peak operation of "Iron Gates I" Hydropower Plant, unsteady flows are induced along both the upstream and downstream river reaches. A number of 117 computational cross-sections were selected and geometrical and morphological input data were prepared according to computational needs. A model calibration has been performed using some adequate stage-discharge records.
For example, a study case run for the multiannual average discharges (i.e. 3,2oo m^3/s at km.1299, 8oo m^3/s at km.62 and 12oo m^3/s at km.136, on the Danube Tisa and Sava rivers, respectively) is briefly described.

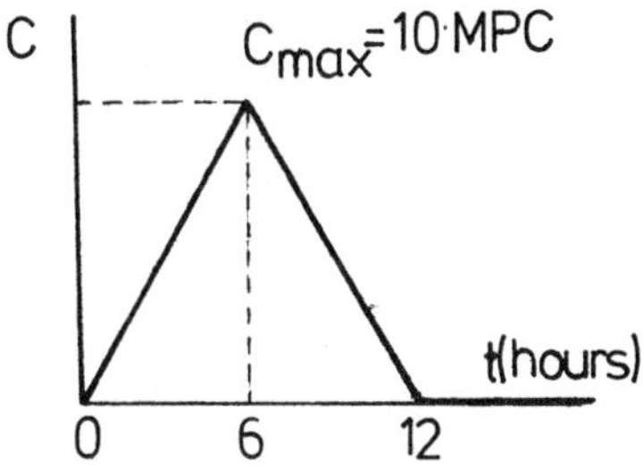

Figure 6. Input radio active concentration in water

A radioactive pollution input as in Figure 6 was assumed at section 1, for a mixture of two radionuclide species: 85-Sr radioisotope (maximum permissible concentration, MPC = $3.10^3 \mu Ci/m^3$, smaller interaction with bottom sediments, K_b = 0,24 m, k_b = $2,8\ 10^{-5} s^{-1}$), and 134-Cs radioisotope (MPC = $10^3 \mu Ci/m^3$, strong interaction with bottom sediment, K_b = 24 m). Resulted time-variation of radioactive concentration in water at "Iron Gates I" dam site is presented in Figure 7. Many details on this example and some others cases of study are included in Popa (1985)

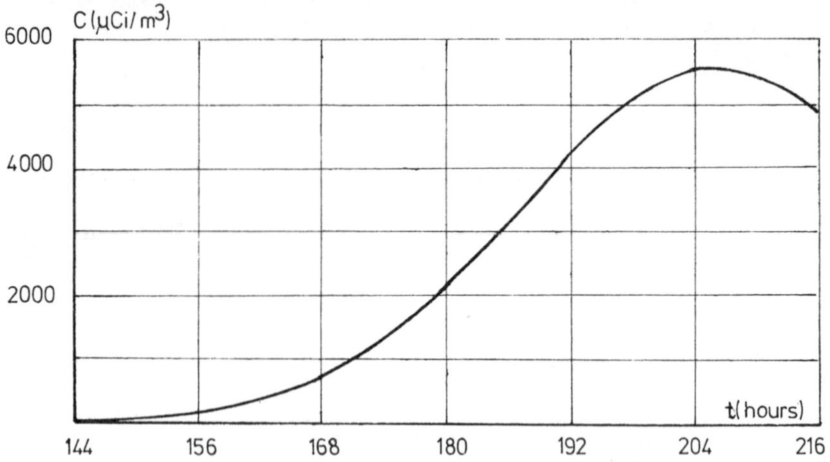

Figure 7. Time-variation of radioactive concentration in water, at IG I dam site

Acknowledgments. Financial support of the International Atomic Energy Agency, Vienna (under research contract no.326o/R1/RB) has made this study possible. Appreciation is due to Dr.M.Miloradov of "Iaroslav Cerni" Institute, Beograd.

REFERENCES

Armstrong, N.E. and Gloyna, E.F. (1968) Radioactivity transport in water - Numerical solutions of radionuclide transport equations and role of plants in Sr-85 transport, Techn.Rep.23, Contr.AT(11-1)-49o, Atomic Energy Comm., The Univ.of Texas

Harleman, D.R., Lee, C.H. and Hall, L.C. (1968) Numerical studies of unsteady dispersion in estuaries ASCE, J.Sanit.Eng.Div., 94, no.SA 5, pp.897-911

Popa, R. (1985) The mathematical modelling of man made radionuclides transfer and transport on the Danube river, in the nuclear accident conditions, Progr.Rep., Res.Contr.no.326o/R1/RB, IAEA, Vienna

Schaffranek, R.W., Baltzer, R.A. and Goldberg, D.E. (1981) A model for simulation of flow in singular and interconnected channels, TWI 7, C3, U.S.Geol. Survey

Shih, G.S. and Gloyna, E.F. (1967) Radioactivity transport in water - Mathematical model for the transport of radionuclides, Techn.Rep.12, Contr. AT(11-1)-49o, Atomic Energy Comm., The Univ.of Texas

VI International Conference on Finite Elements in Water Resources, Lisboa, Portugal, June 1986

A Comparison of Transport Simulations in Two and Three Dimensions Using Alternating Direction Galerkin Techniques

R.D. Burnett, E.O. Frind
Department of Earth Sciences, University of Waterloo, Waterloo, Ontario, Canada, N2L 3G1

ABSTRACT

A set of numerical models based on the Alternating Direction Galerkin technique and consisting of a newly developed 3D model, a 2D vertical cross-section model and a 2D vertically-integrated horizontal plane model, are applied to the simulation of contaminant plumes in a groundwater system. A comparison of the simulations demonstrates some characteristics inherent in 2D transport models that can lead to serious errors in the simulation or the interpretation of the results. The error in the vertical cross-sectional simulation stemming from the omission of the third dimension is found to be significant under many conditions. An assumption of negligible transverse mass loss along the central plane of the plume is therefore rarely justified. This type of error is always conservative, however, as it yields high estimates of concentration. The vertically-integrated horizontal plane model, on the other hand, yields results that are correct in preserving mass, but the average values produced can differ drastically from actual peak concentrations in the aquifer. Because peak concentrations are always higher than averages, an actual plume will extend farther than predicted by a vertically-averaged model.

INTRODUCTION

It is recognized that transport of contaminants in groundwater systems is an inherently three-dimensional process because dispersion acts in all directions. At present, however, most simulations of transport are done in two dimensions, because 3D models are either unavailable or too costly, both in terms of computing and data requirements.

To provide affordable tools for 3D as well as 2D transport simulations, the Principal Direction and Alternating Direction Galerkin techniques were developed. These techniques combine the efficiency of the conventional Alternating Direction technique (Peaceman, 1977) with the convenience of finite elements, and can be formulated in two dimensions (Frind, 1982; Frind and Pinder, 1982; Daus and Frind, 1985) and three dimensions (Frind, 1984; Burnett, 1985). We will use the

Alternating Direction Galerkin models to demonstrate the effect of reducing a 3D system to two dimensions, as is commonly done, either by neglecting the transverse horizontal direction in a vertical cross-sectional model, or by integrating over the vertical to obtain an areal plane model. The effect of neglecting the third dimension in a large thermal plume has been investigated by Frind *et al.* (1985).

GOVERNING EQUATIONS

The general governing equation for transport of a non-reactive, dilute solute in a saturated porous medium is:

$$\frac{\partial u}{\partial t} + \nabla \cdot (u\vec{v}) - \nabla \cdot ([D] \cdot \nabla u) = 0 \tag{1}$$

where u is the mass concentration of the solute, $\vec{v}$ is the average linear velocity vector of the solute, and $[D]$ is the hydrodynamic dispersion tensor (Pinder and Gray, 1977, p. 142). A point source term can be added to Equation 1 to represent internal sources or sinks. The term $\nabla \cdot (u\vec{v})$ is expanded to yield $\vec{v} \cdot \nabla u + u \nabla \cdot \vec{v}$. If the mass of water is conserved in each elemental volume, as in three-dimensional and two-dimensional vertical section modelling, the net divergence of the velocity field is zero and the second term can be neglected. In vertically integrated areal plane modelling, the areal recharge flux causes a divergence of the velocity field; in that case the second term must be retained.

In order to use the classical definition of the dispersion tensor (Bear, 1972) without resorting to the fully general anisotropic form with 36 components, we will assume that there exist a longitudinal dispersivity α_L that is independent of direction and two transverse dispersivities α_{TH} (horizontal) and α_{TV} (vertical). Accordingly, we define the dispersion coefficients for the 3D system as:

$$D_{xx} = \alpha_L \frac{v_x^2}{\bar{v}} + \alpha_{TH} \frac{v_y^2}{\bar{v}} + \alpha_{TV} \frac{v_z^2}{\bar{v}} + D^* \tag{2a}$$

$$D_{yy} = \alpha_{TH} \frac{v_x^2}{\bar{v}} + \alpha_L \frac{v_y^2}{\bar{v}} + \alpha_{TV} \frac{v_z^2}{\bar{v}} + D^* \tag{2b}$$

$$D_{zz} = \alpha_{TV} \frac{v_x^2}{\bar{v}} + \alpha_{TV} \frac{v_y^2}{\bar{v}} + \alpha_L \frac{v_z^2}{\bar{v}} + D^* \tag{2c}$$

$$D_{yx} = D_{xy} = (\alpha_L - \alpha_{TH}) \frac{v_x v_y}{\bar{v}} \tag{2d}$$

$$D_{zx} = D_{xz} = (\alpha_L - \alpha_{TV}) \frac{v_x v_z}{\bar{v}} \tag{2e}$$

$$D_{zy} = D_{yz} = (\alpha_L - \alpha_{TV}) \frac{v_y v_z}{\bar{v}} \tag{2f}$$

where D^* is the effective molecular diffusion coefficient, v_x, v_y, v_z are the velocity components of $\vec{v}$, and $\bar{v} = \sqrt{v_x^2 + v_y^2 + v_z^2}$.

The governing equation for the 3D model thus expands to:

$$\frac{\partial}{\partial x}\left(D_{xx}\frac{\partial u}{\partial x}\right) - v_x\frac{\partial u}{\partial x} + \frac{\partial}{\partial y}\left(D_{yx}\frac{\partial u}{\partial x}\right) + \frac{\partial}{\partial z}\left(D_{zx}\frac{\partial u}{\partial x}\right)$$

$$+ \frac{\partial}{\partial x}\left(D_{xy}\frac{\partial u}{\partial y}\right) + \frac{\partial}{\partial y}\left(D_{yy}\frac{\partial u}{\partial y}\right) - v_y\frac{\partial u}{\partial y} + \frac{\partial}{\partial z}\left(D_{zy}\frac{\partial u}{\partial y}\right)$$

$$+ \frac{\partial}{\partial x}\left(D_{xz}\frac{\partial u}{\partial z}\right) + \frac{\partial}{\partial y}\left(D_{yz}\frac{\partial u}{\partial z}\right) + \frac{\partial}{\partial z}\left(D_{zz}\frac{\partial u}{\partial z}\right) - v_z\frac{\partial u}{\partial z} = \frac{\partial u}{\partial t} \quad (3)$$

To obtain the 2D vertical model, we assume a slice of medium having unit thickness and zero velocity in the y-direction. The governing equation becomes:

$$\frac{\partial}{\partial x}\left(D_{xx}\frac{\partial u}{\partial x}\right) - v_x\frac{\partial u}{\partial x} + \frac{\partial}{\partial z}\left(D_{zx}\frac{\partial u}{\partial x}\right)$$

$$+ \frac{\partial}{\partial x}\left(D_{xz}\frac{\partial u}{\partial z}\right) + \frac{\partial}{\partial z}\left(D_{zz}\frac{\partial u}{\partial z}\right) - v_z\frac{\partial u}{\partial z} = \frac{\partial u}{\partial t} \quad (4)$$

where the dispersion coefficients are defined as:

$$D_{xx} = \alpha_L\frac{v_x^2}{\bar{v}} + \alpha_{TV}\frac{v_z^2}{\bar{v}} + D^* \quad (5a)$$

$$D_{zz} = \alpha_{TV}\frac{v_x^2}{\bar{v}} + \alpha_L\frac{v_z^2}{\bar{v}} + D^* \quad (5b)$$

$$D_{xz} = D_{zx} = (\alpha_L - \alpha_{TV})\frac{v_x v_z}{\bar{v}} \quad (5c)$$

For the horizontal plane model, we assume an aquifer of thickness $l = l(x,y)$ and integrate Equation 1 vertically. The divergence of the velocity field is retained. The resulting governing equation is:

$$\frac{\partial}{\partial x}\left(D_{xx}l\frac{\partial u}{\partial x}\right) - v_x l\frac{\partial u}{\partial x} - ul\frac{\partial v_x}{\partial x} + \frac{\partial}{\partial y}\left(D_{yx}l\frac{\partial u}{\partial x}\right)$$

$$+ \frac{\partial}{\partial x}\left(D_{xy}l\frac{\partial u}{\partial y}\right) + \frac{\partial}{\partial y}\left(D_{yy}l\frac{\partial u}{\partial y}\right) - v_y l\frac{\partial u}{\partial y} - ul\frac{\partial v_y}{\partial y}$$

$$= \frac{\partial u}{\partial t} + \frac{q_z u_2}{\theta}\Big|_{z_2} - \frac{q_z u_1}{\theta}\Big|_{z_1} \quad (6)$$

where $\frac{q_z u_1}{\theta}$ and $\frac{q_z u_2}{\theta}$ are the mass fluxes across the upper and lower boundaries z_1 and z_2 respectively, with θ being the porosity. The dispersion coefficients are now defined as:

$$D_{xx} = \alpha_L\frac{v_x^2}{\bar{v}} + \alpha_{TH}\frac{v_y^2}{\bar{v}} + D^* \quad (7a)$$

$$D_{yy} = \alpha_{TH}\frac{v_x^2}{\bar{v}} + \alpha_L\frac{v_y^2}{\bar{v}} + D^* \tag{7b}$$

$$D_{xy} = D_{yx} = (\alpha_L - \alpha_{TH})\frac{v_x v_y}{\bar{v}} \tag{7c}$$

The boundary conditions for Equation 1 can be of the Dirichlet type

$$u = u_0 \quad \text{on} \quad \Gamma_1 \tag{8}$$

where u_0 is a specified concentration, or of the Cauchy type

$$-D_{\vec{n}}\frac{\partial u}{\partial \vec{n}} + v_{\vec{n}}u = \frac{q_0 u_0}{\theta} \quad \text{on} \quad \Gamma_3 \tag{9}$$

where the left-hand side contains the dispersive and advective mass fluxes normal to the boundary, q_0 is a known Darcy flux normal to the boundary, Γ_1 and Γ_3 are parts of the boundary, and $\vec{n}$ is the inward unit normal vector at the boundary. The Cauchy boundary degenerates to a Neumann boundary when the normal flux $q_0 = 0$.

ALTERNATING DIRECTION GALERKIN SCHEME FOR THREE DIMENSIONS

To formulate the numerical scheme, we first decouple the coordinate directions by setting up an alternating direction time stepping algorithm. We then approximate the spatial derivatives by Galerkin finite elements, using special basis functions that maintain the decoupling.

Writing the left-hand side of Equation 3 in operator notation and approximating the right-hand side by finite differences, we obtain:

$$(L_{xx} + L_{yx} + L_{zx} + L_{xy} + L_{yy} + L_{zy} + L_{xz} + L_{yz} + L_{zz})u + F = \frac{u^{n+1} - u^n}{\Delta t} \tag{10}$$

where subscripts indicate spatial dependence, superscripts indicate the time level, and $\Delta t = t^{n+1} - t^n$.

The corresponding 2D alternating direction scheme (Daus and Frind, 1985) naturally yields a time-centred second-order accurate and unconditionally stable numerical algorithm. The 3D scheme is not as straightforward, unfortunately, and several approaches are possible. Second-order accuracy and unconditional stability are not naturally obtained. Frind (1984) proposed the 'Centred' scheme, which achieves second-order accuracy in time through the use of time weighting. For the 3D scheme, the time step Δt in Equation 10 is split into three partial time steps, each representing one of the spatial dimensions implicitly and the other two explicitly. The corresponding equations are:

<u>Step 1</u>

$$\frac{3}{2}(L_{xx} + L_{yx} + L_{zx})u^{n+1/3} - \frac{1}{2}(L_{xx} + L_{yx} + L_{zx})u^n + (L_{xy} + L_{yy} + L_{zy})u^n + (L_{xz} + L_{yz} + L_{zz})u^n + F = \frac{u^{n+1/3} - u^n}{\Delta t/3} \tag{11a}$$

Step 2 $$(L_{xx} + L_{yx} + L_{zx})u^{n+1/3} + \frac{3}{2}(L_{xy} + L_{yy} + L_{zy})u^{n+2/3}$$
$$- \frac{1}{2}(L_{xy} + L_{yy} + L_{zy})u^{n+1/3} + (L_{xz} + L_{yz} + L_{zz})u^{n+1/3}$$
$$+ F = \frac{u^{n+2/3} - u^{n+1/3}}{\Delta t/3} \quad (11b)$$

Step 3 $$(L_{xx} + L_{yx} + L_{zx})u^{n+2/3} + (L_{xy} + L_{yy} + L_{zy})u^{n+2/3}$$
$$+ \frac{3}{2}(L_{xz} + L_{yz} + L_{zz})u^{n+1} - \frac{1}{2}(L_{xz} + L_{yz} + L_{zz})u^{n+2/3}$$
$$+ F = \frac{u^{n+1} - u^{n+2/3}}{\Delta t/3} \quad (11c)$$

By weighting the implicit term at each partial step with the corresponding term at the explicit level, each term in the equation becomes, on average over the three steps, exactly centred in time at $n+1/2$. The scheme is therefore second-order accurate in time.

The solution domain is discretized into prismatic elements that have quadrilateral sides and that join at the nodes. The element sides can be deformed and follow curvilinear coordinates which will in general be colinear with the principal directions of hydraulic conductivity of the material. The resulting distortion of the prisms is assumed to be small so that a coordinate transformation is unnecessary and the element sides can be represented by average side lengths.

The Galerkin trial solutions for each of the three steps are:

Step 1 $$u \approx \hat{u} = \sum_{j=1}^{N} u_j(t)\, w_j(x) \quad (12a)$$

Step 2 $$u \approx \hat{u} = \sum_{j=1}^{N} u_j(t)\, w_j(y) \quad (12b)$$

Step 3 $$u \approx \hat{u} = \sum_{j=1}^{N} u_j(t)\, w_j(z) \quad (12c)$$

where N is the number of nodes in the grid and $u_j(t)$ are the nodal values of u, with j being a nodal index that increases in the implicit direction at each step. The three sets of basis functions $w_j(x)$, $w_j(y)$, $w_j(z)$ are elementwise linear in the implicit direction and constant halfway across the element in the explicit directions (Burnett, 1985) in order to maintain spatial decoupling.

The Galerkin equations are obtained by substituting the trial solutions (12) into the alternating direction equations (11). The substitution is done for the time derivative as well as the space derivatives, giving a 'consistent' time derivative formulation. The residual is minimized by taking the product of the resulting equations with the basis functions and setting it to zero globally. This results in three sets of triple integral equations, which are first integrated in their respective explicit directions to eliminate two of the spatial dimensions from each equation. The third integration is done by parts in the implicit direction to eliminate the second-derivative terms, yielding a natural boundary term. After rearrangement, three sets of N equations in N unknowns are obtained. In matrix form, these equations are:

<u>Step 1</u>
$$\left(\frac{3}{2}[R_x]+[R_t]\right)\{u\}^{n+1/3} = \left(\frac{1}{2}[R_x]+[R_t]\right)\{u\}^{n}$$
$$+\frac{3}{2}\{F_{yx}\}^{n+1/3}+\frac{3}{2}\{F_{zx}\}^{n+1/3}-\frac{1}{2}\{F_{yx}\}^{n}-\frac{1}{2}\{F_{zx}\}^{n}$$
$$+\{F_{xy}\}^{n}+\{F_{yy}\}^{n}+\{F_{zy}\}^{n}+\{F_{xz}\}^{n}$$
$$+\{F_{yz}\}^{n}+\{F_{zz}\}^{n}+\{F_{s}\}+\{F_{a}\} \qquad (13a)$$

<u>Step 2</u>
$$\left(\frac{3}{2}[R_y]+[R_t]\right)\{u\}^{n+2/3} = \left(\frac{1}{2}[R_y]+[R_t]\right)\{u\}^{n+1/3}$$
$$+\{F_{xx}\}^{n+1/3}+\{F_{yx}\}^{n+1/3}+\{F_{zx}\}^{n+1/3}+\frac{3}{2}\{F_{xy}\}^{n+2/3}$$
$$+\frac{3}{2}\{F_{zy}\}^{n+2/3}-\frac{1}{2}\{F_{xy}\}^{n+1/3}-\frac{1}{2}\{F_{zy}\}^{n+1/3}+\{F_{xz}\}^{n+1/3}$$
$$+\{F_{yz}\}^{n+1/3}+\{F_{zz}\}^{n+1/3}+\{F_{s}\}+\{F_{b}\} \qquad (13b)$$

<u>Step 3</u>
$$\left(\frac{3}{2}[R_z]+[R_t]\right)\{u\}^{n+1} = \left(\frac{1}{2}[R_z]+[R_t]\right)\{u\}^{n+2/3}$$
$$+\{F_{xx}\}^{n+2/3}+\{F_{yx}\}^{n+2/3}+\{F_{zx}\}^{n+2/3}+\{F_{xy}\}^{n+2/3}+$$
$$+\{F_{yy}\}^{n+2/3}+\{F_{zy}\}^{n+2/3}+\frac{3}{2}\{F_{xz}\}^{n+1}+\{F_{yz}\}^{n+1}$$
$$-\frac{1}{2}\{F_{xz}\}^{n+2/3}-\frac{1}{2}\{F_{yz}\}^{n+2/3}+\{F_{s}\}+\{F_{c}\} \qquad (13c)$$

where the vector $\{u\}$ contains the nodal concentration values in the implicit direction, $[R_x]$, $[R_y]$, $[R_z]$ and $[R_t]$ are tridiagonal matrices, $\{F_{xx}\}$, $\{F_{yy}\}$ and $\{F_{zz}\}$ are the explicit direction mass flux terms, $\{F_{yx}\}$, $\{F_{xy}\}$, $\{F_{zx}\}$, $\{F_{xz}\}$, $\{F_{zy}\}$ and $\{F_{yz}\}$ are the cross-derivative mass flux terms, $\{F_s\}$ is the point source mass flux term and $\{F_a\}$, $\{F_b\}$ and $\{F_c\}$ are the boundary mass flux terms.

For the case of a uniform grid spacing $2a$, $2b$ and $2c$ in the x, y and z directions respectively, a typical row in the matrix $[R_x]$ in Equation 13a, for an interior node i, takes the form

$$R_{x_i} = 4bc\left[\left(-\frac{D_{xx}}{2a}-\frac{v_x}{2}\right)_{i-1}\left(\frac{D_{xx}}{a}\right)_{i}\left(-\frac{D_{xx}}{2a}+\frac{v_x}{2}\right)_{i+1}\right] \qquad (14)$$

where the counter i is in the implicit (x) direction. A corresponding row in $[R_t]$, for a consistent time derivative formulation, is:

$$R_{t_i} = \frac{12abc}{\Delta t}\left[\left(\frac{1}{3}\right)\left(\frac{4}{3}\right)\left(\frac{1}{3}\right)\right] \qquad (15)$$

Typical entries for the explicit-direction flux terms $\{F_{yy}\}$ and $\{F_{zz}\}$ are:

$$F_{yy_i}=4ac\left[\left(\frac{D_{yy}}{2b}+\frac{v_y}{2}\right)_{j-1}\quad\left(-\frac{D_{yy}}{b}\right)_j\quad\left(\frac{D_{yy}}{2b}-\frac{v_y}{2}\right)_{j+1}\right]\cdot\begin{Bmatrix}u_{j-1}\\u_j\\u_{j+1}\end{Bmatrix}\tag{16a}$$

$$F_{zz_i}=4ab\left[\left(\frac{D_{zz}}{2c}+\frac{v_z}{2}\right)_{k-1}\quad\left(-\frac{D_{zz}}{c}\right)_k\quad\left(\frac{D_{zz}}{2c}-\frac{v_z}{2}\right)_{k+1}\right]\cdot\begin{Bmatrix}u_{k-1}\\u_k\\u_{k+1}\end{Bmatrix}\tag{16b}$$

where the counters j and k are in the explicit (y and z) directions, and the values of u are taken at the time levels indicated in Equation 13. Cross-derivative terms for node i are:

$$F_{yx_i} = F_{xy_i} = 2c\frac{D_{xy}}{4}\left(u_{i-1,j-1} + u_{i+1,j+1} - u_{i-1,j+1} - u_{i+1,j-1}\right)\tag{17a}$$

$$F_{zx_i} = F_{xz_i} = 2b\frac{D_{xz}}{4}\left(u_{i-1,k-1} + u_{i+1,k+1} - u_{i-1,k+1} - u_{i+1,k-1}\right)\tag{17b}$$

$$F_{zy_i} = F_{yz_i} = 2a\frac{D_{yz}}{4}\left(u_{j-1,k-1} + u_{j+1,k+1} - u_{j-1,k+1} - u_{j+1,k-1}\right)\tag{17c}$$

The point source term $\{F_s\}$ for node i is:

$$F_{s_i} = \frac{Q_{s_i}u_{s_i}}{\theta}\tag{18}$$

where Q_{s_i} is the source fluid flux and u_{s_i} is the concentration. The terms for Steps 2 and 3 in Equation 13 are similar.

In the case of a Dirichlet boundary (8), the matrices are partitioned between boundary and non-boundary nodes, rows corresponding to boundary nodes are eliminated, and column entries are placed as linking terms in either $\{F_a\}$, $\{F_b\}$ or $\{F_c\}$. For a Cauchy boundary condition, the dispersive flux in the natural boundary term in Equation 13 is replaced by substitution of Equation (9), yielding advective flux contributions to the coefficient matrix $[R_x]$ and the boundary flux vector $\{F_a\}$ in Equation 13a. The matrix terms for a Cauchy boundary node i thus become:

$$R_{x_{i,1}} = R_{x_{i,1}} \pm 4bc\cdot v_{x_i}\tag{19a}$$

$$F_{a_i} = 4bc\frac{q_0u_0}{\theta}\tag{19b}$$

The velocity term in Equation 19a is added when the Cartesian $+x_i$ direction coincides with the direction of the inward normal boundary vector $\vec{n}$, and subtracted when the directions are opposite. Daus and Frind (1985) describe the procedure in detail. The same method applies to a Cauchy outflow boundary, but u_0 will be unknown. Similar coefficients can be obtained for a non-uniform grid by performing the integrations over the appropriate prism lengths.

Equations 13 can be solved for the unknown nodal values u at each intermediate time level. The Thomas algorithm for tridiagonal matrices efficiently performs the solution. The implicit level cross-derivative terms are evaluated iteratively; one iteration is usually sufficient to obtain convergence.

NUMERICAL ACCURACY AND STABILITY

The spatial and temporal discretization required to obtain an oscillation-free solution is controlled by the grid Peclet number P and the grid Courant number C (Daus *et al.*, 1985; Frind and Germain, 1986). The Peclet number criterion for the spatial coordinate x_i is:

$$P_i \equiv \frac{v_i \Delta x_i}{D_{ii}} \leq 2 \tag{20}$$

The Courant number criterion is:

$$C_i \equiv \frac{v_i \Delta t}{\Delta x_i} \leq \frac{P_i}{2} \tag{21}$$

Criteria (20) and (21) provide the necessary constraints for the selection of the local grid spacing Δx, Δy and Δz, and for the initial time step Δt. As the solution progresses in time, the steepness of the concentration front decreases and the Courant criterion (21) can be relaxed, allowing the time step to be gradually increased.

The stability of the numerical scheme can be investigated by performing a von Neumann analysis (Peaceman, 1977). The analysis shows that the Centred scheme is conditionally stable. The condition for stability, for both the purely diffusive case and the advective-diffusive case, is $\rho_i \leq \sqrt{27/8}$ ($\approx$1.84), where $\rho_i = \dfrac{D_{ii} \Delta t}{\Delta x_i^2}$, for any of the three coordinate directions. In addition, when a velocity component in any direction is non-zero, there is a stability constraint on the Courant number corresponding to that direction; this constraint, however, is less severe than (21). In all cases, when the accuracy criteria (20) and (21) are satisfied, the stability constraints will also be satisfied.

THREE-DIMENSIONAL SYSTEM

The system we will use to compare 3D and 2D simulations consists of the unconfined aquifer shown in Figure 1. The aquifer has an impermeable base, and the watertable, described by a quarter cosine curve in x, forms the upper boundary. The left boundary is a divide, while the right boundary allows discharge. The system has a length of 200 m, a thickness of 20 to 21 m, and a varying width. The material is homogeneous and isotropic, with a hydraulic conductivity of 1.0 m/day and a porosity of 0.35. Flow is at steady state and all flow components are in the $x-z$ plane. The average annual recharge required to keep this flow system in equilibrium is about 0.3 m.

A contaminant source at the surface provides a mass flux of known strength to the watertable. The contaminant is assumed to be nonreactive and dilute. The source is located at $18.25 \leq x \leq 32.5$ m and $0 \leq y \leq 5.0$ m. The plane $y = 0$ forms a plane of symmetry through the centre of the source; the entire source is 10 m wide. The width of the system is selected such that the generated plume will not reach the transverse horizontal boundary.

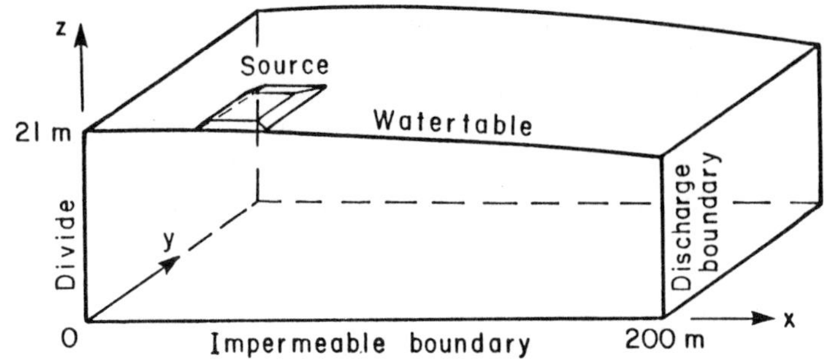

Figure 1 Three-dimensional system

The 2D steady-state flow problem was solved using a streamfunction formulation (Frind and Matanga, 1985) with linear triangular elements and a direct matrix solver. The model calculated streamfunctions and elemental velocities, then interpolated the velocities for the quadrilateral elements used by the alternating direction transport models. The streamfunctions are shown in Figure 2.

The generated flow field was used directly in the two-dimensional vertical section transport simulations. For the 3D simulations, parallel flow fields were projected in the y-direction. The flow field for the 2D horizontal plane model was generated by vertically averaging the horizontal components of the 3D flow field.

For transport, the watertable boundary is of the Cauchy type (9), with $u_0 = 1$ at the source and $u_0 = 0$ elsewhere. All other boundaries are of the Neumann type with zero concentration gradient. At the downstream discharge boundary, the Neumann boundary introduces a slight error which, however, does not affect the rest of the solution.

The three-dimensional effect that cannot be represented easily with a 2D model even when the flow system is two-dimensional is the transverse dispersion in the third dimension. We will therefore compare 3D and 2D simulations while varying the transverse dispersion parameters. The longitudinal dispersivity is kept at a constant value of 3 m, which is of the order of magnitude commonly used for systems of similar scale. The effective coefficient of molecular diffusion is 1×10^{-4} m^2/day.

A recent natural-gradient tracer test measured transverse dispersion on the order of diffusion in the vertical plane, but about 1/10 that of longitudinal dispersion in the horizontal plane (Sudicky, 1985). These findings are supported by stochastic studies (Gelhar and Axness, 1983). Simulations fitting transport parameters to observed plumes have also resulted in greater values of transverse dispersivity in the horizontal plane than in the vertical plane (Anderson, 1979). Accordingly, we will here consider values of transverse vertical dispersivity of zero (pure molecular diffusion) and 0.01 m, and values of transverse horizontal dispersivity of 0.1 and 1.0 m.

According to criteria (20) and (21), the spatial and temporal discretization depends on the transport parameters. To determine the optimal discretization (Frind and Germain, 1986), the flow field is sampled at several points (Figure 2), velocities are noted, and local dispersion coefficients are calculated. The maximum allowable spatial discretization and the corresponding time step are given by:

$$\Delta x = \frac{2D_{xx}}{v_x} \qquad \Delta t = \min\left(\frac{\Delta x}{v_x}, \frac{\Delta z}{v_z}\right)$$

$$\Delta z = \frac{2D_{zz}}{v_z}$$

The discretization in the purely diffusive y-direction was chosen on the basis of the element aspect ratio by satisfying the arbitrary constraint $1/10 \leq \rho_x/\rho_y \leq 10$, as well as the stability constraint. This ensures that the solution roundoff errors remain small.

The resulting discretizations are shown in Table 1. The 3D discretization is a combination of the 2D discretizations.

Vertical Plane Discretization					
α_{TV} (m)	Δx (m) left	Δx (m) right	Δz (m) bottom	Δz (m) top	Δt (days)
0, 0.01, 0.1	1.0	6.0	0.75	1.25	300
Horizontal Plane Discretization					
α_{TH} (m)	Δy (m)		y length (m)		Δt (days)
0.1	1.0		15.0		300
1.	2.0		30.0		300

Table 1 Discretization scheme

COMPARISON OF SIMULATED PLUMES

The three models were applied to simulate the evolution of the contaminant plume up to a time of 12,000 days. The plume evolution obtained with the 3D model, with $\alpha_{TH}=\alpha_{TV}=0.1$ m, at two points in time and contoured at the central vertical section, is shown in Figure 3. As expected, the plume evolves along the flowlines that pass through the source, and it shows relatively little transverse dispersion. Nevertheless, transverse dispersion in the horizontal plane causes the 3D plume to be about 20% shorter than the corresponding plume from the 2D cross-sectional simulation (not shown).

The effect of dispersion in the horizontal transverse direction on the plume shape in the vertical plane is shown in Figure 4. The vertical transverse dispersivity is here set to zero so that vertical spreading is by molecular diffusion only. Figure 4a shows the 2D vertical cross-sectional simulation, which produces a sharply-defined spike-shaped plume. The 3D model with either $\alpha_{TH}=0$ (molecular diffusion in the horizontal as well as in the vertical), or $\alpha_{TH}=0.01$ m, produces a plume that shows no significant difference to the 2D plume within the 200 m

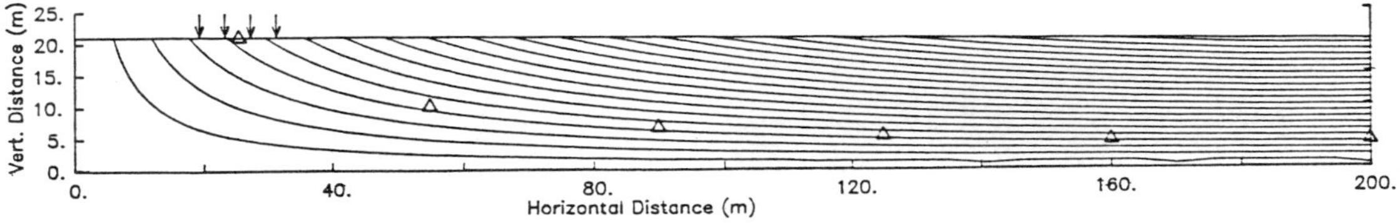

Figure 2 Streamlines of steady-state flow solution, contour interval 0.0075 m^2/day, with points ($\triangle$) used for calculation of grid spacing for transport models

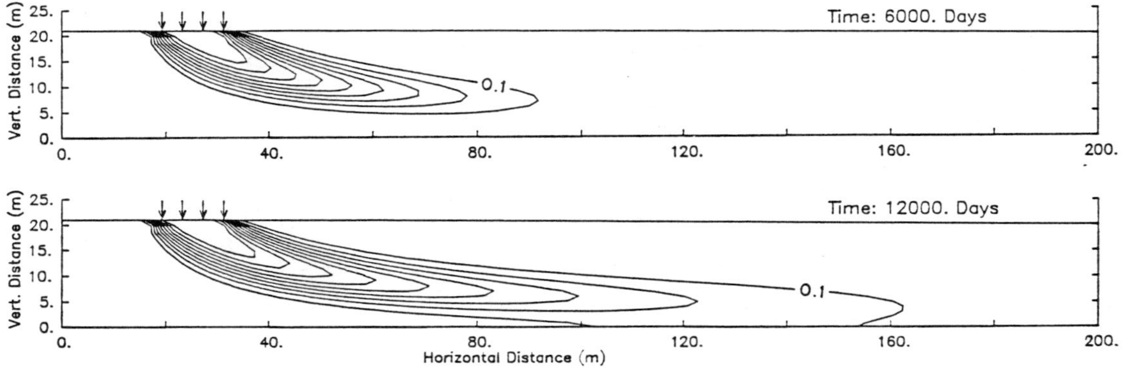

Figure 3 Plume evolution, 3D model at central vertical plane, $\alpha_{TH}=\alpha_{TV}=0.1$ m, contour interval 0.1

length of the model. Some difference, however, is expected at the tip of the plume, which is beyond the downstream model boundary. Increasing the horizontal transverse dispersivity to α_{TH}=0.1 m (Figure 4b) results in a substantial shortening of the plume by about 20%, compared with the 2D plume. A further increase to α_{TH}=1.0 m (Figure 4c) causes a shortening by 65%.

These results show that under conditions of relatively low transverse dispersion, such as might be expected to favour a 2D vertical plane simulation, the effect of the third dimension can be significant. With a transverse dispersivity of 1/30 of the longitudinal dispersivity, and a source width of 10 m, the effect is substantial. The mass removed from the centre section of the plume due to transverse horizontal dispersion becomes noticeable at values of transverse horizontal dispersivity between 0.01 and 0.1 m.

The three-dimensional spreading effect also causes the lower-value concentration contours to be spaced farther apart in the 3D plume than in the 2D plume. Thus, if a 3D plume were observed in the field, such spreading might be interpreted as being caused by an increasing dispersion coefficient (Domenico and Robbins, 1984). In real situations, a scale effect of dispersion might be difficult to distinguish from the 2D effect when using a 2D model. Therefore, in studies where evidence of such a scale effect is sought, the use of a 3D model would appear to be essential.

In the case of the 2D horizontal plane model, the third dimension is the vertical. Figure 5 shows the plume in the horizontal plane for α_{TH}=0.1 m at 12,000 days. The 2D horizontal plane (vertically-integrated) simulation is shown in Figure 5a. The same results can be obtained with the 3D model (Figure 5b) by averaging concentrations over the aquifer thickness. However, the peak concentrations from the same 3D simulation (Figure 5c) are substantially different. At the source, for example, average concentrations are around 0.4, while peak concentrations are about 0.9. More significantly, the vertically averaged model has the tip of the plume, in terms of the 0.1 concentration contour, at about 105 m, while the actual 0.1 concentration peak is at about 200 m. Similar results can be obtained with other combinations of dispersivities. This demonstrates that, although the 2D horizontal plane model correctly accounts for the mass in the system, the results may be grossly misleading in terms of actual point concentrations within the aquifer.

Another effect that differs between the 3D and 2D simulations is local plume stabilization (Germain, 1981). This effect causes regions of stable concentration to form near the source, which gradually expand outward in time to successively lower concentration levels. The 3D plumes are found to stabilize sooner in all cases than the corresponding 2D plumes.

For the 3D and the 2D vertical section simulations, the mass balances were correct within 1.6% or less after the first time step. The level of error either decreased or remained constant through successive time steps until mass reached the boundaries. The vertically-integrated model, which lacks non-zero cross-terms, had a mass balance error of 0.1% or less for each simulation.

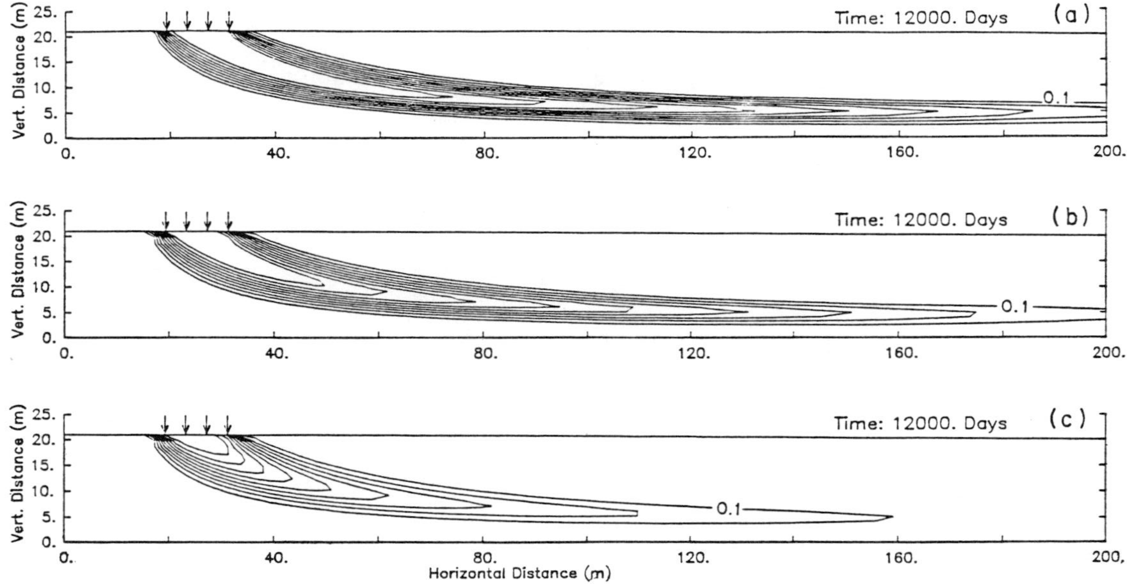

Figure 4 Plumes in central vertical plane, α_{TV}=0.01 m, at 12,000 days
a) 2D vertical cross-section model
b) 3D model, α_{TH}=0.1 m
c) 3D model, α_{TH}=1. m

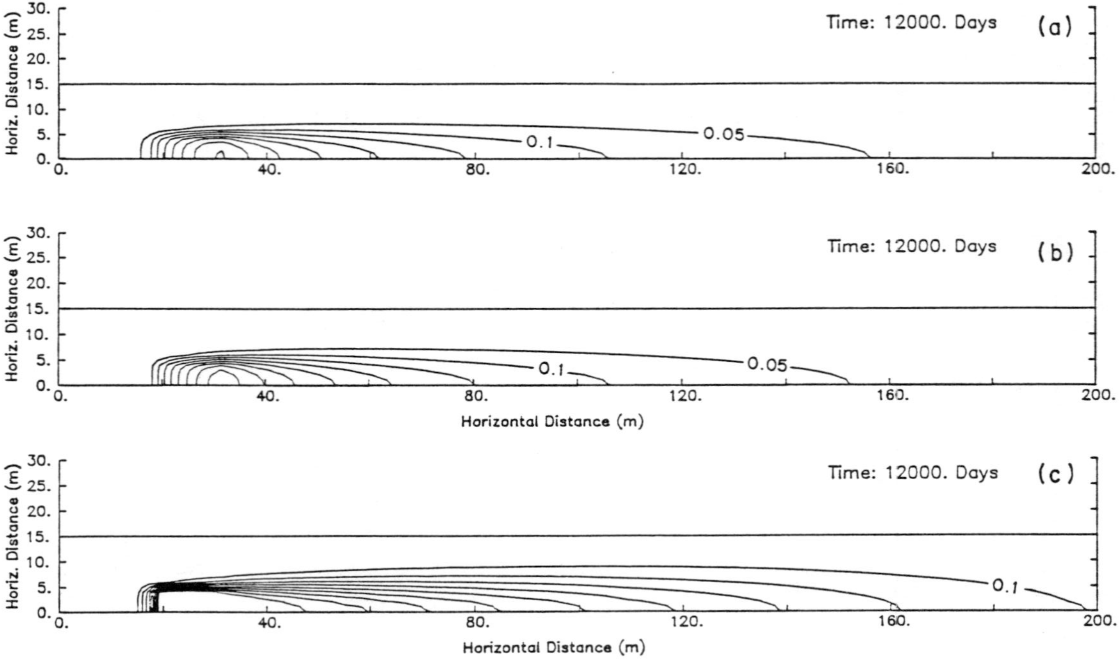

Figure 5 Plumes in horizontal plane, α_{TH}=0.1 m, at 12,000 days
a) 2D horizontal plane model, contour interval 0.05
b) 3D model, α_{TV}=0.01 m, vertically averaged, contour interval 0.05
c) 3D model, α_{TV}=0.01 m, peak concentrations, contour interval 0.1

COST COMPARISON

Probably the greatest obstacle to the use of 3D models has been their prohibitive demands on computing resources, both in terms of execution time and array storage. The 3D ADG model has therefore been developed with an emphasis on computational efficiency and practical utility.

The execution times for the three models used in the comparison are listed in Table 2. All three models are of the ADG-type and source codes were compiled using the FORTRAN H optimizing compiler. All simulations were run on an IBM 4381 machine under VM/CMS batch processing. Each run consisted of 40 uniform time steps.

Model	Nodes	Iterations (total)	CPU (sec)	CPU /time step (sec)	CPU /time step /10^3 nodes (sec)
2D Vertical	55x21=1155	82	14.1	.353	.305
2D Plan	55x17=935	0	12.2	.305	.326
3D	55x17x21=19,635	121	951.7	23.79	1.212

TABLE 2 Execution times for 2D and 3D models

Both the 2D vertical model and the 3D model solved iteratively for the implicit-level cross-derivative terms, while the 2D horizontal model, which for the given situation operates as a principal direction model without cross-derivative terms, can solve directly. On the other hand, the computational effort for the 2D horizontal model increases somewhat, compared with the 2D sectional model, because of the vertical integration. The computational costs for the two 2D models is therefore similar. The unit cost of execution for these models of less than 1/3 seconds per time step per 1000 nodes is very low.

The 3D model required about 23.8 seconds per time step for the entire grid of nearly 20,000 nodes, or about 1.2 seconds per time step per 1000 nodes. The higher unit cost as compared with the 2D models is due to a number of factors, such as the larger number of terms in the governing equation, the splitting of each time step into three partial steps rather than two, and the need to use triply-subscripted arrays. Thus the unit cost of the 3D ADG model is about 4 times higher than that of a corresponding 2D ADG model. In a comparison with a conventional 2D finite element model, this cost factor will, however, be much smaller. The 2D ADG model possesses a much higher degree of efficiency than comparable FE models (Frind and Germain, 1986).

The 2D models required storage for about 11 array entries per node, or a relatively modest 60 kilobytes of array storage for an average simulation. The 3D model required storage for about 17 array entries per node, or an average of 1740 kilobytes of array storage per simulation. The memory requirements for the 3D model are therefore about 30 times as great as for the 2D models, but are well within the capacity of most larger computers.

CONCLUSION

The comparisons show that a 2D vertical cross-sectional simulation of a 3D plume originating at a finite-length source is in general inexact. The error can be substantial for values greater than 10 cm of transverse horizontal dispersivity. Close to the source the error is small, but it increases with distance. The often-made assumption that transverse mass loss is negligible along the central plane of a plume, provided the source is large in extent, is therefore not generally justified. A 2D sectional approximation, however, can be considered conservative in the sense that predicted concentrations will always be greater than actual concentrations. In fitting field observations with 2D transport models, it should be kept in mind that the effect of dispersion in the third dimension is similar to that caused by an increasing longitudinal dispersion coefficient.

A 2D vertically-integrated horizontal plane model can be expected to produce accurate average concentrations. The average concentrations, however, can differ substantially from actual local concentrations in the aquifer unless the vertical transverse dispersivity is very high or the aquifer is very thin. Since the peak concentrations are always ahead of the average concentrations unless complete mixing occurs, the vertically-integrated model will in general not provide conservative results. Thus if predictions of point concentrations are required, a vertically-integrated model may not be an appropriate choice. The discrepancy between the integrated concentrations and the actual point concentrations can be aggravated further by stratifications within the aquifer.

At a computational cost of 1.2 seconds per time step per 1000 nodes, and array storage of about 88 kilobytes per 1000 nodes, the 3D ADG model is sufficiently affordable to be considered a tool of practical value. Although 2D models, both of the vertical cross-sectional type and the horizontal plane type, will continue to play a role for the forseeable future, 3D simulation should be considered in situations where a high degree of accuracy is desired and sufficient data are available.

ACKNOWLEDGEMENT

Financial support for this study was provided by the Natural Sciences and Engineering Research Council of Canada, Grant No. A8368.

REFERENCES

Anderson, M.P., 1979. Using models to simulate the movement of contaminants through groundwater flow systems. CRC Critical Reviews in Environmental Control, 9(2), pp. 97-156.

Bear, J., 1972. *Dynamics of Fluids in Porous Media.* American Elsevier, New York.

Burnett, R.D., 1985. An Alternating Direction Galerkin Technique for simulation of groundwater contaminant transport in three dimensions. M.Sc. thesis, Department of Earth Sciences, University of Waterloo, Waterloo, Canada.

Daus, A.D. and E.O. Frind, 1985. An Alternating Direction Galerkin Technique for simulation of contaminant transport in complex groundwater systems. Water Resources Res., 21(5), pp. 653-664.

Daus, A.D., E.O. Frind and E.A. Sudicky, 1985. Comparative error analysis in finite element formulations of the advection-dispersion equation. Advances in Water Resources, 8, pp. 86-95.

Domenico, P.A. and G.A. Robbins, 1984. A dispersion scale effect in model calibrations and field tracer experiments. J. Hydrology, 70, pp. 123-132.

Frind, E.O., 1982. The Principal Direction Technique: A new approach to groundwater contaminant transport modelling. Proceedings, Fourth International Conference on Finite Elements in Water Resources, Tech. Univ. Hannover, Germany. Springer Verlag, New York, 13: pp. 25-42.

Frind, E.O., 1984. The Principal Direction Technique for advective-dispersive transport simulation in three dimensions. Proceedings, Fifth International Conference on Finite Elements in Water Resources, The University of Vermont, Burlington, Vermont.

Frind, E.O. and D. Germain, 1986. Numerical simulation of advective-dispersive transport: Accuracy control and model comparison. Water Resources Res. (in submission).

Frind, E.O., W. Kinzelbach, T. Soell, P. Ackerer, and M. Berg, 1985. Dimensionality effects in the simulation of transport in natural groundwater systems: A case study. Report No. 85-14 (HWV 065), Institut fuer Wasserbau, Universitaet Stuttgart (61 p.).

Frind, E.O. and G.B. Matanga, 1985. The dual formulation of flow for contaminant transport modelling, 1, Review of theory and accuracy aspects. Water Resources Res. 21(2), pp. 159-169.

Frind, E.O. and G.F. Pinder, 1982. The Principal Direction Technique for solution of the advection-dispersion equation. Proceedings, Tenth World Congress of the International Association for Mathematics and Computers in Simulation, Concordia University, Montreal, Canada.

Gelhar, L.W. and C.L. Axness, 1983. Three-dimensional stochastic analysis of macrodispersion in aquifers. Water Resources Res., 19(1), pp. 161-180.

Germain, D., 1981. Quasi-stable concentration distributions in saturated porous media with a constant solute source. M.Sc. thesis, Department of Earth Sciences, University of Waterloo, Waterloo, Canada.

Peaceman, D.W., 1977. *Fundamentals of Reservoir Simulation.* Developments in Petroleum Science 6; Elsevier, New York.

Pinder, G.F. and W.G. Gray, 1977. *Finite Element Simulation in Surface and Subsurface Hydrology.* Academic Press, New York.

Sudicky, E.A., 1985. Spatial variability of hydraulic conductivity at the Borden tracer test site. Proceedings, International Symposium on the Stochastic Approach to Subsurface Flow, Paris School of Mines, France, June 3-7, 1985.

VI International Conference on Finite Elements in Water Resources, Lisboa, Portugal, June 1986

Accuracy Analysis of the Backwards Method of Characteristics

A.M. Baptista
Laboratório Nacional de Engenharia Civil, 1799 Lisboa Codex, Portugal
E. Eric Adams, K.D. Stolzenbach
Ralph M. Parsons Laboratory, Massachusetts Institute of Technology, Cambridge, MA 82139, U.S.A.

1. INTRODUCTION

Eulerian-Lagrangian methods (ELM) provide promisingly accurate and efficient solutions of the transport equation, even when advection is strongly dominant [1-5,7-10,12-14]. Although several differences exist between proposed ELM, they share the basic idea of splitting advection from diffusion, and handling each kind of transport separately, through appropriate techniques; typically, advection is solved by some (Lagrangian) particle-tracking technique based on a fixed grid, while diffusion is solved by a conventional (Eulerian) FE or FD technique. The solution of advection is typically the limiting factor for accuracy, and special attention should be paid to it, so as to improve available ELM.

In this paper, Fourier analysis is used to discuss the accuracy and convergence of the backwards method of characteristics (BMC), one of the most effective solution techniques for advection.

2. REVIEW OF THE BACKWARDS METHOD OF CHARACTERISTICS

The advection equation

$$\frac{D\,c(x,t)}{Dt} \left(\equiv \frac{\partial c(x,t)}{\partial t} + u(x,t)\,\frac{\partial c(x,t)}{\partial x} \right) = 0 \tag{1}$$

states that concentration remains constant along characteristic lines defined by

$$\frac{dx}{dt} = u(x,t) \tag{2}$$

The BMC explores this concept (Fig.1). In each time step, n, a particle is allocated to each node, j, and tracked backwards, along the appropriate characteristic line, to the previous time step, n-1, where concentrations are known at all nodes; the concentration at the foot of the characteristic line, c(p,n-1), which equals the concentration at the starting point, c(j,n), is found by interpolation between neighbouring nodes.

The backwards tracking can be performed very accurately (e.g., by a Runge-Kutta technique), even for unstructured grids and for complex, multi-dimensional, flows [1]. However, the interpolation to find concentrations at the foot of the characteristic lines introduces numerical damping and dispersion, which increase with increasing sharpness of the transported concentration profile (i.e., with decreasing dimensionless wavelength of the dominant Fourier components).

Several interpolation schemes, proposed by a variety of authors [2,7,9,10,12] were briefly compared in an earlier work [2]. For the present discussion, we selected three of these schemes, that cover a wide range of accuracy/cost characteristics. In increasing order of accuracy and cost per interpolation, the selected schemes are: linear Lagrange interpolation (2P-LI); quadratic Lagrange interpolation (3P-LI); and cubic Hermite interpolation, with estimation of derivatives based on information from five nodes (5P-HI) - Table 1.

3.FOURIER ANALYSIS AND ERROR PROPAGATION

For u=constant, the Fourier representation of the exact solution of Eq.1, in the nodes of a numerical grid, is

$$c(n,j) = \sum_{m=0}^{\infty} A_m.\exp\{i\lambda_m (j-n\beta)\} \tag{3}$$

where A_m are problem-dependent real coefficients, $i=\sqrt{-1}$, $\lambda_m=2\pi\Delta x/L_m$, $\beta=u\Delta t/\Delta x$, L_m is the wavelength of the mth Fourier component, Δx is the interval between adjacent grid nodes, and Δt is the time step.

Because of linearity, each individual Fourier component

$$c_m(n,j) = A_m.\exp\{i\lambda_m (j-n\beta)\} \tag{4}$$

obeys Eq.1. Replacing Eq.4 into the algorithm of a particular numerical method, set between times n and n-1, leads (assuming an exact solution at time n-1) to

$$\tilde{c}_m(n,j) = G_m(\alpha).\ c_m(n,j) \tag{5}$$

where G_m is, in general, a complex function. $|G_m|$ and $\arg(G_m)$ measure, respectively, the amplitude and phase errors introduced to the mth Fourier component during the first step of the numerical solution.

The full numerical solution results by superposition, i.e.

$$\tilde{c}(n,j) = \sum_{m=o}^{\infty} G_m(\alpha) \cdot c_m(n,j) \tag{6}$$

For some numerical methods, amplitude and phase errors repeat themselves from time step to time step, in which case G_m may be considered as an error per time step, and errors after N time steps are simply defined as [6,11]

$$H_m(N,\alpha) = \{G_m(\alpha)\}^N \tag{7}$$

hence

$$a_m(N,\alpha) = |H_m(N,\alpha)| = |G_m(\alpha)|^N \quad \text{amplitude error} \tag{8}$$

$$f_m(N,\alpha) = \arg[H_m(N,\alpha)] = N \arg[G_m(\alpha)] \quad \text{phase error} \tag{9}$$

For the BMC, these simple error propagation characteristics apply when the interpolation scheme is based on 2-nodes core elements (e.g., the 2P-LI). However, error propagation is more complex when the interpolation scheme is based on core elements with 3 (e.g, 3P-LI and 5P-HI) or more nodes, due to the fact that, within any given time step, different errors must be associated with different node types (e.g, corner versus middle nodes, within quadratic elements).

From ongoing research, we summarize error propagation formulae applying when the 2P-LI, 3P-HI and 5P-HI schemes are used (Table 2). These formulae, applied to the complex Fourier series representation of the exact solution of a given reference problem (with u=constant), permit a cheap and accurate simulation of BMC solutions, for any combination of Δx and Δt.

4.ANALYSIS OF ACCURACY AND CONVERGENCE

4.1.General aspects

We consider as a reference the common test problem of uniform advection of a Gauss-hill, which is governed by Eq.1, with constant u, and with boundary and initial conditions:

$$c(x,t) \to o \qquad \text{as } |x| \to \infty \tag{10}$$

$$c(x,o) = \frac{1}{\sqrt{2\pi}\,\sigma} \exp \frac{(x-x_o)^2}{2\sigma^2} \tag{11}$$

In particular, we set u=0.5, σ=264, x_0=2000, and solve the problem in a uniform space-time grid, with $x \in [0,13600]$, and

$t \in [0, T=9600]$ (units are irrelevant, as long as consistent). The problem was solved (a) numerically and (b) using the error propagation formulae of Table 2, for $\Delta x=200$, $\Delta t=96$ (hence $N=T/\Delta t=100$ time steps).

Computed concentration profiles (Fig.2) illustrate the accuracy improvement achieved by increasing the order of the interpolation scheme, and demonstrate the effectiveness of the error propagation formulae of Table 2.

The Fourier representation of the numerical solutions, which is shown in Tables 3 and 4, provides insight on the performance of the BMC and, in particular, illustrates the roles of numerical damping and of numerical dispersion.

For all interpolation schemes, amplitude and phase errors are $(L_m/\Delta x)$-dependent, increasing as $L_m/\Delta x$ decreases. The value and relative importance of these errors is, however, scheme specific.

Indeed, for the 2P-LI, amplitude errors fully dominate, leading to solutions that are strongly damped, but do not exibhit any significant numerical dispersion (no "wiggles"). In the case of the 3P-LI and the 5P-HI, though, amplitudes are fairly well preserved for a larger range of $L_m/\Delta x$, allowing phase errors to show up. Solutions exhibit low to moderate damping and dispersion (this latter showing through quickly damped "wiggles").

For the 3P-LI and 5P-HI schemes, parasitic bursts of energy show up at low $L_m/\Delta x$. They do not significantly affect accuracy, as involved amplitudes are rather small. However, it is interesting to notice that a non-linear mechanism of energy transfer between Fourier components occurs in a linear problem with constant u and uniform grid, as consequence of the different α that are associated to middle and corner nodes. Similar (but eventually more significant) energy transfer should therefore occur, for any scheme, when either the grid or the flow are non-uniform; research is in progress to assess, for such cases, the effect of this transfer on BMC accuracy.

4.2.Convergence

Because errors coming from interpolations in space are dominant, BMC solutions (and ELM/BMC solutions, when advection is dominant) tend, for a fixed time T, to improve as N is reduced, i.e., as Δt increases.

This singular behaviour, which has practical advantages [1], but has inspired some concern on the consistency of ELM/BMC solutions [13], is now discussed. We consider again the reference problem of section 4.1, which we solve for different values of N and Δx, using the error propagation formulae of Table 2.

Figs. 3 and 4 show, for three different Δx, the dependence on N of the global accuracy, as measured by the L2 error-norm

$$\theta = \frac{1}{M(t)} \left\{ \int_{-\infty}^{\infty} [c^{nu}(x,t) - c^{ex}(x,t)]^2 dx \right\}^{1/2} \quad (12)$$

where M(t) denotes total "mass". If we exclude the localized gains of accuracy near integer values of β (Fig.4), which will not prevail in more realistic conditions of non-uniform flow and/or nodal spacing, we indeed detect a clear tendency for accuracy to improve as N decreases (Fig.3).

Results for large values of N suggest that the BMC converges as $N \to \infty$. However, convergence is towards the approximate solution imposed by the space-discretization (rather than to the exact solution), and is achieved "from below", i.e., the limit corresponds to the maximum error.

BMC convergence in space is rather conventional, with accuracy improving as $\Delta x \to 0$ (Fig.5). Tables 2 and 3 suggest the relevant convergence mechanism: for a same problem, reducing Δx implies increasing the dimensionless wavelength of the dominant Fourier components, which are therefore better transported by the numerical technique.

Fig.5 also suggests that the optimal (in a cost/benefit sense) interpolation scheme for BMC depends on the desired level of accuracy, with higher order schemes becoming more cost--effective as more demanding accuracy goals are set.

5.FINAL CONSIDERATIONS

Using Fourier analysis as a basic tool, in a way that extends [6,11], we analysed accuracy and convergence of the BMC.

Accuracy is, commonly enough, found to result from a balance between numerical damping and numerical dispersion. This balance strongly depends on the adopted interpolation scheme, with higher order schemes leading typically (but not always, see [2]) to better accuracy.

For any given scheme, accuracy improves (a) as the dimensionless wavelength of the dominant Fourier components of the solution increases, (i.e., for a given problem, as $\Delta x \to 0$), and (b) as the adopted number of time steps decreases. The BMC is found to converge as $N \to \infty$, but the convergence limit is imposed by the adopted space discretization.

As regard to cost-effectiveness , our analysis suggests that the optimal interpolation scheme for a BMC (hence, a ELM/BMC) significantly depends on the desired accuracy and dominant Fourier components. For pure advection or advection-dominated problems, the choice should most often be restricted to interpolations higher than linear, the 3P-LI and the 5P-HI schemes being good candidates; linear interpolation should be competitive only when physical diffusion is significant.

ACKNOWLEDGEMENTS

The first author gratefully acknowledges the financial support of NATO CCMS and of Comissão INVOTAN to his work.
Thanks are due to Dr. Mendes de Carvalho (LNEC) and to Dr. M. Celia (MIT), for suggestions and helpful discussion, and to Mr. Geadas Cabaço (LNEC), for assistance in the coding and running of computer programs.

REFERENCES

1. Baptista A.M., E.E. Adams and K.D. Stolzenbach - "Eulerian-Lagrangian Analysis of Pollutant Transport in Shallow Water", Tech. Rep. 296, Ralph M. Parsons Lab., MIT, USA, 1984.
2. Baptista A.M., E.E. Adams and K.D. Stolzenbach - "Comparison of several Eulerian-Lagrangian Models to Solve the Advection-Diffusion Equation", Int. Symp. on Refined Flow Modeling and Turbulence Measurements, U. Iowa, USA, 1985.
3. Benque, J.P., G. Labadie and J. Ronat - "A Finite Element Method for Navier-Stokes Equations Coupled with a Temperature Equation", Proc. 4th Int. Symp. Finite Elements in Flow Problems, Tokyo, 1982.
4. Cheng. R.T., V. Casulli and S. Milford - "Eulerian-Lagrangian Solution of the Convection-Disperson Equation in Natural Coordinates", Water Resources Research, 20(7), pp. 944-952, 1984.
5. Glass J. and W. Rodi - "A Higher Order Numerical Scheme for Scalar Transport", Comp. Meth. in Appl. Mech. and Engrg., 31, pp. 337-358, 1982.
6. Gray W.G. and G.F. Pinder - "An Analysis of the Numerical Solution of the Transport Equation", Water Resour. Res., 12, p. 547, 1976.
7. Holly F.M. Jr. and T. Komatsu - "Derivative Approximations in the Two-Points Fourth-Order Method for Pollutant Transport", Frontiers in Hydraulic Engineering ASCE, pp. 349-355, 1983.
8. Holly F.M. Jr., and J.M. Polatera - "Dispersion Simulation in 2-D Tidal Flow", Jour. Hydr. Engrg., ASCE, 110(HY7), pp. 905-926, 1984.
9. Holly F.M. Jr. and A. Preissmann - "Accurate Calculation of Transport in Two Dimensions", Jour. Hydr. Div., ASCE, 103(HY11), pp. 1259-78, 1977.
10. Komatsu T., F.M. Holly Jr. and N. Nakashiki - "Numerical Calculation of Pollutant Transport in Rivers and Coastlines", 4th Congress-Asian and Pacific Div., IAHR, Chiang Mai, Thailand, 1984.
11. Lapidus L. and G.F. Pinder - "Numerical Solution of Partial Differential Equations in Science and Engineering", J. Wiley & Sons, 1982.
12. Leith C.E. - "Numerical Simulation of the Earth's Atmosphere", Methods in Computational Physics, 4, pp. 1-28, 1965.
13. Neuman S.P. - "Adaptive Eulerian-Lagrangian Finite Element Method for Advection-Dispersion", Int. Jour. for Num. Meth. in Engrg., 20, 321-337, 1984.
14. Neuman S.P. and S. Sorek - "Eulerian-Lagrangian Methods for Advection-Dispersion", Proc. 4th Int. Conf. on Finite Elements in Water Resources, Hannover, West Germany, 1982.

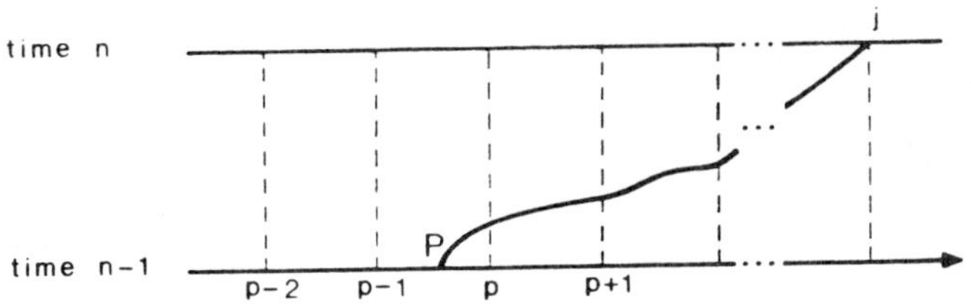

Figure 1 - Illustrative sketch for the BMC

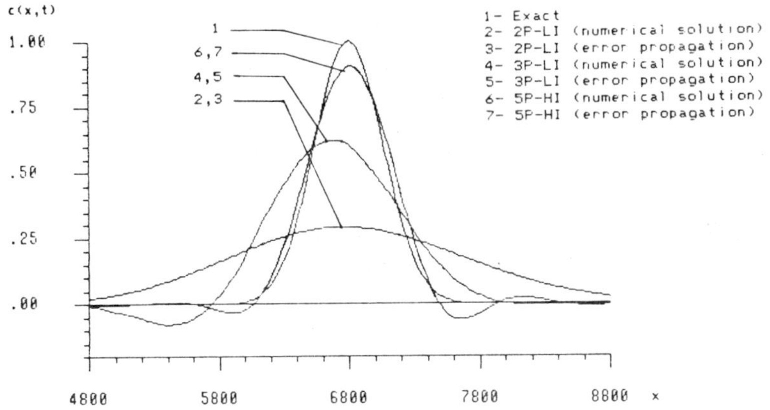

Figure 2 - Solution of the reference problem, at t=T=9600 (Δx=200;N=100)

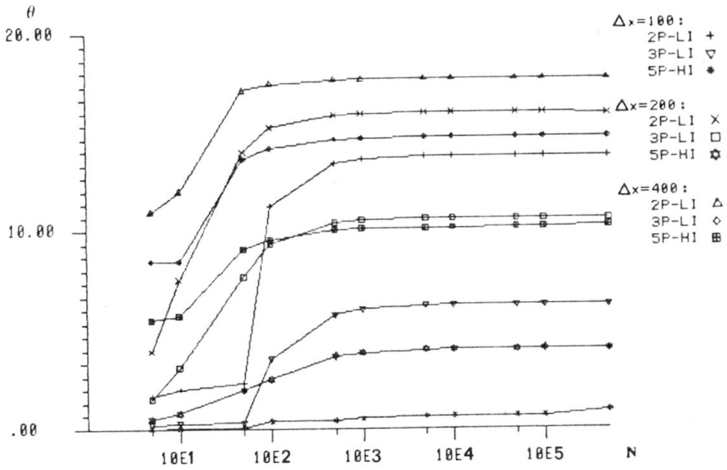

Figure 3 - Global accuracy as a function of N, for t=T=9600

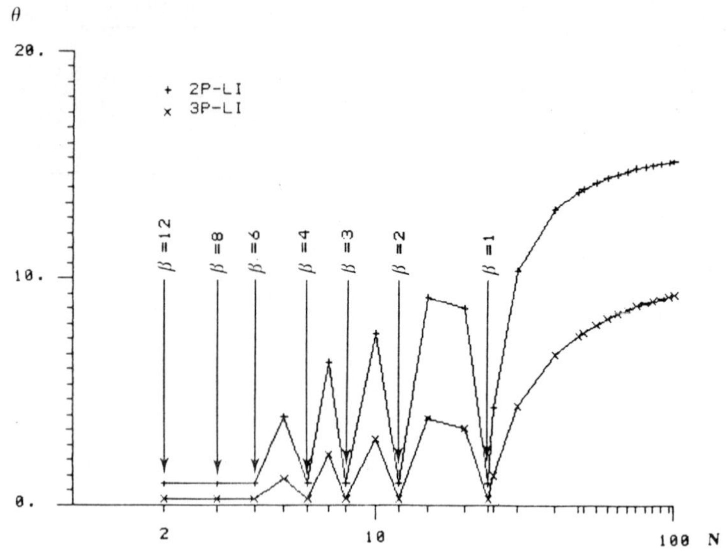

Figure 4 - Illustration of singular accuracy behaviour near integer values of β for t=T=9600, Δx=200.

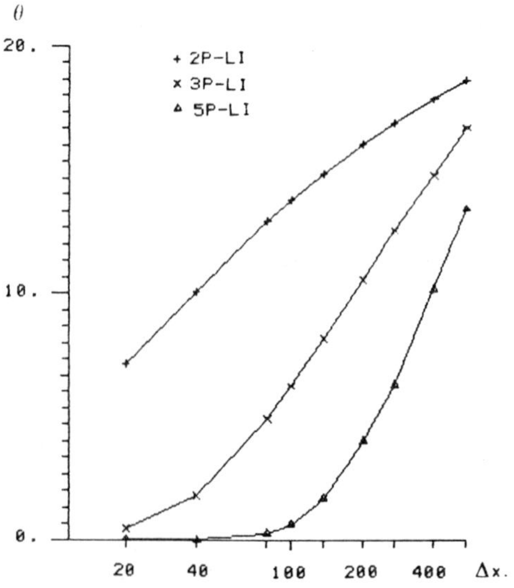

Figure 5 - Global accuracy as a function of Δx, for T=9600 and N=50000.

Table 1 - Definition of the interpolation schemes

Scheme	Core element and relevant nodes	Interpolation formula
2P-LI	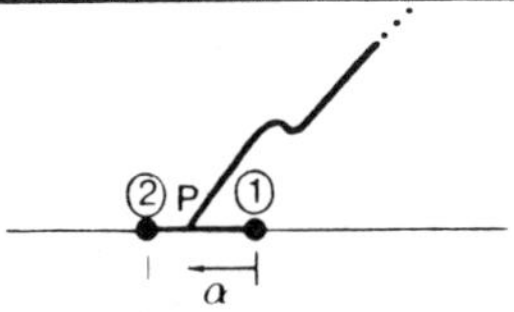$(0 \leqslant \alpha \leqslant 1)$	$c\,(P) = \sum_{i=1}^{2} \phi_i(\alpha)\,.\,c_i$ $\phi_1\ (\alpha) = 1 - \alpha$ $\phi_2\ (\alpha) = \alpha$
3P-LI	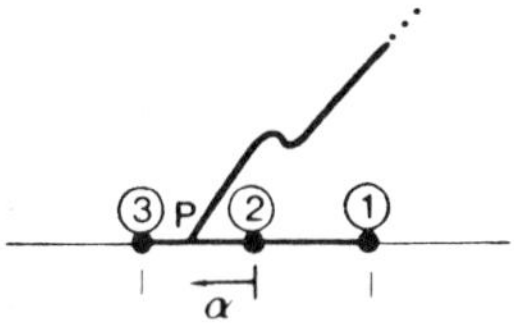$(-1 \leqslant \alpha \leqslant 1)$	$c\,(P) \sum_{i=1}^{3} \phi_i(\alpha)\,.\,c_i$ $\phi_1\ (\alpha) = (\alpha^2 - \alpha)/2$ $\phi_2\ (\alpha) = 1 - \alpha^2$ $\phi_3\ (\alpha) = (\alpha^2 + \alpha)/2$
5P-HI	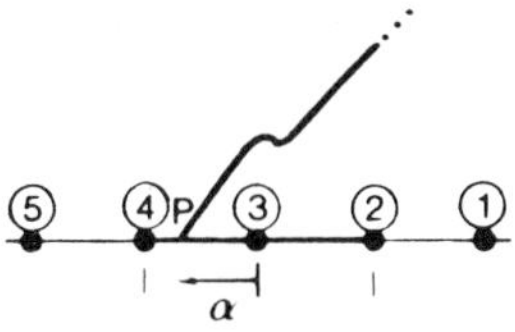$(-1 \leqslant \alpha \leqslant 1)$	$c\,(P) = \sum_{i=1}^{5} \phi_i(\alpha)\,.\,c_i$ $\phi_1\ (\alpha) = -\alpha(\alpha^2 - 1)/12$ $\phi_2\ (\alpha) = (\alpha^3 + 3\alpha^2 - 4\alpha)/6$ $\phi_3\ (\alpha) = 1 - \alpha^2$ $\phi_4\ (\alpha) = -\ (\alpha^3 - 3\alpha^2 - 4\alpha)/6$ $\phi_5\ (\alpha) = \alpha(\alpha^2 - 1)/12$

Table 2 - Error propagation formulae

<table>
<tr><th>Scheme</th><th>General formulae</th><th>Specific functions</th></tr>
<tr><td>2P-LI</td><td>$H_m(N,\alpha) = \{G_m(\alpha)\}^N$
with
$\alpha = \beta - \text{int}(\beta)$</td><td>$G_m(\alpha) = \{\phi_1(\alpha) + \phi_2(\alpha)\, e^{-i\lambda_m}\}\, e^{i\alpha\lambda_m}$</td></tr>
<tr><td>3P-LI</td><td rowspan="2">$H_m(N,\alpha) = \{p_m(N,\alpha) . G_m(\alpha) + q_m(N,\alpha) . G_m(\alpha+s)\} .$
$. \exp(i N\lambda_m \alpha) . \exp(i\lambda_m r)$
with
$p_m(N,\alpha) = S_m(\alpha) . p_m(N-1,\alpha) + S_m(\alpha+s) . q_m(N-1,\alpha)$
$q_m(N,\alpha) = Q_m(\alpha) . p_m(N-1,\alpha) + Q_m(\alpha+s) . q_m(N-1,\alpha)$
$p_1 = 1 - |r|; \quad q_1 = |r|$
$\alpha = \begin{cases} \beta - \text{int}(\beta) & \text{if int}(\beta) \text{ odd} \\ \beta - \text{int}(\beta) + 1 & \text{if int}(\beta) \text{ even} \end{cases}$
$s = \begin{cases} 1 & \text{if int}(\beta) \text{ odd} \\ -1 & \text{if int}(\beta) \text{ even} \end{cases}$
$r = \begin{cases} o & \text{for corner nodes} \\ s & \text{for middle nodes} \end{cases}$</td><td>$G_m(\alpha) = \phi_1(\alpha)\, e^{i\lambda_m} + \phi_2(\alpha) + \phi_3(\alpha)\, e^{-i\lambda_m}$
$S_m(\alpha) = \phi_1(\alpha)\, e^{i\lambda_m} + \phi_3(\alpha)\, e^{-i\lambda_m}$
$Q_m(\alpha) = \begin{cases} \phi_2\, e^{i\lambda_m} & \text{for corner nodes} \\ \phi_2\, e^{is\lambda_m} & \text{for middle nodes} \end{cases}$</td></tr>
<tr><td>5P-HI</td><td>$G_m(\alpha) = \phi_1(\alpha) . e^{i2\lambda_m} + \phi_2(\alpha) . e^{i\lambda_m} + \phi_3(\alpha) + \phi_4(\alpha) . e^{-i\lambda_m} +$
$+ \phi_5(\alpha) . e^{-i2\lambda_m}$
$S_m(\alpha) = \phi_2(\alpha) . e^{i\lambda_m} + \phi_4(\alpha) . e^{-i\lambda_m}$
$Q_m(\alpha) = \begin{cases} \phi_1(\alpha) . e^{i3\lambda_m} + \phi_2(\lambda) . e^{i\lambda_m} + \phi_3(\alpha) . e^{-i\lambda_m} & \text{for corner nodes} \\ e^{is\lambda_m} [\phi_1(\alpha) . e^{i2\lambda_m} + \phi_2(\alpha) + \phi_3(\alpha)\, e^{-i2\lambda_m}] & \text{for middle nodes} \end{cases}$</td></tr>
</table>

Table 3 - Amplitudes and numerical amplifications of the Fourier components, for t=T=9600, N=100 and Δx=200.

$L_m / \Delta x$	Amplitude (exact)	Numerical Amplification 2P-LI	3P-LI	5P-HI
Infinity	.04859	1.000	1.000	1.000
68.00	.04823	.925	.999	1.000
34.00	.04717	.731	.995	1.000
22.67	.04545	.494	.978	1.001
17.00	.04315	.285	.937	1.004
13.60	.04036	.141	.860	1.008
11.33	.03720	.059	.746	1.013
9.71	.03378	.021	.601	1.018
8.50	.03023	.007	.443	1.017
7.56	.02665	.002	.295	1.005
6.80	.02314	.000	.174	.973
6.18	.01981	.000	.090	.910
5.67	.01670	.000	.040	.808
5.23	.01387	.000	.015	.665
4.86	.01136	.000	.004	.492
4.53	.00916	.000	.001	.317
4.25	.00728	.000	.000	.170
4.00	.00570	.000	.000	.070
3.78	.00440	.000	.000	.020
3.58	.00334	.000	.000	.024
3.40	.00250	.000	.000	.052
3.24	.00185	.000	.005	.081
3.09	.00134	.000	.030	.119
2.96	.00096	.000	.083	.156
2.83	.00068	.000	.206	.176
2.72	.00047	.000	.426	.191
2.62	.00032	.000	.781	.188
2.52	.00022	.000	1.182	.182
2.43	.00015	.000	1.533	.133
2.34	.00010	.000	1.700	.100
2.27	.00006	.000	1.833	.000
2.19	.00004	.000	1.250	.000
2.13	.00002	.000	1.000	.000
2.06	.00002	.000	.000	.000
2.00	.00001	.000	.000	.000
1.94	.00001	.000	.000	.000
1.89	.00000	-.000	-.000	-.000
1.84	.00000	-.000	-.000	-.000

Table 4 - Phases of the Fourier components, for t=T=9600, N=100 and Δx=200.

$L_m / \Delta x$	Exact	2P-LI	3P-LI	5P-HI
68.00	3.137	3.138	3.139	3.137
34.00	-.009	.001	.007	-.009
22.67	3.128	-3.132	-3.105	3.128
17.00	-.018	.018	.088	-.018
13.60	3.119	-3.123	-2.988	3.119
11.33	-.028	.014	.214	-.028
9.71	3.109	-3.133	-2.893	3.106
8.50	-.037	.004	.245	-.047
7.56	3.100	-3.140	-2.937	3.077
6.80	-.046	.000	.143	-.089
6.18	3.091	-3.142	-3.058	3.022
5.67	-.055	.000	.039	-.149
5.23	3.082	-3.142	-3.127	2.973
4.86	-.065	.000	.004	-.164
4.53	3.072	-3.142	-3.141	3.009
4.25	-.074	.000	.000	-.084
4.00	3.063	3.142	-3.142	3.104
3.78	-.083	.000	.000	-.002
3.58	3.054	3.142	3.141	-3.118
3.40	-.092	.000	-.001	.050
3.24	3.045	3.142	3.139	-3.064
3.09	-.102	.000	.000	.103
2.96	3.035	3.142	-3.121	-3.019
2.83	-.111	.000	.099	.134
2.72	3.026	-3.142	-2.858	-3.008
2.62	-.120	.000	.571	.124
2.52	3.017	3.142	-2.301	-3.037
2.43	-.129	.000	1.007	.079
2.34	3.008	-3.142	-2.070	-3.090
2.27	-.138	.000	1.046	.026
2.19	2.999	-3.141	-2.240	-3.132
2.13	-.148	.000	.560	.000
2.06	2.990	-3.141	-3.008	-3.141
2.00	-.157	.000	.000	-.001
1.94	2.981	3.141	2.906	3.141
1.89	-.165	.001	-1.260	-.026
1.84	2.972	-3.139	1.636	2.883

VI International Conference on Finite Elements in Water Resources, Lisboa, Portugal, June 1986

Accuracy Criteria for Advection-Dispersion Models

W.K.H. Kinzelbach
Institut für Wasserbau, Universität Stuttgart, Stuttgart, Federal Republic of Germany
E.O. Frind
Institute for Groundwater Research, University of Waterloo, Waterloo, Ontario, Canada

ABSTRACT

The accuracy of numerical solutions of the advection-dispersion equation can depend critically on the discretization chosen. Rigorous criteria to guarantee accuracy are available for 1-D models in the form of constraints on the grid Peclet and Courant numbers, and corresponding criteria for 2-D and 3-D models are often arrived at by analogy. This procedure is however strictly applicable only in principal directions of transport because the cross-derivative terms arising in a general formulation cannot be accounted for.

A 2-D finite element solution using linear elements was investigated and it was found that the accuracy not only depends on the grid size but also on the orientation of the principal axes of the dispersion tensor relative to the grid. This is due to the innate anisotropy of the chosen grid. As a consequence, criteria based on the grid Peclet and Courant numbers only are not sufficient to guarantee exact results if the grid orientation is arbitrary. Several options to control this problem are discussed and guidelines for the design of grids are given.

INTRODUCTION

In the numerical solution of the advection-dispersion equation, certain criteria must be fulfilled to guarantee accuracy. These concern, firstly, the advective part of the equation which introduces hyperbolic behaviour. To keep the equation overall parabolic in character, the discretization must fulfill the Peclet number criterion. Secondly, the Courant number criterion, which limits the temporal discretization, must be satisfied. These criteria are arrived at by rigorous derivation (Daus *et al.*, 1985) in the one-dimensional case. Results can be transferred to the two-dimensional case without difficulty as long as the discretization is oriented along the principal direction of the dispersion tensor, thus decoupling longitudinal advective-dispersive transport and purely dispersive transverse transport. In more than one dimension the two criteria are, however, not sufficient to guarantee accuracy. Particularly in the case of strong anisotropy of dispersion and unrestricted orientation of flow relative to the grid, an inaccuracy may be observed which is due to the dispersive part of the equation. The magnitude of the error depends on the orientation of the grid relative to the principal axes of the dispersivity tensor, or the flow direction.

The same type of error is also present in the solution of the purely parabolic equation of groundwater flow. However, it is not often apparent in flow modelling for two reasons. Firstly, in two-dimensional horizontal-plane modelling, there is usually little or no anisotropy of the transmissivity tensor. Secondly, in two-dimensional vertical-plane modelling, the grid is usually aligned with the stratification and therefore the principal axes of the permeability tensor will automatically coincide with the grid axes.

THE PHENOMENON

The phenomenon of grid anisotropy is demonstrated by using a standard Galerkin finite element model (see for example Kinzelbach, 1986) to solve the advection-dispersion equation in two dimensions for the case of a permanent point source in parallel flow. The physical parameters are:

fluid velocity $u = 1$ m/d
source strength $w = 1$ kg/d
longitudinal dispersivity $\alpha_L = 100$ m
transverse dispersivity $\alpha_T = 10$ to 50 m.

Three test cases are investigated. Discretization and boundary conditions for these three cases are shown in figure 1. The element side lengths are $\Delta x = \Delta y = 50$ m, the time step is $\Delta t = 50$ days, and the final simulation time is 1000 days. The elements are obtained by halving from a square discretization grid, thus arriving at right isosceles triangles. The test cases correspond to:

(1) flow parallel to one of the short sides of the triangle,
(2) flow parallel to the hypotenuse of the triangle,
(3) flow perpendicular to the hypotenuse of the triangle.

The analytical solution for $\alpha_L = 100$ m and $\alpha_T = 10$ m, in the form of concentration contours at 1000 days, is given in figure 2. The corresponding numerical solutions for the three cases are given in figures 3a, b, and c.

In all cases, both the grid Peclet number and Courant number criteria are satisfied. These criteria are defined as (Daus *et al.*, 1985):

$$P = \frac{u\Delta L}{D_{LL}} = \frac{\Delta L}{\alpha_L} \leq 2 \tag{1}$$

$$C = \frac{u\Delta t}{\Delta L} \leq \frac{P}{2} \tag{2}$$

where ΔL is the spatial discretization in the flow direction, Δt is the temporal discretization, u is the fluid velocity, and D_{LL} is the longitudinal dispersion coefficient, with α_L being the longitudinal dispersivity.

From figures 3, we observe that the solution with the flow direction perpendicular to the element hypotenuse is less accurate than the other two solutions. The width of the plume is enlarged artificially. As long as the direction of flow is aligned with the sides of the triangular elements, however, the numerical results are in good agreement with the analytical solution.

We repeat cases 2 and 3 with the transverse dispersivity increased from 10 to 20 and 50 m respectively (figures 4 and 5). At a transverse dispersivity of 20 m, the two grid orientations still produce significantly different results (figures 4a and b), while at 50 m, the directional bias has essentially disappeared (figures 5a and b).

Further experiments (not shown) with flow directions other than at 45 degrees show that the grid bias effect decreases as the flow direction approaches one of the grid lines.

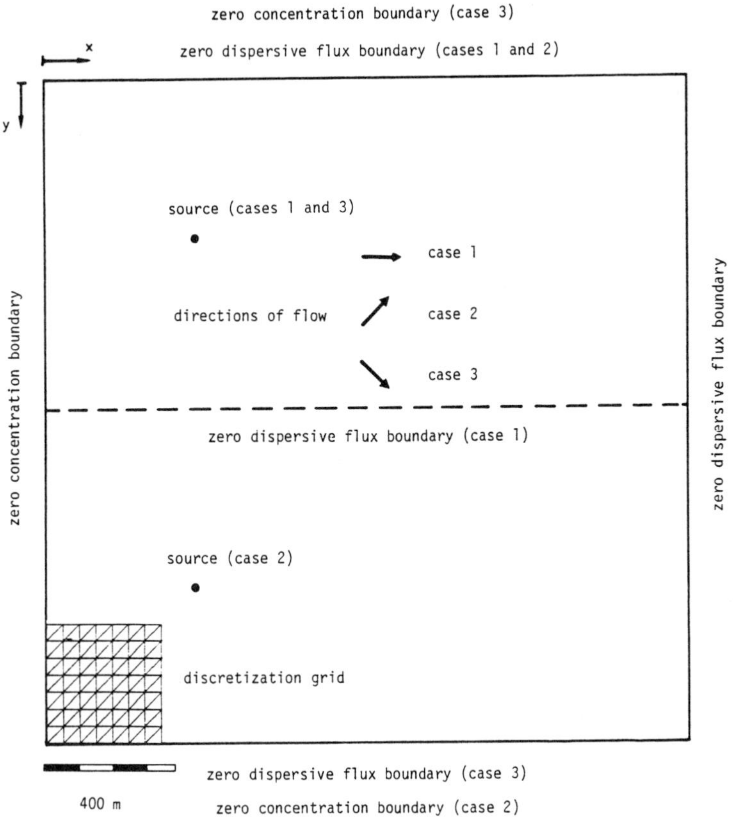

Figure 1 Discretization and boundary conditions for test cases

THE MECHANISM

The reason for the different behaviour of the grid for different directions of flow is easily understood. Figures 6a and b show the interpolation function of the elements in relation to the actual profile of the solution in the transverse cross-section of the plume near the source. If flow is aligned with the hypotenuse of the element, the ridge of the concentration distribution always coincides with a hypotenuse along which the adjacent facets of the interpolation function can fold in a tent-shaped form descending to either side of the ridge. If flow is perpendicular to the hypotenuse of the elements, this is no longer the case. For symmetry reasons, the function values at the two nearest nodes on either side of the ridge must be equal. The sharp ridge cannot be resolved (figure 6b). Instead, the plume is artificially widened. At the same time, the plume shortens to preserve mass. It is this plume shortening that is most apparent in the results.

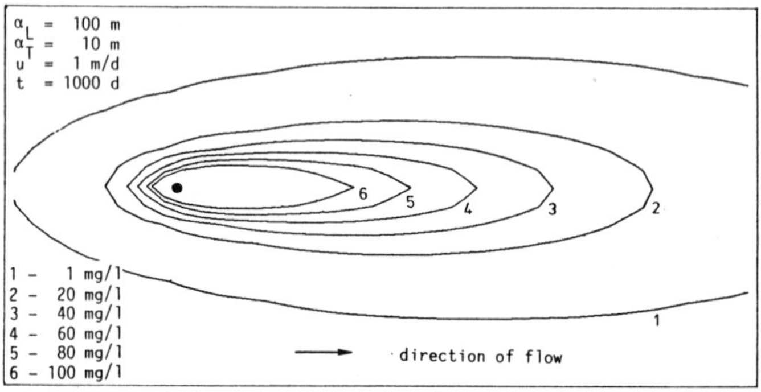

Figure 2 Analytical solution, α_L=100 m, α_T=10 m, at 1000 days

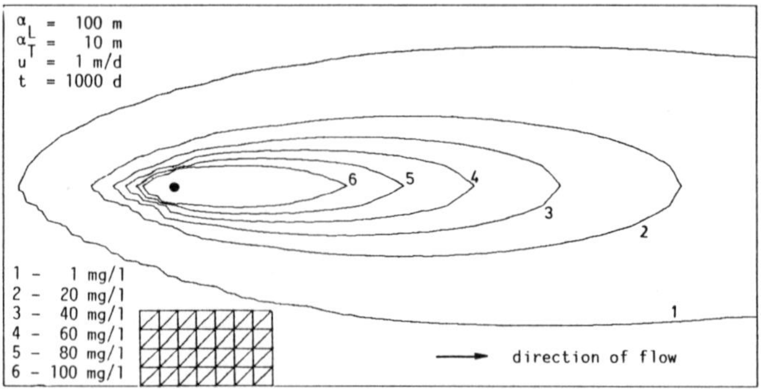

Figure 3a Solution for case 1, α_T=10 m

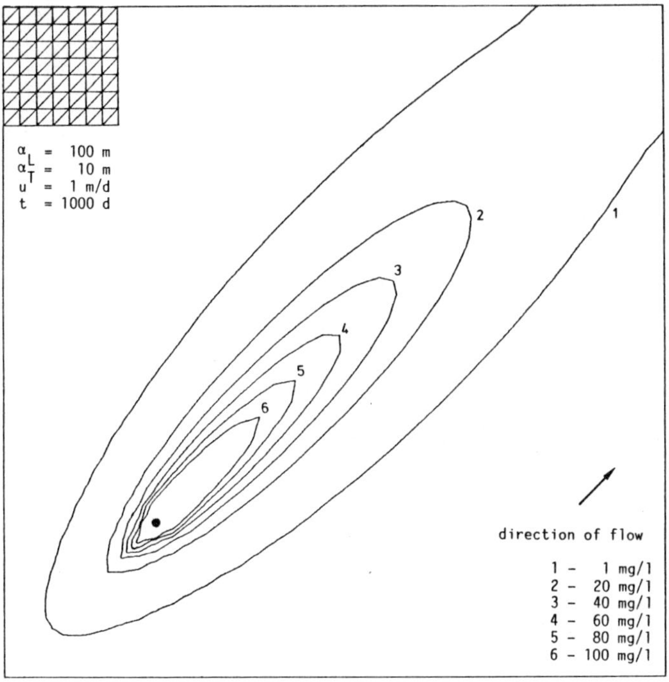

Figure 3b Solution for case 2, α_T=10 m

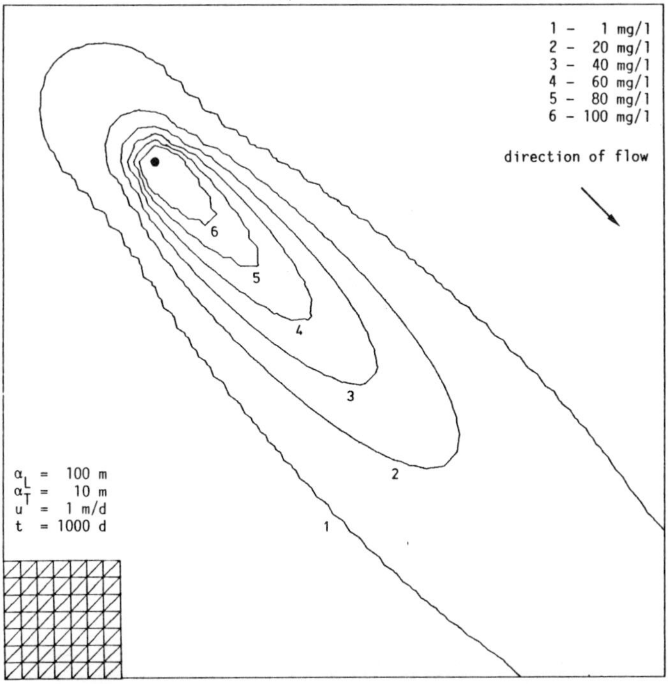

Figure 3c Solution for case 3, α_T=10 m

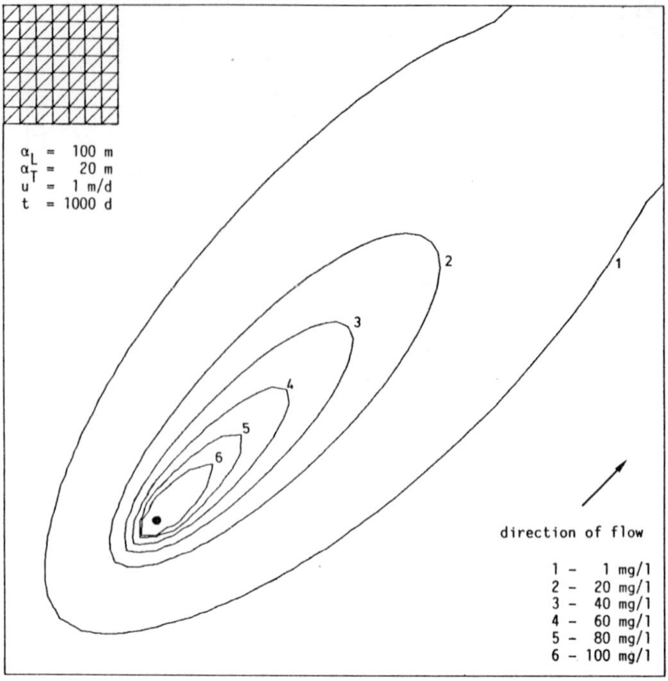

Figure 4a Solution for case 2, α_T=20 m

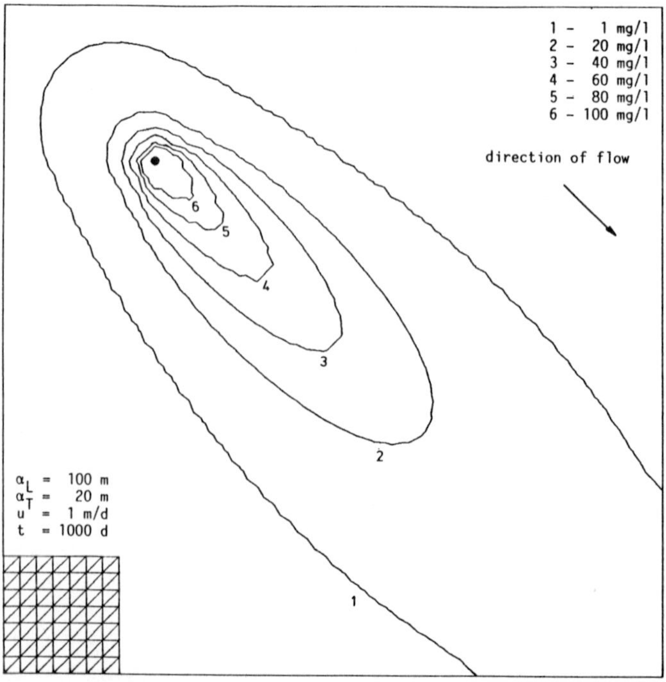

Figure 4b Solution for case 3, α_T=20 m

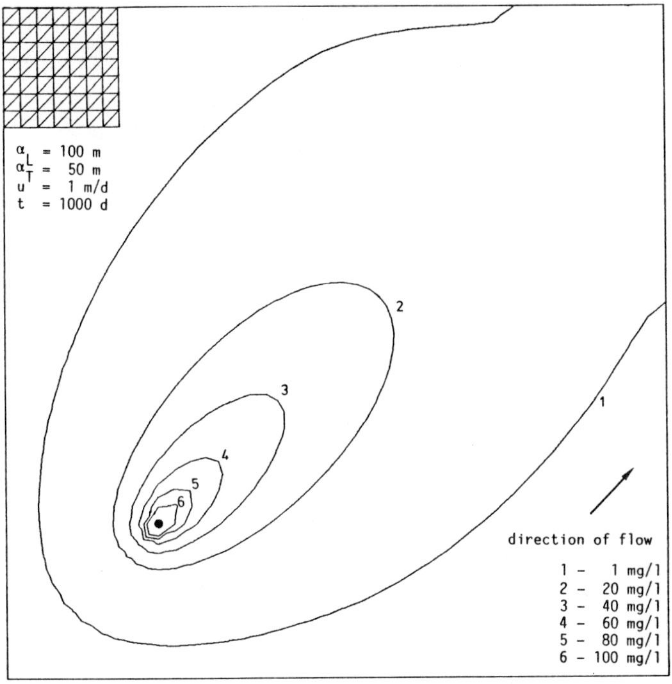

Figure 5a Solution for case 2, α_T=50 m

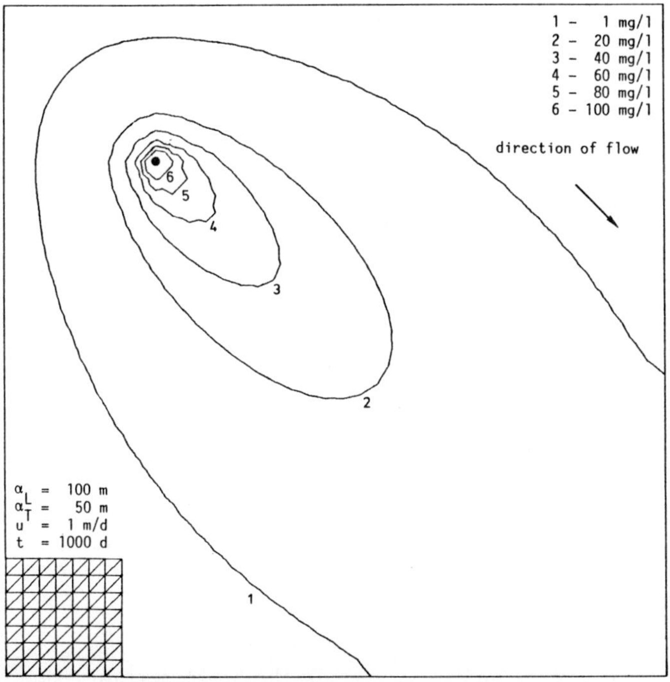

Figure 5b Solution for case 3, α_T=50 m

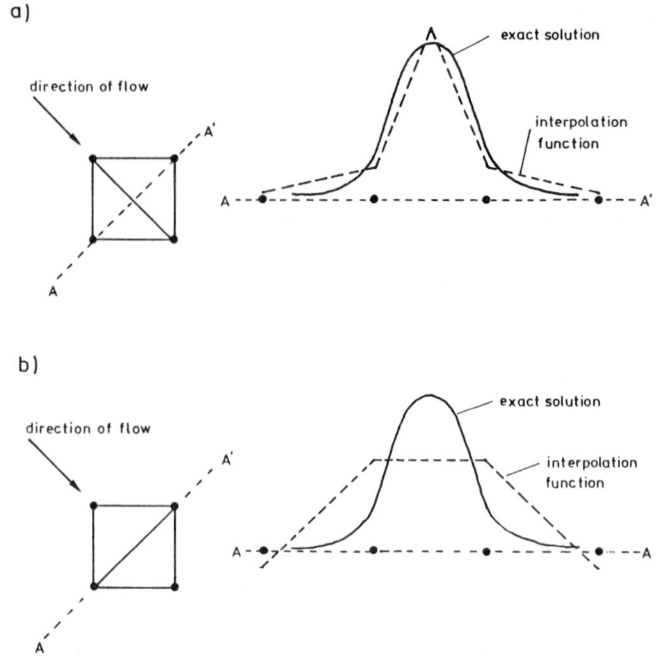

Figure 6 Resolution of plume ridge
(a) Plume axis aligned with element sides
(b) Plume axis orthogonal to element hypotenuse

The evolution of the plume first passes through a transient phase before reaching the steady-state phase. Plume stabilization starts in the region surrounding the source and gradually extends outward and downstream. In order to obtain an accurate numerical solution, the discretization must be adequate for handling both of these phases.

The transient-phase numerical solution can be characterized by a typical time step during which the front is advected over some distance ΔL. If the grid satisfies the Courant criterion, ΔL will be no greater than the element length. A dirac delta function introduced at the beginning of this advective step will be dispersed numerically in the transverse direction by an amount that depends on the resolving power of the grid in that direction. In cases 1 and 2, the numerical solution will spread over 2 elements transversely, while in case 3 it will spread over 3 elements. The standard deviation σ_n of the numerical solution is found to be $1/6\sqrt{6}\Delta x$, $1/6\sqrt{3}\Delta x$, and $\sqrt{5/3}\Delta x$, (0.408 Δx, 0.289 Δx, and 1.291 Δx) for cases 1, 2, and 3 respectively. For no artificial widening, the transverse numerical spread should be no greater than the corresponding physical spread over the same distance. The standard deviation of the transverse profile due to physical dispersion is:

$$\sigma = \sqrt{2\alpha_T \Delta L} \tag{3}$$

where $\Delta L = \Delta x$ in the case of flow in the horizontal direction and $\Delta L = \sqrt{2}\Delta x$ in the case of flow in the diagonal direction. Setting

$$\sigma_n \leq \sigma \tag{4}$$

results in minimum values of $\alpha_T \geq 1/12\Delta x$, $1/24\Delta x$, and $5/12\sqrt{2}\Delta x$ (4.167, 2.083, and 29.46 m) respectively for cases 1, 2 and 3. Thus, case 2 is twice as efficient as case 1 in terms of the transverse discretization required to resolve a given value of α_T, while case 3 is only about one fourteenth as efficient as case 2. This factor of fourteen is solely a result of the different orientation of the hypotenuse of the triangular element.

Unfortunately, the spreading observed in the plumes of figures 3, 4, and 5 is not fully explained by the above analysis of the transient phase behaviour. The plumes for the two opposing flow directions with $\alpha_T = 20$ m (figures 4a and b) still show a large discrepancy between them, while those with $\alpha_T = 50$ m seem to be just in agreement. It may be concluded therefore that with the element hypotenuse perpendicular to the flow direction and the given physical parameters, artificial spreading will persist up to a value of $\alpha_T = 50$ m.

The cause of this spreading will have to be sought in the resolution of the steady-state phase of the plume evolution. The plumes shown in figures 3, 4, and 5 have all reached steady state down to contour 2 at 1000 days. The steady-state analytical solution for a point source (Bear, 1979, p. 274) takes the form of a modified zero-order Bessel function and the ridge that connects to the point source and extends along the plume centerline exists throughout the transient and steady-state phases. It is clear that, unless the element edges coincide with that ridge, the error due to the resolution of the ridge will dominate the numerical solution at all times.

The same effect can be obtained with the steady-state groundwater flow (Laplace) equation when a constant-potential line source is placed at a 45-degree angle in the interior of the grid, using the same grid orientations as above. This supports the contention that the artificial spreading phenomenon is due strictly to the resolution of the dispersive component. The satisfaction of the Peclet and Courant number criteria alone is therefore not sufficient to guarantee the accuracy of the numerical solution of the advection-dispersion equation. Additional criteria must be sought. We will however limit our discussion at this time to qualitative aspects of the phenomenon and leave the more rigorous quantitative analysis for later.

Fortunately, the situation depicted in Figure 3c, where the flow vector crosses the hypotenuse of a right isosceles triangle, is a worst-case situation. The artificial spreading phenomenon will be less pronounced when the flow vector crosses a short side of the triangle, or when there is only a slight deviation of the flow with respect to the grid axes. Also, the point source represents a worst-case situation. Patch or Gaussian-type sources are generally easier to resolve numerically.

IMPLICATIONS AND REMEDIES

One way to reduce the directional bias is by alternating the orientation of the triangles. Figure 7 shows that, in this case, the solution with $\alpha_T = 10$ m will lie between those obtained with the two directionally-biased grids (figures 3b and c).

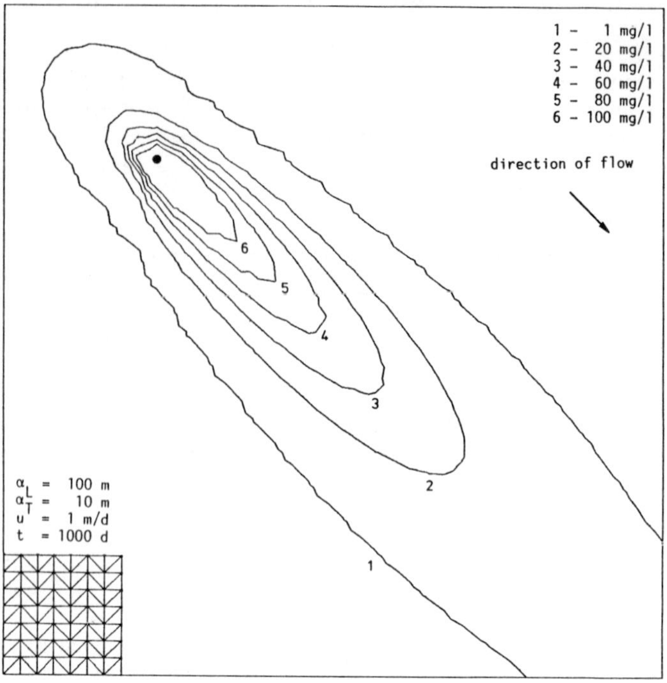

Figure 7 Solution with alternating bias grid, α_T=10 m

Higher degree interpolation functions also show less directional preference as they adapt more flexibly to constraints. An example is given in figure 8 where rectangular elements with bilinear interpolation functions (Wang and Anderson, 1982, p. 155) are used. The bilinear quadrilateral elements can bend, with the sides remaining straight, and they are therefore better able to approximate a ridge than the stiff triangles. This is shown by figure 8 in which flow is diagonally across the elements. The results compare favourably with the analytical solution (figure 2). A cost penalty is paid however because the higher-order elements result in a larger matrix bandwidth.

The main implication, when using stiff elements, is that element sides should be aligned with the flow direction. This is known as a principal direction scheme. In field situations, this is practical only with a curvilinear principal direction coordinate system (Frind, 1982; Frind, 1984) and under steady-state flow conditions. Under general transient flow conditions, perfect alignment of the grid with respect to the flow field at all times is not possible with a fixed grid. It is therefore important in transport modelling to be aware of the potential for artificial spreading due to the directional bias of the grid.

In addition to having the proper grid orientation, a grid should also resolve the plume into a sufficient number of elements. In figures 3b (flow parallel to element hypotenuse) and 5b (flow perpendicular to element hypotenuse), the distance between the source and the 1-percent contour in the transverse direction is resolved by about 7

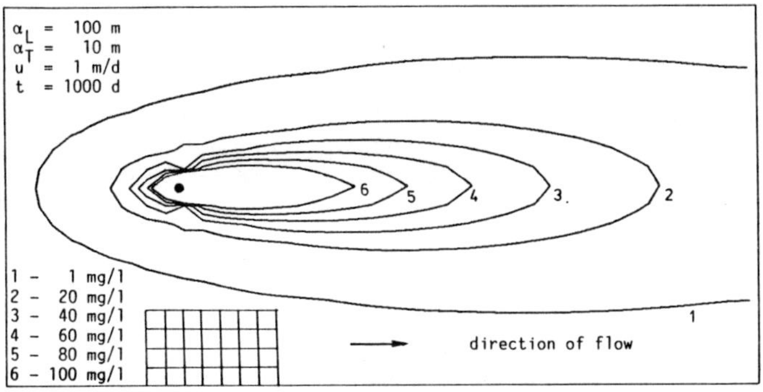

Figure 8a Solution with bilinear elements, case 1, α_T=10 m

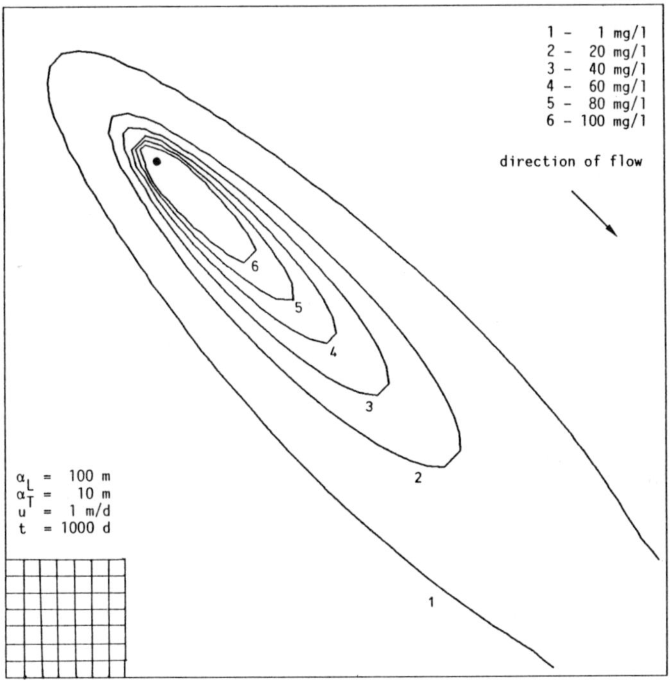

Figure 8b Solution with bilinear elements, case 3, α_T=10 m

elements, the discretizations being $1/2\sqrt{2}\Delta x$ and $\sqrt{2}\Delta x$ respectively. This seems to provide adequate resolution in both cases.

In field situations, transverse dispersivities can be anywhere from one to three orders of magnitude smaller than longitudinal dispersivities. The smaller values are encountered in vertical plane modelling where transverse dispersion can be as low as of the order of molecular diffusion. The grid discretization in the transverse direction will, therefore, be smaller than the longitudinal discretization in general. Fortunately, the width of a plume varies only as $\sqrt{\alpha_T}$, so a two-order-of-magnitude decrease in α_T would require only a one-order-of-magnitude decrease in the element width for an equivalent resolution.

The same type of criterion will of course apply also to the longitudinal dispersive component of the advection-dispersion equation. For most groundwater flow situations, however, the Peclet and Courant number criteria will be more critical as grid discretization constraints in the longitudinal direction. An exception would be the case of transport in a medium having extremely low permeability, where diffusive transport could be of the same order of magnitude as advective transport.

Difference methods also show the effects of directional numerical anisotropy. In upwind schemes, transverse numerical dispersion due to the advective transport aggravates the problem. Method-of-characteristics models that use finite differences in the solution of the dispersive part of the transport equation are susceptible to directional anisotropy as well.

The random walk (particle-tracking) method, on the other hand, is inherently free from directional bias in its basic computing algorithm. However, in order to obtain smooth distributions, large numbers of particles may be required. It is possible to re-introduce directional bias by averaging the particle accumulations over directionally dependent cells.

CONCLUSION

In designing a grid for a numerical advection-dispersion model, the following guidelines apply:

(a) The grid Peclet number criterion must be satisfied. The criterion applies in the direction of flow, but can be resolved into components in the case of arbitrary grid orientation. This provides a constraint on the spatial discretization.

(b) The Courant number criterion must be satisfied. This provides a constraint on the time step.

(c) The grid should be oriented, wherever possible, along principal directions of transport. If flow varies in time, the choice of a principal direction grid corresponding to the average flow field is still advisable.

(d) The plume should be resolved into an adequate number of elements in both the transverse and the longitudinal directions to provide resolution of the dispersive components. About 7-10 elements in the transverse direction between the point source and the 1-percent contour appear adequate. The discretization required for resolution of the dispersive component should vary as the square root of the dispersivity in the same direction.

The above findings should provide a basis for the development of comprehensive quantitative criteria for the design of general grid discretizations.

ACKNOWLEDGEMENTS

We wish to thank Barbara Zimmermann and Philippe Ackerer for their assistance in preparing the figures, and Don Burnett for his help in assembling the final manuscript. Financial support for this study was provided by the Deutsche Forschungsgemeinschaft.

REFERENCES

Bear, J., 1979. *Hydraulics of Groundwater.* McGraw-Hill International Book Company, New York.

Daus, A.D., E.O. Frind and E.A. Sudicky, 1985. Comparative error analysis in finite element formulations of the advection-dispersion equation. Advances in Water Resources, 8, pp. 86-95.

Frind, E.O., 1982. The Principal Direction Technique: A new approach to groundwater contaminant transport modelling. Proceedings, Fourth International Conference on Finite Elements in Water Resources, pp. 13-25 to 13-42. Technical University Hannover, Hannover, Germany.

Frind, E.O., 1984. The Principal Direction Technique for advective-dispersive transport simulation in three dimensions. Proceedings, Fifth International Conference on Finite Elements in Water Resources pp. 363-381. University of Vermont, Burlington, Vermont.

Kinzelbach, W.K.H., 1986. *Groundwater Modeling - An Introduction With Sample Programs in BASIC.* Elsevier Science Publishers, Amsterdam.

Wang, H.F. and M.P. Anderson, 1982. *Introduction to Groundwater Modeling.* W.H. Freeman and Company, San Fransisco.

SECTION 7 COASTAL AND RIVER HYDRODYNAMICS

VI International Conference on Finite Elements in Water Resources, Lisboa, Portugal, June 1986

Three-Dimensional Harmonic Model for Linearized Tidal Circulation

D.R. Lynch, F.E. Werner
Thayer School of Engineering, Dartmouth College, Hanover, NH 03755, U.S.A.

INTRODUCTION

In a previous paper, simulation of vertical detail on finite elements was introduced in the context of the laterally-averaged equations (Lynch and Hazard, 1984). Here we show full 3-D solutions to the linearized hydrodynamic equations for periodic motions. The solutions are obtained in the frequency domain which is especially attractive for the linearized system.

The solution procedure follows that introduced by Lynch and Officer (1985) for analytic cases. The key is the expression of the bottom stress. In the governing equations this is given in terms of the velocity at the bottom of the water column; but a completely equivalent representation may be derived in terms of the vertically averaged velocity. This key finding allows uncoupling of the vertical and horizontal structures, such that existing techniques for solving the 2-D shallow water equations in spectral (harmonic) form may be utilized. The entire 3-D solution is obtained by a single matrix inversion for sea level, and at most 4 tridiagonal matrix solutions for vertical structure beneath each horizontal node.

GOVERNING EQUATIONS

The linearized hydrodynamic equations for periodic motions are

$$j\omega\varsigma + \nabla \cdot (h\bar{\mathbf{V}}) = 0, \tag{1}$$

$$j\omega\mathbf{V} + \mathbf{f} \times \mathbf{V} - \frac{\partial}{\partial z}(N\frac{\partial \mathbf{V}}{\partial z}) = -g\nabla\varsigma, \tag{2}$$

where j is the imaginary unit, ω the radian frequency, and a time variation of the form $exp(j\omega t)$ is assumed. $\mathbf{V}(x,y,z)$ and $\varsigma(x,y)$ are the complex amplitudes of velocity and elevation; $\bar{\mathbf{V}}$ is the vertical average of $\mathbf{V}$; $h(x,y)$ is the bathymetric depth; $\mathbf{f}$ is the Coriolis parameter; $N(x,y,z)$ is the vertical viscosity, assumed known; and z is positive upward. The vertical average of (2) is

$$j\omega\bar{\mathbf{V}} + \mathbf{f} \times \bar{\mathbf{V}} - \frac{N}{h}\frac{\partial \mathbf{V}}{\partial z}\bigg|_{-h}^{0} = -g\nabla\varsigma \tag{3}$$

and boundary conditions at the surface and bottom are

$$N\frac{\partial \mathbf{V}}{\partial z} = h\mathbf{\Psi} \qquad (z = 0) \tag{4}$$

$$N\frac{\partial \mathbf{V}}{\partial z} = k\mathbf{V} \qquad (z = -h) \tag{5}$$

where $h\mathbf{\Psi}$ is the complex amplitude of the atmospheric forcing and k is a real linear slip coefficient.

DECOMPOSITION

The key to our solution technique is the decomposition of the horizontal and vertical structure. The procedure follows that of Lynch and Officer (1985) and has three steps: a) the expression of bottom stress in terms of $\bar{\mathbf{V}}$; b) solution of equations (1) and (3) for ς and $\bar{\mathbf{V}}$; and c) reconstruction of the vertical structure, $\mathbf{V}(x, y, z)$.

a.) Bottom Stress. Lynch and Officer (1985) show that in the absence of wind stress, the bottom stress, equation (5), may be reexpressed in terms of $\bar{\mathbf{V}}$ with both a lossy and a rotational component:

$$\left.\frac{N}{h}\frac{\partial \mathbf{V}}{\partial z}\right|_{-h} = \left(\frac{\tau^+ + \tau^-}{2}\right)\bar{\mathbf{V}} - j\left(\frac{\tau^+ - \tau^-}{2}\right)\hat{\mathbf{z}} \times \bar{\mathbf{V}} \tag{6}$$

The quantities $\tau^{\pm}$ are complex functions of (x, y) and depend on $N(z)$, h, ω, f, and k. They may be simply expressed in terms of the homogeneous solutions of the diffusion equation

$$j(\omega \pm f)\mu - \frac{d}{dz}\left(N\frac{d\mu}{dz}\right) = 0. \tag{7}$$

For simple viscosity structures, μ and therefore $\tau^{\pm}$ may be expressed in closed form (Lynch and Officer, 1985); the case $\partial N/\partial z = 0$ is especially interesting as only exponential functions are involved. For more general cases, we solve (7) on 1-D linear finite elements, requiring only tridiagonal solutions under each horizontal node.

When wind stress is present, we find two additional constant contributions to the bottom stress:

$$\left.\frac{N}{h}\frac{\partial \mathbf{V}}{\partial z}\right|_{-h} = \left(\frac{\tau^+ + \tau^-}{2}\right)\bar{\mathbf{V}} - j\left(\frac{\tau^+ - \tau^-}{2}\right)\hat{\mathbf{z}} \times \bar{\mathbf{V}} +$$

$$\mathbf{\Psi}\left(\frac{\alpha^+ + \alpha^-}{2}\right) - j\left(\frac{\alpha^+ - \alpha^-}{2}\right)\hat{\mathbf{z}} \times \mathbf{\Psi} \tag{8}$$

where $\alpha^{\pm}$ depend on the same parameters as $\tau^{\pm}$. Expressions for both appear in the Appendix.

b.) <u>Horizontal Structure</u>. Incorporation of the bottom stress expression (8) into (3) yields a vertically integrated momentum equation in ς and $\bar{\mathbf{V}}$ only:

$$j\omega\bar{\mathbf{V}} + \mathbf{f}' \times \bar{\mathbf{V}} + \tau'\bar{\mathbf{V}} = -g\nabla\varsigma + \mathbf{\Psi}' \tag{9}$$

$$\text{where} \qquad \tau' = \frac{\tau^+ + \tau^-}{2}, \tag{10}$$

$$\mathbf{f}' = \mathbf{f} - j\left(\frac{\tau^+ - \tau^-}{2}\right)\hat{\mathbf{z}}, \tag{11}$$

$$\mathbf{\Psi}' = \mathbf{\Psi}\left(1 + \frac{\alpha^+ + \alpha^-}{2}\right) - j\left(\frac{\alpha^+ - \alpha^-}{2}\right)\hat{\mathbf{z}} \times \mathbf{\Psi}. \tag{12}$$

Equation (9) is mathematically the same as the conventional vertically averaged form, except that the bottom stress parameter τ' is complex and the rotation and wind terms f' and $\mathbf{\Psi}'$ are "shifted" from their actual physical values. Solution of (1) and (9) can thus proceed as a 2-D problem. As in Lynch (1981 and 1985) we first reexpress $\bar{\mathbf{V}}$:

$$h\bar{\mathbf{V}} = -\left(\frac{(j\omega + \tau')(gh\nabla\varsigma - h\mathbf{\Psi}') - \mathbf{f}' \times (gh\nabla\varsigma - h\mathbf{\Psi}')}{(j\omega + \tau')^2 + f'^2}\right) \tag{13}$$

and use (13) to isolate ς:

$$j\omega\varsigma - \nabla \cdot \left(\frac{(j\omega + \tau')(gh\nabla\varsigma - h\mathbf{\Psi}') - \mathbf{f}' \times (gh\nabla\varsigma - h\mathbf{\Psi}')}{(j\omega + \tau')^2 + f'^2}\right) \tag{14}$$

A Galerkin solution is then obtained for ς and $\bar{\mathbf{V}}$ sequentially, using Integral Lumping. Boundary conditions on ς or $\bar{\mathbf{V}} \cdot \hat{\mathbf{n}}$ are enforced in the usual way. The horizontal structure is thus obtained by inverting only a single complex matrix for ς using a conventional banded solver. With ς known, the $\bar{\mathbf{V}}$ solution is rendered explicit by the Lumping.

c.) <u>Vertical Structure</u>. With ς and $\bar{\mathbf{V}}$ known, the vertical distribution $\mathbf{V} = u\hat{\mathbf{x}} + v\hat{\mathbf{y}}$ is readily calculated. At any point (x, y), the two functions $u \pm jv$ satisfy inhomogeneous versions of (7), with known gravity forcing. The homogeneous solutions of (7) already obtained in part (a) are used to construct $u \pm jv$ beneath each horizontal node. Straightforward conversion of $u \pm jv$ to u and v then completes the 3-D solution. Boundary conditions on normal velocity are enforced in the conventional way – by discarding the calculated version of $\mathbf{V} \cdot \hat{\mathbf{n}}$ in favor of the boundary condition.

COMPUTED RESULTS

As a first test of our approach, we studied the polar test problem as in Lynch and Gray (1979). In the more interesting variable bathymetry cases, the quantities N/h^2 and $(kh)/N$ were kept constant, in order to utilize the analytic solution which requires constant τ. Agreement with the analytic solution was excellent with no surprises.

As a more realistic and interesting test case, we ran this model for the Lake Maracaibo system, which is described by Werner and Lynch (1986). Both the steady, wind-driven circulation and the M_2 tide were computed, each with two assumptions about $N(z)$:
a.) Constant N ... in this case we used the analytic solutions for $\tau^{\pm}$ from Officer and Lynch (1985), with N=0.0025 m^2/sec.

b.) Stratified N ... in this case we solved for $\tau^{\pm}$ numerically, with N=0.0025 m^2/sec everywhere except at mid-depth, where $N = 10^{-5}\,m^2$/sec.

In all cases the bottom slip coefficient k was 0.002 m/sec; the grid was that shown in Werner and Lynch (1986); and 11 equally spaced nodal points were used to resolve the vertical direction. Since h varies with (x, y) so also does Δz. In the figures that follow we compare the flow at the surface nodes and the nodes immediately *above* the bottom-most node; for brevity we will call this latter node the bottom node.

The M_2 results for ς were substantially the same as the inviscid 2-D results (Werner and Lynch, 1986) with expected tuning of the resonance features due to friction. Figures (1a and b) show tidal velocities at the surface and at the bottom for constant N, 3.1 hours into the tidal cycle. Figures (2a and b) show a detail in the Strait of Maracaibo for the same point in time. Note the decrease in magnitude between the surface and the bottom in Figures (1a,b) and the reversal in the flow direction between the two levels at certain locations in Figures (2a,b). A clear illustration of the phase lead of the bottom vs. the top is shown in Figure (3). In Figures (4a and b) we show the effect of including the depth-dependent N; these figures should be compared to Figures (2a,b). Lastly, we show the model results for the steady wind-forced case with a north-easterly wind of magnitude 1.0 dyne/cm^2 in Figures (5a, b and c). The difference between the depth-averaged velocities (Figure 5a), the surface velocities (Figure 5b) and the bottom velocities (Figure 5c) is striking.

CONCLUSION

3-D solutions for linearized periodic motions may be obtained for arbitrary vertical viscosity structures and for arbitrary horizontal domains. The computational expense does not significantly exceed that required for the associated 2-D vertically homogeneous problem, as only tridiagonal systems are required for the vertical representation. The linear solutions are informative and relevant as first approximations to the fuller nonlinear motions. The computed results agree with observed features of the Lake Maracaibo system.

ACKNOWLEDGMENT

We would like to thank Drs. M. Fornerino and J.M. Molines of the Universidad del Zulia for providing information on the Lake Maracaibo system. The assistance of Mr. Gunnar Sidén in making the computer runs and preparing the graphical output was essential. This work was supported by the National Science Foundation, Grant No. CEE-8352226.

REFERENCES

Lynch, D.R. (1981) Comparison of spectral and time-stepping approaches for finite element circulation problems, Proc. OCEANS 81, IEEE Pub. no. 81CH1685-7, pp 810-814.

Lynch, D.R. (1985) Mass balance in shallow water simulations, Comm. Appl. Num. Meths. 1:153-159.

Lynch, D.R. and Gray, W.R. (1979) A wave equation model for finite element tidal computations, Computers and Fluids 7:207-228.

Lynch, D.R. and Hazard, J.L. (1984) Dynamic velocity profiles on simple elements, Proc. 5th Int. Conf. on Finite Elements in Water Resources, Laible et al, eds. Springer-Verlag, pp 67-73.

Lynch, D.R. and Officer, C.B. (1985) Analytic test cases for three-dimensional hydrodynamic models, Int. J. for Num. Meths. in Fluids 5:529-543.

Werner, F.E. and Lynch, D.R. (1986) Field studies with the wave equation formulation. Proc. 6th Int. Conf. on Finite Elements in Water Resources, present volume.

APPENDIX

The bottom stress parameters $\tau^{\pm}$, $\alpha^{\pm}$ in eqaution (8) are summarized here. Let μ_1, μ_2 be homogeneous solutions to the diffusion equation

$$j w \mu - \frac{d}{dZ}\left(\frac{N}{h^2}\frac{d\mu}{dZ}\right) = 0 \qquad (A1)$$

where $Z=z/h$ is the normalized depth. Next define three products of μ_1 and μ_2:

$$A = \det\begin{vmatrix} \dot{\mu}_1(0) & \dot{\mu}_2(0) \\ \mu_1(Z) & \mu_2(Z) \end{vmatrix}, \qquad (A2)$$

$$B = \det\begin{vmatrix} \dot{\mu}_1(0) & \dot{\mu}_2(0) \\ [\mu_1 - N\dot{\mu}_1/(kh)]\big|_{-1} & [\mu_2 - N\dot{\mu}_2/(kh)]\big|_{-1} \end{vmatrix} \qquad (A3)$$

and

$$E = \det\begin{vmatrix} \mu_1(Z) & \mu_2(Z) \\ [\mu_1 - N\dot{\mu}_1/(kh)]\big|_{-1} & [\mu_2 - N\dot{\mu}_2/(kh)]\big|_{-1} \end{vmatrix} \qquad (A4)$$

where the overdot indicates d/dZ. With these quantities,

$$\tau = \frac{j w \bar{A}}{B - \bar{A}} \qquad (A5)$$

$$\alpha = \frac{h}{N(0)}\left(\frac{\tau h \bar{E} - kE(-1)}{B}\right) \qquad (A6)$$

where the overbar indicates the vertical average. The expressions for τ^+ and α^+ are obtained as above with $w = \omega + f$; and for τ^-, α^- with $w = \omega - f$.

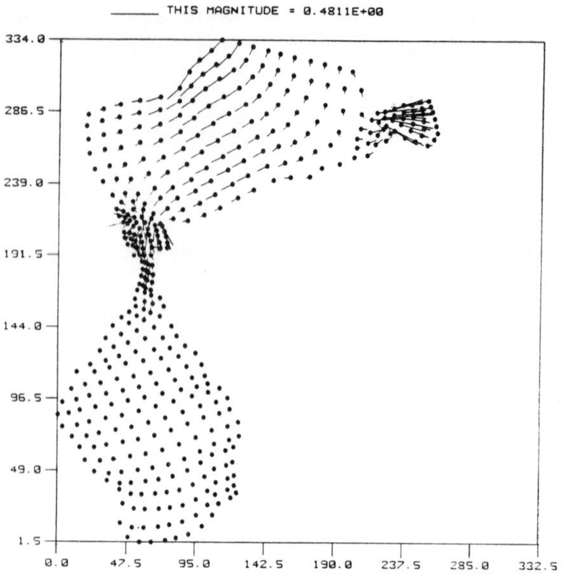

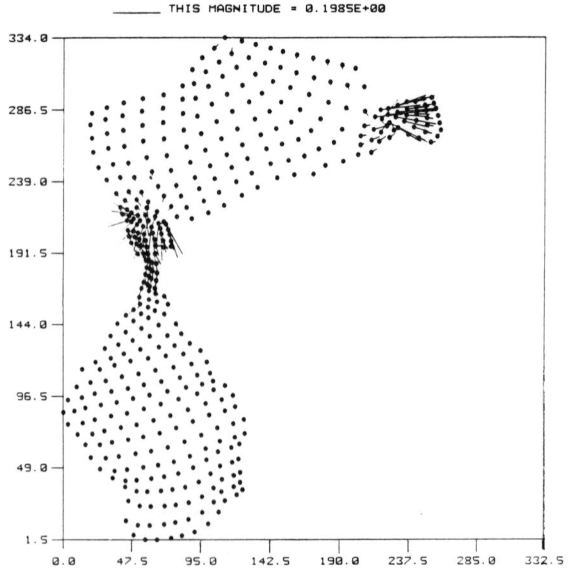

Figure 1. M_2 tidal velocities at 3.10 hours, constant N=0.0025 m^2 sec^{-1}, for the entire Lake Maracaibo system: (a, top) at the surface; and (b, bottom) one level above the bottom. Units are meters/sec, (x, y) axes in Kms.

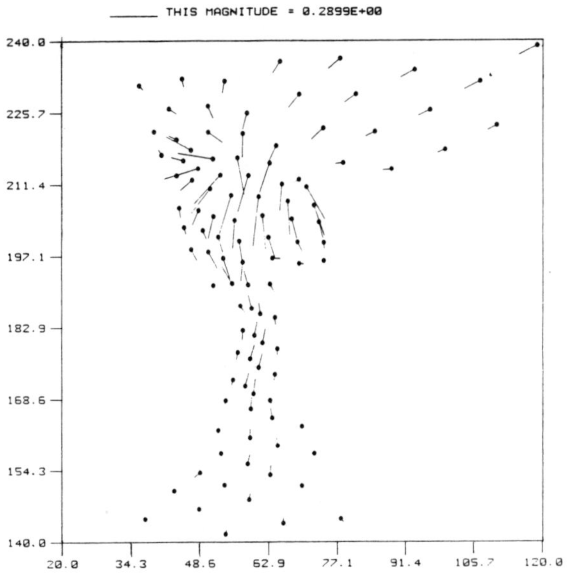

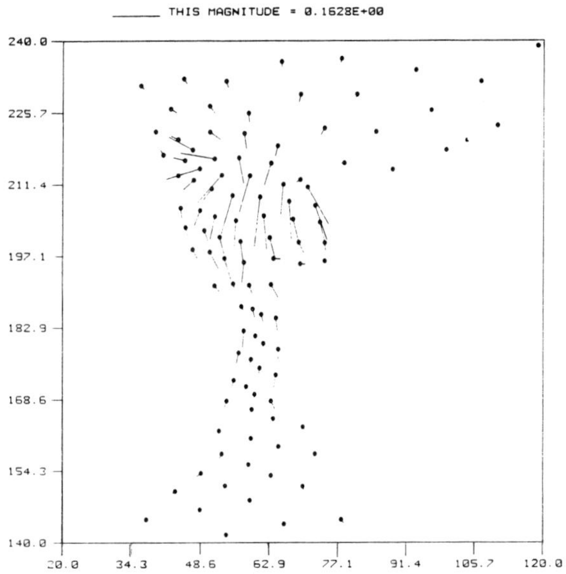

Figure 2. M_2 tidal velocities at 3.10 hours, constant N=0.0025 m^2 sec^{-1}, for the Strait of Maracaibo and El Tablazo Bay: (a, top) at the surface; and (b, bottom) one level above the bottom. Units are m/sec, (x, y) axes in Kms.

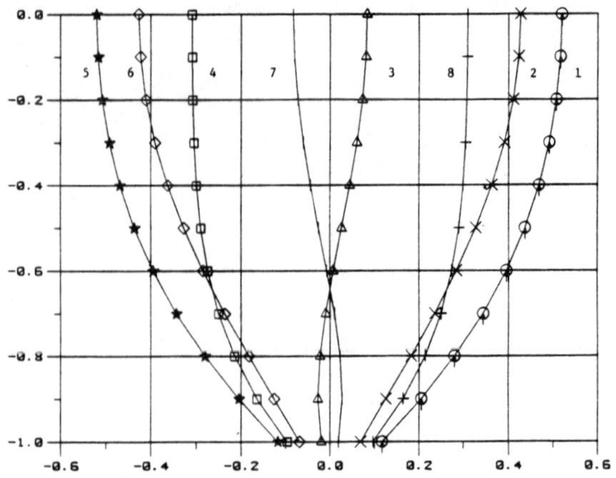

Figure 3. Vertical structure of the north-south tidal velocity at a point in the Strait starting at $t=0$ hours (curve 1) and ending at $t=10.85$ hours (curve 8). Time increment is 1.55 hours. Notice the reversal in current direction in curve (3) corresponding to the time shown in Figures (1 and 2). Horizontal axis in m/sec, vertical axis is normalized depth.

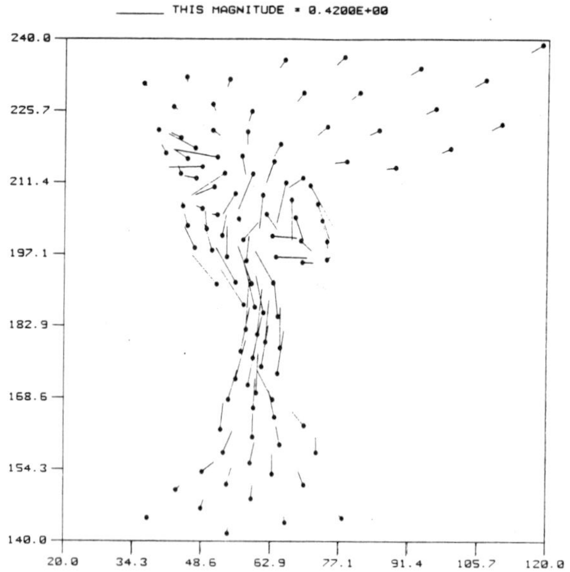

Figure 4a. Tidal velocities at 3.10 hours, variable N (see text), at the surface level. Compare to Figure (2a). Units are m/sec, (x, y) axes in Kms.

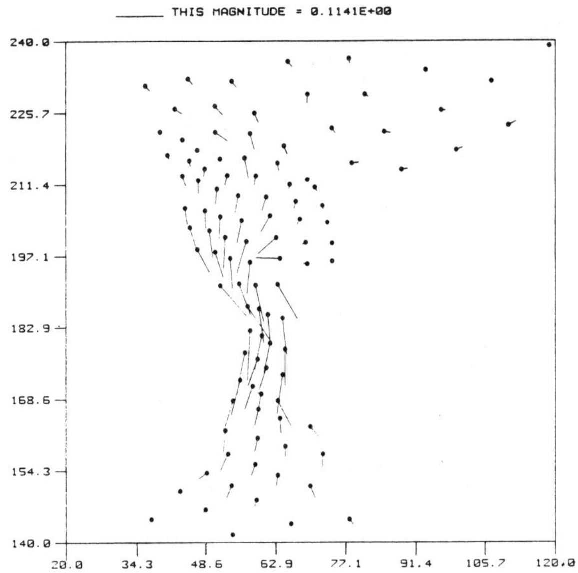

Figure 4b. Tidal velocities at 3.10 hours, variable N (see text), at one level above the bottom. Compare to Figure (2b). Units are m/sec, (x, y) axes in Kms.

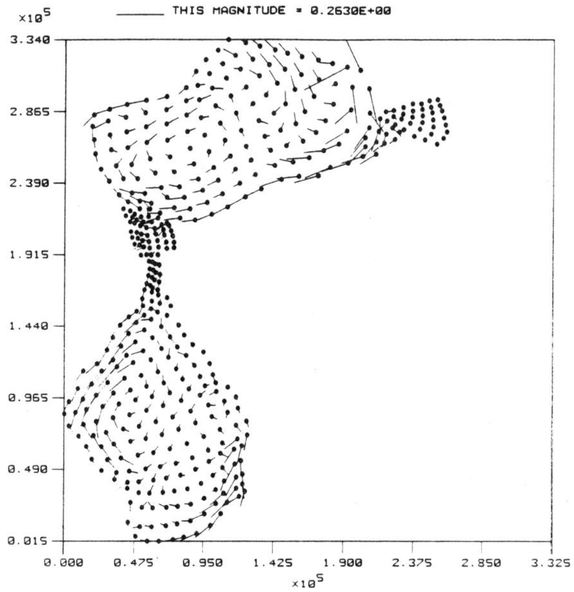

Figure 5a. Vertically averaged velocities for a steady wind (1 dyne cm^{-2}) blowing from the northeast (north is vertically upward). Units are m/sec, (x, y) axes in Kms.

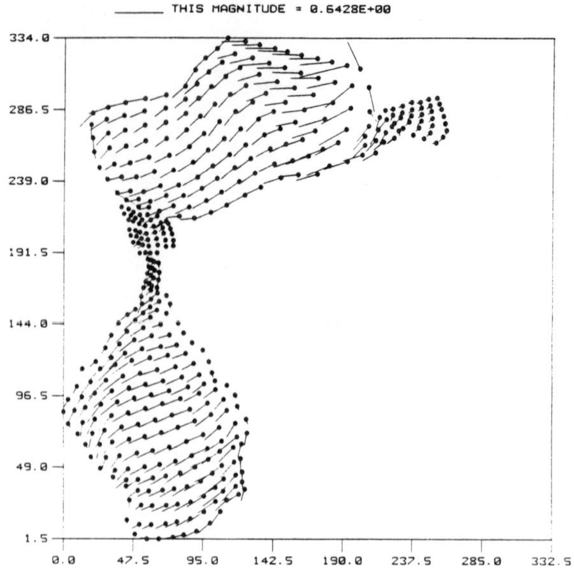

Figure 5b. Surface velocities for a steady wind from the northeast. Units are m/sec, (x, y) axes in Kms.

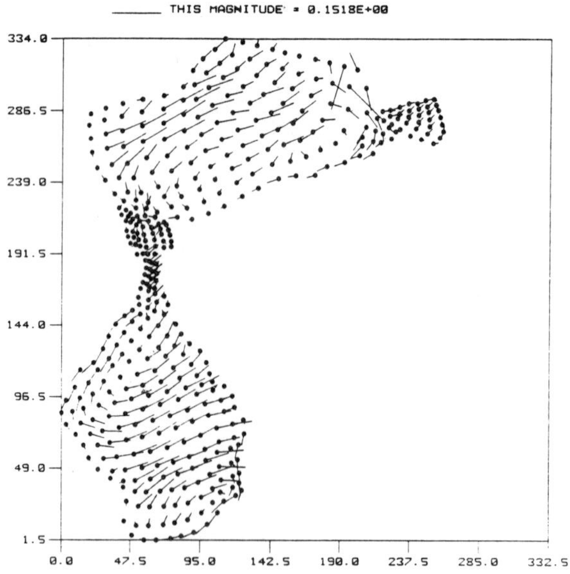

Figure 5c. Velocities one level above the bottom for a steady wind from the northeast. Units are m/sec, (x, y) axes in Kms.

VI International Conference on Finite Elements in Water Resources, Lisboa, Portugal, June 1986

Last Developments Going on with Finite Element Model for Tidal and Storm Surge Computation

S. Dalsecco, N. Goutal, A. Hauguel and J.M. Hervouet
Laboratoire National d'Hydraulique, Direction des Etudes et Recherches, Electricité de France, 6 Quai Watier 78400, Chatou

INTRODUCTION :

Shallow water equations are nowadays used for a wide range of applications. Storm surges, tides, long shore currents are the basis for coastal studies such as dilution or erosion problems.
The CEFALO code was designed at LNH to deal with those topics and finite elements discretisation was chosen to yield a precise description of coastal geometry (e.g. near harbours). The use of special boundary conditions (incident waves) and of spherical coordinates allows the computation of large scale flows. It is thus possible to work out the tides in the Channel or in the North sea. Taking into account the atmospheric forcing terms enables the code to predict the generation and propagation of storm surges. The main work in the last years concerned the interactions between tides and storm surges. In the near future studies will be done to implement a turbulence model so as to improve the accuracy of the program. Concurrently, developments are undertaken to solve problems arising from uncovered tidal flats.

After a rapid review of the equations and algorithms used, the numerical results of storm surges computed with CEFALO will be presented. Then the first results of new developments will be discussed.

I. THE EQUATIONS AND ALGORITHMS :

The shallow water (St Venant) equations are presented hereafter :

$$(1)\quad \frac{\partial z}{\partial t} + \mathrm{div}\,\vec{Q} = 0$$

$$(2)\quad \frac{\partial Q_i}{\partial t} + \mathrm{div}(Q_i\,\vec{U}) + gh\,\frac{\partial z}{\partial x_i} - K\Delta Q_i = F_i \quad (i = 1, 2)$$

z is the free surface elevation
$\vec{Q}$: flow rate (components : Q_1, Q_2)
g : gravity
h : water depth
$\vec{U}$: velocity field
$\vec{F}$: right hand side taking into account Coriolis effect, bottom friction, wind stress, atmospheric pressure gradient.

The equations are split into two parts, following the fractional step method (See [2],[4],[5],[8])

advection step :

$$(3) \quad \frac{\partial Q_i}{\partial t} + \text{div}\,(Q \quad \vec{U}^n) = 0 \qquad (i = 1, 2)$$

this step is achieved with a characteristic method, yielding $\tilde{\vec{Q}}$.

diffusion and propagation step :

$$(4) \quad \frac{\partial z}{\partial t} + \text{div}\,\vec{Q} = 0$$

$$(5) \quad \frac{\partial Q_i}{\partial t} - K\,\Delta Q_i + gh\,\frac{\partial z}{\partial x_i} = F_i \quad (i = 1, 2)$$

with initial conditions z^n , $\tilde{\vec{Q}}$
a semi-implicit discretisation has been chosen, coupled with the Glowinski method [3], this leads to the following system :

$$(6) \quad \alpha^2\, z^{n+1} - K\,\theta\alpha\,\Delta\, z^{n+1} - \theta\,\text{div}\,(C^2\,\beta\,\overrightarrow{\text{grad}}\,z^{n+1}) = W$$

$$(7) \quad \alpha\,\vec{Q}^{n+1} - K\theta\Delta\,\vec{Q}^{n+1} + C^2\beta\,\overrightarrow{\text{grad}}\,z^{n+1} = \vec{T}$$

where $C^2 = gh_m$: h_m mean value of h

$\alpha : \frac{1}{\Delta t}$

θ, β : coefficients of the semi implicitation

$W, \vec{T}$: explicit right hand sides

equation (6) is first solved thanks to the Glowinski method

which gives z^{n+1} on the boundary. Knowing z^{n+1}, Q^{n+1} obtained through equation(7). For further details see [2],[4],[5],[8].

Choice of the finite element discretisation :

All computations were carried out with triangular meshes and quadratic interpolation both for the flow rate and z.

Boundary conditions :

3 types of boundary conditions can be prescribed :

a) flux condition : $\vec{Q}$ given

b) incident wave :

$$\begin{cases} - c^2 z + K \dfrac{\partial \vec{Q}}{n} \cdot \vec{n} + c\, \overrightarrow{Q.n} = (\overrightarrow{n.u} - 1)\, c^2 \psi \\ K \dfrac{\partial \vec{Q}}{\partial n} \cdot \vec{\tau} + c\, \vec{Q} \cdot \vec{\tau} = (\vec{\tau} \cdot \vec{u})\, c^2 \psi \end{cases}$$

$\vec{n}$: exterior normal vector

$\vec{\tau}$: tangent vector

ψ : scalar function describing the wave entering the domain.

Any outgoing wave normal to the boundary may leave the domain without any reflexion.

c) friction condition :

$$\begin{cases} \alpha\, \overrightarrow{Q.t} + K \dfrac{\partial \vec{Q}}{\partial n} \cdot \vec{t} = 0 \\ \vec{Q} \cdot \vec{n} = 0 \end{cases}$$

This condition models the friction on the boundaries, it will be coupled in the future with turbulence models yielding the value of α .

II. SIMULATION OF TIDES AND STORM SURGES :

1. Simulation of the mean tide in the European continental shelf :

With the purpose to determine interaction between tide and surges, a mean tide in the European continental shelf is simulated. Interaction terms being second order terms only the principal semi diurnal (M2) constituant of the tide has been reproduced. The M2 term corresponds approximately to a mean tide. This simulation is a first step towards an accurate description of surge-tide interaction.
The finite element mesh used for the simulation is given in figure [1]. There are 1430 nodes. The domain being very large spherical coordinates have been used.

Since the major contribution to tides on the continental shelf arises from co-oscillation with the neighbouring ocean, the tide has to be specified at the seaward limit. The indicent wave condition described in section I) has been used. The main task is to determine the value of ψ describing the indicent wave entering the domain. Let's take $\psi = A \cos(\omega t - \varphi)$ where A is the amplitude, ω the pulsation and φ the phase of the wave to specify. The different values where found in the literature or interpolated from previous simulations.

The direction of the incident wave $\vec{u}$ was chosen perpendicular to the edge of the continental shelf nearly everywhere except at the southern entrance of the English Channel where the direction is approximately South-West North East.

Figures [2] and [3] represent the results of the simulation showing respectively the semi-marling and the co-tidal phases in the English Channel. They are compared with the results of Joint North Sea Modelling Group using a scale model. The tide was also computed in different harbours and compared with the tides given by the tables for a mean spring tide. The results were in good agreement with the tide - tables except for some ports like Southampton (the reason is that we didn't represent Isle of Wight.
Figure [4] represents the velocity fields computed at a given tide compared to the velocity field given by the Hydrographical Atlas of D.D.R. The velocity field is in good agreement both in magnitude and direction, with the observed velocities. Figure [5] shows the velocities computed at two points in the open sea. The results obtained are compared with data provided by the SHOM (Service Hydrographique et Océanographique de la Marine) and are very satisfactory. The figures presented so far show results obtained within the English Channel but the mean tide has been simulated in the whole continental shelf, the tidal computation being used for storm surges in the same domain.

2) <u>Simulation of the storm surge of 13 to 22 December 1982</u> :

A result of a 9 days storm surge simulation in the continental shelf is simulated. Other results can be found in [13] and [14].
In order to take into account the interaction between tide and surge we carried out a computation including the effects of the tide on the surge propagation. The surge height is then given by the difference between the global result and the tide simulation. Following our results and the meteorological conditions, we can give the following description of the storm. On December the 15th a first depression moves from West to East crossing the northern North sea, generating western winds in the Channel. From 15 to 17 December winds are oriented West North-West and a positive surge is created

propagating from North to South of the North sea. Furthermore another positive surge propagates from West to East in the English Channel. On December the 16th a surge height of 1 meter was observed at Calais and no surge was observed at Roscoff. At the same time a positive surge with increasing height moves Southward in the North sea. On December the 17 th, as winds were rapidly decreasing, the water accumulated in the Dover Straits' region reversed flows in the Channel and in the North sea. From 18 to 20 December a deepened depression passed North of the Shetlands bringing South westerly winds causing an important negative surge on the Eastern coast of great Britain (1,80 m at Lowestoft on December the 19th) and in the Northern part of the Dover Straits (1,30 m at Calais). This negative surge is followed 12 hours later by a positive surge (proceeding partly from a 1st surge coming from the English Channel through the Dover Straits and partly from a second one moving southward along the North sea.
Figure [6] shows the surge levels in Dieppe harbour for two computations :
1) only surge simulation
2) tide + surge simulation minus tide simulation.

In both cases the most important positive surges are well reproduced ; but the presence of the tide reveals important differences in the surge profiles.

In the tide+surge simulation, the computation reproduced short period oscillations corresponding to the observed surge profiles. Although some defaults remain in the simulation (for example over-estimation of the mean surge height at Boulogne), the tide + surge computation generally appears to give a better fit to the observations than did the only surge computations.

The results might be improved by taking into account the second largest constituent of the tide S2. We are now working on the effect of interaction with the velocity field during a storm surge.

III) FURTHER DEVELOPMENTS :

A lot of physical phenomena should be taken into account to improve such a model for coastal problems. Two of them seem to be important and are not included in shallow water equations : turbulence and variations of the coastline. Developments in those directions are undertaken for new applications such as erosion problems, engineering in coastal areas and so on.

1) Turbulence :

Eddies, recirculating flows are difficult problems and there are little data on turbulence with 2D equations. The main work at present is looking for a good turbulence model and testing some "mixing length" ones as well as $k-\varepsilon$ model. Physical experiments achieved at L.N.H. will yield us a way to perform comparisons and enable us to do a final choice. Concurrently, the CEFALO code is prepared for the implementation of such a model. So far two main improvements have been carried out : the friction condition mentioned in section II and the variation of the diffusion coefficient. This allowed immediately the implementation of a simple mixing-length model which is now under validation. Figure [7] shows a CEFALO computation on a backward facing step with slip conditions. Though steady limit conditions are used, the flow happens to be always unsteady, with eddies and recirculations successively appearing and vanishing. That case is under investigation, to see whether the unsteadiness is an artefact of the outflow condition or a real physical phenomenon. Other test cases are studied and even other codes are used to make a decision concerning the choice of a good turbulence model.

2) Intertidal flats :

Many numerical problems arise from moving shorelines due to intertidal flats, rocks awash and sand-banks. Two kinds of solutions may be tried : implementation of a code with a moving grid, and investigations on algorithms solving shallow waters equations and robust enough to give solutions with h = 0 (no water), in some parts of the domain. We have chosen the second solution. In fact, in regions where h tends to 0, Froude number is likely to become greater than one :

$$\left(Fr = \frac{U}{\sqrt{gh}}\right)$$

hence "transcritic" problems have to be solved. It is highly probable that the CEFALO algorithm will not be sufficient. Following the results of a previous L.N.H. study on Euler equations [9] , new formulations of shallow waters equations and new algorithms are tested. Choosing h and U (water depth and velocity) as new variables, we are now implementing an iterative method to solve the diffusion-propagation step (UZAWA algorithm see [15] and [16]). In the advection step, both h and U are advected ; this was the very goal of our formulation because upwinding h in transcritic problems seems to be a good approach. The main features of a somewhat new code would be : fractional steps, advection of h and U with the characteristics method (either in strong or weak formulation ; see [11] , [12]), UZAWA algorithm. The assets of the method would be :

a) treatment of transcritic flows (allowed by the advection of h)
b) possibility of domains with h = 0. The Uzawa algorithm is robust enough to cope with such situations.

Figure [8] displays a first attempt of computations in a one-dimensional problem. A basin with an inclined bottom is emptying because of a negative flux on the left boundary. The obtained results are a validation of points a) and b). The drawback of the method is the fact that conservativity cannot be exactly proved because of the splitting of the continuity equation. Nevertheless, mass conservation was carried out so far in our computations. A 2D code is about to be implemented after the 1D one.

CONCLUSION :

A majority of the results presented here were already obtained in various finite differences codes. It seems now that finite elements are about to give the same results, the advantage being the good description of geometry. An effort must be made as regards computational efficiency ; nevertheless it seems now that finite elements showed their mettle in difficult maritime problems. The CEFALO code is likely to be used now for predictions of storm surges in harbours. The atmospheric data would be in that case provided by a meteorological model. Although the outlook is hopeful with our new algorithm, building a general industrial tool dealing with storm surges, erosion problems, intertidal flats and turbulence still remains a remote goal.

BIBLIOGRAPHIE

[1] BENQUE J.P., LABADIE G., RONAT J. (1983). "A finite element method for the Navier Stokes equations coupled with temperature equation", submitted to the International Journal for Numerical Methods in Fluids.

[2] BENQUE J.P., LABADIE G., LATTEUX B. (1981). "A finite element method for the shallow water equations". 2nd International Conference on Numerical methods for laminar and turbulent flow, Venice, Italy.

[3] BRISTEAU M.O., GLOWINSKY R., PERIAUX J., PERRIER P., PIRONNEAU O., POIRIER G. (1978). "Applications of optimal control and finite element methods to the calculation of transonic flows and incompressible viscous flows". Rapport de recherche 78-294. Inria Laboria, 78150 Le Chesnay-Les-Renardières, France.

[4] ESPOSITO P. "Utilisation des éléments finis pour le calcul des surcotes". Rapport E.D.F. E41/83/23.

[5] ESPOSITO P. "Utilisation des éléments finis pour le calcul des surcotes en Manche". Rapport E.D.F. HE/411-82.55.

[6] FLATHER R.A. (1976). "Results from a storm surge prediction model of the North-West European Continental Shelf for April, November and December 1973". Report n° 24. Institute of Oceanographic Sciences, Bidston, UK.

[7] HEAPS N.S. (1983). "Storm surges 1967-1982" Geophys J.R. astr. Soc. (1983) 74, 331-376.

[8] LABADIE G., DALSECCO S., LATTEUX B. (1982). "Résolution des équations de St Venant par une méthode d'éléments finis". Rapport E.D.F. HE/41/82.15 et HE/42/82.34.

[9] J.M. HERVOUET
MACH 1 : Code de calcul d'écoulements transsoniques de fluides compressibles parfaits, avec hypothèse isentropique Rapport E.D.F. E 41/83.21.

[10] F. HECHT, L. REINHART.
Résolution numérique des équations de Saint-Venant par la méthode des éléments finis. Rapport provisoire INRIA (contrat 80/81.01.1101.1 2D5300).

[11] BENQUE J.P., LABADIE G., RONAT J.
Une méthode d'éléments finis pour la résolution des équations de Navier-Stokes couplées à une équation thermique (communication présentée au 4ème Symposium international sur les méthodes d'éléments finis pour les problèmes de mécanique des fluides. 26-29 juillet 1982 Tokyo - Japon).

[12] J.M. HERVOUET
Application of the method of characteristics in their weak formulation to solving two-dimensional advection equations on mesh grids.

[13] DALSECCO S.
Utilisation des éléments finis pour le calcul des surcotes. Rapport n° 3 - Rapport E.D.F. E 41/84.20

[14] DALSECCO S.
Utilisation des éléments finis pour le calcul des surcotes. Rapport n° 4 - to appear

[15] R. GLOWINSKI, M. FORTIN
Méthodes de Lagrangien augmenté - DUNOD Juin 1982

[16] J. CAHOUET, N. GOUTAL
Modélisation des équations de St Venant en écoulement transcritique : application aux bancs découvrants - Rapport E.D.F. E 41/85.

[17] JONSMOD
Joint North Sea Modelling Group Progress - Report n° 1 - volume 2 - Decembre 1977

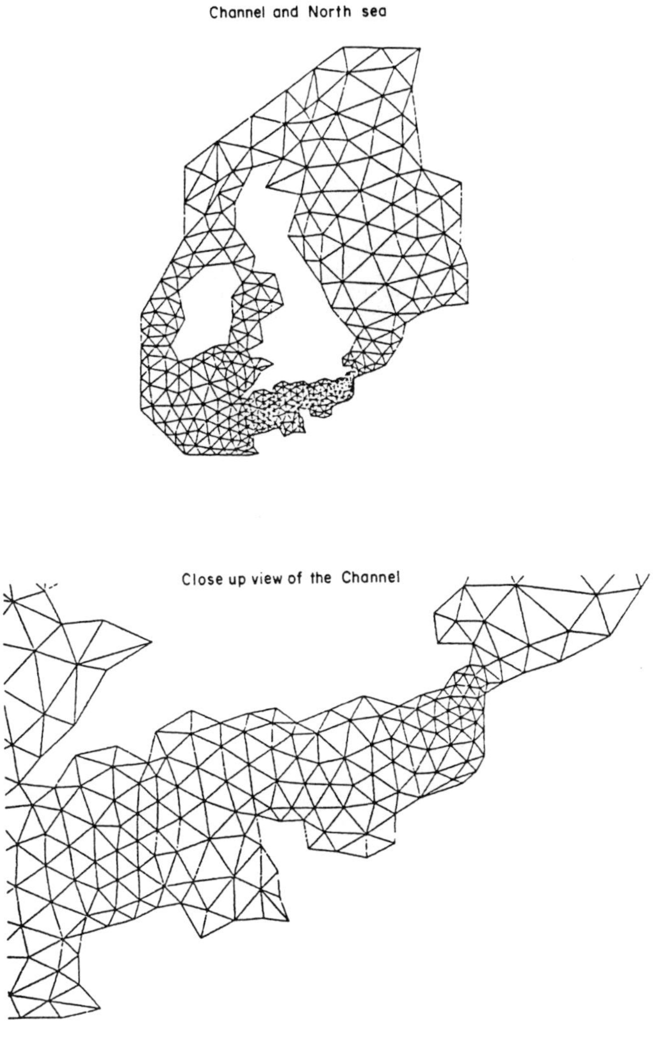

FINITE ELEMENT MESH

Figure 1

Fig.2 : SEMI-MARLING IN THE ENGLISH CHANNEL

(in cm)

CEFALO Code

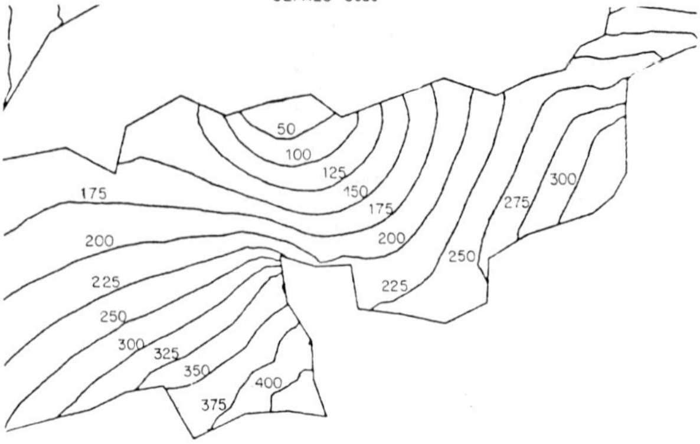

Map after LE PROVOST

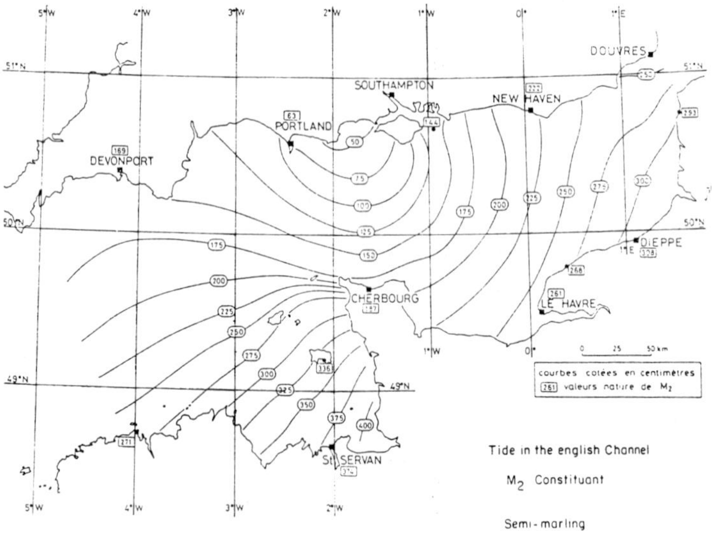

Fig. 3 : COTIDAL PHASES IN THE ENGLISH CHANNEL

(in degrees)

CEFALO Code

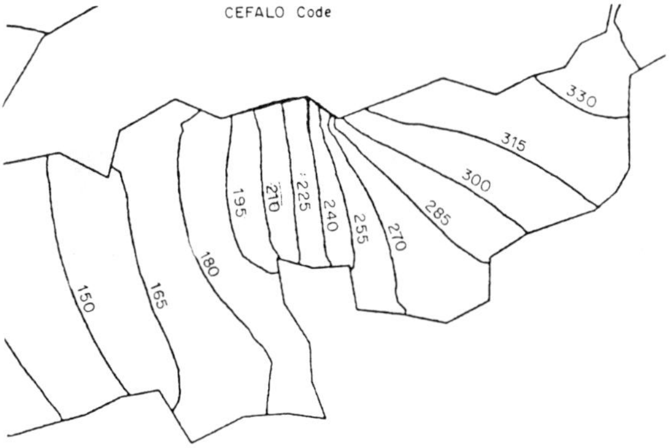

Map after LE PROVOST

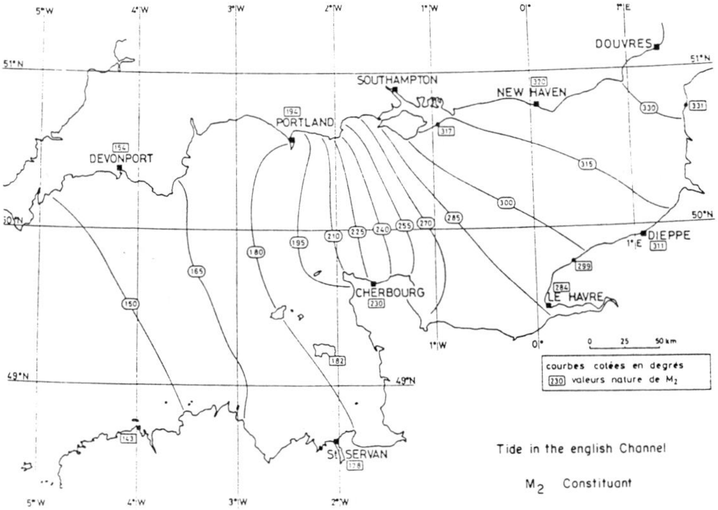

Tide in the english Channel

M_2 Constituant

Cotidal phases

VELOCITY FIELDS IN THE CHANNEL
(Three hours after the transit of the moon at Greenwich meridian)

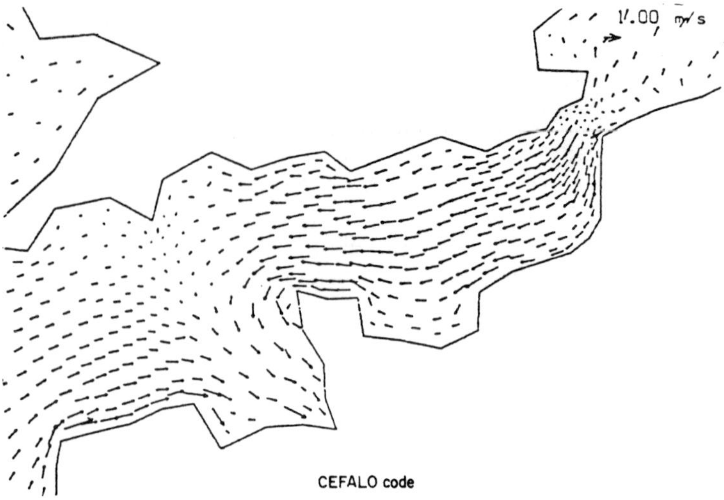

CEFALO code

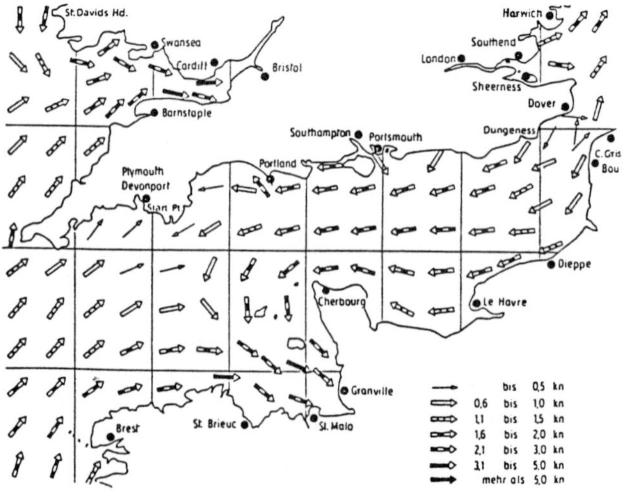

Hydrographical Atlas of DDR (coef. 95)

Figure 4

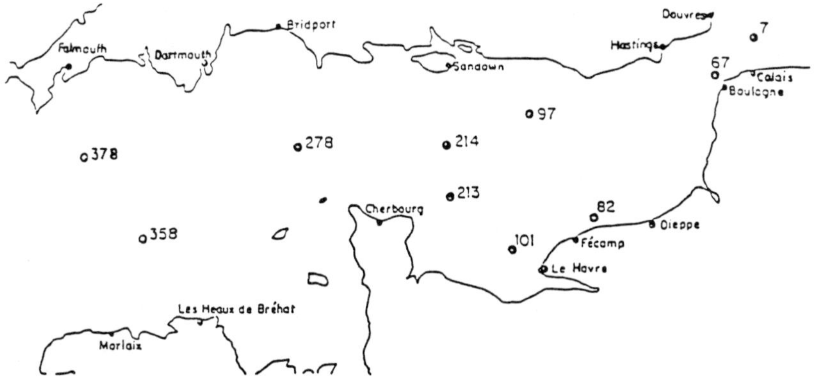

SITUATION OF MEASUREMENTS IN THE CHANNEL

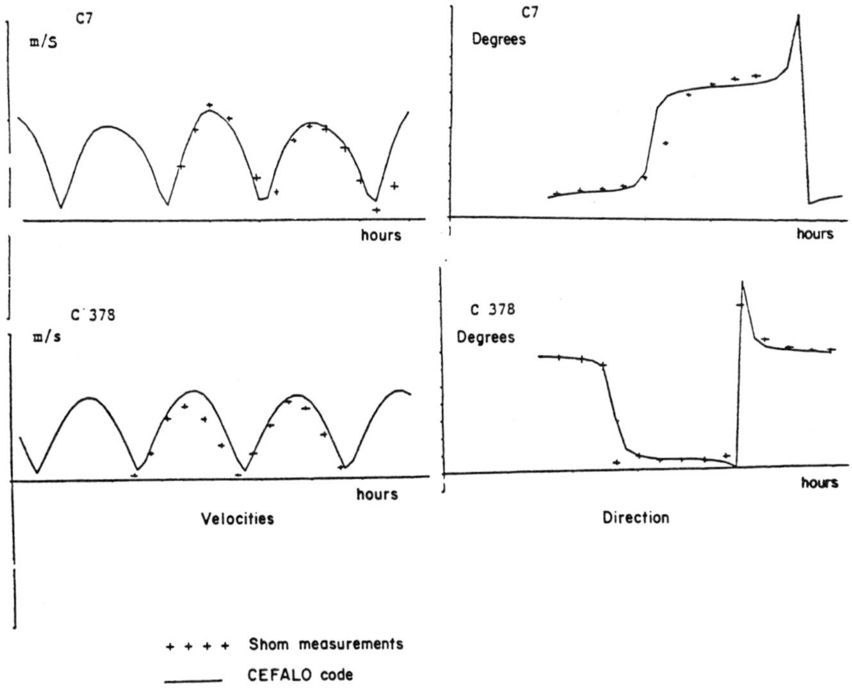

COMPARISON BETWEEN MEASUREMENTS AND COMPUTATION OF CURRENTS IN THE CHANNEL FOR A MEAN TIDE.

Figure 5

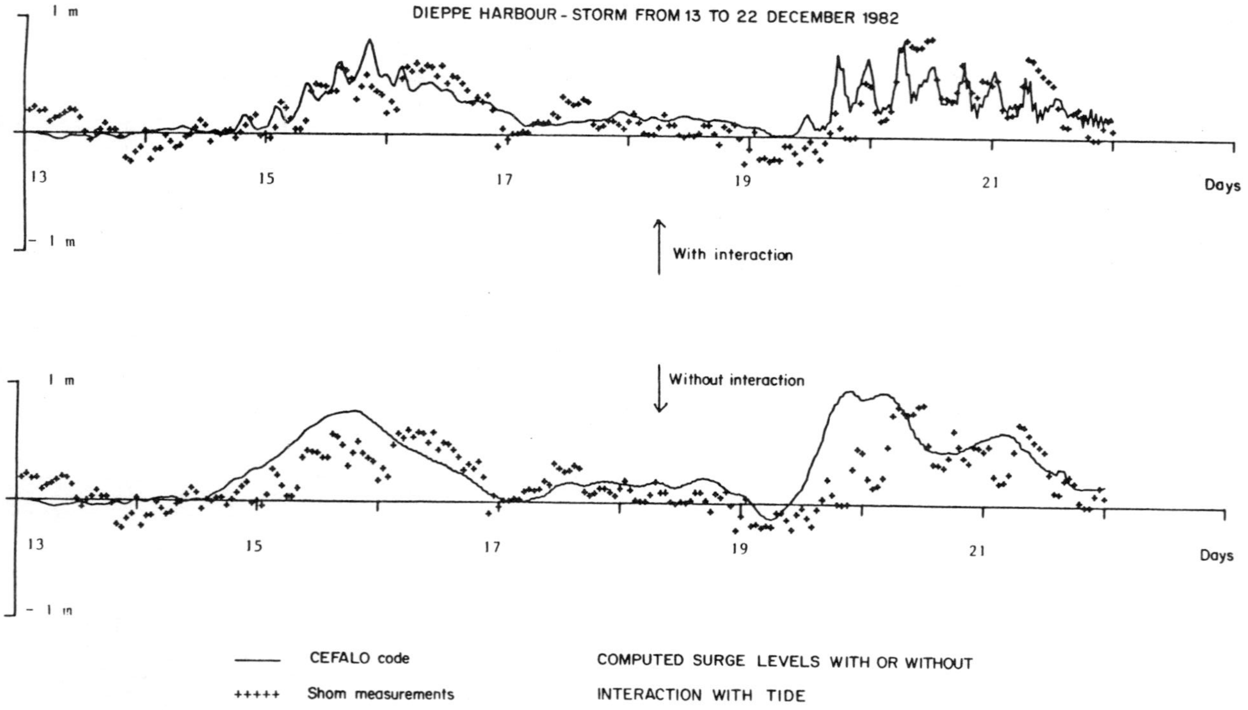
DIEPPE HARBOUR - STORM FROM 13 TO 22 DECEMBER 1982
1 m
- 1 m
13
15
17
19
21
Days
With interaction
Without interaction
CEFALO code
+++++ Shom measurements
COMPUTED SURGE LEVELS WITH OR WITHOUT
INTERACTION WITH TIDE

Figure 6

t = 166.0s

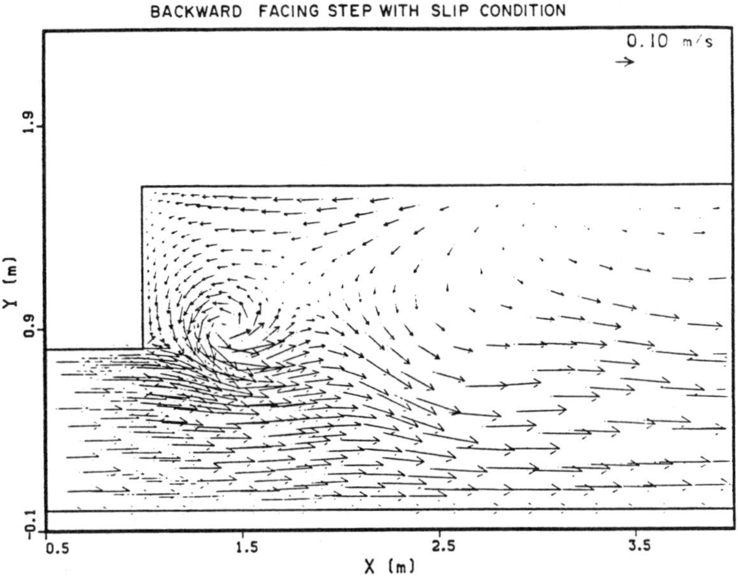

t = 170.0s

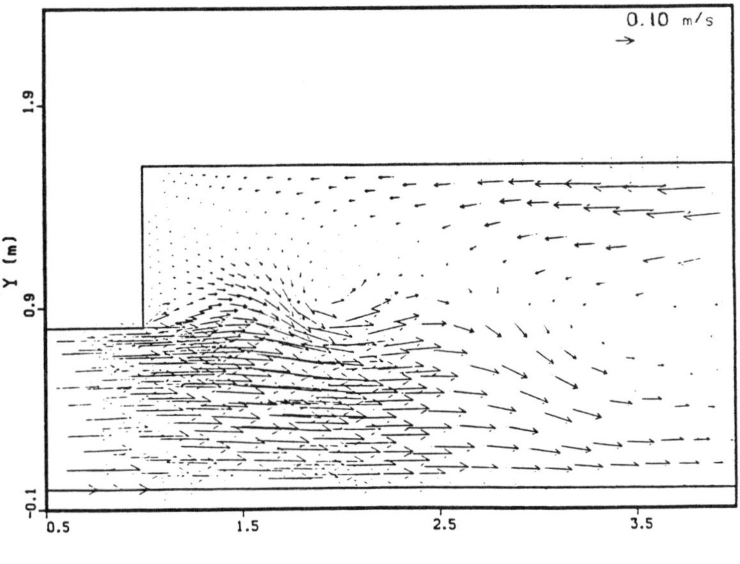

Figure 7

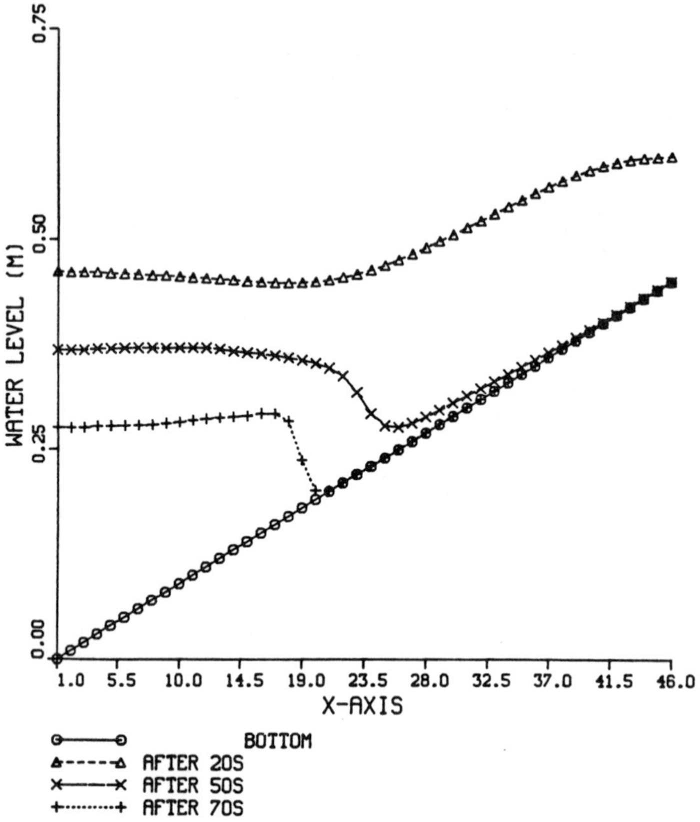

UNCOVERING BEACH

Figure 8

VI International Conference on Finite Elements in Water Resources, Lisboa, Portugal, June 1986

Computation of Steady Recirculating Flow in Complex Geometries

G.K. Verboom
Estuaries and Seas, Delft Hydraulics Laboratory, Delft, The Netherlands
C. Flokstra
Rivers, Navigation and Structures, Delft Hydraulics Laboratory, Delft, The Netherlands
A.K. Wiersma
Harbours, Coasts and Offshore, Delft Hydraulics Laboratory, Delft, The Netherlands

INTRODUCTION

Recirculation flow is an important feature in many engineering problems. In water quality problems constituents can be temporary trapped in an area of recirculating flow, thereby increasing the residence time appreciably. In harbour entrances recirculating flow can strongly influence the navigability of ships as well as change the sediment transport. For structures and closure works recirculating flow can change the discharge coefficient substantially, thereby changing the expected flow characteristics. In these examples the main axis of the recirculating flow is in the vertical direction, though three dimensional features are generally important. However, the use of three dimensional models for engineering applications is still very expensive and so these recirculation flows are usually modelled with two-dimensional averaged depth models. Momentum diffusion plays an important role in the generation of recirculating flow. In steady flow it even is indispensable for the maintenance of recirculating flow, as pointed out by Flokstra (1976).

For many years the reported recirculating flow computations were dominated by numerical diffusion and, in fact, many still are if the advective terms are solved with a first order upwind difference scheme. The results would change drastically if the grid size is reduced, but grid refinement is seldomly reported. In a recent publication Abbott et. al. (1985) suggested that another, not identified, mechanism exists in the finite difference equations that transfers energy from the main stream to the recirculation. But, the examples used to prove this conjecture are questionable at several points. Moreover, in this paper we explain why our example of recirculation flow is insensitive to a change of the eddy viscosity by an order of magnitude whereas the results are shown to be grid independent, i.e. truncation errors are unimportant.

In this paper we report on a study with the objectives to provide a formulation for the eddy viscosity coefficient, ν_t, that can be used for the computation of steady and unsteady recirculation flow in complex geometries.
This study is part of a larger long term applied research program called TOW, that covers among others many aspects of flow and transport problems. This program is financed by Rijkswaterstaat, Department of Public Works and executed in close co-operation with experts of Tidal Waters Division.

The models for ν_t we report on, range from a simple constant value to the rather complex depth-averaged k-ε model, as formulated by Rodi (1980). Results are given for steady flow situations only. Though interesting results are obtained for the backward-step problem, results of which are briefly discussed in the following Section, we concentrate on the case of a complex geometry: the entrance of an estuary with a complex coastline and an accidented bottom profile. The results at maximum (steady) flood velocity are compared with the results of an undistorted hydraulic scale model. The influence of several parameters is investigated and attention is paid to the vorticity generating mechanisms. Next we discuss the work done with a time dependent depth-averaged k-ε model. In the last Section we present the main conclusions.

BACKWARD-STEP RESULTS

Kuipers and Vreugdenhil (1973) were among the first to apply a depth-averaged model, orginally developed by Leendertse (1967) for tidal flows, to steady recirculating flow in a complicated geometry. From these computations it became clear that the representation of recirculating flows induced by a main flow depends rather strongly on diffusion effects contrary to experiences with tidal flows.
Flokstra (1976) showed the importance of a correct representation of the exchange of horizontal momentum for these flows, as accounted for by the effective stresses in the depth-averaged equations. The depth-averaged momentum equations are given by

$$\frac{\partial u}{\partial t} + u\frac{\partial u}{\partial x} + v\frac{\partial u}{\partial y} - fv + g\frac{\partial \zeta}{\partial x} + \frac{\tau_{bx}}{\rho\ H} - \frac{1}{\rho H}\left\{\frac{\partial HT_{xx}}{\partial x} + \frac{\partial HT_{xy}}{\partial y}\right\} = 0, \quad (1)$$

$$\frac{\partial v}{\partial t} + u\frac{\partial v}{\partial x} + v\frac{\partial v}{\partial y} + fu + g\frac{\partial \zeta}{\partial y} + \frac{\tau_{bx}}{\rho\ H} - \frac{1}{\rho H}\left\{\frac{\partial HT_{xy}}{\partial x} + \frac{\partial Ht_{yy}}{\partial y}\right\} = 0, \quad (2)$$

and the continuity reads

$$\frac{\partial \zeta}{\partial t} + \frac{\partial Hu}{\partial x} + \frac{\partial Hv}{\partial y} = 0. \quad (3)$$

The notation is explained at the end of the paper. Flokstra

(1976) showed that Eqs. 1-3 cannot describe main flow induced recirculating flow when the effective stresses are neglected. The effective stresses represent a number of physically different effects of which the exchange of momentum by turbulence is the most important one (Flokstra, 1981).
The structure of the occurring turbulence for these flow cases is rather complicated as the depth is much smaller than the horizontal dimensions of the flow domain. This leads to a rather strong anisotropic turbulence which behaviour is bounded by pure 2D turbulence and 3D turbulence. Most literature is devoted to one of these two extreme turbulence theories. The usual turbulence models concern 3D turbulence; also the standard k-ε model, adapted by Rodi (1980) to finite-depth flows is based on 3D turbulence only.
For applications to engineering problems in which the depth-averaged velocity is of interest instead of the turbulence structure, it may be questioned to which extent the modelling of the turbulence must be physically correct. To investigate this aspect a number of turbulence models, such as a constant coefficient, subgrid scale models and a k-ε model are applied to compare their effects on the flow distribution. In this Section we report on flow past a backward step with a flat bottom and a free surface. The computational method used is derived from the method applied in the well-known TEACH computer program, developed at Imperial College. However, the straightforward up-wind scheme is replaced by a scheme which is up-wind only in the local flow direction. A non-uniform rectangular grid is introduced with refinements in the recirculation zone, about 40 x 50 grid points. The solutions appear to be grid independent.

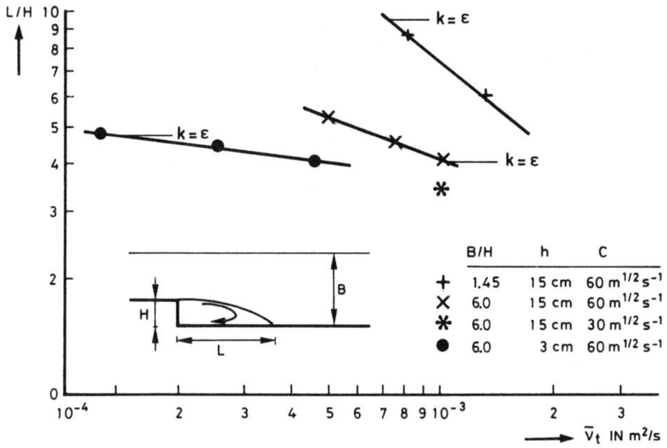

Figure 1 Ratio of reattachment length to step width as a function of $\bar{\nu}_t$, with an indication of the k-ε model results.

The following effects are investigated:

- The influence of the magnitude of the viscosity on the reattachment length. An increase of the viscosity induces a decrease of the reattachment. In fact, the correct reattachment length can be obtained even with a constant coefficient by tuning the magnitude of $\bar{\nu}_t$. However, this value is not universal, it strongly depends on the water depth, the aspect ratio, etc. From the results the impression is gained that a coefficient proportional to depth would fit better than a constant value. This suggests a u*h formulation which results if bottom generated turbulence dominates.
- The reproduction of the reattachment length by the k-ε model.
  By lack of experimental data the reattachment length can be compared only to 2-D flow data (Tropea, 1981), which suggests an underprediction of the reattachment length.
- The influence of the channel width to step width ratio.
  An increase of this ratio leads to a decrease of the reattachment length. For too small a ratio - less than about 4 - pressure effects pushes the recirculation down stream.
- The influence of the water depth and bed roughness.
  An increase of bed roughness leads to a decrease of the reattachment length.
  If the water depth decreased, then the reattachment length decreases in case of a constant eddy viscosity, but increases if the k-ε model is used. With the k-ε model both k and ε increase if depth is decreased, but k^2 increases less than ε, so ν_t decreases and the reattachment length increases.
  In Figure 1 the results are summarized for the constant-coefficient computations and for the k-ε model.

If the reattachment length with a constant eddy viscosity is tuned to the k-ε model results the velocity fields correspond quite well as shown by Figures 2a and b.

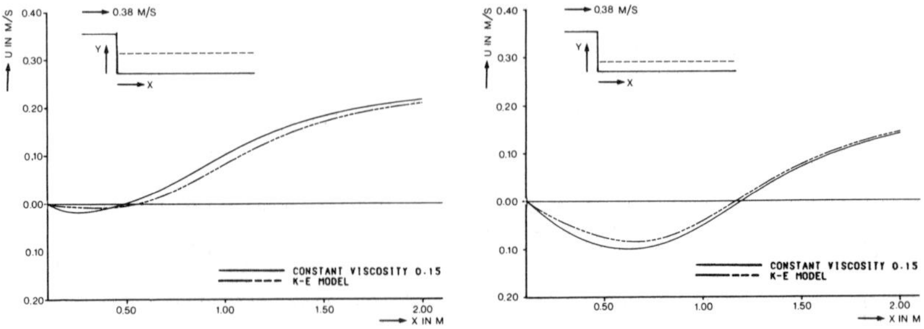

Figure 2 Velocity profiles in the main flow direction at two cross-sectional positions: y = 0.5 H (a) and y = 0.18 H (b). ——— : $\bar{\nu}_t = 1.510^{-4}\ m^2/s$; ----- : k-ε model.

These results suggest a rather large range of flow situations for the application of a constant viscosity model. However, the choice of its magnitude is still a problem to be solved, which may lead to the use of k-ε model.

COMPLEX GEOMETRY

From the flat bottom backward-step computations we learned that for many engineering applications a constant eddy viscosity coefficient might do, provided we can estimate its value. For a simple geometry such as a backward step one might be able to estimate this value from data on half free jets, but for more general cases this is virtually impossible because of a lack of data to estimate the characteristic length scale.
The eddy viscosity is mainly determined by two mechanisms, i.e. turbulence generated at the bottom and in the shear layer between the main flow and the recirculating flow area, Lean and Weare (1979). The influence of the bottom might be rather strong and cannot adequately be investigated in the flat bottom computations. For a more complex geometry we use an area in the entrance of the Eastern-Scheldt estuary. This area is of particular interest because in part it contains the area in which the storm surge barrier is under construction and because measurements are available from prototype and from a (steady) hydraulic scale model. In this paper we concentrate on the (steady) maximum flood situation. The model area is about 2.5 x 1.5 km^2 with a complicated shore line and a pronounced bottom profile, Figure 3.

A rather shallow area, along the shore, depth about 5 m, is separated from the deep main flow area, depth about 35 m, by a steep slope region, upto 1:5. From left (inflow) to right (outflow) the shoreline shows a converging region in which the flow is forced into the deep main flow area, a small harbour entrance and a larger backward-step-like-shaped region, called Anna Friso polder (AFP). At two spots the depth contours bend into AFP. It's here that strong recirculating flows are generated.
The area is modelled with the WAQUA system in which the equations are solved with a finite difference fully implicit ADI-method (Stelling, 1983). The higher order discretization of the advective terms introduces very little numerical diffusion. The effective stress terms in Eqs. 1 and 2 are approximated by $\nu_t \nabla^2 u$ and $\nu_t \nabla^2 v$, respectively. Boundary conditions are taken from a larger area model: velocities at the left and upper boundary (inflow) and water level at the right (outflow) boundary. To get rid of short wave disturbances the boundary conditions are modified with a term that is proportional with the time derivative of the ingoing Riemann invariant (Stelling, 1983; Verboom and Slob, 1984). For a velocity boundary this reads:

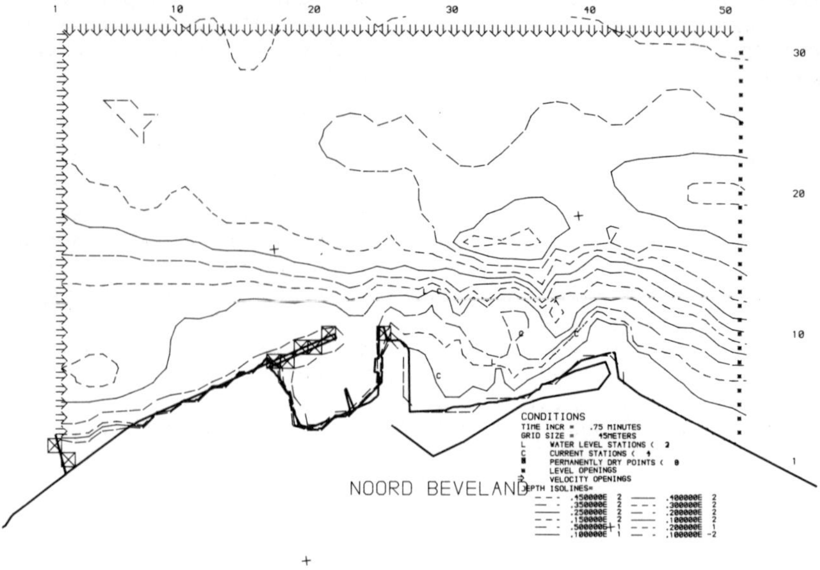

Figure 3 Layout and bottom contours of the Anna Friso polder area.

$$u + \alpha \frac{\partial}{\partial t}\{u + 2\sqrt{g(h+\zeta)}\} = U_o,$$

where $\alpha = 100$ and U_o is the velocity wanted.
For this configuration we investigate the influence of the bottom friction, the bottom profile, and the eddy viscosity coefficient. For ν_t we use three formulations: a constant value, $\bar{\nu}_t$, an u*h-formulation, and a depth averaged k-ε model. To guarantee a Δt independent solution all computations are repeated with half a time step. It is found to be necessary to decrease the time step upto a factor of 7 if $\bar{\nu}_t$ is decreased from 10 to 0.1 m^2/s. No steady solutions are obtained if the time step is choosen too large, but if a steady solution is obtained this solution is Δt independent.
To investigate the influence of the grid spacing, Δx, several computations are repeated with Δx halved, i.e. 22.5 m. For $\nu_t \geq 0.1$ m^2/s the results are found to be grid independent, we come back to this matter later on.
In most computations a period of 9 hours is simulated; each computation is started from rest and the boundary conditions are increased to their final values in a period of 1 hour. In all cases the main flow is established just after this period, but it takes upto 4 hours for the recirculating flow to establish. In Figure 4a the water level in AFP is given as a func-

tion of time for $\bar{\nu}_t$ = 10 m^2/s; if $\bar{\nu}_t$ is decreased to 1 m^2/s or below the final water level decreases by about 5 mm but the (overall) initial period remains the same. This is quite different for the currents in AFP, Figures 4b-d: the initial period is dominated by an oscillation of the recirculating flow area as a whole. The amplitude of this damped oscillation increases when decreasing $\bar{\nu}_t$.
From an order of magnitude estimate it follows that the damping is dominated by the viscous term if $\bar{\nu}_t$ = 10 m^2/s and by bottom friction if ν_t = 0.1 m^2/s, Table 1.

	$\bar{\nu}_t$ = 10 m^2/s	$\bar{\nu}_t$ = 1 m^2/s	$\bar{\nu}_t$ = 0.1 m^2/s
τ_{bot}	3000	3000	3000
$\tau_{\bar{\nu}_t}$	800	8000	80000

Table 1 Time constant of damping mechanisms by order of magnitude

$$\tau_{bot} = \frac{C^2 h}{g\ U};\ \tau_{\bar{\nu}_t} = \frac{4\ \Delta x^2}{\bar{\nu}_t},$$ with C = 45 $m^{1/2}/s$, h = 6 m, and U = 0,4 m/s.

From the results given later on it will become clear that the center of the recirculation flow is found near the largest bottom slope. In AFP there are two locations with a larger slope: in the initial period the center oscillates forward and backward between these two areas with a period of about 0.8 hour independent of $\bar{\nu}_t$ (third and fourth maximum in Figure 4.d).
The (physical) mechanism behind this oscillation is still unknown, but the oscillation period is about the same as it takes a particle to make one revolution around the recirculation. The time step used in these computations decreases from 45 s to 6 s when $\bar{\nu}_t$ is decreased from 10 m^2/s to 0.1 m^2/s. The results change less than 1 promille for the water level and less than 1 percent for the velocities if Δt is halved. If a larger time step is used an oscillation is generated inside AFP that extent in time far beyond the initial period. The oscillation period is markedly different from the initial-period oscillation. At first this oscillation was interpreted as a physical phenomenon: the Strouhal number (related to the longitudinal dimension of AFP) is about 0.15 - 0.2, a figure often found in literature for whistling cavities and such. However, the oscillation disappears when decreasing the time step. Therefore this oscillation is regarded not relevant within the framework of this project and the smaller time step is used. Figures 5a and 5b show the velocity vectors in and just in front of AFP after 9 hours of simulation and for two values of $\bar{\nu}_t$: 10 and 1 m^2/s. The time step used is 45 and 22.5 s respectively. For $\bar{\nu}_t$ = 0.1 m^2/s, the flow field is virtually

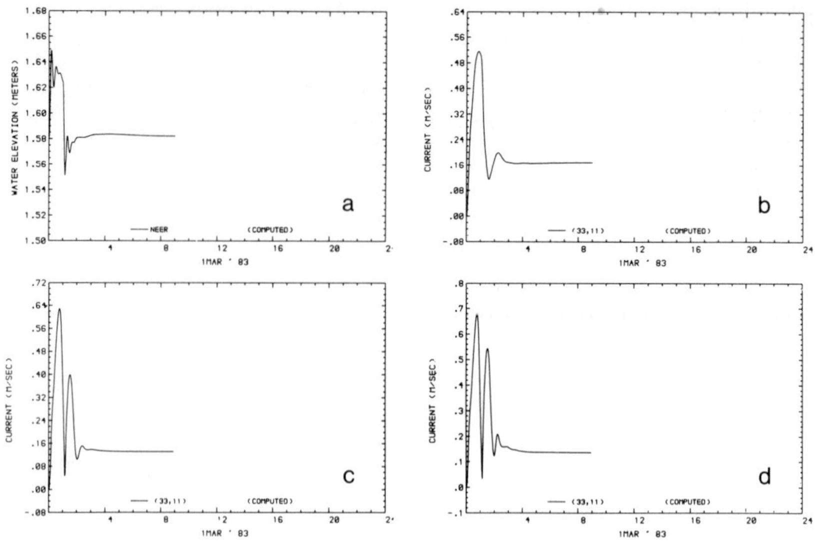

Figure 4 Water level, 4a, and velocities, 4b-4d, as a function of time.

the same as for $\bar{\nu}_t = 1\ m^2/s$, Figure 5c.
There is a large difference between the flows for $\bar{\nu}_t = 10\ m^2/s$ and $\nu_t = 1\ m^2/s$. For $\bar{\nu}_t = 10\ m^2/s$ the recirculation fills AFP completely; there is an elongated center, no pronounced shear layer between the recirculation and the main flow, and the recirculation remains well within the "shadow" of the upstream shore line.
For $\bar{\nu}_t = 1\ m^2/s$ the recirculation doesn't fill AFP completely, a dead water region occurs in the lower left corner and the speed in the recirculation itself increases by up to a factor of two. The center is more circular and concentrates on the spot were the steepest bottom slope is found and a rather pronounced shear layer occurs. At the upstream end of the recirculation a blocking of the flow forces the main flow to move outward. This flow field compares favourable with measurements in an undistorted hydraulic scale model, Figure 5d.
If $\bar{\nu}_t$ is decreased by an other factor of 10 the changes in the flow field can hardly be seen, though when looking at the details the changes are along the same line as before. From Table 1 we know that the viscous terms are negligible compared to the bottom friction for $\bar{\nu}_t = 0.1\ m^2/s$, so the results of these computations seems to agree with Table 1. But, we are dealing with steady recirculating flow for which Flokstra (1976) showed that an integral balance must exist between bottom friction and viscous terms. For this we use the vorticity equation

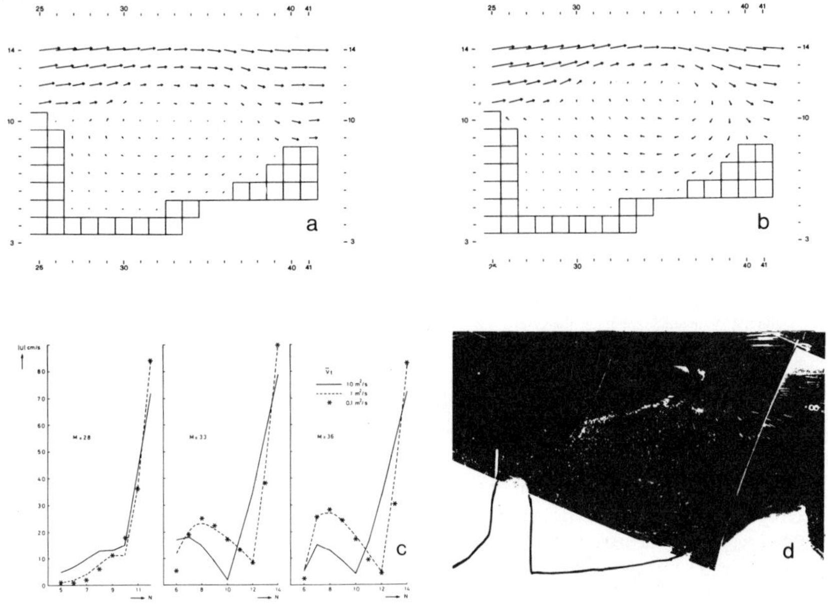

Figure 5 Velocity vector plots after 9 hours of simulation Δx = 45 m and $\bar{\nu}_t$ = 10 m^2/s, 5a, and 1 m^2/s, 5b. Three velocity cross-sections, 5c, and particle tracks in an undistorted hydraulic scale model, 5d. Velocity scale: 1 Δx = 1 m/s.

$$\frac{\partial\omega}{\partial t} + \frac{\partial u\omega}{\partial x} + \frac{\partial v\omega}{\partial y} + f(\frac{\partial u}{\partial x} + \frac{\partial v}{\partial y}) + \frac{\partial\tau_{bx}}{\partial y} - \frac{\partial\tau_{by}}{\partial x} = \bar{\nu}_t(\frac{\partial^2\omega}{\partial x^2} + \frac{\partial^2\omega}{\partial y^2}), (4)$$

where $\omega = v_x - u_y$. Integrating Eq. 4 over an area bounded by a closed streamline, as is possible in a steady recirculating flow, only the last two terms remain. These terms can be written as

$$\int_{\partial 0} \vec{\tau}_b . \vec{t} \; ds = \int_{\partial 0} \bar{\nu}_t \vec{n}.\nabla \; \omega \; ds, \qquad (5)$$

where $\vec{t}$ and $\vec{n}$ are the tangential and outward normal unit vector to the streamline. The left hand side of Eq. 5 is related to the flow field itself and the right hand side to the second order derivatives of the velocities. From this it seems impossible to decrease $\bar{\nu}_t$ by a factor of ten without a noticible change in the flow field; however, exactly this results when ν_t is decreased from 1 to 0.1 m^2/s. Possible explanations are numerical errors, a not entirely steady flow, or a not entirely closed streamline. At the end of the computation the results change in the 5th and 6th decimals only, so we conclude

that the results are truely stationary. This also rules out a not entirely closed streamline because the scheme is strictly mass conservative and there are no sources or sinks in the model; so only numerical errors seem to remain. The velocity gradients in the shear layer are extremely large, so it is not unrealistic to assume that the higher order approximations of the advective terms are not very accurate. As the truncation error of these terms is proportional to Δx^3 we expect a significant influence of halving Δx. From the former results it can be reasoned that the contribution of numerical errors must be of the same order as either one of the integral for $\bar{\nu}_t$ = 1 m^2/s. In Figures 6a and b the results are shown for $\bar{\nu}_t$ = 1 and 0.1 m^2/s, Δx = 22.5 m, and Δt = 6 and 3 s, respectively.
Indeed, the differences are much larger than with Δx = 45 m, but not as much as expected. The influence of the grid refinement on the results with $\bar{\nu}_t$ = 1 m^2/s is very small; if, in fact, only each second velocity vector is shown, there is an almost perfect match with the 45 m-grid results.

The final explanation is found from actually computing the integrals of Eq. 5 along a closed particle track. Both integrals are largely determined along a fraction of the streamline and these fractions do not overlap. The bottom-friction integral is determined in the shallow part and the vorticity related integral is determined at the steep slope. All closed particle tracks are forced through the shear layer and it is just there that $\vec{n}.\nabla\ \omega$ change sign, Table 2.
This enables the flow to counter-balance a decrease of $\bar{\nu}_t$ by shifting the streamline a fraction into or out of the shear layer, while leaving the main part of the flow virtually unchanged.

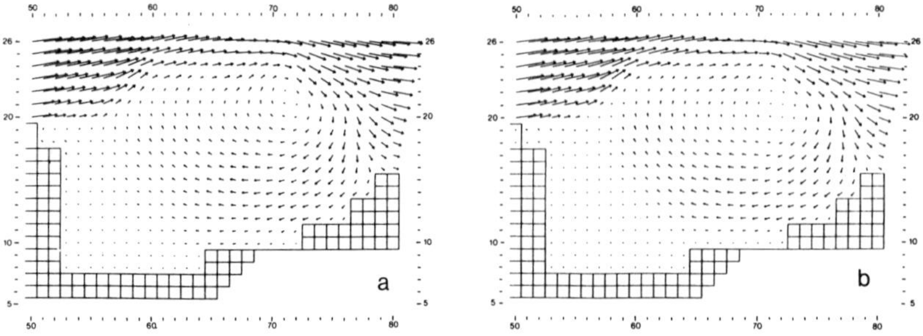

Figure 6 Velocity vector plots after 9 hours of simulation: Δx = 22.5 m and $\bar{\nu}_t$ = 1 m^2/s, 6a, and 0.1 m^2/s, 6b. Velocity scale: 1 Δx = 0.5 m/s.

In Table 3 the values of the integrals of Eq. 5 are given for two particle tracks, $\bar{\nu}_t$ = 1 and 0.1 m^2/s, and Δx = 45 m and 22.5 m. For Δx = 45 m and $\bar{\nu}_t$ = 1 m^2/s both integrals are about the same, but the RHS of Eq. 5 is not able to compensate for a decrease of $\bar{\nu}_t$ to 0.1 m^2/s. This deficit clearly must be compensated by truncation errors. However, for Δx = 22.5 m both integrals are about the same for $\bar{\nu}_t$ = 0.1 m^2/s as well. This proves that truncation errors are unimportant in the fine grid computations for $\nu_t \geq 0.1\ m^2/s$.

$\vec{n}.\nabla\ \omega$				
n	$\bar{\nu}_t = 1\ m^2/s$		$\bar{\nu}_t = 0.1\ m^2/s$	
14	14	10^{-5}	18	10^{-5}
13	-7.2	10^{-5}	-17	$10.^{-5}$
10	1.6	10^{-5}	0.6	10^{-5}

Table 2 Values of $\vec{n}.\nabla\ \omega$ along the line m = 36; Δx = 45 m.

	$\bar{\nu}_t = 1\ m^2/s$				$\bar{\nu}_t = 0.1\ m^2/s$			
	Δx = 45 m		Δx = 22.5 m		Δx =45 m		Δx = 22.5 m	
RHS	2.0	6.0	1.2	5.3	2.2	5.5	9.4	3.2
LHS	1.5	6.3	1.9	5.0	22	1.7	5.1	2.8

Table 3 Integrals of Eq. 5, (* 10^{+3}), for two particle tracks, $\bar{\nu}_t$ = 1 and 0.1 m^2/s, and Δx = 45 and 22.5 m.

In Fig. 7 particle tracks are shown for fine and coarse grid computations. The tracks are not completely closed but this is only due to interpolation errors and not relevant in the context of the findings.

In several computations it was observed that the center of the recirculation is found near the steepest bottom slope. For an explanation we looked at the order of magnitude of the various terms of Eq. 4.

Along a particle track of Fig. 7b ω is maximal, $-1.2\ 10^{-2}s^{-1}$, in the shear layer and a factor of 3 smaller along the rest of the track. The leading terms of Eq. 4 are found to be $\vec{u}.\nabla\ \omega$ and $\omega\ \nabla.\vec{u}$; both terms are about equal but with an opposite sign. The other terms are at least one order of magnitude smaller. The vorticity balance therefore is determined by transport and stretching. With

$$\nabla.\vec{u} = -\frac{\vec{u}.\nabla H}{H}$$

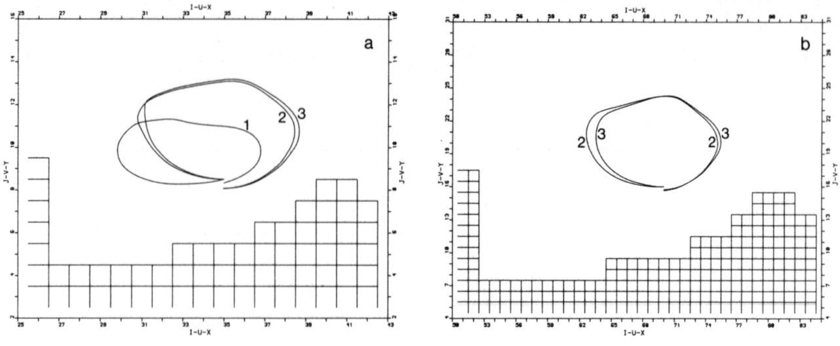

Figure 7 Particle tracks for coarse, 7a, and fine grid, 7b, computations.
ν_t = 10 (1), 1 (2), and 0.1 (3) m^2/s.

it is obvious why the recirculation is found near the steepest bottom slope area.

This finding is confirmed by the following computation: a small area with the steepest slope is filled up. The circulation changes more than in all other computations: the center moves several Δx towards the second steep-slope spot (to the left) and becomes almost circular, and the speed in AFP increases by as much as a factor of three.
When reasoning along the same lines it can also be understood why the influence of decreasing the eddy viscosity in a flat-bottom-backward-step configuration differs so markedly from the results obtained here (Stelling and Wang, 1984).

From these constant-coefficient computations it is found that the absolute value of $\overline{\nu}_t$ is not too important provided $\overline{\nu}_t$ is not too large. Of course, this is not true for the limit $\overline{\nu}_t \to 0$, but for the range 10 - 0.1 m^2/s this seems to be true. If $\overline{\nu}_t$ is decreased, the width of the shear layer decreases but the circulation in the large remains unchanged. Still, there remains the problem of how to choose the value of $\overline{\nu}_t$. For the shear layer one can use the mixing length formula

$$\nu_t = \ell^2 |u_y| . \tag{6}$$

With $\ell \simeq b/5$, $b \simeq x/10$ and $|u_y| \simeq u/2b$ (Schlichting, 1979), where 2b is the width of the shear layer and x the distance from the separation point, there results a value of (0.1 - 1) m^2/s. For AFP a value of 1 m^2/s or less seems to be appropriate. This value is confirmed by comparing the results of the computation with the results of an undistorted hydraulic scale model, Figures 5b and d.

For more general geometries without a well-defined separation point or with a less extreme bottom profile it remains difficult to make an adequate guess for $\bar{\nu}_t$. Therefore we also applied two other formulations: the first is related to bottom generated turbulence only and for the second formulation we used the depth averaged k-ε model as formulated by Rodi (1980). The k-ε results are discussed in the next Section.

For bottom generated turbulence, ν_t can be approximated by (Rodi, 1980)

$$\nu_t \simeq 0.1\, u^* h.$$

For AFP ν_t ranges from 5.10^{-3} or less in the shallow areas to at most 5.10^{-2} m^2/s in the steep slope region. Several computations are done with this formula for ν_t, but the results are virtually identical to those obtained with $\bar{\nu}_t = 0.1$ m^2/s. This agrees with the constant viscosity results.

APPLICATION OF THE DEPTH-AVERAGED k-ε MODEL

The depth-averaged two-dimensional k-ε model as formulated by Rodi (1980) is used. The advection and diffusion are discretised by central differences as long as the local cell Peclet number (e.g. $\sigma_k u\Delta x/\nu_t$ in the k-equation) is less than 2. Otherwise locally first-order upwind is used in the advective terms. (It is stressed that the discretisation of the momentum equations hardly contains any numerical diffusion). The highly nonlinear source and sink terms require special attention since they turn out to have rather complex properties. In a forthcoming paper (Verboom and Wiersma, 1986) some mathematical, physical and numerical aspects of these terms will be discussed.
The k-ε model is applied to the schematization with grid size $\Delta x = 45$ m. The boundary conditions for k and ε are obtained as follows. At inflow k is estimated from the local velocity magnitude: $k = \frac{3}{2}(.1{*}u)^2$; ν_t is estimated by $\nu_t = .077\ u^* h$ and ε is obtained from Eq. 9.
Figures 8a and b show time histories of current magnitude and turbulent viscosity in point (m,n) = (37,11), which is located approximately in the centre of the principal circulation cell. It turns out that after 4 hours a steady state is reached and that the time scales for the current and the turbulent viscosity are roughly the same. The flow field is found to be the same as obtained with a constant viscosity of ≤ 1 m^2/s.
In Table 4 we give ν_t as computed from the k-ε model for the coordinate line m = 36 and we compare it with the local u^*H formulation.
It is clear that inside the shear-layer zone the k-ε model predicts higher turbulent viscosities than the u^*H formulation. Outside the shear layer both formulations give roughly the same order of magnitude. This agrees very well with other

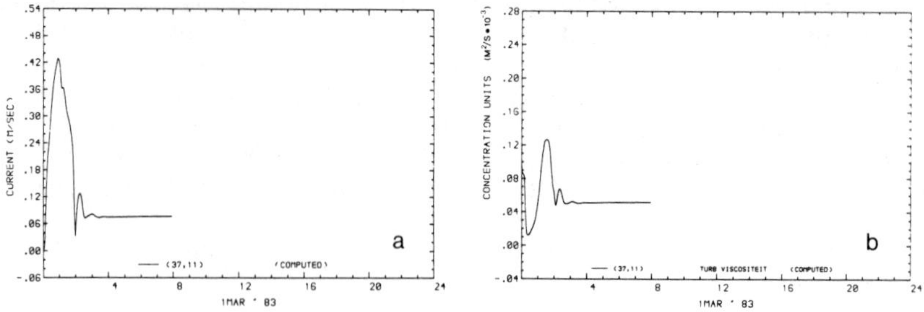

Figure 8 Turbulent viscosity, 8a, and velocity, 8b, as a function of time as obtained with the depth-averaged k-ε model.

n	ν_t(k-ε)	ν_t = .077 u^*H
7	2.4	1.2
8	6.4	5.1
9	12.1	8.0
10	24.0	5.8
11	34.8	3.3
12	21.9	1.9
13	71.3	29.0
14	127.3	117.6

Table 4 Turbulent viscosity, ($*10^{+3}$) from the k-ε model and the u^*h formulation.

experiences that in areas with small velocity gradients the depth-averaged k-ε equations produce viscosities, comparable with those from the u^*H formulation. Inside the shear layer, however, the k-ε model produces a much smaller value than 1 m^2/s as obtained from an order of magnitude estimate, Eq. 6.

CONCLUSIONS

In this paper we report on steady main flow driven recirculating flow in two geometries: a simple flat bottom backward step and a prototype area with a complicated topography. From the results obtained so far we conclude that the bottom topography may be as important a parameter as the value of the eddy viscosity in the shear layer. For the eddy viscosity we used a constant value, a u*h formulation and a depth-averaged k-ε model. The results of the k-ε model agree quite well with the results of an undistorted hydraulic scale model without trimming any parameters. For a constant coefficient the same results can be obtained by choosing an adequate value. For both geometries this value could be estimated from half free yet formulas, but for more general cases this might not be possible. In the prototype case the bottom profile is very important and several unexpected results were obtained. An integral balance along a closed stream line, Eq. 5, is shown to exist also at the finite difference level. There is no need for a new mechanism that transfers energy into the recirculation, but to understand the results we had to look into the very details of the flow and of vorticity generating mechanisms. For the near future we plan to extent these computations to tidal flow cases.

ACKNOWLEDGEMENT

The authors wish to express their gratitude to the members of TOW-B Working Group 1 on 2-D Flow and Transport Problems for the stimulating discussions and critical guidance of this study. In particular they would like to mention the contributions of Dr. Abraham , Dr. Stelling, and Mr. Dijkzeul.

References

Abbott, M.B., Larsen, J. and Jianhua Tao (1985), Modelling circulations in depth-integrated flows. Part 1: The accumulation of the evidence. Journal of Hydraulic Research, Vol. 23, 309-327.

Flokstra, C. (1981), Aspects of modelling horizontal momentum transfer in shallow flow. Delft Hydraulics Laboratory, Report on investigations R1150.

Kuipers, J. and Vreugdenhil, C.B. (1973), Calculations of two-dimensional horizontal flow. Delft Hydraulics Laboratory, Report S163.

Lean, G.H. and Waere, T.J. (1979). Modelling two-dimensional circulating flow. J. Hydr. Div., vol. 105, no. HY1.

Leendertse, J.J. (1967), Aspects of a computational model for long-period water wave propagation. Rand Corp. Mem. RM-5294-PR.

Rodi, W. (1980), Turbulence models and their application in hydraulics - A state of the art review. IAHR State-of-the-art-paper.

Schlichting, H. (1979), Boundary-Layer Theory. McGraw-Hill Book Company, New-York.

Stelling, G.S. (1983), On the construction of computational methods for shallow water flow problems. Thesis Delft University of Technology.

Stelling, G.S. and Wang, L.X. (1984), Experiments and computations on unsteady separating flow in an expanding flume. Delft University of Technology, Dept. of Civil Engineering, Report

2-84.
Tropea, C. (1981), The backward-step flow. Von Karman Institute for Fluid Dynamics, Lecture series 1981-1.
Verboom, G.K. and Slob, A. (1984), Weakly reflective boundary conditions for two-dimensional shallow water flow problems. 5th Int. Conf. Finite Elements in Water Resources, Burlington.
Verboom, G.K. and Wiersma, A.K. (1986). Some properties of the depth-averaged k-ε model. To appear.

Notation

b	width of the shear layer
C	Chézy coefficient
c_j	coefficients in k-ε model
f	Coriolis parameter
g	gravity
H	$h+\zeta$
h	depth below the reference plane $z = 0$
l	mixing length
$P_{k\nu}$, $P_{\varepsilon\nu}$	production terms due to bottom
P_h	production term due to horizontal velocity gradients
T_{ij}	effective stress component
u,v	depth averaged velocity components in x and y direction
u^*	friction velocity
x,y,t	space and time coordinates
α	parameter in the weakly-reflective boundary conditions
ε	turbulent energy dissipation rate
ζ	free surface elevation above the reference plan $z = 0$
κ	turbulent energy
λ	$g\,\vec{u}/C^2H$
$\underline{\nu}_t$	eddy viscosity coefficient
ν_t	averaged, constant, eddy viscosity coefficient
ρ	water density
τ_{bot}	characteristic time scale for bottom friction
$\tau_{\bar{\nu}_t}$	characteristic time scale for viscous terms
τ_{bx}, τ_{by}	x and y component of the bottom friction, $\vec{\tau}_b = \dfrac{\rho g \lvert \vec{u} \rvert \vec{u}}{C^2}$
ω	vorticity, $\omega = \dfrac{\partial v}{\partial x} - \dfrac{\partial u}{\partial y}$
Δx, Δt	space and time step

VI International Conference on Finite Elements in Water Resources, Lisboa, Portugal, June 1986

Field Studies with the Wave Equation Formulation

F.E. Werner, D.R. Lynch
Thayer School of Engineering, Dartmouth College, Hanover, NH 03755, U.S.A.

INTRODUCTION

During the past decade considerable effort has been devoted to the development of sound and accurate finite element solutions of the shallow water equations for the study of coastal seas and oceanic environments. In 1979, Lynch and Gray introduced the Wave Equation approach, which unlike its predecessors, has the ability to keep spurious short-wavelength modes under control without recourse to filters, horizontal viscosity, or other means. In addition to this essential property, the Wave Equation approach also combines most of the economy features which can be realized for shallow water problems: uncoupled calculations for depth and velocity; sparse, symmetric matrices; implicit or explicit options; no matrix inversions required in the explicit option when integral lumping is employed; and for the stable implicit version, matrix inversion for depth only, followed by a pointwise explicit velocity calculation.

Because of the fortuitous combination of all these properties, the Wave Equation has received considerable scrutiny. The bulk of the detailed work since 1979 has involved Fourier analysis of the linearized equations, with important contributions relative to two-dimensional waves, variable bathymetry and mesh spacing, and different kinds of elements (Platzman, 1981; Foreman, 1983 and 1984; Kinnmark and Gray, 1984a and 1985a; and Walters, 1983). Additionally, a global mass balance property of the Wave Equation has been demonstrated (Lynch, 1985); the equivalence of time-stepping results with spectral (harmonic) treatment of the time domain has been established (Lynch, 1981; Walters, 1984); and extensions to moving boundary problems have been shown (Lynch and Gray, 1980).

While all of these studies are necessary and valuable, it is important to conduct concurrent field-scale simulations, to: (a) test ideas under the realistic complications of boundary geometry and nonlinear interactions; and (b) inspire new nonlinear analyses to isolate advective and other difficulties. Kinnmark and Gray (1984b) have shown an application to the North Sea. In this paper, we present results from new field-scale case-studies: (i) the Lake Maracaibo system in **Venezuela and (ii) the Alborán Sea in the western Mediterranean.**

In their primitive form the shallow water equations are:

$$\frac{\partial H}{\partial t} + \nabla \cdot (H\mathbf{v}) = 0 \tag{1}$$

$$\frac{\partial (H\mathbf{v})}{\partial t} + \nabla \cdot (H\mathbf{v}\mathbf{v}) + gH\nabla\varsigma + \mathbf{f} \times H\mathbf{v} + \tau H\mathbf{v} = H\mathbf{\Psi} \tag{2}$$

where $H(x, y, t)$ is the fluid depth, $\varsigma(x, y, t)$ is the free surface elevation above the mean sea level, $h(x, y)$ is the bathymetry defined as $h = H - \varsigma$, $\mathbf{v}(x, y, t)$ is the vertically averaged horizontal velocity vector, g is the acceleration due to gravity, $\mathbf{f}$ is the Coriolis parameter, $\tau(x, y, t)$ is the bottom friction parameter, $\mathbf{\Psi}$ is the atmospheric forcing, the spatial coordinates (x, y) are positive eastward and northward respectively, t is time and ∇ is the horizontal gradient operator.

We employ the Shallow Water Wave Equation in place of (1), obtained by operating on (1) and (2):

$$\frac{\partial^2 H}{\partial t^2} + \tau_0 \frac{\partial H}{\partial t} - \nabla \cdot [\nabla \cdot (H\mathbf{v}\mathbf{v}) + gH\nabla\varsigma + \mathbf{f} \times H\mathbf{v}$$
$$+(\tau - \tau_0)H\mathbf{v} - H\mathbf{\Psi}] = 0 \tag{3}$$

The parameter τ_0 is an arbitrary constant, and its introduction is the only change from the original (Lynch and Gray, 1979) form we employ. This was introduced by Kinnmark and Gray (1985b) as an efficiency feature, as it renders the depth matrix in the implicit scheme stationary. We find that in addition this form stabilizes a very low frequency (10-15 days) drift which otherwise develops in the long-term simulation of tides in Lake Maracaibo.

The Galerkin form of (3) which we employ is:

$$\left\langle \frac{\partial^2 H}{\partial t^2}, \phi_i \right\rangle + \tau_0 \left\langle \frac{\partial H}{\partial t}, \phi_i \right\rangle + \langle [\nabla \cdot H\mathbf{v}\mathbf{v} + gh\nabla\varsigma + \mathbf{f} \times H\mathbf{v}$$
$$+ (\tau - \tau_0)H\mathbf{v} - H\mathbf{\Psi}], \nabla\phi_i \rangle = - \oint \left(\frac{\partial H\mathbf{v}}{\partial t} + \tau_0 H\mathbf{v}\right) \cdot \mathbf{n}\phi_i ds \tag{4}$$

where ϕ_i is the finite element basis and $\langle \cdot, \cdot \rangle$ is the inner product notation. The time domain is handled in a centered, implicit manner exactly as given in Lynch and Gray (1979).

For the velocity calculations, we employ a straightforward Galerkin treatment of the nonconservative momentum equation, as in the original (Lynch and Gray, 1979) paper. However we have adopted the 2-level discretization in time as proposed by Kinnmark and Gray (1982) – essentially a centered implicit treatment of all terms except the advective terms, which are treated explicitly. Our experience agrees with theirs, that is, this scheme eliminates instabilities which develop in long-term simulations with the original leapfrog technique.

When only the linearized periodic motions are of interest, it is advantageous to use the spectral form of the equations (Lynch, 1981):

$$j\omega\varsigma - \nabla \cdot \left(\frac{(j\omega + \tau)(gh\nabla\varsigma - h\mathbf{\Psi}) - \mathbf{f} \times (gh\nabla\varsigma - h\mathbf{\Psi})}{(j\omega + \tau)^2 + f^2} \right) = 0 \qquad (5)$$

$$h\mathbf{v} = -\left(\frac{(j\omega + \tau)(gh\nabla\varsigma - h\mathbf{\Psi}) - \mathbf{f} \times (gh\nabla\varsigma - h\mathbf{\Psi})}{(j\omega + \tau)^2 + f^2} \right) \qquad (6)$$

where j is the imaginary unit and ω is the radian frequency. In both spectral and time-stepping approaches we use Integral Lumping to diagonalize the mass matrix in the momentum equation.

The two cases considered possess widely different dynamical characteristics allowing extreme conditions of the wave equation formulation to be tested. In the Lake Maracaibo system we find shallow co-oscillating tidal basins with the outer basin exhibiting resonance with the M_2 tide. In the Alborán Sea we find an oceanic gyre which appears to be driven by a jet flowing through a narrow strait into a larger basin with a geostrophically balanced anti-cyclonic circulation around the resulting high pressure.

CASE I: The Lake Maracaibo System

The Lake Maracaibo (LM) system is located in the northwest corner of Venezuela and is composed of 4 smaller bodies of water: (i) the Gulf of Venezuela which is approximately 180 Km long and 75 Km wide and averages 30 meters in depth; (ii) the Bay of El Tablazo (27 Km × 24 Km) and averages 2.5 meters in depth; (iii) the Strait which is 37 Km long × 10Km wide (10 meters deep); and (iv) Lake Maracaibo itself which is 120 Km long (North-South) and 110 Km wide (East-West) averaging 25 meters in depth (see Figure 1).

Studies of the semi-diurnal tidal regime in the LM system have uncovered a behavior resembling that of a standing wave produced by the propagation of the tide through the Gulf of Venezuela and reflecting from the head of the Lake. Although the tides in the Caribbean (in the area of Cuba, Santo Domingo, Puerto Rico and the Venezuelan coast) are mixed but predominantly *diurnal*, the measurements at the mouth of the Bay of El Tablazo indicate that the tide there is still mixed but predominantly *semi-diurnal*. This phenomenon has been recognized as a resonance effect on the semi-diurnal tides induced by the dimensions of the Gulf of Venezuela (Redfield, 1961; and Fornerino and Molines, 1983). Specifically, the amplitude of the M_2 component (10 cm) at the entrance to the Gulf amplifies to 41 cm at El Tablazo Bay. The tide retains its semi-diurnal character across El Tablazo and the Strait of Maracaibo. High water is felt almost synchronously along this stretch, is delayed by about 1 hour relative to the high water in the Gulf and has a range that diminishes progressively to the south. While at the northern end of the Lake the tides are greatly reduced, at the southern end the semi-diurnal character of the tide is restored, its amplitude increasing to 3-4 cm. The observed time of high water at that point is 6 hours after high water in the Gulf of Venezuela, i.e., is about 180° out of phase for the M_2 tide.

The mesh used in our studies of the LM system is shown in Figure (2) and contains 718 elements and 433 nodes. As a first approach, tidal amplitudes and phases were computed from the linearized spectral model for the M_2 component and are shown in Figures (3a and b). The agreement with the observations described above is remarkable considering the simplicity of the numerical experiment. A constant amplitude (10 cm) tide with a 15° linearly varying phase was prescribed across the northeastern seaward boundary of the Gulf of Venezuela (the western side leading; Fornerino and Molines, 1983). No normal flow conditions were imposed on the solid boundaries; the bottom bathymetry was realistic (see Figure 1); and the bottom friction was constant and equal to *zero* yielding the linearized inviscid M_2 tidal response. The expected resonance of the tide in the Gulf of Venezuela and its magnitude were accurately reproduced. In the Lake, a nodal line was found in its northern section and amplitudes of 2-3 cm in its southern reaches also in agreement with the observations. The phase of the response showed a 180° shift between the tide in the Gulf and the Lake; details of the phase in the Lake's basin show an amphidromic point occurring just south of the Strait of Maracaibo as described by Fornerino and Molines (1983).

A similar calculation was carried out with the fully non-linear model started from rest, with a uniform Chezy bottom friction parameter of 50 $m^{1/2}\,sec^{-1}$; $\tau_o = 10^{-4}\,sec^{-1}$; a time-step of 360 sec; and a time weighting parameter (θ) of 0.75 (see Lynch and Gray, 1979). Figures (4a and b) show the currents 342.0 hours into the simulation. These flow patterns agree with an observed anti-nodal line in El Tablazo Bay. Consequently, during certain periods of the tidal cycle, the currents of the city of Maracaibo are southward while the flows in the passages from the Gulf of Venezuela are seaward (Brezina, 1975; see Figure 7 therein). The nonlinearities of the system generate higher harmonics than that of the M_2 forcing. Figures (5a and b) show the M_4 and M_6 tidal amplitudes as obtained by the Fourier decomposition of the model-generated time-series during the 12*th* through 15*th* days of the simulation. Note the general reduction in amplitude [compared to the inviscid M_2 tide in Figure (3a)] and the occurrence of the maxima in the Strait where the nonlinearities are expected to be largest. Figures (6a and b) show the M_4 and M_6 velocities for the same time as Figures (4a,b) also obtained by Fourier decomposing the model time-series. It should be mentioned that the Fourier decomposed M_2 signal agreed with the features obtained from the spectral solution. Lastly, Figure (7) shows the tidal height records at a point in the southern section of the Strait and a point in the Lake [just south of the amphidrome shown in Figure (3b).

CASE II: The Alborán Sea

The Alborán Sea is located in the westernmost region of the Mediterranean Sea. Its western limit is the Strait of Gibraltar, its eastern limit is an imaginary line running between Cape Gata (Spain) and Cape Figalo (Algeria). The coastline of

Spain defines its northern boundary while those of Morocco and Algeria define its southern boundary. Its area is approximately 54,000 Km^2 and has depths reaching 1500 m in its western basin and 2000 m in its eastern basin. The Alborán is the first sea coming in contact with surface (fresher) Atlantic waters and the last one the bottom (saltier) Mediterranean waters reach before flowing into the Atlantic through the Strait of Gibraltar. Typically, the Atlantic waters flow through the Strait as a narrow jet, with velocities greater than 1 m/sec, and recirculate in a semi-permanent anti-cyclonic (clockwise) gyre which extends almost from Spain to Morocco (Figure 8). Explanations of the Alborán gyre have ranged from a "dynamical filling process" linked to the relative position of the stagnation point of the jet flowing out of the Strait with respect to where it impinged on the coast of Africa in a laboratory experiment described by Whitehead and Miller (1979), to a standing Rossby wave in a numerical model presented by Preller (1985).

In our studies of the Alborán, Equations (1)-(3) are altered to simulate a reduced gravity calculation whereby a two-layer fluid is assumed to be geostrophically compensated with the lower layer at rest, i.e., fluid motion exists only in the surface layer. Thus, the calculation of the free surface is replaced by the calculation of the interface displacement and hence the action of gravity is reduced by a factor $\Delta\rho/\rho$ where $\Delta\rho$ is the density difference between the two fluids. In the case of the Alborán, the reduced gravity $g' = g(\Delta\rho/\rho) = 0.002\ g$. At the Strait we required an incoming transport of 1 Sv (1 Sverdrup=$1 \times 10^6\ m^3$/sec). The velocities and the interface displacement were left free to adjust to their appropriate values as determined by the dynamics of the governing equations. At the outflow boundary, the interface height was fixed to generate a geostrophic transport of 1 Sv (flowing east) to balance the incoming mass. Additionally, the β- effect (the variation of the Coriolis parameter with latitude) is included. Therefore, f is replaced by $f_o + \beta\ (y - y_o)$ where f_o and y_o are the values of the Coriolis parameter and the y-coordinate at the southern boundary. The value of $\beta(= \partial f/\partial y)$ is $2 \times 10^{-11} m^{-1}\ sec^{-1}$.

The simulation started from rest with a flat interface at 200 m; the time step was 5400 sec; and the time weighting parameter (θ) was 0.75. The model interface displacements (relative to 200 m) and the velocities after 168 days are shown in Figures (9) and (10) repectively. Both results agree with observed dimensions and location of the gyre, and with measured flow patterns. However, the depression of the interface in the western Alborán basin is not as large the observations indicate, and thus, the model velocities are weaker. In a quasi-geostrophic model of the Mediterranean, Loth and Crepon (1984) also found a gyre in the Alborán which was less intense than the observed. Our model results show reversals in the circulation of the gyre, perhaps due to transients generated by the "cold start". Such reversals in the have not, as yet, been verified in the field.

Finally, as opposed to the Lake Maracaibo system's results, which were found to be relatively robust to the values of τ and τ_o, the Alborán Sea simulations proved to be very sensitive with a tendency to become unstable. The value of τ, fixed in the Alborán basin at $5 \times 10^{-6}\ sec^{-1}$, had to be increased exponentially (in the $-x$, or westward direction to $2.5 \times 10^{-5}\,\text{sec}^{-1}$ in the Strait to supress instabilities therein. The role of τ_0 which was set to $5.5 \times 10^{-6}\,\text{sec}^{-1}$, τ and the time step Δt are currently under investigation.

ACKNOWLEGDMENTS

We would like to thank Drs. M. Fornerino and J.M. Molines of the Universidad del Zulia for providing information on the circulation of the Lake Maracaibo system and G. Parrilla of the Instituto Español de Oceanografia and A. Cantos for supplying information on the Alborán Sea. We would also like to acnowledge the assistance of Mr. Gunnar Sidén in making the computer runs and preparing the graphical output. This work was supported by NSF Grant No. CEE-8352226; and by the U.S.-Spain Joint Committee for Scientific and Technological Cooperation, Grant No. CCA-8411047.

REFERENCES

Brezina, J. (1975) Experience with a small scale, highly distorted fixed bed model of the Lake Maracaibo Estuary, Symposium on Modelling Techniques, Vol. 1, 2nd Annual Symp. of the Waterways, Harbors and Coastal Eng. Div. of the ASCE, 675-689.

Foreman, M.G.G. (1983) An analysis of the "Wave Equation" model for finite element tidal computations, J. Comp. Phys., 52:290-312.

Foreman, M.G.G. (1984) A two-dimensional dispersion analysis of selected methods for solving the lnearized shallow water equations, J. Comp. Phys., 56:287-323.

Fornerino, M. and Molines, J.M. (1983) Circulación en el Lago de Maracaibo. Informe Parcial No. 2, Convenio L.U.Z.-ICLAM, 37pp.

Kinnmark, I.P.E and Gray, W.R. (1982) Time weighting of the momentum equation in the explicit wave equation models of surface water flow. Proc. 4th Int. Conf. on Finite Elements in Water Resources, Springer-Verlag, Holz, et al., eds., 5.67-5.77.

Kinnmark, I.P.E. and Gray, W.R. (1984a) A two-dimensional analysis of the wave equation model for finite element tidal computations, Int. J. Num. Meth. in Engg., 20:369:383.

Kinnmark, I.P.E. and Gray, W.R. (1984b) An implicit wave equation model for the shallow water equations. Proc. 5th Int. Conf. on Finite Elements in Water Resources, Burlington, Vt., Springer-Verlag, Laible, et al., eds., 533-543.

Kinnmark, I.P.E. and Gray, W.R. (1985a) Stability and accuracy of spatial approximations for wave equation tidal models, J. Comp. Phys., 60:447-466.

Kinnmark, I.P.E. and Gray, W.R. (1985b) A generalized wave equation formulation of tidal circulation. Proc. 4th Int. Conf. on Num. Meth. in Laminar and Turbulent Flows, Swansea, Taylor et al., eds.

Lanoix, F. (1974) Project Alborán: Etude hydrologique et dynamique de la Mer d'Alborán. NATO Tech. Rep. 66, 39pp.

Loth, L. and Crepon, M. (1984) A quasi-geostrophic model of the circulation of the Mediterranean. In: Remote sensing of shelf-sea hydrodynamics, Elsevier Oceanography Series No. 38, Nihoul (Editor), 277-285.

Lynch, D.R. (1981) Comparison of spectral and time-stepping approaches for finite element modelling of tidal circulation. Proc. Oceans 81, IEEE Pub. No. 81 CH1685-7, 810-814.

Lynch, D.R. (1985) Mass balance in shallow water simualtions, Comm. Appl. Num. Meth., 1:153-159.

Lynch, D.R. and Gray, W.R. (1979) A wave equation model for finite element tidal computations, Computers and Fluids, 7:207-228.

Lynch, D.R. and Gray, W.R. (1980) Finite element simulation of flow in deforming regions, J. Comp. Phys., 36:135-153.

Platzman, G.W. (1981) Some response characteristics of finite-element tidal models, J. Comp. Phys., 40:36-63.

Preller, R. (1985) A numerical study of circulation in the Alborán Sea. Mesoscale Air-Sea Interaction Group, Technical Report, Florida State Univ., Tallahassee, Forida (USA), 126 pp.

Redfield, A.C. (1961) The tidal system of Lake Maracaibo, Venezuela; Limnology and Oceanography, 6:1-12.

Walters, R.A. (1983) Numerically induced oscillations in finite element approximations to the shallow-water equations, Int. J. Num. Meth. Fluids, 3:591-604.

Walters, R.A. (1984) Finite element solution methods for circulation in estuaries. Proc. 5th Int. Conf. on Finite Elements in Water Resources, Burlington, Vt., Springer-Verlag, Laible, et al., eds., 587-596.

Whitehead; J.A. and Miller, A.R. (1979) Laboratory simulation of the gyre in the Alborán Sea, J. Geophys. Res., 84:3733-3742.

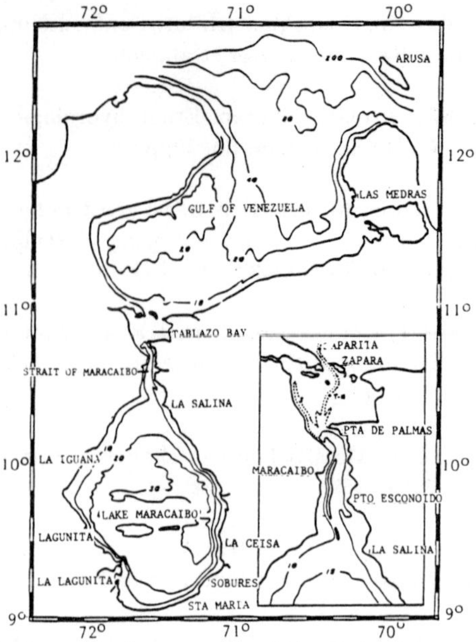

Figure 1. Topography and place names of the Lake Maracaibo system (from Redfield, 1961).

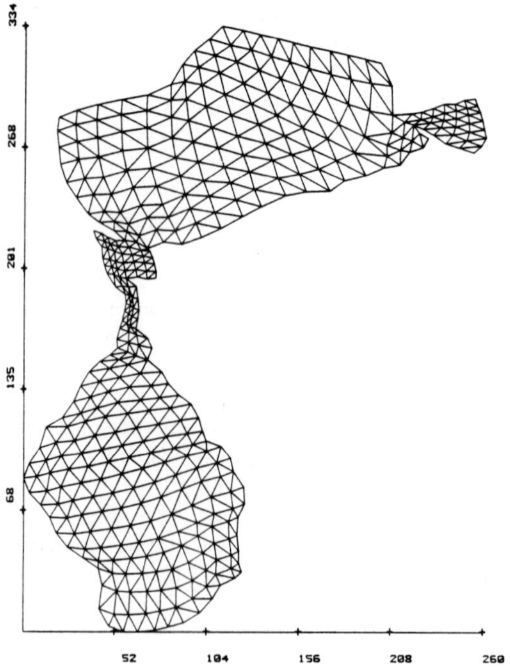

Figure 2. Finite element mesh of the Lake Maracaibo system, (x, y) axes in Kms.

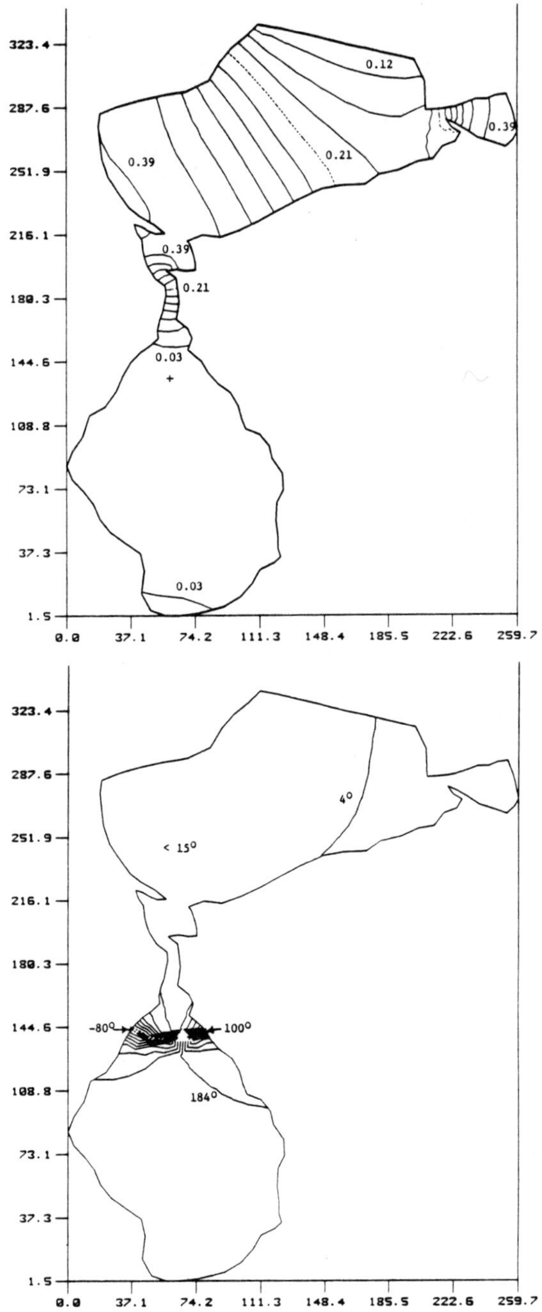

Figure 3. Inviscid spectral model results for the M_2 tidal amplitude in meters (a, top), contour interval is 0.03 meters; and phase (b, bottom), contour interval is 12°, (x, y) axes in Kms.

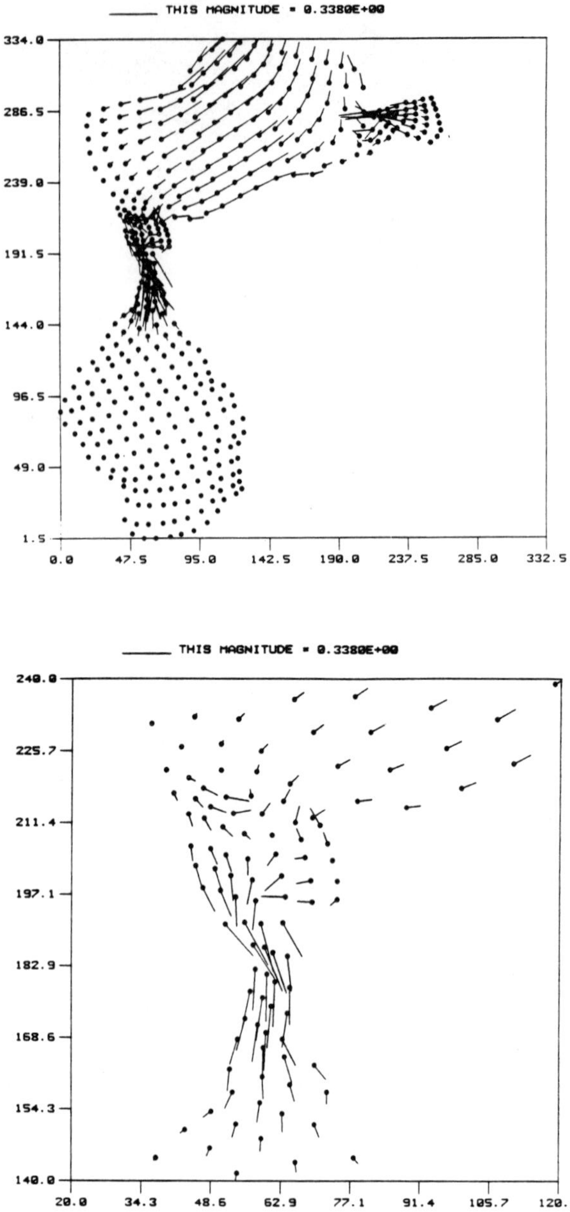

Figure 4. Full nonlinear tidal velocities 342.0 hours into the simulation for the entire domain (a, top); and a detail in the Strait (b, bottom). Units are m/sec, (x, y) axes in Kms.

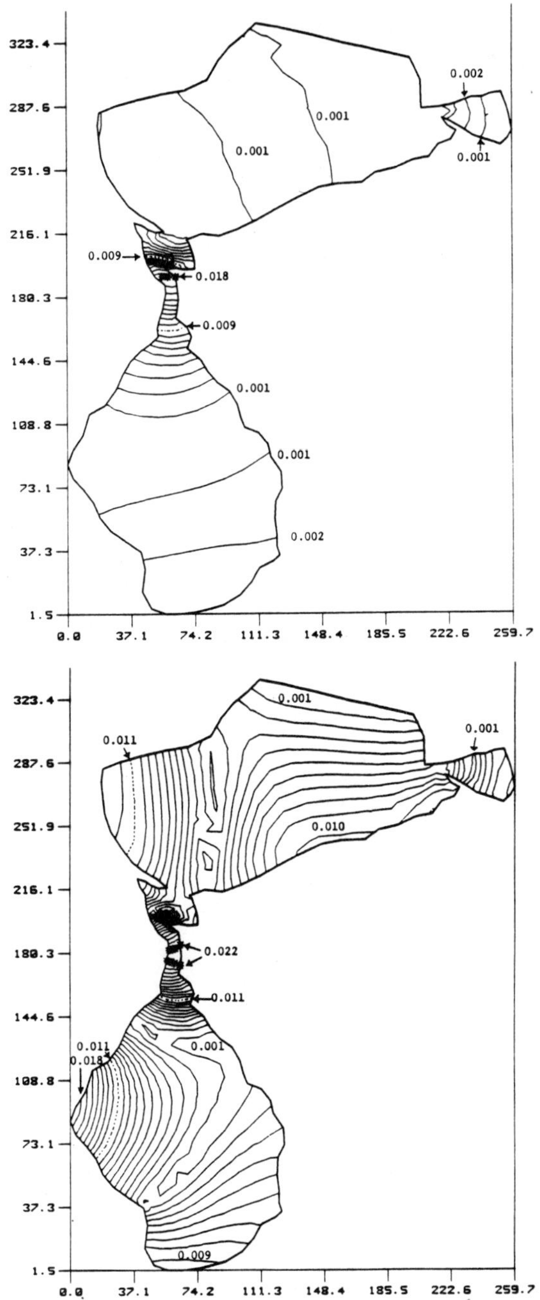

Figure 5. Tidal heights as obtained from Fourier decomposition of the model time series for the M_4 harmonic (a, top), contour interval in 0.001 meters; and the M_6 harmonic (b, bottom), contour interval is in 0.001 meters, (x, y) axes in Kms.

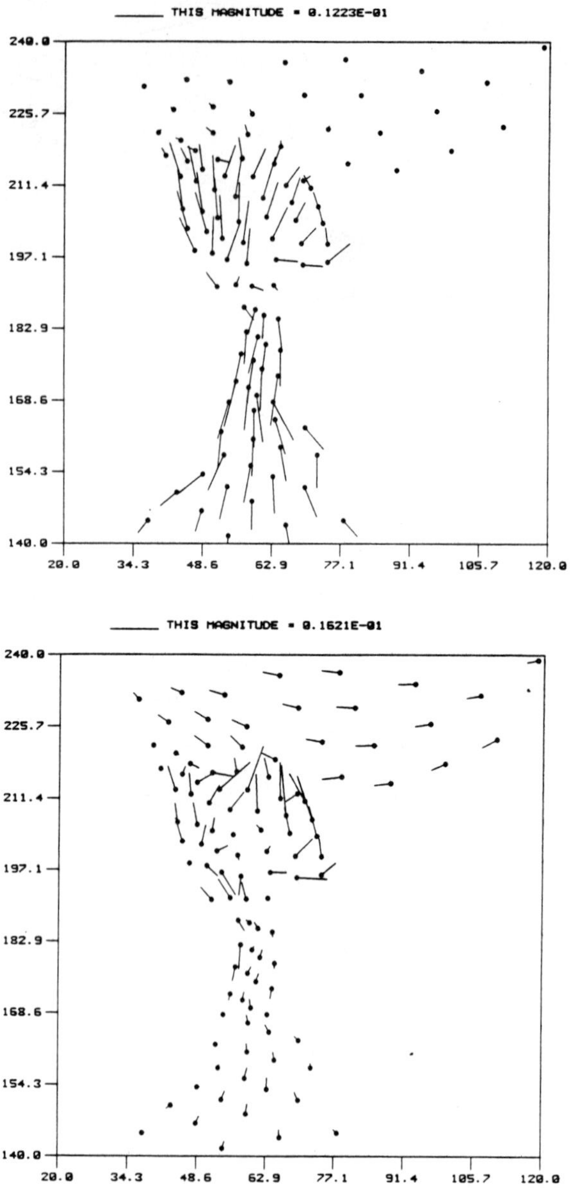

Figure 6. Tidal velocities as obtained from Fourier decomposition of the model time series at the same time in the tidal cycle as in Figures (4a,b) for the M_4 harmonic (a, top); and the M_6 harmonic (b, bottom). Units are m/sec, (x, y) axes in Kms.

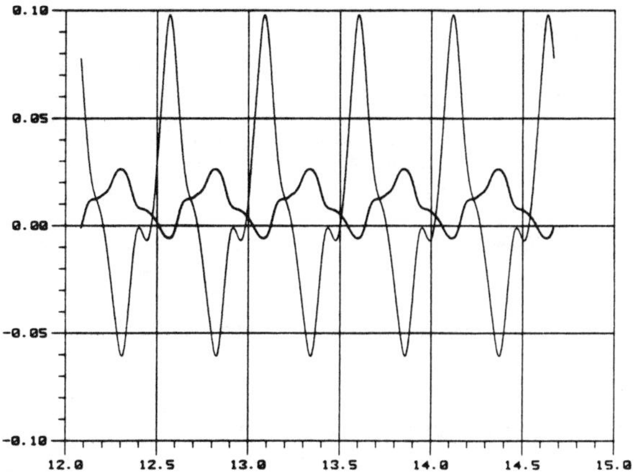

Figure 7. Tidal height record (in meters) between 12 and 15 days of the simulation. The larger amplitude record corresponds to a point in the southern section of the Strait; the smaller amplitude record (darker line) corresponds to a point in the Lake (south of the amphidrome).

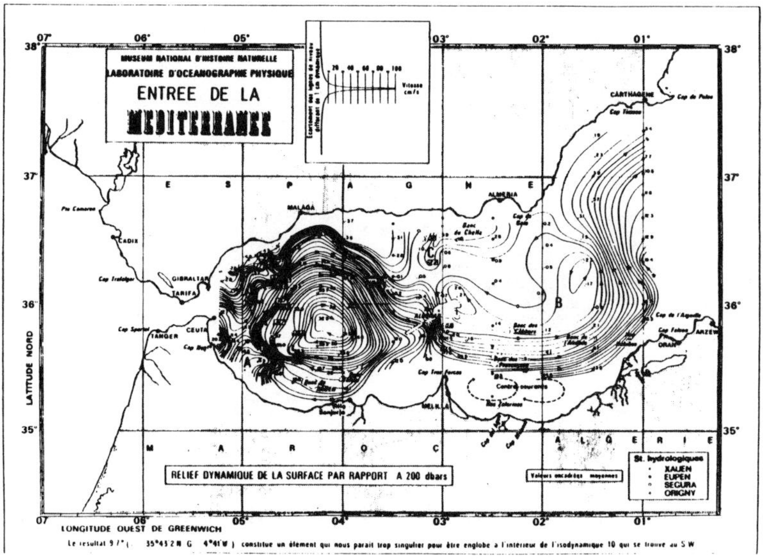

Figure 8. Dynamic height contours and flow patterns of the Alborán Sea (from Lanoix, 1974). Notice the anti-cyclonic gyre in the western basin.

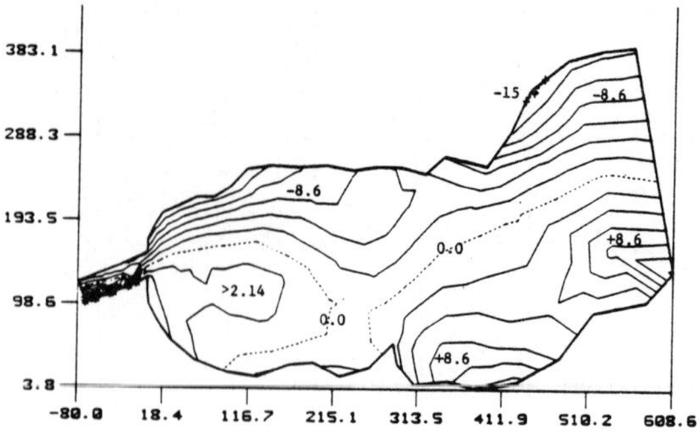

Figure 9. Model interface displacements relative to 200 meters after 168 days. Positive values indicate a depression of the interface; the contour interval is 2.14 meters, (x, y) axes in Kms.

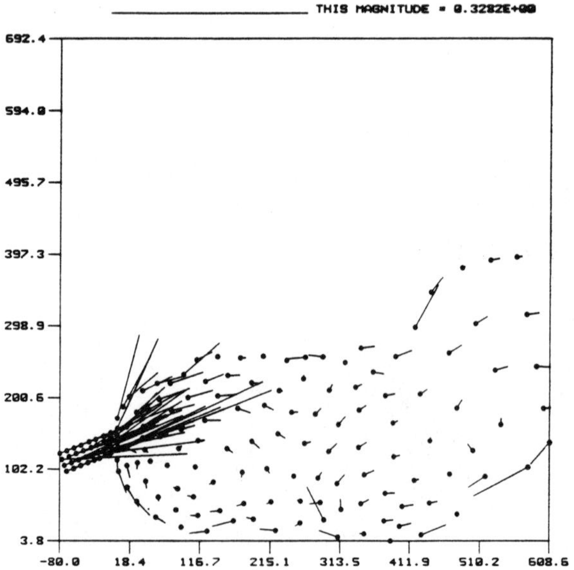

Figure 10. Model velocities after 168 days. Notice the strong currents in the Strait of Gibraltar and the anti-cyclonic gyre in the western basin. Units are m/sec, (x, y) axes in Kms.

VI International Conference on Finite Elements in Water Resources, Lisboa, Portugal, June 1986

A Mathematical Model for Circulation in Maputo Estuary

J.M. Salomao
University Eduardo Mondlane, Maputo, Mozambique

INTRODUCTION

Predicting the circulation pattern is a need that always arises when the consequences of the discharge of wastewater into an estuary have to be assessed. The circulation process can be modelled mathematically and there is already a growing number of cases where the Finite Element Method has been used to satisfaction in the development of an estuarine mathematical model. In this paper a Finite Element Method model for Maputo estuary, that allows the computation of the local truncation error, thus enabling the continuous adjustment of the time increment, is presented. The model was designed as the initial module of a dispersion model for Maputo estuary.

GOVERNING EQUATIONS

The flow of shallow waters can be taken as a two-dimensional process, since the propagation of long period waves is virtually a two-dimensional phenomenon. That is why the governing equations are processed to take this particular form:

$$\frac{\partial q_x}{\partial t} + \frac{q_x}{H}\frac{\partial}{\partial x}(q_x) + \frac{q_y}{H}\frac{\partial}{\partial y}(q_x) = \frac{\partial}{\partial x}(-N_p) - f\,q_y + C_D\,\rho_a\,U_w^2\cos^2\theta_w - \left(\frac{g}{c^2}\right)\frac{1}{\rho}\,\frac{q_x\,(q_x^2+q_y^2)^{1/2}}{H^2} + p_a\frac{\partial H}{\partial x} + \rho\,g\,H\frac{\partial h}{\partial x}, \qquad (1)$$

$$\frac{\partial q_y}{\partial t} + \frac{q_x}{H}\frac{\partial}{\partial x}(q_y) + \frac{q_y}{H}\frac{\partial}{\partial y}(q_y) = \frac{\partial}{\partial y}(-N_p) + f\,q_x + C_D\,\rho_a\,U_w^2\sin^2\theta_w - \left(\frac{g}{c^2}\right)\frac{1}{\rho}\,\frac{q_y\,(q_x^2+q_y^2)^{1/2}}{H^2} + p_a\frac{\partial H}{\partial y} + \rho\,g\,H\frac{\partial h}{\partial y}, \qquad (2)$$

with regard to the conservation of momentum (momentum equations), and:

$$\frac{\partial q_x}{\partial x} + \frac{\partial q_y}{\partial y} + \frac{\partial(\rho H)}{\partial t} = 0 \ , \qquad (3)$$

with regard to the conservation of mass (continuity equation), and where (Figure 1):

x, y	are cartesian coordinates,
q_x, q_y	are components of the mass flux in the x, y directions respectively,
$H = h + \eta$	is the water depth,
N_p	is the force per unit length derived from the internal pressure,
f	is the Coriolis coefficient,
C_D	is the wind drag coefficient,
ρ	is the water density,
ρ_a	is the air density,
U_w	is the wind velocity,
θ_w	is the angle between the wind direction and the x direction,
g	is the gravity acceleration,
c	is the Chézy friction coefficient,
p_a	is the atmospheric pressure,
t	is the time variable.

These equations were obtained after vertical integration, and the momentum equations presented (1,2) already take into account the third momentum equation, that after vertical integration, and disregarding vertical accelerations and the resulting stresses, took the form:

$$p = \rho \, g \, (\eta - h) + p_a \ .$$

Additionally the tide generating forces and the kinematic viscosity terms have been neglected. As shown above the acting forces considered, are those due to the Coriolis effect, the wind on the water surface (**Hicks**, 1972), the bottom friction, the atmospheric pressure, and the water slopes.

To simplify the writing, some of the terms can be brought together, as follows:

$$R_x = \frac{\partial}{\partial x}(-N_p) - f\,q_y + C_D\,\rho_a\,U_w^2 \cos^2\theta_w -$$

$$- \left(\frac{g}{c^2}\right) \frac{1}{\rho} \frac{q_x\,(q_x^2 + q_y^2)^{1/2}}{H^2} + p_a \frac{\partial H}{\partial x} + \rho\,g\,H \frac{\partial h}{\partial x} \ , \qquad (4)$$

$$R_y = \frac{\partial}{\partial y}(-N_p) + f\,q_x + C_D\,\rho_a\,U_w^2 \sin^2\theta_w -$$

$$- \left(\frac{g}{c^2}\right) \frac{1}{\rho} \frac{q_y\,(q_x^2 + q_y^2)^{1/2}}{H^2} + p_a \frac{\partial H}{\partial y} + \rho\,g\,H \frac{\partial h}{\partial y} \ . \qquad (5)$$

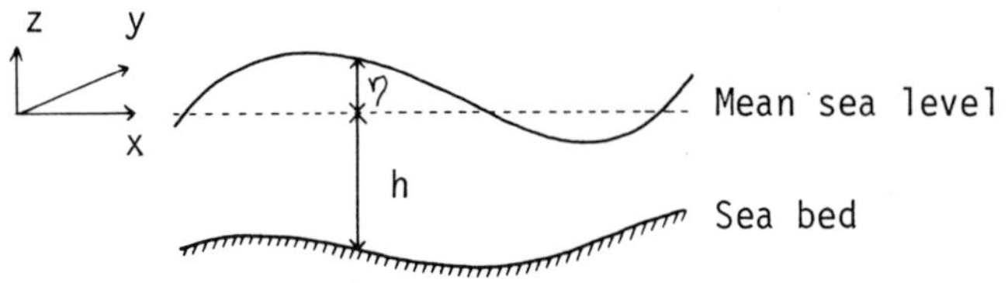

Figure 1 - Vertical section

Boundary and initial conditions

To solve these equations, the boundary conditions have to be specified, and they read (Figure 2):
On a land boundary

$$q_n = 0 \quad , \tag{6}$$

or

$$q_n = \overline{q}_n \quad , \tag{7}$$

being

$$q_n = q_x \cos \alpha + q_y \cos \beta \quad , \tag{8}$$

where a river enters the estuary.
On a sea boundary

$$N_{nn} = - N_p \quad , \tag{9}$$

which is equivalent to

$$H = \overline{H} \quad . \tag{10}$$

The initial conditions are stated as:

$$q_x \,(x, y, t = 0) = 0 \quad , \tag{11}$$

$$q_y \,(x, y, t = 0) = 0 \quad , \tag{12}$$

$$H \,(x, y, t = 0) = h \quad . \tag{13}$$

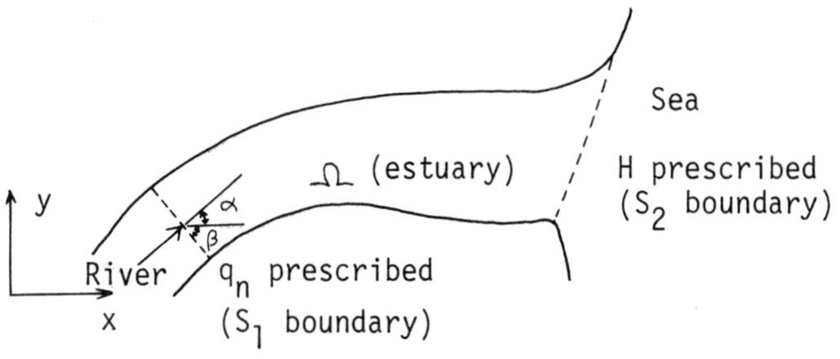

Figure 2 - Domain and boundary conditions

Variational statements

The formulation of variational statements from **Equations** (1, 2, 3), as the first step towards the application of the Finite Element Method (FEM), yields (**Connor et al.**, 1976):

$$\iint_{\Omega}\left\{ \frac{\partial q_x}{\partial t} + \frac{q_x}{H}\frac{\partial}{\partial x}(q_x) + \frac{q_y}{H}\frac{\partial}{\partial y}(q_x) - R_x \right\} \delta q_x \, d\Omega =$$

$$= \int_{S_2} \cos\alpha \, (N_p - \overline{N}_p)\, \delta q_x \, dS \ , \qquad (14)$$

$$\iint_{\Omega}\left\{ \frac{\partial q_y}{\partial t} + \frac{q_y}{H}\frac{\partial}{\partial y}(q_y) + \frac{q_x}{H}\frac{\partial}{\partial x}(q_y) - R_y \right\} \delta q_y \, d\Omega =$$

$$= \int_{S_2} \cos\beta \, (N_p - \overline{N}_p)\, \delta q_y \, dS \ , \qquad (15)$$

$$\iint_{\Omega}\left\{ \frac{\partial q_x}{\partial x} + \frac{\partial q_y}{\partial y} + \frac{\partial(\rho H)}{\partial t} \right\} \delta H \, d\Omega = \int_{S_1} (q_n - \overline{q}_n)\, \delta H \, dS \ , \qquad (16)$$

where:

δq_x, δq_y, δH are arbitrary variations that comply with the mass flux and elevation boundary conditions.

The shape or interpolation functions for the unknown functions and the variations were made identical, with an expression of the type:

$$U = \phi^T U^n \ , \qquad (17)$$

or

$$\delta U = \phi^T \delta U^n \ , \qquad (18)$$

where the index n refers to a generic element in which the domain has been divided.

Taking into account the boundary conditions and integrating by parts the continuity equation (3), we get:

$$\iint_{\Omega} \delta q_x^{n,T}\left\{ \phi\phi^T \frac{\partial q_x^n}{\partial t} + \phi \left[\frac{q_x}{H}\frac{\partial}{\partial x}(q_x) + \frac{q_y}{H}\frac{\partial}{\partial y}(q_x) - \right.\right.$$

$$\left.\left. - R_x \right]\right\} d\Omega = 0 \ , \qquad (19)$$

$$\iint_{\Omega} \delta q_y^{n,T}\left\{ \phi\phi^T \frac{\partial q_y^n}{\partial t} + \phi \left[\frac{q_x}{H}\frac{\partial}{\partial x}(q_y) + \frac{q_y}{H}\frac{\partial}{\partial y}(q_y) - \right.\right.$$

$$\left.\left. - R_y \right]\right\} d\Omega = 0 \ , \qquad (20)$$

$$\iint_{\Omega} \delta H^{n,T}\left\{ \phi\phi^T \rho \frac{\partial H^n}{\partial t} - \left[\frac{\partial \phi}{\partial x} q_x + \frac{\partial \phi}{\partial y} q_y \right]\right\} d\Omega +$$

$$+ \int_{S_1} \delta H^{n,T} \phi \, \overline{q}_n \, dS = 0 \ . \qquad (21)$$

To extend the element equations to the overall domain, these equations are converted into:

$$\sum_N \iint_\Omega \delta q_x^{n,T} \{\phi\phi^T \frac{\partial q_x^n}{\partial t} + \phi \left[\frac{q_x}{H} \frac{\partial}{\partial x} (q_x) + \frac{q_y}{H} \frac{\partial}{\partial y} (q_x) - \right.$$

$$\left. - R_x \right] \} d\Omega = 0 \ , \qquad (22)$$

$$\sum_N \iint_\Omega \delta q_y^{n,T} \{\phi\phi^T \frac{\partial q_y^n}{\partial t} + \phi \left[\frac{q_x}{H} \frac{\partial}{\partial x} (q_y) + \frac{q_y}{H} \frac{\partial}{\partial y} (q_y) - \right.$$

$$\left. - R_y \right] \} d\Omega = 0 \ , \qquad (23)$$

$$\sum_N \iint_\Omega \delta H^{n,T} \{\phi\phi^T \rho \ \frac{\partial H^n}{\partial t} - \left[\frac{\partial \phi}{\partial x} q_x + \frac{\partial \phi}{\partial y} q_y \right] \} d\Omega +$$

$$+ \int_{S_1} \delta H^{n,T} \phi \ \overline{q_n} \ dS = 0 \ , \qquad (24)$$

where N is the number of elements into which the domain has been divided, and the summation Σ is carried out over all the elements.

THE FINITE ELEMENT MESH

From the information available on the hydrodynamics of Maputo estuary (**S.M.A.E.**, 1967; **D.N.A.**, 1983), and through a visit and a discussion of the performance of the physical model of Maputo estuary and bay, it is known that the circulation process in the estuary can be illustrated by what takes place along the main channel. This is the reason why the Finite Element (FE) mesh drawn (Figure 3) covers the development of the main channel that takes an active part in the water flow.

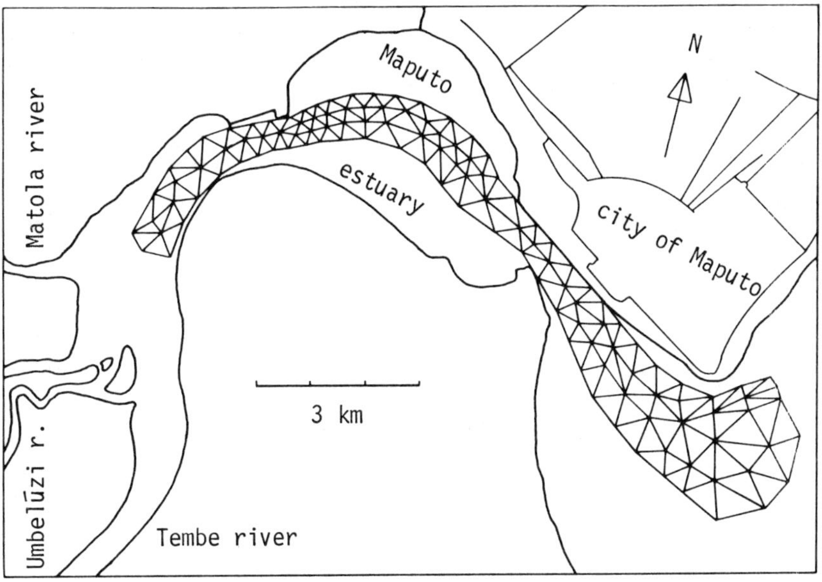

Figure 3 - Maputo estuary and Finite Element mesh

The narrowing and deepening that occur in the estuary have an adverse influence on the numerical integration process, because in the

Fréderick-Courant-Levy formula, the limit of the time increment is prescribed as:

$$\Delta t \leqq \frac{\Delta \ell}{\sqrt{2gH}} \tag{25}$$

where:

Δt is the time increment,
$\Delta \ell$ can be generically called the element size.

CPU REQUIREMENTS

After proper manipulation, a system of equations is derived from **Equations (22, 23, 24).** As the mass fluxes and water depths are variable with time, the system of equations obtained is non-linear and has to be solved in time steps. For the time integration it was decided to use the Runge-Kutta method (4th order), since it provides the necessary accuracy and stability for the time evolutionary problem represented by the model.

The initial time increment computed through the Fréderick-Courant-Levy formula was of the order of 40 seconds (4th order), which meant that for a tidal cycle of 12.4 hours, 1,160 iterations were needed.

TIME INTEGRATION

One difficulty encountered during the first tests of the model, was not being able to evaluate the local truncation error. Moreover, knowing the local truncation error would enable the control of the time increment by comparison with the error limit allowed.

In the 4th order version of the Runge-Kutta method by **Fehlberg** (1970), the solution of the system of equations represented by:

$$\frac{d\vec{y}}{dt} = \vec{f}\,(t,\vec{y}) \;, \tag{26}$$

where:

$$\vec{y}(t_n) = \vec{y}_n \;, \tag{27}$$

has the form:

$$\vec{y}_{n+1} = \vec{y}_n + \Delta t\left(\frac{25}{216}\vec{K}_o + \frac{1408}{2565}\vec{K}_2 + \frac{2197}{4104}\vec{K}_3 - \frac{1}{5}\vec{K}_4\right) + \vec{O}\,(\Delta t^5) \;, \tag{28}$$

the local truncation error being:

$$\vec{O}\,(\Delta t^5) \simeq \Delta t\left(-\frac{1}{360}\vec{K}_o + \frac{128}{4275}\vec{K}_2 + \frac{21997}{75240}\vec{K}_3 - \frac{1}{50}\vec{K}_4 - \frac{2}{55}\vec{K}_5\right) \;, \tag{29}$$

and where:

$$\vec{K}_0 = \vec{f}\,(t_n, \vec{y}_n) \;, \tag{30}$$

$$\vec{K}_1 = \vec{f}\,(t_n + \frac{1}{4}\,\Delta t, \vec{y}_n + \frac{1}{4}\,\Delta t\,\vec{K}_0) \;, \tag{31}$$

$$\vec{K}_2 = \vec{f}\,(t_n + \frac{3}{8}\,\Delta t, \vec{y}_n + \frac{\Delta t}{2}\,(3\vec{K}_0 + 9\vec{K}_1)) \;, \tag{32}$$

$$\vec{K}_3 = \vec{f}\,(t_n + \frac{12}{13}\,\Delta t, \vec{y}_n + \frac{\Delta t}{2197}\,(1932\vec{K}_0 - 7200\vec{K}_1 + 7296\vec{K}_2)) \;, \tag{33}$$

$$\vec{K}_4 = \vec{f}\,(t_n + \Delta t, \vec{y}_n + \Delta t\,(\frac{439}{216}\,\vec{K}_0 - 8\vec{K}_1 + \frac{3680}{513}\,\vec{K}_2 - \frac{845}{4104}\,\vec{K}_3)) \;, \tag{34}$$

$$\vec{K}_5 = \vec{f}\,(t_n + \frac{\Delta t}{2}, \vec{y}_n + \Delta t\,(-\frac{8}{27}\,\vec{K}_0 + 2\vec{K}_1 - \frac{3544}{2565}\,\vec{K}_2 + \frac{1859}{4104}\,\vec{K}_3 - \frac{11}{40}\,\vec{K}_4)) \;. \tag{35}$$

TIME INCREMENT ADJUSTMENT

Using the Fehlberg version of the Runge-Kutta method, and bearing in mind that for a 4th order method (**Conte et al.,** 1980):

$$\overline{\Delta t} \approx \Delta t\,[\varepsilon\,(\Delta t/E)]^{1/4} \tag{36}$$

where:

Δt	is the time increment currently in use,
$\overline{\Delta t}$	is the time increment for the next iteration,
ε	is the upper error limit allowed,
$E/\Delta t$	is the error per unit step;

adjusting the time increment in an iterative process is an easy task now. However, the possibility of time increment change implies an additional computational effort, since each iteration cycle is made longer by the error computations for each unknown, plus the likely risk of repetition of the iteration, if the error limit is exceeded, which means that the time increment in use is too large.

ROUND-OFF ERRORS

To reduce round-off errors, the double precision partial accumulation process was put in practice. It consists of storing the increments of the unknowns in single precision, but their addition to the unknowns, that are stored in double precision, is also made in double precision.

OPERATION OF THE MODEL

The circulation model described was operated in tandem with a dispersion model for Maputo estuary. When running the model, a flux across part of the boundary was considered, to take into account the water exchanges between the storage areas and the main channel. This flux was computed from the tidal prism. The flow from the tributary rivers was neglected, since the currents in the estuary are mainly due to the tidal effect.

CONCLUDING REMARKS

To improve the performance of the model, a few options are available for further research (**Salomão**, 1985):

- Collecting more field data on the flow pattern in the estuary, particularly at the river boundaries, where there is an important exchange of water during a tidal cycle.
- Enlarging the FE domain could be seen as a logical step to follow, but that will more than double the number of mesh nodes, and correspondingly the number of simultaneous equations dealt with in the numerical computations. Memory requirements and CPU time would increase dramatically, and they could make the model unaffordable and heavy to run.

As a final remark it can be said that whereas a theoretical background on estuarine behaviour was necessary before commencing work on the Maputo estuary model, some practical knowledge of the estuary proved quite useful, when the area to be covered by the model was under discussion, or when the mechanisms more active in the circulation process were being evaluated. That is why it is essential that a high sense of critical judgement should always be exercised when working in mathematical modelling.

REFERENCES

Connor, J.J., and Brebbia, C.A. (1976). Finite Element Techniques for Fluid Flow. Butterworth & Co., London.

Conte, S.D., and de Boor, C. (1980). Elementary Numerical Analysis. McGraw-Hill, New York.

Direcção Nacional de Aguas (D.N.A.), (1983). Drenagem e Depuração das Aguas Residuais da Cidade de Maputo. DHV, Maputo.

Fehlberg, E. (1970). Klassiche Runge-Kutta-Formeln Vierter und niedrigerer Ordnung mit Schrittweiten-Kontrolle und ihre Anwendung auf Wärmeleitungsprobleme. *Computing* **6** (1-2), pp. 61-71.

Hicks, B.B. (1972). Some Evaluations of Drag and Bulk Transfer Coefficients over Water Bodies of Different Sizes. *Boundary-Layer Meteorol.* **3**, pp. 201-213.

Salomão, J.M. (1985). Ph.D. thesis. Universidade do Minho.

Serviços Municipalizados de Agua e Electricidade (S.M.A.E.), (1967). Saneamento da Cidade de Lourenço Marques. Hidroprojecto, Lourenço Marques.

VI International Conference on Finite Elements in Water Resources, Lisboa, Portugal, June 1986

Spectral Computations Within the Bight of Abaco Using a Frequency-Time Domain Finite Element Model

J.J. Westerink
Department of Civil Engineering, Princeton University, Princeton, NJ 08540, U.S.A.
J.J. Connor, K.D. Stolzenbach
Department of Civil Engineering, Massachusetts Institute of Technology, Cambridge, MA 02139, U.S.A.

INTRODUCTION

As an alternative approach to time stepping techniques, a number of modelers (Kawahara et al., 1977; Pearson and Winter, 1977; Le Provost and Poncet, 1978; Snyder et al., 1979) have been using harmonic based methods in conjunction with finite differences (f.d.) or finite elements (f.e.) in the numerical simulation of tidal circulation. From a historical perspective harmonic or frequency domain methods have been used in tidal forecasting for more than a century (Dronkers, 1964). However, these methods were abandoned upon the advent of the computer era when f.d. and later f.e. approaches were used. Revived interest in the harmonic approach has come about due to the methods' many unique features. Because of the highly periodic nature of the tidal phenomenon, the harmonic method presents itself as an intrinsically natural solution procedure. The method allows for the accurate resolution of daily tidal fluctuations, it readily accounts for beating effects such as spring tide/neap tide variations and can concisely assess long period fluctuations (steady state, monthly etc.) in a tidal embayment. Each of these capabilities has the potential of being performed with substantial computational savings over standard time stepping schemes.

The harmonic method eliminates the time dependence from the governing shallow water equations and produces sets of quasi-steady equations for each of the harmonic components present in the tidal spectrum at the site of interest. In the deep ocean the only significant tidal species are the astronomical constituents which by definition are directly related to celestial mechanics. In shallow water the nonlinear terms in the governing equations become important and responses at frequencies other than the astronomical forcing frequencies will be generated. These shallow water constituents are classified as either overtides, which correspond to the generation of a response through the nonlinearities by one astronomical component, or compound tides, which are the results of the nonlinear interaction between two astronomical constituents. The amplitudes associated with these shallow water tides generally significantly decrease with higher frequencies and depend on the water depth and the geography of the sea or embayment.

A fundamental requirement for the application of the harmonic method is that the equations which are to be harmonically separated be linear. This necessitates that the nonlinearities be dealt with as linear terms while the associated harmonic coupling between the various constituents be accounted for. Strategies to handle this quasi-linearization have consisted of either pertubation analyses (Kawahara et al., 1977; Askar and Cakmak, 1978) or some type of iterative procedure which treats nonlinearities as pseudo-forcings which are updated with every cycle (Pearson and Winter, 1977; Kawahara and Hasegawa, 1978; Snyder et al., 1979). However these investigators did not take into account the generation of compound tides even though they can constitute a very significant part of the shallow water constituent spectrum. More recently Le Provost (1981a,b) has developed a harmonic based f.e. model which does take into account compound tides. He applies a perturbation analysis and a quasi-linearization for bottom friction such that the full nonlinear coupling between the various astronomical constituents can be accounted for.

In the development of our harmonic based tidal circulation model, we have selected an iterative approach in conjunction with a harmonic analysis technique based on the least squares method. The least squares harmonic analysis method is able to extract extremely closely and irregularly spaced frequency information in a very efficient manner. This entirely general procedure allows for the direct assessment of all the tidal constituents, including the compound tides, and permits the clear cut and complete investigation of their mutual interaction through the nonlinearities. Furthermore we have included the study of the low frequency end of the shallow water constituent spectrum. The capability of evaluating long period fluctuations, which may be regarded as comprising the Eulerian residual circulation, is an especially salient feature which naturally results from our procedure without excessive increases in computational effort. In subsequent sections we shall describe the details of the harmonic based f.e. model TEA-NL (Nonlinear Tidal Embayment Analysis) and then discuss its application to the Bight of Abaco.

MODEL DEVELOPMENT

Governing Equations

The equations used to describe tidal wave propagation are the shallow water equations which are expressed as:

$$\eta_{,t} + [u(h+\eta)]_{,x} + [v(h+\eta)]_{,y} = 0 \tag{1}$$

$$u_{,t} + g\eta_{,x} - fv + c\,\frac{(u^2 + v^2)^{1/2}}{(h+\eta)}\,u + (uu_{,x} + vu_{,y}) = 0 \tag{2}$$

$$v_{,t} + g\eta_{,y} + fu + c\,\frac{(u^2 + v^2)^{1/2}}{(h+\eta)}\,v + (uv_{,x} + vv_{,y}) = 0 \tag{3}$$

where η is the surface elevation relative to mean sea level (MSL), u and v are components of velocity in the x and y directions, t is time, h is depth to MSL, g is acceleration due to gravity, f is the Coriolis factor and c is the bottom friction factor. The boundary conditions associated with these equations are the prescription of elevation, η^*, on the boundary Γ_η, which is usually the open ocean boundary, and the prescription of normal flux, Q_n^*, on Γ_Q, which is typically the land boundary.

Finite Element Formulation

The spatial dependence of the shallow water equations will be resolved by applying the f.e. method. Our procedure requires that the continuity equation be used in order to establish the symmetrical weak weighted residual form. Applying Galerkin's method, the error in the continuity equation is weighted by the variation in elevation, $\delta\eta$, and is integrated over the interior domain, Ω. Furthermore, the natural boundary error is accounted for by weighting the error in the normal boundary flux with $\delta\eta$ and integrating over the natural boundary Γ_Q. It is required that these combined errors vanish and the following expression results:

$$\iint_\Omega \{\eta_{,t} + [u(h+\eta)]_{,x} + [v(h+\eta)]_{,y}\}\delta\eta\, d\Omega + \int_{\Gamma_Q}\{-Q_n + Q_n^*\}\,\delta\eta\, d\Gamma = 0 \tag{4}$$

Applying Gauss' theorem and taking into account certain boundary relationships leads to the symmetrical weighted residual weak form. Moving the nonlinear and boundary loading terms to the right hand side yields the following expression:

$$\iint_\Omega \{\eta_{,t}\delta\eta - uh(\delta\eta)_{,x} - vh(\delta\eta)_{,y}\}\, d\Omega = \int_{\Gamma_Q} Q_n^*\,\delta\eta\, d\Gamma + \iint_\Omega \{u\eta(\delta\eta)_{,x} + v\eta(\delta\eta)_{,y}\}d\Omega \tag{5}$$

The weighted residual forms of the momentum equations are obtained by weighting the associated errors with the residual velocities and integrating over the interior domain. Again the nonlinearities are taken to the right hand side. Furthermore, in order to enhance iterative stability, a linearized friction term is included on both sides. Finally, both equations are multiplied through by depth to allow for symmetricity in the derivative matrices which result in both the f.e. continuity and momentum equations. With these modifications the weighted residual forms of the momentum equations appear as:

$$\iint_{\Omega} \{hu_{,t} + gh\eta_{,x} - fhv + \lambda u\}\ \delta u d\Omega =$$

$$\iint_{\Omega} \{\lambda - c\frac{h}{h+\eta}(u^2+v^2)^{1/2}\}u - h(uu_{,x}+vu_{,y})\,\delta u d\Omega \tag{6}$$

$$\iint_{\Omega} \{hv_{,t} + gh\eta_{,y} + fhu + \lambda v\}\ \delta v d\Omega =$$

$$\iint_{\Omega} \{\lambda - c\frac{h}{h+\eta}(u^2+v^2)^{1/2}\}v - h(uv_{,x}+vv_{,y})\,\delta v d\Omega \tag{7}$$

Equations 5 through 7 serve as the basis of the f.e. formulation. All nonlinear terms appear on the right hand side where they can be conveniently updated with each iteration as pseudo force loadings to a linear problem. Applying the f.e. method to these integral equations results in the following two sets of global nonlinear differentially time dependent matrix equations:

$$\underline{\underline{M}}_{\eta}\,\underline{\eta}_{,t} - \underline{\underline{D}}\,\underline{U} = -\underline{P}_{\eta}^{lin} + \underline{P}_{\eta}^{nl} \tag{8}$$

$$\underline{\underline{M}}_{U}\,\underline{U}_{,t} + \underline{\underline{M}}_{F}\,\underline{U} + \underline{\underline{M}}_{C}\,\underline{U} + g\,\underline{\underline{D}}^{T}\underline{\eta} = \underline{P}_{U}^{nl} \tag{9}$$

where $\underline{\eta}$ is an elevation vector, $\underline{U}$ is a velocity vector, $\underline{\underline{M}}_{\eta}$ and $\underline{\underline{M}}_{U}$ are mass matrices, $\underline{\underline{M}}_{F}$ is a linearized frictional distribution matrix, $\underline{\underline{M}}_{C}$ is the Coriolis matrix, $\underline{P}_{\eta}^{lin}$ is a boundary flux load vector, $\underline{P}_{\eta}^{nl}$ is a nonlinear load vector for finite amplitude effects, $\underline{P}_{U}^{nl}$ is a nonlinear load vector containing the difference between linearized friction and full nonlinear friction and the convective acceleration effects. Both the variable vectors $\underline{\eta}$ and $\underline{U}$, the linear load vector $\underline{P}_{\eta}^{lin}$ and the nonlinear load vectors $\underline{P}_{\eta}^{nl}$ and $\underline{P}_{U}^{nl}$ are all time dependent. Program TEA-NL was implemented with linear expansions for all variables over triangular elements.

Harmonic Decomposition of Governing Equations

The differential time dependence in Equations 8 and 9 are resolved by reducing them to sets of harmonic equations which are coupled through the nonlinear terms. It is assumed that both the responses and load vectors may be expressed as harmonic series of the form:

$$\underline{A}(t) = \mathrm{Re}\left\{\sum_{j=1}^{N_f} \underline{A}_j\, e^{i\omega_j t}\right\} \tag{10}$$

where $\underline{A}$ stands for the responses $\underline{\eta}$ and $\underline{U}$ and any of the load vectors and ω_j represents the N_f frequencies required to adequately represent the significant constituents in the tidal spectrum. Substituting into Equations 8 and 9 for each of the responses and load vectors, taking appropriate time derivatives and grouping terms leads to N_f sets of time independent linear equations of the following type:

$$i\omega_j \underline{\underline{M}}_\eta \underline{\eta}_j - \underline{\underline{D}}\,\underline{U}_j = -\underline{P}^{lin}_{\eta_j} + \underline{P}^{nl}_{\eta_j} \tag{11}$$

$$i\omega_j \underline{\underline{M}}_U \underline{U}_j + \underline{\underline{M}}_F \underline{U}_j + \underline{\underline{M}}_C \underline{U}_j + g\,\underline{\underline{D}}^T \underline{\eta}_j = P^{nl}_{U_j} \tag{12}$$

Iterative Solution Procedure

A direct solution procedure is applied to solve for each set of linear equations associated with the frequencies ω_j. With this scheme $\underline{U}_j$ is solved for with the momentum equation as follows:

$$\underline{U}_j = \underline{\underline{M}}^{-1}_{TOT} (\underline{P}^{nl}_{U_j} - g\,\underline{\underline{D}}^T \underline{\eta}_j) \tag{13}$$

where

$$\underline{\underline{M}}_{TOT} = i\omega_j \underline{\underline{M}}_U + \underline{\underline{M}}_F + \underline{\underline{M}}_C \tag{14}$$

Substituting for $\underline{U}_j$ into the associated continuity equation:

$$(i\omega_j \underline{\underline{M}}_\eta + g\underline{\underline{D}}\,\underline{\underline{M}}^{-1}_{TOT}\underline{\underline{D}}^T)\underline{\eta}_j = -\underline{P}^{lin}_{\eta_j} + \underline{P}^{nl}_{\eta_j} + \underline{\underline{D}}\,\underline{\underline{M}}^{-1}_{TOT}\,\underline{P}^{nl}_{U_j} \tag{15}$$

Hence $\underline{\eta}_j$ is solved for using Equation 15 and subsequently $\underline{U}_j$ is solved for using Equation 13.

The iterative solution strategy starts out with the assumption that the nonlinear loadings are zero. Each of these N_f linear sets of equations are then solved for the boundary loadings imposed. Time histories may then be genereated for both velocities and elevations with Equation 10. This in turn allows time histories of the nonlinear pseudo loading vectors $\underline{P}^{nl}_\eta(t)$ and $\underline{P}^{nl}_U(t)$ to be produced. As was assumed earlier, these time domain pseudo forcings may be approximated as harmonic series. Hence the total nonlinear loadings for continuity and momentum are distributed to all or some of the N_f sets of harmonic equations. Now each of these N_f sets of equations is solved again and the entire procedure is repeated until convergence is reached.

Harmonic Decomposition of Nonlinear Pseudo Load Vectors

The selection of a harmonic analysis procedure for the non-linear pseudo forcing vectors is of vital importance for the efficiency, accuracy and generality of the model. Standard Fourier analysis procedures operate with integer multiples of some base frequency. Therefore they are quite satisfactory when examining one major astronomical tide and its overtides. However when examining a more general tidal spectrum which includes compound tides, Fourier methods become impractical since they then require extremely small frequency steps and an excessive number of time sampling points.

A very attractive alternative to Fourier methods is the least squares harmonic analysis method (Dronkers, 1964; Munk and Hasselman, 1964). This procedure consists simply of a common least squares error minimization procedure which uses a harmonic series as the fitting function. This harmonic series only contains frequencies which are known to exist in the time history record. The method is able to extract extremely closely and irregularly spaced frequency information, yet theoretically only requires a number of time history sampling points equal to twice the number of frequencies contained in the spectrum. The almost infinite frequency resolution and the extremely low number of required time history sampling points make the least squares method the optimal choice for the analysis of the non-linear pseudo forcing time histories representing the nonlinear interaction of various tidal constituents.

COMPUTATIONS OF THE TIDES IN THE BIGHT OF ABACO, BAHAMAS

The Bight of Abaco (Figure 1) offers an ideal opportunity for a study of the nonlinear tidal interactions which occur in shallow embayments both because of its physical characteristics and the amount of available data. The shallow depths within the Bight (between 2 and 8 meters) and the sharp drop in depths at the open ocean boundary (to more than 1000 meters) assure that only astronomical species enter the Bight and that all nonlinear species are generated and almost entirely retained (due to the reflective nature of the boundary) within the Bight. Filloux and Snyder (1979) measured elevation at a total of 25 points throughout the Bight in a series of 3 field experiments. They then harmonically decomposed the measured time history records to obtain amplitudes and phase shifts for the M2, N2, S2, O1, K1, M4 and M6 constituents. The average values of amplitudes over the 3 experiments are listed for the M2, N2, M4 and M6 tides in Table 1 for the sites shown in Figure 3. Snyder et al. (1979) modeled the tides within the Bight using a harmonically based f.d. model which did not consider the generation of steady currents and/or compound tides. Their optimal computations using the standard quadratic friction law overpredicted the amplitudes of the M6 constituent by a factor of roughly 1.9.

TEA-NL computations were performed using the f.e. grid shown in Figure 2. The first series of computations took only the M2 astronomical tide and its overtides (steady, M4, M6, etc.) into consideration. The ocean boundary was forced with the M2 constituent using an amplitude of 40 cm. The boundary was taken as being totally reflective and hence all overtides were specified as zero. The model was then calibrated by varying the friction factor and comparing predictions to measurements for M2 tide only. A constant value of $c = 0.009$ gave the best agreement. This value is physically well justified in the shallow sill region (2-3 meters) where large sand dunes exist. Locally varying c yields no significant improvements in predictions since depths are greater elsewhere in the Bight. Comparison of predicted amplitudes to field data gives standard deviations (after adjusting for variances in field data) of 0.10 for the M2 tide, 0.28 for the M4 tide and 0.95 for the M6 tide. Comparisons of phase data were much better in all cases. Thus TEA-NL overtide runs have the same overprediction problem (by a factor of 1.95) as Snyder et al. (1979).

A second series of runs was performed allowing the full nonlinear interaction to occur between the M2 and N2 astronomical tides and their associated overtides and compound tides. The M2 and N2 tides now both force the open ocean boundary, the boundary was assumed to be fully reflective for all nonlinear constituents and c was taken as 0.009 over the entire Bight. Significant nonlinear tides predicted were the Steady, MN, MN4, M4, 2MN6 and M6 constituents. Results for amplitudes for the astronomical tides and these nonlinear constituents are shown in Figure 3. Comparison of predicted amplitudes to field data gives standard deviations of 0.10 for the M2 tide, 0.09 for the N2 tide, 0.26 for the M4 tide and 0.67 for the M6 tide. Hence it is noted that not only are the compound tides significant relative to the overtides, but that the overpredictions of the M6 tide have substantially decreased (to a factor of 1.67). The M2 and M4 predictions are close to those obtained by considering overtides only. Finally we note from Figure 3 that there is a great deal of similarity in pattern between the overtides and their adjacent compound tides. Detailed data analyses indicate that further improvements in predictions can be obtained by including the full interaction of the M2, N2 and S2 tides and by allowing for slight transmission of the nonlinear tides out of the Bight.

Table 1. Average Values of Amplitudes for Harmonically Decomposed Field Data for M2 and N2 Astronomical Constituents and M4 and M6 Overtides at Locations Indicated in Figure 3 (a,b,f,h).

SITE	M2	N2	M4	M6	SITE	M2	N2	M4	M6
A	19.0	3.5	0.9	0.6	N	29.2	7.6	0.3	0.3
B	18.1	2.3	0.9	0.5	O	14.6	3.3	0.9	0.7
C	17.7	2.8	0.6	0.4	P	38.2	9.9	0.2	0.2
D	16.6	2.3	0.7	0.3	Q	39.2	9.7	0.2	0.3
E	16.4	2.8	0.4	0.3	R	21.8	8.6	0.8	0.5
F	16.3	2.4	0.6	0.6	S	12.7	2.0	0.2	0.3
G	39.4	10.0	0.3	0.2	T	15.3	3.1	0.5	0.7
H	27.9	7.7	0.9	0.3	U	14.8	2.8	0.8	0.9
I	15.0	3.5	0.4	0.4	V	17.6	4.2	1.2	1.5
J	38.8	10.3	0.3	0.2	W	18.0	4.2	1.2	1.0
K	26.9	7.0	0.2	0.4	X	16.8	3.3	1.3	0.3
L	16.9	3.3	0.6	0.6	Y	19.6	3.7	2.1	0.1
M	12.2	2.9	0.2	0.7					

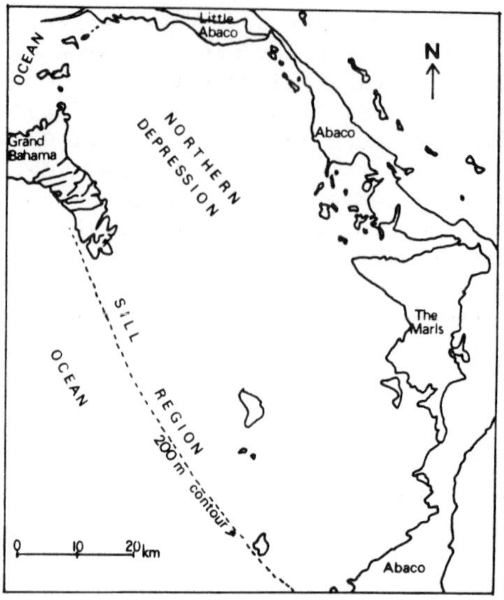

Figure 1. Geography of the Bight of Abaco, Bahamas.

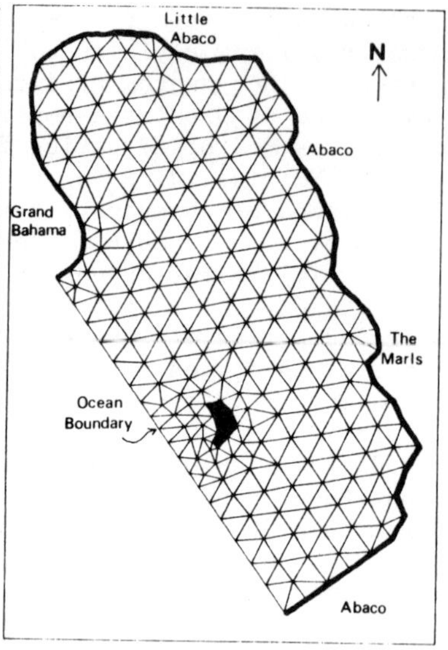

Figure 2. F.E. Discretization of the Bight of Abaco.

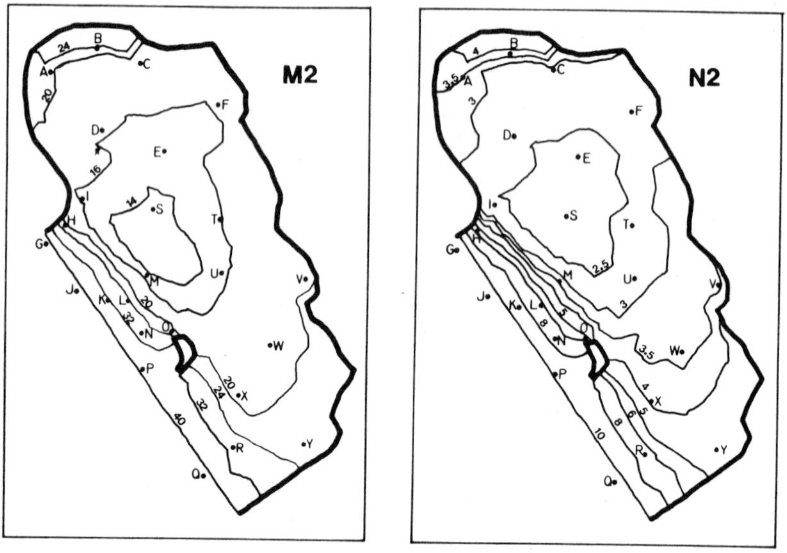

(a) (b)

Figure 3. Compound Tide Computation Results for M2-N2 Tidal Interactions:
(a) M2 amplitude
(b) N2 amplitude

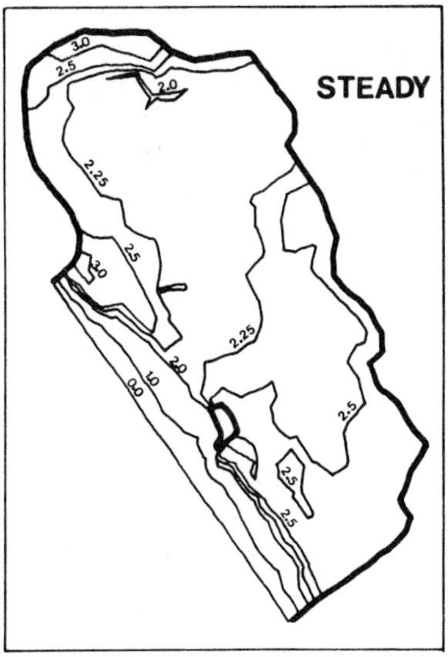

(c)

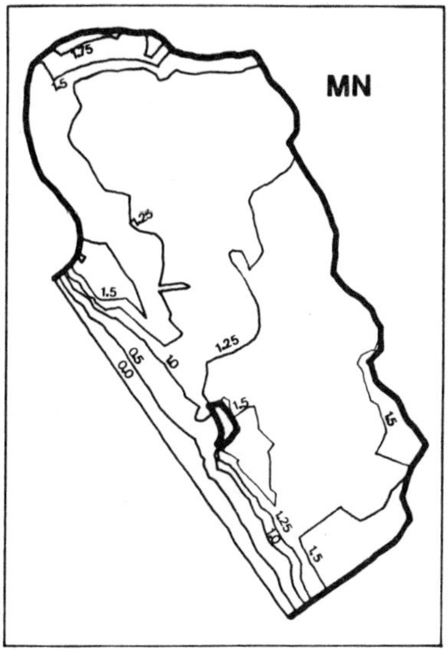

(d)

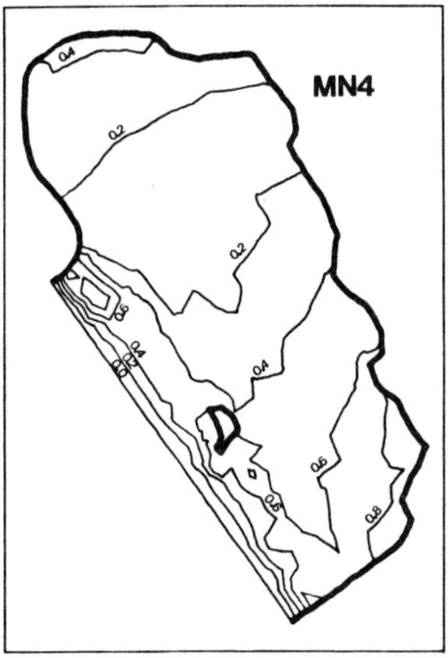

(e)

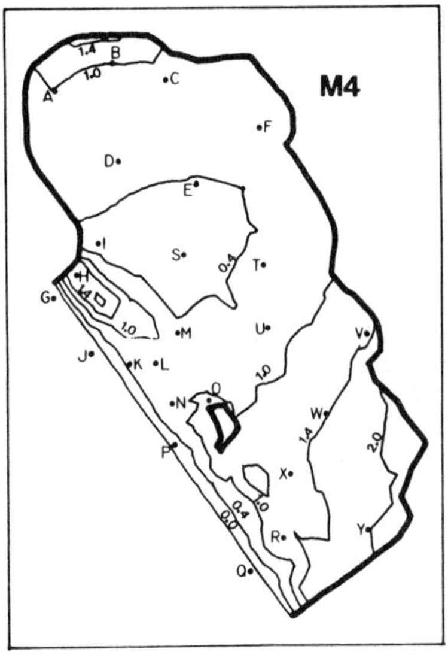

(f)

Figure 3. cont.
(c) Steady amplitude
(d) MN amplitude
(e) MN4 amplitude
(f) M4 amplitude

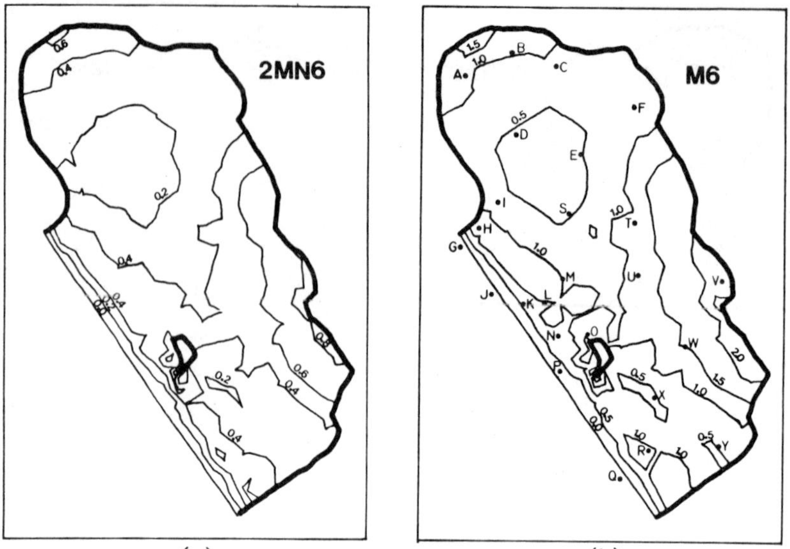

(g) (h)

Figure 3. cont.
(g) 2MN6 amplitude
(h) M6 amplitude

REFERENCES

Askar, A. and A.S. Cakmak (1978) Studies on finite amplitude waves in bounded waterbodies, Adv. Water Res., 4:229-246.

Dronkers, J.J. (1964) Tidal Computations in Rivers and Coastal Waters, North Holland Publ. Co., Amsterdam.

Filloux, J.H. and R.L. Snyder (1979) A study of tides, setup and bottom friction in a shallow semi-enclosed basin. Part I, J. Phys. Ocean., 9:158-169.

Kawahara, M., K. Hasegawa and Y. Kawanago (1977) Periodic tidal flow analysis by f.e. perturbation method. Comp.&Fl.,5:175-189.

Kawahara, M. and K. Hasegawa (1978) Periodic Galerkin f.e.m. of tidal flow, Intl. J. Num. Meth. Eng., 12:115-127.

LeProvost, C. and A. Poncet (1978) F.E.M. for spectral modeling of tides, Int. J. Num. Meth. Eng., 12:853-871.

LeProvost, C., G. Rougier and A. Poncet (1981a) Numerical modeling of the harmonic constituents of the tides with application to the English Channel, J. Phys. Ocean., 11:1123-1138.

LeProvost, C. (1981b) A model for prediction of tidal elevations over the English Channel, Oceanol. Acta, 4:3:279-288.

Munk, W.H. and K. Hasselmann (1964) Super-resolution of tides, Studies in Oceanography, Univ. Wash. Press, 339-344.

Pearson, C.E. and D.F. Winter (1977) On the calculation of tidal currents in homogeneous estuaries, J. Phys. Ocean., 7:4:520-531.

Snyder, R.L., M. Sidjabat and J.H. Filloux (1979) A study of tides, setup and bottom friction in a shallow semi-enclosed basin. Part II, J. Phys. Ocean., 9:170-188.

VI International Conference on Finite Elements in Water Resources, Lisboa, Portugal, June 1986

Finite Element Model for Salt Intrusion Problem in Chao Phraya River

S. Koontanakulvong
Water Resources Engineering Division, Civil Engineering Department, Faculty of Engineering, Chulalongkorn University, Bangkok, Thailand
T. Kawachi
Agriculture Engineering Department, Faculty of Agriculture, Kyoto University, Kyoto, Japan

1. INTRODUCTION

Salt Intrusion problem is one of the major constraints in water resources development on Central plain area of Thailand especially when water requirements for both agricultural, industrial and domestic purposes are increasing with country's economical development. Proper water management is then required in dry season to minimize the amount of water to flush salt water. The one-dimensional FD model has been developed and studied for Chao Phraya River, one of the major rivers of Thailand but the numerical results compared with the field data still need more revision (Tawatchai, 1980).

Finite Element Model on Convection-Diffusion problem has been studied by various investigators. Price(1968) proposed a numerical formulation of high order accuracy based on variational methods for the solution of multi-dimensional diffusion-convection equations. Guymon (1970) also applied variational principle to obtain a finite element solution of the one-dimensional diffusion-convection equation. Though Smith (1973) suggested that previous variational (Rayleigh-Ritz) formulations of finite elements for some problems were misleading and were of limited application when compared with Galerkin's method. He then discussed the accuracy and stability of the Rayleigh-Ritz and Galerkin techniques in relation to the numerical diffusion and dispersion phenomena prevalent in popular finite difference methods. Gray (1976) performed a rourier series analysis to determine the dissipative and dispersive characteristics of the FD and FE methods. The analysis indicates that the phenomena of overshoot of a concentration pulse is due to the inability of the numerical schemes to propagate the small wavelengths which are important to the description of the front. The finite element method was found to be superior to finite difference methods for solution of the convective-dispersive equation. Neuman (1981) proposed a new numerical scheme by combining the utility of a fixed grid in Eulerian coordinates with the computational power of the Lagrangian method in order to eliminate oscillations resulting in overshoot, undershoot and negative concentrations. Hiraoka et.al. (1982)

investigated the stabilities of popular eight schemes to solve the diffusion-convection equation and tried to propose the general form of time-space scheme and stability criteria represented by the figure of Courant no. v.s. Diffusion no..

This paper introduces the development of a one-dimensional finite element model with the aid of Galerkin procedure and the weak formulation of the diffusion-convection equation. Numerical investigations are performed to test the model's stability and accuracy compared with analytical solutions and examine their sensitivities to nondimensional parameters of diffusion-convection equation aiming at the general practical guidelines when applied to the model. In application, all variables in the governing equations: momentum, continuity and diffusion equations are solved simultaneously. The model is applied to the actual computation of Chao Phraya River and the results are compared with the field data and the finite difference results.

2. FINITE ELEMENT EQUATIONS

For well-mixed estuary, salt intrusion problem is adequately represented by one-dimensional unsteady equations. The basic governing equations for the one-dimensional transport phenomena can be shown in matrix form as follows.

$$S_{ij}\dot{X}_j + T_{ij}X_{j,x} + F_i = 0 \qquad (1)$$

where

$$S_{ij} = \begin{bmatrix} 1 & 0 & 0 \\ 1 & B & 0 \\ 0 & 0 & A \end{bmatrix} \qquad X_j = \begin{bmatrix} Q \\ E \\ \rho \end{bmatrix}$$

$$T_{ij} = \begin{bmatrix} 2u & (C_w^2 - u^2)B & \frac{gAh}{2\rho} \\ 1 & 0 & 0 \\ 0 & 0 & Q \end{bmatrix}$$

$$F_i = \begin{bmatrix} u^2\{BS_o - [\frac{\partial A}{\partial h}]_{h=h_o}\} + \frac{gA|Q|Q}{K^2} \\ - q_\ell \\ - \frac{\partial}{\partial x}(AD_x \frac{\partial \rho}{\partial x}) \end{bmatrix}$$

and Q = discharge, E = water level, ρ = density, u = velocity, B = river width at water surface, A = cross sectional area, h = depth, S_o = bed slope, g = gravity acceleration, q_ℓ = lateral flow, wave celerity (C_w) = $\sqrt{gA/B}$, K = CA$\sqrt{R}$ C = Chèzy coefficient, R = hydraulic radius, D_x = diffusion coefficient.

$$-\int_{\ell} M_{\alpha i} \frac{\partial}{\partial x} (AD_x \frac{\partial \rho}{\partial x})\, d\ell = \int_{\ell} AD_x \frac{\partial M_{\alpha i}}{\partial x} \frac{\partial \rho}{\partial x}\, d\ell - \{q_\alpha\} \quad (4)$$

where $q_\alpha = -A D_x \frac{\partial \rho}{\partial x}$

By this formulation, the boundary conditions for diffusion-convection equation are easily substituted.

Assuming that the nodal values of X_β vary linearly between two consecutive time stages having Δt as a time increment, Eq (3) is integrated in time by the aid of the truncated Taylor series, and by assembling over the entire domain, the global finite element equations are derived as follows.

$$K_{qr} X_r^{(n)} = F_r \quad (5)$$

having the known as previously estimated matrices

$$K_{qr} = \sum^{\lambda} (\frac{1}{\Delta t} P_{\alpha\beta} + \theta W_{\alpha\beta})$$

$$F_r = \sum^{\lambda} [\frac{1}{\Delta t} P_{\alpha\beta} - (1-\theta) W_{\alpha\beta}] X_\beta^{(n-1)}$$

where λ is the number of elements, q and r take the integer values 1 to 3N with N being the number of nodes and θ is the weighting coefficient $(0 \leqq \theta \leqq 1)$ of time scheme.

3. ACCURACY INVESTIGATION

In order to investigate the numerical solution of diffusion-convection equation, the computations are performed in the uniform rectangular channel of 10 m. wide, 100 m. long with no bed slope and frictionless. The initial and boundary conditions are set as follows:

Initial condition $Q = 10\ m^3/s$, $E = 1.0$ m., $\rho = 1.0 \times 10^3\ kg/m^3$

Boundary condition a) at $x = 0$ $Q(t) = 10\ m^3/s$

$\rho(t) = 1.03 \times 10^3\ kg/m^3$

b) at $x = L$ $E(t) = 1.0$ m.

$$\frac{\partial \rho(t)}{\partial x} = 0$$

The global finite element equations are then solved simultaneously and the results can then be compared with the exact values calculated from the following equations.

$$\frac{S}{S_o} = \frac{1}{2} \text{erfc} (\frac{x-ut}{2\sqrt{D_x t}}) + \frac{1}{2} \exp (\frac{ux}{D_x}) \text{erfc} (\frac{x+ut}{2\sqrt{D_x t}}) \quad (6)$$

The boundary conditions for the three governing equations are summarized as follows.

at river mouth ($x = 0$) $\quad Q = f(t)$ or $E = g(t)$

and $\rho = h(t)$ when $Q \geqq 0$

or $\dfrac{\partial \rho}{\partial x} = 0$ when $Q < 0$

at upstream side ($x = L$) $\quad Q = f(t)$ or $E = g(t)$

and $\dfrac{\partial \rho}{\partial x} = 0$ when $Q \geqq 0$

or $\rho = h(t)$ when $Q < 0$

where $f(t)$, $g(t)$, $h(t)$ indicate the prescribed time function of variables as boundaries.

The diffusion coefficient in field has been studied by many researches. Here only four types of formula are selected and shown as follows.

(a) D_x as constant value
(b) Harleman formula $D_x = 40.287\ R|u|/C$
(c) Elder formula $D_x = 18.564\ H|u|/C$
(d) Thatcher and Harleman formula

$$D_x = K\left|\frac{\partial(S/S_o)}{\partial(x/L)}\right| + 3\ E_T$$

Where E_T = $63.3\ nuK^{5/6}$, K = constant varied with discharge, n = manning coefficient,
S_o = maximum salinity at river mouth.

For the formulation of the finite element equation, the whole spacewise is then discretized to be finite element subdomains (element) jointed by the nodes at the boundary of each element. The field variables X_j is then approximated by the polynomial expression.

$$X_j = M_{j\beta} X_\beta \tag{2}$$

Where $M_{j\beta}$ and X_β denote interpolation function and a set of nodal values of the field variables respectively. By the Galerkin weighted residual procedure, the following finite element equation can be derived.

$$P_{\alpha\beta}\dot{X}_\beta + W_{\alpha\beta}X_\beta + F_\alpha = 0 \tag{3}$$

where

$$P_{\alpha\beta} = \int_\ell M_{\alpha i} S_{ij} M_{j\beta}\ d\ell$$

$$W_{\alpha\beta} = \int_\ell M_{\alpha i} T_{ij} M_{j\beta,x}\ d\ell + \int_\ell M_{\alpha i} V_{ij} M_{j\beta}\ d\ell$$

$$F_\alpha = \int_\ell M_{\alpha i} F_i\ d\ell$$

With the weak formulation of the diffusion-convection equation, the diffusion term in the equation can be rewritten as follows.

$$\frac{\rho}{\rho_o} = 1 + \beta\,(S-S_o) \tag{7}$$

where S, β and suffix $_o$ indicate the salt concentration, constant and fresh water state respectively.

The degree of accuracy can be defined from the difference between the numerical and exact values. Two indicators are then proposed to indicate the degree of accuracy and shown as follows.

$$\text{Total error (E)} = \left\{ \sum_{i=1}^{nx} (\rho_{i\ exact} - \rho_i)^2 / \sum_{i=1}^{nx} \rho_{i\ exact}^2 \right\}^{\frac{1}{2}} \tag{8}$$

$$\text{Averaged error } (E_{av}) = \sum_{j=1}^{nt} E_j / nt \tag{9}$$

where nx and nt are number of nodes and total computed time cycle respectively.

From the viewpoint of practice, the basic dimensions are considered to be within the following ranges:
$Q = 3\text{-}100\ m^3/s$, $E = 0.3\text{-}10.0$ m, $\theta = 0.0\text{-}1.0$, $\Delta x = 5.0\text{-}20.0$m, $\Delta t = 1.0\text{-}20.0$ sec, $D_x = 0.001\text{-}2000\ m^2/s$

Let U and L be equal to initial velocity and the channel length respectively then the reference values and the nondimensional parameters are in the order as follows.

$U = 1.0$ m/s , $L = 100$ m

$F = 0.05\text{-}4.0$, $G = 2.5{\times}10^{-6}\text{-}1.6{\times}10^{3}$, $P_e = 5{\times}10^{-2}\text{-}10^{5}$

where Courant number (F) = $U\,\Delta t/\Delta x$, Diffusion number (G) = $D_x\,\Delta t/\Delta x^2$ and Peclet number (P_e) = $|u|L/D_x$

<u>Δx-Δt effect</u> From Fig. 1 it can be seen that when Δx and Δt become smaller, the accuracy improves which is generally accepted and the accuracy of numerical solution of Diffusion-convection equation is sensitive to the scale of Δt though as the whole the accuracy of numerical solution is quite acceptable and the error falls in the range of 10^{-3}

<u>θ-effect</u> From the above results, the accuracy of time scheme is then investigated and can be shown in Fig. 2 in terms of total and averaged error. From these figures, when Δt is small. The results of θ less than 0.5 are still favourable but when Δt increases, the accuracy becomes abruptly reduced and when F < 1.0, the computation cannot perform. Crank-Nicolson (θ = 1/2) and Galerkin (θ =2/3) schemes seem to be more accurate than fully Implicit scheme (θ = 1.0) and when inspecting the fluctuating range of error, the Galerkin scheme shows better stability than Crank-Nicolson scheme. The result of Kawachi et al.(1982), who investigated the time scheme of the momentum and continuity equations by Fourier series analysis, also show that the Galerkin scheme exhibits monotonous increase in error and can practically be used without any apprehensions.

D_x-effect From Figs.3 and 4 the accuracy of all D_x values are still in the error range of 10^{-3} though when Peclet number is lower than 1 (or 0.1 with small Δt), the range of total error is remarkably expanded. This shows the trend of instability of numerical solution when the value of D_x is small.

4. MODEL APPLICATION

Chao Phraya River flows through the central plain of Thailand which is the main production land for paddy of the country and flows out to the Gulf of Thailand (see Fig.5) in the south. The problem of salinity intrusion in the Chao Phraya River had been studied by the Asian Institute of Technology (AIT) since 1975. A Salinity FD model with Crank-Nicolson scheme (by Thatcher et.al.(1972)) had been developed to forecast the salinity and the results were recommended as a guideline for water management for salinity problem.

The proposed FE model is then applied to the Chao Phraya River computation. By adopting $\theta = 2/3$, $\Delta x = 4$ km, $\Delta t = 30$ min., the model is first calibrated with the field data of March 21-22 1967 and the roughness coefficient(manning)of 0.025 is selected. The results of water levels velocity and salt concentration (using Thatcher and Harleman formula and shown in Fig.6) are compared with the FD results done by Amnat (1976) and the comparisons show good improvement in forcasting salt concentration. Various types of diffusion coefficient are then tested and the results show that diffusion coefficient with constant value of 600 m^2/s and from Thatcher and Harleman formula give good results with no vibrating phenomena at low tide.

The model is then applied to calculate the salinity at Feb. 18-19, 1970 and the results are shown in Fig.7(b). Numerical results from $D_x = 600$ m^2/s and Thatcher and Harleman formula give close relation and the results at 6 hr. compared with field data at HWS also give good agreement. Compared to the FD results shown in Fig.7(a), the results give better agreement to the field observation in both HWS and LWS periods.

5. CONCLUDING REMARKS

The one-dimensional finite element model for transport phenomena is developed in full forms and the sensitivities of nondimensional parameters toward accuracy and stability are also investigated. The following conclusions can be made from the study.

(1) The developed model with the weak formulation of diffusion-convection equation, which is very convenient for the substitution of derivative-formed boundary condition, can reproduce the solution of transport equation with good accuracy in practical aspects.

(2) In practice, the implicit scheme should be adopted in the computation and among linear time interpolation, the Galerkin scheme seems to give the best solution in terms of overall accuracy and stability.

(3) When the Peclet number is greater than 1.0, the diffusion coefficient does not effect the accuracy and stability of solution, which in practical computation this condition usually can be fulfilled easily, but if the Peclet number gets smaller, the trend of instability can be seen.

(4) The developed model can reproduce the forecast the salinity concentration in the Chao Phraya River with good accuracy computed to the previous FD model which may show the superiority of FE model against FD model.

It is recommended that further studies should be performed especially with higher order of interpolation function.

ACKNOWLEDGEMENTS

The work upon which the paper is based was supported in part by funds provided by the Public Corporation in the Water Resources Development, Chubu Branch and additional support was granted by the Institute of Research and Development, Faculty of Engineering, Chulalongkorn University.

REFERENCES

Amnat A. (1976) Diffusion Process in the Chao Phraya Estuary. AIT Master Thesis No. 852

Guysmon G.L. (1970) A Finite Element Solution of the One-Dimensional Diffusion-Convection Equation, Water Resour. Res., 6(1) : 204-210

Hiraoka M. et.al. (1982) Stability Analysis of Numerical Solution for the Diffusion-Convection Equation. Proc JSCE, 319 : 77-85 (in Japanese)

Kawachi T., A.H. Ghailan and I. Minami (1982) The Effects of the Time Integration Scheme and Boundary value treatment on the Finite Element Solution for Open Channel Flow, Trans. JSIDRE, 102 : 71-77

Price H.S. et.al. (1968) Numerical Methods of Higher-order Accuracy for Diffusion-Convection Equation, Jour. of Society of Petroleum Engineers : 293-300

Sholmo P.Neuman (1981) A Eulerian-Legrangian Numerical Scheme for the Dispersion-Convection Equation Using Conjugate Space-Time Grids, Jour. of Compu. Phy., 41 : 270-294

Smith I.M. et.al. (1973) Rayleigh-Ritz and Galerkin Finite Elements for Diffusion-Convection Problems, Water Resour. Res., 9(3) : 593-606

Tawatchai T. et.al. (1980) Salinity Intrusion Problem During Severe Drought in the Chao Phraya River. AIT Research Report No. 122

Thatcher M.L. and Harleman, D.R.F. (1972) A Mathematical Model for the Prediction of Unsteady Salinity Intrusion in Estuaries, Technical Report No.144, Ralph M. Parsons Laboratory for Water Resources and Hydraulics, Dept. of Civil Engineering, M.I.T. USA.

William G. Gray et.al. (1976) An Analysis of the Numerical Solution of the Transport Equation, Water Resour. Res., 12(3) : 547-555

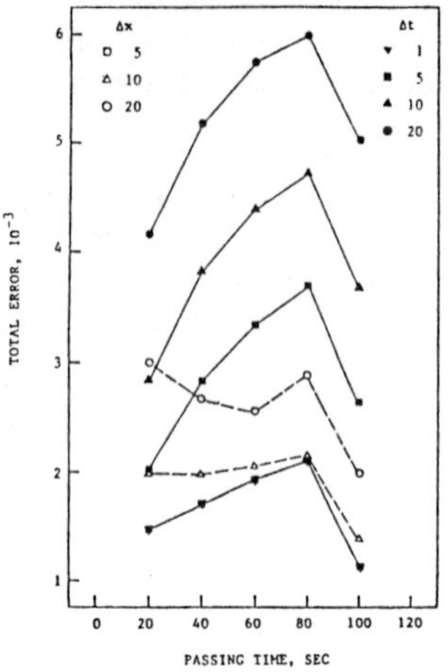

Fig. 1 The effect of Δx-Δt

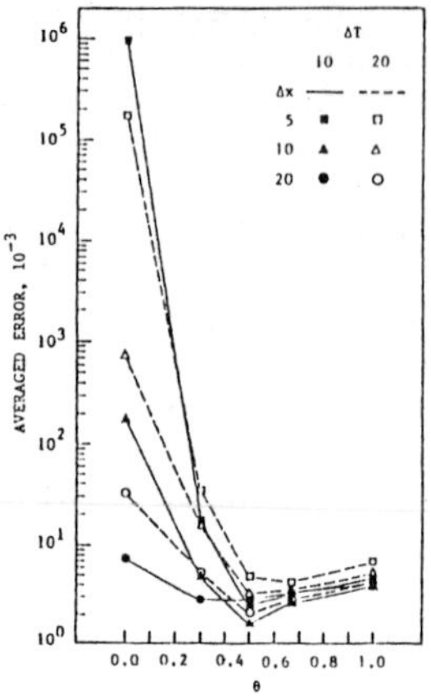

Fig. 2 The effect of θ

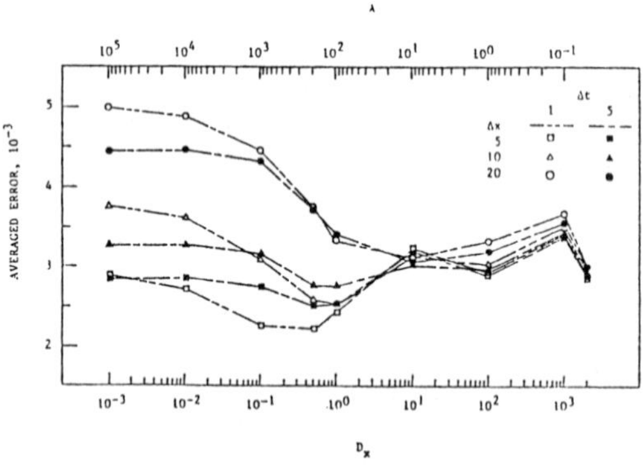

Fig. 3 The effect of D_x (small Δt)

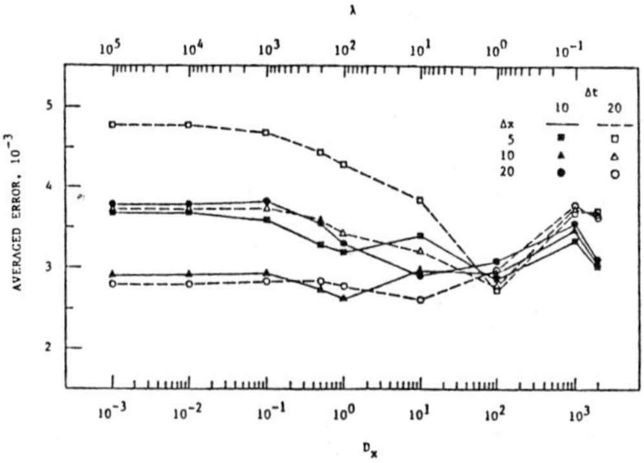

Fig. 4 The effect of D_x (large Δt)

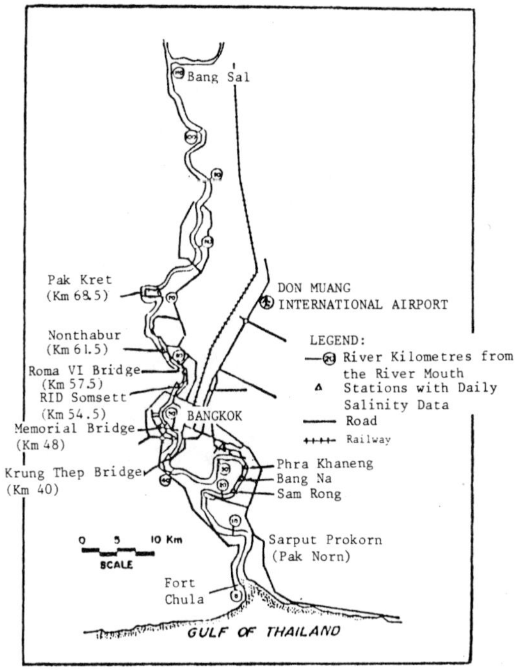

Fig. 5 Map of the Chao Phraya River

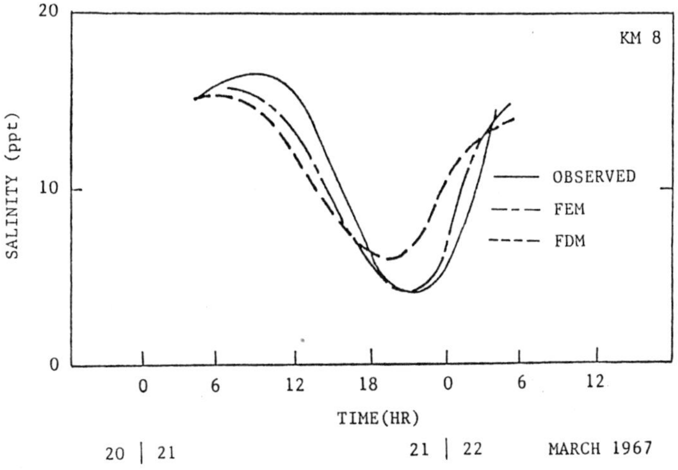

Fig. 6 Calibration results of FD,FE with field data

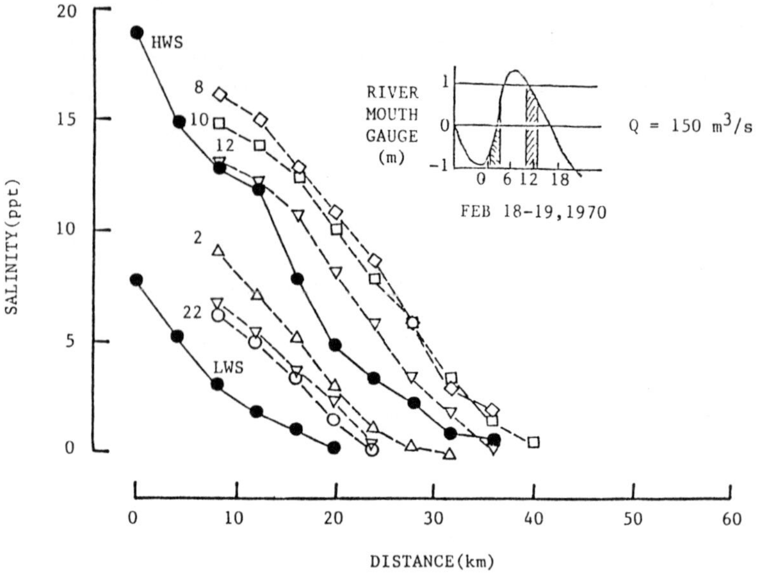

(a) FD results

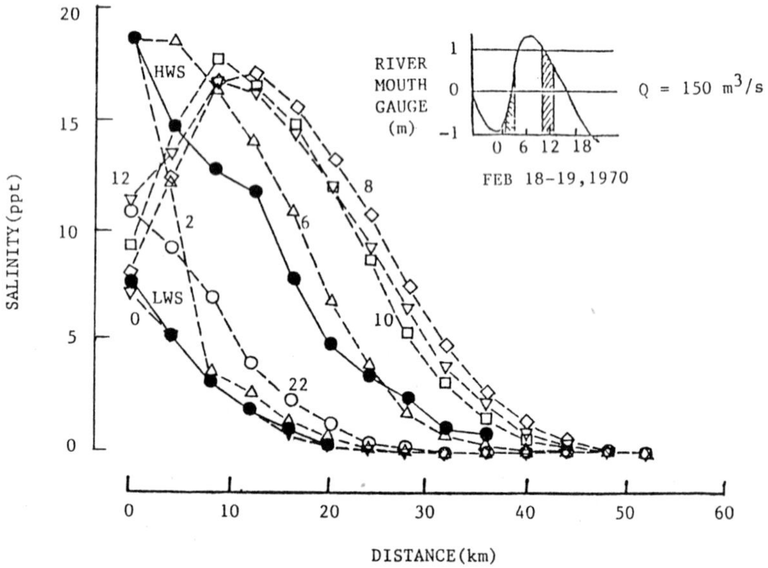

(b) FE results

Fig. 7 The comparison of FD and FE results for the whole tidal cycle

VI International Conference on Finite Elements in Water Resources, Lisboa, Portugal, June 1986

Source Representation in a Numerical Transport Model

E.E. Adams, R. Kossik and A.M. Baptista
Department of Civil Engineering, Massachusetts Institute of Technology, Cambridge, Massachusetts, U.S.A.

INTRODUCTION

Numerical models are routinely used to solve the advection diffusion equation for purposes of simulating pollutant transport in surface waters. A common difficulty in most such applications is to adequately represent concentrations in regions of high concentration gradient. For surface water calculations, strong gradients are found primarily near sources (e.g., pollutant outfalls).

One procedure for handling such problems is to represent the continuous plume near the source as the superposition of discrete puffs that are advected forward in time until they are of sufficient size to be adequately resolved with the numerical grid. Such a procedure is well suited to Lagrangian Transport Models or Eulerian-Lagrangian models in which the advection part of the advection-diffusion equation is simulated by a (Lagrangian) tracking technique.

This approach has been incorporated into the 2-D (depth-averaged) transport model ELA (Baptista et al., 1984a, b). ELA uses a split operator approach solving advection with a backwards method of characteristics using quadratic Lagrange polynomials for interpolation and using an implicit Galerkin Finite Element method for diffusion. Transformation processes such as volatilization are treated separately in a third operation. The technique is illustrated in a simulation of halocarbon concentration distributions resulting from sewage discharges into Boston Harbor.

PROBLEM DESCRIPTION

Figure 1 illustrates a typical problem involving an outfall pipe discharging into a coastal environment discretized with a relatively uniform grid. For purposes of discussion, the near field is defined as that region over which discharge momentum and buoyancy significantly influence local flow patterns. For a typical sewage outfall this dimension may be of order 10-100 m and no attempt is made to resolve concentrations within this region. However, it is desired to simulate realistic distributions as close to the near field as possible.

Theoretical analyses (e.g., Fourier analysis) and numerical experiments by a number of researchers have shown that the ability to successfully advect a pollutant source improves as the dimensionless source size (i.e., characteristic source size divided by characteristic grid dimension) increases. The minimum acceptable source size will depend on the numerical procedure and such parameters as Peclet and Courant number and total simulation time, but will fall in the general range of 3 to 10 (Gray and Pinder, 1976; Baptista et al., 1985). This criterion is not met, in general, for typical grid sizes of order 100-1000 m. As a result, artificial diffusion is introduced, either by the scheme itself, or by the model user who artificially introduces the mass over a larger-than-realistic region. In effect, the concentration distribution becomes artificially and instantaneously spread until it is wide enough to be advected satisfactorily. The result is erroneous prediction over an intermediate region at least as large as that required for physical processes to provide similar mixing. For tidal applications, this intermediate region can easily extend for a distance of one tidal excursion or more. For regions of strong tidal currents such as Boston Harbor, this can represent several kilometers or a significant fraction of the computational domain.

Figure 1 suggests three possible procedures for improving resolution up to the point at which physical processes have spread the pollutant enough to be resolved (i.e., the intermediate field): a) local grid refinement, b) stochastic particle tracking, and c) use of puffs.

With finite element models, grid refinement is conceptually straightforward. However, when the affected area is substantial, and multiple sources are involved, matrix size and bandwidth may increase substantially resulting in a significant increase in computational cost.

Particle tracking has been proposed as a way to resolve strong concentration gradients in Eulerian-Lagrangian models of groundwater transport (Newman, 1984). Using this approach, particles would be released at a rate corresponding to their effluent concentrations and advected by the known flow field. Diffusion can be handled by assigning a random or pseudo velocity component to the advected flow. The process is continued until the particles have diffused over sufficient elements that a smooth concentration field can be computed for subsequent discretized calculation. A major drawback with this approach is that, in order to accurately convert particle density to concentration, a large number of particles must be tracked in relation to the number of grid points.

A third option involves the use of puffs as suggested by Adams et al. (1975) and used by Holly and Usseglio-Polatera (1984). In such an approach, the intermediate field plume is represented by a number of discrete puffs, released one at a time, with a size proportional to the near field mixing zone. As with particles, each puff is tracked forward in time. However, dispersion is handled by dispersing the puffs in accordance with a prescribed dispersion law, e.g., as determined by a tracer study or as estimated from the literature (Okubo, 1971). In contrast with particles, this may involve as little as one tracking per unit of time thus reducing costs. As illustrated below, the present approach is really a hybrid, using up to five trackings per puff in order to better define puff spreading. Nonetheless, the savings should still be substantial.

DETAILS

Figure 2 illustrates, schematically, puff placement for the simple case of a constant current. The elapsed time depicted is $T = N\Delta t$ where Δt is the basic computational time step between alternate advection and diffusion calculations with ELA. (Δt = 3.1h is used in the following calculations.)

Assume $M\Delta t$ is the minimum duration required for the puffs to mature to full size. ($M = 1$ has been used in our calculations.) As indicated by the overlapping circular distributions, puffs are placed around the source corresponding to mass which is physically discharged during the period $(N-M-1)\Delta t < \tau < N\Delta t$. The most recently discharged mass is positioned first (adjacent to the source) and subsequent puffs are created to allow sufficient overlap.

Puffs created during the period of duration Δt from $(N-M-1)\Delta t < \tau < (N-M)\Delta t$ are mapped onto the finite element grid at the beginning of the advection step. Younger puffs, created between $(N-M)\Delta t < \tau < N\Delta t$, are discarded unless a concentration printout is desired, in which case they are mapped onto a highly resolved local grid created only for contouring.

For the illustrative calculations below, symmetrical Gaussian puffs have been used implying isotropic dispersion. (However, different distributions could readily be used.) For each puff, the concentration distribution is thus

$$C = \frac{\dot{m}(t)\Delta\tau}{2\pi h\ \sigma^2} \exp\{-[(x-x_1)^2 + (y-y_1)^2]/2\sigma^2\} \qquad (1)$$

where h is the local depth, $\dot{m}$ is the mass loading rate, $\Delta\tau$ is the time interval associated with the puff (see Figure 2), $(x_1,$

y_1) is the center of mass, and σ is the standard deviation. Puff centers are tracked forward in time by reversing the fourth-order Runge-Kutta integration scheme used by ELA in the backward tracking of characteristics, along with the known space and time dependent variation in current speed. Thus

$$x_1(T) = x_0 + \int_{\tau}^{T} u \, dt$$

$$y_1(T) = y_0 + \int_{\tau}^{T} v \, dt \qquad (2)$$

In principle, puff spreading can be computed from a relationship such as

$$\sigma^2(T) = \sigma_0^2(\tau) + 2\int_{\tau}^{T} D \, dt \qquad (3)$$

where D is an empirical (dispersion) coefficient and σ_0 is the initial standard deviation at the edge of the near field. σ_0 is determined from the near field mixing as

$$\sigma_0 = \frac{SQ_0}{\sqrt{12}\ |u|\ h} \qquad (4)$$

where Q_0 = effluent flow rate, $|u|$ = instantaneous current speed, and S = near field volumetric dilution (determined from measurements or a model as a function of $|u|$ and h).

In a depth-integrated model, D represents physical mixing (dispersion associated with horizontal and vertical current shear as well as turbulent diffusion) plus fluid convergence/divergence effects associated with changing bottom and free surface elevation. Hence D would be expected to change with spatial position and time.

To help separate these effects, and render the intermediate field spreading of puffs similar to the far field mixing handled by finite element, an equivalent "diffusionless" puff distribution at time T can be computed by tracking n - 1 additional particles. These particles are distributed initially at a distance of σ_0 from the source center (x_0, y_0) and are tracked along with the puff center. The equivalent σ is then approximated as the geometric mean of the distances between particles i and the center of mass:

$$\sigma^2 = \prod_{i=2}^{n} [(x_i - x_1)^2 + (y_i - y_1)^2]^{1/(n-1)} \tag{5}$$

If puffs are to be tracked over a long period of time, Equations (5) and (3) can be used sequentially over a number of time steps, with the first term on the right-hand side of Equation (3) taken to be the last value of σ^2 from Equation (5). It is apparent that the major difference between this hybrid method and one using exclusively particles (i.e., Figure 2b) is the way in which diffusion is calculated.

APPLICATION

The above technique has been used to simulate the fate of treated sewage effluent discharged into Boston Harbor on the western shore of Massachusetts Bay. Boston Harbor has approximate mean width and depth of 10 km and 10 m, and is characterized by numerous islands and complicated bottom topography. Flow is primarily tidally driven with mean amplitude of about 1.4 m.

Figure 3 sketches the finite element grids that are used. The largest grid (Figure 3a) includes 888 triangular elements with linear basis functions used to compute circulation with the harmonic circulation model TEA (Westerink et al., 1985). Transport calculations are made with the inner grid (Figure 3b) comprised of triangles with quadratic interpolation functions used for the finite element (diffusion) calculations and for the interpolation component of the advection calculations. The two major effluent sources are indicated (as black dots) on Figure 3b: the Deer Island Treatment Plant (to the north) and the Nut Island Treatment plant (to the south) discharging respectively 18.4 m^3/s and 5.9 m^3/s.

Field measurements indicate that near field dilution is a strong function of tidal phase obeying the following approximate relations:

$$\begin{aligned} S &= 50.5|u| + 6.5 \quad \text{(Deer Is.)} \\ S &= 31.7|u| + 5.5 \quad \text{(Nut Is.)} \end{aligned} \tag{6}$$

where $|u|$ is in m/s. For the Deer Is. outfall, $|u|$ varies from about 0.07 to 0.61 m/s between slack tide and maximum flood resulting in almost a factor of four variation in dilution ($10 < S < 37$). For Nut Is., $0.04 < |u| < 0.25$ m/s resulting in a factor of two variation in dilution ($7 < S < 13$).

Figure 4 illustrates computed concentration contours for the compound 1,1,1-trichloroethane, an industrial solvent discharged through both outfalls at a concentration of approximately 6.7 ppb. Simulations are shown at high tide under conditions of periodic steady-state due to M_2 tidal forcing (period = 12.4 hours), no wind stress (resulting in minimal residual circulation), an ambient diffusion coefficient of $10m^2/s$, and a piston velocity of 10 cm/hr describing volatilization. Measurements of halocarbon concentrations have also been taken in the harbor and substantiate the 2-D assumption. Parallel efforts are now under way aimed at a) model validation, b) establishing the viability of halocarbons as sewage tracers, and c) exploring the process of volatilization by comparing the geochemical fractionation of several related compounds both discharged and measured simultaneously. However, for present purposes, Figure 4 is presented to illustrate the sensitivity of predicted concentrations to the source representation. In particular, note the area of high concentrations west of the discharge from Deer Island and southwest of the discharge from Nut Island. These high concentrations represent effluent that was discharged during low tide when near field dilution is low and that has been advected toward shore during flood tide. Preliminary field measurements have confirmed this phenomenon. Figure 5a depicts corresponding high tide concentrations resulting from only the puffs released near the Deer Island outfall during the most recent 6.2 hours ($M = 1$, $\Delta t = 3.1$ hours) and Figure 5b shows the local grid. The factor of approximately 2.5 between concentrations at the western and eastern edges of the plume (representing discharge at low and high tide respectively) and those in the center (representing discharge during flood tide) is apparent.

The above calculations were made with a time step of 3.1 hours or one-fourth of a tidal period. As such, substantial computational savings were possible by saving, for each of the four tidal phases, both 1) the feet of the characteristic lines emanating backwards from each grid point necessary for computing far field concentration and 2) the intermediate field puff statistics ($\Delta\tau$, x_1, y_1, σ). Using this procedure it is estimated that the CPU time required for a two-week simulation (27 tidal cycles and the approximate time required to reach periodic steady state) is about two times that required for a single tidal cycle. While more accurate calculations would use additional tidal components, with longer repeating intervals, it is likely in many instances that transport calculations would still be required for multiple cycles, hence justifying the storage.

CONCLUSIONS

The above description and application illustrate how puffs can be used efficiently to provide increased resolution near effluent sources in pollutant transport models. Outfall configurations, models parameters (e.g., diffusion coefficients) and puff representation have been kept simple for illustration, but more sophistication can be employed if desired and warranted by available data.

REFERENCES

Adams, E. E.; Stolzenbach, K. D.; and Harleman, D. R. F. (1975) Near and Far Field Analysis of Buoyant Surface Discharges into Large Bodies of Water. Report No. 205, R. M. Parsons Laboratory for Water Resources and Hydrodynamics, M.I.T., Cambridge, Mass.

Baptista, A.; Adams, E. E,; and Stolzenbach, K. D. (1984a) Eulerian-Lagrangian Analysis of Pollutant Transport in Shallow Water. Report No. 296, R. M. Parsons Laboratory for Water Resources and Hydrodynamics, M.I.T., Cambridge, Mass.

Baptista, A. M.; Adams, E. E., and Stolzenbach, K. D. (1984b) The 2-D Unsteady Transport Equation Solved by the Combined Use of the Finite Element Method and the Method of Characteristics. Proc. 5th Int'l Conf. on Finite Elements in Water Resources, U. of Vermont, Burlington, Vt.

Baptista, A. M.; Adams, E. E.; and Stolzenbach, K. D. (1985) Comparison of Several Eulerian-Lagrangian Models to Solve the Advection-Diffusion Equation. Proc. 2nd Int'l Symp. on Refined Flow Modeling and Turbulence Measurements, U. of Iowa, Iowa City, Iowa.

Gray, W. G.; and Pinder, G. F. (1976) An Analysis of the Numerical Solution of the Transport Equation. Water Resources Research, 12:547-555.

Holly, F. M., Jr.; and Usseglio-Polatera, J.-M. (1984) Dispersion Simulation in Two-Dimensional Tidal Flow. Journal of Hydraulic Engineering, 110:905-926.

Neuman, S. P. (1984) Adaptive Eulerian-Lagrangian Finite Element Method for Advection-Dispersion. Int'l Journal for Numerical Methods in Engineering, 20:321-337.

Okubo, A. (1971) Oceanic Diffusion Diagrams. Deep Sea Research, 18:789-802.

Westerink, J. J.; Stolzenbach, K. D.; and Connor, J. J. (1985) A Frequency Domain Finite Element Model for Tidal Circulation. Report No. MIT-EL 85-006, M.I.T. Energy Laboratory, Cambridge, Mass.

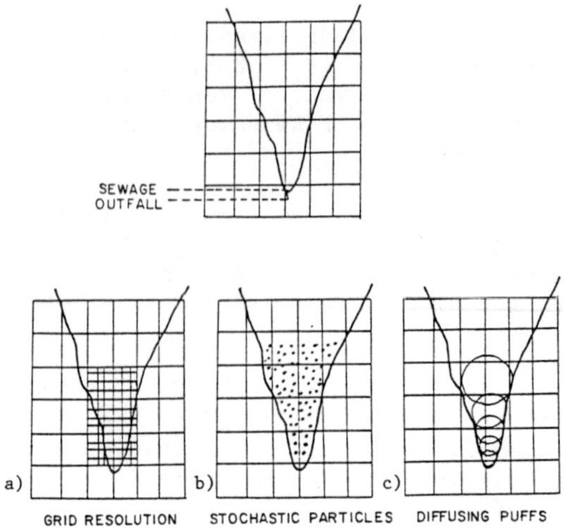

Figure 1. Techniques to Improve Near Source Resolution

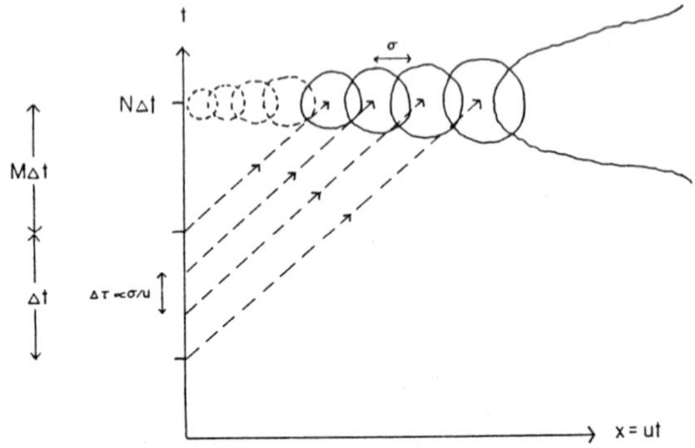

Figure 2. Schematic of Puff Placement

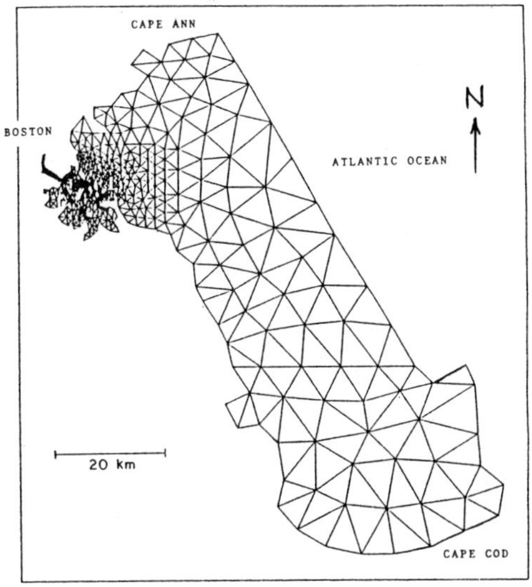

Figure 3a. Finite Element Grid of Massachusetts Bay

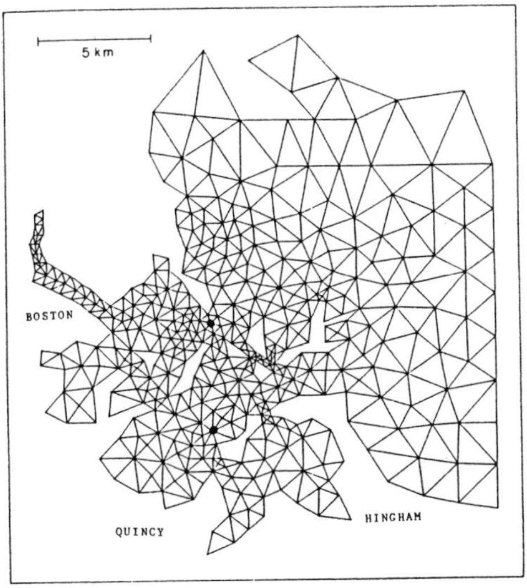

Figure 3b. Finite Element Grid—Detail of Boston Harbor

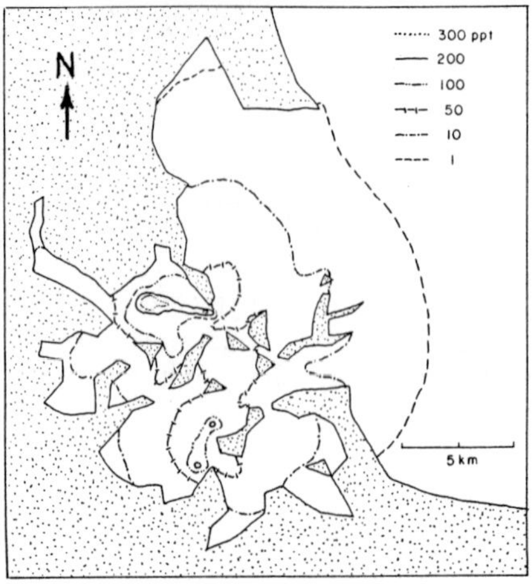

Figure 4. Simulated Intermediate and Far Field Concentration Distribution at High Tide for $Q_o = 24.3\ m^3/s$, $C_o = 6.7$ ppb, $K = 10$ cm/hr, and $D = 10\ m^2/s$

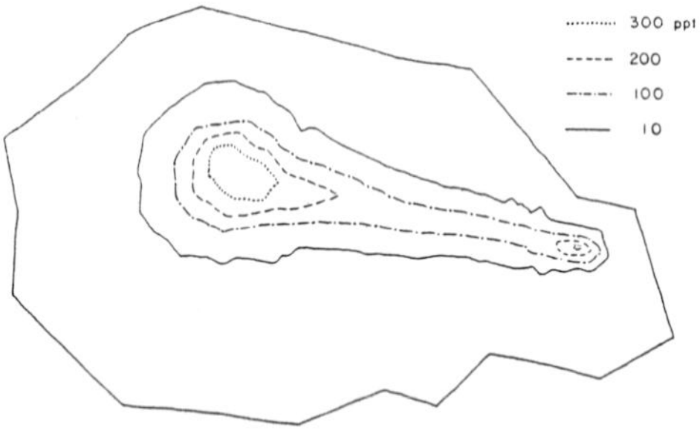

Figure 5a. Simulated Intermediate Field Concentration Distribution at High Tide (Elapsed Time ≃ 6 hrs) Corresponding to Conditions of Figure 4

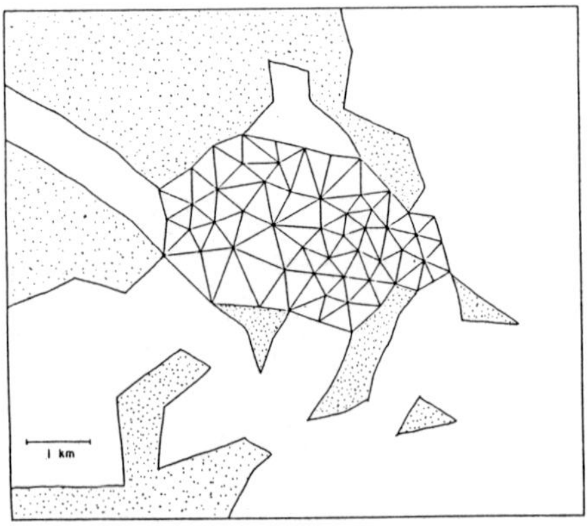

Figure 5b. Detail of Grid Within Border Shown on Figure 5a

VI International Conference on Finite Elements in Water Resources, Lisboa, Portugal, June 1986

A Wave Equation Formulation of River Flow

I.P.E. Kinnmark, W.G. Gray
Department of Civil Engineering, University of Notre Dame, Notre Dame, IN 46556, U.S.A.

INTRODUCTION

The wave equation formulation of the shallow water equations has grown into being a powerful tool for two-dimensional horizontal finite element modeling of estuarine flow. Lynch and Gray (1979) showed that models employing the wave continuity equation effectively avoid spurious spatial oscillations encountered in models using the primitive continuity equation. Kinnmark and Gray (1982) showed the importance of a proper time-weighting in the discretization of the momentum equations, solved in conjunction with the wave continuity equation, to suppress spurious temporal oscillations.

In the present paper the wave equation formulation is applied to the modeling of riverine flow, described by the Saint-Venant equations. The objective is again to suppress spurious oscillations in the numerical solution. The wave equation implementation for riverine flow does however offer some new challenges, in formulating the initial conditions, usually not encountered in estuarine flow. A typical application of estuary models seeks to determine the dynamic steady state for fluid depth and velocity, in response to a periodic tidal forcing. The initial conditions are therefore not of importance in determining the final model results, rather they are chosen to facilitate a smooth start of the simulation. A common procedure is to use a quiescent fluid as initial condition ("cold start") due to its very smooth (constant) spatial distribution. In contrast, a typical application of a riverine model is to determine the transient depth and velocity response caused by a surge moving through the system. Therefore initial conditions do have an impact on model results and initial depths and velocities must be measured or estimated in order to perform a simulation. Wave equation river models contain second order time derivatives thus requiring additional initial conditions which are preferrably determined from already existing initial data.

The wave equation river model will be compared to a primitive equation river model in an application to a Mississippi River dataset.

GOVERNING EQUATIONS

Constant density riverine flow for small bed slopes and hydrostatic vertical pressure in one spatial dimension in the absence of vertical acceleration and Coriolis effect is described by the Saint-Venant equations (see i.e. Strelkoff, 1970). The primitive form of the Saint Venant equations consists of conservation equations for mass and momentum.

Continuity Equation

$$L \equiv \frac{\partial A}{\partial t} + \frac{\partial Q}{\partial x} = 0 \tag{1}$$

Momentum Equation

$$M \equiv \frac{\partial Q}{\partial t} + \frac{\partial (Qu)}{\partial x} + gA \left(\frac{\partial y}{\partial x} - S_o + S_f\right) = 0 \tag{2}$$

where

$$S_f = \frac{n^2 \, Q|Q|}{2.208 \, A^2 \, R^{4/3}} \tag{3}$$

$$U = \frac{Q}{A} \tag{4}$$

$$R = \frac{A}{P} \tag{5}$$

and

A is cross sectional area $[L^2]$
B is width of river at water surface [L]
g is acceleration due to gravity $[L/T^2]$
n is Manning's coefficient $[T/L^{1/3}]$
P is wetted perimeter [L]
Q is volumetric flow rate $[L^3/T]$
R is hydraulic radius [L]
S_o is bottom slope [L/L]
S_f is friction slope [L/L]
t is time [T]
U is velocity [L/T]
x is distance along river [L]
y is depth of flow [L]

For the similar two-dimensional shallow-water equations Lynch and Gray (1979) showed that the introduction of a wave equation formulation of the governing equations effectively suppress spurious spatial oscillations introduced during numerical simulation of the primitive equations. Therefore we will introduce a wave equation formulation of equation (2) using an operator notation following Kinnmark and Gray (1984) and Kinnmark (1986). The operator notation clearly reveals the steps involved in deriving the wave equation formulation from the primitive equations. Note that L and M are defined in equations (1) and (2) respectively.

Operator Form of Wave Momentum Equation

$$W_M \equiv \frac{\partial M}{\partial t} + (\frac{7}{3} S_f + S_o - \frac{\partial y}{\partial x}) gL - gA \frac{\partial}{\partial x} (\frac{L}{B}) = 0 \tag{6}$$

Inserting equations (1) and (2) into Equations (6) and (7) yields the expanded form of the wave momentum equation.

Expanded Form of Wave Momentum Equation

$$W_M \equiv \frac{\partial^2 Q}{\partial t^2} + \frac{2gS_f}{|U|} \frac{\partial Q}{\partial t} + \frac{\partial^2 (QU)}{\partial x \partial t} + \frac{4}{3} gS_f R \frac{\partial B}{\partial t}$$

$$+ (\frac{7}{3} S_f + S_o - \frac{\partial y}{\partial x}) g \frac{\partial Q}{\partial x} - gA \frac{\partial}{\partial x} (\frac{1}{B} \frac{\partial Q}{\partial x}) = 0 \tag{7}$$

The wave momentum equation (7) is solved in conjunction with the continuity equation (1).

NUMERICAL APPROXIMATION

For the numerical solution procedure equations (1) and (7) are replaced by their respective weak formulations

$$\int L \, \phi_i \, dx = 0 \tag{8}$$

$$\int W_M \, \phi_i \, dx = 0 \tag{9}$$

In this Galerkin finite element formulation the basis functions, ϕ_i, were chosen to be linear. The time discretization was chosen to be of minimum time-level type, to avoid spurious temporal oscillations commonly introduced by the use of more time levels than necessary (see i.e. Kinnmark and Gray, 1984). Therefore equation (8) employs a two time level approximation of the following type

$$\frac{\partial W}{\partial t} \approx \frac{W_{t+\Delta t} - W_t}{\Delta t} \tag{10}$$

$$W \approx \theta W_{t+\Delta t} + (1-\theta) W_t \tag{11}$$

Equation (9) employs a symmetric three time level approximation of the following type

$$\frac{\partial^2 W}{\partial t^2} \approx \frac{W_{t+\Delta t} - 2W_t + W_{t-\Delta t}}{(\Delta t)^2} \tag{12}$$

$$\frac{\partial W}{\partial t} \approx \frac{W_{t+\Delta t} - W_{t-\Delta t}}{2\Delta t} \tag{13}$$

$$W \approx \frac{\theta}{2} W_{t+\Delta t} + (1 - \theta)W_t + \frac{\theta}{2} W_{t-\Delta t} \tag{14}$$

After application of spatial and temporal discretization a system of nonlinear equations result, which are solved using a Newton-Raphson procedure.

APPLICATION

The wave equation formulation of the Saint-Venant equations was employed in the simulation of the 1963 spring flood of the 291.2 mile Louisiana reach of the Mississippi River. The upstream boundary is located just south of the confluence between the Red River and the Mississippi River (see Figure 1) and the downstream boundary is to the north of where the Mississippi joins the Gulf of Mexico. The simulated region was subdivided into 24 linear, one-dimensional finite elements. The data for this simulation are based on Hsieh's (1977) work. No further calibration was made of the bottom friction coefficient.

Figure 2 shows the time evolution of the river stage at Baton Rouge. The stages computed by the wave and primitive equations model both agree well with measured data.

Figure 3 shows the spatial distribution of the volumetric flow rate along the river at the first time step, 24 hours after initializing the simulation. We notice the unphysical node-to-node or $2\Delta x$ oscillations generated by the primitive momentum equation. In sharp contrast to this, the wave momentum equation effectively suppresses these spurious oscillations.

An additional feature of interest is that the Newton-Raphson procedure, executed at every time step, only requires approximately half as many iterations for the wave equation formulation as for the primitive equation formulation.

CONCLUSIONS

The wave equation formulation successfully models the Saint-Venant equations. In an application to the Mississippi River the wave equation approach suppressed spurious spatial oscillations in the volumetric flow rate solution generated by the primitive equations. In addition the wave equation approach had approximately half the number of Newton-Raphson iterations per time step compared to the primitive equation approach, in the Mississippi application.

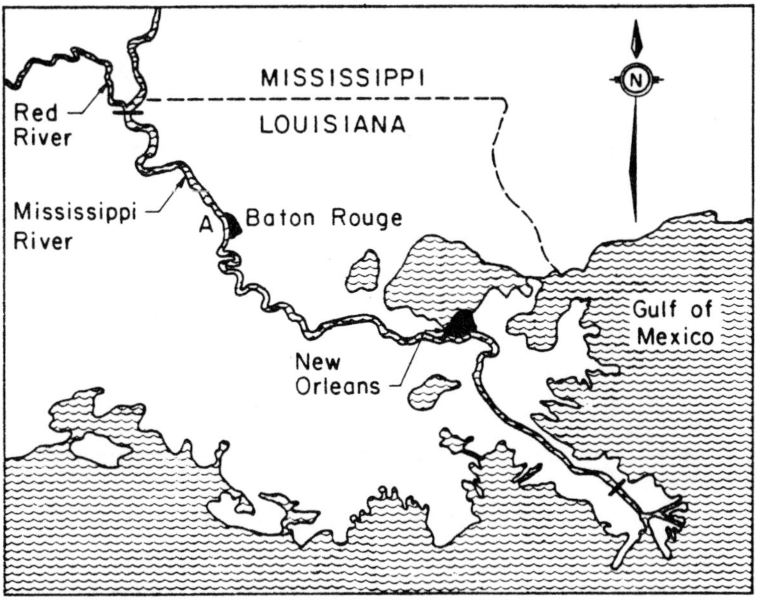

Figure 1. Modeling area in the Mississippi River. At upstream and downstream boundaries, marked with bars (|), stage is specified. Solution obtained at point A is in Figure 2.

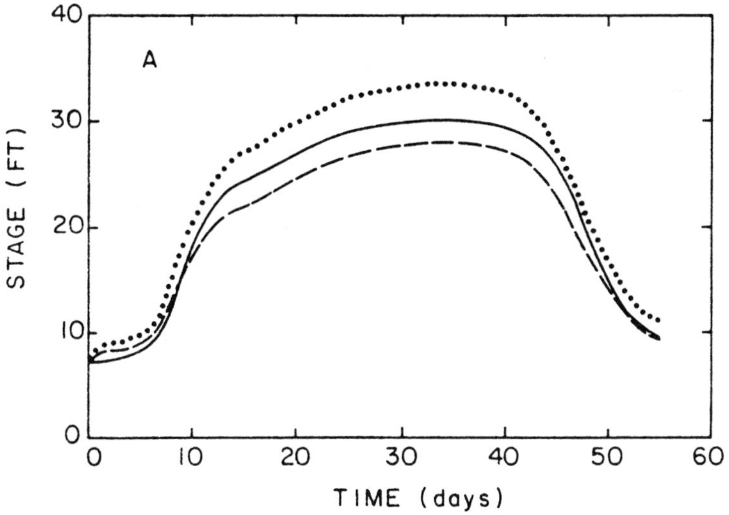

Figure 2. Comparison of computed stages from primitive equation (•••••) and wave equation (--) at Baton Rouge (A) with measured values (—) from Hsieh (1977).

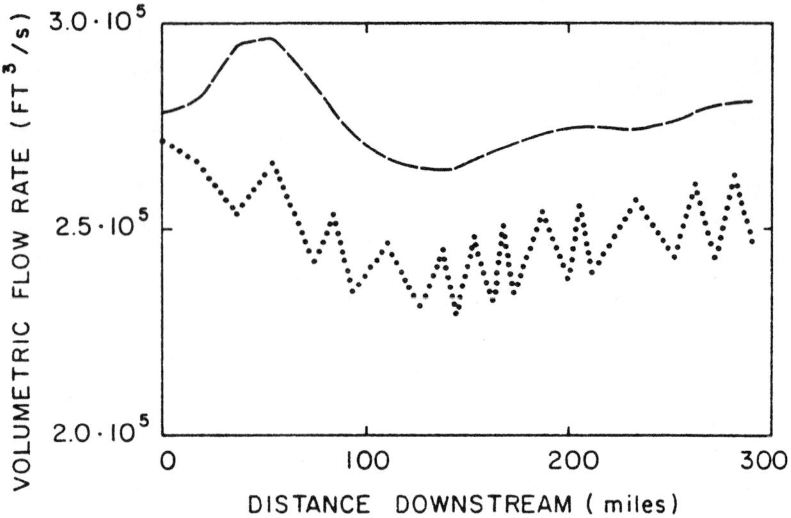

Figure 3. Comparison of computed volumetric flow rates from primitive equation (·····) and wave equation (--) at 24 hours after start of simulation.

ACKNOWLEDGEMENTS

This research has been supported in part through grant number CEE-8419366 from the United States National Science Foundation. The development and simulations were performed on an INTEL 286/310 personal computer provided by the INTEL Corporation. The authors are grateful to Paul Hsieh for providing the Mississippi River data and the primitive equation Mississippi computer model from which the wave equation model was developed.

REFERENCES

Hsieh, P. (1977) Finite Element Simulation of One-Dimensional Open Channel Flow, Senior Thesis, Dept. of Civil Engineering, Princeton University.

Kinnmark, I.P.E. (1986) The Shallow Water Wave Equations: Formulation, Analysis and Application, Lecture Notes in Engineering 15, Springer-Verlag, Berlin.

Kinnmark, I.P.E. and Gray W.G. (1982) Time-Weighting of the Momentum Equation in Explicit Wave Equation Models of Surface Water Flow, Proc. 4th Int. Conf. on Finite Elements in Water Resources, edited by Holz, K.P., Meissner U.,

Zielke W., Brebbia C.A., Pinder G. and Gray W., Springer-Verlag, Berlin, 5.67-5.77.

Kinnmark, I.P.E. and Gray W.G. (1984) A Two-Dimensional Analysis of the Wave Equation Model for Finite Element Tidal Computations, Int. J. Numer. Methods Eng., 20:369-383.

Lynch, D.R. and Gray W.G. (1979) A Wave Equation Model for Finite Element Tidal Computations, Computers and Fluids, 7:207-228.

Strelkoff, T. (1970) Numerical Solution of Saint-Venant Equations, Journal of the Hydraulics Division, 96:223-252.

SECTION 8 COASTAL ENGINEERING

VI International Conference on Finite Elements in Water Resources, Lisboa, Portugal, June 1986

Harbour Resonance Problems: Many Mathematical Aspects

N. Praagman
Svasek B. V., Coastal & Harbour Engineering Consultants, Heer Bokelweg 145, 3032 AD Rotterdam, The Netherlands

INTRODUCTION

A serious problem related to harbour planning concerns the shape of the basins. Relative large movements of moored ships and docks can result if the natural frequencies of the basins and the frequencies of the incoming waves, especially wind waves, approach each other.
In the case that the harbour is of a simple rectangular or circular shape, the natural frequencies of the harbour system may be found utilizing analytical techniques. (see [2]).
However if the shape of the harbour is complicated either expensive model experiments or numerical computations have to be carried out, in order to determine the natural frequencies.
In this paper the basics of a mathematical model called "HARES" are dealt with, as well as the discretization techniques applied and the way of presentation of results. Some plots, taken from a study in which possible extensions of Scheveningen harbour were investigated (see [4]) are shown.
The main advantage of a computer model over a physical model concerns its flexibility. In a computer model all types of alterations, related to
- the direction of the incoming waves
- the bathymetry of the region of interest
- the boundary geometry of the harbour

are incorporated easily. Hence many different layouts can be investigated quickly and for a reasonable price.

MATHEMATICAL FORMULATION

The mathematical equation which forms the basis of the numerical model is derived using several assumptions:
- the fluid is supposed to be ideal, hence no viscosity
- the fluid is incompressible and well-mixed
- the amplitudes of the incoming waves are small compared to the depth
- the elevation of the water surface is simple harmonic in time:

$$\eta = \eta_1 \cos wt - \eta_2 \sin wt = \mathrm{Re}(\eta * \exp(iwt))$$

with $\eta = \eta_1 + i\eta_2$.

Utilizing these assumptions the following model equation can be derived for the complex-valued function η : (see [1], [3])

$$\frac{\partial}{\partial x}\left(h \frac{\partial \eta}{\partial x}\right) + \frac{\partial}{\partial y}\left(h \frac{\partial \eta}{\partial y}\right) + (k^2 h + \gamma i k)\eta = 0, \forall\, x,y \varepsilon \Omega c R^2 \qquad (1)$$

where:

η : wave elevation with respect to the still water level
x,y : cartesian coordinates
h : depth, function of the position (x,y)
k : wave number of the incoming waves
γ : coefficient to incorporate bottom friction (see [3])
Ω : region of interest
$\partial\Omega$: boundary of region of interest

Once the angular velocity ω is prescribed the wave number k can be computed by the so called dispersion relation

$$\omega^2 = g * k * \tanh (k * h) \qquad (2)$$

where g is the acceleration of gravity.

BOUNDARY CONDITIONS

In order to obtain a well-posed mathematical problem boundary conditions have to be specified along the boundary $\partial\Omega$ of the region of interest.
In a general setting three types of conditions can be specified:
- the elevation η is prescribed on part of the boundary
- a reflection condition of the form

$$\frac{\partial \eta}{\partial n} + a * k * \eta = 0 \qquad (3)$$

is imposed on the reflecting part of the boundary, where η is the outside pointing normal and a=a1+ia2 is a theoretical non-dimensional complex reflection coefficient

- a radiation condition of the form

$$\frac{\partial \eta}{\partial n} - i * k * \eta = \frac{\partial \eta_I}{\partial n} - i * k * \eta_I \qquad (4)$$

where η_I is the incoming wave which satisfies:

$$\eta_I = ampl * \exp((-i * k * r)*(\cos(\theta-\alpha))) \qquad (5)$$

in a polar system (r,θ). The numerical solution of equations (1) and (2) with the conditions (3), (4) and (5) is treated in the following sections.

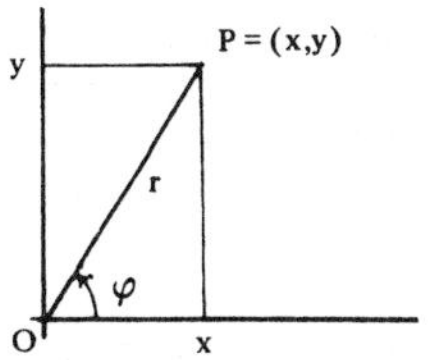

figure 1: polar coordinate system and cartesian coordinate system

DISCRETIZATION

Equation (1), being a Helmholtz-equation, is encountered in many disciplines. Due to the fact that in most applications the depth is variable and the region of interest is irregular the finite element method is a natural choice to discretize equation (1).
In order to replace equation (1) by a system of linear equations the standard Galerkin finite element method is applied to the weak formulation of (1).
Use is made of a triangulation of Ω and of basisfunctions which are linear and continuous over each element, hence

$$\eta = \sum_i \eta_i * \phi_i \ (x,y) \qquad (6)$$

with

$$\phi_i \ (x_j, y_j) = \delta \ (i,j), \qquad (7)$$

ϕ_i is linear and continuous over Ω,

and

(x_j, y_j) is the j'th nodal point,

δ the Kronecker delta

The system of equations which results reads:

$$S * \eta + M(k,\gamma) * \eta + F(\eta) = 0 \qquad (8)$$

and $\eta|\partial\Omega$ is prescribed.

Several steps of the process which leads to the building and solution of system (8), such as mesh generation, assembly and solution, can be done automatically which increases reliability and turnaround time.

AUTOMATIC MESH GENERATION

In order to discretize a region Ω in triangles two mesh generators have been built, called respectively "General" and "Meshharbour".

Mesh generator "General"

To activate "General" the user has to specify:
- points on the boundary of the domain together with a given coarseness in order to approximate the boundary curve of Ω
- the lines which connect these points to create Ω and the way in which internal points on these lines have to be created. The following possibilities are available:
  1. connecting lines are straight -
     - internal points are equidistant, the user specifies the number of line elements
     - length of the elements increases constantly along the line, the user gives the multiflication factor
     - internal points are computed in such a way that the coarseness of begin and end-point of the line are matched smoothly
  2. connecting lines are arcs -
     - same possibilities as for straight lines are available.

After calling "General" a triangulation of the domain is obtained in such a way that the resulting triangles are as regular as possible, the optimal triangle being equilateral. This objective is striven for using three criteria, in each substep in the triangulation process:

1 - lines that are created to split a polygon into two new, but smaller polygons should have angles which are as close to 60 degrees as possible.

2 - The number of points to be created on a split-line has to be as close as possible to an integer.

3 - After the final step of the triangulation, repositioning is performed:
each point is placed in the barycenter of its neighbours.

Due to the fact that the triangulation of the domain is performed in a very general way the numbering of the nodal points is such that the bandwidth of the matrices which result after the assembling of the element contributions is far from optimal. Therefore a Cuthill-MacKee renumbering is performed as a final step in "General". An example of a mesh created by "General" is shown in figure (2).

Mesh generator "Mesh-harbour"

Although the numbering provided by "General" is quite good it is never optimal. To get a better result the triangulation can be created utilizing the generator "Mesh-harbour". This generator is semi-automatic. The user has to specify the boundary points, lines along which the boundary points are connected and the number of points to be created on that special line.
Using "Mesh-harbour" an optimal bandwidth can be obtained. Especially when many different frequencies have to be computed through, an optimal numbering with respect to computation time is important. As an example of a mesh created by "Mesh-harbour" see figure (3).

ASSEMBLING OF THE EQUATIONS

The assembling process is performed in the usual way: element matrices are computed and added to the large matrices. Boundary conditions specified for each type of boundary are incorporated after the assembling process.

NUMERICAL SOLUTION

A solution of the system of equations may be obtained in two ways. Either a direct Gaussian elimination method or an iterative method is applicable. If a Gaussian method is used the bandwidth plays an important role, hence "Mesh-harbour" should be used. If an iterative (Chebyshev, since the system is complex-valued) method is used "General" is preferable. In that case the availability of a good initial guess is of course very important.

REPRESENTATION TECHNIQUES

Once the solution has been computed facilities have to be provided in order to obtain a quick insight in the results.
In the "HARES" package three plotting techniques are available:

1 - contour plotting:
lines of equal elevation for the amplitudes showing the wave pattern in the harbour.

2 - 3-D plotting of the elevation at some special time T.
Rotation of the pictures may increase the understanding of the harbour behaviour (see figure (4)).

3 - histories:
resulting values of the elevation for a number of ω values are plotted in a η-ω diagram. The ω-values which are near to resonance values are found easily (see figure (5)).

Of course printing of the results for part or the total harbour is also possible. Interpretation of that many values is however difficult.

ENGINEERING OBSERVATIONS

For the application of the program to practical situations a statistical approach is used. A two-dimensional matrix is made connecting the direction of waves and its chance of appearance in one year. For each of these situations a computation is made, in which the aberration of the incoming waves due to refraction outside the harbour is taken into account. Results of these computations are tabulated to give for the special layout studied and for each dock location the expected number of days that the local undulation is too large with respect to working conditions for loading and unloading of moored ships.

CONCLUSION

A mathematical model to study harbour layouts has been treated in a general way. It has been shown that many mathematical problems are encountered during such a study. For instance:
- mathematical derivation and formulation of the problem
- choice of discretization technique
- mesh generation
- renumbering techniques
- finite element assembling of equations
- incorporation of several types of boundary conditions
- solution techniques for large systems of complex-valued linear equations
- graphical representation techniques
- statistical representation of results.

Although all these problems have not been treated here in detail keys to solve these problems have been dealt with.

LITERATURE

(1) Berkhoff, J.C.W. (1976) Mathematical models for simple harmonic linear water waves. Wave diffraction and refraction.
Ph.D. Thesis, Delft University of Technology.

(2) Ippen, A.T. (ED) (1966) Estuary and coastline hydrodynamics.
McGraw-Hill, Incorporated, New York.

(3) Walker, S and Brebbia, C.A. (1978) Harbour resonance problems using finite elements.
Advances in water resources, Vol. 1, No. 4 PP 205-211.

(4) Possibilities and consequences of a fourth basin for Scheveningen harbour.
Project 473, Svasek B.V., Rotterdam, 1984.

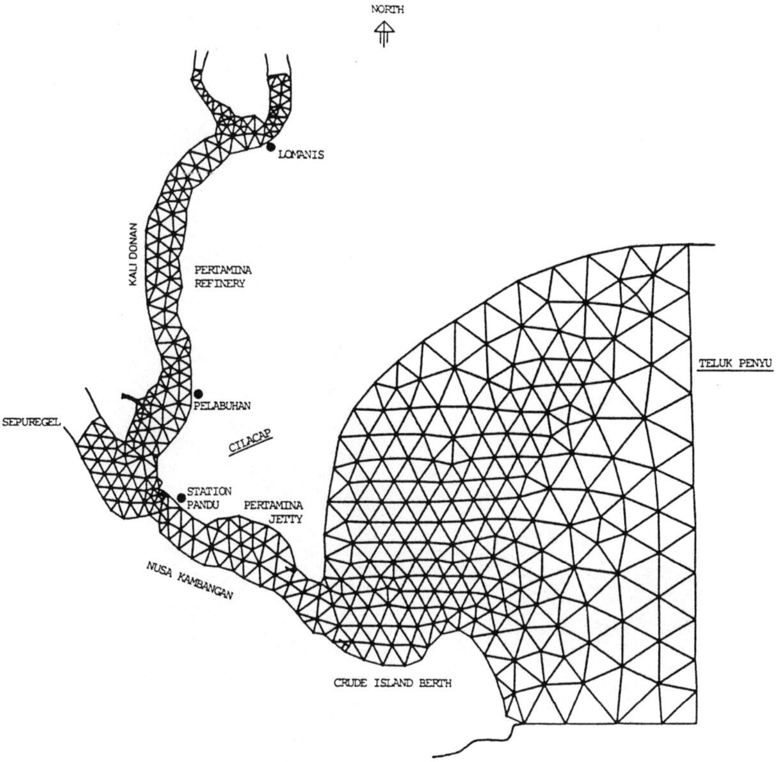

figure 2: Triangulation of irregular domain;
Result of application of "General".
(Finite element discretization of the
Kali Donan River and the Teluk Penyu Sea,
Indonesia).

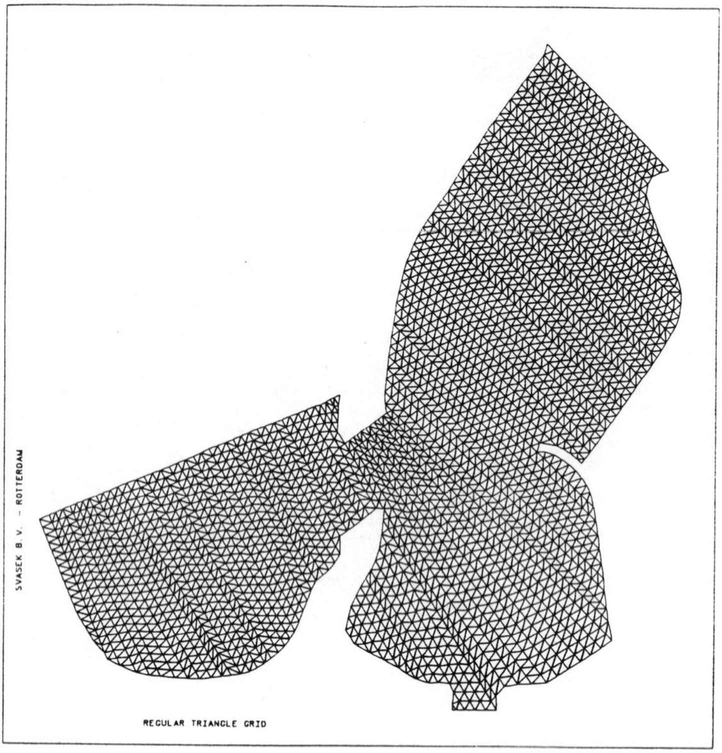

figure 3: Triangulation of irregular domain;
Result of application of "Mesh-harbour".

(Finite element discretization of
Scheveningen harbour, The Netherlands).

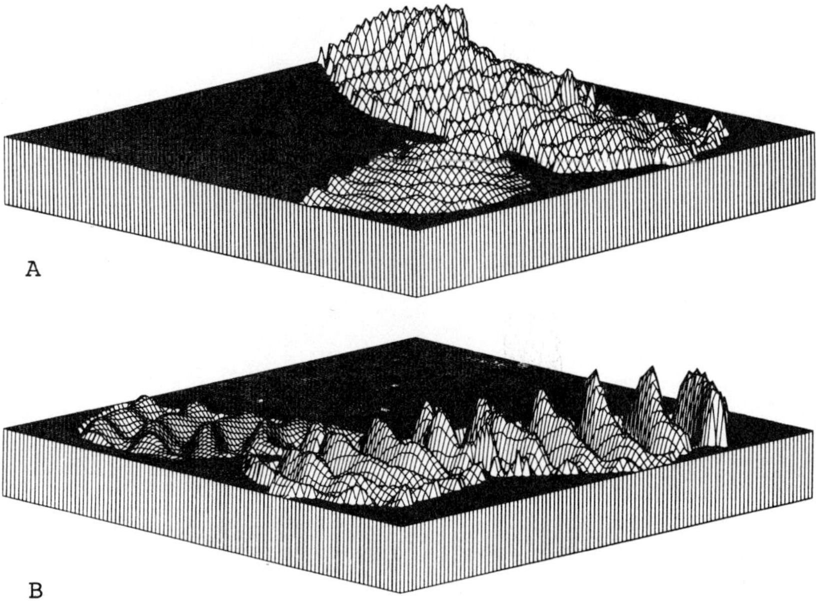

figure 4: Computed wave elevation for new layout of Scheveningen harbour to be investigated.
A : seen from the South-East
B : seen from the North-East

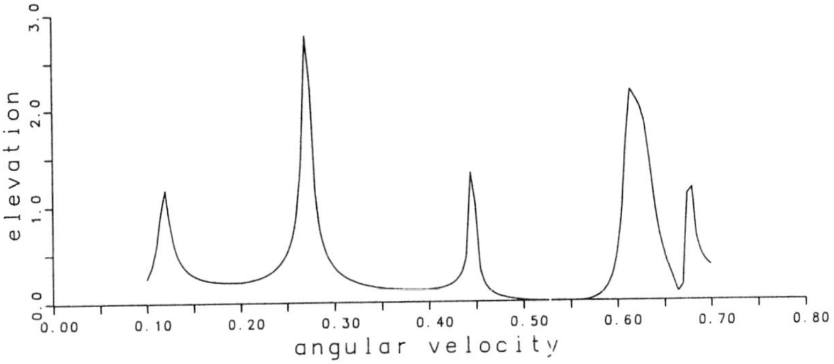

figure 5: η–ω diagram for special harbour lay-out. Resonance values are determined easily.

VI International Conference on Finite Elements in Water Resources, Lisboa, Portugal, June 1986

Boundary Type Finite Element Modelling of Harbour Oscillations

K. Kashiyama, M. Kawahara
Department of Civil Engineering, Chuo University, Kasuga 1-13-27, Bunkyo-ku, Tokyo 112, Japan

INTRODUCTION

The analysis of harbor oscillations is becoming more important from the point of view of planning and control of harbors. Various numerical methods have been presented to study the harbor oscillation problems. Lee (1971) and Mattioli (1978) presented a boundary element model. Some combination methods based on finite element method are also presented, since the finite element method can easily treat the arbitrary shape and variable water depth. Chan and Mei (1974) and Tsay and Liu (1983) presented the combination method of finite elements and analytical solutions. This method is called as hybrid finite element method. Berkhoff (1972) and Zienkiewicz et al. (1979) presented the combination method using boundary elements. Bettess et al. (1977,1984) presented the combination method using infinite elements. In recent papers, the authors (1985, 1985) presented the combination method based on boundary type finite element method. The key feature of this method is that the interpolation equation which satisfies the governing equation is employed. However, all of above models have been restricted without the effect of energy dispersion. Consequently, the resonance peak of harbor is always high compared with experimental and observed ones. More recently Ganaba et al. (1982) and Chan (1984) presented dissipative finite element model.

This paper presents a combination method based on boundary type finite element method for harbor oscillations considering the effect of friction. Chan's dissipative model is used in this paper, since it is simple and effective in applications. The efficiency of the present method is tested against a fully rectangular harbor and a circular harbor. The computed results are compared with the existing theoretical and experimental results. It is shown that the present method is useful for the analysis of harbor oscillation problems.

BASIC EQUATIONS

Consider the harbor with a straight coastline as shown in Figure 1. Assuming the infinitismal amplitude wave on variable water depth in shallow water, the surface displacement ζ and horizontal velocity u_i must satisfy the following equations.

$$\frac{\partial \zeta}{\partial t} + (hu_i),_i = 0 \tag{1}$$

$$\frac{\partial u_i}{\partial t} + \frac{1}{\rho} p,i + \varepsilon u_i = 0 \tag{2}$$

where p is the hydrostatic fluid pressure, h is water depth, ρ is the water density and ε is the complex friction coefficient.

A potential function ϕ is introduced as follows.

$$p = -\rho \frac{\partial \phi}{\partial t} - \rho g z \tag{3}$$

where g is the gravity acceleration. It follows from the hydrostatic assumption that

$$\zeta = -\frac{1}{g}\frac{\partial \phi}{\partial t} \tag{4}$$

Since the waves are assumed to be sinusoidal in time with radian frequency ω, the following relation can be introduced.

$$\left.\begin{aligned} \zeta(x,y;t) &= \eta(x,y)\exp(-i\omega t) \\ u_i(x,y;t) &= U_i(x,y)\exp(-i\omega t) \\ \phi(x,y;t) &= \Phi(x,y)\exp(-i\omega t) \end{aligned}\right\} \tag{5}$$

where η is amplitude factor and i is the imaginary unit.

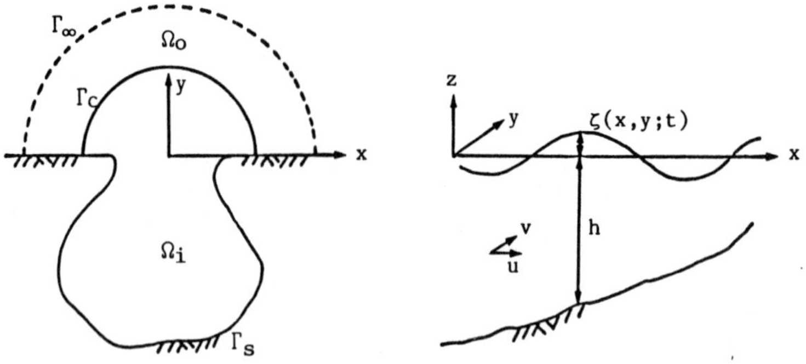

Figure 1. Definition sketch

Substituting (3) and (5) into (2), the following equation can be obtained.

$$U_i = \lambda \Phi,_i \tag{6}$$

where

$$\lambda = 1 / (1 + \frac{i\varepsilon}{\omega})$$

Substituting (4), (5) and (6) into (1), the governing equation considering the effect of friction can be written in the following form.

$$(\lambda h \eta,_i),_i + \frac{\omega^2}{g}\eta = 0 \tag{7}$$

If there is no friction, ε=0, then the equation (7) is to be the Helmholtz equation.

The complex friction coefficient can be assumed as follows.

$$\varepsilon = \beta \frac{\omega A}{kh} e^{i\gamma} \tag{8}$$

where β is nondimentional friction coefficient, A is incident wave amplitude and γ is phase difference from the flow velocity. The wave number is related to ω and h through the dispersion relation.

$$k = \omega(gh)^{\frac{1}{2}} \tag{9}$$

As the boundary condition, the following conditions are introduced on the boundary.

$$\eta,_n = \frac{\partial \eta}{\partial n} = \alpha \eta \qquad \text{on } \Gamma s \tag{10}$$

$$\lim_{r \to \infty} \sqrt{r}(\eta sc,_n - ik\eta sc) = 0 \qquad \text{on } \Gamma_\infty \tag{11}$$

where n means the normals to the boundary and α can be expressed in terms of the reflection coefficient as:

$$\alpha = ik\frac{1 - Kr}{1 + Kr} \tag{12}$$

where Kr denotes the reflection coefficient.

COMBINATION METHOD USING BOUNDARY TYPE FINITE ELEMENTS

For the purpose of efficient numerical computations, wave field Ω is divided into two domains, one of which is the inner domain Ωi with variable water depth and other is the outer domain Ωo

with constant water depth. In the inner domain Ω_i, the boundary type finite element method is applied and the boundary solutions are introduced in the outer domain Ω_o to deal with the radiation condition.

Since the wave is linear wave, the amplitude factor η is assumed to be the sum of the incident wave η_{in} , reflected wave η_{re} and scattered wave η_{sc} as:

$$\begin{aligned} \eta &= \eta_{in} + \eta_{re} + \eta_{sc} && \text{in } \Omega_i \\ \bar{\eta} &= \eta_{in} + \eta_{rc} + \bar{\eta}_{sc} && \text{in } \Omega_o \end{aligned} \tag{13}$$

where η_{in} and η_{re} are known value and are given as follows.

$$\begin{aligned} \eta_{ir} &= \eta_{in} + \eta_{re} \\ &= 2A \sum_{n=0}^{\infty} \varepsilon_n i^n J_n(kr)\cos n\theta_0 \cos n\theta \end{aligned} \tag{14}$$

in which A denotes incident wave amplitude, ε_n is Neumann number, J_n is the Bessel function of order n and θ_0 is incident wave angle, respectively.

The scattered wave within outer domain $\bar{\eta}_{sc}$ must satisfy the Helmholtz equation and the radiation condition, and can be represented by the Fourier-Bessel expansion as:

$$\bar{\eta}_{sc} = \sum_{n=0}^{\infty} \beta_n H_n(kr)\cos n\theta \tag{15}$$

where β_n denotes the unknown constants and H_n is the Hankel function of order n.

The following continuity conditions should be satisfied on Γ_c.

$$\left.\begin{aligned} \eta &= \bar{\eta} \\ \lambda h \eta_{,n} &= \lambda h \bar{\eta}_{,n} \end{aligned}\right\} \quad \text{on } \Gamma_c \tag{16}$$

For the discretization of the spatial variable η, the variational functional can be introduced. Generally, the variational functional to be minimized is expressed as follows.

$$\begin{aligned} \Pi = \frac{1}{2}\int_{\Gamma_i}[\lambda h(\eta,_i)^2 - \frac{\omega^2}{g}\eta^2]d\Omega - \frac{1}{2}\int_{\Gamma_s}\alpha\lambda h\eta^2 d\Gamma \\ + \int_{\Gamma_c}\lambda h[(\frac{1}{2}\bar{\eta}_{sc} - \eta_{sc})\bar{\eta}_{,n} - \frac{1}{2}\bar{\eta}_{sc}\eta_{ir,n}]d\Gamma \end{aligned} \tag{17}$$

Integrating the first term by parts, the variational functional can be transformed into the following form.

$$\Pi = \frac{1}{2}\int_{\Gamma_i}\lambda h\eta\eta,_n d\Gamma - \frac{1}{2}\int_{\Omega}\lambda h\eta(\eta,_{ii}+\frac{k^2}{\lambda}\eta)d\Omega - \frac{1}{2}\int_{\Gamma_s}\alpha\lambda h\eta^2 d\Gamma$$

$$+ \int_{\Gamma_c}\lambda h[(\frac{1}{2}\bar{\eta}_{sc}-\eta_{sc})\bar{\eta},_n - \frac{1}{2}\bar{\eta}_{sc}\eta_{ir},_n]d\Gamma \qquad (18)$$

Assuming that the interpolation equation for amplitude factor satisfies the governing equation (7) in each element, equation (18) can be simplified as follows.

$$\Pi = \frac{1}{2}\int_{\Gamma_i}\lambda h\eta\eta,_n d\Gamma - \frac{1}{2}\int_{\Gamma_s}\alpha\lambda h\eta^2 d\Gamma$$

$$+ \int_{\Gamma_c}\lambda h[(\frac{1}{2}\bar{\eta}_{sc}-\eta_{sc})\bar{\eta},_n - \frac{1}{2}\bar{\eta}_{sc}\eta_{ir},_n]d\Gamma \qquad (19)$$

where Γi expresses the boundary of each finite element.

For the interpolation equation of finite element, trigonometric function series is employed based on a three node triangular element as:

$$\eta = \left[\cos(\frac{k}{\sqrt{2\lambda}}x)\cos(\frac{k}{\sqrt{2\lambda}}y) \quad \cos(\frac{k}{\sqrt{2\lambda}}x)\sin(\frac{k}{\sqrt{2\lambda}}y) \quad \sin(\frac{k}{\sqrt{2\lambda}}x)\cos(\frac{k}{\sqrt{2\lambda}}y)\right]\begin{Bmatrix}\alpha_1\\ \alpha_2\\ \alpha_3\end{Bmatrix} \qquad (20)$$

where $\alpha_1 \sim \alpha_3$ are constants and k is wave number which takes the value at the centroid of each element. This interpolation equation satisfies the governing equation (7).

The configuration and the coordinate system are shown in Figure 2. The origin of the local coordinate system is placed at the centroid of each element. Figure 3 shows the typical form of the function in case that the ratio between element length s and wave length L are 0.1 and 0.4 respectively. It can be seen that the shape of the interpolation function varies according to the value of wave number.

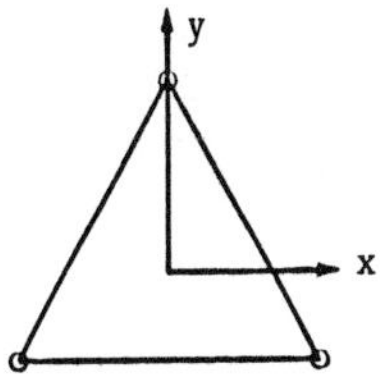

Figure 2 Element and coordinate system

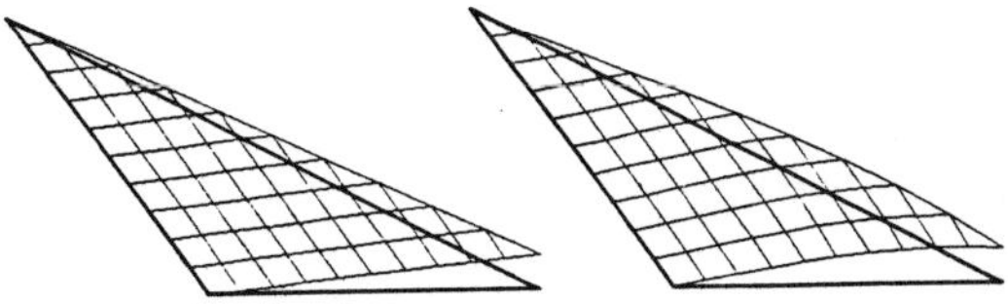

s/L = 0.1 s/L = 0.4

Figure 3 Typical form of interpolation function

On the other hand, the boundary solutions are used in the outer domain Ωo. In this method, the boundary of Γc is assumed to be a circle of radius R, then the integral of Γc can be evaluated analytically.

Minimizing the functional (19), it is obtained that

$$\frac{\partial \Pi}{\partial \eta_i} = 0 \qquad i = 1,2,\cdots,E \tag{21}$$

$$\frac{\partial \Pi}{\partial \beta_i} = 0 \qquad i = 1,2,\cdots,M \tag{22}$$

where E and M are total number of nodal point and total number of coefficient in the expansion of outer domain (15).

From equation (21) and (22), a set of linear algebraic equation for $\{\eta\}$ and $\{\beta\}$ is obtained. Eliminating the constants $\{\beta\}$, the matrix equation for $\{\eta\}$ can be derived in the following form.

$$[K]\{\eta\} = \{F\} \tag{23}$$

where $[K]$ is stiffness matrix which is symmetric and $\{F\}$ is the external source to excite the wave motion.

NUMERICAL EXAMPLE

In order to show the validity of present method, several numerical computations have been carried out, comparing with the analytical solution and experimental results.

At first, consider a fully open rectangular harbor with a straighat coastline as shown in Figure 4. Theoretical analysis has been made by Ippen and Goda (1963) ,Lee (1971) and so on. A series of experiments has been also conducted by them. The finite element idealization is shown in Figure 4. The total number of finite elements and nodal points are 118 and 86, respectively. The incident wave angle θ_0 is assumed to be $-\pi/2$.

The computed results are compared with the theoretical results versus kl in case that there is no friction, $\varepsilon=0$. The percentage errors at the center of the backwall (point P) are plotted in Figure 5 comparing them with the results obtained by the conventional combination method using linear interpolation function. It can be seen that the present method is good in accuracy compared with the conventional conbination method.

Figure 6 shows the amplification factor $|\eta|/2A$ at the point P comparing them with the exist experimental results by Lee (1971) and Ippen and Goda (1963). In this figure, dotted line represents the theoretical results obtained by Lee, Solid line represents the computed results which uses the nondimensional friction coefficient $\beta=10$ and the phase difference $\gamma=-\pi/4$.

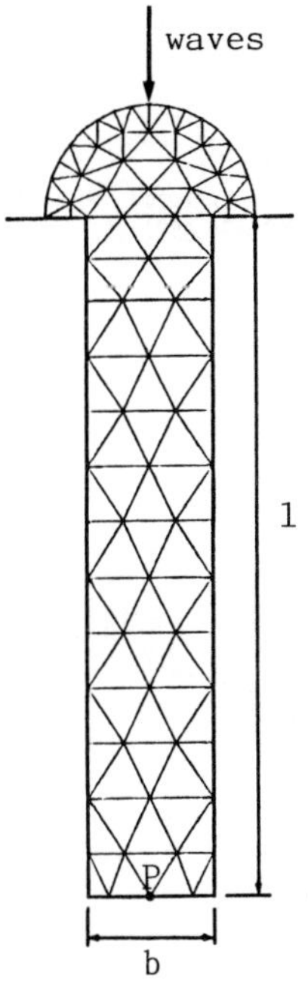

b=2.38in.
1=12.25in.
h=0.844ft.

Figure 4 Finite element idealization for a rectangular harbor

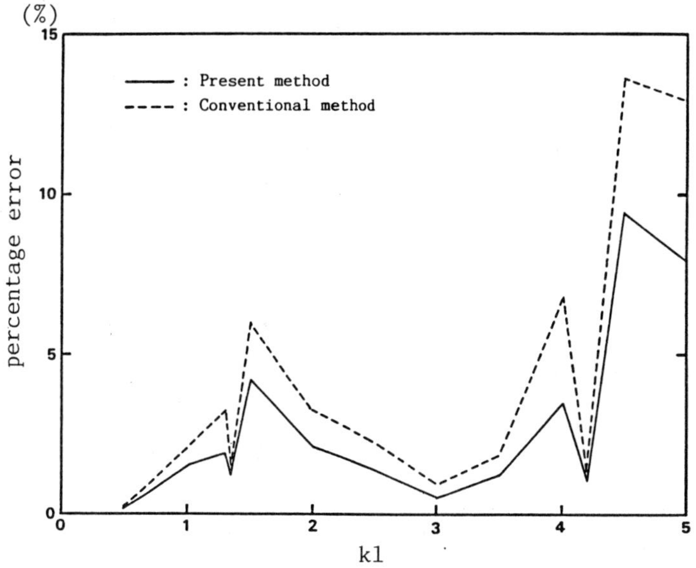

Figure 5 Percentage error of amplification factor at point P

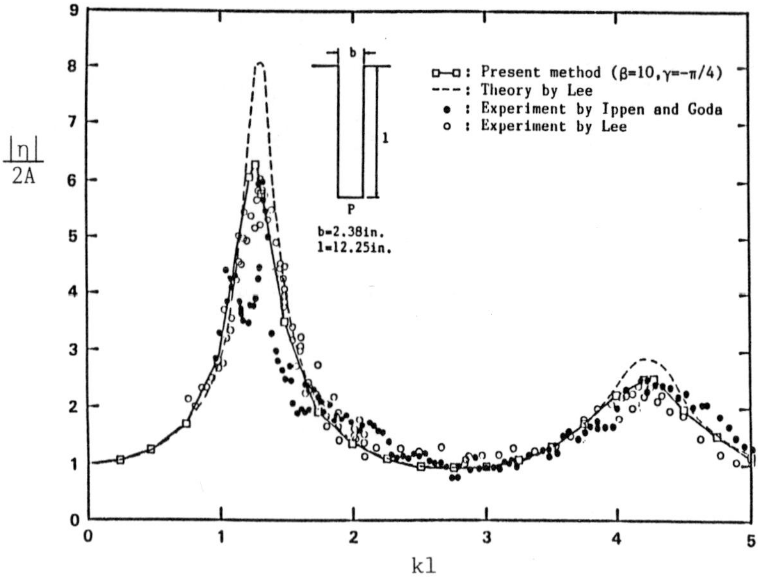

Figure 6 Computed amplification factor at point P

Secondly, consider a circular harbor with a 60° opening as shown in Figure 7. The total number of finite elements and nodal points are 224 and 136, respectively. Figure 8 shows the amplification factor at the point P inside a harbor comparing them with the theoretical and experimental results obtained by Lee (1971). In this figure, dotted line represents the theoretical results and solid line represents the computed results which uses one and the same friction coefficient and phase difference.

From these examples, it can be seen that the computed results considering the friction by the present method is well in agreement with the existing experimental results.

CONCLUSION

The Combination method using the boundary type finite element method has been presented for the analysis of harbor oscillations considering the energy dissipation. The key feature of this method is that the interpolation equation has been chosen to satisfy the governing equation in each element. It follows that the final equation can be formulated by the calculation of line integral along the boundary of element.

From the numerical example, it can be seen that the present method is extremely useful for the analysis of harbor oscillation problems.

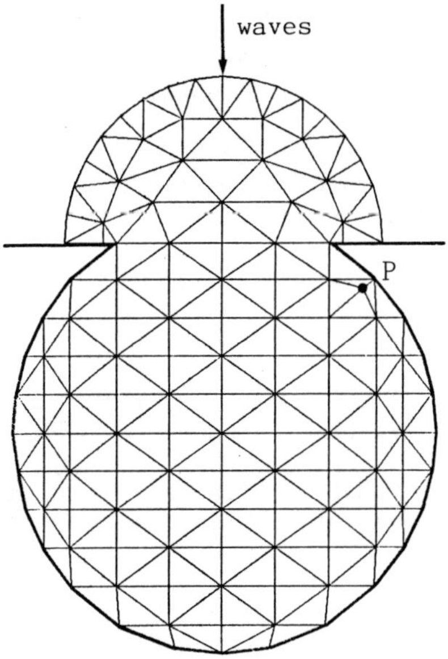

Figure 7 Finite element idealization for a circular harbor

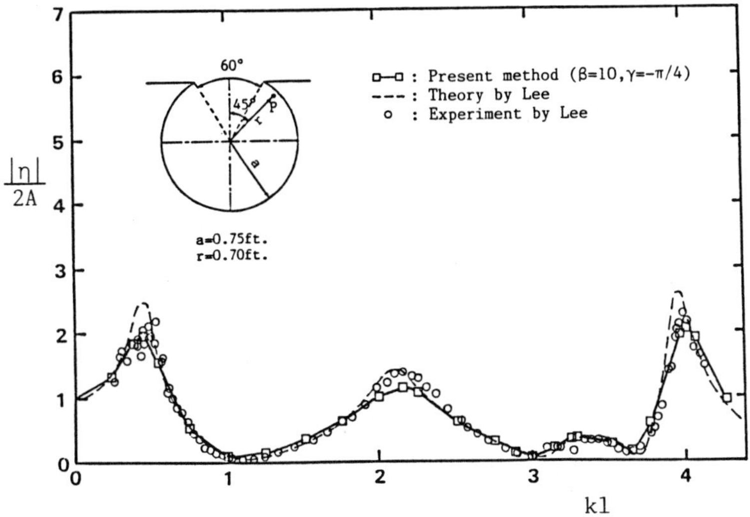

Figure 8 Computed amplification factor at point P

REFERENCES

Berkhoff, J.C.W. (1972) Computation of combined refraction and diffraction, Proc. 13th Conf. Coastal Eng., ASCE, 471-490.

Bettess, P. and Zienkiewicz, O.C. (1977) Diffraction and refraction of surface waves using finite and infinite elements, Int. J. Numer. Methods Eng., 11:1271-1290.

Bettess, P., Emson, C. and Chiam, T.C. (1984) A new mapped infinite element for exterior wave problems, in Lewis, R.W. et al. (ed), Numerical Methods in Coupled System, 489-504.

Chan, H.S. and Mei, C.C. (1974) Oscillations and wave forces in an offshore harbor, Ralph M. Persons Lab., Report 190, MIT.

Chan, H.S. (1984) Hybrid finite element modeling of harbor resonance, Proc. 4th Int. Conf. on Applied Numerical modeling, tainan, 312-316.

Ippen, A.T. and Goda, Y. (1963) Wave induced oscillations in harbors: the solution for a rectangular harbor connected to the open-sea, Raiph M. Persons Lab., Report No.59, MIT.

Ganaba, M.B., Welford, C. and Lee, J.J. (1982) Dissipative finite element models for harbor resonance problems, in Kawai, T. (ed), Finite Element Flow Analysis, 451-459.

Kawahara, M. and Kashiyama, K. (1985) Boundary type finite element method for surface wave motion based on trigonometric function interpolation, Int. J. Numer. Method Eng., 21:1833-1852.

Kashiyama, K. and Kawahara, M. (1985) Boundary type finite element method for surface wave problems, Proc. of JSCE, No.363/2(Hydraulic and Sanitary Eng.):205-214.

Lee, J.J. (1971) Wave induced oscillations in harbors of arbitrary geometry, J. Fluid Mech., 45:375-394.

Mattioli, F. (1978) Wave induced oscillations in harbors of variable depth, Computer and Fluids, 6:171-172.

Tsay, T.K. and Liu, P. L-F, (1983) A finite element model for wave refraction and diffraction, Applied Ocean Research, 5:30-37.

Zienkiewicz, O.C., Kelly, D.W. and Bettess, P. (1979) Marriage a la mode - the best of both worlds (finite elements and boundary integrals), in Glowinski, R. et al., Energy Methods in Finite Element Analysis, 81-107.

VI International Conference on Finite Elements in Water Resources, Lisboa, Portugal, June 1986

Wave Action Studies for Alcala Beach (Canary Islands). A Case Study of Joint Application of Physical and Mathematical Models in a Convergence Zone

J.M.A. Covas
Laboratório Nacional de Engenharia Civil, Av. Brasil, 1799 Lisboa Codex, Portugal

INTRODUCTION

A state-of-the-art review of wave propagation modelling in a convergence zone

One of the practical problems confronting the coastal design engineer is to determine a design wave for a coastal structure in an area where a strong convergence of wave orthogonals, often resulting in the development of caustics, can occur. In convergence zones reliability of the results of conventional refraction diagram techniques is at its lowest. Feasible modelling techniques of wave propagation in convergence zones are: (1) the combined use of a physical model of wave action and a mathematical model of wave refraction; (2) the use of a special technique of interpretation of wave refraction diagrams such as the "Monte-Carlo approach" to computation of refraction of water waves derived by Bouws and Battjes (1982) eventually in connection with experimental model tests; (3) the computation of refraction of wave spectra using an irregular wave refraction mathematical model; (4) the use of a refraction-diffraction mathematical model based upon the mild slope equation derived by Berkhoff; (5) the use of a refraction-diffraction mathematical model using the parabolic approximation of the Berkhoff's mild slope equation.

Several authors have given contributions to modelling of wave propagation in a convergence zone.

Arthur (1946) derived some analytical solutions for wave refraction by islands and shoals with circular bottom contours analytically defined. Pierson (1951) presented a physical interpretation and an analytical study of wave propagation in a convergence zone. Pierson's work is an important contribution to the understanding of the phenomena and to the interpretation of wave refraction diagrams. Whalin (1971) carried out an experimental investigation to assess the limits of applicability of linear wave refraction theory in a convergence zone.

These works were developed in the field of the analytical formulation and physical interpretation of wave refraction phenomena in a convergence zone.

As far as mathematical modelling of refraction of irregular waves is concerned, Abernethy and Gilbert (1975) and Abernethy, Snell and Stuert (1977) established an irregular wave refraction mathematical model based on the integration of the directional wave spectra evolution equation along the wave rays. Wang and Shiau (1977) developed a mathematical model for refraction of wave spectra based on the assumption that wave energy associated with a narrow frequency band stays within this band upon refraction when waves propagate from deep into shallow waters.

Computations of wave propagation in a convergence zone are also possible with a wave refraction-diffraction mathematical model. Barailler and Gaillard (1964) presented a wave refraction-diffraction mathematical model combining the ray-method and a boundary integral equation method. Svendsen (1967) derived a one-dimensional wave refraction-diffraction equation. Berkhoff (1972) derived the mild slope equation, a two-dimensional differential equation for combined refraction-diffraction of water waves. Schönfeld (1972) derived in a different way a two-dimensional refraction-diffraction equation similar to Berkhoff's one. Biésel (1972) developed a ray-model, combining wave refraction with the so-called "moderate diffraction." Biésel's model accounts for the wave amplitude gradient accross the crest through corrections to the wave number. Smith and Sprinks (1975) gave a formal derivation of Berkhoff's mild slope equation. Berkhoff (1976) used a variational formulation for the mild slope equation and reflection boundary condition, combined with a source distribution along the boundary Γ_2 between the regions of constant and variable depth. Numerical treatment is based on the finite element method in combination with a finite source distribution along the boundary Γ_2. Chen and Mei (1974,1975 and 1976) proposed a hybrid element method to solve the diffraction Helmholtz equation in an infinite fluid region of constant depth and they succeeded in establishing a variational principle which incorporates, as natural boundary conditions, the matching conditions along the boundary of the finite element region. Chen, Mei and Yue (1976) developed a hybrid element method for calculating three-dimensional water wave scattering. Bettess and Zienkiewicz (1977) developed a wave refraction-diffraction mathematical model in which a variational formulation for Berkhoff's equation and respective boundary conditions, is used as basis for finite and infinite elements. Houston (1981) using a hybrid finite element method, originally developed by Chen and Mei (1974), presented a two-dimensional finite element numerical model that calculates combined refraction-diffraction of short waves. He succeeded in establishing a variational principle for Berkhoff's equation and boundary conditions, and that incorporates, as natural boundary conditions, the matching conditions between the regular finite element of the variable-depth region and the super-element used to cover the constant-depth infinite region. These are the main refraction-diffraction mathematical models based on Berkhoff's elliptic-type mild slope equation.

In Radder (1979) a parabolic approximation to the mild slope equation is derived from splitting the wave field into transmitted and reflected components. By assuming that the reflected field is negligible, a parabolic equation is obtained for the transmitted field.

Southgate (1981) developed a mathematical model based on a ray method which combines the effects of depth refraction with diffraction around breakwaters and reflections from harbour boundaries. Bowers and Southgate (1982) checked the results of this mathematical model against a physical model.

Berkhoff, Booy and Radder (1982) performed a verification of three numerical wave propagation models for simple harmonic linear water waves: the refraction model, the parabolic refraction-diffraction model and the full refraction-diffraction model. A comparison of the computational results of these models against measurements in a hydraulic scale model together with the conclusions on the practical use of the models are given by these authors.

Alcala Beach's wave action studies

Spanish official authorities of the Canary Islands planned the construction of a fishing harbour breakwater at the site known as Alcala Beach in the Tenerife Island (Canary Islands, Spain).

Hand made wave refraction diagrams, computed at INTECSA consulting engineers, had shown that the area was an important convergence zone. Subsequent studies undertaken at LNEC with a mathematical model of wave refraction and a physical model of wave action confirmed INTECSA's wave refraction diagram results.

The analysis of INTECSA's former studies showed

the worst storms for proposed breakwater area proceeded from directions between WSW and S. The design wave's deep water significant period and height values were Ts = 12 s and Hs = 5.4 m.

Mathematical model did allow the analysis of a great number of situations and the selection of a few cases which were then studied more deeply with the physical model.

As pointed out in the previous section the combined use of a physical and a mathematical model is one of the methods of analysis of wave propagation in a convergence zone.

WAVE REFRACTION COMPUTATIONS FOR ALCALA BEACH

LNEC's wave refraction mathematical model is a ray-model based on equations of Arthur and Munk (1951).

Two different sets of water depths, organized from two hydrographic charts, were used for the computation of large grid and small grid wave refraction diagrams (Figure 1).

Three groups of large grid wave refraction diagrams were computed. The first one concerned the monochromatic waves defined by deep water wave directions SW-20°-N, SW-10°-N, SW, SW-10°-S and SW-20°-S, and, on one hand, wave periods 8, 10 and 14 seconds and mean water level and, on the other hand, period 12 seconds and high and low water sea levels. For deep water wave directions SW, SW-10°-S and S-20°-S, period 9 seconds and high and low water sea levels a second group of wave refraction diagrams was computed. The third of set of refraction diagrams regarded wave directions SW-5°-S, SW-15°-S, SW-25°-S, SW-30°-S, periods 10 and 12 seconds and mean water level and period 9 seconds and high water sea level and direction SW-35°-S, periods 9 and 12 seconds and high water sea level. At last for monochromatic waves defined by SW, SW-10°-S and SW-20°-S deep water wave directions, periods 9 and 12 seconds and mean water level, small grid wave refraction diagrams were computed (Figure 2).

The main conclusions from the wave refraction computations were: (1) for deep water wave directions north of SW the convergence zone, arising from bottom topography, was far from the area of proposed breakwater construction where divergence of wave orthogonals occurred. Wave height values in this area were expected to be lesser than deep water ones; (2) deep water wave directions between SW and SW-20°-S gave rise to a strong convergence of wave orthogonals in the area where construction of the breakwater was intended. Computed wave refraction coefficients indicated an important effect of wave energy concentration along the breakwater: (3) for deep water directions south of SW-20°-S wave energy concentration along the breakwater was unimportant.

As a result of wave refraction computations it was decided to perform experimental model tests for monochromatic waves corresponding to deep water wave directions SW, SW-10°-S and SW-20°-S, periods 9 and 12 seconds and high and low water sea levels.

MODEL TESTS OF WAVE ACTION FOR ALCALA BEACH

A physical model of scale 1/125 was constructed in one of the LNEC wave basins equipped with a ten-meter-long translation type regular wave generator. A two-quilometer long section of the coastline together with the bottom topography up to the 65 m water depth were reproduced in the model (Figure 3).

A total of 30 tests was carried out for incoming wave directions, periods and sea water levels referred to in the previous section along with deep water wave heights varying from 1 m to 5.4 m. Breakwater itself was obviously not incorporated in the model, but its centre line position was indicated with a full line.

Deep water wave heights were measured in five points along a line two meters distant from the wave generator. At the same time a set of four probes measured wave heights over the study area using a half-meter-side reference mesh.

Values of Krsd coefficient - due to refraction, shoaling and diffraction - at measuring points in the study zone were expressed in percentage of deep water wave height values.

Physical model experiments have shown the occurrence of an important wave energy concentration in the area of proposed breakwater construction.

In fact values of Krsd along the breakwater ranged from 50 up to 300% (Figure 4) for the incoming wave direction from the SW, from 50 up to 280% for the direction SW-10°-S and from 50 up to 400% for the direction SW-20°-S.

CONCLUSIONS FROM ALCALA BEACH WAVE ACTION STUDIES

Alcala Beach wave action studies performed at LNEC with both a wave refraction mathematical model and a regular wave physical model have clearly shown that the area of proposed fishing harbour breakwater construction was an important convergence zone where a strong wave energy concentration occurred as a result of wave refraction by underwater topography, for a wide range of wave periods and incoming wave directions.

In its final report LNEC stated that construction of a harbour sheltering breakwater at Alcala Beach should be avoided once the expected wave environment in the area would impose a heavy and very expensive coastal structure. At the same time very difficult navigation conditions in the area together with an insufficient shelter for fishing boats inside the harbour were to be expected.

SOME REMARKS ON JOINT APPLICATION OF PHYSICAL AND MATHEMATICAL MODELS

Although mathematical models are an important tool for study of natural phenomena, they involve some approximations such as modelling prevailing phenomena without accounting for second order ones. This procedure, valid under some initial conditions, may induce important errors if these conditions are not verified.

Faults associated with construction and calibration of physical models and respective experimental measuring devices, and with processing of results of model tests may also give rise to model deviations from prototype behaviour.

However physical modelling is still a mean of validation of mathematical models and it is also the only available technique for the phenomena whose mathematical modelling is not yet possible.

Physical and mathematical models are then complementary tools of natural phenomena modelling.

It is a frequent situation to use in a physical or mathematical model boundary conditions computed from another mathematical model or from a campaign of prototype observations and measurements.

Previous computations with a mathematical model can be used for selection of the cases to be studied more deeply in the physical model. Model tests allow then a good calibration of mathematical model and/or a better interpretation of its results. Extrapolation of physical model results may then be performed with mathematical model to account for situations not studied in the physical model.

This case study is a practical example of joint application of physical and mathematical models for solution of hydraulic engineering problems.

Mathematical model was used to define the entire region to be reproduced in the physical model as well as the experimental conditions for the model tests. These ones as well as wave refraction computations were then used to access the wave environment in the area of proposed breakwater construction.

For Alcala Beach, in addition to reported studies a quantitative comparison was made between the results of both the physical model of wave action and the refraction mathematical model, for a 12 second, SW deep water incoming, monochromatic wave and a high water sea level.

Small grid wave refraction diagram was subdivided into several partial refraction diagrams each one corresponding to an independent wave train. Values of H/Ho corresponding to overlapped independent wave trains have been added up for the reference mesh of wave height measurements on the physical model.

Measurements on the physical model and results of wave refraction computations do agree quite well (Figure 5).

ACKNOWLEDGEMENTS

The author wishes to express his thanks to Dr. Climaco Pereira, co-author of Alcala Beach wave action studies, who was in charge of the physical model tests.

REFERENCES

ABERNETHY, C.L. and GILBERT, G. (1975) Refraction of wave spectra. Wallingford, Hydraulics Research Station, Report n. INT 117.

ABERNETHY, C.L., SNELL, R.J. and STUERT, K.B. (1977) Computation of the refraction of wave spectra. Wallingford, Hydraulics Research Station, Report n. IT 131.

ARTHUR, R.S. (1946) Refraction of water waves by islands and shoals with circular bottom contours. Transactions, American Geophysical Union, Washington D.C. 27(2).

ARTHUR, R.S. and MUNK, W.H. (1951) Wave intensity along a refracted ray. Proc. of the National Bureau of Standards Semi-centennial Symposium on Gravity Waves, Washington, U.S.A..

BARAILLER, L. and GAILLARD, P. (1964) Exemple de réalisations de modèles mathématiques à Sogreah pour des études de propagation de houle. Proc. of 9th Conference on Coastal Engineering, Lisbon, Portugal.

BERKHOFF, J.C.W. (1972) Computation of combined refraction-diffraction. Proc. of the 13th International Conference on Coastal Engineering, Vancouver, Canada.

BERKHOFF, J.C.W. (1976) Mathematical models for simple harmonic linear water waves. Wave diffraction and refraction. Ph. D. dissertation, Delft University of Technology.

BERKHOFF, J.C.W., BOOY, N. and RADDER, A.C. (1982) Verification of numerical wave propagation models for simple harmonic linear water waves. Amsterdam,

Coastal Engineering, 6.
BETTESS, P. and ZIENKIEWICZ, O.C. (1977) Diffraction and refraction of surface waves using finite and infinite elements. International Journal for Numerical Methods in Engineering, Vol. 11, n. 8.
BIÉSEL, F.(1972) Réfraction de la houle avec diffraction modérée. Proc. of the 13th International Conference on Coastal Engineering, Vancouver, Canada.
BOUWS, E. and BATTJES, J.A. (1982) A Monte-Carlo approach to the computation of refraction of water waves. J. of Geophysical Research, Vol. 87, n. C8.
BOWERS, E.C. and SOUTHGATE, H.N.(1982) Wave diffraction, refraction and reflection. A comparison between a physical model and a mathematical ray model. Wallingford, Hydraulics Research Station, Report n. IT 240.
CHEN, H.S. and MEI, C.C. (1974) Oscillations and wave forces in an offshore harbour. Ralph and Parsons Laboratory for Water Resources and Hydrodynamics, M.I.T., Report n. 190, Cambridge, U.S.A..
CHEN, H.S. and MEI, C.C. (1974) Oscillations and wave forces in a man-made harbour in the open sea. Proc. of the 10th Symposium on Naval Hydrodynamics, Office of Naval Research, U.S.A..
CHEN, H.S. and MEI, C.C. (1975) Hybrid element method for water waves. Proc. Symposium on Modelling Techniques, San Francisco, U.S.A..
CHEN, H.S. and MEI, C.C. (1976) A hybrid element method for steady linearized free-surface flows. International Journal for Numerical Methods in Engineering, Vol. 10, n. 5.
CHEN, H.S., MEI, C.C. and YUE, D.K.P. (1976) A hybrid element method for calculating three-dimensional water-wave scattering. Massachusetts Institute of Technology, Report n. MITSG 76-10, Cambridge, U.S.A..
HOUSTON, J.R. (1981) Combined refraction and diffraction of short waves using the finite element method. Applied Ocean Research, Vol. 3, n. 4.
INTECSA INTERNACIONAL DE INGENIERIA Y ESTÚDIOS TÉCNICOS (1974) Alcala Beach fishing harbour breakwater. Analysis of its feasibility by means of a study of the wave environment in the area. Intecsa, Madrid. (In Spanish).
NATIONAL LABORATORY OF CIVIL ENGINEERING (LNEC). HARBOURS AND BEACHES DIVISION (1979) Wave action studies for Alcala Beach (Canary Islands). Internal Report, Lisbon, LNEC. (In Portuguese).
PEREIRA, M.A.M. CLIMACO and COVAS, J.M. AFONSO (1981) Wave action studies for Alcala Beach (Canary Islands). A case study of joint application of physical and mathematical models in a convergence zone. Lisbon, LNEC, Memoir n. 555. (In Portuguese).

PIERSON, W.J.P. (1951) The interpretation of crossed orthogonals in wave refraction phenomena. Washington, BEB Technical Memorandum n. 21.

RADDER, A.C. (1979) On the parabolic equation method for water-wave propagation. J. Fluid Mechanics, Vol. 95, part 1.

SCHÖNFELD, J.C. (1972) Propagation of two-dimensional short waves . Delft University of Technology.

SMITH, R. and SPRINKS, T. (1975) Scattering of surface waves by a conical island. J. Fluid Mechanics, Vol. 72, Part 2.

SOUTHGATE, H.N. (1981) Ray methods for combined refraction and diffraction problems. Wallingford, Hydraulics Research Station, Report n. IT 214.

SVENDSEN, I.A. (1967) The equation for gravity waves in water of gradually varying depth. Copenhagen, Coastal Engineering Laboratory and Hydraulics Laboratory, Technical University of Denmark, Basic Research Progress Report 15.

WANG, H. and SHIAU, J.C. (1977) Wave energy transformation over irregular bottom. Proc. of ASCE, J. of Waterway, Port, Coastal and Ocean Division, WW1.

WHALIN, R.W. (1971) The limit of aplicability of linear wave refraction theory in a convergence zone. Vicksburg, U.S. Army Engineer Waterways Experiment Station, Research Report H-71-3.

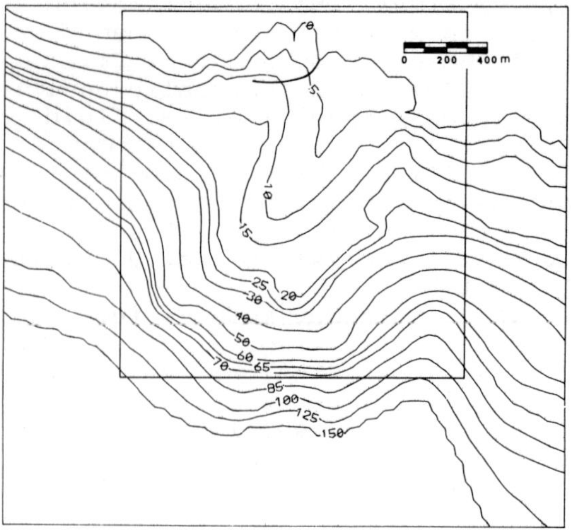

Fig. 1 - Alcala Beach's bottom topography used for large grid computations of wave refraction diagrams

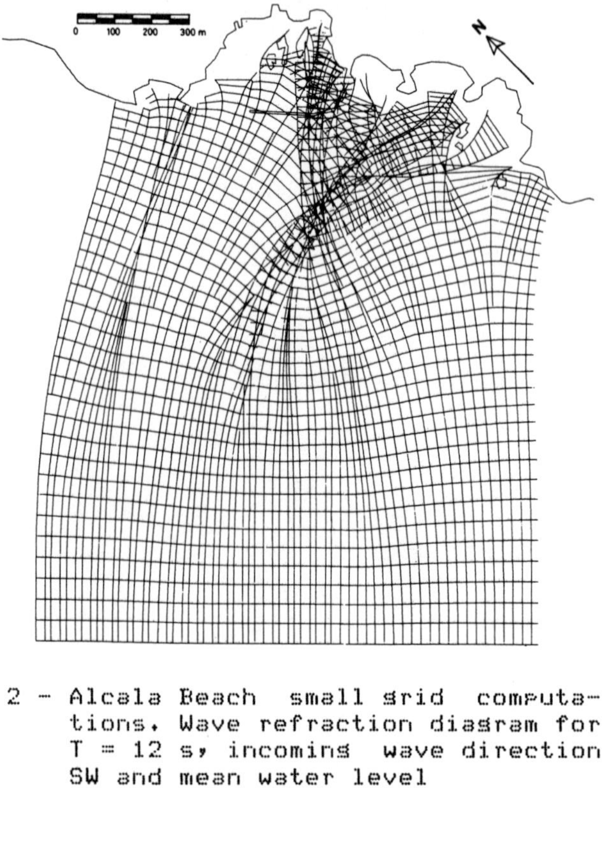

Fig. 2 - Alcala Beach small grid computations. Wave refraction diagram for T = 12 s, incoming wave direction SW and mean water level

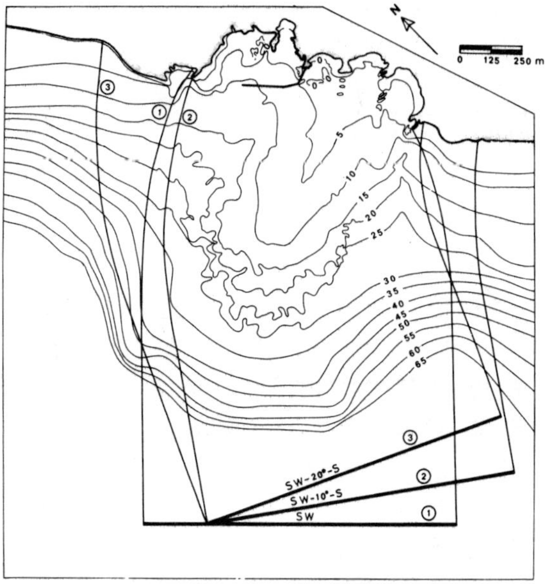

Fig. 3 - Alcala Beach's physical model lay-out showing wave generator and guiding walls' positions

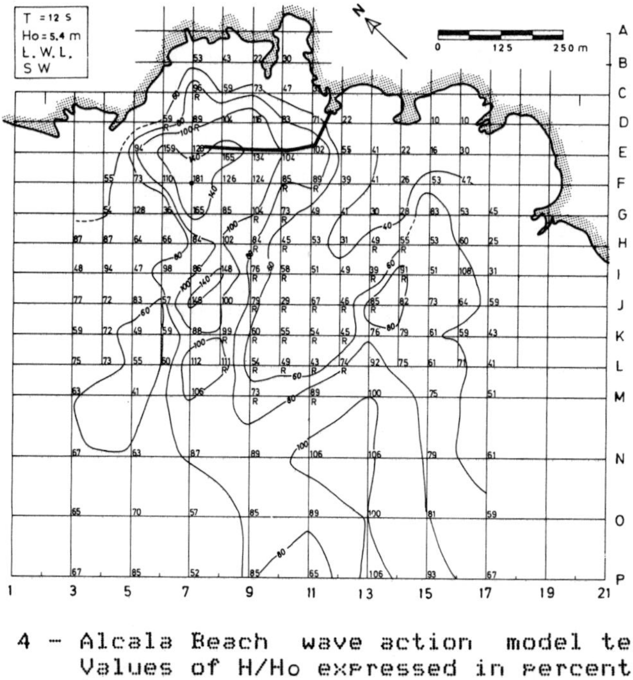

Fig. 4 - Alcala Beach wave action model tests. Values of H/Ho expressed in percentage of deep water wave height values

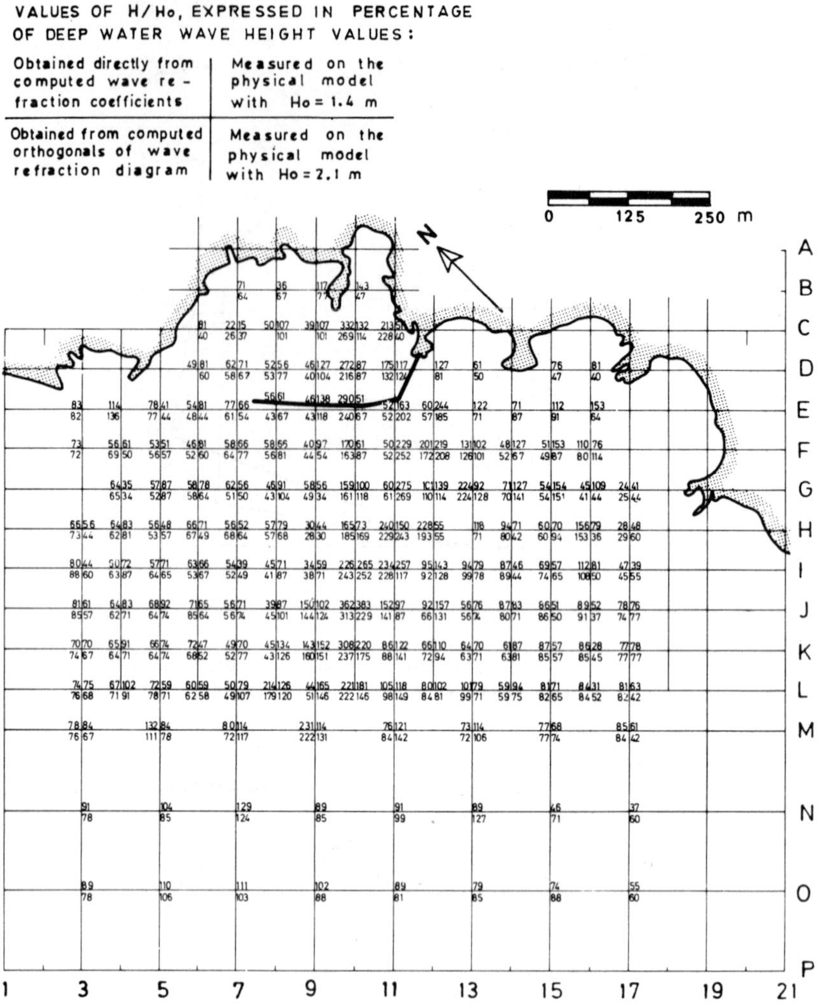

Fig. 5 - Alcala Beach. Values of H/Ho obtained from wave refraction computations and from physical model's measurements

VI International Conference on Finite Elements in Water Resources, Lisboa, Portugal, June 1986

Dynamic Analysis of Sea Dykes Under Breaker Impact

U. Meissner, Th. Hartmann
University Hannover, Hannover, West Germany

INTRODUCTION

For the protection of the German coastline at the North Sea, large parts of sea dykes had to be improved after the storm and flooding disaster of 1962. Since then, great efforts have been made in order to gain an optimization of these structures for better resistance against wave forces and an improvement of stability. As far as the study of wave run-up, wave impact, energy dissipation and the construction of revetments and filter layers are concerned, it seemed neccessary to set up a 1:1 scale model for a simulation of the natural phenomena in a laboratory, because in situ measurements were not sufficient and especially problematic under severe climate conditions. Since 1983, "The Large Wave Channel" (GWK), an inter-institutional facility of the University Hannover and the Technical University Braunschweig, which was erected under the sponsorship of the German Research Association (DFG), is under operation in Hannover. In this channel of 324 m length, 5 m width, and 7 m depth, waves between 1 sec and 15 sec period with heights up to 2 m can be generated by a hydraulically driven spectrum wave generator (9oo kW) of the combined plunger-paddle-type. For the investigation of sea dykes at the far end of the channel, a 1:4 slope model was built (Figure 1) consisting of a sandfill core and covered by an asphalt concrete revetment. The displayed test field is instrumentated with surface, soil and pore pressure transducers for the measurement of wave forces acting on the revetment and stresses within the core induced by wave and breaker impact. In addition, the laboratory investigations are accompanied by the development of adequate numerical models to simulate the dynamic processes within dykes for a wide range of applications. In the following report, initial results of a comparison between numerical model studies and collected measurements are presented.

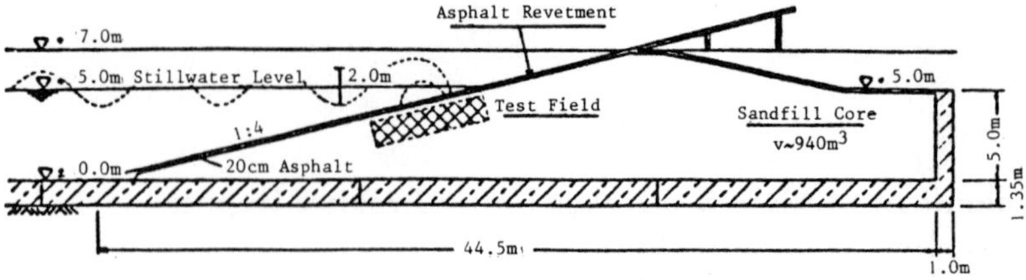

Figure 1: Dyke Model in the Large Wave Channel

From the standpoint of continuum and soil mechanics the behaviour of the dyke structure under dynamic loadings is of high interest because of its complexity as a multi-component continuum (solid, water, air) and its dynamic characteristics of constitutive relationships. In the practice of dyke construction, it is most important to analyse the phenomena of deformation, fluid flow and liquefaction especially in the zones of wave impact in order to achieve an optimization of these structures, because severe damage to natural dykes must be prevented, e.g. Brösskamp (1976).

THEORETICAL MODEL

Considering the phenomena which are relevant to the stability of natural dykes, the load cases and effects illustrated in Fig. 2 were included in the formulation of a mechanical-mathematical model.

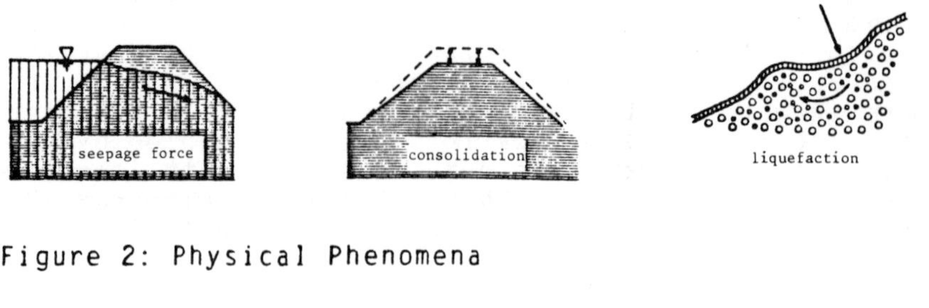

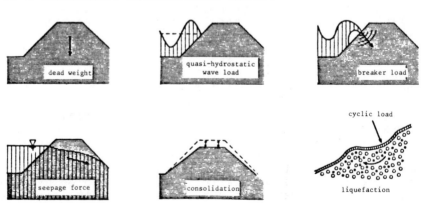

Figure 2: Physical Phenomena

Most important is the internal interaction between the deformation of the porous soil material and the fluid flow through the pore volume under cyclic loading conditions from waves and breakers striking the dyke revetment. According to investigations by Führböter (1985) breaking waves on dyke surfaces under storm conditions release enormous energy and may cause concentrated loads of breaker impact (e.g. in the GWK: 60000 Pa within a small zone from 0.2 m to 0.4 m). For an optimal construction, it is therefore important to analyse the dynamic response of the dyke system and to calculate the stress and pressure distributions within the soil material (e.g. sand or clay) and the pore water. This can adequately be achieved only by a model which couples the relevant equations for the dynamics of solid particles and for the transient seepage flow, and leads to a theory for a multi-component continuum (Figure 3). The model applied herein follows the principles developed by Zienkiewicz et al. (1984) and Hoeborn, Schröder (1981) and neglects as a first approximation the dynamic influence of the airy component.

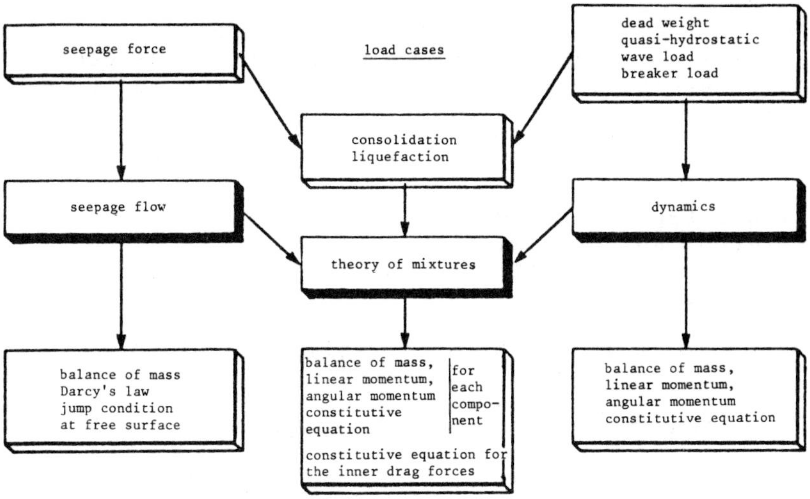

Figure 3: Mechanical Model

The physical behaviour of each component is described by the principles for the conservation of mass and momentum and by constitutive equations concerning the materials properties. In the water-saturated soil the coupling mechanism between the two phases of solid skeleton and water is due to two major factors (Figure 4): (a) the pressure interaction between solid grains and pore water and (b) inner drag forces caused by the flow of water through the porous material.

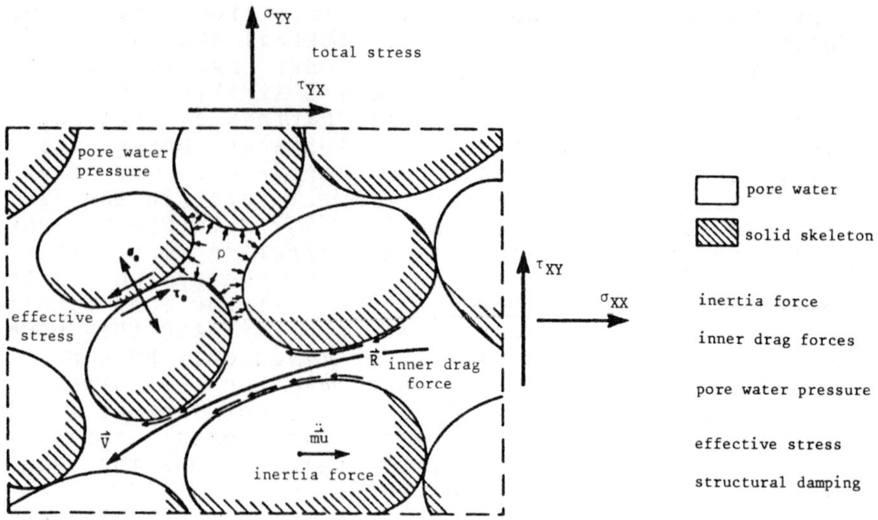

Figure 4: Multi-Component Continuum

Each deformation of the multi-component continuum causes a change of effective stresses between the solid grains and the seepage flow. Especially under cyclic dynamic shock loads the danger of large deformations and liquefaction may occur if pore water pressures attain the total stresses in the continuum.

Using a Lagrangian formulation with respect to the solid skeleton and an Eulerian formulation for the fluid flow the basic equations describing the problem can be specified as follows:

Conservation of momentum for solid and fluid:

$$\operatorname{div} \underset{\sim}{T}' - (1-\varphi)\operatorname{grad} p + \rho_s \vec{f} = \rho_s \ddot{\vec{u}} - \vec{R} \qquad (1)$$

$$-\varphi \operatorname{grad} p + \rho_f \vec{f} = \rho_f \left[\ddot{\vec{u}} + \partial\vec{v}/\partial t + (\operatorname{grad}\vec{v})\vec{v}\right] + \vec{R} \qquad (2)$$

Conservation of mass for fluid:

$$\dot{\rho}_f = -\operatorname{div}(\rho_f \vec{v}) \qquad (3)$$

with the following notations: u displacement of solid, v velocity of fluid, E tensor of effective stresses, p pore pressure, φ porosity, ρ_s density of solid, ρ_f density of fluid, R internal drag force, f body force.

Regarding small volume changes of the solid skeleton and of the fluid a linear relationship with the pore pressure distribution can be assumed using Eqn. (3)

$$\dot{p} * [(1-\varphi)/K_s + \varphi/K_f] = -\varphi \operatorname{div} \vec{v} - \operatorname{tr} \dot{\underset{\sim}{E}} \tag{4}$$

where K_s, K_f denote the bulk moduli of the solid and the fluid resp., and E is defined by :

$$\underset{\sim}{E} = \frac{1}{2}(\operatorname{grad} \vec{u} + \operatorname{grad} \vec{u}^T) \tag{5}$$

as the linearized Cauchy-Green strain tensor.

For a Darcy-type flow of water through the pore volume of the solid skeleton, the internal drag force can be sufficiently approximated by a linear viscous law

$$\vec{R} = D \cdot \vec{v} \tag{6}$$

where D is proportional to the inverse permeability coefficient.

If the non-linear convective term in Eqn. (2) is neglected under the assumption, that its contribution is of minor influence in Darcy Flow, Equations (1,2) and (4,5,6) can be assembled in the following way :

$$\rho_s \ddot{\vec{u}} - D(\dot{\vec{w}} - \dot{\vec{u}}) - \operatorname{div} \underset{\sim}{T}' + (1-\varphi) \operatorname{grad} p = \rho_s \vec{f} \tag{7}$$

$$\rho_f \ddot{\vec{w}} + D(\dot{\vec{w}} - \dot{\vec{u}}) - \varphi \operatorname{grad} p = \rho_f \vec{f} \tag{8}$$

$$p = -Q \operatorname{div} [(1-\varphi)\vec{u} + \varphi \vec{w}] \quad \text{with} \quad 1/Q = (1-\varphi)/K_s + \varphi/K_f \tag{9}$$

where $\dot{\vec{W}} = \dot{\vec{U}} + \vec{V}$ defines mathematically the velocity of fluid particles in a Lagrangian reference system.

In addition, a constitutive law relating effective stresses T' to strains and displacements of the solid material is needed in order to solve these equations. For a non-linear analysis regarding ultimate load conditions, appropriate relationships depending on the type of material, are given by e.g. Desai/Siriwardane (1984), Gudehus (1979), Kolymbas (1978). For the type of dynamic exitation presently investigated in the Large Wave Channel, a restriction to the linear material law :

$$\underset{\sim}{T}' = \lambda \, \mathrm{tr} \, \underset{\sim}{E} \, 1 + 2\mu \, \underset{\sim}{E} \tag{10}$$

seemed to be sufficient. Further modifications will be necessary in future when the breaker impact is increased and laboratory test are performed destroying the dyke model.

NUMERICAL MODEL

The elimination of effective stresses T' and pressure p from Eqn. (7,8) by use of the constitutive equations (9, 10) leads to the formulation of a deformation model, where the only unknowns are the displacements u, w and their time derivatives. At present, the dyke problem is analysed by a two-dimensional plane strain model representing a cross-section of the dyke. For its discretization, nine-node finite elements of the Lagrangian type are used with a bi-quadratic spatial approximation :

$$\vec{u} = \underline{N}(x,y,z)\,\underline{U}(t) \quad , \quad \vec{w} = \underline{N}(x,y,z)\,\underline{W}(t) \tag{11}$$

of the displacement field. Using the standard Ritz-Galerkin procedure of minimizing weighted residuals, the finite element formulation finally leads to the following matrix equation :

$$\begin{bmatrix} \underline{M}_u & 0 \\ 0 & \underline{M}_w \end{bmatrix} \cdot \begin{bmatrix} \ddot{\underline{U}} \\ \ddot{\underline{W}} \end{bmatrix} + \begin{bmatrix} \underline{C} & -\underline{C} \\ -\underline{C}^t & \underline{C} \end{bmatrix} \cdot \begin{bmatrix} \dot{\underline{U}} \\ \dot{\underline{W}} \end{bmatrix} + \begin{bmatrix} \underline{K}_1 & \underline{K}_2 \\ \underline{K}_2^t & \underline{K}_3 \end{bmatrix} \cdot \begin{bmatrix} \underline{U} \\ \underline{W} \end{bmatrix} = \begin{bmatrix} \underline{R}_u \\ \underline{R}_w \end{bmatrix}$$

$$\underline{M} \cdot \ddot{\underline{X}} + \underline{D} \cdot \dot{\underline{X}} + \underline{K} \cdot \underline{X} = \underline{R} \tag{12}$$

in which system matrices are symmetric. By this relationship, the phenomena of fluid flow and vibration of solid material are mathematically coupled. In addition, structural damping effects are accounted for by use of Rayleigh-damping terms. The solution of the time-dependent problem is obtained by use of Newmarks step-by-step time integration procedure.

For practical applications the constitutive parameters of the numerical model must be determined. Special difficulties arise from the estimation of the damping parameters. Here, the field tests in the Large Wave Channel are used to calibrate the numerical model. For this purpose, an automatic calibration procedure was developed by Meissner/Narten (1984) which is applied to adjust the numerical response of the model to the measured field data.

MEASUREMENTS

Many series of experiments with different characteristics for regular and irregular waves have been performed in the Large Wave Channel. Führböter (1985) has reported about initial results concerning the wave impact on a dyke revetment. In the report herein, one experiment with a wave height of 1,25 m and a period of 4 sec is depicted for the comparison of numerical and experimental results. Fig. 5 illustrates the location of transducers within the dyke test field and a preliminary discretization for the numerical model.

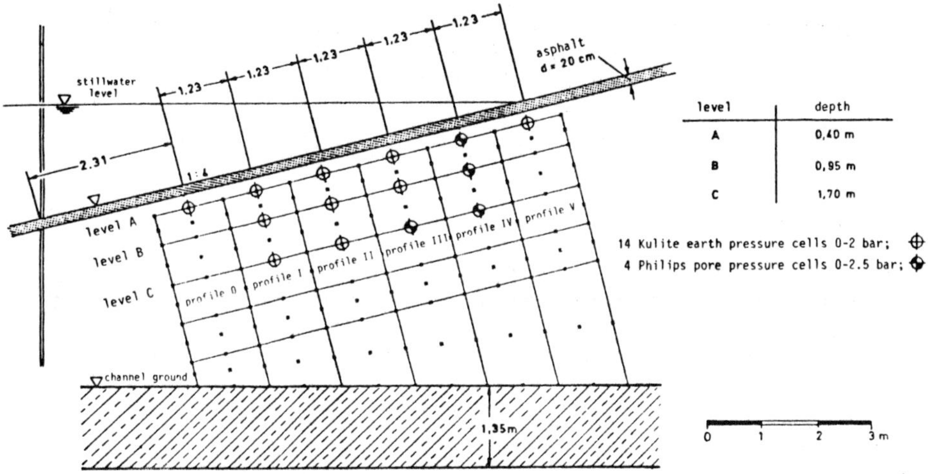

Figure 5: Test Field and Discretization

Fourteen soil pressure transducers are installed at three different levels parallel to the dykes surface and register pressure components in six profiles normal to these levels. The measuring signals are digitized and registered at a rate of 50 Hz. Figure 6 displays two recordings of registered soil pressure at level B, profiles III, IV within the drained dyke. Further details concerning instrumentation and measurements are reported by Richwien/Wehner (1985).

Despite the regularity in wave period, the samples display the random character of induced wave impact. The breaker impact on the revetment causes a rapid change of soil pressure with a high frequency content followed by a moderate change due to the wave motion.

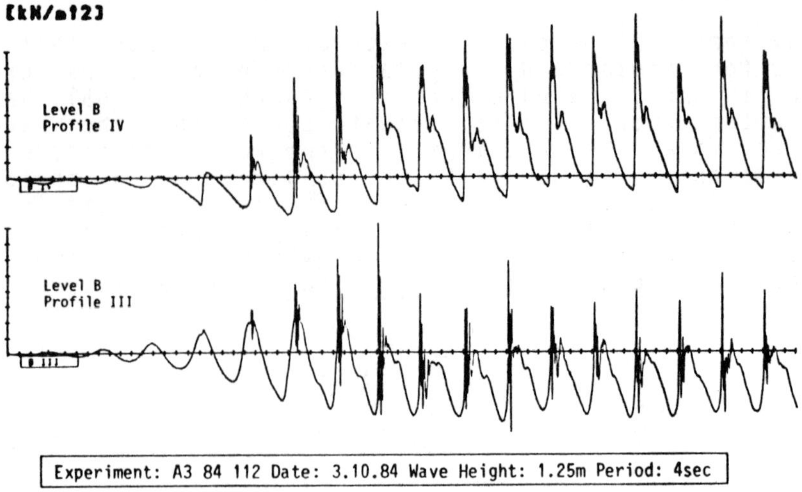

Figure 6: Measured Soil Pressure

The frequency content of the recordings was analysed by a Fourier transformation in order to distinguish between different influencies. Fig. 7 shows the harmonic analysis of the pressure recording at level A, profile III.

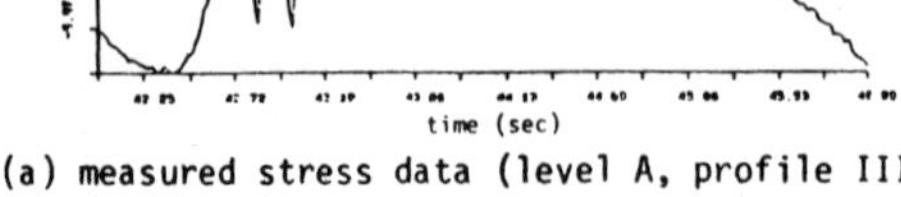

(a) measured stress data (level A, profile III)

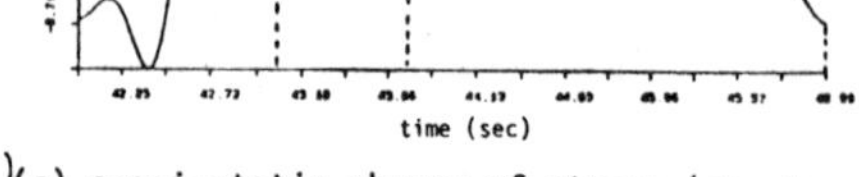

(c) quasi-static change of stress (spectrum I)

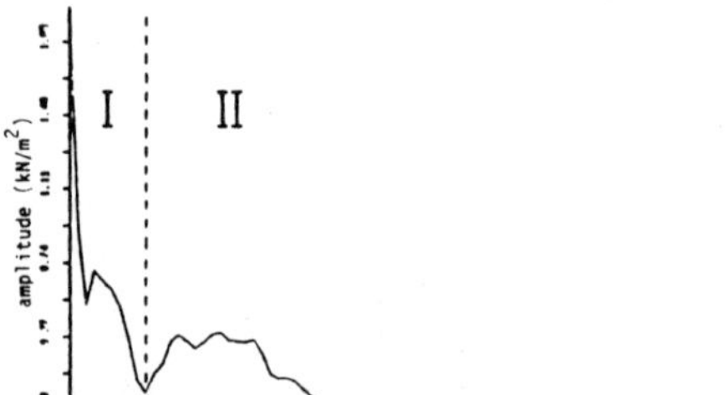

(b) spectrum of amplitudes

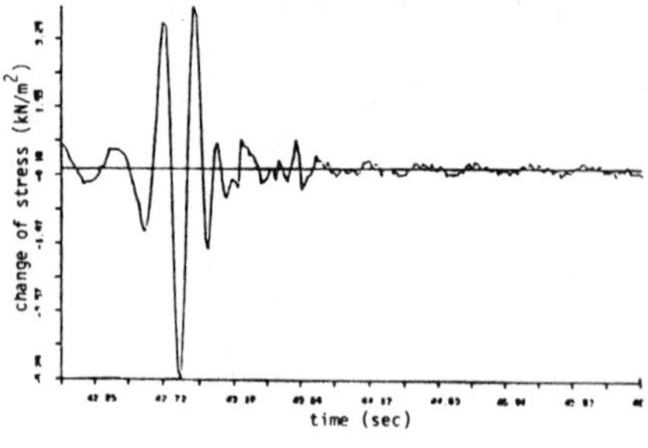

(d) oscillatory change of stress (spectrum II)

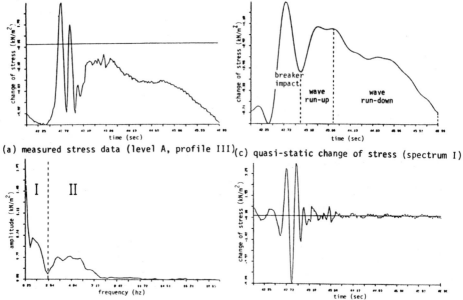

Fig. 7: Harmonic Analysis

The amplitude spectrum (b) can be divided into two parts. The artificial assembly (c) of the low frequency part I (0.25 - 2.5 Hz) displays the influence of breaker impact, wave run-up and wave run-down on the change of stresses. Within the high frequency range II (2.5 - 10 Hz), a strongly damped oscillation of stresses (d) occurs which apparently is initiated by the breaker impulse(0.01-0.06 sec) and can be interpreted as the system (revetment, sandfill core) reaction to the impact. Fig. 8 illustrates the propagation of this oscillatory reaction along level A.

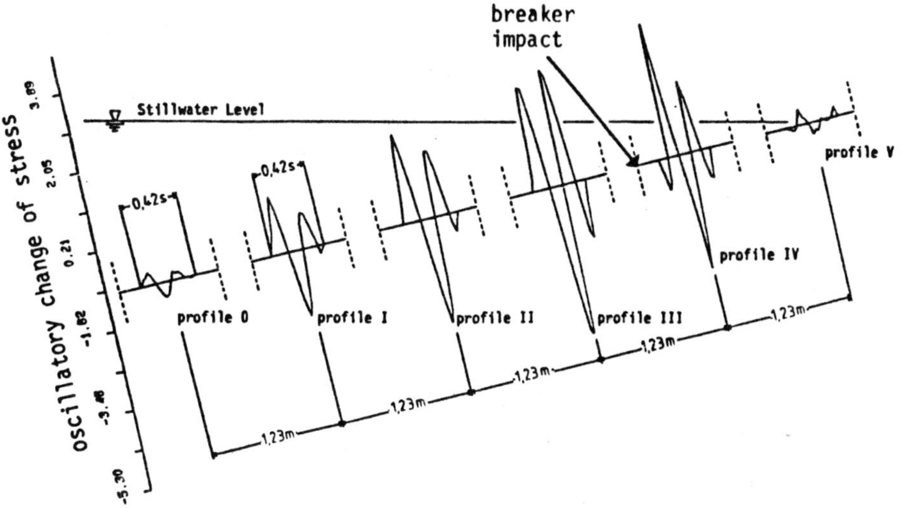

Figure 8: Propagation of Oscillatory Stresses

The linear amplitude decay to the seaward side is moderate, whereas the reaction vanishes rapidly above the still water level towards the landward side of the dyke. Overall the measured soil pressure decreases quite rapidly with respect to depth in the drained dyke. At level C the amplitudes are approximately only 30 % of the values at level A.

NUMERICAL RESULTS

For the numerical simulation of the dynamic response to the breaker impact exitation, a simple model for the dyke test field beneath the revetment was chosen (Fig. 5) as a first approximation. For this model, the field data from measurements at the top level A (Fig. 7) serve as boundary conditions, whereas the data from the remaining transduces are used for comparing calculated and measured reactions. Assuming a linear material behaviour of the drained dyke the constitutive parameters of Eqn. (10) were obtained from soil mechanics laboratory tests (λ = 3370 kN/m2, μ = 3080 kN/m2). For the estimation of damping parameters, laboratory tests were not available. Therefore the amount of Rayleigh damping was determined using the automatic calibration of the numerical model by a comparing calculated and measured stress data. Fig. 9 illustrates the results at two different levels of profile IV.

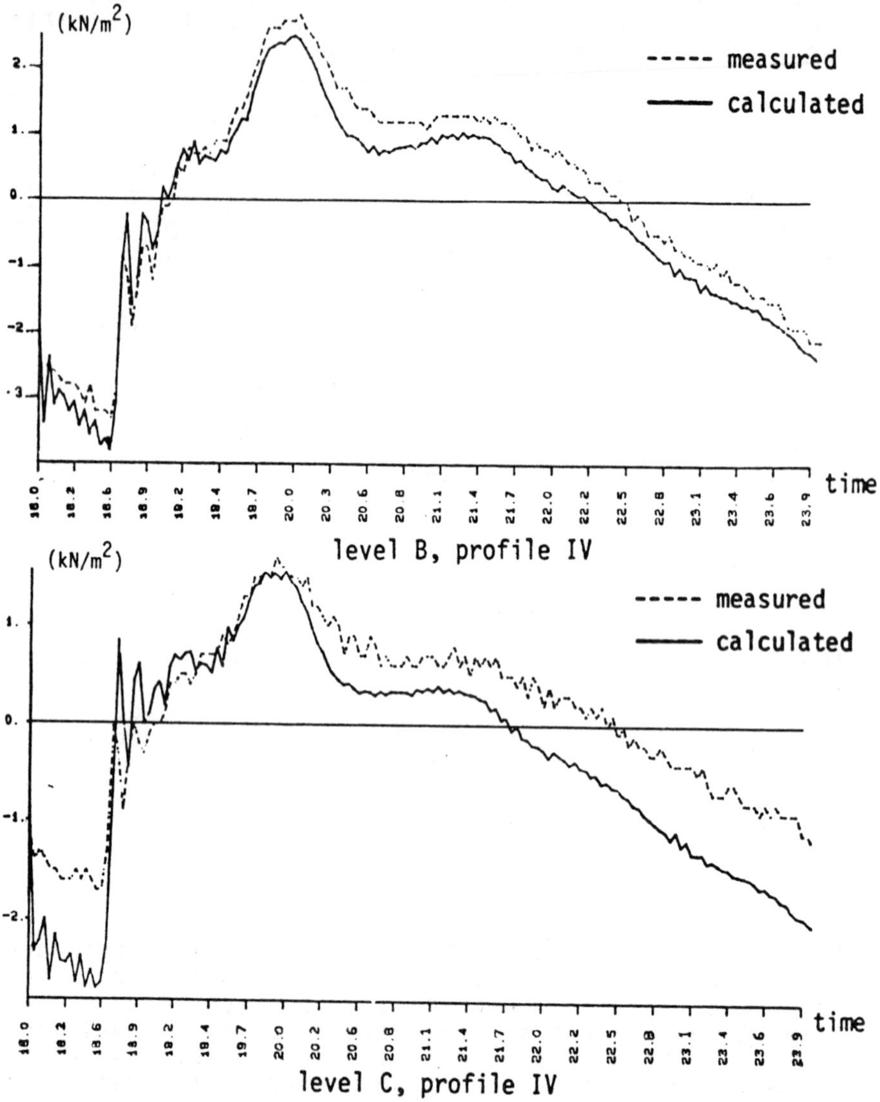

Fig. 9: Comparison of Measured and Calculated Normal Stresses

Despite the simplicity of the model, the quality of agreement is quite satisfactory and validates the reliability of the theoretical approach in general. In order to eliminate the remaining discrepancies, the model has to be extended over the whole cross-section and must include the revetment layer as well as the particular mass of water above it. Special concern has to be focussed on the energy dissipation of the dynamic process in this complex model of the Large Wave Channel.

CONCLUSION

First results of numerical studies compared to measurements from laboratory tests are presented. As the research in the Large Wave Channel proceeds to the simulation of ultimate load processes the numerical model has to be developed further. The non-linear interaction of soil excitation and flow through the saturated and unsaturated medium is of particular interest. The dynamic behaviour of the revetment must be included and the effects of filter layers taken into consideration in order to approach a structural optimization by numerical analysis.

REFERENCES

Brösskamp, K.H. (1976): Seedeichbau in Theorie und Praxis. Vereinigung der Naßbaggerunternehmungen e.V. Hamburg.

Desai, C.S., Siriwardane (1984): Constitutive Laws for Engineering Materials. Prentice Hall.

Führböter, A. (1985): Model and Prototype Tests for Wave Impact and Run-up on an Uniform Slope 1:4. Proceedings Water Wave Research, Hannover.

Gudehus, G. (1979): Stoffgesetze der Bodenmechanik. Grundbautaschenbau.

Hoeborn, D. (1981): Eine Konsolidationstheorie für bindige Böden auf der Grundlage eines Zweikomponentenkontinuums. Dissertation, Wuppertal.

Kolymbas, D. (1978): Ein nichtlineares viskoplastisches Stoffgesetz für Böden., Veröffentlichung Inst. f. Bodenmechanik und Felsmechanik, Heft 74, Karlsruhe.

Meissner, U., Narten, M. (1984): On the Automatic Calibration of Tidal and Transport Models. Finite Element in Water Resources, Burlington, Vermont, USA.

Richwien, W., Wehner, T. (1985): Entwicklung und Aufbau einer Versuchseinrichtung im Großen Wellenkanal, Hannover-Marienwerder, zur Ermittlung seegangserzeugter Beanspruchungen von Böden.
Wasser und Boden, 11.

Zienkiewicz, O.C., Shiomi, T. (1984): Dynamic Behavior of Saturated Porous Media, the Generalized Biot Formulations and its Numerical Solution.
Int. J. Num. Anal. Meth. Geomech., 8.

SECTION 9 FLUID MECHANICS

VI International Conference on Finite Elements in Water Resources, Lisboa, Portugal, June 1986

Comparison Between Finite Element and Finite Difference Simulation of Viscous Flow Through Cylinders

J. Ganoulis, F. Durst
Lehrstuhl für Strömungsmechanik, Universität Erlangen-Nürnberg, Egerlandstr. 13, 8520 Erlangen, Federal Republic of Germany

INTRODUCTION

Numerical integration of the Navier-Stokes equations has become a powerful tool for simulating complex flows. Originally the Finite Difference Method (FDM) (Richtmyer and Morton, 1967; Roache, 1972) and over the past decade the Finite Element Method (FEM) (Connor and Brebbia, 1976; Chung, 1978; Baker, 1983) have been extensively used to predict laminar and turbulent flows for different flow geometries. For incompressible fluid flow, several numerical algorithms of various degree of sophistication have been developed. Some of the numerical calculation procedures are formulated to use as variables the velocities and pressure; examples are in FEM, the penalty function formulation (Hughes, Liu and Brooks, 1979) and in FDM the algorithms of artificial compressibility (Yanenko, 1965; Chorin, 1967) and of the perturbated system equations (Temam, 1969; Ganoulis and Thirriot, 1976). Other, use the stream function and the vorticity together with the FEM (Smith and Brebbia, 1973; Durin and Ganoulis, 1978) or together with FDM (Roache, 1972).

Although a large number of articles on the algorithms for numerical solutions to the Navier-Stokes equations have appeared in the literature, reliability measures of the numerical results are scare and mostly refer to specific cases of rectilinear flow boundaries. For complex situations of flows in domains with curved boundaries, where separation of the main stream and recirculating flow regions are observed, the calibration and validation of the numerical results are highly desirable.

This study has been motivated by the aim to understand the flow of viscoelastic fluids through porous media. Such liquids, as

* On sabbatical leave from School of Technology, Aristotle University of Thessaloniki, Thessaloniki, Greece

solutions of water soluble polymers, exhibit abnormal flow behaviour in the pore scale and their flow modelling can lead to various applications in Petroleum Engineering (Enhanced Oil Recovery). To validate the numerical predictions based on FEM and FDM for a Newtonian and a non-Newtonian flow through porous media, non intrusive experimental investigations, based on laser-Doppler anemometry (LDA), have been designed and are currently under development. By comparing numerical and experimental results, the ultimate goal is to produce a robust, reliable and easy to operate computer package, to simulate flows in domains with curved boundaries. More specifically, the aim of this paper is to compare numerical results obtained independently by using FEM and FDM computer simulation codes. The comparative study is performed for laminar separated flows through cylinders in parallel rows. This is the prototype of a porous medium through which the flow, depending on the Reynolds number, shows various features of complexities. In the sections to follow, the physical problem and two numerical algorithms based on FEM and FDM are described. Numerical results obtained by these models are presented and compared.

THE PHYSICAL PROBLEM

Figure 1 shows the idealized porous medium used in this study. Cylindrical obstacles of constant diameter D are placed in rows parallel to the x_1 axis. The minimum gap e between two cylin-

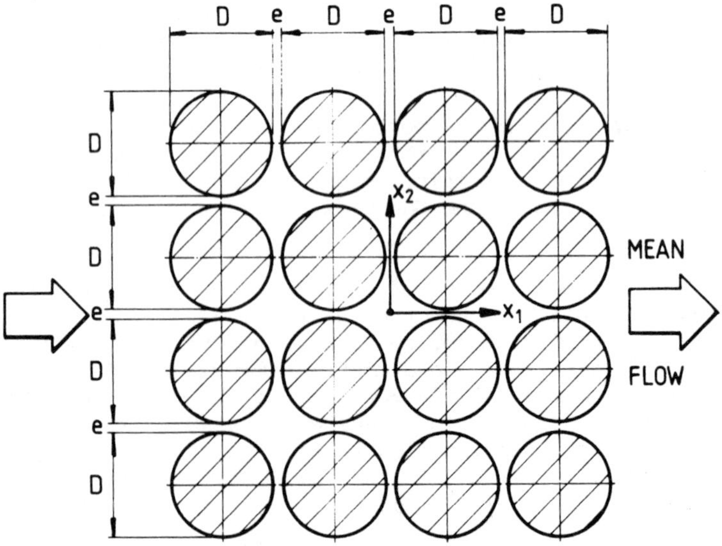

Figure 1. Porous medium composed by cylinders.

ders is the same along the x_1 and x_2 directions. This forms a periodical porous structure in the two-dimensional space, theoretically extending from minus infinity to plus infinity in both x_1 and x_2 directions.

This geometry has been selected because it is relatively simple and preserves the basic properties of a porous medium. Because of the periodical flow conditions along the x_1 and x_2 axes, the mean flow parallel to the x_1 axis can be studied in a finite portion of pores. This is explained in the following section.

The porosity of this medium is a function of the ratio e/D. For the design of the experimental set-up and the measurements using laser-Doppler anemometry the values e = 2 mm and D = 20 mm have been chosen. This gives a porosity equal to 35%. The same geometry has also been used for the numerical simulations.

MATHEMATICAL FORMULATION

Basic Equations

The periodic in space structure of the porous medium leads to a periodic flow along the x_1 and x_2 axes. Therefore, the flow can be studied in the elementary channel shown in Figure 2.

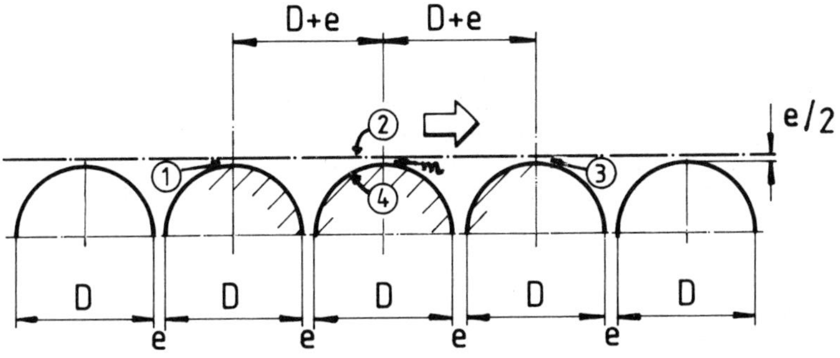

Figure 2. The flow field.

For the unsteady, incompressible viscous flow of a Newtonian fluid, the momentum and mass balance are given by the Navier-Stokes and continuity equations. In the absence of external forces, these equations are written in the following non-dimensional form

$$\frac{\partial u_i}{\partial t} + \frac{\partial}{\partial x_j}(u_i u_j) = -\frac{\partial p}{\partial x_i} + \frac{1}{Re}\nabla^2 u_i \qquad (1)$$

$$\frac{\partial u_j}{\partial x_j} = 0 \qquad (2)$$

where $x_i = x_i'/L$, $u_i' = u_i'/U$, $t = Ut'/L$, $p = p'/\rho U^2$ are respectively dimensionless space coordinates, velocity components, time and pressure. $Re = UL/\nu$ is the Reynolds number, U and L the reference velocity and length and ν the kinematic viscosity of the fluid.

Introducing the dimensionless vorticity $\zeta = L\ /U$ and stream function $\Psi = \Psi'/UL$, the above equations take the following form

$$\frac{\partial \zeta}{\partial t} + u_j \frac{\partial \zeta}{\partial x_j} = \frac{1}{Re} \nabla^2 \zeta \qquad (3)$$

$$\zeta = -\nabla^2 \Psi \qquad (4)$$

Boundary Conditions

Because the flow field is periodic along the x_1 axis (Figure 2), an arbitrary velocity profile imposed at the entry would lead, after some transition length, to a periodic form of the simulated flow. As this requires much computational time, the following technique is adopted in this study. The length of the flow field is taken equal to two wavelengths. At every time step the computed values of u_1 , Ψ and ζ in the mid-cross-section m (Figure 2) are transfered as new boundary conditions to the entry 1 and exit 2 boundaries. This procedure of adjustment of the flow periodicity has proved very efficient.

The following boundary conditions are imposed on the external boundaries of the flow field

a) At the entry 1 and the exit 3 a prescribed velocity profile is imposed, initially arbitrary and afterwards computed according to the periodicity procedure.
b) Along the axes of symmetry (boundary 2 and rectilinear part of boundary 4) the following conditions are implied.

$$u_1 = u_{max},\ u_2 = 0,\ \Psi = \text{const.},\ \zeta = 0$$

c) At the rigid wall (curved part of boundary 4) non slip conditions are imposed in the form

$$u_1 = 0,\ u_2 = 0,\ \Psi = \text{const.}$$

On the wall, the values of ζ are computed in terms of the stream function Ψ following the procedure described by Latinopoulos and Ganoulis (1979).

NUMERICAL SIMULATION

Finite Element Algorithm

In the FEM simulation the vorticity ζ and the stream function Ψ are used, according to the equations (3) and (4). The algorithm follows the standard Galerkin method, as applied for the Navier-Stokes equations by Durin and Ganoulis (1978) and Latinopoulos and Ganoulis (1979). For the problem studied here, a grid generating computer routine has been developed, allowing the division of the flow field into triangular elements. Refinement of the grid near the solid boundaries is possible according to an exponential law. Figure 3 shows an example of finite element grid used in most of the numerical computations reported here. In the portion of the flow field used for the

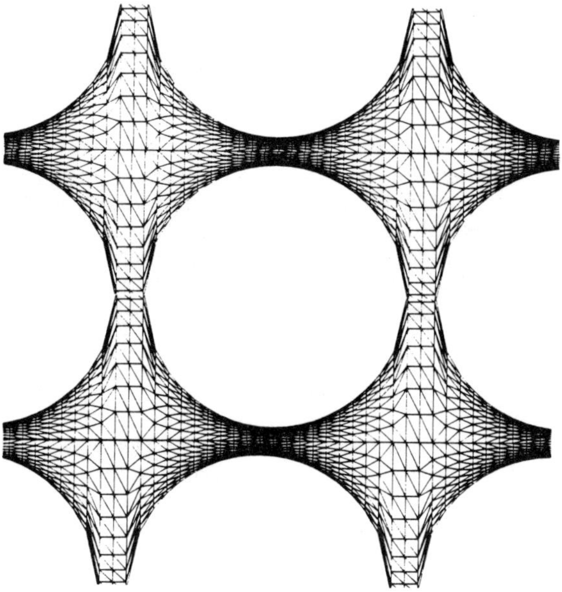

Figure 3. Finite element grid.

numerical simulation (Figure 2) this grid contains 704 triangular elements and 405 computational nodes.

The discrete form of the equations (3) and (4) according to the explicit FEM algorithm, the computational steps and the approximate stability criteria are given by Latinopoulos and Ganoulis (1979). Starting from a steady flow, a transient state flow is obtained by suddenly modifying the fluid viscosity. For every Reynolds number, the new steady flow is obtained as the asymptotic limit of the transient regime, when the time becomes large enough.

Finite Difference Algorithm

The FDM simulation algorithm is based on the computer code PERSEFS (PERturbated System Equations Flow Simulator) (Ganoulis, 1974; Ganoulis and Thirriot, 1976). Mathematically this follows an application on the original equations (1) and (2) of a Cauchy-Kowalevski type perturbation (Temam, 1969). According to this procedure, instead of the velocity components

u_i and the pressure p, the perturbed functions $u_{\varepsilon i}$ and p_ε are introduced. These new variables satisfy the Navier-Stokes equations (1) and the following perturbation form of the continuity equation

$$\varepsilon\frac{\partial p_\varepsilon}{\partial t} + \frac{\partial u_{\varepsilon j}}{\partial x_j} = 0 \qquad (5)$$

where ε is a positive very small perturbation parameter, very close to zero. Numerically, an asymptotic solution can be reached at every time step, so that the first term in equation (5) tends to zero and the incompressibility condition (2) is satisfied.

For the numerical integration of the perturbed system of equations the algorithm follows a fractional step computation of the velocities and pressure over a staggered grid. The discrete form of the equations, the treatment of the boundary conditions, the stability criteria, the optimum selection of the perturbation parameter ε and examples of computation using the code PERSEFS can be found in Ganoulis (1974) and Ganoulis and Thirriot (1976).

NUMERICAL RESULTS AND DISCUSSION

For the definition of the Reynolds number, the mean velocity in the constricted section and the mean width of the channel (12 mm) have been used. Stable numerical computations have been run on a CDC CYBER 173 computer for Reynolds number between 1 and 400. Laboratory experiments using LDA have been performed for Re = 66, 203, 340, 584 and the obtained results are being presently analysed.

Using the FEM comupter code, the stream function, velocity and vorticity distributions could be obtained directly. Figure 4 shows an example of velocity vector distribution, for steady flow at Re = 203.

A separation and two large laminar eddies are observed behind every cylinder. Close to the symmetry line two other eddies of very small intensity are developed. As shown in Figure 5, separation starts from low Reynolds numbers (Re $\simeq$ 10). The presented streamlines have been computed using the PERSEFS code based on FDM. The grid size has taken as $\Delta x = \Delta y = 1/24$ (0.5 mm). Previous experience (Ganoulis, 1974) has indicated that for this size, grid independent numerical solutions can be obtained. By the FDM, a step like polygonal line is used to approximate the boundary form.

Figure 6 shows the capability of PERSEFS code to compute a non steady flow, which follows a sudden variation of the Reynolds number. Two eddies appear in the diverging section of the flow and their intensity grows, till a steady flow is established.

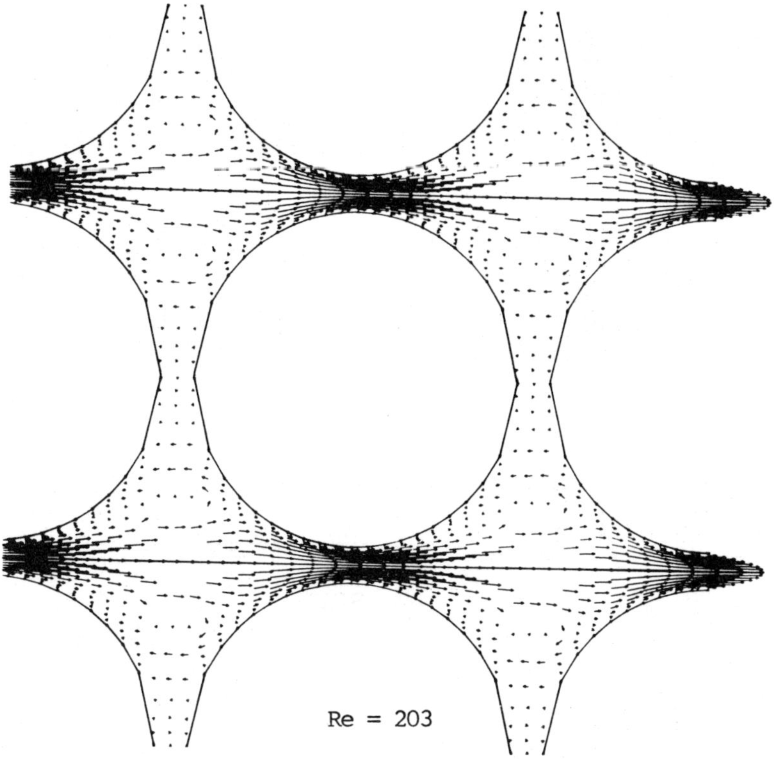

Figure 4. Velocity vector distribution computed by FEM.

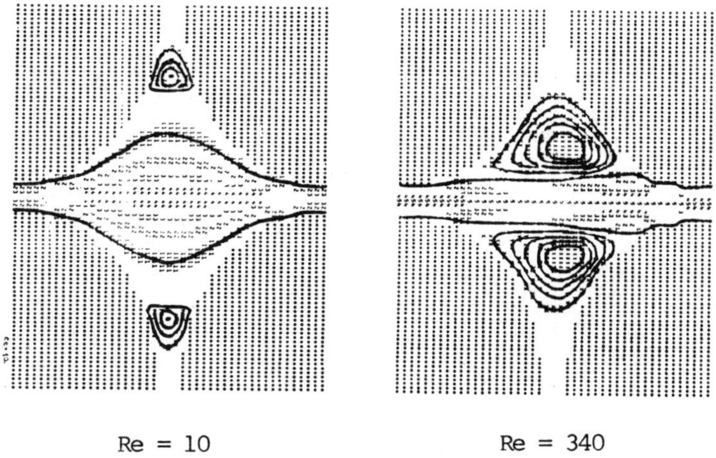

Figure 5. Streamlines computed by FDM. Steady flow, Re = 10(a) and 340(b).

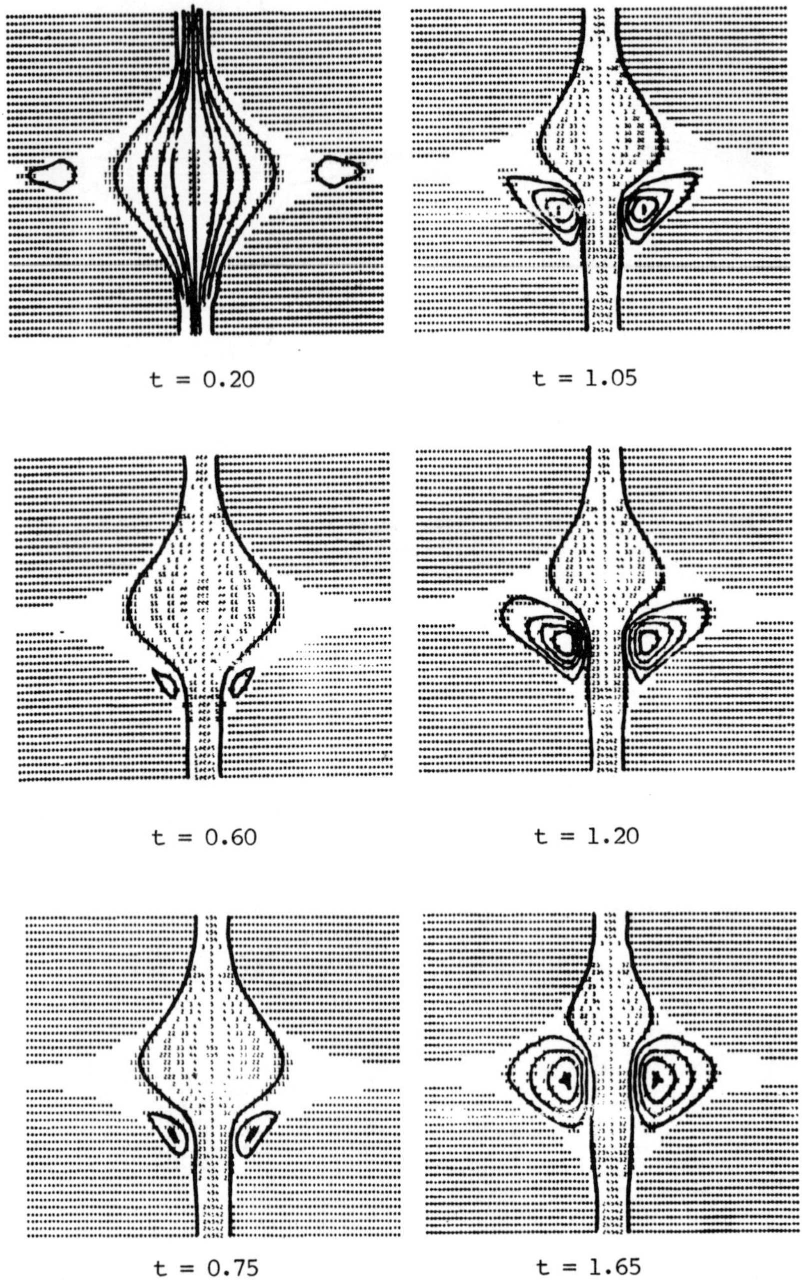

Figure 6. Streamlines in unsteady flow computed by FDM. Re = 400.

Figure 7 shows a comparison between the u_1 velocity profiles in non-dimensional form, computed at various cross-sections of the pores by the FEM and FDM codes. The mean velocity in the mean-width opening is taken as the reference velocity. The consistancy and agreement of the obtained results is generally good.

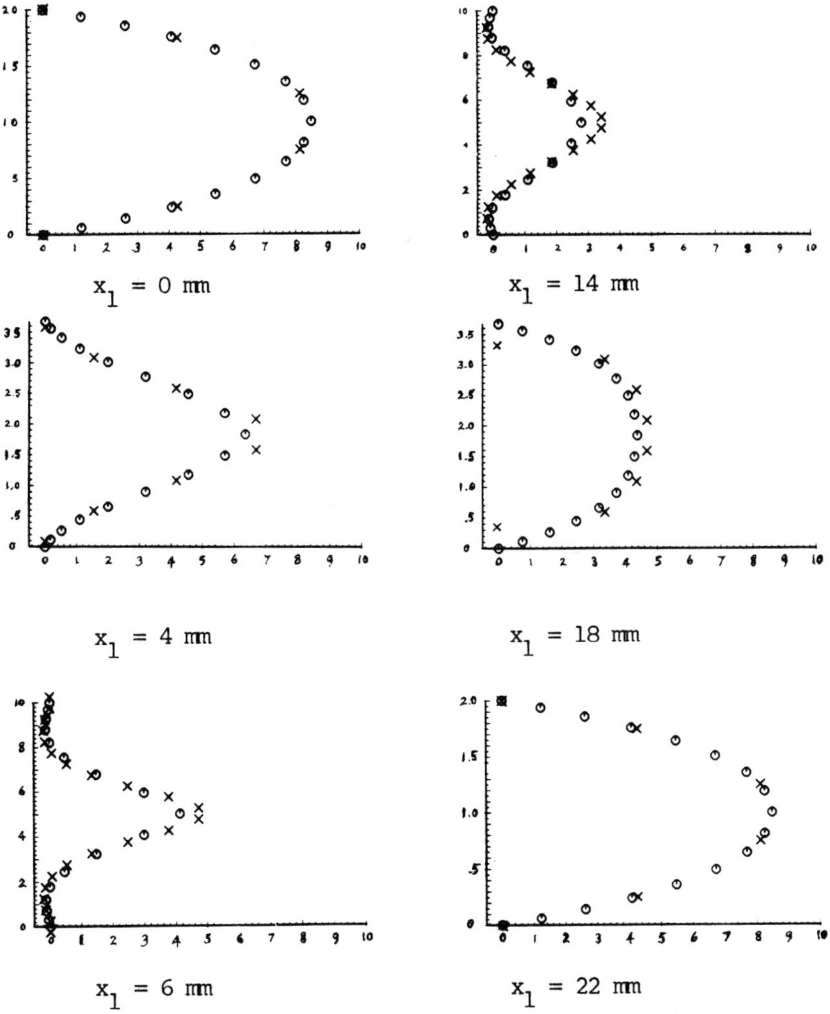

Figure 7. Comparison between the u_1 velocity distributions computed by FEM(0) and FDM(X). Steady flow, Re = 203.

Considering the above presented results together with other computations and the preliminary LDA measurements, the following conclusions can be drawn:

a) The FEM and FDM computer simulation codes, used in this work, led to compareable numerical solutions.
b) Further inspection of the output and preliminary comparisons with the LDA measurements indicated that the FEM simulation comes closer to the experimental data. This can be explained by the fact that a better description of the curved boundaries is incorporated in the FEM, while a rough zero-order approximation of the geometry of the boundaries is used in the FDM.
c) As a counterpart, more computational effort to generate the grid and more computer time is needed for the FEM simulation. As an indication, 1.055 s computer time is necessary per time step on CYBER 173 computer for the FEM computation. This is 30% less using the PERSEFS/FDM computer code.

Further confrontation between the FEM, FDM simulations and LDA measurements will allow to incorporate the more attractive features of the two methods in a reliable computer simulation package.

ACKNOWLEDGEMENTS

The writers are grateful to the Alexander-von-Humboldt Foundation for the support provided for this research.

REFERENCES

Baker, A.J. (1983) Finite Element Computational Fluid Mechanics, McGraw-Hill, New York.
Chorin, A.J. (1976) A numerical method for solving incompressible viscous problems, J. Computational Phys., 2.
Chung, T.J. (1978) Finite Element Analysis in Fluid Dynamics, McGraw-Hill, New York.
Connor, J.J. and Brebbia, C.A. (1976) Finite Element Techniques for Fluid Flow, Newnes-Butterworths, London.
Durin, M. and Ganoulis, J. (1978) Stresses in oscillatory converging and diverging flow by finite element simulations, Proceedings 2nd ICFEM, 3.85-3.95, Pentech Press, London.
Ganoulis, J.(1974) Thèse d'Etat, Univ. Paul Sabatié, Toulouse.
Ganoulis, J. and Thirriot, C. (1976) Lecture Notes in Physics, 59: 191-196, Springer Verlag, Berlin.
Hughes, T., Liu, W.K. and Brooks, A. (1979) Finite Element Anlalyis of incompressible viscous flows by the penalty function formulation, J. Computational Phys., 30:1-60.
Latinopoulos, P. and Ganoulis, J. (1979) Numerical Simulation of Oscillating Flow Through Idealized Sclerotic Arteries, Comp. Meth. in Appl. Mech. and Eng., 20:270-290.
Richtmyer, R.D. and Morton, K.W. (1967) Difference Methods of Initial-Value Problems, Interscience, New York.
Roache, P.J. (1972) Computational Fluid Dynamics, Hermosa.
Smith, S. and Brebbia, C.A. (1975) Finite Element Solution for Vortex Stress Development, J. Computational Phys. 17, No. 3.
Temam, R. (1969) Arch. Rational Mech. Anal. 32:135, 33:377.
Yanenko, N. (1965) Methode à pas fractionnaires, Novosibirsk.

VI International Conference on Finite Elements in Water Resources, Lisboa, Portugal, June 1986

Wave Forces Induced on Horizontal Floating Structures

A.C. Mendes
Instituto Superior Técnico, Universidade Técnica de Lisboa, Portugal

ABSTRACT

The paper deals with the numerical modelling of waves-structure interaction. An algorithm is developed to calculate the first-order forces that are induced on rigid floating bodies. It deals with horizontal cylinders of any rounded section which oscillate in a three-degree-of-freedom harmonic motion. An integral-equation method is used to resolve the hydrodynamic problem, by writing out a set of Fredholm equations. These equations are then numerically solved by means of a boundary-element approach. Some graphical results are finally presented.

1. INTRODUCTION

A significant improvement has been achieved in the numerical calculation of wave forces induced on floating bodies, since T. F. Ogilvie's work (1963) on the subject. For the past ten years, however, some of the experience gathered on this field has also been exploited in modelling ocean wave-energy devices. The present paper attempts to pursue the same objective, by using a dipole-method to evaluate the first-order hydrodynamic forces that are exerted by regular waves upon rigid floaters. The method is developed to deal with horizontal structures of arbitrary profile which perform a three-degree-of-freedom oscillatory motion, under conveniently imposed linear constraints.

The linearized problem is formulated in section 2.1 in terms of the scattered and radiating potentials. The diffraction and radiation solutions are not completely independent, as has been pointed out by J.N. Newman (1975). Nevertheless, these two contributions will be separately obtained from direct resolution of the necessary equations. The total hydrodynamic forces are then obtained by integrating the global potential along the body surface.

The numerical methods that are commomly used in the study of body-waves interaction were revised by C.C. Mei (1978). In order to resolve our problem we retain an integral-equation method. We refer to the work of P. Guevel (1975), who generalized the source method of W. Frank (1967) to the case of floating sections with non-vertical side walls. Instead of the source operators, however, we shall be handling a distribution of normal dipoles that fulfill the requirement of kinematic equivalence to the floating body. The integral representation of the problem is established on four Fredholm equations of the first kind, which we obtain in section 2.2. A numerical resolution of these equations is then achieved in section 3, by means of a boundary-element approach.

Results that have recently been obtained on a resonant SALTER profile are presented in section 5. We finally draw some general conclusions and outline future work, with a particular emphasis on the study of wave-energy converters of brackwater type.

2. FORMULATION

Let us consider a horizontal cylinder of irregular profile, as shown in fig.1. The body is floating in the surface of a deep fluid and (C) is the contour of the immersed cross-section. The unit vector $\vec{n}$ is normal to the contour and points towards the exterior fluid domain (D). The Cartesian co-ordinates (Oxyz) define an undisturbed surface level (SL) for (y=0). The y-axis is pointing upwards and Oz is parallel to the cylinder's generator. Monochromatic waves of amplitude (a) and period T are generated at $(x=-\infty)$, and travel towards the cylinder along Ox. The floater responds to the incident waves by oscillating in a combination of sway (Ox), heave (Oy) and rolling (Oz) harmonic motions having complex amplitudes (amplitude and phase) a_k (k=1,2,3).

2.1 Governing equations

The formulation of the problem is simplified by a certain number of assumptions. We first assume that the cylinder is infinitely long, so that we shall be concerned with a body element of unit length along Oz. This elementary cylinder is immersed in an ideal and incompressible fluid of infinite depth. The incident waves and body motions have very small amplitudes and a common angular frequency ω. We last assume that the fluid flow is irrotational along (Oxy). Our approach to the problem is therefore two-dimensional and based on the existence of a harmonic velocity-potential: $\vec{V}$ = GRAD $\Phi(z,t)$, z=x+iy being the usual complex co-ordinates.

The potential function Φ is the solution of a boundary-value problem over the Laplace equation, with a linearized condition on the free surface and a condition of regularity at great depths;

$$\Delta\Phi = 0 \ ; \quad \frac{\partial^2\Phi}{\partial t^2} + g\,\frac{\partial\Phi}{\partial y} = 0 \quad (y=0) \ ; \quad \Phi = 0 \quad (y \to -\infty) \tag{2.1}$$

The global potential will be searched in the frequency-domain as a superposition of the incident, diffraction and radiation fields:

$$\Phi = \mathrm{Re}\,\{\phi c^{i\omega t}\}, \quad \phi = \omega L^2 A\,[\phi_I + \phi_D + iA_k\phi_k] \tag{2.2}$$

where L is a typical length of the body; A=a/L is the relative amplitude of the incident waves and $A_k = a_k/a$ are reduced amplitudes of the body elementary motions (k=1,2,3). The incident potential ϕ_I is due to regular waves of unit amplitude

$$\phi_I = -(1/k_o L)\, e^{-ik_o z} \tag{2.3}$$

$k_o = \omega^2/g$ being the wavenumber. ϕ_D associate to the diffraction of the incident waves on the fixed body and ϕ_k are due to radiating waves. These waves are caused by unit-amplitude forced motions of the body in calm water. The four potentials individually satisfy a kinematic boundary condition over the cylinder contour:

$$\left(\frac{\partial\phi_D}{\partial n}\right)_C = -\left(\frac{\partial\phi_I}{\partial n}\right)_C ; \quad \left(\frac{\partial\phi_k}{\partial n}\right)_C = n_k \tag{2.4}$$

which will be respected at the hydrostatic equilibrium position of the floater. Here n_k are the generalized components of the normal along (Oxyz), where n_3 is the z-component of vector $(\vec{r} \wedge \vec{n})$. Finally we assume that ϕ_D results in transmitted and reflected waves and that ϕ_k behave as outgoing waves, according to the radiation conditions at $(x = \pm\infty)$.

2.2 Integral representation

We choose to represent the potential function described in 2.1 by means of a singularity distribution. The superficial distribution is composed of Havelock-Kelvin dipoles, having as an only support the immersed surface of the cylinder. These singularities induce a potential $\Phi(z,t)$ in every point of the exterior fluid domain $(z \in D)$ which satisfies at once the equations (2.1) and the radiation condition. Their pulsating strength will then be appointed by the kinematic boundary conditions (2.4).

The complex amplitude of the double-layer potential can be presented in the integral form:

$$\phi(z) = \int_C \mu(z')\,(C - iD)\,d\ell(z') \tag{2.5}$$

where μ is the complex-valued density of dipoles on each point of the body contour $(z' \in C)$. The integral kernels appearing in equation (2.5) are written as follows

$$C(z,z') = -\frac{1}{2\pi}\,\mathrm{Im}\left\{\frac{e^{i\alpha(z')}}{z-z'} - \frac{e^{-i\alpha(z')}}{z-\bar{z}'} - 2ik_o e^{-i\alpha(z')} J(-ik_o(z-\bar{z}'))\right\}$$

$$D(z,z') = k_o \;\mathrm{Re}\left\{ e^{-i\alpha(z')}\; e^{-ik_o(z-\bar{z}')}\right\} \tag{2.5A}$$

α being the argument of a vector tangent to the contour. $J(\zeta)$, $\zeta = -ik_o(z-\bar{z}')$, is a function which can be obtained from the exponential integral $E_1(\zeta)$ in the following manner:

$$\begin{cases} J(\zeta) = e^{\zeta}\,\{E_1(\zeta) + i\pi\},\ \mathrm{Im}(\zeta) > 0 \\ J(\zeta) = e^{\zeta}\,\{E_1(\zeta) - i\pi\},\ \mathrm{Im}(\zeta) < 0 \end{cases} \tag{2.6}$$

where

$$E_1(\zeta) = -\nu - \log\zeta - \sum_{n=1}^{\infty} (-1)^n \frac{\zeta^n}{n\, n!}, \qquad |\mathrm{Arg}\,\zeta| < \pi \tag{2.7}$$

is the series expansion that has been given for that function in M. Abramowitz and I. Stegun (1965).

To find the exact densities $\mu(z')$ that could generate a potential ϕ respecting all the boundary conditions of the problem, we still have to guarantee the impermeability of the body contour. At this point it seems appropriate to distinguish between the diffraction and radiation dipole-intensities, as we have done with the global potential in equation (2.2)

$$\mu = \omega L^2 A\,[\mu_D + iA_k\,\mu_k] \tag{2.8}$$

Next we obtain the dipole generated potential (2.5) as a solution of the rigid-boundary equations (2.4). If the elementary densities defined above are taken into account, this leads up to:

$$\int_C \mu_D(z')\,(P - iQ)\,L^2\,d\ell(z') = -\,e^{-i[k_o z - \alpha(z)]} \tag{2.9}$$

$$\int_C \mu_k(z')\,(P - iQ)\,L^2\,d\ell(z') = n_k\,, \qquad (k = 1,2,3) \tag{2.10}$$

The kernels (P-iQ) are obtained by calculating the component of the fluid velocity which is normal to the body surface, i.e. by taking the normal derivatives in equations (2.5A);

$$P(z,z') = -\frac{1}{2\pi}\mathrm{Re}\left\{e^{i\alpha(z)}\left[\frac{e^{i\alpha(z')}}{(z-z')^2} - \frac{e^{-i\alpha(z')}}{(z-\bar{z}')^2}\right]\right\} - \frac{k_o}{\pi}\mathrm{Im}\left\{e^{i\alpha(z)}\left[\frac{e^{-i\alpha(z')}}{z-\bar{z}'}\right]\right\}$$

$$-\frac{k_o^2}{\pi}\mathrm{Re}\left\{e^{i\alpha(z)}\left[e^{-i\alpha(z')}J(-ik_o(z-\bar{z}'))\right]\right\} \qquad (2.11)$$

$$Q(z,z') = -k_o^2\,\mathrm{Re}\left\{e^{i\alpha(z)}\left[e^{-i\alpha(z')}e^{-ik_o(z-\bar{z}')}\right]\right\}$$

In the second member of equation (2.9) use has been made of the incident potential that was given in (2.3). As for equations (2.10), it should be noted that n_k is associated to 3 elementary oscillations whose velocities are prescribed in $\cos(\omega t)$: two translatory modes along the x,y-axis (k=1,2) and a rotary mode about Oz (k=3).

The four Fredholm equations (2.9,10) stand for a canonic integral formulation of the global hydrodynamic problem. Their solutions are the elementary dipole-densities μ_D and μ_k (k=1,2,3) which enable us to build the diffraction-radiation field, through equations (2.2,5), and consequently determine the flow-properties that we seek.

3. RESOLUTION

A numerical approach to the problem is now introduced, in order to find the approximate solutions of the integral equations (2.9,10). The discretized problem is resolved for a set of boundary elements.The contour (C) is for that purpose divided into N linear elements S_j(j=1..,N) which are defined by their extremity points Z_j and Z_{j+1}, expressed in reduced co-ordinates (Z=z/L). These contour elements are the support of the dipole singularities, that are distributed there with uniform complex densities μ_{Dj} and μ_{kj}.

3.1 Algebraic systems

The Fredholm equations are hence reduced to four algebraic equations, each of these containing N unknown dipole intensities. To find the numerical values of these densities we have to procure N control points in which we write the kinematic boundary condition. If the opacity of the body is thereby observed at the middle point of every element, $\tau_i=(Z_i + Z_{i+1})/2$, the following linear systems are obtained:

$$\sum_{j=1}^{N}\mu_{Dj}(P_{ij}-iQ_{ij})L = -\{(Z_{i+1}-Z_i)/|Z_{i+1}-Z_i|\}e^{-iK_o\tau_i} \qquad (3.1)$$

$$\sum_{j=1}^{N}\mu_{kj}(P_{ij}-iQ_{ij})L = n_{ki}, \quad (k=1,2,3) \qquad (3.2)$$

valid for (i=1..,N). $K_o=\omega^2L/g$ is a non-dimensional wavenumber, reduced by means of the reference length L. The influence-coefficients $(P_{ij} - iQ_{ij})$ associate to elementary effects in normal velocity, which are induced on each point τ_i by a discrete distribution of dipoles with unit density. These coefficients arise from the integration of the kernels (2.11), as

$$L\,P_{ij} = -\frac{1}{2\pi}\,\mathrm{Re}\left\{\frac{Z_{i+1}-Z_i}{|Z_{i+1}-Z_i|}\left[\frac{Z_{j+1}-Z_j}{(\tau_i-Z_{j+1})(\tau_i-Z_j)} - \frac{\bar{Z}_{j+1}-\bar{Z}_j}{(\tau_i-\bar{Z}_{j+1})(\tau_i-\bar{Z}_j)}\right]\right\}$$

$$-\frac{K_o}{\pi}\,\mathrm{Im}\left\{\frac{Z_{i+1}-Z_i}{|Z_{i+1}-Z_i|}\left[J(-ik_o(\tau_i-\bar{Z}_{j+1})) - J(-iK_o(\tau_i-\bar{Z}_j))\right]\right\} \tag{3.3}$$

$$L\,Q_{ij} = -K_o\ \mathrm{Im}\left\{\frac{Z_{i+1}-Z_i}{|Z_{i+1}-Z_i|}\left[e^{-iK_o(\tau_i-\bar{Z}_{j+1})} - e^{-iK_o(\tau_i-\bar{Z}_j)}\right]\right\}$$

In the body surface, the normal velocity of the fluid equals the component of the body velocity in that direction. For the three elementary modes of unit amplitude (k=1,2,3) we easily obtain:

$$\left\{\begin{array}{l} n_{1i} = \mathrm{Im}\,\{(Z_{i+1} - Z_i)/|Z_{i+1} - Z_i|\} \\ n_{2i} = -\mathrm{Re}\,\{(Z_{i+1} - Z_i)/|Z_{i+1} - Z_i|\} \\ n_{3i} = -0.5\,\{(Z_{i+1}\,\bar{Z}_{i+1} - Z_i\,\bar{Z}_i)/|Z_{i+1} - Z_i|\} \end{array}\right. \tag{3.4}$$

in the second member of equations (3.2).

3.2 Discrete potential

The evaluation of the pressure-field acting on the solid boundaries, requires the knowledge of the velocity potential which is induced within the fluid adjacent to the contour. That potential can be obtained from equation (2.5), as soon as we dispose of the convenient dipole intensities. From this viewpoint a distribution of dipoles is not as advantageous as a Green's distribution of source-dipole singularities, to which any further calculations for that purpose would not be necessary. If we then combine equations (2.3) and (2.5), the global potential that is induced in every point (τ_i) of the fluid is:

$$\phi(\tau_i) = -\,\omega L^2 A\left\{(1/K_o)\,e^{-iK_o\tau_i} - \sum_{j=1}^{N}\mu_j(C_{ij} - iD_{ij})\right\} \tag{3.5}$$

where $\mu_j = \mu_{Dj} + iA_k\mu_{kj}$ are the total dipole intensities along the discrete contour. The potential influence-coefficients $(C_{ij} - iD_{ij})$ are calculated from direct integration of equations (2.5A). They are found to be

$$C_{ij} = \frac{1}{2\pi}\,\mathrm{Im}\left\{\log\left(\frac{\tau_i - Z_{j+1}}{\tau_i - Z_j}\right) + \log\left(\frac{\tau_i - \bar{Z}_{j+1}}{\tau_i - \bar{Z}_j}\right)\right\}$$

$$+ \frac{1}{\pi}\,\mathrm{Im}\left\{J(-iK_o(\tau_i-\bar{Z}_{j+1})) - J(-iK_o(\tau_i-\bar{Z}_j))\right\} \qquad (3.5A)$$

$$D_{ij} = \mathrm{Im}\left\{e^{-iK_o(\tau_i-\bar{Z}_{j+1})} - e^{-iK_o(\tau_i-\bar{Z}_j)}\right\}$$

$\log\{(\tau_i-Z_{i+1})/(\tau_i-Z_i)\}=-i\pi$, whenever τ_i belongs to (C) and (i=j).

At this stage the diffraction-radiation problem can be considered as being solved. To manipulate the numerical algorithm it is only necessary to describe the shape of a specific body section, with an adequate number of discrete elements.

4. HYDRODYNAMIC FORCES

In order to calculate the wave forces that are induced on the immersed structure, an integration of the fluid dynamic pressure is performed along the body wet surface. If we call this pressure P(z), defined at a current point of the body contour ($z \in C$), we have:

$$F_p = -\int_C P(z)\, n_p\, d\ell, \quad (P=1,2,3) \qquad (4.1)$$

These are the x,y-components of the resulting force (p=1,2) and its moment (p=3) about the origin of (Oxy). We are going to confine the following analysis to the evaluation of first-order hydrodynamic efforts.

4.1 Total force and moment

The pressure-field that exists within the fluid is directly appointed by Lagrange equation. In linear theory, equation (4.1) is simply reduced to the integration of a time-derivative of the velocity potential. For the time-harmonic function ϕ,

$$F_p = \mathrm{Re}\{\mathcal{F}_p\, e^{i\omega t}\}, \qquad \mathcal{F}_p = i\,(\omega\rho)\int_C \phi(z)\, n_p\, d\ell \qquad (4.2)$$

where $\mathcal{F}_p$ are the generalized complex-amplitudes (amplitude and phase) of the force components. If we take the global potential ϕ from equation (2.2), these frequency-dependent amplitudes can still be written as:

$$\mathcal{F}_p = i\,(\omega^2\rho L^2)\, A \int_C [(\phi_I + \phi_D) + iA_k\,\phi_k]\, n_p\, d\ell \tag{4.3}$$

Here $\mathcal{F}_3 = \mathcal{M}_z/L$, $\mathcal{M}_z$ being the moment amplitude. In equation (4.3) it is clear that the total hydrodynamic forces held by the structure result from two different contributions. The forces due to the scattered waves $(\phi_I + \phi_D)$ are known as "exciting forces", and the ones caused by the forced waves $(A_k\phi_k)$ will be called "radiation forces".

4.2 Numerical equations

The hydrodynamic forces and moment are now determined, in the case of the discretized contour that has been considered in section 3. A numerical integration of (4.3) and the use of the discrete potential (3.5), allow the generalized forces to be presented as in

$$\mathcal{F}_p = -i\,(\omega^2\rho L^3)\, A \sum_{i=1}^{N} \left\{ (1/K_o)\, e^{-iK_o\tau_i} - \sum_{j=1}^{N} \mu_j (C_{ij} - iD_{ij}) \right\} \chi_{ip} \tag{4.4}$$

The dipole intensities $\mu_j = \mu_{Dj} + iA_k\mu_{kj}$ are composed of four elementary densities that were previously obtained from the algebraic systems (3.1,2). As for the parameters $\chi_{ip} = n_p(\tau_i)d\ell/L$,

$$\begin{cases} \chi_{i1} = \mathrm{Im}\{Z_{i+1} - Z_i\} \\ \chi_{i2} = -\mathrm{Re}\{Z_{i+1} - Z_i\} \\ \chi_{i3} = -0.5\{Z_{i+1}\bar{Z}_{i+1} - Z_i\bar{Z}_i\} \end{cases} \tag{4.4A}$$

they only depend on the geometrical description of the body profile.

Equations (4.4) suggest a systematic study of the wave forces on a given geometry, for a wide range of wavenumbers. The numerical procedure consists of the calculation of the exciting forces and hydrodynamic coefficients, followed by the resolution of a complete set of equations for the body motion. It naturally requires information about the inertia, damping and restoring characteristics of the system. The amplitudes of oscillation of the floater are finally used to build the global diffraction-radiation potential, from which the total hydrodynamic forces are immediately obtained.

5. RESULTS

In this section we present some results that have been obtained on a floater of a two-dimensional configuration. These results illustrate the use of the numerical model to calculate the hydrodynamic forces which are induced on the structure, per unit length along Oz, by incident waves of unit amplitude and normalized frequency $K_o = \omega^2 T/g$. The floater draft is the characteristic length. We work with an average of N=50 input points. The curves presented in figs.2 and 3, refer to the total wave-forces induced on a SALTER profile that operates with one-degree-of-freedom. The irregular-frequency effects were ignored here. Fig. 2 shows the amplitudes of the horizontal $F_x=(\omega^2\rho L^3)^{-1}\,|\mathcal{F}_1|$ and vertical $F_y=(\omega^2\rho L^3)^{-1}\,|\mathcal{F}_2|$ components of the total hydrodynamic force, and its moment $M_z=(\omega^2\rho L^3)^{-1}\,|\mathcal{F}_3|$ about the origin of (Oxy). These results are valid for a free-rolling section having $B_o/T=2.5$ and $\beta=41.8^o$. The origin (O) is the centre of rotation. The homogeneous floater has its natural frequency at $\omega_o=(1.5g/T)^{0.5}$. The vertical pressure-forces and the torsional moment become the main parameters, in the design of a structure working with incident waves of wavelength bigger than 12 times the floater draft. The force induced by small waves of 3.7 s (a=1) in a device of unit draft, can easily reach 2 ton/m of frontage. If we now constrain the body to oscillate in resonance with incident waves of wavenumber $K_o=1$, by means of some inertial-restoring arrangement, the hydrodynamic efforts become as it is shown in fig. 3. These curves are valid in the situation where the device is absorbing wave-energy. The floater is completely tuned for a frequency $\omega=(g/T)^{0.5}$ with the help of a linear damper. The mechanical damping-constant equals the hydrodynamic damping coefficient for the rolling motion of the floater, at $K_o=1$. These are merely the conditions for maximum wave-power absorption. The forces induced on a device equipped with a floater working among incident waves of wavelength between 4 and 25 times its draft, now experience a considerable reduction. This is precisely the frequency-bandwidth in which the device presents the highest efficiency in absorbing the incident wave-energy.

CONCLUSIONS

The algorithm that we have developed can provide useful information for the design of oceanic structures which operate in deep beam-sea. The model is particularly helpful to the study of wave-energy converters of oscillating-body type. It has shown that significant efforts can be induced on the shaft of a stationary device, as a result of dynamic interactions with long incident waves. A dipole-method was used to solve the hydrodynamic problem. The diffraction and radiation solutions were obtained independently; we hope that in this manner it should be possible to reproduce the discrete pressure-charge acting on the body surface. The "irregular-frequencies" phenomena is here an important limitation for certain wavenumbers. It is not easy to twist this problem around, because we don't know the double-layer potential which is induced in the interior of the body in the rolling mode. Dealing with simpler Green functions is one obvious advantage of the method. However, the regeneration of the potential adjacent to the body is an additional difficulty. The matrix of the velocity-coefficients doesn't show a dominant diagonal and therefore, a reenforcement of the number of discrete elements is necessary in order to obtain results having the desirable accuracy. As we have solved a linearized problem in the frequency-domain, the model is unable to account for the existing non-linearities; it is thereby valid within applications involving slow motions of short amplitude. In future research we wish to extend the model to simulate oscillating thin plates and oscillating water-column devices. The method is particularly suitable in these situations, although a proper study of the segments arriving on the free surface and at immersed edges is still needed.

ACKNOWLEDGMENTS

The author is indebted to Professor Pierre Guevel for his kind support and valuable guidance on the subject, during the author´s stay at the Naval Hydrodynamics Laboratory of "Ecole Nationale Supérieure de Mécanique" in Nantes, France. The stay was made possible by a scholarship received from the French Government.

REFERENCES

Abramowitz, M. and Stegun, I. (1965). Handbook of mathematical functions. Dover Publications Inc., New York.

Frank, W. (1967). Oscillations of cylinders in or below the free surface of deep fluids. NSRDC, Rep. 2375, Washington D.C.

Guevel, P. and Kobus, J.M. (1975). Flotteurs cylindriques horizontaux soumis à des oscillations forcées de très faibles amplitudes. Bull. Ass. Tech. Marit. et Aéronaut., 75, 183-204.

Mei, C.C.(1978). Numerical methods in water-wave diffraction and radiation. Ann. Rev. Fluid Mech., 10, 393-416.

Mendes, A.C. (1983). Hydrodynamic forces on thin barriers immersed in deep water among surface waves (in Portuguese). Proc. 3rd. Portuguese Congress on Theoretical and Applied Mechanics, Lisbon.

Newman, J.N.(1975). Interaction of waves with two-dimensional obstacles: a relation between the radiation and scattering problems. J. Fluid Mech., 71, 273-282.

Ogilvie, T.F. (1963). First and second-order forces on a cylinder submerged under a free surface. J. Fluid Mech., 16, 451-472.

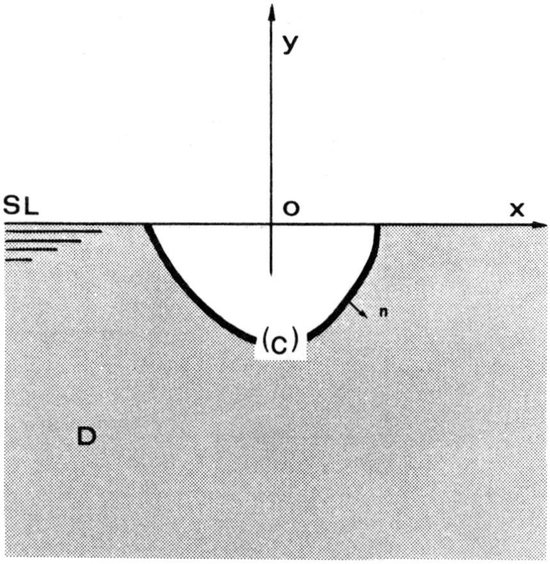

Figure 1. Horizontal floating structure of arbitrary profile.

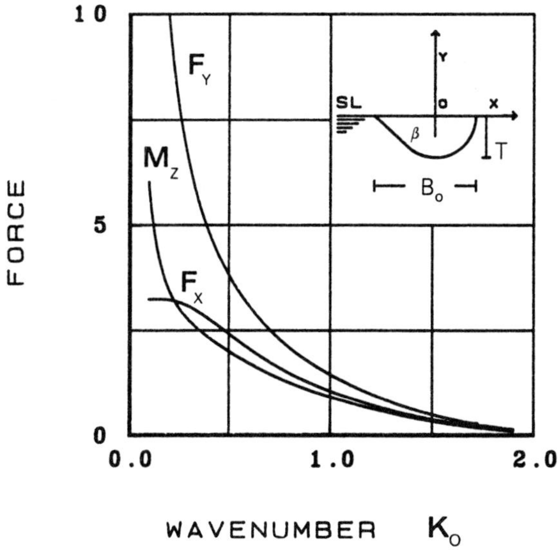

Figure 2. Total hydrodynamic efforts induced on a free-rolling SALTER profile ($B_o/T = 2.5$ and $\beta = 41.8^o$) for wave-numbers $K_o = \omega^2 T/g$.

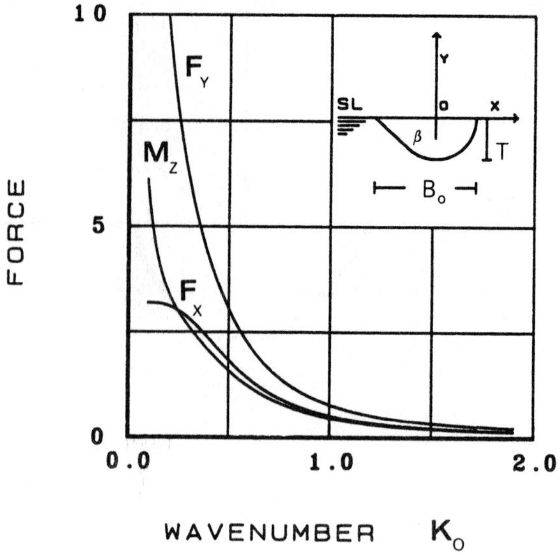

Figure 3. Total hydrodynamic efforts induced on a SALTER profile ($B_o/T = 2.5$ and $\beta = 41.8^o$) in constrained rolling, tuned for a wavenumber $K_o = \omega^2 T/g = 1$.

VI International Conference on Finite Elements in Water Resources, Lisboa, Portugal, June 1986

Modelling of Flow under Sluice Gates with FEM

F.L. Heng, E. Mitsoulis
Department of Chemical Engineering, University of Ottawa, Ottawa, Ontario, Canada K1N 9B4
P. Prinos
Department of Civil Engineering, University of Ottawa, Ottawa, Ontario, Canada L1N 9B4

INTRODUCTION

The regulation of flows in hydraulic structures is usually achieved by the use of sluice gates. Design of such devices is based on the appropriate analysis of gravity flow under a sluice gate with particular emphasis on the determination of the upstream and downstream free-surface profiles and the prediction of discharge for a given total head and gate opening.

The analysis of this problem has been undertaken by a number of investigators which have opted for several analytical and/or numerical methods. A recent review of these efforts can be found in Masliyah et al. (1985). The ever-increasing use of computers for engineering problems has made the numerical analysis a strong favorite. Both finite difference methods (FDM) and finite element methods (FEM) have been used for the analysis of flows under sluice gates. The advantages of the finite element method for classes of problems with complex geometries and the presence of free surfaces have been discussed in standard textbooks (Zienkiewicz, 1977; Huebner and Thornton, 1982).

Finite elements for the analysis of gravity flows under sluice gates have been used so far by McCorquodale and Li (1971), Chan et al. (1973), Isaacs (1977), Diersch et al. (1977). Although the heart of the finite element analysis in each of these efforts remains the solution of a Laplace equation either for the stream function ψ or the potential function ϕ, different numerical algorithms have been applied. This stems from the variety that exists in choosing the boundary conditions in conjunction with the presence of the unknown free surfaces and flow rate.

In the present paper, we re-examine the problem of flow under sluice gates using a different iterative technique and also specifying natural boundary conditions on the downstream free surface. The results show good agreement with past numerical simulations and experimental data available in the literature for cases of vertical and several radial sluice gates.

MATHEMATICAL MODELING AND BOUNDARY CONDITIONS

The flow under sluice gates is assumed to be steady, two-dimensional, incompressible and irrotational. The governing flow equation is a Laplace equation for the stream function ψ in cartesian coordinates (x,y):

$$\frac{\partial^2\psi}{\partial x^2} + \frac{\partial^2\psi}{\partial y^2} = 0 \qquad (1)$$

The above equation is solved in the domain shown in Fig. 1 along with a set of boundary conditions. These can be either essential (Dirichlet) or natural (Neumann) type boundary conditions. The essential boundary conditions require specification of ψ, while the natural boundary conditions require specification of $\frac{\partial\psi}{\partial n}$, the normal to the boundary derivative of ψ. Along the upstream and downstream free surfaces EF and CD, respectively, the additional equation applies:

$$\frac{V_s^2}{2g} + h = H \qquad (2)$$

where V_s is the magnitude of the velocity vector, g is the gravity constant and h is the local elevation.

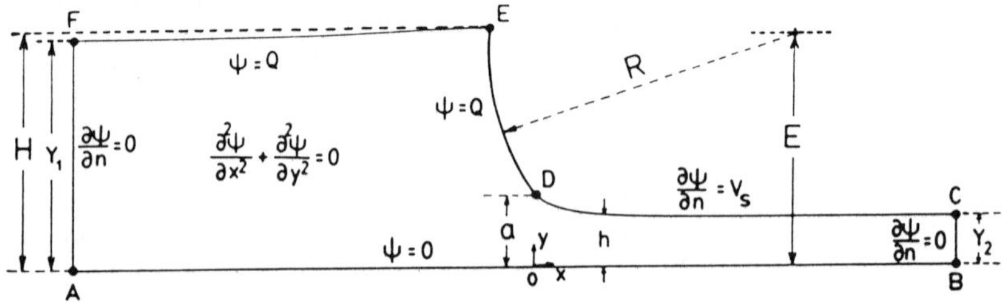

Figure 1. Notation and boundary conditions for flow analysis under sluice gates.

The boundary conditions that have been applied in this study are:

On AB : $\psi = 0$ (3)

On BC : $\frac{\partial\psi}{\partial n} = 0$ (4)

On CD (free surface) : $\frac{\partial\psi}{\partial n} = V_s = \sqrt{2g(H-h)}$ (5)

On DE (sluice gate) : $\psi = Q$ (6)

On EF (free surface) : $\psi = Q$ (7)

On FA : $\dfrac{\partial \psi}{\partial n} = 0$ (8)

NUMERICAL ALGORITHM

For a given gate geometry, including the gate opening, a, and the available total head H, we mush find the flow rate Q and the upstream elevation Y_1 and downstream elevation Y_2 by locating the free surfaces. The numerical procedure we have adopted is somewhat similar to the one used by Isaacs (1977) and it can be summarized by the following steps:

1. Assume a discharge Q.
2. Locate point C by finding the height Y_2 of far downstream surface according to:
$$\frac{Q^2}{2gY_2^{\,2}} + Y_2 = H \tag{9}$$
3. Assume arbitrary downstream free surface from point C to point D.
4. Upstream free surface FE is taken as horizontal for 1st iteration.
5. Assign proper boundary conditions (Equations 3-8).
6. Solve the Laplace Equation (1) for the stream function ψ.
7. Calculate $v_x = \dfrac{\partial \psi}{\partial y}$ and $v_y = -\dfrac{\partial \psi}{\partial x}$.
8. Calculate pressure, $p = H - \dfrac{V_s^2}{2g} - h$, on CDEF.
9. Update the upstream free surface FE by:
$$h = H - \frac{V_s^2}{2g} \tag{10}$$
and the downstream free surface DC by:
$$\delta H = \frac{Q-\psi}{\frac{\partial \psi}{\partial y}} = \frac{Q-\psi}{v_x} \tag{11}$$
10. If the free surface does not converge, repeat steps 5 through 9.

Usually, 6-10 iterations were required to obtain a converged free surface with relative changes less than 10^{-4} of Y_2, depending upon the initial guess and the gate geometry (radial gates gave better convergence). Once the free surfaces have converged, the numerical value of V_s at point D is checked against the fixed value of V_D

$$V_D = \sqrt{2g(H-a)} \tag{12}$$

which is dictated by the energy level at point D. In general, the calculated value V_{SD} differs from V_D, and a new discharge Q is assumed to bring the calculated energy level at D closer to the specified value. A Newton-Raphson method for Q is therefore employed, that consists of the following steps:

- For the initially assumed discharge Q_1, find $f_1 = (V_{SF}-V_D)_1$.
- Alter the discharge by a small amount δQ to a new value $Q_2 = Q_1 + \delta Q$, and find $f_2 = (V_{SD} - V_D)_2$.
- Use Q_1 and Q_2 to find an improved value for Q according to Newton's method:

$$Q = Q_1 - \frac{f_1}{f_1'} \tag{13}$$

where

$$f_1' = \frac{f_2 - f_1}{Q_2 - Q_1} \tag{14}$$

With this procedure, it was found that 3 to 5 finite element analyses of the internal flow region were sufficient to obtain convergence for the discharge Q that satisfied the energy level at D (Equation 12).

FINITE ELEMENT MODEL

The present simulations have been carried out with a standard 6-node triangular element using a quadratic variation for the stream function ψ (Diersch et al. 1977). Although the matrix of coefficients is symmetric and banded and a standard Choleski method can be used, we have opted for a frontal method of solution for unsymmetric matrices (Taylor and Hood, 1981). The frontal method greatly reduces storage requirements as it solves for a nodal variable as soon as all contributions from all elements to a particular nodal point have been assembled. The complete matrix is, therefore, never assembled. It was found that for the number of variables handled here (about 1000), the frontal needed about half the CPU time than the Choleski decomposition.

The contribution to the load vector from the surface integrals (natural boundary conditions, Equation 5) is handled by assuming a quadratic variation of the velocities along the boundary lines. The integrations are carried out numerically at the 4 Gaussian points.

To facilitate changes in grid density, a preprocessing program was used for the finite element discretization. The program can handle cartesian and polar subdivisions of a domain, which are useful in sudden contractions like the flow under sluice gates. It also rearranges the numbering of nodes and elements, as to give the minimum bandwidth and frontwidth (Durocher and Gasper, 1979). A postprocessing program plots the grid, streamlines, velocity vectors and pressures.

RESULTS AND DISCUSSION

Several cases of vertical and radial gates have been examined, for which experimental and theoretical data exist in the literature. The calculations for vertical gates have been performed for openings of a/H equal to 0.1, 0.2, 0.3 and 0.4. The finite element grid used extends up to -2H upstream and 2H downstream. A typical final F.E. grid is shown in Fig. 2 for a vertical gate. It consists of 444 elements, 975 nodes (13 points across). The corresponding streamlines are shown in Fig. 3. The stream function has been normalized to take the values between 0 and 1 (by dividing by the discharge Q) and the streamlines are plotted with intervals of 0.1 in between. The calculated values for the contraction coefficient C_c

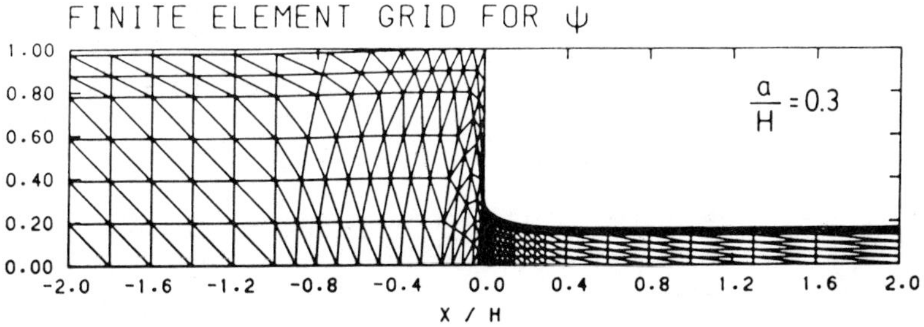

Figure 2. Final finite element grid for a vertical sluice gate (a/H = 0.3).

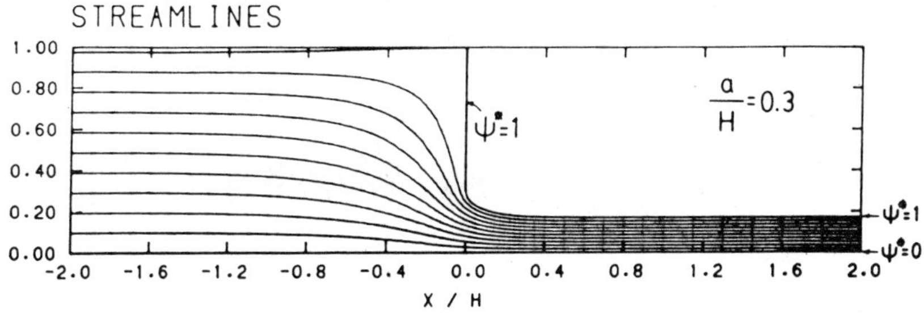

Figure 3. Streamline pattern for flow under a vertical sluice gate (a/H = 0.3).

$$C_c = \frac{Y_2}{a} \tag{15}$$

and the discharge coefficient C_d

$$C_d = \frac{Q}{a\sqrt{2gY_1}} \tag{16}$$

were found to be very sensitive to the density of the grid. This prompted an investigation for different grids and the results for C_d are shown in Fig. 4, along with the experimental results of Henry (1950) and other theoretical values available in the literature. It becomes evident that more elements bring the results closer to the experimental data, but our method gave slightly lower discharge coefficients than other numerical analyses. Nevertheless, the agreement is quite satisfactory for all practical purposes.

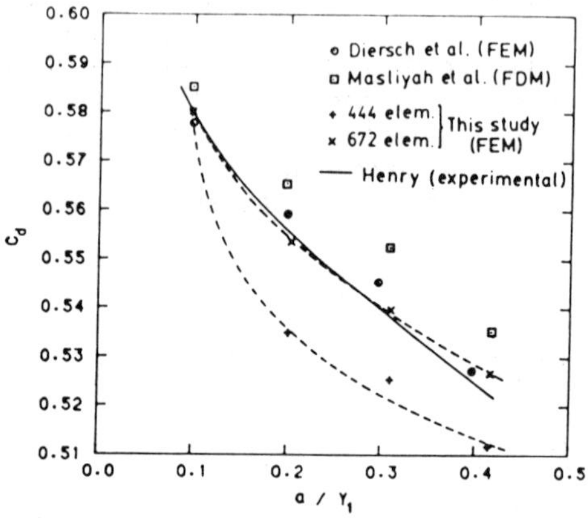

Figure 4. Discharge coefficients for vertical sluice gates.

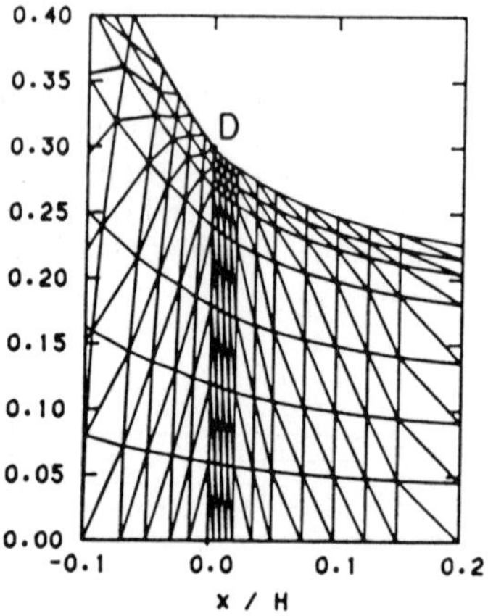

Figure 6. Blown-up section for grid of Fig. 5 near the gate opening.

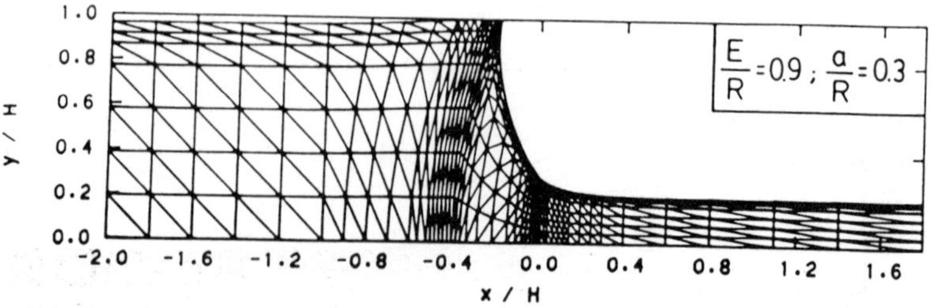

Figure 5. Final finite element grid for a radial sluice gate (E/R = 0.9, a/R = 0.3).

In view of the above findings and for the rest of the calculations for radial gates, we have opted for the finite element grid with 672 elements, 1455 nodes (15 nodes across, 97 nodes along the datum level AB). For a typical case of a radial gate, Fig. 5 shows the overall domain discretization. A blown-up section near the gate opening is shown in Fig. 6. For this case, the normalized streamline pattern is shown in Fig. 7.

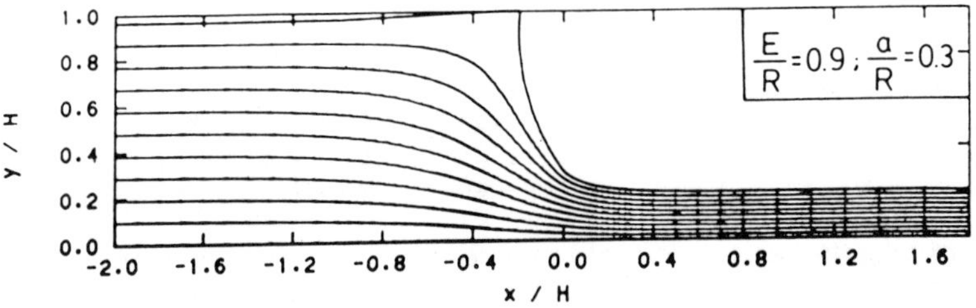

Figure 7. Streamline pattern for flow under a radial sluice gate (E/R = 0.9, a/R = 0.3).

The results for the discharge coefficients C_d for radial gates with E/R = 0.9 are shown in Fig. 8 for two cases of a/R, for which experimental and theoretical data are available. The agreement is again quite satisfactory.

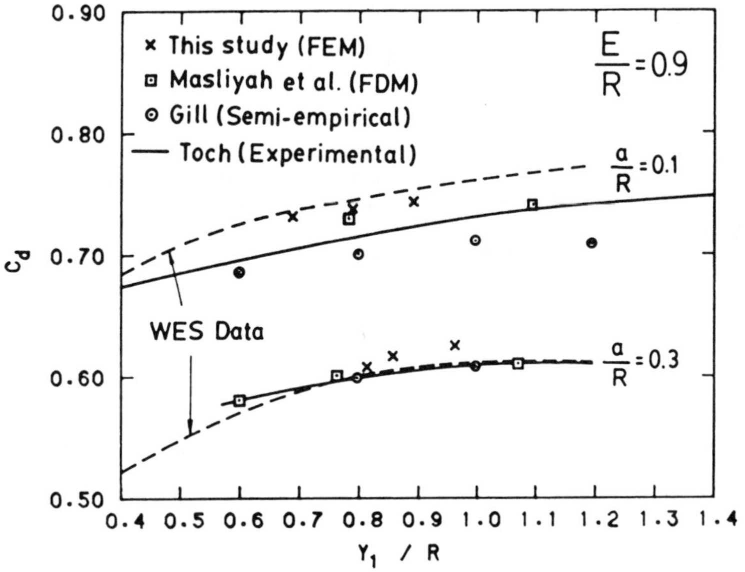

Figure 8. Discharge coefficients for radial sluice gates with E/R = 0.9.

Furthermore, we have studied the case of a radial gate with $E/R = 0.538$, $a/R = 0.2796$ and $a/H = 0.3835$, also examined by Larock (1970) and Isaacs (1977). The results from the three investigations are compared in Table 1. The agreement is excellent.

Table 1: Flow under a radial sluice gate with $E/R = 0.538$, $a/R = 0.2796$ and $a/H = 0.3835$. Comparison among several investigations.

Investigation	Y_1/Y_2	C_c	C_d
Larock (1970)	4.000	0.621	0.555
Isaacs (1977)	3.959	0.627	0.559
This work	4.035	0.617	0.552

The discharge and contraction coefficients for both vertical and radial sluice gates are shown in Figs. 9 and 10, respectively, for various a/H ratios. Radial sluice gates of $a/R = 0.1$ and $E/R = 0.9$ perform better when compared with the vertical gate, having greater discharge and contraction coefficients. However, for $a/R = 0.28$ and $E/R = 0.538$, the performance of both vertical and radial gates is similar. From a hydraulic design viewpoint, the above figures can indicate the appropriate selection of a sluice gate for certain hydraulic conditions.

CONCLUSIONS

A numerical analysis of gravity flows under vertical and radial sluice gates has been undertaken using the finite element method. The present analysis incorporates both essential and natural boundary conditions. The unknown discharge and upstream and downstream free surfaces have been found by means of an iterative algorithm that employs Newton's method for the discharge and velocity boundary conditions (Neumann conditions) on the downstream free surface. The study showed that the results are very sensitive to the finite element grid used. A fine discretization is necessary near the lip of the sluice gate, the stagnation point at the gate top and also near the free surfaces. Contraction and discharge coefficients obtained with a dense grid show very good agreement with other theoretical and experimental investigations available in the literature for a variety of vertical and radial sluice gates.

ACKNOWLEDGEMENTS

Financial assistance from the Natural Sciences and Engineering Research Council of Canada (NSERC) is gratefully acknowledged.

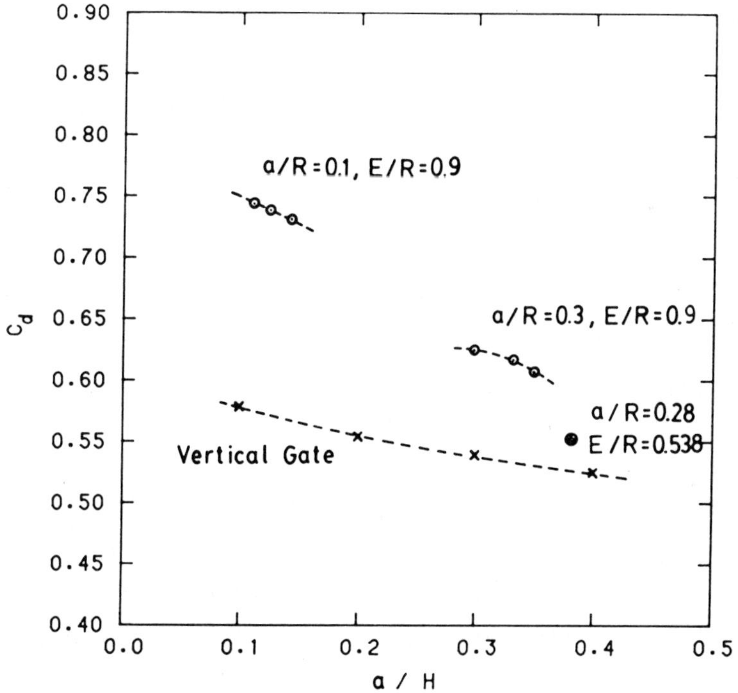

Figure 9. Comparison of discharge coefficients between vertical and several radial sluice gates.

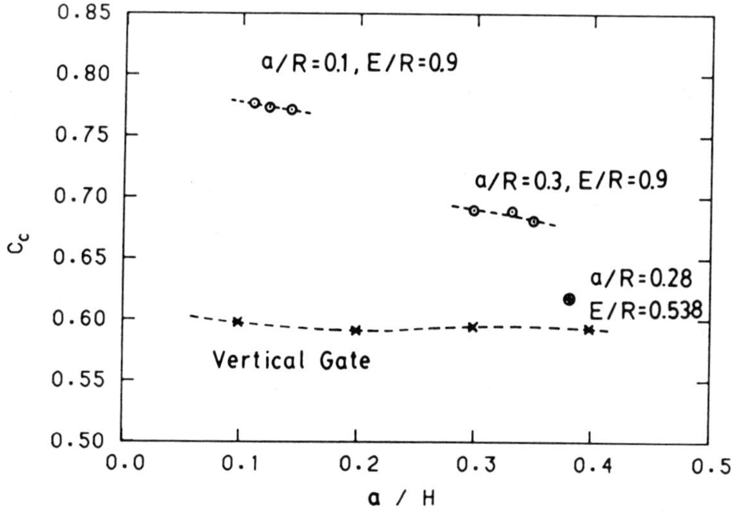

Figure 10. Comparison of contraction coefficients between vertical and several radial sluice gates.

REFERENCES

Chan, S.T.K., Larock, B.E. and Hermann, L.R. (1973) Free Surface Ideal Fluid Flows, J. Hydr. Div., ASCE, 99:959-974.

Diersch, H-J., Schirmer, A. and Busch, K.-F. (1977) Analysis of Flows with Initially Unknown Discharge, J. Hydr. Div., ASCE, 103:213-231.

Durocher, L.L. and Gasper, A. (1979) A Versatile Two-dimensional Mesh Generator with Automatic Bandwidth Reduction, Comp. & Struct., 10:561-575.

Gill, M.A. (1982) Discharge Characteristics of Radial Gate, Wat. Power & Dam Constr., 34:39-41.

Henry, H.R. (1950) Discussion of "Diffusion of Submerged Jets", by M.L. Albertson et al., Trans. ASCE, 115:687.

Huebner, K.H. and Thornton, E.A. (1982) The Finite Element Method for Engineers, 2nd edition, J. Wiley, New York.

Isaacs, L.T. (1977) Numerical Solution for Flow under Sluice Gates, J. Hydr. Div., ASCE, 103:473-481.

Larock, B.E. (1970) A Theory for Free Outflow beneath Radial Gates, J. Fluid Mech., 41:851-864.

Masliyah, J.H., Nandakumar, K., Hemphill, F. and Fung, L. (1985) Body-Fitted Coordinates for Flow under Sluice Gates, J. Hydr. Eng., 111:922-933.

McCorquodale, J.A. and Li, C.Y. (1971) Finite Element Analysis of Sluice Gate Flow, Trans. Eng. Inst. Can. Vol. 14, No. C-2.

Taylor, C. and Hughes, T.G. (1981) Finite Element Programming of the Navier-Stokes Equations, Pineridge Press, Swansea, U.K.

Toch, A. (1955) Discharge Characteristics of Tainter Gates, Trans., ASCE, 120:290-300.

Zienkiewicz, O.C. (1977) The Finite Element Method, 3rd edition, McGraw-Hill, New York.

VI International Conference on Finite Elements in Water Resources, Lisboa, Portugal, June 1986

A Model for Undular and Breaking Bores

N.D. Katopodes
Department of Civil Engineering, University of Michigan, Ann Arbor, MI 48109, U.S.A.

INTRODUCTION

In a variety of engineering applications, it is of interest to simulate the dynamic formation of a bore under a wide range of initial and boundary conditions. The two basic approximate theories commonly used for the description of surface waves are based on the assumption that the wave length is significantly larger than the depth of flow. Then, the momentum equation in the vertical is approximated by either a zero of a first-order expansion of the vertical velocity. Since the first-order theory contains the zero-order one, it is plausible to assume that a numerical model based on the former theory could easily be used to simulate problems that are well described by the latter, such as, the formation and propagation of a hydraulic bore. Unfortunately, both zero and first-order theories are incomplete and, in principle, fail to describe wave breaking. Interestingly enough the lower order theory yields quite satisfactory results in the description of steep fronts and bores, if it is employed in certain numerical formulations known as weak solutions of conservation forms. Wave breaking in such a theory is represented by a discontinuity of the free-surface profile, which invalidates the differential form of the flow equations. On the other hand, a numerical model that has the ability to suppress nonlinear instabilities without excessive artificial dissipation and dispersion, can be a very satisfactory means for simulation of steep fronts.

Numerical models based on the first-order theory are primarily judged on their ability to accurately simulate the dispersion effects, which are described by third order derivatives, while keeping phase and amplitude dissipation to a minimum. This is by no means an easy task, since at least fourth order accuracy is required in order to avoid potential contamination of the dispersion terms by truncation error. The practical result is a complete segregation of the two theories. The zero-order approximation is limited to nonlinear, non-dispersive waves, while the first-order one is limited to nonlinear dispersive waves of moderate amplitude. The transition from the dispersive to the non-dispersive theory is strictly prohibited, and it is practically manifested in the numerical solution in the form of spurious oscillations.

Despite all these theoretical arguments, physical reality indicates a gradual transition from the state of an undular wave front to a breaking, turbulent bore. For wave heights to depth ratios slightly exceeding unity, a wave train is formed manifesting the radiation of energy away from the front. For intermediate depth ratios, the leading undulation becomes steeper and eventually breaks. Finally, for even larger values of wave height to depth ratios, the undulations completely disappear. All energy conversion now takes place at the front by means of turbulent dissipation and the wave has the form of the well-known hydraulic bore.

The model presented in this paper utilizes the first-order theory but includes some additional terms that account for higher order effects. As a result, the computation is allowed to continue well into the breaking zone without catastrophic instabilities, although the justification of the higher-order terms is only heuristic. The numerical solution is obtained by means of an explicit finite-element method, which is second-order accurate with respect to the time increment. The model uses exclusively linear elements and is simple to formulate and execute.

GOVERNING EQUATIONS

With reference to Fig. 1, equations for continuity and momentum in a frictionless channel can be obtained by extending the classical Boussinesq theory to third order(Dingemans, 1973)

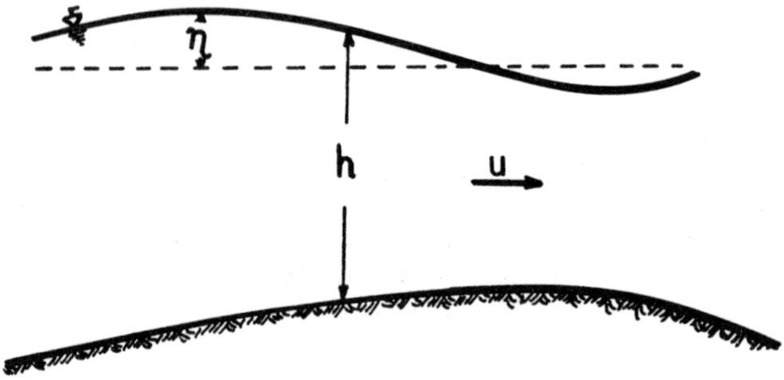

Fig. 1. Definition sketch for flow variables

$$\frac{\partial \eta}{\partial t} + \alpha \frac{\partial (u\eta)}{\partial x} + \frac{\partial (uh)}{\partial x} = O \tag{1}$$

$$\frac{\partial u}{\partial t} + \alpha u \frac{\partial u}{\partial x} + \frac{\partial \eta}{\partial x} = O(\beta) + O(\alpha\beta) + O(\beta^2) \tag{2}$$

In Eqs. 1 and 2, all variables are dimensionless and defined as follows:

$$\alpha = \frac{H}{h} \tag{3}$$

$$\beta = \frac{h^2}{L^2} \tag{4}$$

η = displacement of free surface from its mean level
h = depth of flow

$u =$ average horizontal velocity
$x =$ distance
$t =$ time
$H =$ characteristic wave height
$L =$ characteristic wave length.

The higher order terms appearing in the momentum equation represent the three possible levels of approximation, i.e., zero, first and second order theories, as described above. These terms can be written explicitly as follows

$$O(\beta) = \beta \left[\frac{1}{2} h \frac{\partial^3 (uh)}{\partial x^2 \partial t} - \frac{1}{6} h^2 \frac{\partial^3 u}{\partial x^2 \partial t} \right] \tag{5}$$

$$O(\alpha\beta) = \alpha\beta \frac{\partial}{\partial x} \left\{ u \left[\frac{1}{2} h \frac{\partial^2 (uh)}{\partial x^2} - \frac{1}{6} h^2 \frac{\partial^2 u}{\partial x^2} \right] \right\} - \alpha\beta \frac{\partial}{\partial t} \left\{ \eta \left[\frac{1}{2} \frac{\partial^2 (uh)}{\partial x^2} - \frac{1}{6} h \frac{\partial^2 u}{\partial x^2} \right] \right\} +$$

$$\alpha\beta \frac{\partial}{\partial x} \left[\eta \frac{\partial^2 (uh)}{\partial x \partial t} - \frac{\partial (uh)}{\partial x} \frac{\partial^2 uh}{\partial x^2} \right] \tag{6}$$

$$O(\beta^2) = \frac{1}{6} \beta^2 h^2 \frac{\partial^2}{\partial x^2} \left[\frac{1}{2} h \frac{\partial^3 (uh)}{\partial x^2 \partial t} - \frac{1}{6} h^2 \frac{\partial^3 u}{\partial x^2 \partial t} \right] - \beta^2 \left[\frac{1}{24} h^3 \frac{\partial^5 (uh)}{\partial x^4 \partial t} - \frac{1}{120} h^4 \frac{\partial^5 u}{\partial x^4 \partial t} \right] \tag{7}$$

It is obvious from Eqs. 1 and 2 that for $\alpha < 1$ (i.e., wave height less than the total depth) the zero and first-order approximations are meaningful, provided that β is also less than unity, which is embedded in the fundamental hypothesis of long wave motion. In particular, if $\alpha < 1$ while $\beta << 1$, zero-order accuracy is quite adequate for describing the flow. If on the other hand α is of the same order as β, the first order approximation is necessary. The latter approximation is not appropriate, however, if α is so large compared to β, that the second-order terms containing $\alpha\beta$, are more important than the first-order ones containing β.

In plain terms this means that the relative size of α and β is of great importance in selecting the appropriate order of approximation. In addition, there is no guarantee that these parameters will remain constant over the course of the solution and therefore neither order of approximation can describe completely any given wave motion.

This mathematical incompleteness of the governing equations has been the subject of numerous analytical investigations. The undisputed conclusion of all types of analyses can be summed up as follows. As the ratio of wave height to depth becomes larger, some basic assumptions of both the zero and first-order theory begin to break down. It is interesting to note, however, that the zero-order approximation responds to the physical wave steepening by developing a spontaneous discontinuity in the solution. On the two sides of this discontinuity, the free surface is adequately desribed by the zero-order theory, so if one uses the governing equations in integral or weak form, mass and momentum can be conserved across the jump and the solution is quite satisfactory. The relative simplicity of the lowest-order model accounts for its popularity in engineering applications. It is also obvious that a major effort is required in order to obtain a solution based on the complete second-order theory, which may allow the computation to continue for large values of α.

In this paper an attempt is made to employ some but not all of the second-order terms in Eq. 2. This is not very agreeable from a theoretical point of view, since inclusion of some terms while omission of others may destroy the consistency of the governing equations with respect to convergence to the true solution. The present approach is only justified from a computational point of view. The models introduced by Katopodes and Wu(1986a,b,c) for the zero and first order theories, have led to satisfactory results for moderate values of α. Unfortunately, the solution becomes unstable when α exceeds approximately 0.3, which is not all that surprising. It should be mentioned that the models referenced above exhibit no instabilities for smooth initial data even for values of α as high as 0.8. In problems of bore formation, however, the discontinuity in the initial(or boundary) conditions leads almost always to instabilities at large wave heights.

Since it is suspected that it is large values of α rather than β that create problems near breaking, we have retained the terms of order $\alpha\beta$, i.e., Eq. 6, but left out the terms of order β^2, i.e., Eq. 7. This is obviously very convenient, since the numerical approximation of Eq. 7 would require a rather major effort, while that of Eq. 6 presents no conceptual difficulties over those already present in a numerical solution of the first-order theory. There is also some rational in the present approach, in that for the intended applications, α assumes rather large values, while β maintains more or less the same order of magnitude.

FINITE ELEMENT FORMULATION

The approach followed in the formulation of the present problem is very similar to that employed by Katopodes and Wu (1986). The method is based on the Taylor-Galerkin approach introduced by Donea(1983) with some modifications accounting for the mixed time-space derivatives. It is assumed that the nodal values of the dependent variables, u and η can be expanded in terms of a Taylor series, as follows

$$[u]_j^{n+1} = [u]_j^n + \Delta t \left[\frac{\partial u}{\partial t}\right]_j^n + \frac{1}{2}(\Delta t)^2 \left[\frac{\partial^2 u}{\partial t^2}\right]_j^n \tag{8}$$

$$[\eta]_j^{n+1} = [\eta]_j^n + \Delta t \left[\frac{\partial \eta}{\partial t}\right]_j^n + \frac{1}{2}(\Delta t)^2 \left[\frac{\partial^2 \eta}{\partial t^2}\right]_j^n \tag{9}$$

in which j and n are indices representing spatial and temporal discretization, respectively. Equations 1 and 2 are next written in the following form

$$\frac{\partial \eta}{\partial t} = f\left(\eta, u, \frac{\partial \eta}{\partial x}, \frac{\partial u}{\partial x}\right) \tag{10}$$

$$\frac{\partial u}{\partial t} - \frac{\partial}{\partial t}\left[f\left(\frac{\partial (uh)}{\partial x}, \frac{\partial^2 (uh)}{\partial x^2}\right)\right] = f\left(\frac{\partial (uh)}{\partial x}, \frac{\partial^2 (uh)}{\partial x^2}, \frac{\partial^3 (uh)}{\partial x^3}\right) \tag{11}$$

Although quite complicated, it is easy to see that the continuous space derivatives can be replaced by appropriate discrete approximations in Eqs. 10-11 and thus provide two equations for the determination of $\frac{\partial u}{\partial t}$ and $\frac{\partial \eta}{\partial t}$. To obtain similar equations for the second time derivatives that appear in Eqs. 8-9, Eqs. 10-11 are differentiated with respect to time. The resulting expressions are very complicated and again, it is not possible to isolate all time and spatial derivatives. The two additional equations can be written, however, in a form very similar to that of Eqs. 10-11, as follows

$$\frac{\partial^2 \eta}{\partial t^2} - \frac{\partial^2}{\partial t^2}[f(spatial\ derivatives)] = f(spatial\ derivatives) \tag{12}$$

$$\frac{\partial^2 u}{\partial t^2} - \frac{\partial^2}{\partial t^2}[f(spatial\ derivatives)] = f(spatial\ derivatives) \tag{13}$$

Since up to third order spatial derivatives appear in Eqs. 10-13, the C^0 elements adopted in this study are inadequate for the spatial discretization. Once again, in order to simplify the present model, we compromise by eliminating all third-order derivatives in space using the low-order relations that transform them to third-order mixed space-time derivatives(Dingemans, 1973). Some loss of accuracy is introduced but now we are in a position to use linear chapeau functions for both trial and test functions. Then, following integration by parts all degrees of continuity are transferred to the test functions leaving only first-order spatial derivatives. Thus, linear chapeau trial functions are sufficient for the discretization of the problem, which results in a significantly simpler algorithm. The only real sacrifice involved concerns the boundary integrals resulting from the integration by parts, which are brutally neglected in this paper. We simply avoid solving any problems with other than essential boundary conditions and dismiss the issue for the sake of simplicity. The resulting system of linear equations is well-behaving and its solution rather trivial. It is worth mentioning, however that the method is only conditionally stable and since no formal stability analysis is available at the present time, the selection of the discretization increments is made with extreme caution. Experience has shown that approximately 50 computational nodes per wave length are necessary for the types of problems presented in the following and the time step is arbitrarily selected to be approximately of order $\frac{\Delta x}{10}$.

COMPUTATIONAL RESULTS

The problem of interest in this paper concerns the sudden release of water in a horizontal, frictionless channel of unit width. Initially still water of uniform depth equal to 1m occupies the entire length, which is 24m. The computational domain is divided in 196 uniform elements and the time step is fixed at 0.01 sec. At $t = 0^+$ the depth is instantaneously increased at a specified constant value at the upstream end and remains fixed throughout the computation. At the downstream end the velocity is fixed to zero at all times, so that the problem is equivalent to the sudden raising of a sluice gate in a channel terminated by a dead end. The cases presented in the following correspond to values of α of 1.05, 1.1, 1.3, 1.5, 1.7 and 1.9. Since the initial depth is equal to one, η is identical to α in this problem. The solid curves show the computed free-surface profile at various times while the dashed lines represent the zero-order solution and are presented for purposes of qualitative comparison. The results are quite interesting. The model responds to the increasing influence of the nonlinear terms rather satisfactorily. The undular bore at low values of α compares very well with results from first-order models. As α increases, the undulations are pushed towards the ever steepening front leaving behind a flat free surface. At very large values of α, isolated nonlinear instabilities of wave length $2\Delta x$ appear next to the front but this is characteristic to the handling of discontinuities by most Taylor-Galerkin methods. The solution does not match perfectly the zero-order profile, as one would like, but considering the approximations involved, the agreement is not bad.

Summarizing, the proposed model was shown to bridge the gap between undular and breaking bores without major increase in computational effort. Although some of the approximations involved are not theoretically rigorous, the computed results are satisfactory and the model may be of practical use in cases of sudden releases from reservoirs and canal structures.

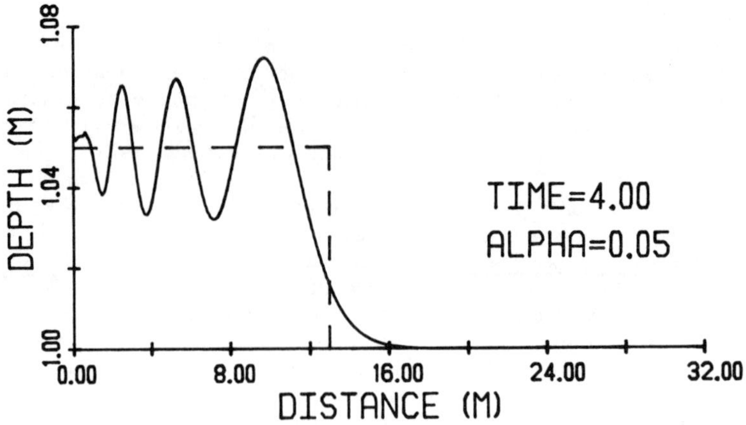
1.08
1.04
1.00
DEPTH (M)
0.00
8.00
16.00
24.00
32.00
DISTANCE (M)
TIME=4.00
ALPHA=0.05

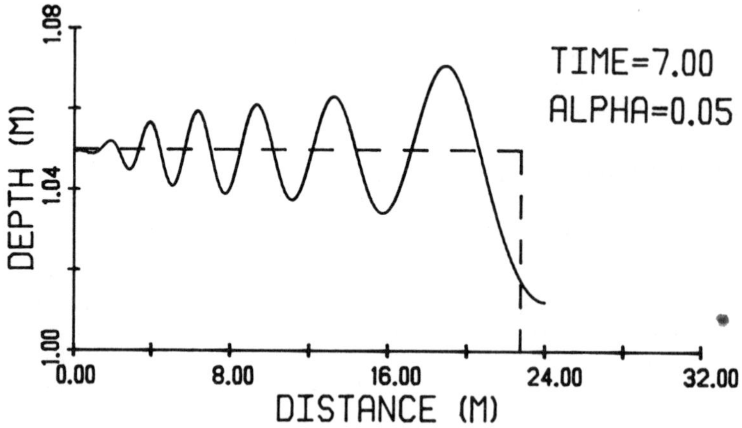
1.08
1.04
1.00
DEPTH (M)
0.00
8.00
16.00
24.00
32.00
DISTANCE (M)
TIME=7.00
ALPHA=0.05

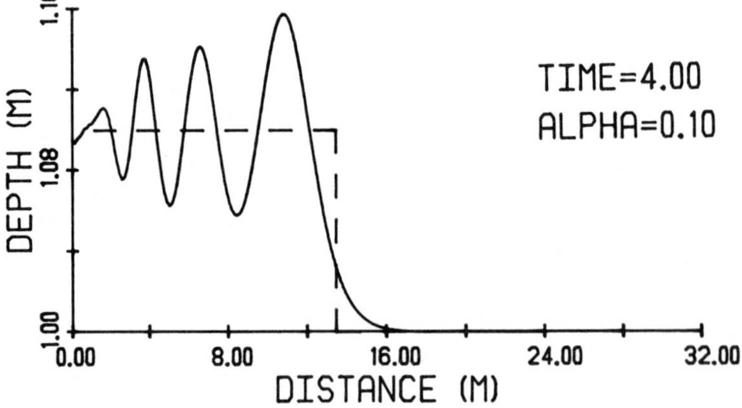
1.16
1.08
1.00
DEPTH (M)
0.00
8.00
16.00
24.00
32.00
DISTANCE (M)
TIME=4.00
ALPHA=0.10

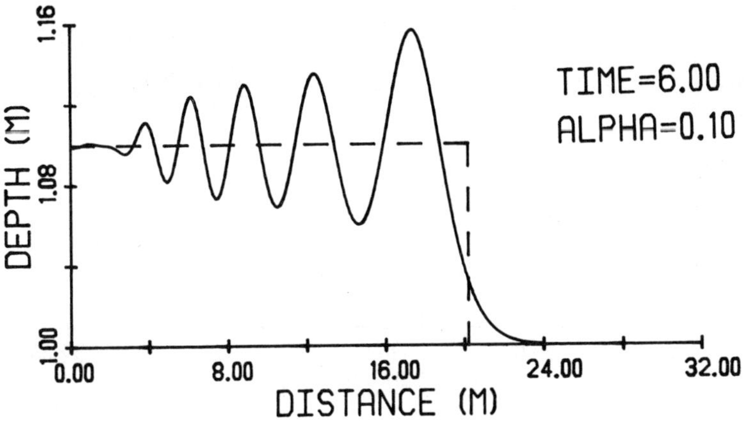
TIME=6.00
ALPHA=0.10
DEPTH (M)
1.16
1.08
1.00
0.00
8.00
16.00
24.00
32.00
DISTANCE (M)

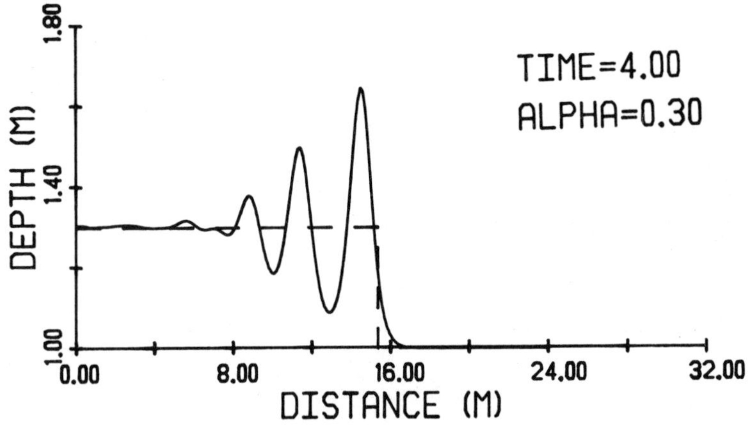
TIME=4.00
ALPHA=0.30
DEPTH (M)
1.80
1.40
1.00
0.00
8.00
16.00
24.00
32.00
DISTANCE (M)

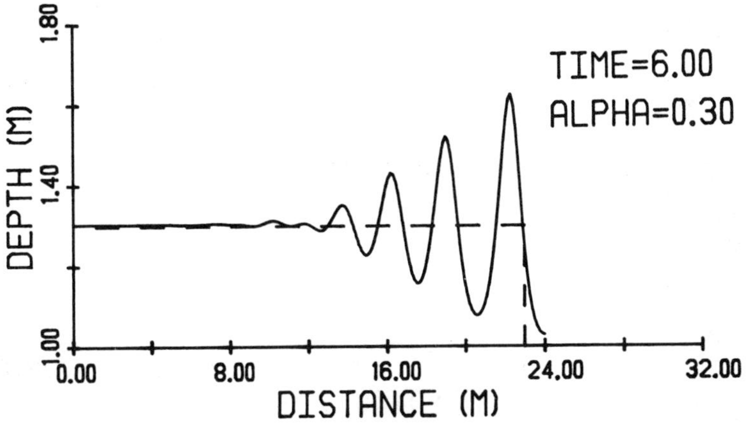
TIME=6.00
ALPHA=0.30
DEPTH (M)
1.80
1.40
1.00
0.00
8.00
16.00
24.00
32.00
DISTANCE (M)

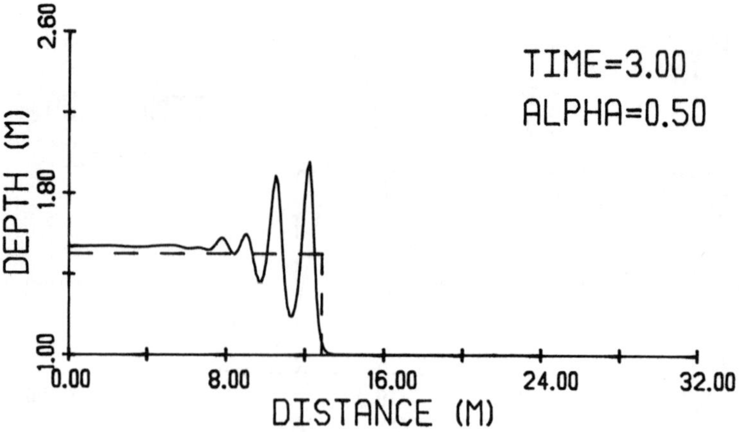
TIME=3.00
ALPHA=0.50
DEPTH (M)
2.60
1.80
1.00
0.00
8.00
16.00
24.00
32.00
DISTANCE (M)

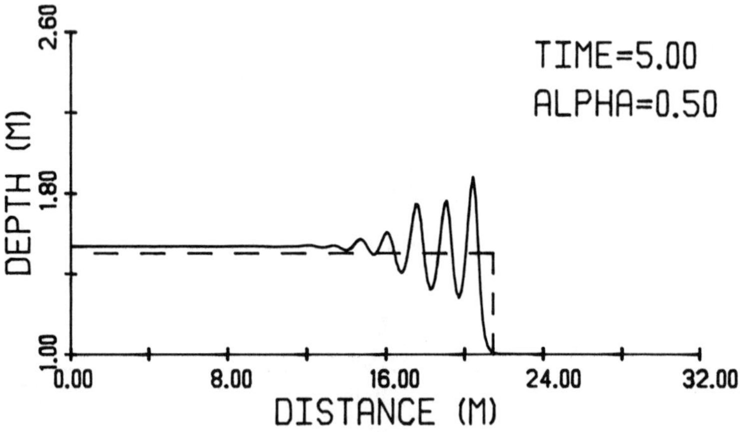
TIME=5.00
ALPHA=0.50
DEPTH (M)
2.60
1.80
1.00
0.00
8.00
16.00
24.00
32.00
DISTANCE (M)

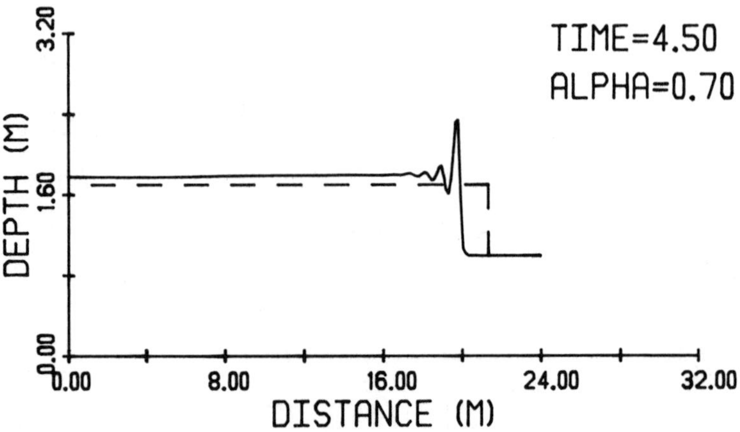
TIME=4.50
ALPHA=0.70
DEPTH (M)
3.20
1.60
0.00
0.00
8.00
16.00
24.00
32.00
DISTANCE (M)

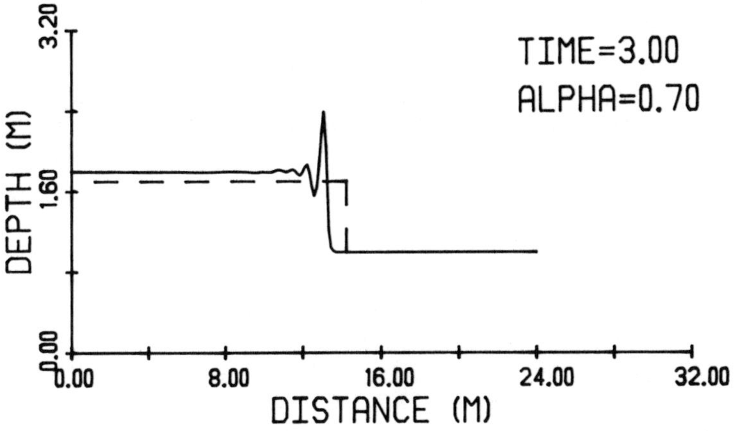
TIME=3.00
ALPHA=0.70
DEPTH (M)
3.20
1.60
0.00
0.00
8.00
16.00
24.00
32.00
DISTANCE (M)

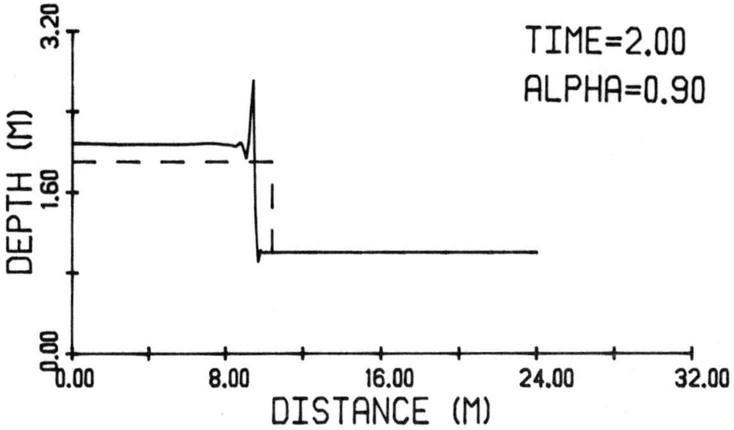
TIME=2.00
ALPHA=0.90
DEPTH (M)
3.20
1.60
0.00
0.00
8.00
16.00
24.00
32.00
DISTANCE (M)

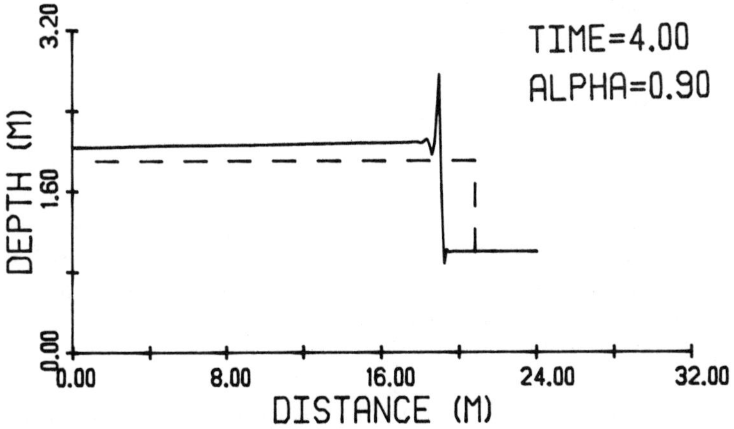
TIME=4.00
ALPHA=0.90
DEPTH (M)
3.20
1.60
0.00
0.00
8.00
16.00
24.00
32.00
DISTANCE (M)

REFERENCES

Abbott, M.B. and G.S. Rodenhuis (1972), "A Numerical Simulation of the Undular Hydraulic Jump," Journ. Hyd. Res., Vol. 10, No. 3, pp. 239-257.

Alexander, M.E. and Morris, J.L., (1979), "Galerkin Methods Applied to some Model Equations for Non-Linear Dispersive Waves," Journal of Comput. Physics, 30, pp.428-451.

Binnie, A.M. and Orkney, J.C. (1955),"Experiments on the Flow of Water from a Reservoir through an Open Horizontal Channel. II. The Formation of Hydraulic Jumps," Proc. Roy. Soc. A., 230, 237-246.

Dingemans, M.W., "A Discussion of Long-Wave Equations,"Delft Hydraulics Laboratory, R 729-II, December 1973

Donea, J., "A Taylor-Galerkin Method for Covective Transport Problems,"Numerical Methods in Laminar and Turbulent Flow, Pineridge Press, 1983.

Jones, L.E. (1964)"Some Observations on the Undular Jump," Journal of the Hydraulics Division, ASCE, No. 5, pp. 69-82.

Katopodes, N.D., (1984),"Finite Element Simulation of the Undular Hydraulic Jump," 2nd International Conference in Computational Methods and Experimental Method, QE2, New York-Southampton.

Katopodes, N.D. and Wu, C.T.

(1984),"Simulation of Shallow-Water Waves at Ursell Numbers of Order Unity," 5th International Conference on Finite Elements in Water Resources, Burlington, Vermont.

(1986a), "Explicit Computation of Discontinuous Channel Flow," J. of Hydr. Eng., ASCE, in press

(1986b), "A Model for Unidirectional Water Waves," Journal of Engineering Mechanics, ASCE, in press

(1986c), "Computation of Finite-Amplitude Dispersive Waves," Journal of Waterway, Port, Coastal and Ocean Engineering, ASCE, in press

Meyer, R.E., (1967), "Note on the Undular Jump," Journ. Fluid Mech., Vol. 28, Part 2, pp. 109-221.

Peregrine, D.H. (1967),"Calculations of the Development of the Undular Bore," Journal of Fluid Mechanics, Vol. 25, Part 2, pp. 321-330.

Rodenhuis, G.S. (1973), "Difference Method for Higher-Order Equations of Flow," Journ. Hyd. Div. ASCE, Vol. 99, N. HY3, pp. 471-483.

Sanz-Serna, J.M. and Christie, I. (1981),"Petrov-Galerkin Methods for Nonlinear Dispersive Waves," Journ. of Comput. Physics, Vol. 39, pp. 94-102.

Witting, J.M.(1984) "A Unified Model for the Evolution of Nonlinear Water Waves," Journal of Computational Physics, 56, pp. 203-236.

VI International Conference on Finite Elements in Water Resources, Lisboa, Portugal, June 1986

Natural Convection in Sloping Porous Layers

D.J. Powers, K. O'Neill
U.S. Army Cold Regions Research and Engineering Laboratory, Hanover, NH 03755, U.S.A.

ABSTRACT

2-D finite difference simulations of natural convection in a laterally confined, saturated porous medium show distinctive cell patterns and heat transfer characteristics when the medium is inclined relative to the horizontal. A perfectly horizontal layer heated from below exhibits the classical Benard type convection cells, while a vertical medium heated on one side forms a single Rayleigh cell. Progressing from the horizontal to the vertical one sees an evolution of cell forms, each typically featuring a pattern of cell types which alternate longitudinally along the slope. Benard cells rotating in harmony with the Rayleigh forces grow, eventually consuming their weakened counter-rotating neighbors. The latter gradually diminish to the status of transition cells between the dominant types which flank them. Identifiable transitions in flow configuration and cell morphology cause dramatic changes in the efficiency of transverse heat transfer through the layer. These changes have previously been interpreted only as scatter in experimental data.

INTRODUCTION

Natural convection in fluid saturated porous media is important in such diverse applications as geothermal reservoirs, aquifers, insulation, and snow layers. Much work has been done on convection in horizontal porous layers: both the basic physics of and the mean heat transfer by convection have been extensively studied. However, in realistic situations the porous layer is frequently inclined, in which case the convection phenomena are more complex.

There is a close analogy between the porous media problem and the classic problem of convection in a confined fluid layer. Benard considered a horizontal fluid layer heated from below,

Figure 1. Bottom: Streamlines for classic Benard cells in a porous layer heated from below. top: Isotherms for the same.

and observed a striking polycellular convective form. Bories and Combarnous (1973) and others have observed the same form in porous media. Figure 1 shows the classic Benard cells in 2-computed for a porous layer at conditions just beyond those which will initiate thermally driven convection. The streamlines form closed loops in cells with aspect ratios of about 1.0, and convection distorts the isotherms from their initially flat distribution between the isothermal cold top and warm bottom. (The right and left ends are adiabatic.) Rising and falling plumes transfer heat beyond what would occur if only conduction took place. Temperature gradients are driven up in hit the boundaries, and overall this natural convection enhances heat transfer through the layer. If the drive on the system is increased, e.g. by increasing the temperature difference between the top and bottom, convection is enhanced further, as illustrated in Figure 2. Here the drive has been doubled relative to the case in Figure 1. This tends to create narrower cells and a greater density of counterflowing plumes, so that relatively greater mixing occurs between the top and bottom of the domain. The effective thermal conductivity of this construct is also increased in the sense that the net heat transfer through the domain is greater, per degree temperature difference between the two boundaries.

For a fluid layer tilted at 90°, Lord Rayleigh observed a unicellular pattern with fluid flowing up along the warm wall and down along the cold wall. This form has also been observed in porous media (i.e., Chan et al., 1970). Figure 3 shows Rayleigh convection computed for a container rotated 90 degrees counterclockwise relative to that in Figure 2, with conditions otherwise the same. Here we note that most of the flow is parallel to the vertical hot and cold boundaries and to the

Figure 2. Same as Figure 1, but with convective drive doubled.

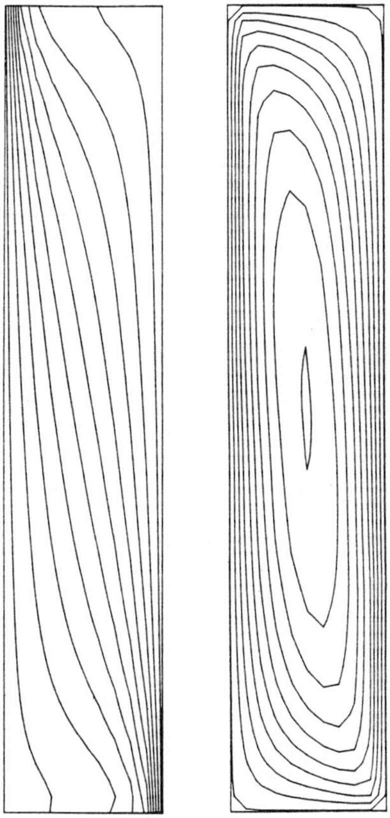

Figure 3. Same as Figure 2, but rotated 90° so that isotherms are on left.

isotherms, and the only transverse flows occur at the ends. These transverse flows affect the heat transfer, as is evident from the isotherm plot. However, the enhancement of effective thermal conductivity of the container is not so much inherent in Rayleigh convection as it is forced by the confinement: If the box were infinitely long, no transfer of fluid would occur, and the rate and pattern of transverse heat transfer would be indistinguishable from that in a stagnant medium under the same conditions.

When a saturated porous medium (or a fluid layer) is inclined at some angle between 0 and 90°, we expect some sort of transition cell forms. This is observed in experiments by Bories and Combarnous (1973). Their results compare closely with results in fluid layers (Hart, 1971). Bories and Combarnous describe a transition from unicellular flow (Rayleigh convection) to hexagonal cells or longitudinal coils as the temperature difference across the layer increases. For the conditions considered, polyhedral cells were observed only at inclinations of less than about 15° relative to the horizontal (Benard) case. The cells and rolls are described as being a juxtaposition of the forms observed in the horizontal case over the unicellular Rayleigh convection.

In a laterally infinite layer, the Rayleigh form of convection does not transfer heat because the flow is parallel to the isotherms. If, however, the layer is laterally confined, the flow is perpendicular to the isotherms at each end, and thus heat is transferred by the flow. The presence of lateral confinement should also influence the cell form. The aim of this paper is to examine heat transfer and cell forms in laterally confined porous layers, with particular attention to changes in cell morphology and flow structure as a function of inclination. We examine the phenomena using finite difference solutions of the coupled heat and flow equations, restricting ourselves to two dimensions to simplify the analysis. A two-dimension analysis is clearly adequate for the simple unicellular Rayleigh convection: it is a cell pattern that is uniform in one dimension thus eliminating the need for analysis in that dimension. The existence of longitudinal coils cannot be examined with a two-dimensional model. The cell form, described as "adjacent coils climbing up along the slope" by Bories and Cambarnous (1973) cannot exist as described, and would violate continuity under confined conditions. Hexagonal cells, which constitute a well established three-dimensional cell form, cannot be fully described in 2-D. Instead, they will appear as a 2-D transverse rolls, with axis parallel to the contour. We assume that these transverse rolls parallel the hexagonal cells in the way they accomplish changes in heat transfer and respond qualitatively to imposed conditions.

GOVERNING RELATIONS AND ANALYSIS

Thermal Convection in Porous Media

For our present purposes we define the Rayleigh number as

$$Ra = \frac{\rho_o g\beta(\Delta T)HK}{\mu_f \kappa} \tag{1}$$

where ρ_o is the fluid density at a reference temperature T_o, g the acceleration due to gravity, β the coefficient of thermal expansion ($°C^{-1}$), ΔT a characteristic temperature difference, H the layer depth, K the permeability (m^2), and μ_f the fluid viscosity. The parameter κ is a thermal diffusivity (m^2/s) defined as $k_m/(\rho C_p)_f$ where k_m is the thermal conductivity of the porous medium/fluid system and $(\rho C_p)_f$ the volumetric heat capacity of the fluid alone. Thus the parameter κ is not a real physical diffusivity, but rather is the ratio of the ability of the system to conduct heat to its ability to convect heat. The remaining parameters describe the ratio of buoyancy forces to viscous drag.

Most previous work has been done on convection between isothermal, impermeable, horizontal hot (lower) and cold (upper) planes. Lapwood (1948) found the theoretical critical Rayleigh number to be $4\pi^2$ for this case, with ΔT equal to the temperature difference across the layer. That is, for lower values of Ra, dissipative effects dominate and incipient instabilities are quelled such that there is no significant fluid flow and all heat transfer is by conduction. Above the critical Ra arbitrary perturbations will be amplified by bouyancy forces, producing convection and enduring circulation. Experimental studies (e.g. Katto and Masuoka, 1967; Elder, 1967) have repeatedly confirmed this result. The critical Rayleigh numbers for many other sets of boundary conditions have been derived by Nield (1967). The only experimental work on any other boundary conditions seems to be that of Powers et al. (1985), who found good agreement with Nield's predictions for a horizontal layer with a constant heat flux bottom.

A common indicator of the intensity of convection is the Nusselt number

$$Nu = \frac{k_{eff}}{k_m} \tag{2}$$

where k_{eff} is the ratio of the horizontally averaged heat flux to the average temperature gradient. Thus Nu is equal to the ratio of the actual net transverse heat flux to that which one would obtain from pure conduction under the same boundary conditions (i.e. to $k_m\ \Delta T/H$). Calculating k_{eff} in numerical solutions is straightforward because the temperature and velocity distributions are known throughout the solution domain, and numerically consistent expressions for boundary fluxes may be adduced.

Experimental and numerical results for heat transfer between horizontal, isothermal, impermeable boundaries are best summarized by the relation proposed by Elder (1967):

$$Nu = 1 + \left(\frac{Ra}{Ra_{cr}} - 1\right) , \qquad Ra \geq Ra_{cr} \tag{3}$$

where Ra_{cr} is the critical Rayleigh number. Below Ra_{cr}, Nu is uniformly equal to 1, while above Ra_{cr} it rises smoothly and monotonically.

Results for sloped layers are more sparse. Bories and Combarnous (1973) measure heat transfer in a container of dimensions 66.3 x 46.3 x 5.0 cm, where the smallest dimension is the height of the layer. Thus the lateral dimensions were an order of magnitude greater than the height. Their results are in agreement with the theoretical results of Weber (1975), indicating that (3) described heat transfer well, and that the critical Rayleigh number was given by $Ra_{cr,o}/\cos\phi$, where $Ra_{cr,o}$ is the critical Rayleigh number for an identical horizontal layer and ϕ the angle of inclination from the horizontal.

Kaneko et al. (1974) measure heat transfer in a container of dimensions 18 x 3 x 6 in., where the last dimension is the height and the largest dimension is parallel to the slope. Their experiment thus forced only two-dimensional convection. End effects are important because the length to height ratio is only three. However end effects are ignored in their analysis, which makes their conclusions ambiguous. They reason that the critical Rayleigh number is less than $4\pi^2$ for some systems, based on their measurements of heat transfer. This contradicts the generally accepted notion that Ra_{cr} increases with increasing ϕ in accordance with $Ra_{cr,o}/\cos\phi$. Thus one suspects these heat transfer results are due to the combination of Rayleigh convection with end effects and not to Benard convection. In what follows, we shall see that the two forms can mix in ways that create complex but explicable relations between Ra, ϕ, and Nu.

Analysis

Governing Equations

The governing equations for the flow of an incompressible fluid through a saturated porous medium at steady state are

$$- \nabla p - \frac{\mu_f}{K} \underset{\sim}{v}' + \rho_f \underset{\sim}{g} = 0 \tag{4a}$$

$$\nabla\cdot(k_m\nabla T') = (\rho C_p)_f\ \nabla\cdot(\underset{\sim}{v}T') \tag{4b}$$

$$\nabla\cdot\underset{\sim}{v}' = 0 \tag{4c}$$

where p is the pressure, $\underset{\sim}{v}$ the fluid velocity, K the intrinsic permeability of the porous medium, T the temperature and g the acceleration due to gravity. ρ_f, C_{pf}, and μ_f are the density, heat capacity, and dynamic viscosity of the fluid, respectively. Primes denote variables which will later be nondimensionalized. We assume here that the Boussinesq approximation is valid, and use a linear relation for the equation of state of the fluid:

$$\rho_f = \rho_o\ (1 - \beta)(T'-T_o) \tag{4d}$$

where β is the coefficient of thermal expansion and ρ_o the fluid density at reference temperature T_o. By substituting the expression in Equation (4d) into (4a), and then taking the cross product of the result, the pressure term drops out and the equation of motion becomes

$$-\frac{\mu_f}{K}\ (\nabla x\underset{\sim}{v}') = \rho_o\beta\nabla\ x\ \underset{\sim}{g}(T'-T_o) \tag{5}$$

We then introduce as scaling factors ΔT, κ/H and H for temperature, velocity and distance respectively. The equation of motion and the heat equation are then respectively

$$-\ (\nabla x V) = \frac{\rho_o\beta K H(\Delta T)}{\mu_f\kappa}\ \nabla x(\underset{\sim}{g}T) \tag{6}$$

$$\nabla^2 T = \nabla\cdot(\underset{\sim}{v}T) \tag{7}$$

In two dimensions the gravity vector is $g(-\cos\phi,\ -\sin\phi)$. Thus equation (6) becomes

$$\frac{\partial w}{\partial x} - \frac{\partial u}{\partial z} = Ra\left[\cos\phi\ \frac{\partial T}{\partial x} - \sin\phi\ \frac{\partial T}{\partial z}\right] \tag{8}$$

where u and w are the x and z components of the Darcy velocity. Finally, we introduce a stream function

$$u = -\frac{\partial\psi}{\partial z}\quad,\quad w = \frac{\partial\psi}{\partial x} \tag{9}$$

and equation (8) becomes

$$\nabla^2\psi = Ra\left[\cos\phi \frac{\partial T}{\partial x} - \sin\phi \frac{\partial T}{\partial z}\right] \qquad (10)$$

Boundary Conditions

The boundary conditions which have received the most attention in the literature are impermeable, isothermal upper and lower boundaries, and impermeable, adiabatic lateral boundaries. In terms of the stream function and nondimensional temperature introduced here, we express the boundary conditions as

$$T(x,0) = 0$$

$$T(x,1) = -1 \qquad \frac{\partial T}{\partial x}(0,z) = \frac{\partial T}{\partial x}(L,z) = 0 \qquad (11)$$

where z=0 on the lower boundary and x=L on the right hand boundary. ψ=0 on all boundaries.

Numerical Solution

A finite difference scheme is used to approximate equations (7) and (10). A rectangular mesh with equal and uniform grid spacings in both directions is used. Three point central differences are used for the second derivatives. The first derivative convection term in (7) is approximated using upwind differences, and the system was solved using an ADI-SOR scheme. After setting the initial conditions to those of no flow and a linear temperature profile, a small, transient temperature perturbation is introduced to initiate instability. The algebraic equivalent of (10) is solved iteratively until

$$\frac{\max \left| \psi^{\ell+1}_{i,j} - \psi^{\ell}_{i,j} \right|}{\left| \max \psi_{i,j} \right| + \left| \min \psi_{i,j} \right| + 0.01} < \varepsilon \qquad (12)$$

where ℓ denotes the iteration number. Values of ε equal to 10^{-5} were found to be sufficient. Velocity values were then calculated using (9). Central differences were used at interior points with the appropriate second order 3-point forward or backward differences at the boundary.

A false transient similar to that of Ribando (1977) is introduced into (7) to relax the solution to a final steady state. Equation (7) is solved using ADI as a time stepping scheme. Nusselt numbers were calculated at steady state by solving for the heat flux through the boundary using a control volume about each node on the boundary.

RESULTS

The most general result obtained from this study is illustrated in Figures 4 through 9. These figures show streamlines comput-

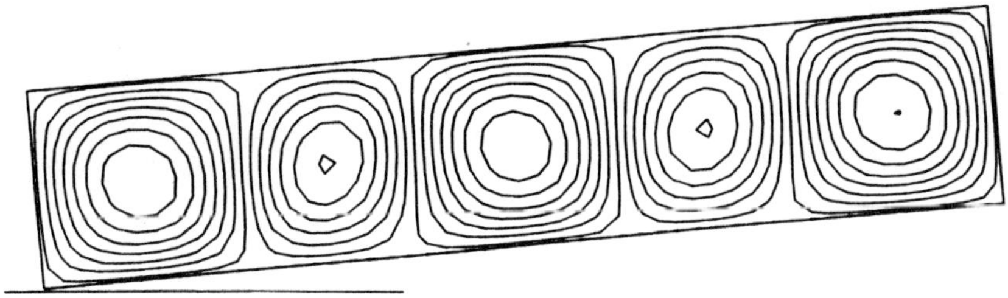

Figure 4. Porous layer of aspect ratio 5, at Ra = 100, inclined at 5°.

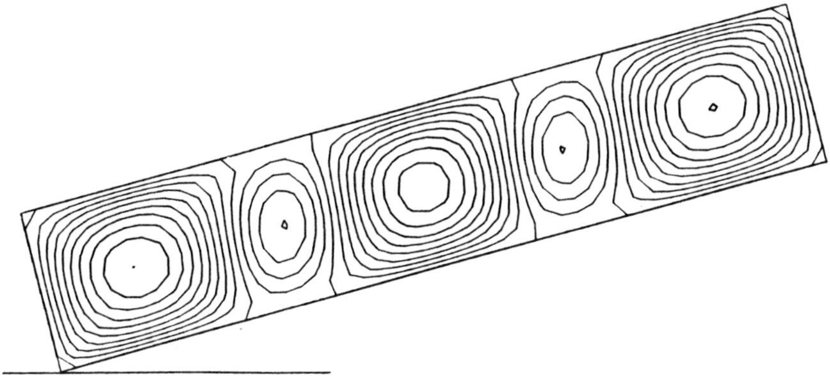

Figure 5. 15° inclination.

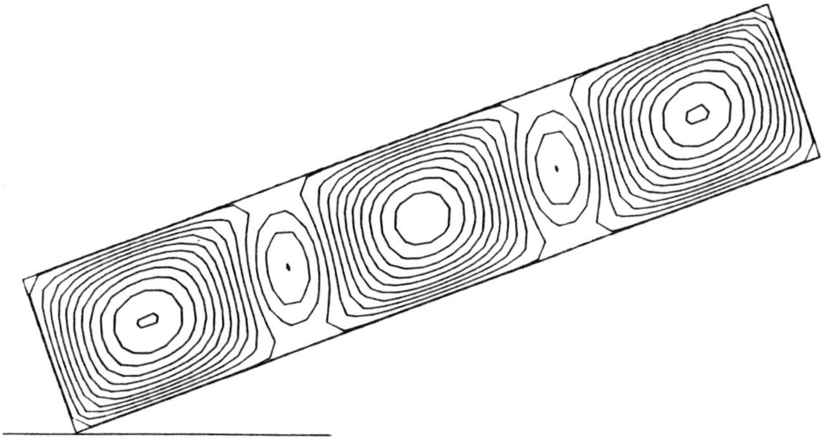

Figure 6. 20° inclination.

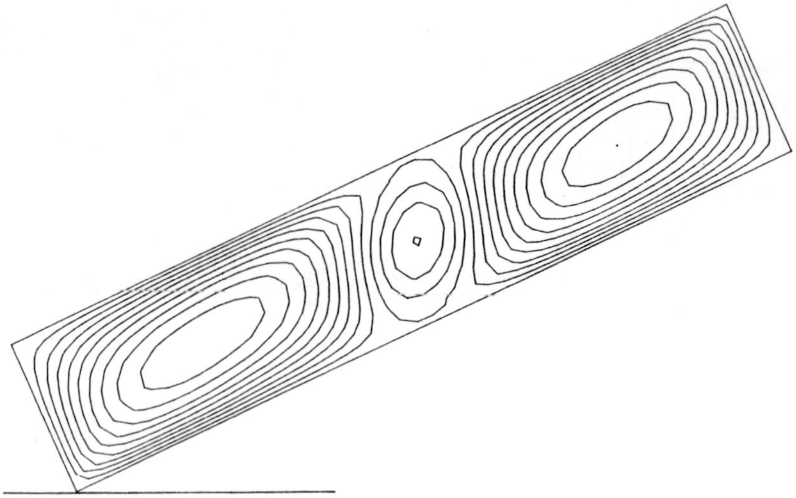

Figure 7. 25° inclination.

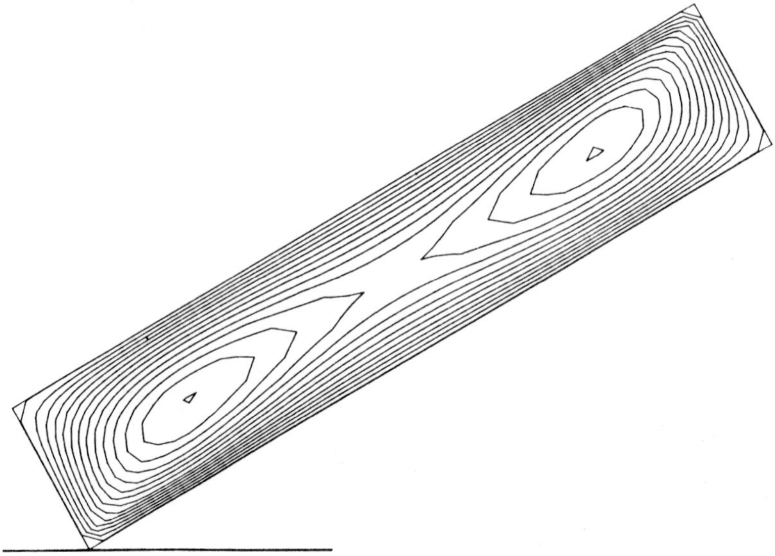

Figure 8. 30° inclination.

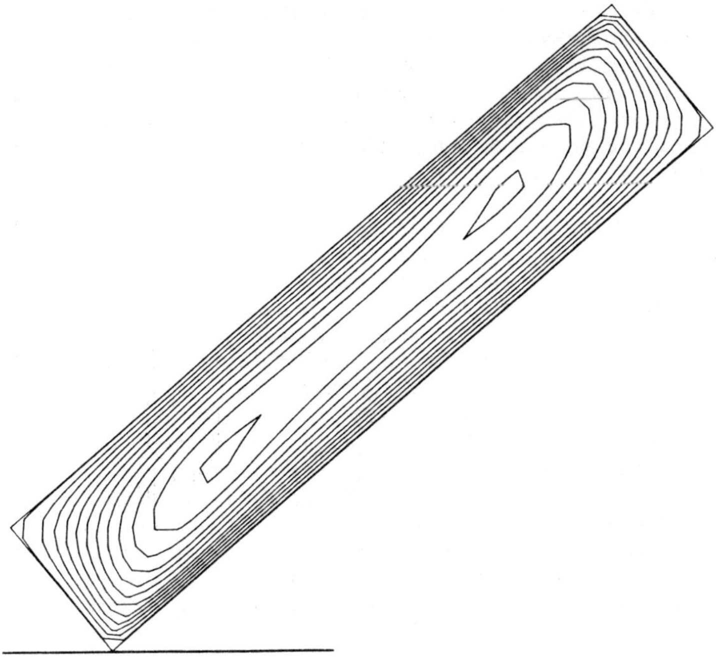

Figure 9. 40° inclination.

ed at different inclinations for the same case as in Figures 2 and 3, that is, for Ra = 100 and aspect ratio of 5. While other simulations showed trends and differences resulting from changes in Ra and aspect ratio, the overall patterns of transition were the same, hence we examine only this case.

Figure 4 shows the porous layer inclined at 5°. Even at such a small inclination one notes that the number of cells has decreased from 7 to 5. This is presumably due in part to the reduction of the drive for Benard type convection, which depends on $\cos\phi$, but is likely due more to a proportionally greater assertion of Rayleigh drives, dependent on $\sin\phi$. The fact that Rayleigh forces favor the counterclockwise rotating cells means that every other interior cell is discouraged by the increased inclination. The fact that the number of cells jumped from the initial number to the next lower odd number is also an illustration of the rise of Rayleigh forces. Simulations showed this phenomenon at both odd and even aspect ratios, over a range from about 1 to 9. This is because a counterclockwise cell always develops at each end, to accommodate the tendencies for downward and upward flow at the downslope and upslope ends, respectively.

As inclination increases, the counterclockwise cells are favored increasingly, as is evident in Figures 5 and 6. The clockwise cells weaken and are encroached upon increasingly by their counterclockwise neighbors. Some streamlines from the dominant cells loop slightly over and under the weaker cells but do not link; despite the fact that the system has conformed increasingly to Rayleigh drives, no streamlines make a complete circuit of the domain and the flow is still distinctly broken up into (unequal) Benard cells. While the governing equations and their assumed physics do not contain viscous shear terms which can enforce no-slip type conditions, still the system will tend to avoid discontinuities in velocity. In particular, the flow field will tend not to reduce to, say, three cells all like the dominant ones in Figure 6, because downward and upward flows would come in direct lateral contact. Thus the weaker cells rotating in the "wrong" direction act as transition cells between those with the "right" orientation.

Between about 22.5 and 25.0 degrees of inclination the system jumps from five cells to three, as shown in Figure 7. It is interesting that this occurs as such a threshold phenomenon. Not only are the transition cells reduced, but the central counterclockwise cell has been suddenly consumed as well, with a weaker clockwise transition cell remaining in its place. All remaining cells are skewed slightly, reflecting a residual Benard tendency to produce vertical transverse plumes.

Between about 27.5 and 30.0 another abrupt transition occurs, as the two end cells consume the last transition cell (Figure 8). Here we see a startling flow configuration tantamount to two Benard cells wholly contained within a single larger Rayleigh flow. The system resists giving up the Benard flow altogether, but a close brush of counterflows is avoided by the development of a blurred region of low flow around the middle of the box. At 40° (Figure 9) we see some last remnants of recirculation near the ends, as very small portions of the flow "short circuit" across the overall pattern. With further inclination the system gradually approaches the single Rayleigh cell of Figure 3.

Figure 10 shows consequences of these changes in cell morphology and orientation in terms of Nusselt number. Slight inclination increases Nu, even while the number of cells is reduced. This is because Benard convection is still vigorous enough to support many transverse plumes, and they are strengthened as Rayleigh drives reinforce the counterclockwise cells. Even as the transition cells wane, the increasingly dominant cells intensify so that the overall transverse mixing retains its potency. There is little change in Nu between about 5 and 22.5 degrees. When the number of cells drops from 5 to 3, the ability of the system to accomplish transverse heat transfer also drops sharply. Nu then stabilizes very briefly while the system retains the new configuration, even increasing slightly as greater inclination intensifies the remaining dominant cells. However, when the system jumps from 3 cells to the

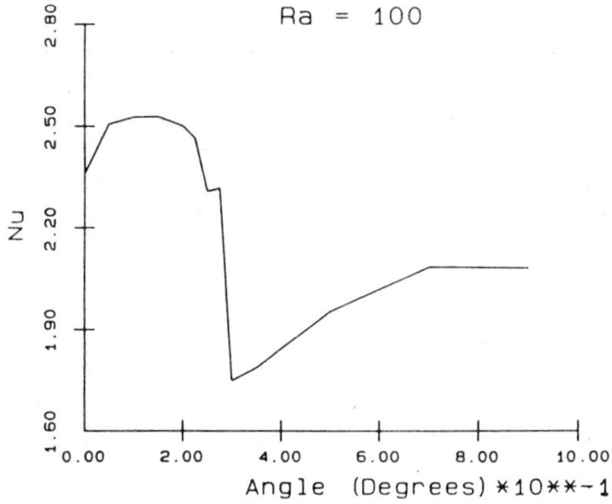

Figure 10. Nu vs inclination.

configuration in Figure 8, Nu plummets. While a certain amount of circulation across the middle of the domain tenaciously remains, no real transverse plumes exist. Flow along the boundaries is approximately parallel to those boundaries and to the nearby isotherms. Thus, the residual interior circulation does little to enhance heat transfer into and out of, hence across the domain. In a sense, the Benard influences merely add confusion which is ironed out with increased inclination. Rayleigh flow becomes smoother and more intense, resulting in sharper gradients near the confining ends (Figure 3) which produce an enhanced Nu.

These results explain away some ambiguity in previously published investigations. Kaneko et al. (1974) show experimental results for inclined media which, when plotted on a log-log basis, resemble the linear arithmetic relation of Elder (Equation 3) for horizontal cases. They summarize their findings with a closest fit of the form

$$Nu = a \cdot (Ra \cos\phi)^b \tag{13}$$

where a and b are positive constants. Thus their proposed relation is monotic, as Nu increases with Ra and decreases with ϕ. Spread of the data within an apparently reasonable envelope around the line is regarded as scatter. However this neglects the role of rising Rayleigh forces as Benard drives diminish, and it masks fluctuations in heat transfer due to changes in cell structure. Close examination of the apparent scatter in the data suggests systematic variations of the sort shown in Figure 10 here. On the whole, the formula in Equation (13) obscures the true pattern of the system's response under diverse circumstances.

SUMMARY

Finite difference simulations have shown distinctive flow patterns that evolve in confined, inclined porous layers. Changes in Nusselt number with inclination are not monotonic, but fluctuate as the flow system passes through transitions in the number and kind of cells present. The greatest, most abrupt change in Nu occurs when inclination is increased until the configuration drops from three to fewer cells. From the point of view of the flow field, this transition is smoothed by the existence of a heretofore unseen Benard type circulation contained wholly within a larger Rayleigh flow. From the heat transfer perspective, however, this transition suddenly eliminates all the internal thermal plumes which passed wholly across the domain. Thus most flow near the boundaries takes place along the isotherms and net heat transfer through the domain is substantially diminished. After this transition Nu rises somewhat with increased inclination as the ultimate Rayleigh cell intensifies.

References

Bories, S.A. and Combarnous, M.A. (1973) "Natural Convection in a Sloping Porous Layer," J. Fluid Mech., 57, 63-70.

Chan, B.K.C., Ivey, C.M. and Barry, J.M. (1970) "Natural Convection in Enclosed Porous Media with Rectangular Boundaries," J. Heat Transf., 2, 21-27.

Elder, J. (1967) "Steady Free Convection in a Porous Media Heated from Below," J. Fluid. Mech., 27, 29-48.

Hart, J.E. (1971) "Stability of the Flow in a Differentially Heated Inclined Box," J. Fluid. Mech., 47, 547-576, (1971).

Kaneko, T., Mohtadi, M.F. and Aziz, K. (1974) "An Experimental Study of Natural Convection in Inclined Porous Media," Int. J. Heat Mass Transf., 17, 485-496.

Katto, Y. and Masuoka, T. (1967) "Criterion for the Onset of Convective Flow in a Fluid in a Porous Medium," Int. J. Heat Mass Transf., 10, 297-309.

Lapwood, E.R. (1948) "Convection of a Fluid in a Porous Medium," Proc. Cam. Phil. Soc., 44, 508-521.

Nield, D.A. (1967) "Onset of Thermohaline Convection," Water Res. Res., 4, 553-560.

Powers, D.J., O'Neill, K. and Colbeck, S.C. (1985) "Theory of Convection in a Snow Cover," J. Geophys. Res., 90, 10,642-10,649.

Ribando, R.J. (1977) "Geothermal Energy Related Problems of Natural Convection in Porous Media," Ph.D. Thesis, Cornell Univ.

Weber, J.F. (1975) "Thermal Convection in a Tilted Porous Layer," Int. J. Heat Mass Transf., 474-485.

VI International Conference on Finite Elements in Water Resources, Lisboa, Portugal, June 1986

Compressible Boundary Layer: A New Approach

F. Martelli, G. Bidini
Department of Energetics, University of Florence, Via S. Marta 3, 50139 Florence, Italy

Abstract

The paper presents a method for compressible laminar boundary layer calculation. The method is based on the use of finite element of hermitian type for the determination of the velocity profile coupled with a space marching procedure in the streamwise direction. The particular formulation developed is discussed both under the theoretical side and under the consequent numerical discretization. The proposed method is applied to simple calculations, of which the exact solutions are shown in literature. The comparison between the obtained results and the exact solution shows the affidability and the correctness of the present approach.

1. INTRODUCTION

The determination of profile losses is an important step in the turbomachinery fluidodynamic design. This calculation is performed via Boundary Layer. Two classical approaches are used for B.L. calculations: integral equations and differential approach.

The first technique is very quick and simple to be use. The differential techniques purpose the solution of B.L. equations on their basic formulation, perhaps improved by suitable turbolence model. The advantage of to no required the empirical support, excluding the transition and separation criteria, is paid on term of calculation complexity and considerable time calculation. For this reason it is prepared a method which tries to connect the advantages of the two approaches, maintaining an interesting level of quickness and management simplicity.

The basic idea of the method is to obtain an integral formulation with a representation of the velocity distribution on the B.L. by the finite elements.

This paper wants to present the theoretical and numerical aspects of the method.

SYMBOLS

u, v; $\bar{u}$, $\bar{v}$	velocity components and I-S velocity components
x, y; $\bar{x}$, $\bar{y}$	Cartesian coordinates and I-S coordinates
U_∞	flow velocity potential
Re	Reynolds number
p	pressure
R	profile curving ray
T	temperature
h	enthalpy
c_p	specific isobaric heat
k	thermal conductivity coefficient
Pr	Prandtl number
M	Mach number
h, H	Hermite's polynomial coefficient
H_A, H_I; H_O, H_V	matrix (see the text)
g	velocity unknown function
S	temperature unknown function
δ	boundary layer thickness
ρ	density
μ	dynamic viscosity coefficient
τ	shearing stress
ν	kinematic viscosity coefficient
ψ	stream function
η	nondimensional ordinate

SUBSCRIPTS

1	measures referring to the external flow of the boundary layer
o	stagnation measures
∞	flow potential measures

2. BASIC EQUATIONS

The classical equations which hold the laminar boundary layer are:

$$\frac{\partial}{\partial x}(\rho u) + \frac{\partial}{\partial y}(\rho v) = 0 \qquad \text{continuity} \qquad (1)$$

$$\rho u\frac{\partial u}{\partial x} + \rho v\frac{\partial u}{\partial y} = -\frac{\partial p}{\partial x} + \frac{\partial}{\partial y}(\mu\frac{\partial u}{\partial y}) \qquad \text{flow} \qquad (2)$$

$$\rho c_p(u\frac{\partial T}{\partial x} + v\frac{\partial T}{\partial y}) = u\frac{\partial p}{\partial x} + \frac{\partial}{\partial y}(k\frac{\partial T}{\partial y}) + \mu(\frac{\partial u}{\partial y})^2 \qquad \text{energy} \qquad (3)$$

The following contour conditions are associated to the system being analyzed:

for $y = 0.$
$u = v = 0.$ $\quad \partial T/\partial y = 0.$ adiabatic wall (4)
$\quad T = T_W$ isothermal wall

for $y = \infty$
$u = u_1\ (x)$ $\quad T = T_1\ (x)$ (5)

By using the Illingworth-Stewartson /1/ transformation and the Sutterland's formula for the viscosity functions $\mu(T)$ it is possible to rewrite the equations in a more suitable form where in the energy equation the nondimensional Pr and M have been introduced. u and v are the velocity components which refer to the x, y coordinates of I-S. For more details see Schlicting /1/ or Martelli /5/.
To obtain the solution of the differential equations system, a further transformation of coordinates, proposed by Von Mises /1/, is needed. This utilizes the stream function which satisfies automatically the continuity function. The final system becomes:

$$\frac{1}{2}\frac{\partial g}{\partial \bar{x}} = (A[\bar{x}])(1 + S) + \nu_o\frac{\partial^2 g}{\partial \psi^2}\frac{\bar{u}}{2} \qquad (6)$$

$$\frac{\partial S}{\partial \bar{x}} = B[\bar{x}]\frac{\partial}{\partial \psi}(\bar{u}\frac{\partial g}{\partial \psi}) + \frac{\nu_o}{Pr}\frac{\partial}{\partial \psi}(\bar{u}\frac{\partial S}{\partial \psi}) \qquad (7)$$

Being

$$g = \bar{u}^2 \ ; \ A[\bar{x}] = \bar{u}_1\frac{d\bar{u}_1}{d\bar{x}} \ ;$$

$$B|\bar{x}| = \frac{\nu_o}{\bar{u}_1^2} \frac{Pr-1}{Pr} \frac{1/2\ (\gamma - 1)M_1^2}{1+1/2(\gamma-1)M_1^2}$$

the contour conditions become

for $\psi = 0.$

$g = 0$ $\qquad \left\{ \begin{array}{ll} \partial S/\partial\psi = 0. & \text{adiabatic wall} \\ S = S_W & \text{isothermal wall} \end{array} \right.$

for $\psi = \infty$

$g = \bar{u}_1^2$ $\qquad S = 0.$

From the computational point of view, one of the delicate aspects is that at the wall the flow equation presents an undesirable singularity since, if $\psi = 0$, being $u = 0$, we have

$$\frac{\nu_o}{2} \frac{\partial^2 g}{\partial\psi^2} \bar{u} \neq 0 \qquad \text{and therefore} \qquad \frac{\partial^2 g}{\partial\psi^2} = \infty \ . \tag{8}$$

This problem is obviously tied to the flow, near the velocity profile surface, which is obtainable from the compatibility conditions.

3. NUMERICAL SOLUTION

By trying to obtain an adequate representation of the velocity profile, keeping limited the number of calculations points and the consequent memory overlaod, a solution has developed which foresees the representation of the local velocity profile with finite Hermitian type monodimensional elements and the integration step by step in the flow direction ($\bar{x}$) of the resulting matrix ordinary equation. Be it noticed that the Hermitian elements allow the representation of a function guaranteeing the continuity of the function and of its derivative between elements. We have generally:

$$f(x) = f_1h_1 + f_2h_2 + f_3h_3 + f_4h_4$$

where:

$$f_1 = f(x_1)\ ;\ f_2 = \left(\frac{df}{dx}\right)_{x=x_1}\ ;\ f_3 = f(x_2)\ ;\ f_4 = \left(\frac{df}{dx}\right)_{x=x_2}$$

for an element for extremes x_1, x_2. After having discretized the equations by the classical Finite Element approach and applying the weighed residual technique, we obtain:

$$\int_0^{\infty} \left[\frac{\partial g}{\partial \bar{x}} H_j - 2A[\bar{x}](1+S)H_j - \nu_o \frac{\partial^2 g}{\partial \psi^2} \bar{u} H_j \right] d\psi = 0$$

$$\int_0^{\infty} \left[\frac{\partial S}{\partial \bar{x}} H_j - B[\bar{x}] \frac{\partial}{\partial \psi} \left(\bar{u} \frac{\partial g}{\partial \psi}\right) H_j - \nu_o \frac{1}{Pr} \frac{\partial}{\partial \psi}\left(\bar{u} \frac{\partial S}{\partial \psi}\right) H_j \right] d\psi = 0 \qquad (9)$$

with j = 1, N. Then the integration can be carried out. From these expressions we can reach a formula in matrix terms which, once the vector, $\{q\} = \{{g \atop s}\}$ has been established, can be written in the following compact form:

$$\begin{bmatrix} H_A & 0 \\ 0 & H_A \end{bmatrix} \begin{pmatrix} \dot{g} \\ \dot{S} \end{pmatrix} = \begin{bmatrix} \nu_o [H_U] & 2A[H_A] \\ -B[\bar{x}][H_O] & -\frac{\nu_o}{Pr}[H_O] \end{bmatrix} \begin{pmatrix} g \\ S \end{pmatrix} + \begin{bmatrix} 2A[H_I] \\ 0 \end{bmatrix} \qquad (10)$$

$$[H_1] \cdot \{\dot{q}\} = [H_2] \cdot \{q\} + [T.N.] \qquad (10')$$

The point superscript means derivative with respect to x. For the solution of the problem connected to the presence of a singularity at the wall, it is necessary to implement the Hermitian polynomial with a f function so that on the wall $f = f' = 0$; $f'' = \infty$, on the other node of the element $f=f'=0$. Hermite's polynomial takes on therefore the form $g = \Sigma_i g_i + f$; $g = \Sigma_i g_i + f = G + f$.

We have now to search for a suitable expression of $f(\psi)$ to match our constrains. Further to the above mentioned conditions we have to take into account the constraint which comes from eq. 7, i.e.:

$$\lim_{\psi \to 0} \frac{\partial^2 g}{\partial \psi^2} \cdot \bar{u} = q$$

here q is a known function of $\bar{x}$.

We suppose $z = \psi^a$ ($a = 1/m$ with m integer: $a < 1$) and $f(\psi) = f(z) = \Sigma_i b_i z^i$ $i = n, \ldots\ldots, n1$ and n, n1 integer to ne chosen.Because $f' = 0$ n must be greater than m, but because $f'' \to \infty$ n must be less than $2 \cdot m$. The conditions: $G = G' = 0$ and $G'' \neq 0$ at $\psi = 0$ lead to say that G has the minimum exponent equal to two and then the limit

$g'' \sqrt{g} = (f'' + G'') \sqrt{f + G} = q$ is possible only if $f'' \cdot \sqrt{f}$ is independent of ψ. This condition must be verified on the terms with minimun exponent as follows:

$$n/m - 2 + n/(2 \cdot m) = 0.$$

Then $n/m = 4/3$ which defines the first exponent of the polynomion f. Because $f(0) = f'(0) = 0$ are automatically satisfied the polynomion must have only 3 terms to match the other conditions:

$$f(z) = b_4 z^4 + b_5 z^5 + b_6 z^6 \quad \text{and} \quad z = \psi^{1/3}.$$

This expression is then patched in the code.

4. CALCULATION EXAMPLES

The calculation procedure has been applied, in order to verify its accuracy, to some of the problems whose exact solution is known.

4.1 Incompressible Calculations

The calculation on a flat blade has been chosen as the first test case, using the values obtained by H. Blasius solution as comparison. The results obtained (see Fig. 1) show the accuracy of the procedure being used. Fig. 2 shows how the percentage error spreads in different ways to the various ordinates according to the variations of Δx.

This is due to the fact that at the wall and upper border of the boundary layer, the known contour conditions have been set, while the intermediate nodes are calculated with finite differences and therefore the excessive values of Δx produce unacceptable errors. An in-dept study of the stability characteristics could be made later-on.

A second test case is relative to the flow on a wedge with an opening of $\pi\beta$. The analytical reference solution is the one reached by D.R. Hartree. In Fig. 3, 4 the results obtained for $\pi\beta = 90°$ and $\pi\beta = 36°$ are reported, these stress both the increase in thickness of the boundary layer and the similarity of the solutions. In Fig. 3 the attention is focused on the influence of the surface singularity. The adding of the above mentioned function f(z) at the first element allows to better the solution.

The circular cylinder, (Blasius reference solution), with a symmetric axis perpendicular to the direction of the flow is at last being studied. The results obtained are shown in

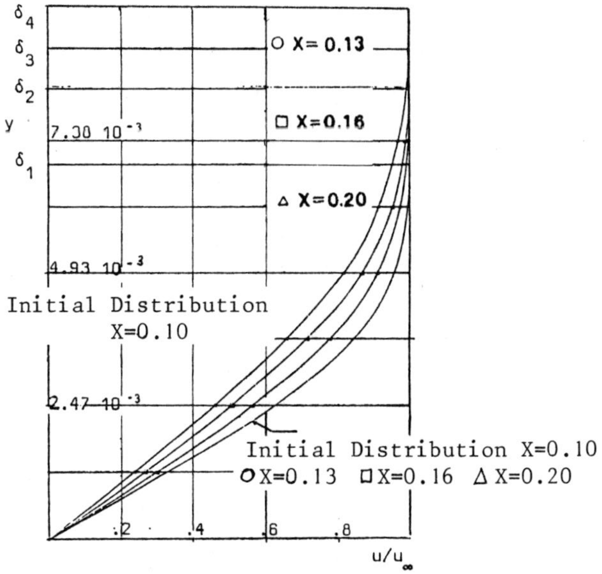

Fig. 1 - Velocity profile $M_\infty = 0$.

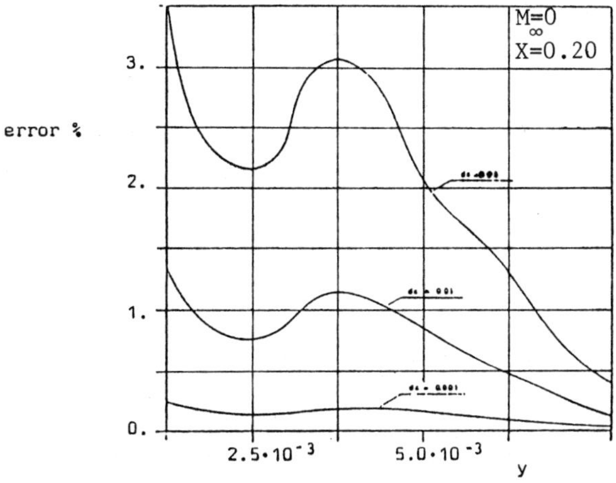

Fig. 2 - Percentual error variation on the velocity profile, for the integration step variations.

Fig. 5; Fig. 6 shows the shearing stress pattern. The accuracy reached is quite satisfying.

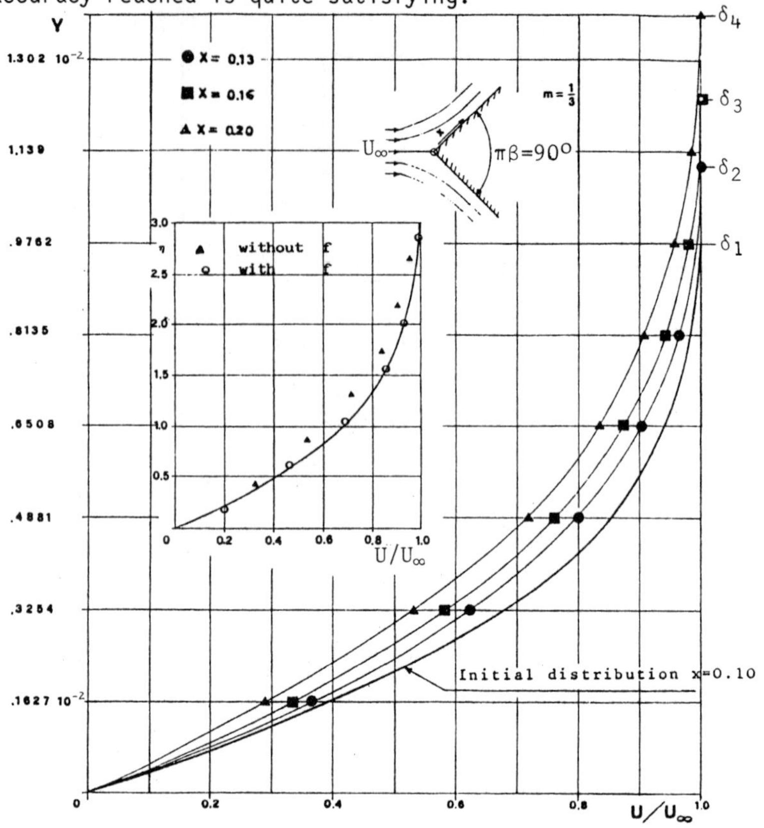

Fig.3 - Velocity profile $M_\infty = 0$.

4.2 Compressible Calculations

The proposed method has been applied to the calculation on a flat blade whose exact solution is available for Pr=1. Fig. 7 and 8 show the results obtained for $M_\infty = 2$. In this case, besides verifying the similarity of the solutions of the velocity profile, one can also compare the results obtained in terms of temperature distribution; this comparison shows a satisfying accuracy. These first experiences have shown the interesting capability and reliability of the method and suggest its further improvement so as to optimize its calculation under the computational and accuracy aspects. It's interesting to note

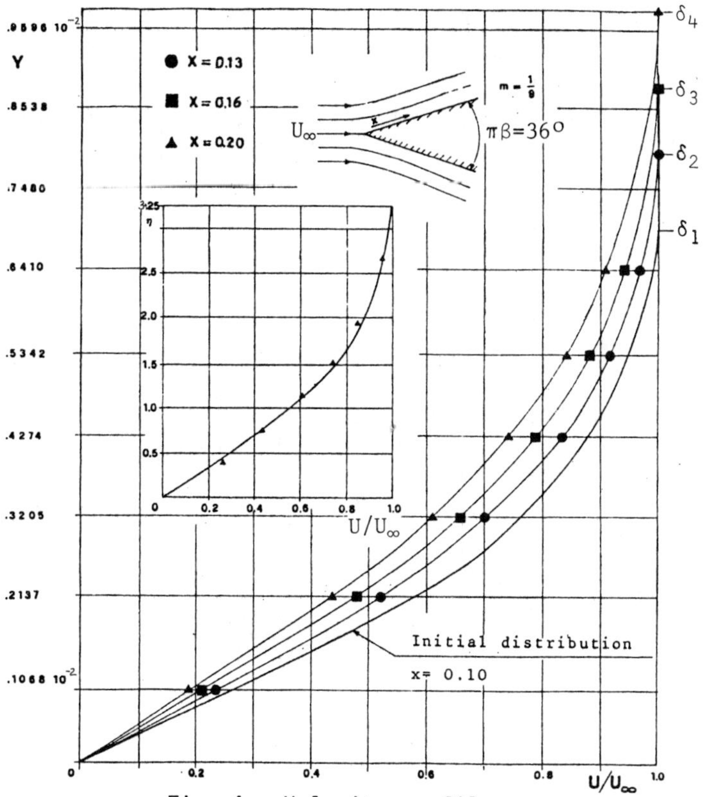

Fig. 4 - Velocity profile

that from the examined tests a good calculation stability has come up even though there are no theoretical methods to define the best integration step. Nevertheless further developments must be foreseen to short the computational time mainly by the overcoming of the heavy evaluation of the nonlinear terms at each step. Finally work is in progress to extend the method to turbulent flow.

REFERENCES

1. Schliching, Boundary layer theory, Mc Graw Hill, 1968.
2. Bruch, Zyvoloski, A finite element solution to a general two dimensional non symmetric parabolic partial differental equation, Computer & Fluids, vol. 3, Pergamon Press, 1975.
3. Gear, Numerical initial value problems in ordinary differential equations, Englewood Cliffs, N.J., 1977.
4. Forsythe, Malcon, Malet, Computer methods for mathematical computation, Englewood Cliffs, N.J., 1977.
5. Martelli, F., Bidini, G., Compressible boundary layer calculation by finite element mixed approach, 4th Int. Conf. on Num. Meth. in Lam. and Turb. Flow, Swansea, July 1985.

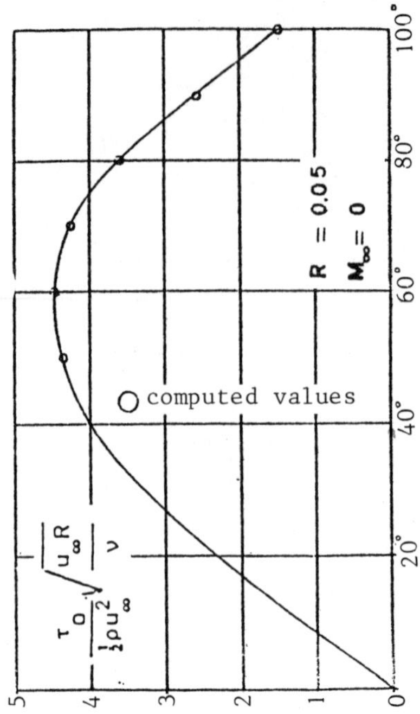

Fig.6 - Shearing stress

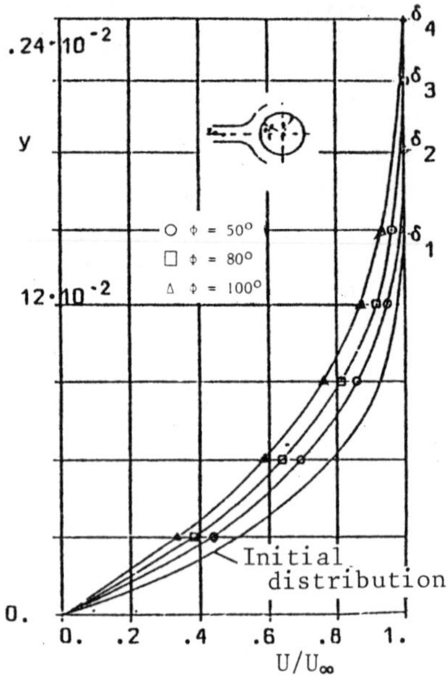

Fig.5 - Velocity profile

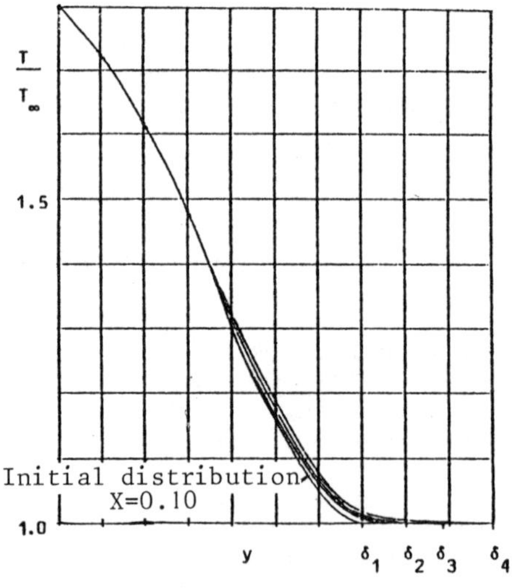

Fig. 7 - Temperature profile

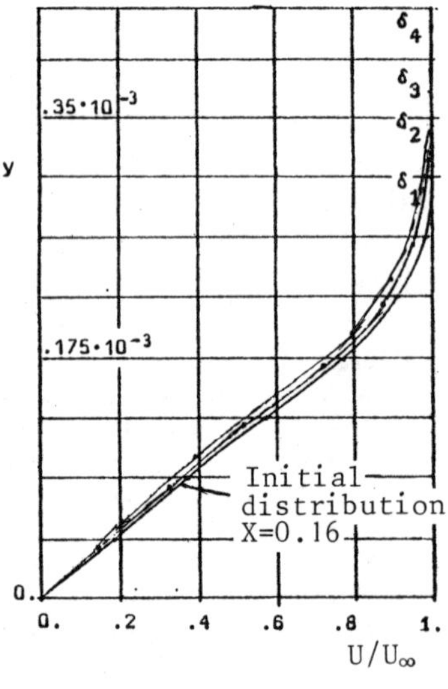

Fig.8-Velocity profile

SECTION 10 NUMERICAL TECHNIQUES

VI International Conference on Finite Elements in Water Resources, Lisboa, Portugal, June 1986

Calculation of Diffusion, Advection-Diffusion and Boussinesq Flow by Integral Methods

J.A. Liggett
School of Civil and Environmental Engineering, Cornell University, U.S.A.
A. Taigbenu
Department of Civil Engineering, University of Benin, Nigeria

INTRODUCTION

The boundary integral equation method (BIEM) has enjoyed two distinct advantages over the finite element method. The better known of these advantages is the efficiency of calculation. The more important is the efficiency in problem formulation, including the discretization. The latter means a considerable saving in personnel costs, usually the most expensive part of any calculation. Balancing these advantages are a number of serious disadvantages. These have included the inability of the method to compute problems in which the governing equations or boundary conditions were not linear or did not have constant coefficients.

In this paper three types of problems are solved by integral methods, if not precisely the BIEM. The methods retain the second and most important of the above advantages while relaxing the most serious disadvantages. In most problems the user of the resulting computer programs can view the calculation as a boundary method even though the program must utilize the interior of the solution domain. The computational efficiency advantage over the domain methods may or may not be retained.

Time dependent diffusion in a uniform medium fits the criteria for boundary methods in that the equation is linear with constant coefficients and the Green's function is known. However, it has proved to be a difficult problem to realize the efficiencies that have come to be expected of the method except where transform methods are used. When advection is added, the equation has non-constant coefficients and the Green's function is not known. Moreover, the solution of the diffusion - advection equation has proved to be extraordinarily difficult even by domain methods. The Boussinesq equation is nonlinear and as such is not amenable to boundary methods.

The applications of all of these solutions are in the field of flow of groundwater through porous media. The diffusion equation governs the flow of water through a confined aquifer, the advection-diffusion equation has application in the transport of pollutants, and the Boussinesq equation applies to the flow on a large scale in an unconfined aquifer.

In each of these cases the idea of a boundary calculation is discarded in favor of more general integral equation techniques.

DIFFUSION

The parabolic diffusion equation can easily be transformed to an elliptic equation by means of the Laplace transform (Rizzo and Shippy, 1970; Liggett and Liu, 1979). In that way the solution of the time dependent equation is replaced by a few solutions of the modified Helmholtz equation. The difficulty is that the transform must be inverted in order to return to the physical variables and the inversion process sometimes means a great loss of accuracy; indeed, the form of the solution must be known in order to define a suitable inverse transform. On the other hand the diffusion equation can be treated directly by means of the time-dependent Green's function (Banerjee and Butterfield, 1981; Liggett and Liu, 1979; Shaw, 1974). In doing so the method requires either repeated boundary integrations or frequent evaluations of the domain integral, either of which tends to spoil the computational efficiency and can spoil the accuracy of the calculation if not done carefully (Taigbenu and Liggett, 1985). The equation under consideration is

$$\nabla^2\Phi = \frac{\partial\Phi}{\partial t} \tag{1}$$

which applies over some region Ω with either Φ or its normal derivative defined over all parts of Ω.

Green's second identity is

$$\int_\Omega [H\nabla^2 G - G\nabla^2 H]\, dA = \int_{\partial\Omega} [H\nabla G - G\nabla H]\cdot\underline{n}\, ds \tag{2}$$

in which H and G are twice differentiable in Ω. Ordinarily H would be identified with the dependent variable (Φ) and G with the Green's function (i.e. the Green's function which is the fundamental solution to 1). Now H is taken as the dependent variable but G is the Green's function to the steady state portion of (1), G=ln r, where r is the distance between a base (source) point and a field (target) point; that is, the Green's function to Laplace's equation is used. The central idea is to find the fundamental solution to the portion of the equation with the highest order space derivatives while leaving the time derivatives to be treated separately. The result is

$$\lambda\Phi = \int_{\partial\Omega} [\Phi \frac{\partial}{\partial n} \ln r - \ln r \frac{\partial\Phi}{\partial n}] \, ds + \int_{\Omega} \ln r \frac{\partial\Phi}{\partial t} \, dA \tag{3}$$

in which λ is the angle at the base point

$\lambda = 2\pi$ if the base point is in the interior of Ω,
$\lambda = \pi$ is the base point is on a smooth part of the boundary, and
$\lambda =$ the interior angle of the boundary if at a kink.

The first integral is over the boundary of the solution domain whereas the second is over the solution domain itself. The dependent variable is interpolated along the boundary in the usual fashion for the BIEM. (In our case linear interpolation is used between nodes at the ends of the elements.) The examples presented herein are all two dimensional.

The domain integration is accomplished by discretizing Ω into suitably small regions and using two-dimensional interpolation functions over the small areas. (In our case triangles were used.) The time derivative is approximated by the finite difference

$$\frac{\partial\Phi}{\partial t} = \frac{1}{\Delta t} [\Phi^{t+\Delta t} - \Phi^{t}] \tag{4}$$

in which Δt is the finite difference time step. The result of using (4) in (3) is a matrix equation

$$\Theta[[R] \{\Phi\}^{t+\Delta t} - [L]\{\frac{\partial\Phi}{\partial n}\}^{t+\Delta t}] + \frac{1}{\Delta t} [T] \{\Phi\}^{t+\Delta t} + \{V\} = 0 \tag{5}$$

where Θ positions the time derivative between the known time, t, and the unknown time, $t+\Delta t$ ($0 \leq \Theta \leq 1$). [R] and [L] are the standard matrices stemming from the BIEM equation and represent the second and first terms of the first integral of (3). [T] comes from the discretization of the domain integral. {V} is a vector of known quantities which results from the solution at time t and is given by

$$\{V\} = (1-\Theta)\{[R]\{\Phi\}^{t} - [L]\{\frac{\partial\Phi}{\partial n}\}^{t}\} - \frac{1}{\Delta t}[T]\{\Phi\}^{t} \qquad (6)$$

The matrices [R], [L], and [T] are dependent only on the geometry of Ω and do not change throughout the calculation; thus the boundary and domain integrals need to be done only once. The unknowns of (4) are Φ or $\partial\Phi/\partial n$ on the boundary, depending on which boundary conditions are applied, and Φ in the interior of the domain. The assembly of the system into unknowns Φ and $\partial\Phi/\partial n$ depends on the boundary conditions but does not change throughout the calculation. Thus, the simultaneous equations can be assembled into a coefficient matrix which does not change throughout the calculation and must be decomposed only once. The solution at each time step consists only of the back substitution and can be done efficiently. The method is at least competitive with that of Taigbenu and Liggett (1985) which uses an optimum combination of domain integration and repeated boundary integration. More details are given in Taigbenu and Liggett (1986a).

The computational stability of the system can be obtained with respect to the discretization of the time derivative and the choice of the weighting function, Θ. The analysis indicates that Θ should be between 0.5 and 0.6 (Taigbenu and Liggett, 1986a). However, it is less expensive to perform the boundary integration accurately than the domain integration. With that consideration the analyst may wish to use the fully implicit method, Θ=1, in order to lessen the dependence of the result on the domain integration; that is, to use the full contribution of the boundary at the advance time step in (5). Also, the fully explicit method (Θ=0) gives a singular coefficient matrix in some problems and thus should be avoided. As in all such calculations greater accuracy results from smaller time increments, Δt.

An example of a diffusion type solution is the classical well problem of Theis. The differential equation written in cylindrical coordinates is

$$\frac{1}{r}\frac{\partial}{\partial r}\left(r\frac{\partial\Phi}{\partial r}\right) = \frac{\partial\Phi}{\partial t}$$

with the conditions

$$\Phi(r,0) = \Phi_0 \qquad \lim_{r\to 0} 2\pi\frac{\Phi}{\partial r} = Q \qquad \Phi(\infty,t) = \Phi_0$$

in which Q is a (dimensionless) flow into the well and Φ_0 is the level of water in the aquifer at the initial time and at infinity. Theis (1935) gives the exact solution to the problem which is plotted in Figure 1.

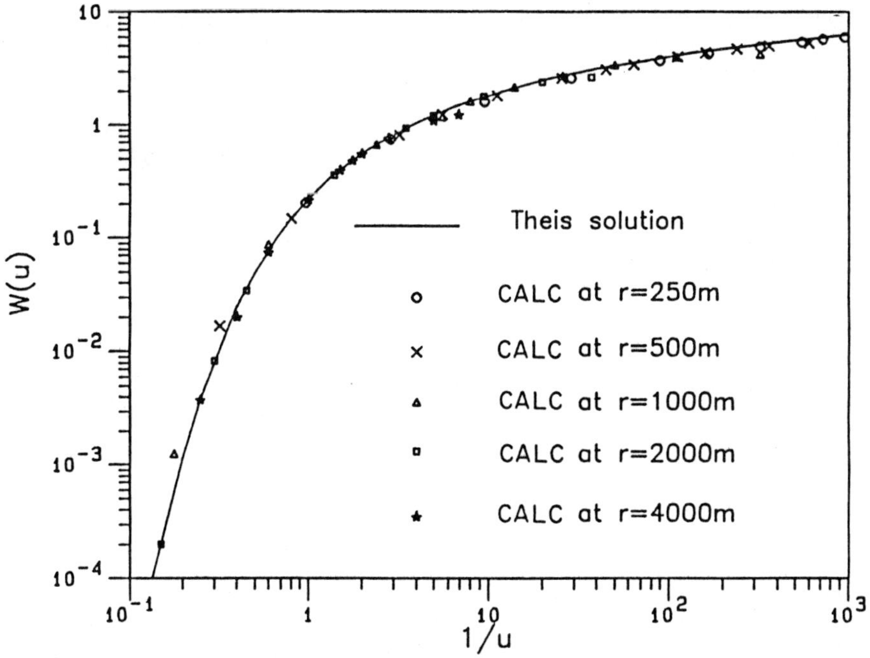

Figure 1. The integral solution for the Theis problem of flow into a well in a confined aquifer.

ADVECTION-DIFFUSION

When advection is combined with diffusion the resulting equation is of the form

$$\frac{\partial c}{\partial t} + \nabla \cdot (\underline{v}c) = \nabla^2 c \qquad (7)$$

where c is the concentration of some substance (e.g. a pollutant) and $\underline{v}$ is the velocity vector of the fluid. Again, the equation has been made dimensionless and the physical constants are absorbed in the variables.

Although (7), or similar equations, is important to a variety of transport problems, it has proved extraordinarily difficult to solve accurately. There have been a large number of papers written on various techniques, almost all of which use finite differences or finite elements (Anderson, 1979). The equation becomes "stiff" at high Peclet numbers (strong advection or weak diffusion) leading to problems near sharp gradients in the concentration. These problems take the form of spurious oscillations and/or numerical diffusion. The oscillations can be smoothed although they are certainly aesthetically undesirable. The numerical diffusion is more insidious in that the analyst has no way to differentiate between the diffusion that is actually present in the problem and that which is introduced by the numerical method. Partial elimination of these features has involved "upwinding" or some combination of orthogonal collocation and weighting (Heinrich, et al. 1977; Pinder and Shapiro, 1977; Sun and Yeh, 1983; Yeh, 1984). Most such methods are somewhat ad-hoc in that they require an analysis of the problem before solution and some critical choices of parameters. A primary objective of the formulation as explained herein was to develop an easy to use method, one that has the advantages of the BIEM and does not involve difficult parameter choices on the part of the analyst.

The general technique follows immediately from the solution of the diffusion equation. The integral equation (3) becomes

$$\lambda c = \int_{\partial\Omega}[c \frac{\partial}{\partial n} \ln r - \ln r \frac{\partial c}{\partial n}]\, ds + \int_{\Omega} \ln r \,[\frac{\partial c}{\partial t} + \nabla \cdot (\underline{v}c)]\, dA \qquad (8)$$

which contains the same technique of resolving the highest order space derivatives in the boundary integral while the remainder of the equation remains in the domain integral. If the velocity, $\underline{v}$, is given as part of the problem, the numerical technique follows from the diffusion solution, the difference being that the advection terms are included in the domain integration and in the resulting matrices.

Three integration methods have been explored for computing the domain integral (Taigbenu and Liggett, 1986b). In general it is found that the simpler methods with denser discretization hold an advantage for accuracy per unit time over those which use more integration points with less dense discretization; however, there is obviously more that can be done to study the best techniques of performing domain integrals. In contrast to the diffusion equation, not all of the matrices remain constant throughout the computation in the presence of advection. The [T] matrix is dependent on the velocity, which may change in a time dependent problem if the underlying flow is unsteady, requiring that a new integration be performed at each time step and that the equations be fully solved.

Not enough studies have been done to draw definite conclusions about spurious oscillations and numerical diffusion. It appears that the method behaves about the same on both of these problems as does the best of the finite element and finite difference methods. Figure 2 shows a calculation near a very sharp front compared to the finite element method of Yeh (1984). The integral equation method shows slightly more overshoot and slightly less numerical diffusion. The Peclet

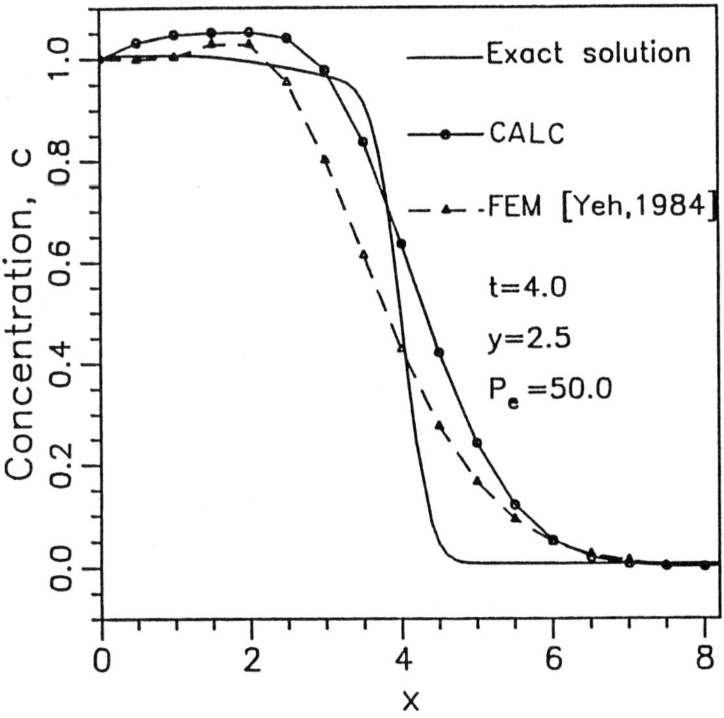

Figure 2. Calculation around a steep front with grid Peclet number 50 compared with Yeh (1984).

number is based on the spatial discretization. In the comparison with the solution of Yeh, it should be kept in mind that there is no upwinding of any type in the current method; the computation is straightforward and there is no concession made to the type of problem, the direction of the flow, etc. In most calculations the domain can be automatically discretized for integration without the intervention of the analyst. Thus, from the analyst's point of view the method operates only on the boundary. Exceptions may occur in odd shaped regions where the method for automatic discretization fails or produces areas over which it is impossible to obtain accurate integrals.

THE BOUSSINESQ EQUATION

In most regional groundwater studies the thickness of the aquifer is small compared to the typical horizontal dimensions. In such a case the vertical pressure gradients result only from gravity and the vertical component of flow can be neglected. Thus the use of a three-dimensional method is unnecessarily expensive when the vertical dimension can be suppressed. The resulting differential equation (again, dimensionless with the physical coefficients absorbed in the variables) is

$$\frac{\partial \Phi}{\partial t} = \nabla \cdot (\Phi_0 \nabla \Phi) \tag{9}$$

in which Φ_0 is the thickness of the aquifer. Of current interest is the case where the aquifer is unconfined so that the hydraulic head itself is the thickness and (9) becomes

$$\frac{\partial \Phi}{\partial t} = \nabla \cdot (\Phi \nabla \Phi) \tag{10}$$

If the flow is steady, (10) becomes Laplace's equation in Φ^2 and can be solved by a standard BIEM technique.

In the unsteady case (10) is written

$$\frac{\partial}{\partial t} (\Phi^2)^{1/2} = \frac{1}{2} \nabla^2 \Phi^2 \tag{11}$$

so that the dependent variable is Φ^2 but the left side of (11) is considered nonlinear. The integral equation is

$$\lambda \Phi^2 = \int_{\Omega} [\Phi^2 \frac{\partial}{\partial n} \ln r - \ln r \frac{\partial \Phi^2}{\partial n}] ds + \int_{\partial\Omega} \ln r [\frac{\partial \Phi}{\partial t}] dA \tag{12}$$

Following (4) the time derivative is written

$$\Delta t \frac{\partial \Phi}{\partial t} = [\frac{\Phi^2}{\Phi_*}]^{t+\Delta t} - \Phi^t \tag{13}$$

in which Φ_* is an estimate of Φ. The solution procedure is iterative. Φ_* is set equal to Φ at the previous time step (unless that value is zero). Then the problem is solved for the Φ at time $t+\Delta t$. The new value of Φ is used as Φ_* in a second solution and the process is repeated until there are no further significant changes; that is, until Φ_* is sufficiently close to Φ in each node. Error criteria consist of setting a bound on the total of the root-mean-square error

$$R = [\sum (\Phi_{k+1} - \Phi_k)^2]^{1/2} \tag{14}$$

and a bound on the maximum error

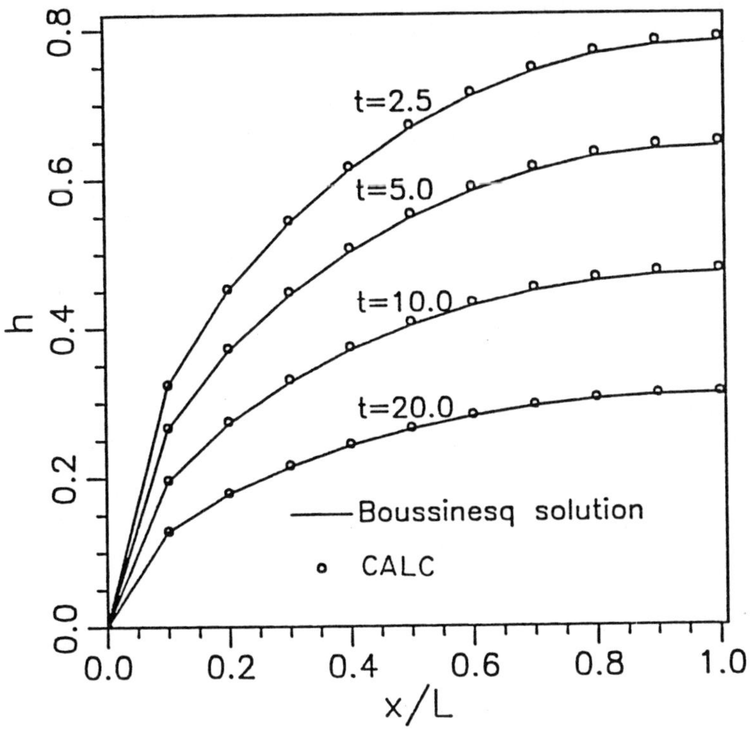

Figure 3. The integral solution of the Boussinesq problem compared to the exact solution.

$$\varepsilon < [\Phi_{k+1} - \Phi_k] \tag{15}$$

in which the subscript is the iteration number. Often the criteria can be satisfied with a single iteration, except in those cases of rapidly changing solutions.

A demonstration of the solution of a Boussinesq problem is given by solving the following problem proposed by Boussinesq (1904). It uses (10) with the boundary conditions

$$\Phi(0,t) = 0 \qquad \frac{\partial \Phi}{\partial x}(L,t) = 0 \qquad \Phi(x,0) = H\,F(x/L)$$

in which H is the head at x/L=1 and F is a function defined implicitly by the equation

$$\frac{x}{L} = 0.3865 \int_0^{\frac{F(x/L)}{H}} (1-u)^{-1/2}\, u^{-1/3}\, du$$

The solution to the problem is shown in Figure 3 together with that given by Boussinesq (1904).

CONCLUSIONS

Integral techniques based on boundary methods are clearly capable of solving nonlinear and nonhomogeneous problems. The efficiency of the method, compared to the boundary integral equation method, suffers from the necessary interior integration, but is at least competitive with the finite element method. In terms of data and problem preparation, which is often the primary cost of numerical solutions, the integral method is vastly superior to the finite element or finite difference method.

Not enough work has been done on the solutions of the diffusion-advection equation to determine the properties of the integral solution. The few calculations that have been done indicate that it is reasonably well behaved, at least comparable to the finite element solutions. At the same time it appears that the integral solution requires less analysis and insight by the operator of the program.

REFERENCES

Anderson, M. P., "Using models to simulate the movement of contaminant through groundwater flow systems", CRC Crit. Rev. Environmental Control, Vol. 9, No. 2, 1979, pp. 97-156.

Banerjee, P. K., and R. Butterfield, Boundary Element Methods in Engineering, McGraw-Hill, London, 1981.

Boussinesq, J., "Recherches theoretiques sur l'ecolement des nappes d'eau infiltrees dans sol et sur le debit des sources", J. de Mathematiques pures et Appliquees, Vol. 10 (5th series), pp. 5-78, 1904.

Heinrich, J. C., P. S. Huyakorn, O. C. Zienkiewicz and A. R. Mitchell, "An upwind finite element scheme for two-dimensional convective transport equation", International Journal for Numerical Methods in Engineering, Vol. 11, 1977, pp. 131-143.

Liggett, J. A., and P. L-F. Liu, "Unsteady flow in confined aquifers -- a comparison of two boundary integral methods", Water Resources Research, 15, No. 4, August, 1979, pp. 861-866.

Liggett, J. A., and P. L-F. Liu, "Unsteady interzonal flow in porous media", Water Resources Research, 15, No. 2, April, 1979, pp. 240-246.

Pinder, G. F., and A. Shapiro, "A new collocation method for the solution of convective-dominated transport equation", Water Resources Research, Vol. 19, No. 6, 1983, pp. 1489-1500.

Rizzo, F. J., and D. J. Shippy, "A method of solution for certain problems of transient heat conduction", Journal of the American Institute for Aeronautics and Astronautics, 8, No. 11, 1970, pp. 2004-2009.

Shaw, R. P., "An integral equation approach to diffusion", International Journal of Heat and Mass Transfer, 17, 1974, pp. 693-699.

Sun, N-Z., and W. W-G. Yeh, "A proposed upstream weight numerical method for simulating pollutant transport in groundwater", Water Resources Research, 19, No. 6, December, 1983, pp. 1489-1500.

Taigbenu, A. E., and J. A. Liggett, "An integral solution for the diffusion-advection equation", manuscript submitted for publication, 1986a.

Taigbenu, A. E., and J. A. Liggett, "An integral formulation applied to the diffusion and Boussinesq equations", International Journal for Numerical Methods in Engineering (In press), 1986b.

Taigbenu, A. E., and J. A. Liggett, "Boundary element calculations of the diffusion equation", Journal of the Engineering Mechanics Division, ASCE, 111, No. EM2, April, 1985.

Theis, C. V., "The relation between the lowering of the piezometric surface and the rate and duration of discharge of a well using groundwater storage", Transactions of the American Geophysical Union, Vol. 16, 1935, pp. 519-524.

Yeh, G. T., "Solution of contaminant transport equations using an orthogonal upstream weighting finite element scheme", Proc. of the Fifth International Conference on Finite Elements in Water Resources (J. P. Liable, et al., eds.), Burlington, Vermont, June, 1984. pp. 285-297.

VI International Conference on Finite Elements in Water Resources, Lisboa, Portugal, June 1986

A Preprocessor for the Improved Isoparametric Element

M.A. Celia
Ralph M. Parsons Laboratory, Room 48-207, Department of Civil Engineering, Massachusetts Institute of Technology, Cambridge, MA 02139, U.S.A.
W.G. Gray
Department of Civil Engineering, University of Notre Dame, Notre Dame, IN 46556, U.S.A.
L.A. Ferrand
Department of Civil Engineering, Princeton University, Princeton, NJ 08544, U.S.A.

ABSTRACT

An improved isoparametric coordinate transformation has recently been developed for both quadratic and cubic finite elements (Celia and Gray, 1984, 1986). This transformation produces significant improvements over the standard nonlinear transformation by allowing flexibility in locating nodes in the local space. Implementation of the new procedure requires several significant modifications to be made in a standard finite element code. The present work introduces a preprocessing algorithm that allows existing codes to take advantage of the improved formulation without significant modification. All needed information is developed in the preprocessor, and communicated to the finite element code through the input data. The preprocessor carries insignificant computational requirements, and makes the improved isoparametric coordinate transformation readily accessible to any code that employs quadratic or cubic elements.

INTRODUCTION

The isoparametric coordinate transformation (ICT) has become a standard tool in finite element computations. It allows complex geometries to be treated in a direct and systematic way. A fact that is sometimes overlooked is that the standard ICT can, in some cases, cause serious problems in finite element solutions. These problems arise when nonlinear (degree greater than one) isoparametric elements are used with node placements that are not uniformly spaced. Such nonlinear mappings generally lead to reduced accuracy in the numerical solution. Under certain conditions, application of the ICT can preclude the computation of any solution.

These problems were first recognized by Jordan (1970). Since then, a number of investigators have studied the problem; an excellent review is provided by Atluri (1983). The degenerate nature of particular ICT's has even been used to advantage in specialized fracture mechanics problems (Henshell and Shaw, 1975; Barsoum, 1976; Pu, et al., 1978). However, the fact remains that the standard nonlinear ICT can produce serious problems when node placements are not carefully considered.

Celia and Gray (1984, 1986) have recently presented a modified ICT, for both quadratic and cubic elements, which eliminates the problems inherent in the standard mapping. The new ICT is applicable to general, curve-sided elements. It involves a redefinition of the basis functions in the local space, due to the movement of node locations away from their usual equidistant spacing. While additional computational requirements (execution time, storage) are minimal, there is a substantial reprogramming requirement to apply the new ICT to existing finite element codes. It is the purpose of this paper to present a preprocessing/postprocessing algorithm that allows existing finite element codes to be used without modification.

The presentation begins by reviewing the basic concepts of the new ICT of Celia and Gray. The preprocessing algorithm is then described in detail. An example calculation illustrates the advantages of the new ICT, and verifies the performance of the proposed preprocessor.

THE IMPROVED ISOPARAMETRIC TRANSFORMATION

The development of a new isoparametric coordinate transformation is motivated by the following observations: (1) the standard nonlinear ICT produces a noninvertible mapping whenever the node locations within an element are sufficiently irregular, and (2) even when the map is invertible, undesirable distortions are generally introduced in the basis functions, due solely to the coordinate mapping; these distortions reduce the accuracy of the resulting finite element solution. The first of these problems is easily demonstrated by analyzing one-dimensional quadratic and cubic elements. For a quadratic element of length L, with node locations $x_1 = 0$, $x_2 = x_2$, $x_3 = L$ (see Figure 1a), any values of $x_2 \leq L/4$ or $x_2 \geq 3L/4$ will produce a noninvertible map when the standard ICT is used. For a cubic element with nodes at $x_1 = 0$, $x_2 = aL$, $x_3 = bL$, $x_4 = L$ (Figure 1b), choices of (a,b) corresponding to the unshaded portion of Figure 1c produce noninvertible mappings under the standard ICT. Each of these results is generated by defining the standard ICT and requiring $\det J = \frac{dx}{d\xi}$ to be non-zero for all $-1 \leq \xi \leq 1$, where ξ is the local coordinate. Whenever the geometric mapping is not invertible, a solution can, in general, not be computed.

The second problem listed above, involving the distortion of functions due to the coordinate mapping, occurs whenever $x_2 \neq L/2$ in the quadratic case, and $(a,b) \neq (L/3, 2L/3)$ in the cubic case. The problem is a direct result of the nonlinear nature of the ICT. This is discussed in detail by Celia and Gray (1984), and is illustrated via simple numerical calculations presented therein.

The development of the new ICT is based on the recognition that the deviation of the ICT from linear behavior is the root cause of the problems. These problems can be eliminated by allowing the nodes in the local space to move away from their standard equi-spaced locations. In particular, the node corresponding to x_2 in the quadratic case is not forced to reside at $\xi = 0$; similarly, for the cubic case, nodes 2 and 3 are not restricted to the locations $(\xi_2, \xi_3) = (-1/3, +1/3)$. These node locations in the local space are chosen so that they are spaced in the same proportion as the global spacing. For example, for the quadratic case, the local node location for the interior node, call it α, is chosen as

$$\frac{\alpha - (-1)}{1 - (-1)} = \frac{x_2 - x_1}{x_3 - x_1} = \frac{x_2}{L}$$

or,

$$\alpha = \frac{2x_2}{L} - 1 \tag{1}$$

Under these node placements, the quadratic ICT reduces to a linear CT, so that nonlinear effects are elminated. The modified ICT for the cubic case uses a similar proportionality relationship for the local node placements. These shifted placements completely eliminate both of the problems discussed above for these one-dimensional elements.

The results of this one-dimensional analysis are used to guide the development of the two-dimensional ICT. The general idea is to consider each side separately, and to use the length ratio presented above to decide on the local node placements. A general two-dimensional, serendipity quadratic element is shown in Figure 2, with the local node placements along the sides denoted by α, β, γ, ε. A listing of the associated basis functions is provided in Table 1. These basis functions differ from the standard functions due to the non-zero values of α, β, γ, ε.

The only difficulty in this approach is that the length ratios on which the local node locations are based are not known a priori when the element sides are curved. For example, consider the curved side illustrated in Figure 3. The equation used to define α is, by analogy to Equation (1),

$$\alpha = 2\frac{\ell_2}{\ell_3} - 1 \qquad (2)$$

where ℓ_2 is the arc length between nodes 1 and 2, and ℓ_3 is the arc length between nodes 1 and 3. These lengths can be computed by using the ICT definition, since

$$\ell_i = \int_{-1}^{S} \sqrt{\left(\frac{dx}{d\xi}\right)^2 + \left(\frac{dy}{d\xi}\right)^2}\; d\xi, \qquad (3)$$

where $S = \alpha$ when $i = 2$ and $S = 1$ when $i = 3$. The global coordinates x and y are related to the local coordinates ξ and η via the ICT. Since the basis functions used in the ICT expansion are functions of α (see Table 1), the right-hand side of Equation (3) is a function of α. This means that Equations (2) and (3) must be solved iteratively for the local node placement α. Iterative procedures have been defined in detail by Celia and Gray (1984, 1986) for both the quadratic and cubic cases. Convergence has been rapid in all cases tested.

The iterative procedure of Equations (2) and (3) is applied for each element side. Once the local placements α, β, γ, and ε are determined, the basis functions of Table 1 are completely defined. These bases are then used to define both the trial function and the ICT, and the finite element computations are carried out.

Several example calculations have demonstrated the improvements due to the new ICT. For example, following Celia and Gray (1984), consider the Laplace equation defined over the arc domain of Figure 4,

$$\nabla^2 h = 0, \qquad (4)$$
$$h = h_1, \ \theta = 0$$
$$h = h_o, \ \theta = \pi/2$$
$$\frac{\partial h}{\partial r} = 0, \ r = 1, \ r = 2.$$

This equation is solved, in x - y space, using the finite element discretization shown in Figure 4. Let the side nodes along the lines of constant θ (denoted by r_{s1} through r_{s5}) be shifted alternatively toward and away from the inner radius, deviating from their centered positions at r = 1.5 (see Figure 4). Solutions computed using both the standard ICT and the new ICT are plotted as functions of node displacement in Figure 4. The figure clearly shows both the singular nature of the standard ICT and the improved accuracy, for all values of displacement, that the new ICT provides.

While the new ICT can produce obvious improvements in finite element solutions, it requires a substantial number of program modifications. In particular, side lengths and node placements must be calculated, and the basis function definitions must be modified as per Table 1. While the actual CPU time is hardly affected (the calculations need to be done only once), the modification of existing codes can be time consuming. This motivates the development of a preprocessing algorithm that allows existing finite element codes to take advantage of the new ICT without modification.

A PREPROCESSING ALGORITHM

The general concept of the preprocessor is to perform the geometric calculations prior to entering the main finite element program. The novelty is that, based on the geometric considerations discussed in the previous section, the preprocessor introduces new node locations which allow the standard finite element procedure to be used without modification. That is, by appropriate modification of the node coordinates in the input data, the preprocessor causes the standard finite element algorithm (using the standard ICT) to generate solutions that exactly match those obtained using the new ICT.

As input, the preprocessor requires the geometric information that defines the finite element discretization, namely node locations and element incidences. Then, for each element side in the domain, the preprocessor uses the iterative algorithm described above (Equations (2) and (3)) to define the local node locations. With this information in hand, the basis functions of Table 1 are defined. Finally, using these basis functions, the modified ICT is defined by

$$x(\xi,\eta) = \sum_{j=1}^{8} X_j \, \phi_j(\xi,\eta;\underset{\sim}{\alpha}) \tag{5a}$$

$$y(\xi,\eta) = \sum_{j=1}^{8} Y_j \, \phi_j \, (\xi,\eta;\underset{\sim}{\alpha}) \tag{5b}$$

where (X_j, Y_j) is the global coordinate location of node j, ϕ_j is the modified local basis function associated with node j, and the vector $\underset{\sim}{\alpha} = (\alpha,\beta,\gamma,\varepsilon)$ corresponds to the local node locations of Figure 2.

The procedure of Celia and Gray (1984) employs Equations (5) to define the ICT, and uses the basis functions of Table 1 to define the trial function. The finite element calculations are then carried out directly. As an alternative to this computational procedure, consider the definition, within the preprocessor, of a new set of node locations, $\{(X_j^*, Y_j^*)\}$. Let these global coordinate values correspond exactly to the centered points along each side, under the mapping of Equation (5). That is, using the local node numbering of Figure 2, the new location of node 2, for example, is defined by

$$X_2^* = \sum_{j=1}^{8} X_j \phi_j(0,-1;\underset{\sim}{\alpha}) \tag{6a}$$

$$Y_2^* = \sum_{j=1}^{8} Y_j \phi_j(0,-1;\underset{\sim}{\alpha}) \tag{6b}$$

Similar expressions are written for nodes 4, 5, and 7. The corner nodes 1, 3, 6, and 8 maintain their original global coordinates. Now, if the finite element grid is changed so that the locations (X_j^*, Y_j^*) are used instead of the original (X_j,Y_j), then every element side in the entire domain will have equispaced node points. Thus, if the standard ICT is employed, using the standard basis functions $\{\phi_j(\xi,\eta;\underset{\sim}{0})\}$, in conjunction with node coordinates $\{(X_j^*,Y_j^*)\}$, the resulting finite element solution should be identical to that obtained using the new ICT. Therefore, as output, the preprocessor produces a list of the vectors $\underset{\sim}{\alpha}$, and, most importantly, the list of modified nodal coordinates $\{X_j^*,Y_j^*)\}$. If the values (X_j^*,Y_j^*) are used as input to a standard finite element code (using a standard ICT), then the problems associated with the standard ICT will be elminated. Therefore standard finite element codes require no modification to take advantage of the improved ICT, so long as the input data is modified by the preprocessing algorithm.

The only remaining task is a minor postprocessing of the solution before it is printed or displayed. This is required because the printed nodal solutions must correspond to the original node locations, not the modified locations. This postprocessing involves a simple interpolaton, using the trial function definition, to define the solution at the desired spatial location. As an example, consider node number 2 of Figure 2. Let the nodal values of the computed finite element solution be denoted by the vector $\underset{\sim}{U}^*$. These values correspond to the locations $(\underset{\sim}{X}^*,\underset{\sim}{Y}^*)$. To evaluate the solution at the original node locations, the trial function is simply evaluated at the local coordinates corresponding to those node locations. For node number 2, the solution is computed as

$$U_2 = \sum_{j=1}^{8} U_j^* \, \phi_j(\alpha,-1;\underset{\sim}{0})$$

Other nodal values are computed in an analogous manner. The proper solution is now ready for display. Notice that this postprocessing is performed only when the solution is to be displayed. For time marching algorithms, the solution $\underset{\sim}{U}^*$ is always used in the actual finite element computations.

An additional advantage of using the preprocessor relates to quadrature considerations. Gray and van Genuchten (1978) have shown that a significant computational saving can be achieved by using numerical integration formulas for which the sampling points coincide with local coordinate node locations. When the nodes are equispaced in local space, this feature is more easily achieved. The preprocessor facilitates such integration schemes while preserving the benefits of the improved coordinate transformation.

As verification of the preprocessing algorithm, several of the examples presented by Celia and Gray (1984) were resolved using the preprocessing approach. One of these examples is given by Equation (4), and Figure 4, of this paper. The solutions using the preprocessing algorithm coincide with those of the new ICT. Thus the preprocessing approach affords the same benefits as the modified ICT.

SUMMARY

A preprocessing algorithm has been presented that allows existing finite element codes to take direct advantage of the improved isoparametric coordinate transformation. No reprogramming is required within the finite element algorithm. The preprocessor provides modified input data so that the standard finite element algorithm (using the standard ICT) produces results that are identical to those computed using the modified ICT, and modified basis functions, of Celia and Gray (1984). Potential geometric problems, inherent in the standard ICT, are elminated by the preprocessing step. The preprocessing is performed only once, and carries an insignificant computational requirement. The algorithm can be applied to any finite element code that uses quadratic or cubic basis functions.

REFERENCES

Atluri, S. N. (1983) "Higher Order, Special and Singular Finite Elements," in State-of-the-Art Surveys on Finite Element Technology, N. K. Noor and W. Pilkey, eds, ASME, 87-126.

Barsoum, R. S. (1976) "On the Use of Isoparametric Finite Elements in Linear Fracture Mechanics," Int. J. Num. Meth. Eng., 10:25-37.

Celia, M. A. and W. G. Gray (1984) "An Improved Isoparametric Transformation for Finite Element Analysis," Int. J. Num. Method. Eng., 20:1443-1459.

Celia, M. A. and W. G. Gray (1986) "Improved Coordinate Transformations for Finite Elements: The Lagrange Cubic Case," submitted to Int. J. Num. Math. Eng.

Gray, W. G. and M. Th. van Genuchten (1978) "Economical Alternatives to Gaussian Quadrature over Isoparametric Quadrilaterals," Int. J. Num. Math. Eng., 12:1478-1484.

Henshell, R. D. and K. G. Shaw (1975) "Crack Tip Finite Elements are Unnecessary," Int. J. Num. Meth. Eng., 9:495-507.
Jordan, W. B. (1970) "Plane Isoparametric Structural Elements," A.E.C. Research and Development Report KAPL-M-7112.
Pu, S. L., M. A. Hussain and W. E. Lorensen (1978) "The Collapsed Cubic Isoparametric Element as a Singular Element for Crack Problems," Int. J. Num. Meth. Eng., 12:1727-1742.

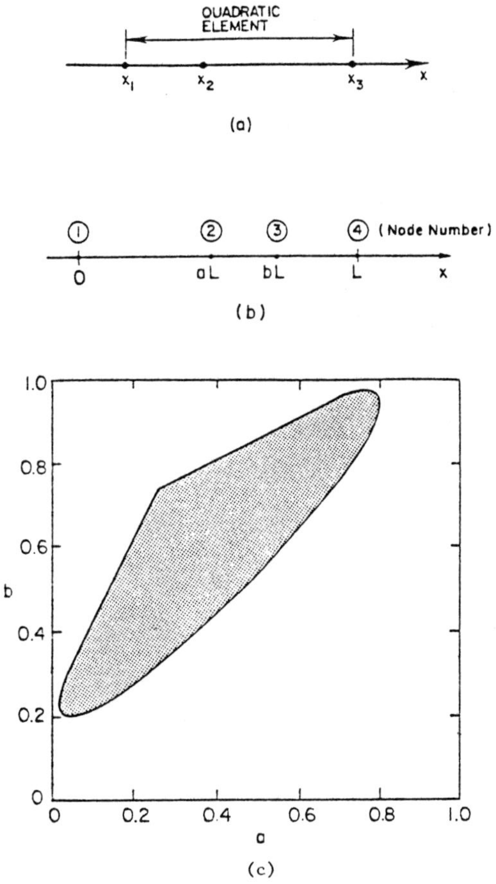

Figure 1 -- Typical quadratic (a) and cubic (b) element, showing global node locations. Values of a, b for which the cubic ICT remains well-defined are shown by the shaded portion of (c).

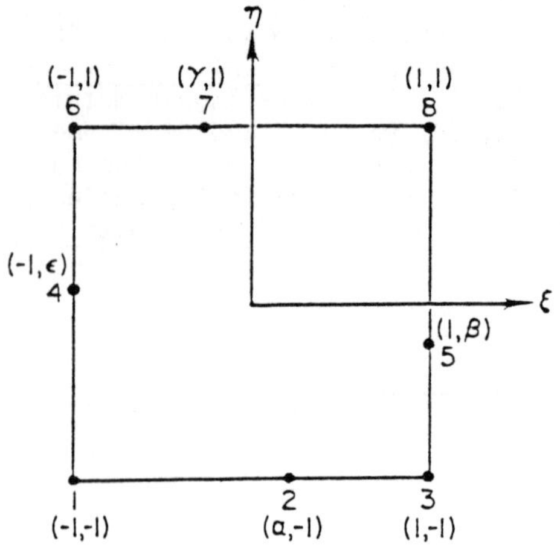

Figure 2 - Typical quadratic serendipity element showing node locations in the local space.

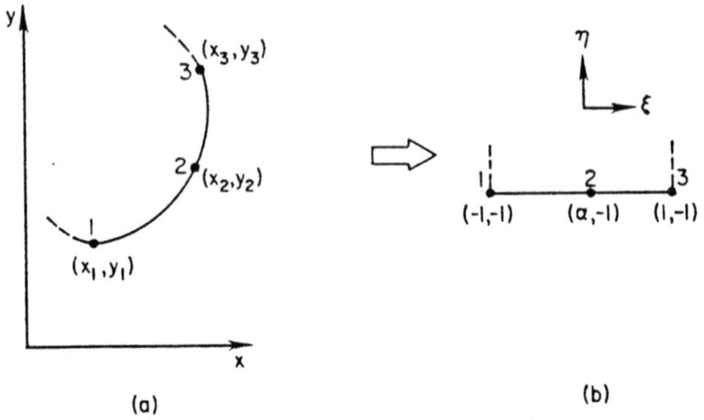

Figure 3 -- A curved element side (a) being mapped to the local coordinate system (b).

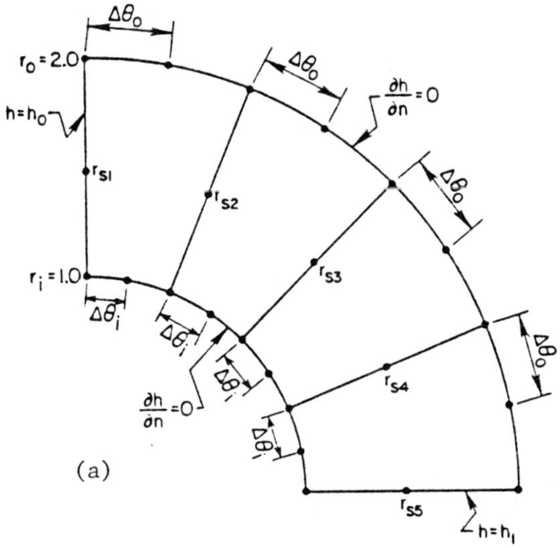

(b)

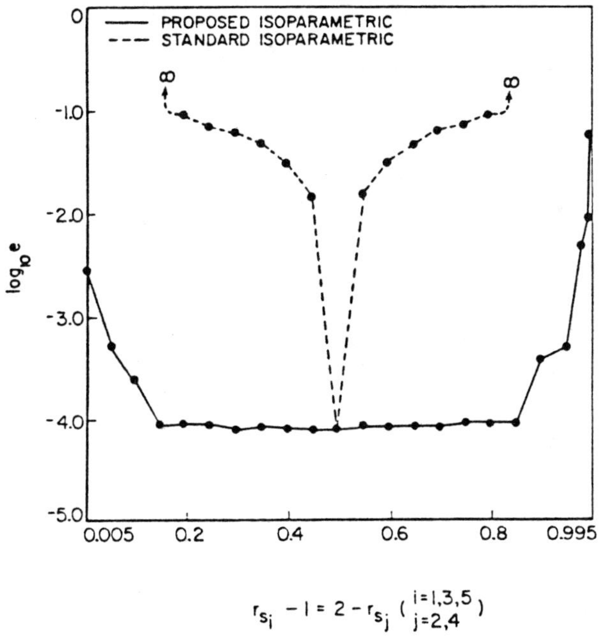

Figure 4 -- Domain, showing node locations and elements (a), used for the example problem. The values of $\Delta\theta_o$ and $\Delta\theta_i$ are held at $\pi/16$. Error norms are plotted as functions of node placement (b) for both the standard ICT and the new ICT.

Node Coordinates (ξ_i, η_i)	ϕ_i	Basis Function
(-1,-1)	ϕ_1	$\frac{1}{4}(1-\xi)(1-\eta)\left[\frac{(1+\alpha)(1+\varepsilon) - (1+\alpha)(1+\eta) - (1+\varepsilon)(1+\xi)}{(1+\alpha)(1+\varepsilon)}\right]$
$(\alpha,-1)$	ϕ_2	$\frac{1}{2}(1-\eta)\left[\frac{1-\xi^2}{1-\alpha^2}\right]$
(1,-1)	ϕ_3	$\frac{1}{4}(1+\xi)(1-\eta)\left[\frac{(1-\alpha)(1+\beta) - (1-\alpha)(1+\eta) - (1+\beta)(1-\xi)}{(1-\alpha)(1+\beta)}\right]$
$(1,\beta)$	ϕ_5	$\frac{1}{2}(1+\xi)\left[\frac{1-\eta^2}{1-\beta^2}\right]$
(1,1)	ϕ_8	$\frac{1}{4}(1+\xi)(1+\eta)\left[\frac{(1-\gamma)(1-\beta) - (1-\gamma)(1-\eta) - (1-\beta)(1-\xi)}{(1-\gamma)(1-\beta)}\right]$
$(\gamma,1)$	ϕ_7	$\frac{1}{2}(1+\eta)\left[\frac{1-\xi^2}{1-\gamma^2}\right]$
(-1,1)	ϕ_6	$\frac{1}{4}(1-\xi)(1+\eta)\left[\frac{(1+\gamma)(1-\varepsilon) - (1+\gamma)(1-\eta) - (1-\varepsilon)(1+\xi)}{(1+\gamma)(1-\varepsilon)}\right]$
$(-1,\varepsilon)$	ϕ_4	$\frac{1}{2}(1-\xi)\left[\frac{1-\eta^2}{1-\varepsilon^2}\right]$

Table 1 -- Local coordinate basis functions for element in Figure 2.

VI International Conference on Finite Elements in Water Resources, Lisboa, Portugal, June 1986

New Developments in Numerical Mathematics

W.C. Conley
Departments of Mathematics and Business Administration, The University of Wisconsin at Green Bay, Green Bay, Wisconsin 54302, U.S.A.

INTRODUCTION

A new numerical mathematics solution technique called multi stage Monte Carlo optimization (MSMCO) is presented along with several examples of its application. It is a general purpose optimization technique that could find many applications in water resource problems.

Multi variate multi population sample size problems are easier to solve with MSMCO. In many cases this reduces the number of samples needed for a specified general level of confidence. Linear homogeneous differential equations with constant coefficients are easily solvable with MSMCO as are certain types of Lagrange multiplier optimization problems.

Multivariate reliability theory problems from finite or continuous distributions is another area of application along with scheduling problems.

Linear and nonlinear systems of equations with integral, real and or complex coefficients (constrained or not) can be solved with multi stage.

These developments could be of interest to scientists in water resource studies.

A FINITE ELEMENT TECHNIQUE SYSTEM

The finite element method is discussed by Steffens (1985) and a five equation six variable linear system is presented and solved in a mechanical equilibrium setting using standard linear techniques. However that problem and other finite element problems (linear or nonlinear) could be attempted with multi stage Monte Carlo optimization (MSMCO) after appropriate transformations have been made. As an example find a solution to the system

$$10X_1=16(X_2-X_1) \quad (1)$$
$$16(X_2-X_1)=5(X_3-X_2) \quad (2)$$
$$5(X_3-X_2)=40(X_4-X_3) \quad (3)$$
$$40(X_4-X_3)=8(X_5-X_4) \quad (4)$$
$$8(X_5-X_4)=20(X_6-X_5) \quad (5)$$
$$20(X_6-X_5)=4(X_7-X_6) \quad (6)$$
$$4(X_7-X_6)=80 \quad (7)$$

in the region $1 \leq X_i \leq 100$, for i=1,2,.....7. This problem is similar to the Steffens (1985) example in form but a little larger.

We transform the system to minimize

$$f(X_1,X_2,X_3,X_4,X_5,X_6,X_7)=|10X_1-16(X_2-X_1)|+|16(X_2-X_1)-5(X_3-X_2)| +|5(X_3-X_2)-40(X_4-X_3)|+|40(X_4-X_3)-8(X_5-X_4)|+|8(X_5-X_4)-20(X_6-X_5)| +|20(X_6-X_5)-4(X_7-X_6)|+|4(X_7-X_6)-80| \quad (8)$$

subject to $1 \leq X_i \leq 100$ for i=1,2,....7.
The MSMCO algorithm draws a sample of 20,000 potential answers inside the seven dimensional "cube" (centered at (50,50,50,50, 50,50,50) and bounded by $1 \leq X_i \leq 100$.) and stores the best one (smallest f value). Then the "cube" is divided in half in each dimension and a sample of 20,000 more potential answers is drawn inside this new smaller cube, always centered around the best answer so far. Then a new "cube" (with each of the seven dimensions divided in half again) is sampled 20,000 times for better answers and the best one stored. This process is repeated until the solution is produced. $f(X_1,X_2,X_3,X_4,X_5,X_6,X_7)$ was minimized to zero after a total of 140,000 samples out of the 100,000,000,000,000 feasible solutions had been looked at with the MSMCO algorithm. The solution produced to the above transformed system was
$X_1=8$, $X_2=13$, $X_3=29$, $X_4=31$, $X_5=41$, $X_6=45$, $X_7=65$
with total error =0.

The bounds can be widened and different sampling schemes can be used (all revolving around the law of large numbers and the central limit theorem) as the problem and theory dictate.

MSMCO APPLIED TO A DIFFERENTIAL EQUATION

Consider the homogeneous linear differential equation

$$\frac{d^{25}y}{dx^{25}} + \frac{d^{24}y}{dx^{24}} + \frac{d^{23}y}{dx^{23}} + \ldots\ldots \frac{d^{2}y}{dx^{2}} + \frac{dy}{dx} + y=0 \quad (9)$$

Employing the standard polynomial operator $D=\frac{d}{dx}$, all that needs to be done is to solve the corresponding characteristic polynomial (using MSMCO)

$$\sum_{j=0}^{25} D^j=0 \quad (10)$$

for its twenty-five roots to obtain the primitive.

We solve the characteristic polynomial

$$\sum_{j=0}^{25} D^j=0 \tag{11}$$

by transforming it to

$$f_1(a,b)=\left|\sum_{j=0}^{25} D^j\right| \tag{12}$$

where D=a+bi is complex and a and b are real numbers. Then $f_1(a,b)$ is minimized to zero with MSMCO by twenty-one times drawing 125 sample complex numbers in ever decreasing size rectangles centered about the best answer so far. The rectangles shoot across the feasible solution space of f_1 to a minimum of zero hence producing the first root r_1. Then r_1 is factored out by defining

$$f_2(a,b)=\left|\left\{\sum_{j=0}^{25} D^j\right\}/(D-r_1)\right|. \tag{13}$$

Then f_2 is minimized by the same converging multi stage Monte Carlo process just described for f_1. The 21x125 sample answers provide a trail to the second root r_2. Then r_2 is factored out by defining

$$f_3(a,b)=\left|\left\{\sum_{j=0}^{25} D^j\right\}/\{(D-r_1)(D-r_2)\}\right|. \tag{14}$$

f_3 is then minimized similarly producing r_3.

This process continues until lastly

$$f_{25}(a,b)=\left|\left\{\sum_{j=0}^{25} D^j\right\}/\left\{\prod_{i=1}^{24}(D-r_i)\right\}\right| \tag{15}$$

is minimized to zero producing r_{25}. The roots are listed in the following table.

Table 1

The Roots of $\sum_{j=0}^{25} j=0$

Root Number	Real Part	Complex Part	Error Term
1	-.748510748171	.663122658341	.000000000001
2	.568064746731	.822983865894	.000000000001
3	-.568064746731	-.822983865894	.000000000000
4	.354604887042	-.935016242685	.000000000001
5	-1.000000000000	-.000000000000	.000000000000
6	-.120536680255	.992708874098	.000000000000
7	.970941817426	-.239315664288	.000000000001
8	-.120536680255	-.992708874098	.000000000001
9	-.354604887042	.935016242685	.000000000001
10	.885456025653	.464723172044	.000000000000
11	.748510748171	-.663122658241	.000000000000
12	-.970941817426	-.239315664288	.000000000000
13	-.970941817426	.239315664288	.000000000000

Root Number	Real Part	Complex Part	Error Term
14	.354604887043	.935016242685	.000000000000
15	-.748510748171	-.663122658241	.000000000000
16	.120536680255	-.992708874098	.000000000000
17	-.568064746731	.822983865894	.000000000000
18	.885456025653	-.464723172044	.000000000000
19	.748510748171	.663122658241	.000000000000
20	-.354604887043	-.935016242685	.000000000000
21	.970941817426	.239315664287	.000000000000
22	-.885456025653	-.464723172044	.000000000000
23	-.885456025653	.464723172044	.000000000000
24	.120536680255	.992708874098	.000000000000
25	.568064746731	-.822983865894	.000000000000

The technique is completely general and should work on any polynomial. The one page FORTRAN IV program is easy to use and runs quickly on various computers. Also the absolute value transformation could be generalized. Consider the system of equations (linear or nonlinear with real or complex coefficients)

$$A_1(X_1,X_2,X_3,X_4,X_5)=C_1 \quad (16)$$

$$A_2(X_1,X_2,X_3,X_4,X_5)=C_2 \quad (17)$$

$$A_3(X_1,X_2,X_3,X_4,X_5)=C_3 \quad (18)$$

$$A_4(X_1,X_2,X_3,X_4,X_5)=C_4 \quad (19)$$

$$A_5(X_1,X_2,X_3,X_4,X_5)=C_5 \quad (20)$$

Define

$$g(X_1,X_2,X_3,X_4,X_5)=|A_1-C_1|+|A_2-C_2|+|A_3-C_3|+|A_4-C_4|+|A_5-C_5| \quad (21)$$

and minimize using multi stage MSMCO. This technique works with a variety of linear and nonlinear systems.

This brings up the possibility of developing and or solving more complex operator systems involving multivariate polynomials and or nonlinear systems of equations. Knowing that a solution to the general nonlinear system of equations can be attempted with MSMCO could be of some use to differential equations operator researchers.

MULTIVARIATE RELIABILITY THEORY

Three examples are presented here. The first one involves a system with eleven components that work with set probabilities. The question is how many backups are needed in order to reach a given level of confidence in the device. The second problem involves a device with nine components that fail over time as a function of nine different normal distributions. The problem is to use the correct number of backup components to meet a certain level of reliability for the device. The third example is like the second problem but costs are also considered and there are 35 components involved. The three examples demonstrate that functional form differences are easily handled with MSMCO. Therefore comments about other types of reliability problems that could be solved in this manner are made.

Example 1 - Fixed Probabilities

A device with eleven components in series is to be made. The probability of each component working is given in table 2.

Table 2
Reliability of Components

component	probability of working
1	$p_1=$ .65
2	$p_2=$ .75
3	$p_3=$ .60
4	$p_4=$ .95
5	$p_5=$ .80
6	$p_6=$ .90
7	$p_7=$ .80
8	$p_8=$ .85
9	$p_9=$ .90
10	$p_{10}=$ .70
11	$p_{11}=$ .65

The manufacturer requires that this device work with overall probability .99. Therefore the question of how many backups to use for each component can be found by solving

$$\prod_{i=1}^{11} (1-(1-P_i)^{X_i})=.99 \qquad (22)$$

where $1\leq X_i\leq 25$ for $i=1,2,.....25$ and X_i is the number of backups plus one. The company has decided not to use more than twenty four backups to any one component.

Therefore the problem is transformed to minimize

$$f(X_1,X_2,X_3,.........X_{11})=\left|\prod_{i=1}^{11} (1-(1-P_i)^{X_i})-.99\right| \qquad (23)$$

subject to $1\leq X_i\leq 25$ (and the X_i's are whole numbers) and solved with MSMCO. Five solutions are presented here (there are many).

Table 3
Solutions

$X_1=18$, $X_2=19$, $X_3=23$, $X_4=19$, $X_5=11$, $X_6=18$, $X_7=22$,
$X_8=17$, $X_9=2$, $X_{10}=23$, $X_{11}=21$

$X_1=22$, $X_2=15$, $X_3=20$, $X_4=13$, $X_5=24$, $X_6=11$, $X_7=19$,
$X_8=19$, $X_9=2$, $X_{10}=14$, $X_{11}=22$

$X_1=16$, $X_2=18$, $X_3=23$, $X_4=7$, $X_5=19$, $X_6=2$, $X_7=15$,
$X_8=24$, $X_9=23$, $X_{10}=24$, $X_{11}=20$

$X_1=20$, $X_2=17$, $X_3=23$, $X_4=21$, $X_5=21$, $X_6=2$, $X_7=25$,
$X_8=10$, $X_9=20$, $X_{10}=17$, $X_{11}=16$

$X_1=19$, $X_2=14$, $X_3=25$, $X_4=11$, $X_5=22$, $X_6=11$, $X_7=11$,
$X_8=17$, $X_9=2$, $X_{10}=14$, $X_{11}=23$

Example 2 - Continuous Probabilities

A company is to make a device that has nine components in series. Each one of the nine components has a length of life described by a different normal distribution as given in table 4.

Table 4
Length of Life of Components

component	normally distributed length of time it should work in hours	
1	$u_1 = 11000$	$\sigma_1 = 1500$
2	$u_2 = 9000$	$\sigma_2 = 1000$
3	$u_3 = 8500$	$\sigma_3 = 1250$
4	$u_4 = 12000$	$\sigma_4 = 2000$
5	$u_5 = 10000$	$\sigma_5 = 1400$
6	$u_6 = 6000$	$\sigma_6 = 500$
7	$u_7 = 14000$	$\sigma_7 = 1750$
8	$u_8 = 5000$	$\sigma_8 = 1800$
9	$u_9 = 7000$	$\sigma_9 = 1100$

How many backups should each component have so that the device stands at least a 95% chance of lasting 25,000 hours?

Recalling that the sum of n normally distributed random variables with mean u and standard deviations σ is also normally distributed with mean nu and standard deviation $\sqrt{n}\sigma$, this fact along with the standard normal distribution and the standard normalizing Z transformation

$$Z=\frac{X-u}{\sigma} \tag{24}$$

(where X is normally distributed) are programmed into the MSMCO algorithm and the number of backups is found (for each component) such that

$$\prod_{i=1}^{9}\{P(Z_i \geq 25{,}000 \text{ hours})\} \geq .95 \text{ for } i=1,2,.....9$$

where $P(Z_i \geq 25{,}000)$ is the probability that the ith component plus its backups lasts at least 25,000 hours.

One solution produced was (there are others) 16 backups for component 1, 36 backups for component 2, 22 for component 3, 9 for component 4, 2 for component 5, 6 for component 6, 25 for component 7, 6 for component 8 and finally 19 backups for component 9.

Example 3 - Continuous Probabilities and Cost Consideration

A company has embarked on a project where component reliability is essential. They have an opportunity to make a device for under sea data collection, but the president of the company wants to be 99.5% sure that the device lasts for five years (the projected length of life of the under sea data collection mission) and doesn't cost much more than $500,000 dollars for the components to build it.

Therefore the president and the chief engineer decide to make five identical devices to package together for the under sea data mission. All five will be submerged together and report back data. But the mission will be considered successful as long as at least one of the five units lasts for the full five years. Therefore requiring a .995 success rate means no more than a .005 failure rate therefore

$$.005=X^{1/5}. \quad (25)$$

So X=.3466. Therefore if each of the five units stands about a 65.5% chance of lasting five years or 43,800 hours, then the president of the company will be about 99.5% sure that at least one of the five units lasts the five year length of the data gathering mission.

Now each unit has 35 components (with separate normal distribution length of life rates) in series. So all thirty five must work for the unit to keep working. The Table gives the length of life rates and cost per unit for each component.

Table 5
Length of Life and Costs

component	normally distributed length of time it should work in hours		costs per unit
1	u_1=10,000	σ_1=1000	c_1=\$100.
2	u_2=12,000	σ_2= 900	c_2= 250.
3	u_3= 6,000	σ_3= 800	c_3= 195.
4	u_4=11,000	σ_4=2000	c_4= 600.
5	u_5=19,000	σ_5=3000	c_5= 250.
6	u_6=14,000	σ_6=1000	c_6= 800.
7	u_7=12,000	σ_7=1500	c_7= 350.
8	u_8=15,000	σ_8=1800	c_8= 280.
9	u_9= 8,000	σ_9=1500	c_9= 175.
10	u_{10}=11,500	σ_{10}=1400	c_{10}= 50.
11	u_{11}=16,500	σ_{11}=2000	c_{11}= 700.
12	u_{12}=17,000	σ_{12}=3000	c_{12}= 400.
13	u_{13}=16,000	σ_{13}=2500	c_{13}= 295.
14	u_{14}=12,500	σ_{14}=3000	c_{14}= 458.
15	u_{15}=13,000	σ_{15}=2500	c_{15}= 265.
16	u_{16}=17,500	σ_{16}=2100	c_{16}= 703.
17	u_{17}= 7,000	σ_{17}=1000	c_{17}= 258.
18	u_{18}= 9,000	σ_{18}=2000	c_{18}= 390.
19	u_{19}=12,000	σ_{19}=4000	c_{19}= 550.
20	u_{20}=14,000	σ_{20}=3000	c_{20}= 604.
21	u_{21}= 9,000	σ_{21}=2500	c_{21}= 880.
22	u_{22}=11,000	σ_{22}=2000	c_{22}= 75.
23	u_{23}=20,000	σ_{23}=5000	c_{23}= 490.
24	u_{24}=16,500	σ_{24}=4000	c_{24}= 609.
25	u_{25}=21,000	σ_{25}=4500	c_{25}= 715.
26	u_{26}=14,500	σ_{26}=3000	c_{26}= 250.
27	u_{27}=19,500	σ_{27}=6000	c_{27}= 525.
28	u_{28}=12,000	σ_{28}=4500	c_{28}= 418.
29	u_{29}=17,000	σ_{29}=3500	c_{29}= 640.
30	u_{30}=24,000	σ_{30}=6500	c_{30}= 780.

31	u_{31}=16,500	σ_{31}=4000	c_{31}= 800.
32	u_{32}=15,500	σ_{32}=5000	c_{32}= 705.
33	u_{33}=11,000	σ_{33}=3000	c_{33}= 680.
34	u_{34}=18,000	σ_{34}=5000	c_{34}= 500.
35	u_{35}=14,000	σ_{35}=4500	c_{35}= 359

Therefore given the one half million dollar budget for the five identical units and the 99.5% requirement the MSMCO algorithm must solve the simultaneous equations

$$\prod_{i=1}^{35} \{P(Z_i \geq 43{,}800 \text{ hours})\} = .655 \quad \text{and} \tag{26}$$

$$\sum_{i=1}^{35} C_i X_i = 100{,}000 \text{ dollars} \tag{27}$$

where $P(Z_i \geq 43{,}800$ hours) is the probability that the ith component plus its backups lasts at least five years and C_i is the unit cost of component i and X_i is the number of backups of component i plus one.

The problem is implicity a function of the X_i's so MSMCO minimizes

$$f(X_1, X_2, X_3 \ldots X_{35}) = \left| \prod_{i=1}^{35} \{P(Z_i \geq 43{,}800)\} - .655 \right| + \left| \sum_{i=1}^{35} C_i X_i - 100{,}000 \right| \cdot .00001 \tag{28}$$

(Note that the .00001 weight on the last term "balances" the equations to make the solution easier to find) yielding the solution in Table 6.

Table 6

X_i is the number of components of type i to use (backups plus one).

X_1=5	X_2=5	X_3=32	X_4=7	X_5=5
X_6=6	X_7=5	X_8=7	X_9=9	X_{10}=10
X_{11}=5	X_{12}=3	X_{13}=20	X_{14}=6	X_{15}=8
X_{16}=8	X_{17}=8	X_{18}=7	X_{19}=6	X_{20}=5
X_{21}=8	X_{22}=6	X_{23}=4	X_{24}=5	X_{25}=7
X_{26}=4	X_{27}=8	X_{28}=5	X_{29}=3	X_{30}=3
X_{31}=5	X_{32}=5	X_{33}=7	X_{34}=3	X_{35}=5

Overall Probability is .656644
Cost is \$100,861.

Interpreting the solution, the company should have four backups for component 1, four for component 2, thirty one for component 3 and so on for all 35 components. They should make five of these units at about \$100,861 cost of components each.

More accuracy could be had with other solution runs, but the 65.66% and \$100,861 versus our goals of 65.5% and \$100,000 seem accurate enough given the normal estimated length of life errors that are probably inherent in those projections. Several price lists could be simultaneously compared from different suppliers with different levels of quality components. Fixed and continuous probability distributions of varying type (not all normal etc.) could be considered together as well as components wired in series and or parallel. Minimum cost solutions within certain standards could be pursued with the MSMCO algorithm in reliability problems. More multi stage (MSMCO) examples are in Conley (1984).

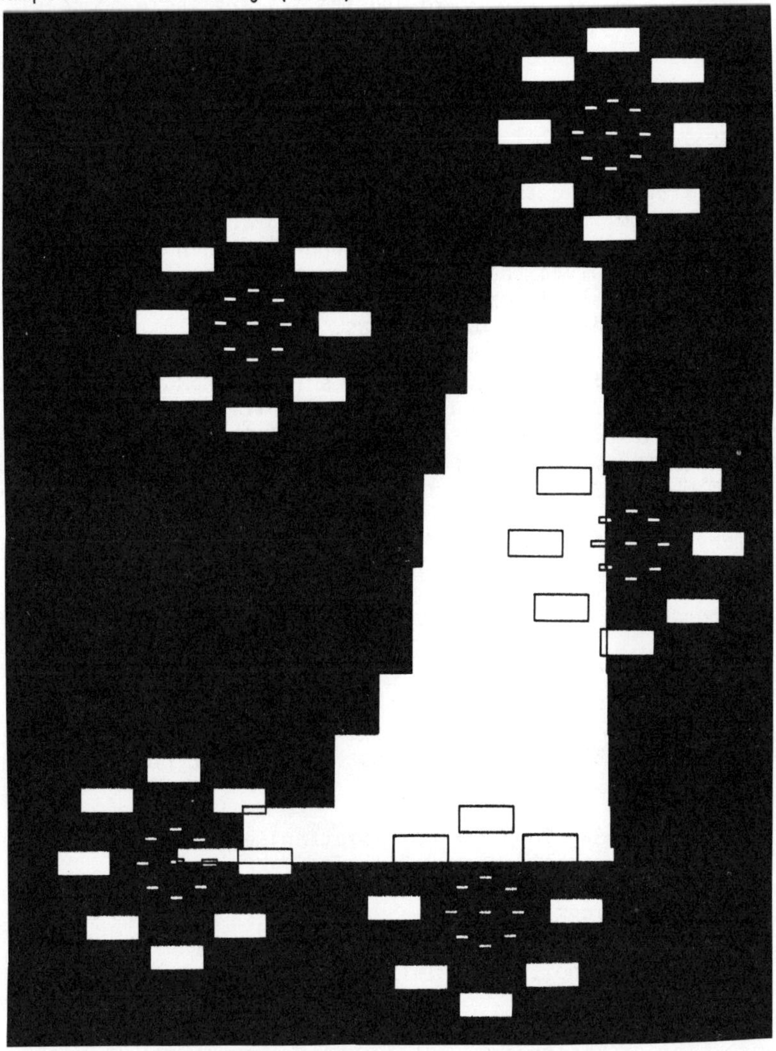

Figure 1. Four MSMCO preliminary discovery samples show the way across the sampling distribution of the transformed system to the solution represented by the cluster in the lower left hand corner of the distribution.

CONCLUSION

MSMCO was used to solve a thirty equation thirty variable nonlinear system of the form

$$X_i X_j^2 = C_k \qquad (29)$$

for $1 \le i \le 30$, $1 \le j \le 30$, $k=1,2,3,\ldots 30$, $1 \le X_i \le 100$, $1 \le X_j \le 100$ for $i=1,2,3,\ldots 30$, $j=1,2,3,\ldots 30$ and the X's are whole numbers. The unique whole number solution out of $1X10^{60}$ feasible solutions was produced using the MSMCO sampling scheme illustrated in Figure 1.

Figure 1 is a partial statistical representation of the sampling distribution of a nonlinear optimization problem (such as the transformed thirty by thirty system mentioned above). The cluster of rectangles (ever reducing and moving across thirty dimensional space) in the lower left hand corner of the distribution solved the system after the other four clusters led the way by taking preliminary Bayesian discovery samples to find out where the solution was.

Woodside (1984) showed that Conley's (1982) MSMCO solution to a multivariate Lagrange multipliers problem was correct, demonstrating that MSMCO works on problems that can be solved with Lagrange or Newton Rhapson techniques. Conley (1983) uses MSMCO to solve multivariate constrained sample size problems that can reduce the cost of sampling 10 or 20 percent in many cases for a specified overall confidence level. The flexibility of MSMCO is its best feature.

REFERENCES

Conley, W. (1982) An Economic Order Quantity Problem, Int. J. Math. Educ. Sci. Technol., 13:265-268.

Conley, W. (1983) BASIC II Advanced. Petrocelli Books, Princeton.

Conley, W. (1984) Computer Optimization Techniques Revised Edition. Petrocelli Books, Princeton.

Steffens, K. (1985) Obtaining "Know How" in Material Forming Technology by Means of Computer Simulation, Int. J. Math. Educ. Sci. Technol., 16:191-195.

Woodside, W. (1984) A Multiple Commodity Inventory Problem with Storage Constraint, Int. J. Math. Educ. Sci. Technol., 15:1-5.

VI International Conference on Finite Elements in Water Resources, Lisboa, Portugal, June 1986

Finite Element Error Estimates for Nonlinear Variational Inequalities

M.A. Noor
Mathematics Department, College of Science, King Saud University, Riyadh 11451, Saudi Arabia

ABSTRACT

Variational inequality theory provides us not only a unified and general view point for studying many unrelated moving and free boundary problems arising in fluid flow through porous media, contact problems in elasticity and many other branches of mathematical and engineering sciences but also gives a natural framework for applying numerical methods. Finite element techniques are being used effectively for numerically solving variational inequalities. In this paper, we derive the error estimates for the finite element approximations of a class of highly nonlinear variational inequalities characterizing a fluid flow problem in porous media in an arbitrary domain and show that these are of order h in the energy norm. The results obtained are an improvement as well as extension of the previously known results for elliptic variational inequalities.

1. INTRODUCTION

Variational inequalities theory as developed mainly by the Italian and French schools in the early 1970's constituted a significant extension of the variational principles and led to new and numerous applications in diverse fields of mathematical and engineering sciences. The variety of the problems to which the variational inequality techniques may be applied is impressive and amply representative for the richness of the field. Variational inequalities techniques provide a sound basis for an approximate solutions of moving and free boundary value problems. In 1971, Baiocchi proposed a new way of formulating flow problems through porous media in terms of variational inequalities, which has proved highly effective in both theoretical and numerical respects. The general problem of the fluid flow through porous media in an arbitrary domain is one of the most difficult problem both analytically and numerically. The issue of existence of solution to such problem in most cases is still open. Inherent in these free boundary problems is the free-surface problem of identifying the unknown free surface. In addition to these difficulties, the formulation of these problems in terms of variational inequalities give rise to non-differentiable forms.

In recent years, significant advances have been made to overcome these formidable difficulties by using numerical methods including finite element technique which has emerged as a new discipline combining approximation theory, numerical analysis and computer science together. The success of the finite element technique is mainly attributed to its gnerality, versatility and ability to analyze complex configurations. To-day finite element can be used on any physical problem which can be formulated in terms of differential, integral or integro-differential equations. In this article, we use the finite element technique to find error estimates for the approximate solutions of a class of highly nonlinear variational inequalities arising in the study of a fluid flow problem in porous media and show that these are of order h in the energy norm. However, it should be emphasized that the kind of numerical problems which occur in lubrication, laminar flow and contact problems can be formulated in terms of these nonlinear variational inequalities and the error estimates are the same.

Following this introductory section, variational inequality formulation problem is considered in Section 2 in a general framework. In Section 3, we derive the general error estimates for the finite element approximations of the variational inequalities and show that these error estimates are of order h in the energy norm for a problem of fluid flow through porous media. Due to the space limit, we only give the main outlines of our results. Full details will appear elsewhere.

2. FORMULATION AND BASIC RESULTS.

We, first of all, consider the formulation of variational inequalities in the setting of larger spaces of functions than those containing the classical solutions. We thus start in a Hilbert space context and later are specialized. We now introduce some notions.

Let H be a real Hilbert space with its dual H', whose inner product and norm are denoted by (.,.) and $\|\cdot\|$. respectively. The pairing between the elements of H' and H is denoted by <.,.> and M is a closed convex subset of H.
Let a(u,v) be a coercive and continuous bilinear form on H and the form $b(u,v): H\times H \longrightarrow \mathbb{R}$ satisfy the following properties:

(1) b(.,.) is linear in the first variable.
(ii) b(.,.) is bounded, that is there exist a constant $\gamma > 0$ such that

$$|b(u,v)| \leq \gamma \| u \| \| v \|, \quad \text{for all } u,v \in H.$$

(iii) b(.,.) is either convex or linear in the second variable.
(iv) $|b(u,v)-b(u,w)| \leq b(u,v-w)$, for all $u,v,w \in H$.

We now consider the problem of finding the minimum of the functional I[u], defined by

$$I[v]=a(v,v)+b(v,v)-2f(v), \quad \text{for all } v \in H, \quad (1)$$

on the convex set M in H. It has been shown by Baiocchi and Capelo [1984], Crank [1984], and Oden and Kikuchi [1980] that the fluid flow problem through porous media in an arbitrary region can be formulated in terms of the functional I[u], defined by (1). In fact, the functional I[v] represents the potential energy (virtual work) associated with the fluid flow problem. We would like to point out that almost the whole theory of variational principles can be based on the minimum of the functional I[v] for the time independent problems.
For the linear continuous functional f, the minimum of I[v] on M in H is equivalent finding $u \in M$ such that

$$a(u,v-u)+b(u,v)-b(u,u) \geq \langle f, v-u \rangle, \text{for all } v \in M, (2)$$

a case considered by Oden and Pires [1981]. For a differentiable nonlinear continuous functional, using the technique of Noor [1982], we can show that the minimum of I[v] on M can be characterized by a class of variational inequalities of the type.

$$a(u,v-u)+b(u,v)-b(u,u) \geq \langle f'(u),v-u \rangle, \text{ for all } v \in M, \quad (3)$$

where f'(u) is the Frechet differential of f at $u \in H$.

Special Cases:
I. If the form $b(u,v) \equiv 0$, then it is clear that the minimum of I[v] on M can be characterized by

the following classes of variational inequalities:

$$a(u,v-u)\geq\langle f, v-u\rangle, \quad \text{for all } v\in M. \tag{4}$$

and

$$a(u,v-u)\geq\langle f'(u),v-u\rangle, \text{ for all } v\in M. \tag{5}$$

The variational inequality (4) is due to Lions and Stampacchia [1967] and whereas (5) was introduced by Noor [1975]. For the finite element approximations of these variational inequalities, see Ciarlet [1978] and Noor [1984].

II. If we restrict the dependence of the form $b(u,v)$ to its second variable only, that is $b(u,v)\equiv j(v)$, then the minimum of $I[v]$ on M in H may be characterized by the following variational inequalities

$$a(u,v-u)+j(v)-j(u)\geq\langle f,v-u\rangle, \quad \text{for all } v\in M \tag{6}$$

and

$$a(u,v-u)+j(v)-j(u)\geq\langle f'(u),v-u\rangle \text{ , for all } v\in M. \tag{7}$$

For the piecewise finite element approximations of the solutions of variational inequalities (6) and (7), it has been shown that the error estimates are of order h in the energy norm, see Noor [1984] and Noor [1986] for the existence and uniqueness of the solution of these variational inequalities alongwith the error estimates and applications. It is obvious from the above discussion that the variational inequality (3) is most general and include the previously known ones as special cases.

3. GENERAL ERROR ESTIMATES.

We now establish a general error estimate for the finite element approximations of the solution of the variational inequality (3). Our estimates are quite general and hold for any finite element subspace S_h and approximate convex set M_h. Our results represent a significant improvemtn of all the error estimates for elliptic variational inequalities that can be found in the literature.
In order to derive the error estimates for approximate solutions for variational inequality (3), we consider an approximate form of these inequalities. Thus, let S_h be a finite dimensional subspace of H and $M_h\subset H$ be a finite dimensional convex set; for the

construction of S_h and M_h, see Ciarlet [1978] and Oden and Carey [1984].
An approximate form of (3) is that of finding $u_h \varepsilon M_h$ such that

$$a(u_h, v_h - u_h) + b(u_h, v_h) - b(u_h, u_h) \geq \langle f'(u_h), v_h - u_h \rangle, \tag{8}$$

for all $v_h \varepsilon M_h$.
Similarly we can also construct an approximation of (2), (6) and (7) of the form:

$$a(u_h, v_h - u_h) + b(u_h, v_h) - b(u_h, u_h) \geq \langle f, v_h - u_h \rangle, \text{ for all } v_h \varepsilon M_h. \tag{9}$$

$$a(u_h, v_h - u_h) + j(v_h) - j(u_h) \geq \langle f, v_h - u_h \rangle, \text{ for all } v_h \varepsilon M_h \tag{10}$$

$$a(u_h, v_h - u_h) + j(v_h) - j(u_j) \geq \langle f'(u_h), v_h - u_h \rangle, \text{ for all } v_h \varepsilon M_h. \tag{11}$$

respectively.
With these preliminaries established, we can now derive the main result of this paper.

Theorem 1
Let $u \varepsilon M$ and $u_h \varepsilon M_h$ be the solutions of (3) and (8) respectively, then

(i) For $M_h \subset M$,

$$\begin{aligned} \|u - u_h\| \leq C[&\|u - v_h\| + \|v - u_h\|^2 + \|v_h - v\| \\ &+ \{(\|f'(u) - Tu\| \, \|u - v_h\|)^{\frac{1}{2}} + (\|f'(u_h) - Tu_h\| \, \|u_h - v\|)^{\frac{1}{2}} \\ &+ (\|u\| (\|u_h - v\| + \|u - v_h\|))^{\frac{1}{2}}\}], \end{aligned}$$

for all $v \varepsilon M$, and $v_h \varepsilon M_h$. (12)

(ii) For $M_h \not\subset M$,

$$\begin{aligned} \|u - v_h\| \leq C[&\|u - v_h\| + (\|f'(u_h)\| \, \|u - v_h\|)^{\frac{1}{2}} \\ &+ (\|u\| \, \|u - v_h\|)^{\frac{1}{2}}], \quad \text{for all } v_h \varepsilon M_h, \end{aligned} \tag{13}$$

where $a(u,v) = \langle Tu, v \rangle$, for all $v \varepsilon H$.

Proof.
(1) $M_h \subset M$.

Since $u \varepsilon M$ and $u_h \varepsilon M_h$ are solutions of (3) and (8), respectively, then adding (3) and (8), we have

$$a(u,u)+a(u_h,u_h)\leq\langle f'(u),v-u\rangle+\langle f'(u_h),v_h-u_h\rangle+b(u,u)$$
$$-b(u,v)+b(u_h,v_h)-b(u_h,v_h).$$

Subtracting $a(u,u_h)+a(u_h,u)$ from both sides and rearranging terms, see Noor [1986], we obtain

$$a(u-u_h,u-u_h)\leq a(u-u_h,v-u_h)+a(u-u_h,u-v_h)+\langle f'(u)$$
$$-f'(u_h),v_h-v\rangle+\langle f'(u)-Tu,u-v_h\rangle+\langle f'(u_h)-Tu_h,u_h-v\rangle$$
$$+b(u-u_h,u-u_h)+b(u,u_h-v)+b(u_h,u-v). \qquad (14)$$

Now by using the coercivity, continuity of $a(u,v)$, Lipschitz continuity of f' and the inequality $ab\leq\varepsilon a^2 + \frac{1}{4\varepsilon}b^2$, for positive a,b and any $\varepsilon>0$, we obtain the required estimate (12).

(ii) $M_h\not\subset M$.
Setting $v=u_h$ in (14), we obtain,

$$a(u-u_h,u-v_h)\leq a(u-u_h,u-v_h)+\langle f'(u)-f'(u_h),v_h-u_h\rangle$$
$$+\langle f'(u)-Tu,u-v_h\rangle+b(u-u_h,u-u_h)+b(u_h,u-v_h).$$

From the coercivity, continuity of $a(u,v)$, boundedness of $b(u,v)$ and rearranging terms, we obtain, the required estimate (13).

Special Case
If f is independent of the solution u, that is $f(u)\equiv f$, then our results represent an improvement of the results of Pires and Oden [1981-82]. In this case theorem 1 becomes:

(i) $M_h\subset M$;

$$\|u-u_h\|\leq c\{\|u_h-v\|+[\|Tu-f\|\,\|u-v_h\|+\|u_h-v\|]^{\frac{1}{2}}$$
$$+[c\|u\|_H(\|u-v_h\|+\|u_h-v\|)]^{\frac{1}{2}}\}, \quad \text{for all } v\in M, v_h\in M_h.$$

(ii) $M_h\not\subset M$;

$$\|u-u_h\|\leq c\{\|u-u_h\|+(\|Tu-f\|\,\|u-v_h\|)^{\frac{1}{2}}$$
$$+(c\|u\|_H\|u-v_h\|)^{\frac{1}{2}}\}, \quad \text{for all } v_h\in M_h.$$

For other special cases and full details, see Noor [1986].

4. APPLICATIONS.

The general problem of finding the dicharge of the water flow through a partially saturated arbitrary domain, see Baiocchi and Capelo [1984] and Oden and Kikuchi [1982], for mathematical and physical formulation of this model, can be characterized by a class of variational inequality of the type (3):

$$a(u,v-u)+b(u,v)-b(u,u)\geq\langle f'(u),v-u\rangle \text{ for all } v\in M. \quad (15)$$

Here

$$a(u,v)= \int_\Omega \nabla u.\nabla v dxdy$$

$$\langle f'(u),v\rangle=\int_\Omega f(u)vdxdy;$$

$$b(u,v) = \int_\Omega[\text{conv}(u)^+-v]^+dxdy$$

$$H=\{v\varepsilon H^1(D): v=0, \text{a.e on } D\}, \text{ a Hilbert space,}$$

$$M=\{v\varepsilon H;\ v\geq 0 \text{ on } D\}, \text{ a closed convex set in } H.$$

D is the whole domain, Ω is the unknown domain. Here and throughout this paper, we emply notations and conventions commonly used in the study of partial differential equations, see Ciarlet [1978]. Since the bilinear form a(u,v) is symmetric and positive, thus it is possible to associate with (15), the functional

$$I[v] = a(v,v)+b(v,v)-2f(v),$$

which is known as the potential energy functional. We now use the results of the previous section to derive the error estimates. To do so, we consider $\{T_h\}_{h>0}$ be a regular family of triangulation of D and define, see Ciarlet [1978],

$$S_h=\{v_h:\ v_h\varepsilon C^0(D);\ v_h/_T\varepsilon P_1 \text{ for all } T\varepsilon T_h\},$$

where P_1 is the set of all polynomials on $\mathbb{R}^2$ of degree ≤ 1. Clearly S_h is the finite dimensional subspace of H. The finite dimensional convex set M_h is defined as:

$$M_h=\{v_h:v_h\varepsilon S_h;\ v_h\geq 0 \text{ at every vertex of } T_h\}.$$

It is clear that $M_h\not\subset M$. We also need the following result, which can be easily proved using the method of Noor [1983].

Lemma 1:
There exists a constant C_1 such that

$$||f'(u_h)||_{L_2(D)} \leq C_1, \quad \text{for all } h>0.$$

For simplicity, we consider the special case of theorem 1(ii), where $M_h \subset M$. Using lemma 1 and the standard results of the approximation theory, see Ciarlet [1978], we obtain

$$||u-u_h||_1 = O(h^{\frac{1}{2}}),$$

which shows that the error estimate for the finite element approximation of a general class of variational inequalities is of order $h^{\frac{1}{2}}$ in the energy norm.

5. CONCLUSION.

In this paper, we have introduced and studied a new class of variational inequalities. The problem of fluid flow through porous media can be studied in the frame of these variational inequalities. Finite element techniques are used to derive the error estimates. The development and implementable algorithm for solving numerical different classes of variational inequalities requires further research efforts. A complete study of the moving and free boundary problems arising in the formulation of flow in the porous media (and contact problems in elasticity) is an interesting and very difficult problem both from the engineering and mathematical point of view.

ACKNOWLEDGEMENT

This research is supported by the Research Center of College of Science, King Saud University, Riyadh, under grant No. Math./1406/.

REFERENCES

Baiocchi, C. and Capelo, A. (1984), Variational and quasi variational inequalities, J. Wiley and Sons, New York.

Ciarlet, P.G. (1978), The finite element method for elliptic problems, North-Holland, New York.

Crank, J. (1984), Free and moving boundary problems, Oxford Press, London, U.K.

Lions, J. and Stampacchia, G. (1967), Variational inequalities, Comm. Pure Appl. Math. 20, 493-519.

Noor, M.A. (1982), Mildly nonlinear variational inequalities, Math. (Cluj), 47, 99-110.

Noor, M.A. (1983), Error analysis of mildly nonlinear variational inequalities, Carr. J. Math. 1(2), 49-62.

Noor, M.A. (1984), Finite element analysis of a class of contact problems, C.R. Math. Rep. Acad. Sci. Canada, 6,249-254.

Noor, M.A. (1985), Finite element analysis of a Signorini problem, Int. J. Engg. Sci. 23.

Noor, M.A. (1985), Nonlinear variational inequalities with applications to contact problems in elastostatistics, J. Math. Anal. Appl. (submitted).

Oden, J.T. and Carey, G. (1984), Finite elements (V), Prentice-Hall, N.J., U.S.A.

Oden, J.T. and Kikuchi, N. (1980), Theory of variational inequalities with applications to problems of flow through porous media, Int. J. Engg. Sci. 18, 1173-1284.

Oden, J.T. and Pires, E., (1981), Contact problems in elastostatics with non-local friction law, TICOM/8, University of Texas, Austin, U.S.A.

Pires, E. and Oden, J.T. (1981-82), Error estimates for the approximation of a class of variational inequalities rising in unilateral problems with friction, Num. Funct. Analy. and Opt. 4, 397-412.

VI International Conference on Finite Elements in Water Resources, Lisboa, Portugal, June 1986

An Element by Element Preconditioner for Iterative Equation Solvers

H.P. Langtangen, T. Rusten, A. Tveito and S.Ø. Wille
Institute of Informatics, University of Oslo, Norway

Abstract.

An element by element Incomplete Gaussian Elimination preconditioner is developed and tested with several linear equation solvers. An Inner Iteration procedure is used to speed up convergence. Also a new iterative linear equation solver is developed. The equation solvers are tested on the two dimensional convection-diffusion equation.

Introduction.

When differential equations are discretized by the Finite Element Method, linear equation systems of the form

$$\mathbf{Ax} = \mathbf{b} \quad \mathbf{A} \in \Re^{n,n}, \quad \mathbf{x}, \mathbf{b} \in \Re^{n} \tag{1}$$

must be solved. In the present paper we will be concerned with iterative solution of (1) when $\mathbf{A}$ is large sparse and nonsymmetric. For small n (1) is usually solved by standard Gaussian Elimination. When $\mathbf{A}$ is symmetric and positive definite the Conjugated Gradient method of Hestenes and Stiefel (1952) is usually applied. Recently a number of Generalized Conjugated Gradient methods to solve non-symmetric linear equation systems have been available. Numerical experiments with nine such iterative methods are presented here.

Preconditioning is used to improve the rate of convergence of iterative methods. Several methods for preconditioning have been proposed. Incomplete Gaussian Elimination, IGE, seems to be the fastest and most stable method, for a discussion confer Behie (1985) or Eisenstat et al (1985). The IGE-method is well suited for FEM-problems since FEM produces large and very sparse matrices.

Let

$$L(\phi) = f \quad \phi, f : \Omega \rightarrow \Re, \quad \Omega \subset \Re^2 \tag{2}$$

be a linear second order differential equation defined on Ω with boundary conditions on $\partial\Omega$. The domain Ω is divided into n_x, n_y parts in the x and y direction respectively. This gives $n_{el} = n_x n_y$ non-overlapping elements and $n_{no} = (n_x + 1)(n_y + 1)$ nodes. The equation (2) is discretized by bilinear elements. When the boundary conditions have been incorporated, a linear equation system of the form (1) arises with $n = n_{no}$ and where $\mathbf{x}$ gives the value of the approximate solution at each node. The matrix $\mathbf{A}$ is stored as element matrices i.e. no assembling in a global stiffnes matrix is done. This storage technique handles any geometry in both two and three dimensions and the storage requirement is only a function of n_{el} and the number of unknowns at each node. The algorithms of this paper are investigated on two dimensional regular grids with one unknown at each node. The element by element preconditioner will later be extended to handle any grid in both two and three dimensions.

Iterative methods.

There is a large number of linear equation solvers available for nonsymmetric problems. Eight of the most promising methods are chosen for numerical experiments. Also a new iterative method which will be presented in the next section, has been tested. All equation solvers are tested with and without element by element Incomplete Gaussian Elimination preconditioning.

These methods are:

1) Orthomin — see Vinsome (1976) or Wallis (1983).
2) Orthores — see Young and Jea (1980) or Wallis (1983).
3) Orthodir — see Young and Jea (1980).
4) Orthominres — see next section.
5) Lanczos-Orthomin — see Jea and Young (1983) or Fletcher (1975).
6) Lanczos-Orthores — see Jea and Young (1983) or Lanczos (1952).
7) Lanczos-Orthodir — see Jea and Young (1983).
8) Craigs Method — see Craig (1955).
9) The Conjugated Gradient Method for $\mathbf{A}^T\mathbf{A}\mathbf{x} = \mathbf{A}^T\mathbf{b}$ — see Hestenes and Stiefel (1952).

Lanczos-Orthomin is identical with the Biconjugated-Gradient method studied by Fletcher (1975). For an overview over Conjugate Gradient-Like methods see Saad and Schultz (1985).

Orthominres.

In this section a new iterative linear equation solver will be developed. The method is an extension of Orthores.

Let $\mathbf{x}^0, \mathbf{x}^1, \cdots, \mathbf{x}^i$ be approximations to $\mathbf{x}$ in (1), and define the residual vectors $\mathbf{r}^j = \mathbf{b} - \mathbf{A}\mathbf{x}^j, \quad j = 0, 1, \cdots i$. The new approximation to $\mathbf{x}$ is computed by

$$\mathbf{x}^{i+1} = \omega_1 \mathbf{p} + \omega_2 \mathbf{r}^i + \sum_{j=0}^{i} \alpha_j \mathbf{x}^j \tag{3}$$

where the parameters $\omega_1, \omega_2, \alpha_j \quad j = 0, 1, \cdots i$ and the vector $\mathbf{p}$ must be selected. Let

$$\sum_{j=0}^{i} \alpha_j = 1. \tag{4}$$

Then the new residual vector has the form

$$\mathbf{r}^{i+1} = \mathbf{b} - \mathbf{A}\mathbf{x}^{i+1} = -\omega_1 \mathbf{A}\mathbf{p} - \omega_2 \mathbf{A}\mathbf{r}^i + \sum_{j=0}^{i} \alpha_j \mathbf{r}^j. \tag{5}$$

The residual vectors is chosen to be orthogonal i.e.

$$(r^{i+1}, \mathbf{r}^m) = 0 \quad m = 0, 1, \cdots, i. \tag{6}$$

Then it follows from (5) that

$$\alpha_m = \omega_1 \frac{(\mathbf{A}\mathbf{p}, \mathbf{r}^m)}{(\mathbf{r}^m, \mathbf{r}^m)} + \omega_2 \frac{(\mathbf{A}\mathbf{r}^i, \mathbf{r}^m)}{(\mathbf{r}^m, \mathbf{r}^m)} \quad m = 0, 1, \cdots, i. \tag{7}$$

Equation (4) and (7) determine all the parameters α_j and ω_2 as functions of ω_1.

If we put $\omega_1 = 0$, the algorithm Orthores is obtained. This algorithm has one serious disadvantage, it does not minimize the norm of the residual vector. Our idea is to add a vector $\mathbf{p}$ in the approximation of $\mathbf{x}$ and minimize the residual in the direction of $\mathbf{p}$.

Define $E(\omega_1) = \|\mathbf{r}^{i+1}\|_2^2$. The parameter ω_1 is chosen to minimize the function E. Since

$$E(\omega_1) = (\sum_{j=0}^{i} \alpha_j \mathbf{r}^j - \omega_1 \mathbf{A}\mathbf{p} - \omega_2 \mathbf{A}\mathbf{r}^i, \sum_{j=0}^{i} \alpha_j \mathbf{r}^j - \omega_1 \mathbf{A}\mathbf{p} - \omega_2 \mathbf{A}\mathbf{r}^i)$$

where α_j and ω_2 are known functions of ω_1, E is a second degree polynomial in ω_1 and its minimum is uniquely determined by requiring

$$\frac{dE}{d\omega_1} = 0.$$

All the scalar parameters are now determined, it remains to choose the vector $\mathbf{p}$. There are several possible choices. A steepest descent choice would be $\mathbf{p} = -\nabla f(\mathbf{x}^i)$ where $f(\mathbf{x}) = \frac{1}{2}\mathbf{x}^T\mathbf{A}^T\mathbf{A}\mathbf{x} - (\mathbf{A}^T\mathbf{b})^T\mathbf{x}$, that is

$$\mathbf{p} = \mathbf{A}^T\mathbf{r}^i. \tag{8}$$

Another possibility is to choose

$$\mathbf{p} = \mathbf{A}\mathbf{r}^i. \tag{9}$$

Define the i-*th* Krylov space $K_i = \{\mathbf{r}^0, \mathbf{A}\mathbf{r}^0, \ldots, \mathbf{A}^{i-1}\mathbf{r}^0\}$. For the choice (9) we have $\mathbf{r}^i \in K_{2i}$. Both (8) and (9) have been implemented and tested. It turns out that (8) has two serious disadvantages compared with (9): *i*] (8) seems to give slower convergence, *ii*] an extra matrix-vector multiplication must be performed in (8) for each iteration. Because of this, $\mathbf{p} = \mathbf{A}\mathbf{r}^i$ is chosen.

Since the residual vectors are orthogonal, Orthominres will in absence of round-off errors converge to the exact solution of equation (1) in at most n iterations.

As for Orthomin, Orthores and Orthodir this algorithm should be truncated. Let k be a positive integer. The algorithm is truncated by only requiring that the i-*th* residual vector is orthogonal to the k previous residual vectors. Then the new approximative solution is formed by

$$\mathbf{x}^{i+1} = \omega_1 \mathbf{A}\mathbf{r}^i + \omega_2 \mathbf{r}^i + \sum_{j=max(0,i-k+1)}^{i} \alpha_j \mathbf{x}^j.$$

On computational form the following algorithm is obtained.

Algorithm Orthominres.

choose ε

$$\mathbf{x} := \mathbf{x}^0, \quad \mathbf{r}^0 := \mathbf{b} - \mathbf{A}\mathbf{x}^0$$

$$\rho_0 := (\mathbf{r}^0, \mathbf{r}^0), \quad e_0 := \rho_0$$

$$e := 1, \quad n := 0$$

while $e \geq \varepsilon$ *do*

begin

$$m := min(n,k), \quad n := n+1$$

$$\ell := mod(n,k+1), \quad j := mod(n-1,k+1)$$

$$\mathbf{p} := \mathbf{A}\mathbf{r}^j, \quad \mathbf{v} := \mathbf{A}\mathbf{p}$$

$$\xi_i := (\mathbf{p},\mathbf{r}^i), \quad \tau_i := (\mathbf{v},\mathbf{r}^i), \quad i = 0,1,\ldots,m, \quad i \neq \ell$$

$$s_1 := \sum_{\substack{i=0\\ i\neq\ell}}^{m} \frac{\tau_i}{\rho_i}, \quad s_2 := \sum_{\substack{i=0\\ i\neq\ell}}^{m} \frac{\xi_i}{\rho_i}$$

$$\gamma_i := (s_2\tau_i - s_1\xi_i)/s_2, \quad i = 0,1,\ldots,m, \quad i \neq \ell$$

$$h_1 := (\mathbf{p},\mathbf{v}), \quad h_2 := (\mathbf{p},\mathbf{p}), \quad h_3 := (\mathbf{v},\mathbf{v})$$

$$\omega_1 := \frac{\sum_{\substack{i=0\\ i\neq\ell}}^{m} \gamma_i\xi_i/\rho_i - h_1 + h_2 s_1/s_2}{s_2\left(-\sum_{\substack{i=0\\ i\neq\ell}}^{m} \gamma_i^2/\rho_i - 2h_1 s_1/s_2 + h_3 + (s_1/s_2)^2 h_2\right)}$$

$$\omega_2 := (1 - \omega_1 s_1)/s_2$$

$$\alpha_i := (\frac{\xi_i}{s_2} + \omega_1\gamma_i)/\rho_i, \quad i = 0,1,\ldots,m, \quad i \neq \ell$$

$$\mathbf{x}^\ell := \omega_1\mathbf{p} + \omega_2\mathbf{r}^j + \sum_{\substack{i=0\\ i\neq\ell}}^{m} \alpha_i\mathbf{x}^i, \quad \mathbf{r}^\ell := -\omega_1\mathbf{v} - \omega_2\mathbf{p} + \sum_{\substack{i=0\\ i\neq\ell}}^{m} \alpha_i\mathbf{r}^i$$

$$\rho_\ell := (\mathbf{r}^\ell,\mathbf{r}^\ell)$$

$$e := \sqrt{\frac{\rho_\ell}{e_0}}$$

end.

Incomplete Gaussian Elimination, IGE.

Let $\mathbf{M} \in \Re^{n_{no},n_{no}}$ be a nonsingular matrix, then the linear equation system $\mathbf{Ax} = \mathbf{b}$ may be replaced by

$$\mathbf{M}^{-1}\mathbf{Ax} = \mathbf{M}^{-1}\mathbf{b}. \tag{10}$$

The rate of convergence of the equation solvers tested here is strongly dependent of the condition number of the equation matrix. By solving another equivalent equation system where the matrix has a lower condition number, the rate of convergence will be increased.

We want the preconditioning matrix $\mathbf{M}$ to have the following properties (Gustafsson, 1980).

1) $\mathbf{M}$ is a good approximation of $\mathbf{A}$.
2) $\mathbf{M}$ is easily computed.
3) $\mathbf{M}$ do not require too much storage.
4) Equations of the form $\mathbf{Mx} = \mathbf{c}$ is easily solved ($O(n_{no})$ operations).

One way to compute a preconditioning matrix is to perform an IGE. This method is carefully studied by Meijerink and Van der Vorst (1977), Kershaw (1978), Gustafsson (1980) and Axelsson and Barker (1984). In this section it will be shown how IGE may be applied when the equation matrix is stored as element-matrices.

The IGE method computes an incomplete LU-factorization of $\mathbf{A}$, i.e. $\mathbf{M} = \tilde{\mathbf{L}}\tilde{\mathbf{U}}$. IGE is performed as usual Gaussian Elimination but all the fill-in terms are discarded. The preconditioning matrix may also be stored as element-matrices. The matrix $\mathbf{M} = \tilde{\mathbf{L}}\tilde{\mathbf{U}}$ does fulfill the requirements 1),2),3),4). The equation system $\mathbf{Mx} = \mathbf{c}$ is solved by a forward sweep and a backward substitution as in plain Gaussian Elimination.

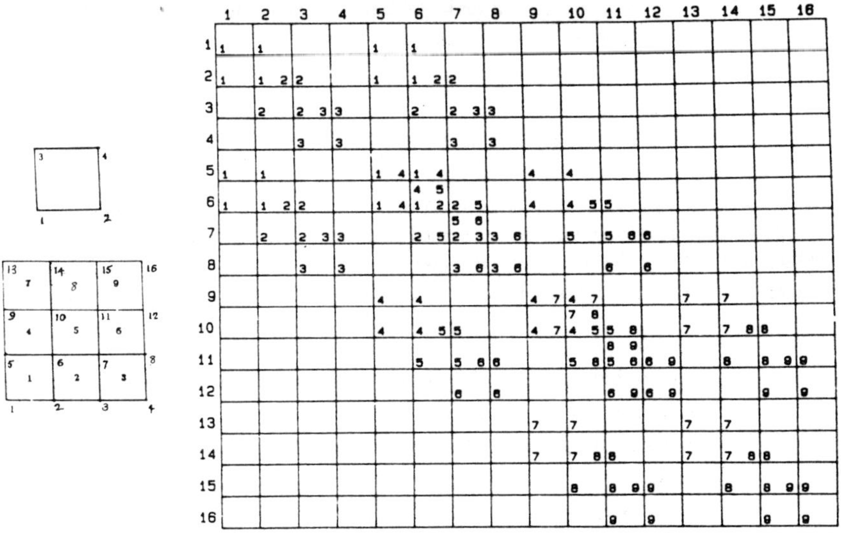

Figure 1. *The lower left part of this figure shows the element and global node ordering when $n_x = n_y = 3$, and the upper left the lokal node ordering. The right part shows how each element contribute to the matrix-locations. The numbers in the matrix are element numbers.*

The local and global numbering of the nodes are shown in figure 1. In figure 1 it is also indicated how each element contribute to the different matrix locations. When eliminating the element-matrices figure 1 is very helpful in checking that every term in the matrix is eliminated.

IGE for element-matrices.

for $n := 1$ *to* n_y *do*
begin
  for $k := 1$ *to* $n_x - 1$ *do*
  begin
    $e := n_x(n-1) + k$
    Eliminate local node # 1 in element # e.
    Add into the next element.
    Add into the element above.
  end
  * Elementboundary on the right hand side.
  $e := n_x \cdot n$
  Eliminate local node #1 and # 2 in element # e.
  Add into the element above.
end

```
* Upper elementboundary.
for k := 1 to n_x - 1 do
begin
   e := n_x(n_y - 1) + k
   Eliminate local node #1 and # 3 in element # e.
   Add into the next element.
end
e := n_el
Eliminate local node #1, 2, 3 in element # e.
```

To solve equation-systems of the form $\tilde{\mathbf{L}}\tilde{\mathbf{U}}\mathbf{x} = \mathbf{c}$, we first solve $\tilde{\mathbf{L}}\mathbf{y} = \mathbf{c}$ and then solve $\tilde{\mathbf{U}}\mathbf{x} = \mathbf{y}$. The first part can be performed similar to the IGE algorithm above. The solution of $\tilde{\mathbf{U}}\mathbf{x} = \mathbf{y}$ deserves some attention.

Backsubstitution: Solve $\tilde{\mathbf{U}}\mathbf{x} = \mathbf{y}$.

```
e := n_el
Determine the value of local node # 4 in element # e.
* Upper elementboundary.
for k := n_x downto 1 do
begin
   e := n_x(n_y - 1) + k
   Determine the value of local node # 3 in element # e.
end
for n := n_y downto 1 do
begin
   * Elementboundary on the right hand side.
   e := n_x · n
   Determine the value of local node # 2 in element # e.
   Determine the value of local node # 1 in element # e.
   for k := n_x - 1 downto 1 do
   begin
      e := n_x(n - 1) + k
      Determine the value of local node # 1 in element # e.
   end
end
```

In some of the algorithms listed in section 3, also equation-systems of the form $\mathbf{M}^T\mathbf{x} = \mathbf{c}$ must be solved. Since $\mathbf{M} = \tilde{\mathbf{L}}\tilde{\mathbf{U}}$, we must be able to solve the system

$$\tilde{\mathbf{U}}^T\tilde{\mathbf{L}}^T\mathbf{x} = \mathbf{c}. \tag{11}$$

To design an algorithm to solve (11) is slightly more complicated than just interchange the forward and backward substitution due to the fact that $\tilde{\mathbf{L}}$ is an unit lower triangular matrix, while $\tilde{\mathbf{U}}^T$ is only lower triangular.

Inner Iteration.

When linear systems are solved by preconditioned iterative methods, equation systems of the form $\mathbf{Az} = \mathbf{c}$ are solved approximately in each iteration. This is done by using an approximate factorization $\mathbf{M}$ of $\mathbf{A}$ and solving $\mathbf{Mz}^{i-1} = \mathbf{c}$ exact. Consider $\mathbf{z}^{i-1}$ as an approximation to $\mathbf{z}$ and define the residual vector $\tilde{\mathbf{r}}^{i-1} = \mathbf{c} - \mathbf{Az}^{i-1}$. Let us improve our approximation by a vector $\mathbf{s}^i$. Define the new approximation $\mathbf{z}^i = \mathbf{z}^{i-1} + \mathbf{s}^i$ where the vector $\mathbf{s}^i$ is chosen to reduce the residual. The new residual vector has the form $\tilde{\mathbf{r}}^i = \tilde{\mathbf{r}}^{i-1} - \mathbf{As}^i$, hence a proper choice of $\mathbf{s}^i$ would be the solution of $\mathbf{Ms}^i = \tilde{\mathbf{r}}^{i-1}$. We have then obtained a presumably better approximation $\mathbf{z}^i$ to $\mathbf{z}$. This improvement of the approximative solution is called an *inner iteration*. The following algorithm performs I inner iterations.

$$
\begin{aligned}
&\mathbf{z}^0 = \mathbf{M}^{-1}\mathbf{c} \\
&for\ i := 1\ to\ I\ do \\
&\quad \tilde{\mathbf{r}}^{i-1} := \mathbf{c} - \mathbf{Az}^{i-1} \\
&\quad \mathbf{s}^i := \mathbf{M}^{-1}\tilde{\mathbf{r}}^{i-1} \\
&\quad \mathbf{z}^i := \mathbf{z}^{i-1} + \mathbf{s}^i
\end{aligned}
\tag{12}
$$

$I = 0$ corresponds to standard preconditioning.

The algorithm (12) may be used to improve standard preconditioning of all the methods mentioned earlier. The inner-iteration method is tested on Orthomin and $I = 1$ seems to be an optimal choice.

Test-problem.

Let $\vec{v} = (u, v)$ where u, v are known constants. Consider the differential equation

$$
\begin{aligned}
\vec{v} \cdot \nabla\phi = \nabla^2\phi \quad & for\ \ (x,y) \in \Omega = (0,1)\mathrm{x}(0,1) \\
\phi = \phi_0 \quad & (x,y) \in \Gamma_0, \quad \Gamma_0 \neq \emptyset \\
\frac{\partial\phi}{\partial n} = 0 \quad & (x,y) \in \Gamma_1.
\end{aligned}
\tag{13}
$$

Here $\Gamma_0 \cap \Gamma_1 = \emptyset$ and $\Gamma_0 \cup \Gamma_1 = \partial\Omega$. This two dimensional stationary convection-diffusion equation is a well suited test-problem. By different choices of $\vec{v}$, symmetrical and non-symmetrical, and good and poor conditioned matrices can be generated. When $\|\vec{v}\|$ becomes large (13) approaches a hyperbolic problem where the solution is constant along the characteristics determined by $\vec{v}$. A discontinuous Dirichlet boundary condition will then produce a front in the solution.

Results.

In the experiments $k = 5$ direction vectors have been used for Orthomin, Orthores, Orthodir and Orthominres. When no preconditioning is used, k must be increased if the problem is poorly conditioned. When preconditioning is used, it is rarely necessary to use more than $k = 5$ direction vectors.

In table 1 the number of iterations the equation solvers used to obtain convergence is listed. The lower part of table 1 indicates how Inner Iterations effects the number of global iterations. The table shows that the number of iterations are greatly reduced when preconditioning is applied, and that the number of global iterations are further reduced by Inner Iterations. When reading table 1 it is important to be aware of the fact that the number of iterations are not a very good measure of the computational work. There are differences in the amount of computational work within an iteration for the different equation solvers. In the other figures the number of arithmetic operations (multiplications and divisions) needed to obtain convergence have been computed. This gives a reliable comparison of the methods.

Table 1.

This table gives the number of iteration required for each method to solve the differential-equation $10(\frac{\partial\phi}{\partial x} + \frac{\partial\phi}{\partial y}) = \nabla^2\phi$ *when* $n_{no} = 1369$ *(unknowns).*

Method	Without precond.	With precond.
Orthomin(5)	78	25
Orthores(5)	119	24
Orthominres(5)	53	12
Lanczos-Orthomin	82	21
Lanczos-Orthores	83	21
Lanczos-Orthodir	81	20
Conjugated Gradients for $\mathbf{A}^T\mathbf{A}$	612	59
Craigs Method	636	59

For the above problem, this table show how inner iterations reduces the number of global iterations .

Number of Inner Iterations	0	1	2	3	4	5
Orthomin(5) with Inner Iterations	25	15	12	9	8	7

Table 2.

Nine different versions of equation (13) was solved and the average number of arithmetic operations was computed for each equation solver. The number of unknowns was $n_{no} = 1369$. *This table shows the average number of arithmetic operations counted in millions. Because of its instability, Orthodir does not appear in the table.*

Method	Computational work
Preconditioned Orthominres(5)	1.2
Preconditioned Orthores(5)	1.5
Preconditioned Orthomin(5)	1.6
Preconditioned Lanczos-Orthomin	1.6
Preconditioned Lanczos-Orthores	1.8
Preconditioned Lanczos-Orthodir	1.8
Preconditioned Conj. Grad. for $\mathbf{A}^T\mathbf{A}$	4.6
Preconditioned Craigs Method	4.6
Lanczos-Orthomin	5.1
Orthominres(5)	5.3
Lanczos-Orthores	5.5
Lanczos-Orthodir	5.5
Orthomin(5)	5.8
Orthores(5)	6.7
Conjugated Gradients for $\mathbf{A}^T\mathbf{A}$	27.3
Craigs method	27.8

In table 2 the average number of arithmetic operations for nine different problems with $n_{no} = 1369$ are listed. From the table the following results are obtained.

1) The new method, Orthominres, is fastest.
2) Preconditioning reduces the computational work considerably.
3) If no preconditioning is used, Lanczos-Orthomin is fastest.
4) Conjugated Gradients for $\mathbf{A}^T\mathbf{A}$ and Craigs method converge very slow, especially when no preconditioning is used.

Figure 2 show that one Inner Iteration seems to minimize the computational work. Orthomin with Inner Iterations has been tested on other problems with the same result.

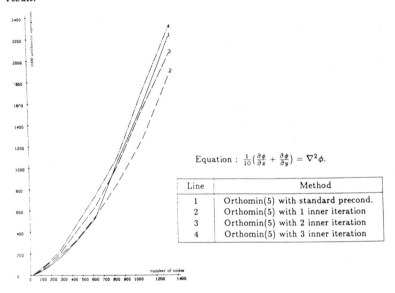

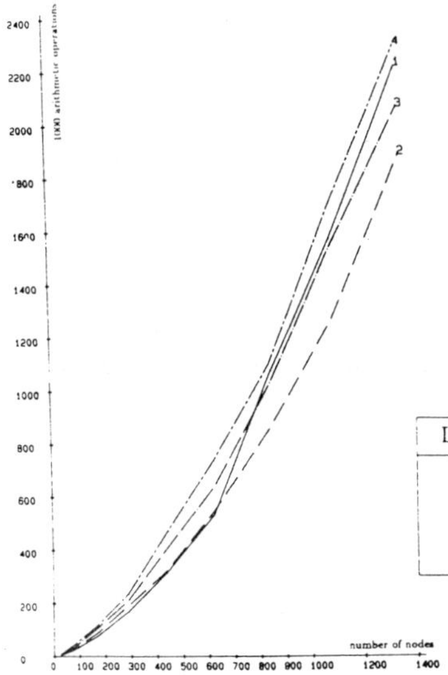

Equation : $\frac{1}{10}\left(\frac{\partial\phi}{\partial x} + \frac{\partial\phi}{\partial y}\right) = \nabla^2\phi.$

Line	Method
1	Orthomin(5) with standard precond.
2	Orthomin(5) with 1 inner iteration
3	Orthomin(5) with 2 inner iteration
4	Orthomin(5) with 3 inner iteration

Figure 2.

The figure shows the computational work as a function of the number of nodes for Orthomin with inner iterations. For this problem one inner iteration was the optimal choice.

The Lanczos–methods has the advantage of requiring less storage than Orthomin, Orthores, Orthodir and Orthominres. The four latter methods use about the same amount of storage when the number of direction vectors k are equal.

Breakdown is a serious problem when using iterative equation solvers for nonsymmetric problems. From the experiments we draw the conclusion that Orthodir is unstable, and when Orthodir converges it seem to require more computational work than Orthomin, Orthores and Orthominres. The other methods seem roughly equally stable. Breakdowns also occur for these methods, but no regular pattern has been observed.

Conclusion.

Several numerical experiments with iterative equation solvers have been performed. The convergence of these methods may be very slow when no preconditioning is used. The element by element IGE preconditioning has worked well, it reduces the computational work at least by a factor of two. One Inner Iteration further reduces the amount of work. The new iterative equation solver, Orthominres, compares favourably with the other methods.

References.

Axelsson, O. and Barker, V.A. (1984) Finite Element Solutions of Boundary Value Problems. Theory and Computation, Academic Press, New York.

Behie, A. (1985) Comparison of nested factorization, constrained pressure residual and incomplete factorization preconditioners, in Society of Petroleum Engineers of AIME, proceedings of the eighth symposium on reservoir simulation, Dallas.

Craig, E.J. (1955) The N-step iteration procedure, J. Math. Phys., 34: 65-73.

Eisenstat, S.C., Elman, H.C. and Schultz, M.C.(1985) Block-preconditioned Conjugate-Gradient-like methods for numerical reservoir simulation, in Society of Petroleum Engineers of AIME, proceedings of the eighth symposium on reservoir simulation, Dallas.

Fletcher, R. (1975) Conjugate Gradient Methods for Indefinite Systems, in Proceedings of the Dundee Biennal Conference of Numerical Analysis, (ed: G. A. Watson) Springer, New York.

Gustafsson I. (1980) On modified incomplete factorization methods, Numerical Integration of Differential Equation and Large Linear Systems, Proceedings, Biefield, (ed: Juergen Hinze) Springer-Verlag.

Hestenes, M.R and Stiefel, E.(1952) Methods of Conjugate Gradients for Solving Linear Systems, J. Res. Nat. Bur. Standards, 49:409-436.

Jea, K.C. and Young, D.M. (1983) On the Simplification of Generalized Conjugate-Gradient Methods for Nonsymmetrizable Linear Systems, Lin. Alg. and its Appl. 52,53:399-417.

Kershaw, D.S. (1978) The incomplete Cholesky-Conjugate Gradient Method for the Iterative Solution of Systems of Linear Equations, J. Comput. Phys. 26:43-65.

Lanczos, C. (1952) Solution of Systems of Linear Equations by Minimized Iterations, J. Res. Nat. Bur. Standards, 49:33-53.

Meijerink, J.A. and van der Vorst, H.A. (1977) An iterative solution method for linear systems of which the coefficient matrix is a symmetric M-matrix, Math. Comp., 31:148-162.

Saad, Y. and Schultz, M.H. (1985) Conjugate Gradient-Like Algorithms for Solving Nonsymmetric Linear Systems, Math. Comp., 44:417-424.

Vinsome P.K.W. (1976) Orthomin, an iterative method for solving sparse sets of simultaneous linear equations, in Society of Petroleum Engineers of Aime, Proceedings of the fourth symposium on reservoir simulation. Los Angeles.

Wallis, J.R. (1983) Incomplete Gaussian elimination as a preconditioning for generalized Conjugate Gradient acceleration, in Society of Petroleum Engineers of AIME, Proceedings of the seventh symposium on reservoir simulation, San Francisco.

Young, D.M. and Jea, K.C. (1980) Generalized Conjugate-Gradient Acceleration of Nonsymmetrizable Iterative Methods, Lin. Alg. and its Appl., 34:159-194.

VI International Conference on Finite Elements in Water Resources, Lisboa, Portugal, June 1986

Numerical Aspects of Adjoint Solutions

N.R. Thomson, J.F. Sykes
Department of Civil Engineering, University of Waterloo, Waterloo, Ontario, N2L 3G1, Canada

INTRODUCTION

The major objective of sensitivity analysis of simulation models is to determine the change in model results as a result of changes in the model input or system parameters. Conventional sensitivity analysis utilizes direct parameter sampling in which parameters are perturbed one by one and the complete set of system equations are resolved. Sensitivity coefficients for each of these perturbed parameters may be derived by a finite difference approximation. An efficient alternative is the adjoint sensitivity method (Sykes et al 1985, Sykes and Wilson, 1984) which requires the solution of only two system matrix equations in order to determine the sensitivity of a user selected system performance function to all parameters. The finite element solution of the primary or forward problem yields the nodal state variables while the adjoint equation or backward problem is solved for the adjoint state variables. Sensitivity coefficients for the performance function can then be expressed in terms of these two solutions and derivatives of the forward problem equations. While the forward problem may be non linear, the related backward problem will always be linear.

There has been much investigation of the numerical properties of the discretized primary problem. For example, cell Péclet and Courant numbers (O'Neill, 1981) are utilized in selection of temporal and spatial discretization for advective-dispersion problems. Upstream weighting schemes (e.g. Hughes, 1978), lumped time formulations (e.g. Huyakorn, 1976) and various finite difference time schemes (e.g. Smith, 1976) are often used to control problems such as numerical dispersion and oscillations.

Comparatively, there have been few investigations of the numerical properties of the discretized backward problem or adjoint equation. In the case of transient problems, the adjoint equations are solved backward in space and time. Normal performance functions are in the form of Dirac delta functions at user selected points in space and time.

This paper addresses some of the numerical problems that may occur when solving for the adjoint state variable. The primary and adjoint equations for both transient flow and mass transport are presented. The numerical details for the treatment of the discretized form of the performance measure is outlined. Results of numerical experiments utilizing the one-dimensional mass transport equation are presented.

ADJOINT STATE EQUATIONS

A performance or response function is user selected and for a transient flow or mass transport problem it may be written as

$$P = \int_t \int_A f(\phi,\underline{\alpha},\underline{x},t)\ dAdt \qquad (1)$$

where $f(\phi,\underline{\alpha},\underline{x},t)$ is a specified function of the system state variable ϕ, the vector of system parameters $\underline{\alpha}$, of the Cartesian coordinate system $\underline{x}$ and time t.

Flow

The governing equation for the vertically integrated transient groundwater flow problem written in tensor notation is

$$S\frac{\partial h}{\partial t} = \frac{\partial}{\partial x_i}\left[T_{ij}(h)\frac{\partial h}{\partial x_j}\right] + Q \qquad (2)$$

where S is the storativity, h is the hydraulic head (L), T_{ij} is the transmissivity tensor (L^2/T) and Q is the areal recharge or discharge ($L^3/T/L^2$). The boundary conditions associated with (2) are

$$h(\Gamma_1,t) = \hat{h} \text{ on } \Gamma_1 \qquad (3a)$$

$$q_i(\Gamma_2,t)\ n_i = \hat{q} \text{ on } \Gamma_2 \qquad (3b)$$

where $\hat{h}$ is the prescribed head on boundary Γ_1, $\hat{q}$ is a prescribed normal flux to boundary Γ_2 (as designated by the components of the unit outward normal n_i), and $\Gamma_1+\Gamma_2 = \Gamma$ represents the external boundary of the spatial domain. The initial conditions required by (2) are determined from the steady state flow equation

$$\frac{\partial}{\partial x_i}\left[T_{ij}(h_o)\frac{\partial h_o}{\partial x_j}\right] + Q = 0 \tag{4}$$

with boundary conditions

$$h_o(\Gamma_1,0) = \hat{h}_o \text{ on } \Gamma_1 \tag{4a}$$

$$q_i(\Gamma_2,0)\, n_i = \hat{q}_o \text{ on } \Gamma_2 \tag{4b}$$

where h_o is the initial hydraulic head (L), $\hat{h}_o$ is the initial prescribed head on Γ_1, and $\hat{q}_o$ is the initial prescribed normal flux to boundary Γ_2.

In conjunction with the performance measure (1), the governing equation (2), boundary conditions (3) and initial conditions (4) there exists a linear adjoint governing equation expressed in terms of ψ^*, the adjoint state variable (also known as the importance function):

$$-S\frac{\partial\psi^*}{\partial t} - \frac{\partial}{\partial x_j}\left[T_{ij}(h)\frac{\partial\psi^*}{\partial x_i}\right]$$

$$+\frac{\partial T_{ij}(h)}{\partial h}\frac{\partial h}{\partial x_j}\frac{\partial\psi^*}{\partial x_i} - \frac{\partial f}{\partial h} = 0 \tag{5}$$

In combination with (5) are the following boundary conditions

$$\psi^*(\Gamma_1,t) = 0 \text{ on } \Gamma_1 \tag{6a}$$

$$T_{ij}\frac{\partial\psi^*}{\partial x_i}(\Gamma_2,t)\, n_j = 0 \text{ on } \Gamma_2 \tag{6b}$$

and final conditions

$$\psi^*(x_i,t_f) = 0 \tag{7}$$

where t_f represents the final time. The initial adjoint state value ψ_o^* is coupled to the initial condition adjoint variable β^* by

$$\psi^*(t_o)S - \frac{\partial}{\partial x_j}\left[T_{ij}(h_o)\frac{\partial\beta^*}{\partial x_i}\right] + \frac{\partial T_{ij}(h_o)}{\partial h_o}\frac{\partial h_o}{\partial x_j}\frac{\partial\beta^*}{\partial x_i} = 0 \tag{8}$$

with boundary conditions

$$\beta^*(\Gamma_1) = 0 \text{ on } \Gamma_1 \tag{9a}$$

$$T_{ij}\frac{\partial\beta^*}{\partial x_i}n_j(\Gamma_2) = 0 \text{ on } \Gamma_2 \tag{9b}$$

where t_o represents the initial time.

Equation (5) is solved backwards in time from the final adjoint state value at t_f, equation (7), to the initial time, t_o. The adjoint state variable for the initial time t_o, is then utilized as a component in the forcing or load to determine the initial or steady state adjoint state value, β^*. Of importance is the impact on equation (5) of the derivative of the integrand of the performance measure with respect to the state variable h.

Marginal sensitivity coefficients are calculated based on the forward problem solution and adjoint state variables ψ^* and β^* as

$$\frac{\partial P}{\partial \alpha_k} = \int_t \int_A \left[\frac{\partial f}{\partial \alpha_k} - \psi^* \frac{\partial S}{\partial \alpha_k} \frac{\partial h}{\partial t} - \frac{\partial \psi^*}{\partial x_i} \frac{\partial T_{ij}(h)}{\partial \alpha_k} \frac{\partial h}{\partial x_j} + \psi^* \frac{\partial Q}{\partial \alpha_k} \right] dA dt$$

$$- \int_t \int_{\Gamma_1} \frac{\partial \hat{h}}{\partial \alpha_k} T_{ij} \frac{\partial \psi^*}{\partial x_i} n_j \, d\Gamma_1 \, dt$$

$$+ \int_t \int_{\Gamma_2} \psi^* \frac{\partial \hat{q}}{\partial \alpha_k} \Gamma_2 \, dt$$

$$+ \int_A \left[\frac{\partial \beta^*}{\partial x_i} \frac{\partial T_{ij}(h_o)}{\partial \alpha_k} \frac{\partial h_o}{\partial x_j} - \beta^* \frac{\partial Q}{\partial \alpha_k} \right] dA$$

$$+ \int_{\Gamma_1} \frac{\partial \hat{h}_o}{\partial \alpha_k} T_{ij} (h_o) \frac{\partial \beta^*}{\partial x_i} n_j \, d\Gamma_1$$

$$- \int_{\Gamma_2} \beta^* \frac{\partial \hat{q}_o}{\partial \alpha_k} d\Gamma_2 \qquad (10)$$

where α_k is a member of the vector of system parameters $\underline{\alpha}$.

The first term in (10) represents the direct effect of α_k on the performance measure while the following five terms represent transient contributions to the marginal sensitivity from storativity, components of the transmissivity tensor, recharge or discharge, prescribed boundary heads and prescribed boundary flux, respectively. The remaining four terms reflect contributions from the parameters used to derive the initial conditions.

Transport

The primary advection dispersion equation can be written in tensor notation as

$$\frac{\partial C}{\partial t} = \frac{\partial}{\partial x_i}\left[D_{ij}\frac{\partial C}{\partial x_j}\right] - V_i\frac{\partial C}{\partial x_i} \tag{11}$$

with the following initial and boundary conditions

$$C(x_i, 0) = \hat{C}_o \text{ on } D \tag{12}$$

$$C(x_i, t) = \hat{C} \text{ on } \Gamma_1 \tag{13a}$$

$$\left[-D_{ij}\frac{\partial C}{\partial x_j} + V_i C\right] n_i = J \text{ on } \Gamma_2 \tag{13b}$$

where C is concentration (M/L^3), t is time (T), V_i is the average linear velocity (L/T), D_{ij} is the dispersion tensor (L^2/T), $\hat{C}_o$ is the initial concentration, $\hat{C}$ is the prescribed concentration on boundary Γ_1, J is the prescribed mass flux normal to the boundary Γ_2, and $\Gamma_1 + \Gamma_2 = \Gamma$ represents the external boundary of the spatial domain.

The adjoint state equation for the mass transport equation (11) with initial conditions (12), boundary conditions (13) and performance measure (1) is

$$\frac{\partial \psi^*}{\partial t} + \frac{\partial}{\partial x_j}\left[D_{ij}\frac{\partial \psi^*}{\partial x_i}\right] + \frac{\partial(\psi^* V_i)}{\partial x_i} + \frac{\partial f}{\partial C} = 0 \tag{14}$$

with final conditions

$$\psi^*(x_i, t_f) = 0 \tag{15}$$

and boundary conditions

$$\psi^*(\Gamma_1, t) = 0 \text{ on } \Gamma_1 \tag{16a}$$

$$D_{ij}\frac{\partial \psi^*}{\partial x_i} n_j = 0 \text{ on } \Gamma_2 \tag{16b}$$

It is the inclusion of the final term in equation (14) that necessitates special consideration.

Marginal sensitivity coefficients which are based on the forward problem and the adjoint state variable ψ^* are calculated from the following

$$\frac{\partial P}{\partial \alpha_k} = \iint\limits_{t\,A} \left[\frac{\partial f}{\partial \alpha_k} - \frac{\partial \psi^*}{\partial x_i} \frac{\partial D_{ij}}{\partial \alpha_k} \frac{\partial C}{\partial x_j} + C \frac{\partial}{\partial x_i} \left(\frac{\partial V_i}{\partial \alpha_k} \psi^* \right) \right] dAdt$$

$$+ \int\limits_A \psi^*(t_o) \frac{\partial \hat{C}_o}{\partial \alpha_k} dA$$

$$- \iint\limits_{t\,\Gamma_1} \frac{\partial \hat{C}}{\partial \alpha_k} D_{ij} \frac{\partial \psi^*}{\partial x_i} n_j \, d\Gamma_1 \, dt$$

$$- \iint\limits_{t\,\Gamma_2} \psi^* \frac{\partial J}{\partial \alpha_k} d\Gamma_2 \, dt. \tag{17}$$

The first term in (17) represents the direct effect of α_k on the performance function while the following terms represent the contributions to the marginal sensitivity from the components of the dispersion tensor, the linear velocity, initial concentrations, prescribed boundary concentration and the prescribed mass flux respectively.

DISCRETE EQUATIONS

The finite element solution to the non-linear transient flow equation (2) or the linear advection dispersion equation (11) and the associated boundary conditions can be approximated in general by

$$\underline{\underline{S}} \frac{d\underline{\phi}}{dt} = \underline{\underline{H}}(\underline{\alpha},\underline{\phi}) + \underline{h}(\underline{\alpha},\underline{\phi}) \tag{18}$$

where $\underline{\phi}$ is a vector representing the primary state variable, $\underline{\underline{S}}$ is a system matrix, $\underline{\underline{H}}$ is a banded coefficient matrix, $\underline{h}$ is a load vector, $\underline{\alpha}$ is a vector of system parameters. Discretizing the temporal term yields

$$\underline{\underline{A}}(k)\ \underline{\phi}(k) = \underline{\underline{B}}(k-1)\ \ \underline{\phi}(k-1) + \underline{c}(k) \tag{19}$$

where

$$\underline{\underline{A}}(k) = \frac{1}{\Delta t_k} \underline{\underline{S}} - \theta\ \underline{\underline{H}}(\underline{\alpha},\underline{\phi}'), \tag{20a}$$

$$\underline{\underline{B}}(k-1) = \frac{1}{\Delta t_k} \underline{\underline{S}} + (1-\theta)\ \underline{\underline{H}}(\underline{\alpha},\underline{\phi}'), \tag{20b}$$

$$\underline{c}(k) = \theta \underline{h}(\underline{\alpha},\underline{\phi}(k)) + (1-\theta)\ \underline{h}\ (\underline{\alpha},\underline{\phi}(k-1)), \tag{20c}$$

$k = 1,2,3,\ldots N$ representing the time level,
θ is the time weighting coefficient,
$\underline{\phi}'$ is the non-linear state variable evaluated between $\underline{\phi}(k)$ and $\underline{\phi}(k-1)$.

The adjoint state variable for this discrete equation (19) can be derived by the method described by Sykes and Wilson (1984) which yields the following written in Vetter notation

$$\left[\underline{\underline{A}}(k) + \frac{\partial \underline{\underline{A}}(k)}{\partial \underline{\phi}^T} (\underline{\underline{I}} * \underline{\phi}(k)) - \frac{\partial \underline{c}}{\partial \underline{\phi}^T} \right]^T \Delta t_k \, \underline{\psi}^*(k) =$$

$$\left[\underline{\underline{B}}(k) + \frac{\partial \underline{\underline{B}}(k)}{\partial \underline{\phi}^T} (\underline{\underline{I}} * \underline{\phi}(k)) \right]^T \Delta t_{k+1} \underline{\psi}^*(k+1) + \frac{\partial \underline{f}(k)}{\partial \underline{\phi}^T} \Delta t_k \qquad (21)$$

where $\underline{\psi}^*$ is the vector representing the adjoint state variable associated with the primary problem (18), the operator * is the Kronecker or outer product and $\frac{\partial \underline{f}(k)}{\partial \underline{\phi}^T}$ is the partial of the discretized performance function. It is this term that is the source of the numerical problems that develop while solving for the adjoint state variable. The spatial and temporal increments over which the term is integrated must be carefully considered. The calculated sensitivity coefficients will be a function of these increments.

Equation (21) is solved backward in time from the final value of the adjoint state variable, $\psi^*(N)$. The time step increment contained within the matrix $\underline{\underline{A}}(k)$ and $\underline{\underline{B}}(k)$ are not the same, $\underline{\underline{A}}(k)$ contains the time increment Δt_k while $\underline{\underline{B}}(k)$ contains Δt_{k+1}. This results as a consequence of the transposed matrix system or a reversal in space.

A typical form of the continuous performance measure (1) is

$$P = \iint_{t\ A} g(x,t)\ \phi\ (x,t)\ dAdt \qquad (22)$$

where g(x,t) is user-selected weighting function identifying the region and time of importance. For a particular value of the state variable at location $\hat{x}$ at time $\hat{t}$ the weighting function takes the following form

$$g(x,t) = \delta(x-\hat{x})\ \delta(t-\hat{t}). \qquad (23)$$

Thus, the marginal sensitivity coefficients derived by using such a performance function provide information on the change in the state variable at $\hat{x}$ and $\hat{t}$ to a change in system parameters over all space for time less than or equal to $\hat{t}$. Based on (23) the discretized form of (22) is

$$P = \sum_{i=1}^{n} \sum_{k=1}^{N} g_i(k)\ \phi_i(k)\ \Delta t_k \tag{24}$$

where $g_i(k)$ is the importance weighting function for node i at time level k, and n is the total number of nodes.

In order to match the weighting function for the continuous situation in (23), the question arises as to what is the appropriate time increment. Since the summation in (24) is over the number of time steps it is suitable to use a weighted average that encompasses $\hat{t}$. For instance $g_i(k)$ may take the following form

$$g_i(k) = \delta(i-\hat{i}) \left[\gamma \frac{\delta(k-\hat{k})}{\Delta t_{\hat{k}}} + \frac{(1-\gamma)\ \delta(k-\hat{k}+1)}{\Delta t_{\hat{k}-1}} \right] \tag{25}$$

where $\hat{i}$ is the ith node that corresponds to location $\hat{x}$, $\hat{k}$ and $\hat{k}-1$ are time steps that bound $\hat{t}$ and γ is the weighting factor which enables the importance of the time steps $\hat{k}$ and $\hat{k}-1$ to be altered. Substituting (25) into (24) and summing results in a performance measure of

$$P = \gamma\ \phi_{\hat{i}}\ (\hat{k}) + (1-\gamma)\ \phi_{\hat{i}}\ (\hat{k}-1). \tag{26}$$

Equation (26) provides an average of $\phi_{\hat{i}}$ over the period $\Delta t_{\hat{k}}$.

The load vector $\dfrac{\partial\ \underline{f}(k)}{\partial \underline{\phi}^T}$ which appears in (21) is null for all nodes and time steps except for the $\hat{i}^{th}$ entry which contains $(1-\gamma)$ when $k=\hat{k}-1$ and γ when $k=\hat{k}$. For a weighting value of $\gamma=1$, the load vector contains only the value unity at time step $\hat{k}$ for the $\hat{i}^{th}$ entry. With such a forcing on the adjoint state system (21), oscillations and numerical dispersion can occur as a result of improper spatial and temporal discretization. However, with increased numerical detail (both spatially and temporally) around the location $\hat{x}$ at time $\hat{t}$, improved solution accuracy may be obtained.

NUMERICAL RESULTS

To illustrate some of the numerical difficulties that may occur while solving for the adjoint state variable or importance function, a one-dimensional advection dispersion equation will be utilized. For constant coefficients, this equation takes the form

$$\frac{\partial C}{\partial x} = D \frac{\partial^2 C}{\partial x^2} - V \frac{\partial C}{\partial x} \tag{27}$$

with initial and boundary conditions of

$$C(x,0) = 0 \qquad \text{for } t \leq 0 \tag{28}$$

$$C(0,t) = 1.0 \qquad \text{for } t > 0 \tag{29a}$$

$$\frac{\partial C}{\partial x}(L,t) = 0 \qquad \text{for } t > 0 \tag{29b}$$

where L is the total length. The parameters used to describe the spatial and temporal domain and other properties are listed in Table 1. Figure 1 shows some results for the primary problem using a constant time step of ten units and several cell Péclet numbers (Pe_c). These results replicate many of the standard problems (overshoot and numerical dispersion) that have been previously reported by many investigators while solving this problem. The primary problem was solved using linear interpolation functions for the spatial terms and an implicit finite difference representation of the time derivative.

The adjoint state variable was determined based on the performance measure represented by (24) with $\hat{i}$ taking the midpoint node number corresponding to a normalized length (x/L) of one-half and $\hat{k}$ the value of the final time step number. For all simulations of the backward problem the weighting factor γ was set to unity.

The sensitivity coefficients generated from this performance measure indicate the change in the midpoint concentration at the final time to:

i) a change in the initial concentrations at each node at the initial time,

ii) a change in each elemental value of velocity and dispersion coefficient for all time steps,

iii) a change in the prescribed concentration for all time steps.

Figures 2, 3 and 4 present the behaviour of the importance function ψ^* to a change in nodal spacing. These three figures correspond to the primary problem solutions presented in Figure 1. The three curves on each of the figures show the propogation of the importance function backward in time. As the nodal spacing increases the importance function develops severe oscillations and numerical dispersion. These problems are then propogated backward in time subject to some damping effects. Decreasing the Pe_c to a value of one-half and reducing the time step size to satisfy a Courant number of unity produces a much improved representation of the importance function as shown in Figure 5. The importance of the information upstream of the midpoint node has now become apparent.

Table 2 lists the sensitivity coefficients and numerical details for all the solutions. The sensitivity coefficients are summed up over all elements and time steps and normalized. Comparing the sensitivity coefficients to those calculated from a perturbed approximation of the analytical solution reveals that the accuracy of the numerical solution results are suspect. However, this is not the case as the sensitivity coefficients generated by Run 1 and Run 4 validate with perturbed results from the numerical models.

CONCLUSIONS

Adjoint sensitivity methods can be used to calculate the sensitivity of user selected performance measures to the system parameters. The developed sensitivity coefficients are local derivatives; that is, they are dependent on both the specific parameters of the problem of interest as well as the spatial and temporal discretization of the numerical solution procedure. A change in parameters or discretization may change the calculated sensitivities. The impact of changing the discretization is illustrated in Table 2. The sensitivities changed significantly as a result of the changing discretization. For each analysis however, the calculated sensitivities could be validated by perturbing the parameters of the discretized forward problem. The sensitivities are thus relevant in a numerical sense only and must be calculated using the same discretization options for both the forward and backward problem.

As is the case with some forward problems, the backwards or adjoint problem can be subject to numerical dispersion and oscillation problems. The occurrence of the latter is of particular concern as oscillations of the adjoint state variable may produce sensitivity coefficients that are incorrect in terms of numerical magnitude and sign. Spatial and temporal discretization selections must satisfy the numerical requirements of both the forward and backward problems.

REFERENCES

Hughes, T.J.R., A simple scheme for developing 'upwind' finite elements, Intl. J. Num. Methods. Eng., 12, pp. 1359-1365, 1978.

Huyakorn, P.S., An upwind finite element scheme for improved solution of the convection-diffusion equation, Research Report number 76-WR-2, Dept. of Civil Eng., Princeton Univ., 1976.

O'Neill, K., Highly efficient, oscillation-free solution of the transport equation over long times and large spaces, Water Resour. Res., 17(6), 1665-1675, 1981.

Smith, I.M., Integration in time of diffusion and diffusion-convection equations, paper presented at the 1st International Conference on Finite Elements in Water Resources, Vol. 1, Princeton Univ., New Jersey, July 1976.

Sykes, J.F. and J.L. Wilson, Adjoint sensitivity theory for the finite element method, paper presented at the 5th International Conference on Finite Elements in Water Resources, Burlington, Vermont, June 1984.

Sykes, J.F., J.L. Wilson and R.W. Andrews, Sensitivity analysis for steady state groundwater flow using adjoint operators, Water Resour. Res., 21(3), 359-371, 1985.

Table 1 Parameters for Numerical Experiments

Parameter	Value
Length (L)	20.0 units
Initial Time (t_o)	0.0 units
Final Time (t_f)	150.0 units
Velocity (V)	0.05
Dispersion (D) Coeffcient	0.0125
System Péclet (Pe) Number	80.0

Table 2 Sensitivity Coefficients and Numerical Details

Run	Δx	Δt	Pe_c	C_o	SN_V [1]	SN_D [2]
1	0.5	10.0	2.0	1.0	3.794	0.345
2	1.25	10.0	5.0	0.4	3.310	0.282
3	2.5	10.0	10.0	0.2	2.489	0.174
4	0.125	2.5	0.5	1.0	5.395	0.757
Analytical Solution	---	---	---	---	6.615	1.169

1. $SN_V = \frac{\partial P}{\partial V} \cdot \frac{V}{P}$ (Velocity sensitivity)

2. $SN_D = \frac{\partial P}{\partial D} \cdot \frac{D}{P}$ (Dispersion coefficient sensitivity)

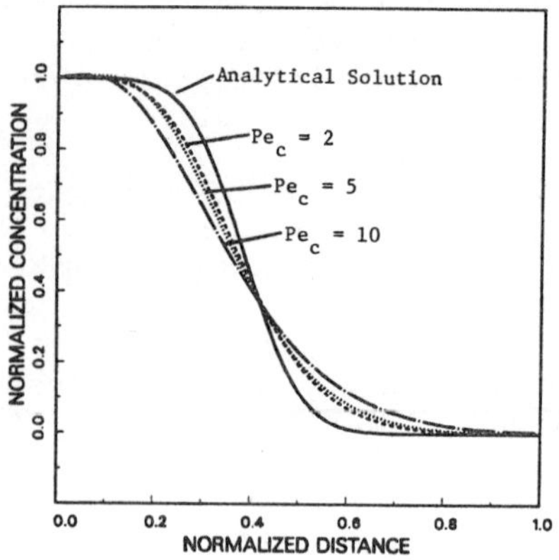

Figure 1. Forward problem results.

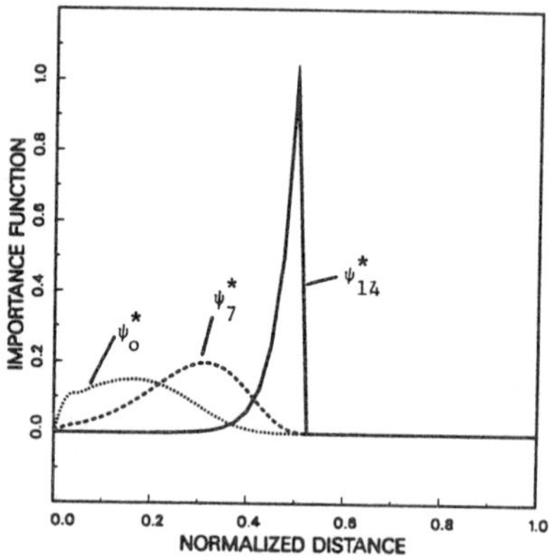

Figure 2. Importance function for $Pe_c=2$ and $C_o=1.0$.

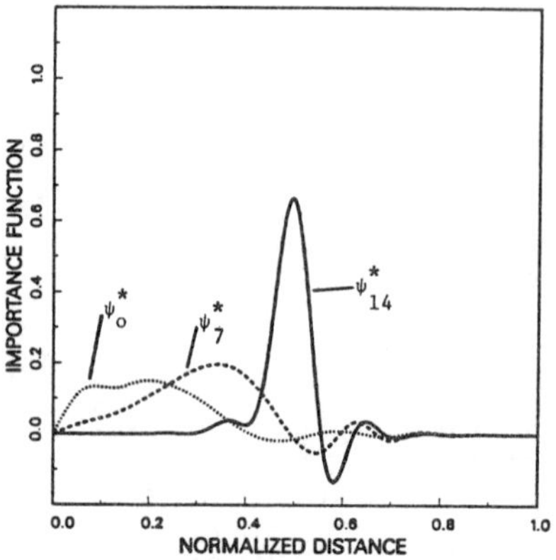

Figure 3. Importance function for $Pe_c=5$ and $C_o=0.4$.

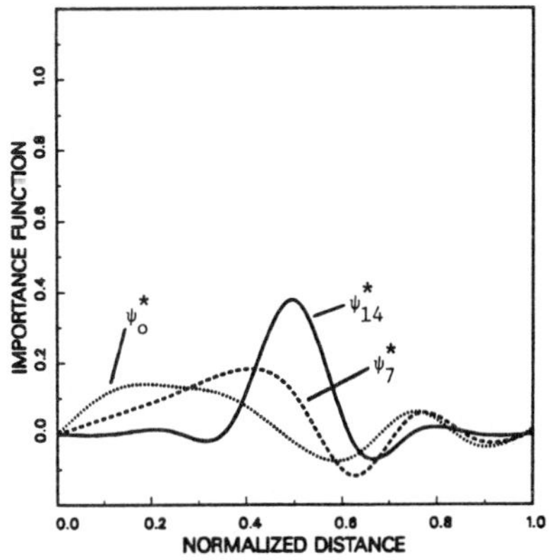

Figure 4. Importance function for Pe_c=10 and C_o=0.2.

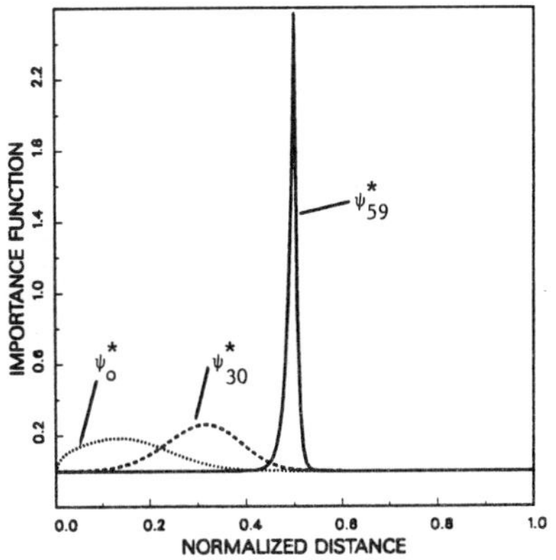

Figure 5. Importance function for Pe_c=0.5 and C_o=1.0.

VI International Conference on Finite Elements in Water Resources, Lisboa, Portugal, June 1986

A Finite Element Method with Linear Trial Functions for Steady-State Two-Dimensional Flows

C. Urban, W. Zielke
Institute of Fluid Mechanics, University Hannover, Federal Republic of Germany

The earliest FE-methods for the calculation of steady-state two-dimensional flows date back almost 15 years. Since the publication of Hood/Taylor (1973), it has been accepted to work at least with mixed trial functions for the approximation of velocities or fluxes, and pressures or water levels. This procedure requires excessive computing time and core capacity. Therefore, the development of a more efficient method for the calculation of stationary flows was initiated by the authors.

By means of this method, a system of equations is solved only for the water levels or pressures at the element nodes. Fluxes or velocities are calculated separately for each element by a matrix multiplication. It was possible to include the convective acceleration terms which, until then, had been an obstacle for the realization of this method. In contrast to the procedures applied until now, exclusively linear trial functions are used, thus the newly developed method contradicts the opinion widely found in literature, that steady-state flows can only be described by trial functions of higher order. Whereas the approach with mixed interpolation (quadratic/linear) in conjunction with triangle elements results in element matrices of 15 x 15, the newly developed method leads to 3 x 3 matrices. The system of equations is correspondingly small. Test calculations demonstrate the rapid convergence of this method for free surface flows as well as for gas flows.

MATHEMATICAL CONCEPT AND FINITE ELEMENT APPROXIMATION

The method will be exemplified by the well-known equations describing the 2D-steady-state free surface flow. With the notations explained in Fig. 1, the equations for momentum and continuity are as follows:

$$v_{i,j} q_j + gH h_{,i} + \frac{\lambda}{H^2} |q| q_i - HT v_{i,jj} = 0 \qquad (1)$$

$$q_{i,i} = 0 \qquad (2)$$

The inertial terms as well as the longitudinal pressure gradients are included, the bottom friction with the friction parameter λ and the horizontal eddy viscosity represented by means of an Boussinesq approximation where parameter T can also be prescribed in anisotropic form.

Since only flows with Froude numbers <1 are discussed here, we are confronted with an elliptic boundary value problem. The region of integration of elliptic differential equations is shown in Fig. 2. The differential equation is valid for the area Ω. For the boundary, the unknown function, or its derivation in the outward normal direction, or a combination of both must be prescribed.

The first boundary condition used here is of Dirichlet type and prescribes the water level at the open boundary Γ_1. By means of the second boundary condition, the flow at the open boundary Γ_2 in the direction of the outer normal can be given directly by setting β equal zero. A closed boundary is modelled with α and β equal zero. For $\alpha \neq 0$ and $\beta \neq 0$ the Cauchy boundary condition represents a linearized loop rating curve. Boundary friction, originating from turbulence at the boundary, is considered along the closed boundary Γ_3.

Mixed trial functions have been used until now for the approximative solution of the boundary value problem by means of the finite element method. This is necessary because the exclusive use of linear trial functions leads to singular algebraic equation systems (Dixon et al., 1978). This is due to the direct approximation of the continuity equation. Singularities do not occur when the equations for instationary flows are approximated, because the local time derivations result in a sufficiently strong occupation of the diagonal in the coefficient matrix.

Singularities which occur when linear trial functions are used can be avoided if the equation of motion is solved in order to determine the constant fluxes in each element and to insert them into the continuity equation:

$$q_i = -K_{ij} h_{,j} + L_i^* \qquad (3)$$

$$-(K_{ij} h_{,j})_{,i} + L_{i,i}^* = 0 \qquad (4)$$

In this way, with eq.(4) an equation for the water level H is obtained.

It is, therefore, called h-model. The total algebraic equation system is smaller by two thirds compared to direct approximation of the individual equations. When the fluxes within the elements have been derived by means of equation (3), the equation system is established for the water levels (equ. 4) and then solved. As a next step, the fluxes in the single elements are determined (equ. 3) by means of the nodal water levels computed in the step before. The elements of matrix K_{ij} are functions of h and q. Since the flux is found in the denominator, this must be given as starting value for the iterative solution.

The first h-model for instationary flows was developed by Herrling at the Institute for Fluid Mechanics and presented in 1977, with the exclusive intention to reduce the equation system. In the stationary case, here discussed, it is possible to use exclusively linear trial functions with the help of this procedure. No mixed trial functions are required (Urban, 1986).

When eddy viscosity is included, third derivations of the velocity components are obtained in the term $L^*_{i,i}$ (equ. 4) in addition to the second derivatives of the water level. If exclusively linear trial functions are to be used for the approximative solution of the water level equation by means or the FE method, the order of eq. (4) has to be downrated. In order to achieve this, the equations of motion and of continuity must be transformed into equivalent functional equations and subsequently integrated partially. This procedure is known from literature (Oden/Reddy, 1976) and will not be discussed here. First, the weak form of the equation of motion is obtained:

$$<\psi, v_{i,j}\, q_j + gHh_{,i} + \frac{\lambda}{H^2}\,|q|\,\xi + <\psi_{,j}, HTv_{i,j}{}^e - \int_{\Gamma^e} \psi H\hat{T}_{ij} u_j \qquad (5)$$

It contains only derivatives of first order, because the second derivatives are transferred to the function ψ. Boundary friction due to turbulence can be included in the boundary integral as a natural boundary condition.

Using the FE approximation, an equation system is established for water levels only, whereas the equations of motion are dealt with separately for each element. In the equations of motion, therefore, the form function ψ of the FE approach is found at the place of test function φ. The solution of the fluxes q_i is also possible, because the integrands which consist of the terms of the equarions of motion are constant for each element. The integrals over ψ and $\psi_{,j}$ occur as additional factors.
At last, the following equation is obtained for q_i:

$$q_i = - K_{ij}\, h_{,j} + L_i \qquad (6)$$

The term L_i contains the eddy viscosity and the boundary integral obtained by partial integration.

The weak form of the equation of continuity reads:

$$<\varphi, q_{i,i}>: = - <\varphi_{,i}, q_i> + \int_\Gamma \varphi q_i u_i \, d\Gamma \qquad (7)$$

The boundary integral offers the possibility to prescribe the normal flux to the boundary as a natural boundary condition. With fluxes q_i from eq. (6)inserted in eq. (7), we obtain

$$b(\varphi,h) = l(\varphi) \qquad (8)$$

which is the required equation for the water level. For the case without impulse convection and eddy viscosity, the bi-linear form $b(\varphi,h)$ is symmetrical. The linear form $l(\varphi)$ represents the external load of the system, e.g. flux normal to the boundary, boundary friction, or fetch from wind.

FE approximation of equations (6) and (7) by means of the Bubnow-Galerkin method results, corresponding to eq. (8), in an element matrix $\underline{\underline{I}}^e$ of (3 x 3) format:

$$\underline{\underline{I}}^e: = gH^e \, [\underline{\underline{X}}^T \underline{\underline{K}}o\underline{\underline{N}} + \underline{\underline{Y}}^T \underline{\underline{K}}u\underline{\underline{N}}]\underline{h}^e = [\underline{\underline{X}}^T \underline{\underline{K}}o\underline{T}o + Y^T \underline{\underline{K}}u\underline{T}u] - \int_\Gamma \underline{\Lambda} q_q \, d\Gamma \qquad (9)$$

This is considerably smaller than the (15 x 15) matrices in the procedures used until now. In eq. (9), $\underline{\underline{X}}$, $\underline{\underline{Y}}$, and $\underline{\underline{N}}$ are matrices which result from the Galerkin approach. H^e is the medium water depth in the element, and $\underline{h}^e$ is the vector of the nodal water levels. The matrix $\underline{\underline{K}}$ and the vector $\underline{T}$ contain the coefficients and the eddy viscosity including boundary friction; $\underline{\Lambda}$ is the vector of the form functions in the element.

The convergence behaviour of the procedure depends, among others, largely on the computation of representative coefficients for each element as well as on the linearization of the equations. For the iterative computation of the coefficients, depending on the solution of the former iteration steps, a new method had to be developed. The procedure is totally different from the h-models in use until now. and will be discussed in more detail. It is particularly important to define the element averaged water depth H^e (viz. eq. (9)), which is not computed by arithmetic averaging from the nodal values, but in dependence on the flow direction in the element. It contributes decisively to the fact that no lateral velocity components are present in the computed velocity distribution of a straight channel.

The velocity gradients required for the inclusion of the convective terms are obtained by a linear interpolation by means of the derived form functions:

$$v^e_{i,j} = \sum_{k=A,B,C} \frac{\partial \lambda_k}{\partial x_j} \frac{q_i}{H_k} \quad (k \rightarrow \text{element nodes}) \qquad (10)$$

Generally, this procedure is rather simple. The problem lies in determining the nodal velocities. First the nodal velocities were found by averaging the local values, as usual in the h-models for instationary flow. This procedure failed when models with complicated geometry, or with strong topographic irregularities had to be computed. A similar procedure of Samuels (1983) to average the velocity gradients from the values of the surrounding element leads, in the author's opinion, to numerical problems when models with complicated geography are involved. In connection with the general conception to approximate the equations of motion separately for each element, the nodal velocities are also computed separately for each element. The problems connected with the convective terms could be overcome by this procedure. Later, this led to a procedure by which the velocity gradients could be calculated in the element center point without using the nodal velocities:

$$v^e_{i,j} = - \sum_{k=A,B,C} \frac{q_i}{(H^e)^2} \frac{\partial \lambda_k}{\partial x_j} H_k \qquad (11)$$

The computation of models with complicated geometry and strong topographical properties, including convective terms, no longer presents any problem. Furthermore, the time-consuming averaging of the nodal velocities, which introduces errors, becomes superfluous.

Another special item is linearization. Normally, the values of the previous iteration step are required for the computation of the coefficients. They are marked by index o:

$$uv = u^o v + O(h) \qquad (12)$$

The friction term can be linearized this way without any problem, whereas the convective terms can only be included when the derivations of the velocities are represented as coefficients $u^o v$, as shown in the linearization of first order. With uv^o, the convective terms are automatically left out as a consequence of the FE formulation. Consequently, when carrying out a linearization of 2nd order

$$uv = u^o v + \underline{uv^o} - u^o v^o + O(h^2)$$

the term uv^o cannot be of any effect on the inclusion of the convective terms.

TEST CALCULATIONS AND APPLICATIONS

In the following examples, the iterative calculation ends when the difference of the maximum fluxes between two subsequent iteration steps is less than 1 °/oo.

The first example is a straight channel of 5,000 m length, 2,000 m width, and an undisturbed water depth of 10 m. As boundary condition, a water level of h = 1 m was given at the nodes 0,1, and 2, and h = 0 m at the nodes 15,16,17. With the prescribed level difference of 1 m, the iteration ends after 5 steps. For the first iteration a velocity was given which is approximately identical with the calculated velocity at the channel entrance. The calculated water levels are given in Fig. 3, they are virtually identical with the results found by a one-dimensional backwater calculation carried out for comparison. Fig. 3 shows that the water level distribution is equal over each cross-section. The flux is consistent on the entire channel length, mass losses do not occur. No lateral components are present in flux or velocities.

The second example is a river with flood plain taken from a hydraulic experiment (Könemann, 1980). A 2 m section of the 60 m experimental channel was taken for the FE-calculation. It was discretized with 107 nodes and 188 elements (Fig. 4). Fig. 5 displays the cross-section. The step between flood plain and river bed was replaced by a slope of o.1 m, for reasons of numerical stability. The values for parameter λ of bottom friction was found with the help of the Moody-diagram, using the roughness values given in Könemann's paper. Very good agreement between computed and measured (in hydraulic test) flux distribution values (Fig. 6) was found: calibration was not required. The differences were smaller than 2% for small water depths and even less than 1% for greater depths.

A channel with a 90° bend is used as an example to show that the convective terms could be included without carrying numerical problems. This is a good prerequisite for implementing turbulence models which can only be used effectively when the diffusion generated numerically is insignificant in comparison to the exchange caused by physical factors.
Fig. 7 shows the channel, discretized with 67 nodes and 105 elements. A water depth of H = 11 m was given as a boundary condition at the inflow boundary, and H = 10 m at the outlet boundary. The value 0.005 was chosen for bottom friction parameter λ. The results of calculation with and without convective terms led to very small differences in the neighbourhood of the inner edge. Fig. 8 displays the computed velocity distribution. When eddy viscosity is included, a recirculation behind the inner corner is established.

The method here presented was also useful for calculating floods in river valleys. The next example is a flood situation in the Aller valley north of Hannover. The maximum transport capacity of the river without overland flow is in this part of the valley nearly 60 m^3/s. During a flood the transport may increase up to 400 m^3/s. The river section under consideration has a length of 1.5 km and is characterized by very strong irregularities in the topography (Fig. 9). It is discretized with 229 nodes and 402 elements as shown in Fig. 9.

With a water depth of 5 - 6 m in the river channel and 0 - 2 m in the flood plains, the water level difference between inflow and outflow boundary is 0.15 m (taken from field data). Convergence is achieved after 8 iterations without convective terms and 12 iterations with them. This proves convincingly how much more efficient the steady-state calculations are as compared to time-dependent solution schemes. Fig. 10 displays that the method is capable of simulating water depth-dependent boundaries in order to study, in an quasi-steady manner, the flooding and receding currents on the flood plain.

REFERENCES

Dixon, L.C.W., Morgan, D.J., Harrison, D., (1978) On singular cases arising from Galerkin' Method, MAFELAP 18.-21.4., Brunel University.

Herrling, B. (1977) Eine hybride Formulierung in Wasserständen zur Berechnung von Flachwasserwellen mit der Methode finiter Elemente, VDI-Verlag, Düsseldorf.

Hood, P., Taylor, C. (1974) Navier-Stokes Equations using mixed interpolation, Finite Element Method in Flow Problems, Huntsville, UAH-Press.

Könemann, N. (1980) Der wechselseitige Einfluß von Vorland und Flußbett auf das Widerstandsverhalten offener Gerinne mit gegliederten Querschnitten, Dissertation, TH Darmstadt.

Oden, J.T., Reddy, J.N. (1976) An introduction to the mathematical theory of finite elements, J. Wiley and Sons, New York.

Samuels, P.G. (1983) Two Dimensional Modelling of flood flows using the finite element method, Report IT 250, Hydraulics Research, Wallingford (UK).

Urban, C. (1986) Ein Finite-Element-Verfahren mit linearen Ansätzen für stationäre zweidimensionale Strömungen, Bericht Nr. 22/1986, Institut für Strömungsmechanik und elektronisches Rechnen im Bauwesen, Universität Hannover.

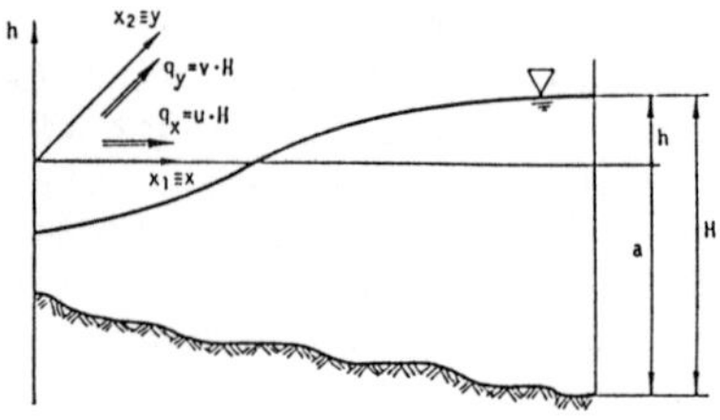

Figure 1. Twodimensional coordinate-system with notation

q_i = horizontal flux, v_i = corresponding velocities, a = undisturbed depth, h = water level, H = water depth.

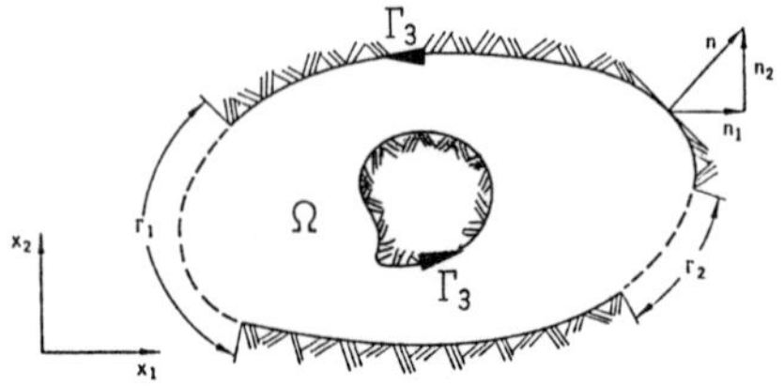

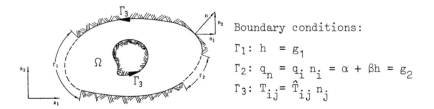

Boundary conditions:

Γ_1: $h = g_1$

Γ_2: $q_n = q_i\, n_i = \alpha + \beta h = g_2$

Γ_3: $T_{ij} = \hat{T}_{ij}\, n_j$

Figure 2. Domain Ω with boundary conditions.

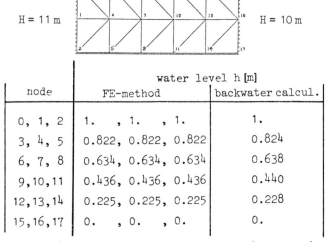

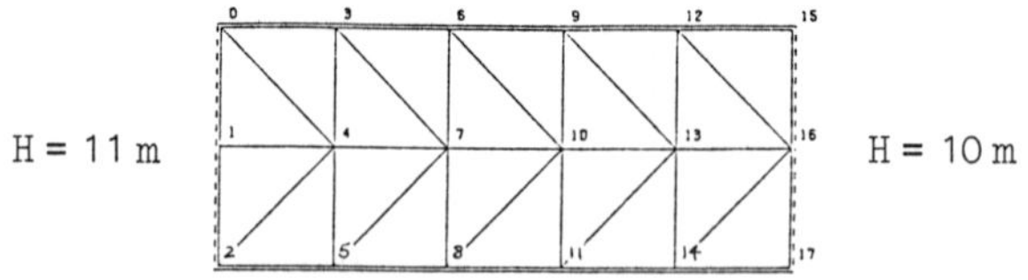

node	water level h [m] FE-method	backwater calcul.
0, 1, 2	1. , 1. , 1.	1.
3, 4, 5	0.822, 0.822, 0.822	0.824
6, 7, 8	0.634, 0.634, 0.634	0.638
9,10,11	0.436, 0.436, 0.436	0.440
12,13,14	0.225, 0.225, 0.225	0.228
15,16,17	0. , 0. , 0.	0.

Figure 3. Comparison of computed water levels in a straight channel.

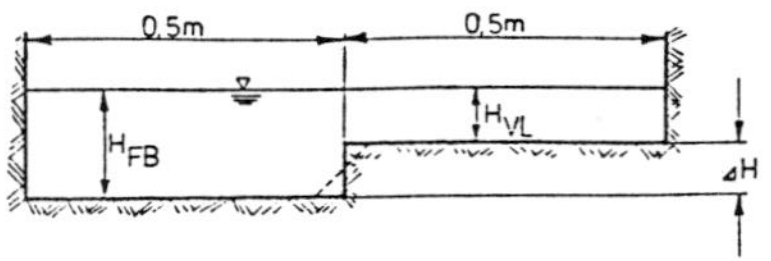

Laboratory channel	G1G	G1R	G2G	G2R
Riverbed width (m)	0.5	0.5	0.5	0.5
Floodplain width (m)	0.5	0.5	0.5	0.5
Riverbed depth (m)	0.05	0.05	0.1	0.1
Slope (°/oo)	1.1	1.1	1.0	1.0
Grain roughness Riverbed/Floodplain (mm)	0,1/0,1	0,1/1,83	0,1/0,1	0,1/1,83

Figure 4. Cross-section, topographic data and roughness of the hydraulic model used by Könemann

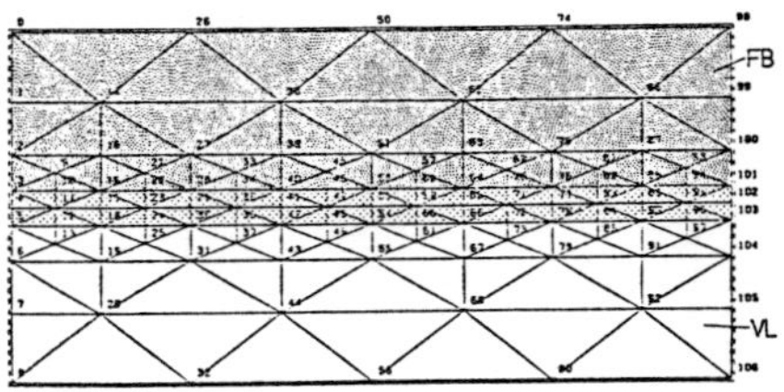

Figure 5. Discretized river flood plain model with 107 nodes and 188 elements

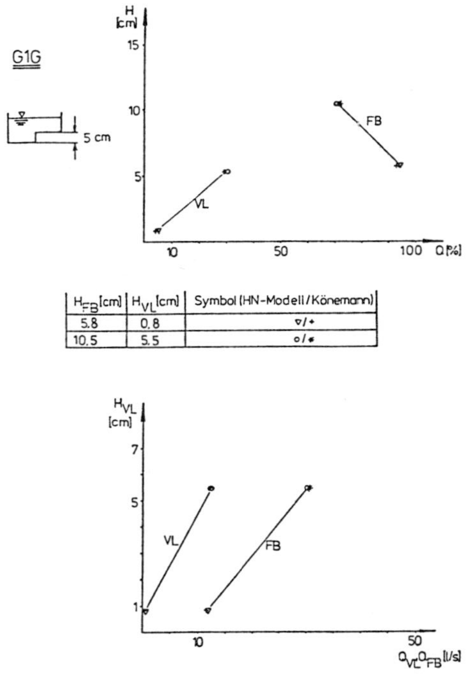

H_{FB} [cm]	H_{VL} [cm]	Symbol (HN-Modell/Könemann)
5.8	0.8	▽/+
10.5	5.5	o/*

Figure 6. Flux distribution in channel G1G Comparison between FE-Computation and hydraulic result

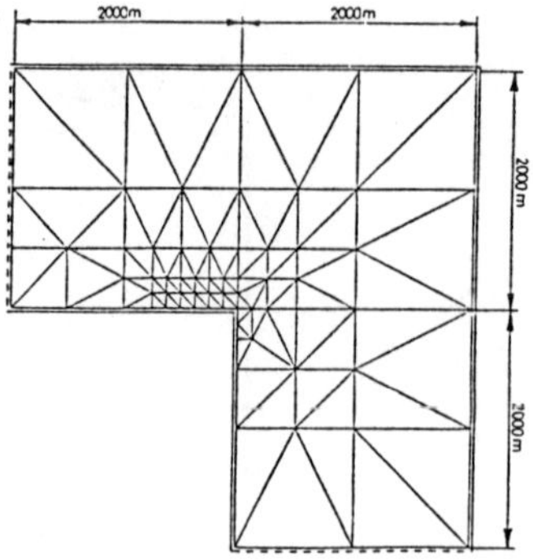

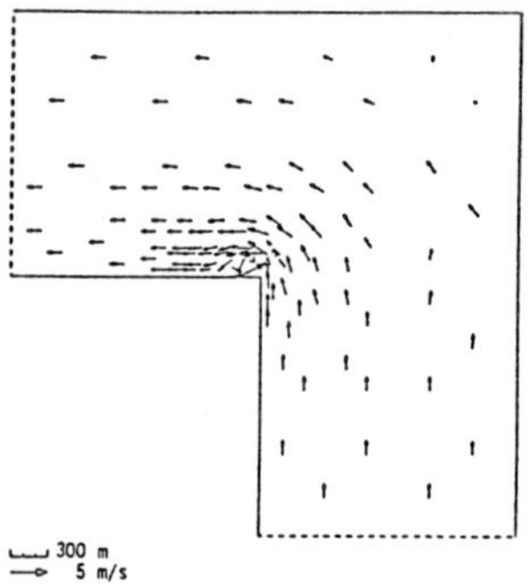

Figure 7. Finite Element Discretization of a channel with 90° bend

Figure 8. Computed velocity distribution

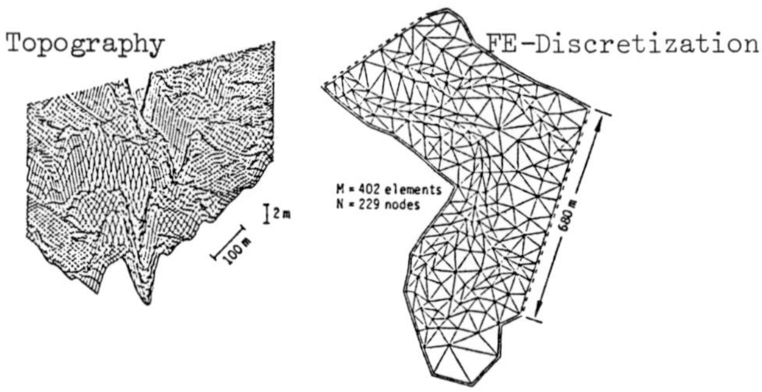

Figure 9. Part of the Aller-Valley in northern Germany downstream of Celle

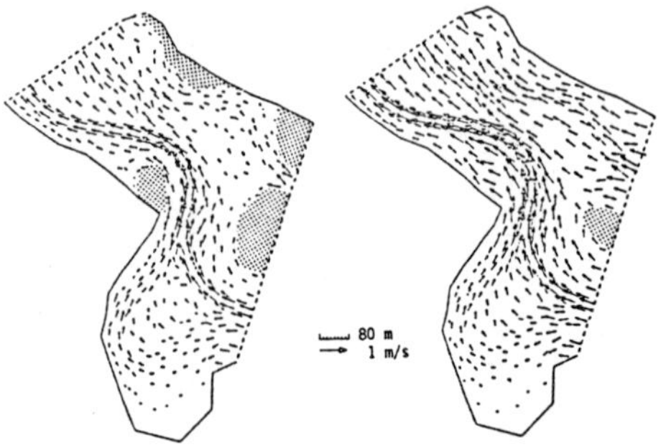

Figure 10. Computed velocity distribution for different water depths

VI International Conference on Finite Elements in Water Resources, Lisboa, Portugal, June 1986

The Dual Reciprocity Boundary Element Formulation for Transient Heat Conduction

L.C. Wrobel
On leave from COPPE-UFRJ, Brazil
C.A. Brebbia, D. Nardini
Computational Mechanics Institute, Southampton, U.K.

INTRODUCTION

It is now widely accepted that the Boundary Element Method (BEM) is a very powerful technique for solution of problems governed by elliptic partial differential equations such as Laplace's, Helmholtz's, Navier's and others (Brebbia et al., 1984).

In addition, many different formulations have been proposed for extending the BEM to deal with parabolic and hyperbolic partial differential equations. These include finite difference approximations of the time derivative (Curran et al., 1980), use of Laplace transforms (Rizzo & Shippy, 1970), and time dependent fundamental solutions (Chang et al., 1973 ; Brebbia and Wrobel, 1979). The latter is by far the most successful one and has been extended to deal with axisymmetric and fully three-dimensional heat conduction (Wrobel & Brebbia, 1981a; Pina and Fernandes, 1983), convection-diffusion (Brebbia & Skerget, 1984), viscous flow (Skerget et al., 1984), elastodynamics (Mansur and Brebbia, 1985), among other problems.

In spite of its success and its high - second order - accuracy (Onishi, 1981), this formulation is not without its drawbacks. Usually, the initial conditions are taken into account through a domain integration which removes the "boundary-only" character of the technique. To overcome this , a time-stepping technique where previous solutions are advanced in time through the boundary integrals was proposed by Wrobel and Brebbia (1981b) . Although mathematically elegant, this technique may be time consuming if the number of time steps in the problem is large.

Because of all this it was required to develop a BEM technique for parabolic and hyperbolic problems which could retain the "boundary-only" character of the method (thus its main source of efficiency and simplicity) without sacrificing its high accuracy. Such a technique was proposed by Brebbia and Nardini (1983)and Nardini and Brebbia(1985a)in the context of elastodynamics, and is extended in this work for the solution of transient heat conduction problems.

BEM FORMULATION FOR STEADY PROBLEMS

Let us start by reviewing the formulation of a boundary integral equation for steady problems. Assume that one wants to apply the BEM for solution of the equation

$$k\,\nabla^2 u(x) = 0 \qquad \text{in } \Omega \tag{1}$$

subject to the boundary conditions

$$u(x) = \bar{u}(x) \qquad \text{on } \Gamma_1 \tag{2a}$$

$$q(x) = k\,\frac{\partial u(x)}{\partial n(x)} = \bar{q}(x) \qquad \text{on } \Gamma_2 \tag{2b}$$

in which k is a (constant) conductivity coefficient and n(x) is the unit outward normal at point x.

In what follows, the fundamental solution to equation (1) will be used. This is represented by u* which, in two dimensions, is of the form

$$u^*(\xi,x) = \frac{1}{2\pi k}\ln\frac{1}{r} \tag{3}$$

where r is the Euclidian distance from the source point ξ to the field point x. Function u* is the solution to Equation (1) with a discrete singularity at the source point, i.e. the solution of

$$k\,\nabla^2 u^*(\xi,x) = -\,\Delta(\xi,x) \tag{4}$$

in which Δ is the Dirac delta function.

Applying Green's second identity to functions u and u* gives

$$\int_\Omega (u^*\,k\,\nabla^2 u - u\,k\,\nabla^2 u^*)\,d\Omega = \int_\Gamma (u^* q - q^* u)\,d\Gamma \tag{5}$$

with

$$q^*(\xi,x) = k\,\frac{\partial u^*(\xi,x)}{\partial n(x)} \tag{6}$$

Note that, in the above equation, u and q are functions of x, u* and q* are functions of ξ and x and the integrations are carried out with respect to the variable x.

Substituting Equation (4) into (5) yields

$$\int_{\Omega} u^* \, k \, \nabla^2 u \, d\Omega = - u_i + \int_{\Gamma} (u^*q - q^*u) d\Gamma \tag{7}$$

with u_i denoting the value of u at the source point ξ.

Taking the source point ξ to the boundary and accounting for the jump of the integral in q*, the following integral equation is obtained,

$$\int_{\Omega} u^* \, k \, \nabla^2 u \, d\Omega = - c_i u_i + \int_{\Gamma} (u^*q - q^*u) d\Gamma \tag{8}$$

where c_i is a function of the internal angle the boundary Γ makes at point ξ, and the integral in q* is computed in the Cauchy principal value sense.

For steady problems, one can further substitute Equation (1) into (8), resulting in the well-known boundary integral equation (Brebbia, 1978; Brebbia et al., 1984),

$$c_i u_i = \int_{\Gamma} (u^*q - q^*u) d\Gamma \tag{9}$$

PROPOSED FORMULATION FOR TRANSIENT PROBLEMS

Let us propose a new BEM formulation for solution of the diffusion equation

$$\nabla^2 u(x,t) = \frac{1}{\kappa} \frac{\partial u(x,t)}{\partial t} \tag{10}$$

with boundary conditions as given by Equation (2). In the above equation, κ is the diffusivity coefficient, assumed to be constant both in space and time.

Rewriting Equation (10) as

$$\kappa \, \nabla^2 u = \dot{u} \tag{11}$$

with the dot denoting temporal derivative, one can substitute this into Equation (8) to obtain:

$$\int_\Omega u^* \dot{u} \, d\Omega = - c_i \, u_i + \int_\Gamma u^* q \, d\Gamma - \int_\Gamma q^* u \, d\Gamma \qquad (12)$$

with k (the conductivity coefficient) replaced by κ (the diffusivity coefficient) in Equations (2b), (3) and (6).

Let us now approximate function $\dot{u}$ at any point inside the domain by a set of N coordinate functions multiplied by unknown functions of time, i.e.:

$$\dot{u}(x,t) = \sum_{j=1}^{N} f^j(x) \, \dot{\alpha}^j(t) \qquad (13)$$

With this substitution, the domain integral becomes:

$$D = \int_\Omega u^* \dot{u} \, d\Omega = \sum_{j=1}^{N} \dot{\alpha}^j \int_\Omega f^j \, u^* \, d\Omega \qquad (14)$$

Let us assume that for each function $f^j(x)$ there exists a function $\psi^j(x)$ such that $\nabla^2\psi^j = f^j$. Using this substitution, the domain integral becomes

$$D = \sum_{j=1}^{N} \dot{\alpha}^j \int_\Omega \nabla^2\psi^j \, u^* \, d\Omega \qquad (15)$$

Applying the transformation given by Equation (8), one arrives at a boundary integral equation of the form:

$$c_i u_i + \int_\Gamma q^* u \, d\Gamma - \int_\Gamma u^* q \, d\Gamma = \sum_{j=1}^{N} \frac{1}{\kappa}\Big(c_i \psi_i^j + \int_\Gamma q^* \psi^j \, d\Gamma$$

$$- \int_\Gamma u^* \eta^j \, d\Gamma\Big)\dot{\alpha}^j \qquad (16)$$

Note that the above equation involves only boundary integrals. The reduction has been accomplished by a double application of reciprocity principles. Because of this the resulting technique is called the Dual Reciprocity Boundary Element Method.

Next, one can approximate the variation of functions u, q, ψ and η (= $\kappa \, \partial\psi/\partial n$) within each boundary element by using a unique set of interpolation functions $\underset{\sim}{\phi}$, i.e.:

$$u = \underset{\sim}{\phi}^T \underset{\sim}{u}_e \qquad \psi^j = \underset{\sim}{\phi}^T \underset{\sim}{\psi}^j_e$$
$$q = \underset{\sim}{\phi}^T \underset{\sim}{q}_e \qquad \eta^j = \underset{\sim}{\phi}^T \underset{\sim}{\eta}^j_e \tag{17}$$

with the subscript e denoting a particular boundary element. It should be noted that functions ψ and η need not necessarily be approximated over the boundary in the above manner, as they are known functions once the f sequence is chosen. However, doing so will, with some sacrifice in the accuracy, dramatically reduce the necessary boundary integrations.

Applying Equation (16) to all boundary nodes, taking into account the above approximations, results in the following system of equations:

$$\underset{\sim}{H}\,\underset{\sim}{U} - \underset{\sim}{G}\,\underset{\sim}{Q} = \frac{1}{\kappa}\,(\underset{\sim}{H}\underset{\sim}{\psi} - \underset{\sim}{G}\underset{\sim}{\eta})\,\dot{\underset{\sim}{\alpha}} \tag{18}$$

By evaluating the expression (13) at all boundary nodes the following relation is obtained:

$$\dot{\underset{\sim}{U}} = \underset{\sim}{F}\,\dot{\underset{\sim}{\alpha}}$$

which, upon inversion, produces the relation:

$$\dot{\underset{\sim}{\alpha}} = \underset{\sim}{F}^{-1}\,\dot{\underset{\sim}{U}}$$

Substituting the above into Equation (18) results in:

$$\underset{\sim}{C}\,\dot{\underset{\sim}{U}} + \underset{\sim}{H}\,\underset{\sim}{U} = \underset{\sim}{G}\,\underset{\sim}{Q} \tag{19}$$

with $\underset{\sim}{C} = \frac{-1}{\kappa}\,(\underset{\sim}{H}\underset{\sim}{\psi} - \underset{\sim}{G}\underset{\sim}{\eta})\underset{\sim}{F}^{-1}$.

System (19) is similar in form to the one obtained using the finite element method. Hence, any standard direct time integration scheme can be used to find a solution to (19). Note, however, that vectors $\dot{\underset{\sim}{U}}$, $\underset{\sim}{U}$ and $\underset{\sim}{Q}$ in (19) have the dimension of the number of boundary nodes only, thus matrices $\underset{\sim}{C}$, $\underset{\sim}{H}$ and $\underset{\sim}{G}$ are of the size of standard boundary element matrices. It should also be noted that the vector of fluxes $\underset{\sim}{Q}$ is present in Equation (19) thus rendering it a system of equations of mixed type, as opposed to "displacement" only finite element equivalent formulations.

In this work, we employ a simple two-level time integration

scheme. Using a linear approximation for $\underset{\sim}{U}$ and $\underset{\sim}{Q}$ within each time step gives:

$$\underset{\sim}{U} = (1-\theta)\underset{\sim}{U}^{m} + \theta\,\underset{\sim}{U}^{m+1}$$

$$\underset{\sim}{Q} = (1-\theta)\underset{\sim}{Q}^{m} + \theta\,\underset{\sim}{Q}^{m+1}$$

$$\dot{\underset{\sim}{U}} = \frac{1}{\Delta t}(\underset{\sim}{U}^{m+1} - \underset{\sim}{U}^{m})$$

Substituting these approximations into (19) yields:

$$\left(\frac{1}{\Delta t}\underset{\sim}{C} + \theta\,\underset{\sim}{H}\right)\underset{\sim}{U}^{m+1} - \theta\,\underset{\sim}{G}\,\underset{\sim}{Q}^{m+1} = \left(\frac{1}{\Delta t}\underset{\sim}{C} - (1-\theta)\underset{\sim}{H}\right)\underset{\sim}{U}^{m} + (1-\theta)\underset{\sim}{G}\,\underset{\sim}{Q}^{m} \qquad (20)$$

The right side of Equation (20) is known at all times. Upon introducing the boundary conditions at time $(m+1)\Delta t$, one can rearrange the left side of (20) and solve the resulting system of equations by using a direct solution procedure, such as Gauss elimination.

Note that the elements of matrices $\underset{\sim}{C}$, $\underset{\sim}{H}$ and $\underset{\sim}{G}$ depend only on geometrical data. Thus, they can all be computed once and stored. If we keep the value of Δt constant, the system matrix can be reduced only once as well, and the time procedure will consist of a simple recursive scheme with only additions and products involved.

CHOICE OF COORDINATE FUNCTIONS

The success of the proposed method is strongly dependent on the choice of the coordinate functions $f^j(\underset{\sim}{x})$, used to approximate the time derivatives of the solution in the domain. Nardini and Brebbia (1985b) proposed a number of different classes of coordinate functions, such as polynomial expressions, trigonometric series and concentrated nodal functions. In the present work, we combine functions of this last class, which uses the simple formula

$$f^j(\underset{\sim}{x}) = r(\underset{\sim}{x}, \underset{\sim}{x}_j) \qquad j = 1,\ldots,N \qquad (21)$$

where r is the Euclidian distance between any point in Ω and the jth nodal point, with a constant function

$$f^{N+1}(\underset{\sim}{x}) = c \qquad (22)$$

applied at a fixed internal point. The inclusion of the constant function, which can simulate the heating up of the whole body by a constant value, was found to improve the accuracy of the numerical solution.

EXAMPLES OF APPLICATION

In what follows, two simple examples of application of the proposed formulation are presented, in order to show the high accuracy and efficiency which can be produced using only simple elements and rather coarse discretizations.

i) One-dimensional Problem

A one-dimensional problem of an infinite slab subjected to a thermal shock is herein analysed as a two-dimensional one with mixed boundary conditions, i.e. $u = 1$ prescribed along the faces $x_1 = \pm L$ and $q = 0$ along the faces $x_2 = \pm \ell$ of a rectangular region with zero initial conditions. The numerical values adopted for the cross-section and the material constant were $L = 5$, $\ell = 4$ and $k = 1$.

Following a standard procedure, the thermal shock was applied in a smoothed form as shown in Figure 1. The discretization employed used only 7 constant boundary elements over one quarter of the region, taking symmetry into account by reflection and condensation as described by Brebbia et al. (1984) . Results are shown in Figure 2 for the temperature at some boundary and internal points, for $\theta = 1$ and a rather large Δt value of 1, compared to the analytical solution given by Carslaw and Jaeger (1959).

ii) Convection Problem

This example studies a square region with unit initial temperature convecting into a surrounding medium at zero temperature. The heat transfer coefficient is constant all over the surface and equal to 2 while the thermal diffusivity was assumed to be unity.

The boundary element discretization employed only 8 constant elements over one quarter of the region, due to the double symmetry of the problem. Results are shown in Figure 3 for the temperature at some boundary and internal points, for $\theta = 1$ and $\Delta t = 0.05$, together with the analytical solution of Carslaw and Jaeger (1959).

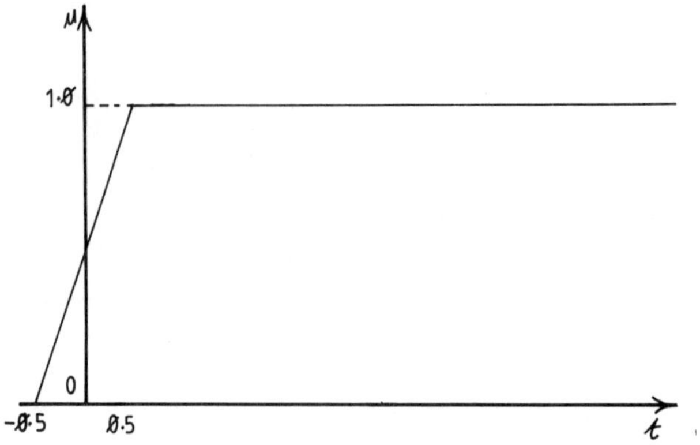

Figure 1. Smoothing of Thermal Shock

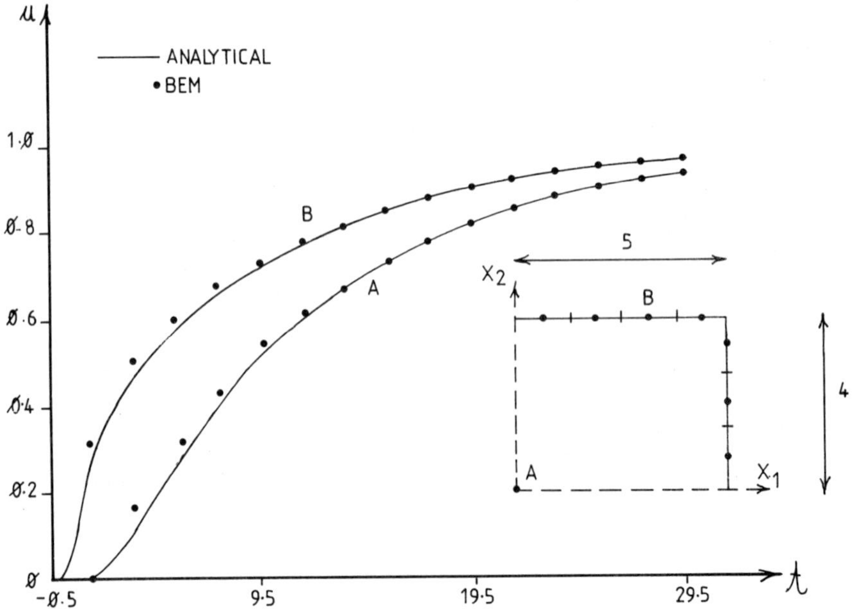

Figure 2. Temperature at some points (Ex.1)

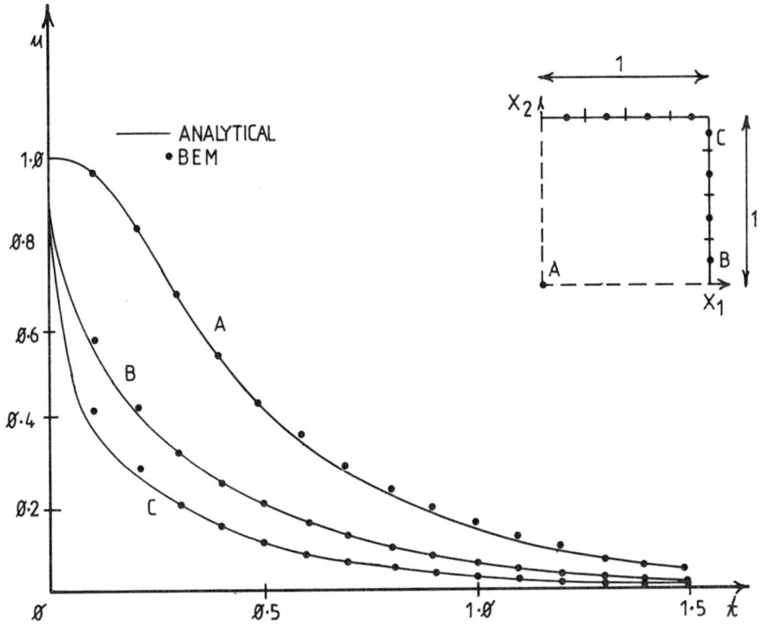

Figure 3. Temperature at some points (Ex. 2)

CONCLUSIONS

This paper has presented an efficient BEM formulation for solution of transient heat conduction problems. The essence of the method is to apply a standard weighted residual technique only to the part of the differential equation which does not include time derivatives. The remaining terms are then approximated over the domain as in the standard finite element method. However, with an appropriate choice of the interpolation functions, it is possible to reduce the resulting domain integrals, ending with a boundary-only formulation. Thus, the main advantages of the BEM for elliptic equations are all preserved.

This technique, called the Dual Reciprocity Boundary Element Method,is currently being implemented in the BEASY system (Brebbia et al., 1985) which allows for higher order elements and subregions. Thus, it will be possible to fully test the capabilities of the technique by solving practical engineering problems. Results of these developments will be published in a forthcoming paper.

REFERENCES

1. BREBBIA, C.A. (1978) The Boundary Element Method for Engineers, Pentech Press, London.

2. BREBBIA, C.A. and WROBEL, L.C. (1979) "The boundary element method for steady-state and transient heat conduction", in Numerical Methods in Thermal Problems (R.W. Lewis and K. Morgan, Eds.), Pineridge Press, Swansea.

3. BREBBIA, C.A. and NARDINI, D. (1983) "Dynamic analysis in solid mechanics by an alternative boundary element procedure", Int. J. Soil Dynamics and Earthquake Engng., Vol.2, 228-233.

4. BREBBIA, C.A., TELLES, J.C.F. and WROBEL, L.C. (1984) Boundary Element Techniques: Theory and Applications in Engineering, Springer Verlag, Berlin.

5. BREBBIA, C.A. and SKERGET, P. (1984) "Diffusion-convection problems using boundary elements", in Finite Elements in Water Resources V (J.P. Laible et al., Eds.), Springer Verlag, Berlin.

6. BREBBIA, C.A., DANSON, D. and BAYNHAM, J. (1985) "BEASY Boundary Element Analysis System", in Finite Element Systems, A Handbook (C.A. Brebbia, Ed.), Springer Verlag, Berlin, NY.

7. CARSLAW, H.S. and JAEGER, J.C. (1959) Conduction of Heat in Solids, 2nd edn.,Clarendon Press, Oxford.

8. CHANG, Y.P., KANG, C.S. and CHEN, D.J. (1973) "The use of fundamental Green's functions for the solution of problems of heat conduction in anisotropic media", Int. J. Heat Mass Transfer, Vol.16, 1905-1918.

9. CURRAN, D.A.S., CROSS, M. and LEWIS, B.A. (1980) "Solution of parabolic differential equations by the boundary element method using discretization in time", Appl. Math. Modelling, Vol.4, 398-400.

10. MANSUR, W.J. and BREBBIA, C.A. (1985) "Transient elastodynamics", in Topics in Boundary Element Research, Vol.2 (C.A. Brebbia, Ed.), Springer Verlag, Berlin & New York.

11. NARDINI, D. and BREBBIA, C.A. (1985a) "Boundary integral formulation of mass matrices for dynamic analysis", in Topics in Boundary Element Research, Vol.2 (C.A. Brebbia Ed.), Springer Verlag, Berlin & New York.

12. NARDINI, D. and BREBBIA, C.A. (1985b) "The solution of parabolic and hyperbolic problems using an alternative boundary element formulation", in Boundary Elements VII (C.A. Brebbia, Ed.), Springer Verlag, Berlin.

13. ONISHI, K. (1981) "Convergence in the boundary element method for heat equation", TRU Mathematics, Vol.17, 213-225.

14. PINA, H.L.G. and FERNANDES, J.L.M. (1983) "Three-dimensional transient heat conduction by the boundary element method", in Boundary Elements V (C.A. Brebbia et al., Eds.), Springer-Verlag, Berlin.

15. RIZZO, F.J. and SHIPPY, D.J. (1970) "A method of solution for certain problems of transient heat conduction", AIAA Journal, Vol.8, 2004-2009.

16. SKERGET, P., ALUJEVIC, A. and BREBBIA, C.A. (1984) "The solution of Navier-Stokes equations in terms of vorticity-velocity variables by boundary elements", in Boundary Elements VI (C.A. Brebbia, Ed.,), Springer Verlag, Berlin.

17. WROBEL, L.C. and BREBBIA, C.A., (1981a) "A formulation of the boundary element method for axisymmetric transient heat conduction", Int. J. Heat Mass Transfer, Vol.24, 943-950.

18. WROBEL, L.C. and BREBBIA, C.A. (1981b) "Time-dependent potential problems", in Progress in Boundary Element Methods, Vol.1 (C.A. Brebbia, Ed.), Pentech Press, London.